WHITE'S DEVON

WHITE'S DEVON

A reprint of

History, Gazetteer and Directory of Devonshire

by
WILLIAM WHITE
1850

With new introduction by
W. E. Minchinton

DAVID & CHARLES REPRINTS

7153 4276 2

This book was first published in 1850
© Introduction W E Minchinton 1968

Printed in Great Britain by
Redwood Press of Trowbridge Wiltshire
for
David & Charles (Publishers) Limited
South Devon House Newton Abbot Devon

INTRODUCTION

The first directories appeared at the end of the seventeenth century in the form of lists of commercial addresses. In England they were first published for London and gradually spread to other towns large enough to warrant their production. By the early nineteenth century they were a well-established institution and it was considered that no town of any importance could do without its directory. Thus, the first Exeter directory, *The Exeter Pocket Journal; or Westcountry Gentleman & Tradesman's Memorandum book* appeared in 1807[1] and the earliest Plymouth directory in 1812. Other Devon towns followed: Newton Abbot in 1830[2], Torquay in 1832 and Sidmouth in 1836. The fact that the first directories contained trade information probably indicates that they originated to serve the commercial needs of the area concerned and provided a guide to the services available for the use of both private individuals and other traders, but it was not until well into the nineteenth century that directories began to include advertisements. From providing purely trade information, directories came also to include private addresses, a development encouraged by the compilation of directories by post office officials for their own use. In the course of the nineteenth century too, many directories began to include sections on the history and topography of the area, perhaps to widen the potential market by serving as guides as well as directories. Devon is first seriously catered for by *Pigot and Co.'s London and Provincial New Commercial Directory for 1823-4*[3] but the first county directory of Devon of any real historical value is *William White's History, Gazetteer, and Directory of Devonshire* published in 1850.

Little is known of William White, senior, who was responsible for the compilation of the *Devonshire Directory*. Few details of his life can be traced but it is said that his involvement with directories began in Newcastle-on-Tyne in 1822 when he was working under Edward Baines on his directories of Yorkshire. Then, in collaboration with William Parson, he published directories of Hull (1826), Lincolnshire (1826), Durham and Northumberland (1827), Cumberland and Westmoreland (1829) and Yorkshire (1830). In 1830 William White moved to Sheffield and from then on published many directories on his own account, mainly covering the northern and eastern parts of England. His *Devonshire Directory* was his first venture outside these areas and the reason for this experiment is unknown. Later he made a further foray outside his main area in

publishing directories of Hampshire from 1859. At some point, William White's son, also called William, joined him in the business, which he took over on his father's death in 1868. William White, junior, did not long survive his father, dying two years later in 1870[4]. The business was then taken over by his brother, although the directories continued to be published under the name of William White.

If we can guess at the reasons why directories were compiled, much less is known about how the directories were compiled. And only detailed analysis and comparison with other relevant material such as parish registers, rate books, poll books and so on will reveal exactly what sorts of people were included in the directories. White emphasised the learned character and accuracy of his directories. In the preface to the Devonshire volume he acknowledges the many 'literary and official Gentlemen' who have provided him with 'valuable Communications' and claims that 'Every parish, and almost every house, in this extensive county' has been 'visited by the Author's Assistants, and the information either collected or verified on the spot'. But in this case at least his claim was challenged as in the following year a number of local subscribers brought a case against White in the Plymouth County Court on the grounds that the directory was 'full of inaccuracies, and not such a book as the prospectus represented it should be.' Errors in the directory were pointed out and Judge Praed 'ruled that the defence set up was valid, and observed that inasmuch as the book was not of the quality represented, he should give judgement for the defendants.'[5]

White's directories were among the best known of the second half of the nineteenth century. They covered a wide area and were revised fairly frequently. Together with Frederic Kelly and James Pigot, he provided a systematic survey of the country and no other publishers achieved their degree of success. But there were challengers. All directory publishers were liable to have their material pirated by others and William White was no exception. Indeed White had himself been accused of piracy early in his career over the production of his Sheffield directory of 1833 and he was obliged to issue a disclaimer in which he stated 'W. W. hopes that the following pages bear not the slightest resemblance to those of Mr. T's *Register*'. White was particularly troubled by Francis White, also of Sheffield, who claimed to be a relative. Francis White not only pirated information but went further by producing directories which closely resembled those of his namesake's. In her *Guide to Directories*, Jane Norton discusses this situation:[6]

> William White refrained from taking any steps to protect himself he says from 'a natural dislike to the entanglements of the law' but perhaps because there really was a family connection. When he did finally apply for an injunction it was against E. S. Drake & Co. for pirating his directory of Leicestershire. An account of the case is given in the preface to W. White's

Directory of Norfolk (1864).[7] In this he refers to 'the cupidity of certain illiterate individuals, who, in 1854, under the name of "Francis White & Co." published a pirated and spurious edition' of his directory of Norfolk for 1845, in which 'most of the information was copied verbatim, while the form and general arrangement were identical'. Miss Norton then comments: Francis White's directories are certainly less honest and competent than William White's and should be clearly distinguished from them.

The first edition of the *History, Gazetteer and Directory of Devonshire*, published in 1850 and reprinted here, was a small and easily handled octavo volume of 804 pages, containing no advertisements. The price to subscribers was 14s in calf binding or 12s 6d in boards. The towns and villages were arranged under the old county divisions of hundreds, an inconvenient system which was characteristic of White's earlier directories. The second edition of 1878 was a considerably larger quarto volume containing 1116 pages together with 30 pages of advertisements. The price was now 36s for the cloth edition and 40s for the half-bound edition. The chapters on the history of Devonshire and Exeter were revised and the directory included what White called 'County Scientific Essays'—chapters on the geology, mines and mining, botany and vital statistics by named contributors. Other new features included a list of fairs in Devonshire, a street directory of Exeter and a classified Devonshire trades directory. A map was provided and the arrangement of the contents was improved by listing the entries in alphabetical order which made its use easier.

A third edition, again a quarto volume, containing 1323 pages and also 28 pages of advertisements, with the entries again arranged alphabetically, was published in 1890 at the same price as the second edition. The histories were further revised but there was less change in the other entries. New features were a list of polling districts, polling places and places of election; the electoral divisions; a list of County Council members; and a street directory of the Three Towns (Plymouth, Devonport and Stonehouse). A new and enlarged map was bound into the volume before the advertisements. The preface to the third edition promised further issues but no more seem to have appeared.

White's *Directory* appeared at a time when important economic and social changes were taking place in Devon. The old industries of cloth-making and mining had passed their peak and farming, although the major source of employment in the county, was not highly regarded by contemporary observers. Carpet-making had also recently come to an end, the number of paper mills in Devon was declining and the hand-lace industry was suffering from the competition of the machine-made product. The pilchard fisheries in the south-west of the county were also less active. Other industries, such as silk and ribbons, glove-making, rope-making and pottery were carried on but on a fairly small scale. There was

also some shipbuilding both in north and south Devon. But by 1850 it was clear that Devon had—perhaps happily—missed the full flood of the industrialisation process.

Nevertheless the coming of the railway was an important agency of change. By providing an improved transport service with the rest of England, it was, in due course, to open wider markets to the agricultural produce of Devon while, at the same time, it brought visitors in growing numbers to savour the delights of the holiday resorts both in north and south Devon. Dawlish, Teignmouth and Torquay particularly benefited from the coming of the railway. The result of all these changes was that the population of Devon grew more slowly than in the country as a whole. Until 1831 Devon had been the fourth most populous county, by 1851 it had dropped to sixth place and by 1881 to ninth place. It should be noted, moreover, that White's population figures are drawn from the 1841 census, almost a decade before the *Directory* was published. And with slackening growth came some redistribution. The coming of the railways eroded away other forms of transport and, as a result, many of the market towns in the county began to decline from the 1840s. People also began to leave the poorer and more isolated parts of the county. According to the 1851 census, which provides for the first time, a satisfactory analysis of the occupations of the people, the population of Devonshire had risen to 567,090 in that year. Much detail about who they were and how they gained a livelihood is to be found in the pages of the *Directory* which follow. But it should be remembered that, as is commonly the case with trade directories, while the professional classes, the gentry and the self-employed are reasonably covered, the employed worker scarcely figures in these pages. For a fuller picture of the employment position, the enumeration returns of the 1851 census should be consulted.

No such compilation as White's *Directory* is likely to be completely free from error but the standing of this *Directory* amongst historians is high. It is of value because it provides us with the first detailed contemporary account of the ways in which the people of Devon won a living for themselves in the middle of the nineteenth century.

W. E. Minchinton

Notes.—

1. J. Davidson, *Bibliotheca Devoniensis* (Exeter, 1852), p. 28 has an entry: 'Trewman's Exeter Journal, Exeter 1790–1852. An Annual Register and Directory' but the earliest extant edition is that for 1807 of which the Guildhall Library, London has a copy.
2. Not issued separately as a directory but appended to D. M. Stirling, *The history of Newton-Abbott.*
3. About twenty Devon towns appear in *Bailey's Western & Midland Directory for 1783* and *for 1784*. Devon entries are fuller in *The Universal British Directory of Trade, Commerce and Manufactures . . . Volume the Third* (1794) where the Exeter entries cover 29 pages but *Holden's Triennial Directory for 1805, 1806* and *1807* is much briefer. Devon has a separate section of 60 pages in *Pigot & Co.'s London & Provincial New Commercial Directory for* 1823–4. Later editions of Pigot were published in 1830, 1844 and 1852–3. There were also Devon entries in *Robson's Commercial Directory of London & the Western Counties* of 1840.
4. In the *Sheffield Telegraph* appeared the announcement of the 'premature death in the prime of life of our friend and townsman, Mr. Wm. White, publisher of county and borough directories. In this business, Mr. White succeeded a few years ago to his late father, who, having commenced directory work under the late Edward Baines, Esq., M.P. for Leeds, settled in Sheffield in 1830, and very ably and successfully carried on business on his own account, so that the reputation of Wm. White's directories stood very high, not only here and in the adjoining counties but in many other parts of England.'
5. See the *Plymouth and Devonport Weekly Journal*, 2 January 1851.
6. Jane E. Norton, *Guide to the National and Provincial Directories of England and Wales, excluding London, published before 1856* (London: Royal Historical Society, 1950), p. 67.
7. Also in his *Leicestershire*, 1863.

HISTORY,
GAZETTEER, AND DIRECTORY

OF

DEVONSHIRE,

AND THE

CITY AND COUNTY OF THE CITY OF EXETER;

COMPRISING

A GENERAL SURVEY OF THE COUNTY OF DEVON,

AND THE DIOCESE OF EXETER;

WITH SEPARATE

HISTORICAL, STATISTICAL, & TOPOGRAPHICAL

DESCRIPTIONS OF ALL THE

Boroughs, Towns, Ports, Bathing Places,

UNIONS, PARISHES, TOWNSHIPS, VILLAGES, HAMLETS, &c.;

SHEWING THEIR EXTENT AND POPULATION;

Their Agricultural and Mineral Productions; their Manufactures, Fisheries, Trade, Commerce, Markets, and Fairs; their Churches, Chapels, Charities, and Public Institutions; their eminent Men; the Patrons, Incumbents, and Value of the Benefices; the Tithe Commutations; the Lords of the Manors and Owners of the Soil; the Civil and Ecclesiastical Jurisdictions; the Addresses of the principal Inhabitants; the Mediums of Public Conveyance; the Post-Office Regulations; the

Seats of the Nobility and Gentry;

MAGISTRATES AND PUBLIC OFFICERS;

AND A VARIETY OF OTHER USEFUL INFORMATION.

IN ONE VOLUME, WITH A MAP OF THE COUNTY.

BY WILLIAM WHITE,

AUTHOR OF SIMILAR WORKS FOR YORKSHIRE, NORFOLK, SUFFOLK, ESSEX, AND MANY OTHER COUNTIES.

PRINTED FOR THE AUTHOR,

BY ROBERT LEADER, INDEPENDENT OFFICE, SHEFFIELD;

And Sold by WM. WHITE, *Broom Bank, Sheffield,*

BY HIS AGENTS, AND SIMPKIN, MARSHALL, AND CO., LONDON.

PRICE TO SUBSCRIBERS, 14s. IN CALF BINDING, OR 12s. 6d. IN BOARDS.

—

1850.

PREFACE.

The Author, in presenting to an indulgent Public this first essay towards a popular History, Topography, and Directory of the extensive and highly interesting County of Devon, has to tender his grateful acknowledgments to many literary and official Gentlemen for the valuable *Communications* with which they have furnished him, in answer to his multifarious inquiries; and also to nearly three thousand *Subscribers*, who have honoured him with their support. The prompt and extensive patronage which the Author has received in this and many other counties, shews clearly that Works of this description are useful and interesting to all classes; especially in large and populous counties like Devonshire, where the want of such *a book of general reference* has long been felt, not only by Merchants, Tradesmen, &c.; but by the Nobility, Gentry, Clergy, Yeomen, and Farmers. *Authenticity* being the grand requisite of topography, all possible care has been taken to avoid errors in the following 804 closely printed pages, which embrace more matter than is usually found in two quarto volumes. *Every parish*, and almost *every house*, in this extensive county having been visited by the Author's Assistants, and the information either collected or verified on the spot, it is hoped that this comprehensive Volume will be found as free from inaccuracies as is compatible with its vast body of information, and great variety of subjects. Among many other works which have been consulted in its compilation, are those of *Sir Wm. Pole*, who died in 1636; *Tristram Risdon*, who died in 1640; *Thos. Westcote*, who died about the same year; and the *Rev. Richard Polewhele*, who published his " Chorographical Description, or Parochial Survey of the Archdeaconry of Exeter," in 1793; and afterwards issued a brief notice of the Archdeaconries of Barnstaple and Totnes. The only works giving anything like a regular parochial history of Devon, are those of Polewhele, Risdon, and the two Lysons, the latter of which was published in 1822, as part of the *Magna Britannia*, by the Rev. Daniel Lysons and Samuel Lysons, Esq. The Devonshire Volume of the " *Beauties of England and Wales*," published in 1803; the History of Devonshire, by the *Rev. Thomas Moore*, published in 1829; and all the local histories,

guides, and hand-books of Exeter, Plymouth, and other towns, have also been consulted; but most of the statistical information has been drawn from *personal inquiry in every parish*, and from the voluminous *Parliamentary Reports of Public Charities, Population, Church Livings, &c.* The Report of the *Devon Charities* forms two large folio volumes, the substance of which has been incorporated in the following pages.

The PLAN OF THE WORK embraces a *General Survey of the County*, with lists of the Magistrates and Public Officers; followed by a *History of the City and Diocese of Exeter;* and Histories and Directories of all the *Hundreds, Boroughs, Towns, Parishes, Townships, Villages,* and *Hamlets* in the county. The *Poor Law Unions, Petty Sessional Divisions, Archdeaconries,* and *Deaneries,* to which the parishes respectively belong, are shewn in the general descriptions of the *Hundreds.* (See page 26.) The value of the Benefices in the *King's Book,* or *Libra Regis,* according to the valuation made in 1535, is distinguished by the contraction K.B., to which is added the annual value of each living in 1831; the amount of the tithe commutations; the number of glebe acres, &c. The *Directory* of each Town or Parish follows its History; and, though the parishes are printed in connexion with the Hundreds in which they are situated, the following copious Indexes give the work all the advantages of an Alphabetical Gazetteer, by enabling the reader instantly to refer to any place or subject; whilst the arrangement of the work enables him to read connectedly the history of a whole Hundred or District.

WM. WHITE.

Sheffield, June 10th, 1850.

INDEX OF PLACES IN DEVON.

INDEX OF SUBJECTS.

EXETER AND PLYMOUTH INDEXES.
(See after page 24.)

COUNTY OFFICERS, &c. OF DEVON.

Lord Lieutenant *and Custos Rotulorum*, Right Hon. Earl Fortescue, F.R.S.
High Sheriff (till March, 1851,) W. A. Yeo, Esq., Fremington House.
Under Sheriff, Thomas Hooper Law, Barnstaple.
Acting Under Sheriff, Charles Brutton, Exeter.
County Clerk, John Bradford Ellicombe, Exeter.
Clerk of the Peace, Richard Eales, Esq.; *Deputy*, T. E. Drake, gent., Exeter.
Clerk of the Lieutenancy General Meetings, J. G. Pearse, gent., Southmolton.
Treasurer of the County Rates, Edmund W. Paul, gent., Exeter.
County Solicitor, Thomas Edward Drake, gent., Exeter.
Treasurer to the Trustees of Exeter Turnpikes, H. M. Ellicombe, gent., Exeter.
Clerk to the Trustees of Exeter Turnpikes, Mark Kennaway, gent., Exeter.
Surveyor to the Trustees of Exeter Turnpikes, Mr. Jas. Howard, Alphington.
Coroners.—Totnes District, Joseph Gribble, Esq., Ashburton.—Stoke Damerel District, Allan B. Bone, Esq., Devonport.—Honiton District, R. H. Aberdein, Esq., Honiton.—Barnstaple District, Richard Bremridge, Esq., Barnstaple.—Okehampton District, H. A. Vallack, Esq., Torrington.—Crediton District, Frederick Leigh, Esq., Cullompton.
Chaplain to the County Prisons, Rev. W. B. Hellins; *Assistant ditto*, Rev. Theodore Coldridge.

Governor of High Gaol and Keeper of House of Correction, Mr. W. Cole.—
Under Keeper, Mr. E. H. Rose.—*Matron*, Mrs. M. Rose.—*Surgeon*, Mr.
C. K. Webb.
Keeper of Sheriff's Ward, Mr. Thomas Burch.
Surveyor of County Bridges, Mr. Thomas Whitaker, Exeter.
Surveyor of County Buildings, Mr. John Hayward, Exeter.
Keeper of the Castle, Mr. W. Snow.
Inspectors of Weights and Measures.—Exeter, Mr. R. Taylor ; Barnstaple,
Mr. Frederick Jones; Honiton, Mr. Henry Hurd ; Modbury, Mr. John
Walter ; Newton Abbot, Mr. W. Hearder ; Okehampton, Mr. W. Pons-
ford ; Plympton, Mr. Jonathan Walter ; Tiverton, Mr. Thomas Mitchell.

MAGISTRATES FOR THE COUNTY OF DEVON,

With the Petty Sessional Divisions *in which they act.*

The periods of holding *Petty Sessions* are noticed at subsequent pages,
with the histories of the places which give name to the *Divisions*.
(See also page 26.)

AXMINSTER.

Hon. Sir J. Talbot, K.C.B., LymeRegis
Rev. Wm. Palmer, D.D., Yarcombe
John Hussey, Esq. Lyme Regis
A. H. D. Acland, Esq. Axminster
N. T. Still, Esq. Axminster
Hon. A. N. Hood, Cricket, St Thomas, Chard
J. L. Lee, Esq. Dillington House
W. Tucker, Esq. Coryton
Sir H. Bayly, Burley Villa
H. B. Farnall, Esq. High Cliff Lodge
R. J. Elton, Esq. Crewkerne
C. W. Loveridge, Esq. Crewkerne
W. H. Richards, Esq. Lea-Coombe
C. A. Macalister, Esq. Loup Cottage
Sir J. G. R. De la Pole, Shute House
Rev W. Bernard, Clatworthy
Clerk, Mr C. Pond, Axminster

BLK.TORRINGTON&SHEBBEAR

Lord Clinton, Heanton House
G. L. Coham, Esq. Upcot Avenel
H. Mallett, Esq. Ash, Hatherleigh
J. Oldham, Esq. Strawbridge
S. C. Hamlyn, Esq. Leawood
J.H. Veale, Esq. Passaford
J. M. Woollcombe, Esq. Ashbury
Rev P. Glubb, Torrington
W. H. B. Coham, Esq. Dunsland
Rev J. Penleaze, Black Torrington
Clerk, H. Hawkes, Okehampton

BRAUNTON.

Sir B. P. Wrey, Bart. Tawstock
W. A. Yeo, Esq. Fremington House
Sir J. P. B. Chichester, Bart., Arlington
T.W. Harding, Esq. Upcott, Barnstaple
J. May, Esq. Barnstaple
J. Whyte, Esq. Pilton

R. Harding, Esq. Lynton, Minehead
Rev C. P. Coffin, East Down
Rev J. Dene, Horwood
Rev S. T. Gully, Berrynarbor
Rev H. B. Wrey, Tawstock
N. Vye, Esq. Ilfracombe
Rev J. Pyke, Parracombe
J. Marshall, Esq., Barnstaple
R. Chichester, Esq., Hall, Barnstaple
C. H. Webber, Esq., Buckland Hs.
Clerk, Mr J. S. Clay, Barnstaple

CREDITON.

J. W. Buller, Esq. Downes
Sir H. R. F. Davie, Bart., Creedy
J. H. Hippesley, Esq., Fulford Park
J. Quicke, Esq., Newton St Cyres
J. Sillifant, Esq., Coombe, Crediton
Rev H. A. Hughes, Clannaborough
Clerks, Messrs Smith, Crediton

CROCKERNWELL.

B. Fulford, Esq., Great Fulford
J. N. Stevenson, Esq., Moreton
Rev W. Hames, Chagford
Rev W. Ponsford, Drewsteignton
Clerk, Mr M. W. Harvey, Moreton

CULLOMPTON.

Sir G. P. Adams, Wiveliscombe
Rev Dr Tripp, Silverton
J. Bere, Esq., Milverton
R. H. Clarke, Esq., Bridewell, Culptn
F. Hole, Esq., Collipriest Cott. Tivert.
J. Heathcoat, Esq., Tiverton
E.A.Sanford, Esq., Ninehead,Welgtn.
J. F. Worth, Esq., Worth, Tiverton
W. Hole, Esq., Clare House, Tiverton
Rev J. Huyshe, Clisthydon
C. N. Welman, Esq., Norton Manor, Taunton

B.Walrond, Esq. Montrath, Cullomp.
J. White, Esq., Churchstanton
Rev J. P. Sydenham, Cullompton
Rev G. S. Cruwys, Cruwys Morchard
Rev W. Rayer, Tiverton
Rev W. P. Thomas, Wellington
J. Chichester Nagle, Esq., Calverleigh
E. S. Drewe, Esq., Grange, Honiton
T. Carew, Esq., Collipriest, Tiverton
W. A. Sanford, Esq., Ninehead
Clerk, Mr F. Leigh, Cullompton
ERMINGTON AND PLYMPTON.
C.B.Calmady,Esq.,Langdon, Plympt.
H. R. Roe, Esq., Gnaton, Plympton
R.Robertson,Esq.,Membland,Modby.
G. Strode, Esq., Newnham, Modbury
J. C. Harris, Esq., Radford, Plymth.
W. Pode, Esq., Slade, Ivybridge
Earl of Morley, Saltram, Plymouth
T.Lockyer,Esq.,Wembury,Plymouth
R.Z.Mudge,Esq. Beechwood,Plympt.
J. L. Templer, Esq., Ivybridge
Wm. M. Praed, Esq., Delamoor
G. W. Soltau, Esq., Efford Lodge
Rev R. Lane, Coffleet, Plympton
J. B. Yonge, Esq., Puslinch
G. Woollcombe, Esq., Hemerdon
Clerk, Mr Thos. Kelly, Yealmpton
GREAT TORRINGTON.
W. Tardrew, Esq., Annery, Bideford
Rev P. Glubb, Great Torrington
L. W. Buck, Esq., M.P., Moreton
C. Carter, Esq., Bideford.
B. Prust, Esq., Woolfardisworthy
J. H. Furse, Esq., Torrington
J. Gould, Esq., Knapp, Bideford
J. T. Kirkwood, Esq., Bideford
Sir Trevor Wheler, Bart., Cross Hs.
H. Hole, Esq., Ebberley, Torrington
Rev J. L. Harding, Monkleigh
R. Shute, Esq., Burkish, Bideford
Rev J. T. P. Coffin, Portledge
G. S. Buck, Esq., Hartland Abbey
C.H.Hotchkys,Esq.,CleverdonHouse, Bradworthy
T. Wren, Esq., Lenwood, Bideford
J. R. Best, Esq., Abbotsham Court, Bideford
Clerks, MrW.G.Glubb,GreatTorrington; Mr H. A. Harvie, Bideford
HOLSWORTHY.
J. Vowler, Esq., Parnacott
Rev S. Hart, Alternun, Launceston
G. L. Coham, Esq., Upcot Avenel
W. H. B. Coham, Esq., Dunsland

C. H. Hotchkys, Esq., Cleverdon Hs.
Rev F. Parker, Luffincott
Rev T. H. Kingdon, Bridgerule
J. N. Vowler, Esq., Parnacott, Pywor.
Clerk, Mr E. Shearm, Stratton
HONITON.
SirE.S.Prideaux,Bart.,NethertonHall
C. Gordon, Esq., Heavitree
Rev V. H. P. Somerset, Honiton
Sir E. M. Elton, Widworthy Court
G. B. Northcote, Esq., Feniton
W. M. Smyth, Esq., Deer Park
Rev. T. J. Marker, Gittisham
Hon. W. W. Addington, Upottery
W. Porter, Esq., Hembury Fort
Clerks, Townsend & Stamp, Honiton
LIFTON.
W. A. H. Arundell, Esq., Trebursie
Sir J. S. G. Sawle, Bart., Penrice
E. B. Gould, Esq., Lew Trenchard
G. Gurney, Esq., Woodleigh
A. Kelly, Esq., Kelly, Lifton
J.H.Tremayne,Esq., Sydenham Hs
T. J. Phillipps, Esq., Landue
Rev. Dr. Fletcher, Callington
T. Pearse, Esq., Launceston
J. K. Lethbridge, Esq., Tregane
Clerks, J. C. Braddon, Camelford; S. Pattison & J.L. Cowlard, Launcest.
MIDLAND ROBOROUGH.
Sir R. Lopes, Bart., Maristow
J. H. Gill, Esq., Bickham
Sir A. Buller, Pound, Plymouth
Erving Clarke ,Esq., Efford
Rev. W. Radcliffe, Warleigh
J. Pedler, Esq., Meavy, Plymouth
Massy Lopes, Esq., Maristow
Clerk, Mr. J. Giles, of Jump
PAIGNTON.
Sir J. B. Y. Buller, Bart., Lupton
G.H.Cutler,Esq.,Upton Lodge,Brixh.
J. Garrow, Esq., Braddons, Torquay
J.B.Y. Buller, Esq., Churston Court
R. Sheddon, Esq., Tor Abbey
J. Harry, Esq., Paignton
C. Mallock, Esq., Cockington
E. Vivian, Esq., Torquay
Sir L. V. Palk, Bart., Haldon House
J. Hack, Esq , Torquay
E. Carlyon, Esq., Greenway, Totnes
Rev T. Kitson, Shiphay
H. C. M. Phillipps, Esq., Torquay
J. Belfield, Esq., Primley Cottage
C. B. Baldwin, Esq., Torquay
Clerk, Mr G. Hearder, Torquay

ROBOROUGH.

Sir A. Buller, Pound, Plymouth
Sir J. J. G. Bremer, Compton
W. P. Daykin, Esq., Plymouth
J. Foote, Esq., Stonehouse
G. Foot, Esq., Plymouth
E. St Aubyn, Esq., Devonport
J. Shephard, Esq., Stonehouse
J. Williams, Esq., Penlee, Devonport
W. Hodge, Esq., Devonport
W. Hancock, Esq., Stoke
J. Ingle, Esq., Stonehouse
Sir S. Pym, Plymouth
J. A. Parlby, Esq., Manadon
Rev T. H. Ley, Maker
T. Gill, Esq., Buckland Abbey
C. H. Seale, Esq., Plymouth
G. B. Kingdon, Esq., Compton Hall
J. H. Gill, Esq., Bickham
T. W. Fox, Esq., Plymouth
Philip W. Pedler, Esq., Mutley House
Clerk, Mr. A. B. Bone, Devonport

SOUTHMOLTON.

Earl Fortescue, Castle Hill
Viscount Ebrington, Castle Hill
Lord Poltimore, Court Hall
Rev C. Tucker, Morchard Bishop
Hon. N. Fellowes, Heywood House
J. Budd, Esq., Landkey
Rev P. Johnson, Wembworthy
Rev W. Karslake, Dolton
Rev W. H. Karslake, Meshaw
J, Nott, Esq., Bydon, Barnstaple
Rev J. P. Benson, Witheridge
Clerks, Messrs. Pearse, Son, and
Crosse, Southmolton

STANBOROUGH & COLERIDGE.

Hon. & Rev Lord H. F. C. Kerr
W. J. Clark, Esq., Buckland
W. R. Ilbert, Esq., Horswell
J. Parrott, Esq., Dundridge, Totnes
Sir H. P. Seale, Bart., Dartmouth
Rev Archdeacon Froude, Dartington
A. B. E. Holdsworth, Esq., Wide-
combe House
A. B. Savile, Esq., Holne
W. L. Pearse, Esq., Kingsbridge
G. S. Cary, Esq., Follaton, Totnes
J. Allen, Esq., Coleridge House
R. Peek, Esq., Hazlewood
F. Wells, Esq., Slade, Kingsbridge
H. Champernowne, Esq., Dartington
J. Cornish, Esq., Black Hall
H. Studdy, Esq., Watton Court
Clerk, Mr T. Harris, Kingsbridge

TEIGNBRIDGE.

Lord Clifford, Ugbrook
Hon. C. H. Clifford, Ugbrook
Sir L. V. Palk, Bart., Haldon Hs
Sir W. H. Tonkin, Teignmouth
Lord Cranstoun, Bagtor
A. Chichester, Esq., Stokelake
J. Caunter, Esq., Ashburton
G. S. Curtis, Esq., Teignmouth
C. H. Monro, Esq., Ingsdon
C. Parr, Esq., Dawlish
M. E. N. Parker, Esq., Whiteway
John Divett, Esq., Bovey Tracey
J. Sweetland, Esq., Teignmouth
H. Cartwright, Esq., Ford
W. Hole, Esq., Park, Bovey Tracey
W. J. Watts, Esq., Teignmouth
Rev T. Kitson, Shiphay
C. Kelson, Esq., Teignmouth
Clerk, Mr. W. Flamank, Newton Ab.

TAVISTOCK.

J. Rundle, Esq., Tavistock
Rev E. A. Bray, Tavistock
W. Courtenay, Esq., Walreddon
Clerk, Mr R. Luxton, Tavistock

WONFORD.

Earl of Devon, Powderham Castle
Lord Poltimore, Poltimore
Lord Courtenay, Powderham Castle
Hon. & Rev J. Fortescue, Poltimore
Sir T. D. Acland, Bart., Killerton
Sir L. V. Palk, Bart., Haldon House
Sir J. T. B. Duckworth, Bart., M.P.,
Topsham
T. D. Acland, Esq., Killerton
J. B. Creswell, Esq., Newcourt
A. H. Hamilton, Esq., Retreat
W. Miles, Esq., Exeter
J. H. Ley, Esq., Trehill
Charles Gordon, Esq., Heavitree
J. C. Luxmoore, Esq., Alphington
J. Milford, Esq., Coaver House
H. S. Northcote, Esq., Pynes
W. Nation, Esq., Exeter
J. S. Pitman, Esq., Dunchideock
F. B. Short, Esq., Bickham
A. Stowey, Esq., Kenbury
J. Truscott, Esq., Brockhill
Rev W. H. Palk, Ashcombe
Rev H. F. Strangways, Rewe
W. Ley, Esq., Woodlands, Kenn
S. T. Kekewich, Esq., Peamore
M. B. Bere, Esq., Barley House
G. Fursdon, Esq., Bramfordspeke
Rev A. Atherley, Heavitree

R. L. Pennell, Esq., Exeter
C. Shirreff, Esq., Pinhoe
D. B. Davy, Esq., Topsham
L. Palk, Esq., Haldon
Clerk, Mr T. E. Drake, Exeter

WOODBURY.

Sir John Kennaway, Bart., Escot
T. W. Buller, Esq., Strete Raleigh
E. Divett, Esq., M.P., Bystock
Rev Archdeacon Stevens, Otterton
Rev H. W. Marker, Aylesbeare
General Thomas, Strete Raleigh
Rev J. Huyshe, Clisthydon
J. Garratt, Esq., Bishop's Court

H. Porter, Esq., Winslade, Exeter
Gen. Sir H. Browne, K.C.B., Exmth
J. Tyrrell, Esq., Sidcliff, Sidmouth
W. C. Cole, Esq., Exmouth
C. J. Cornish, Esq., Sidmouth
Rev H. Fellowes, Sidbury
R. Hunt, Esq., Sidbury
W. R. Bayley, Esq., Cotford House
J. Garratt, jun., Esq., Bishop's Court
G. Smith, Esq., Salcombe Mount
J. M. Wolcott, Esq., Knowle House
S. Parr, Esq., Clist St George
E. Lousada, Esq., Peak House
J. Carslake, Esq., Sidmouth
Clerk, Mr F. G. Coleridge, Ottery

REVENUE OFFICERS.

Barnstaple...*Collector of Customs*, Rd. White, Esq..*Comptroller*, W. A. Gent, Esq.
Bideford..... „ H. Rodd, Esq.... „ Jas. John Paxton, Esq.
Dartmouth.. „ A. Moore, Esq... „ J. H. Sparke, Esq.
Exeter...... „ H. L. Grove, Esq. „ A. Stewart, Esq.
Plymouth ... „ Geo. Jones, Esq. „ Wm. Lockyer, Esq.

Collectors of Inland Revenue, including Excise, Stamps, Land, Assessed, Property and Income Taxes, Wm. Schofield, Esq., *Exeter*—office, 86, South street, Exeter ; John Mc'Culloch, Esq., *Plymouth ;* J. Johnstone, Esq., *Barnstaple.*

Inspector of Stamps, Taxes, and Property and Income Taxes, for Devon and Cornwall, James Michell, Esq., 3, Upper Lemon Villa, Truro ; *Deputy Ditto,* Mr. Nicholas Michell, Truro.

Surveyors of Taxes, Mr. Joseph Welch ; *Assistant Surveyor,* Mr. W. Richardson ; Office, No. 4, Park place, Exeter ; Mr. J. Gilbert, Newport, near Barnstaple ; Mr. W. Kite, Honiton ; Mr. Robert Watterworth, Plymouth ; Mr. George Webb.—*Assistant Surveyor,* Mr. — Michell, Totnes.

Distributor of Stamps for Devon, Mark Kennaway, Esq. ; *Deputy,* Mr. Edwin Martin, Stamp Office, Bampfylde street, Exeter.

Sub-distributors of Stamps.—*Ashburton,* R. Dobell ; *Axminster,* T. Chapple ; *Bampton,* W. Crudge ; *Barnstaple,* J. Harris ; *Bideford,* W. L. Vellacott ; *Brixham,* O. H. Bartlett ; *Chudleigh,* Eliz. Petherick ; *Chulmleigh,* T. Croote ; *Colyton,* J. Spence ; *Crediton,* M. Pinson ; *Cullompton,* T. Mitchell ; *Dartmouth,* John Soper ; *Devonport,* J. Gilbard ; *Exmouth,* C. W. H. Spencer ; *Hatherleigh,* Samuel Hooper ; *Holsworthy,* S. Fry ; *Honiton,* M. Murch ; *Ilfracombe,* J. Banfield ; *Kingsbridge,* Jane Prideaux ; *Modbury,* ——— ; *Moreton,* S. Treleaven ; *Newton,* John Alsop ; *Okehampton,* G. Lacey ; *Ottery,* C. D. Mayne ; *Paignton,* H. D. Carnell ; *Plymouth,* E. Nettleton ; *Plympton,* T. Sherwill ; *Sidmouth,* John Harvey ; *Stonehouse,* M. Huss ; *Southmolton,* R. Tepper ; *Tavistock,* J. Hamley ; *Teignmouth,* G. Collings ; *Tiverton,* F. Boyce ; *Torquay,* G. Hearder ; *Torrington,* E. Handford ; *Totnes,* Samuel Hannaford ; *Witheridge,* Henry Pullen.

CLERKS TO COMMISSIONERS OF INCOME TAX.

Divisions.	Clerks and Assistants.
Axminster, Philip Mules, Hen. C. Mules, Honiton.	
Barnstaple, Chas. J. Dene, Barnstaple	
Bideford, C. Carter, jun., Bideford	
Coleridge and Stanborough, (Morleigh,) Ts. Harris, jun., Kingsbridge	
Colyton, J. H. Townsend, Edmund Stamp, Honiton	
Crediton, Thos. Pring, Crediton	
Devonport, A. B. Bone, John Gedye, Devonport	
East Budleigh and Cliston, F. G. Coleridge, C. D. Mayne, Ottery St Mary	
East Axminster (Castle of Exeter,) T. E. Drake, Exeter	
Ermington and Plympton, (Yealmpton,) J. Walters, Plympton	
Exeter, (City,) Edwin Force, Exeter	

Divisions.	Clerks and Assistants.
Hatherleigh, H. Hawkes, Okehampton	
Haytor and Wonford South, (Newton,) Wm. Heardor, Newton ; G. E. Hearder, Torqy	
Holsworthy, R. W. Cock, Holsworthy	
North Roborough, G. Giles, W. Lethbridge	
North Tawton, J. Price, Torrington	
Plymouth, C. C. Whiteford, L. Kent	
South Molton, R. M. Riccard, South Molton	
Tavistock, C. V. Bridgman, A. W. Barnett, Tavistock	
Teignbridge and Exminster West, (Highweek Newton,) G. Caunter, Ed. Foote, Ashburton	
Tiverton, T. L. T. Rendell, Jas. Wood	
Torrington, C. E. Palmer, Barnstaple	
West Wonford, (Crockernwell,) M. W. Harvey, Moretonhampstead	
Witheridge, T. M. Commins, Witheridge	

NEW COUNTY COURTS.

These Courts are held monthly, or oftener, in each District, and their jurisdiction fees, &c., are noticed at page 71. The County is divided into two *Circuits*, and the *Judges, Districts, Clerks,* and *High Bailiffs,* are as follow :—

CIRCUIT No. 58.—EAST and NORTH DEVON.—*Judge,* John Tyrrell, Esq ; *Treasurer,* James Terrell, Esq., Bartholomew square, Exeter.

The residences of the Clerks and High-bailiffs are in the Court Town, unless otherwise expressed.

AXMINSTER District.— *Clerk,* Charles Bond ; *High-bailiff,* Thos. Pickering

BARNSTAPLE District.— *Clerk,* L. T. Bencraft ; *High-bailiff,* H. K. Thorne

BIDEFORD District.—*Clerk,* Jas. Rooker ; *High-bailiff,* Richard Buse

CREDITON District.—*Clerk,* Geo. Tanner ; *High-bailiff,* Francis Lee

EXETER District.— *Clerk,* John Daw : Office, 13, Bedford circus ; *High-bailiff,* Rt. Collins

HONITON District.—*Clerk,* Robert H. Aberdein ; *High-bailiff,* John Manley

SOUTH MOLTON District.—*Clerk,* Jas. Pearse ; *High-bailiff,* John Manning

TIVERTON District.—*Clerk,* Thos. Leigh Teale Rendell ; *High-bailiff,* William Webster

TORRINGTON District.— *Clerk,* Wm. Anthony Deane ; *High bailiff,* Frederick Holwell

CIRCUIT No. 59.—WEST DEVON and PART OF CORNWALL.—*Judge,* Wm. Mackworth Praed, Esq. ; *Treasurer,* Jas. Terrell, Esq., Bartholomew square, Exeter.

CAMELFORD District.— *Clerk,* John Darke, Launceston ; *Assistant Clerk,* R. H. Burt ; *Bailiff,* Samuel Scott

HOLSWORTHY District.— *Clerk,* John Darke, Launceston ; *Assistant Clerk,* J. Lisle ; *High-bailiff,* Wm. Bassett

KINGSBRIDGE District. — *Clerk,* P. Pearce, Newton Abbot ; *Assistant Clerk,* T. Harris, jun. ; *High-bailiff,* Nicholas Southwood

LAUNCESTON District. — *Clerk,* John Darke ; *High-bailiff,* Joseph Short

NEWTON ABBOTT District.—*Clerk,* P. Pearce ; *Assistant Clerk,* F. I. Stokes ; *High-bailiff,* Edward Burch

OKEHAMPTON District.—*Clerk,* P Pearce, Newton Abbot ; *Assist. Clerk,* H. Hawkes ; *High-bailiff,* John H. Hawkes

PLYMOUTH District.—*Clerk,* Wm. Jacobson ; *High-bailiff,* J. H. Williams ; *Office,* Eldad place

TAVISTOCK District.—*Clerk,* Christopher V. Bridgman ; *High-bailiff,* John Brownson

TOTNES District.—*Clerk,* Chas. Edwards ; *High-bailiff,* Thomas Welch

☞ The COUNTY COURT DISTRICTS, with the following and a few other exceptions, comprise all the parishes in the *Poor Law Unions* bearing the same names. EXETER DISTRICT comprises the parishes of the City and County of the City of Exeter, and all those in *St. Thomas's Union.* PLYMOUTH DISTRICT comprises Stonehouse, the Boroughs of Plymouth and Devonport, and all the parishes of *Plympton St. Mary Union.*

The BANKRUPTCY COURT is noticed at page 71, and is now held at Plymouth, as well as at Exeter.

EXETER APPENDIX

Consisting of alterations and Additions since the Directory was printed.

Aggassiz Lewis, Esq. 2 Colleton crescent
Aldridge Capt. R.N., 1 Mont-le-grand
Alger A. lodgings, 3 St James place
Allen H. H. smith, Goldsmith street
Arthur Miss, 6 Northernhay place
Ashby Mr E. 31 Paris street
Ayre Abrm. builder, 3 Lansdown terrace
Babb Daniel, tinner, Paris street
Badgery Andrew, butcher, 23 Magdalen st
Bailey Eliz. milliner, 245 High street
Baker Mrs L. 1 Manston terrace
Baker J. lodgings, 3 Bystock terrace
Barratt J. tea dealer, 41 Magdalen street
Beal J. butcher, 32 Russell street
Beard John, slate dealer, Friars walk
Beer S. and M. milliners, 241 High street
Bellamy Charles, hairdresser, Preston st
Bennett Misses, Friars walk
Bennett Miss, academy, David's hill

Bere Miss & Mr., Mount Vernon
Bicknell Mrs. 5 St Leonard's terrace
Blackmore Joseph, baker, 16 North street
Bouter Misses, school, Cowick terrace
Brissenden Mr J. 8 Longbrook terrace
Brown E. lodgings, 8 Windsor terrace
Bullen James, blacksmith, Alphington st
Burdett Mrs George, 4 Dix's field
Butcher Wm. hatter, 65 High street
Camm Mr H. 2 Hampton place
Carslake Wm. blacksmith, Pancras street
Cawne Miss, 9 Hill's court
Chapman Mrs. 8 Radnor place
Chapple Mr J. C. *Lion's Holt*
Church R Esq. 5 Regent park, H
Coggin Eliza, shopkeeper, Milk street
Coniam Wm. butcher, Cowick street
Cook Major, 5 Prospect place, Topsham road

Coombes Thomas, mason, Cricklepit lane
Cornish H. lodgings, 2 Upr. Southernhay st
Cox Captain, 5 Higher Mt. Radford terrace
Crabb John, broker, Guinea street
Cumming G. W. civil engineer, Cath. yd
Davis Wm. painter, Alphington street
Dicken Captain, 6 Regent Park
Dunning Mr. 3 Park place, Mt. Radford
Ebbles F. coal dealer, Bartholomew street
Edye John, surgeon, Southernhay
Fernandez B. G. Esq. Hr. Mt. Radford tr
Fox Mrs. lodgings, 8 Friars walk
Frampton H. agent to Chimney Sweeping
  Co. 93 North street
Fulford Mrs. 1 Bicton place
Furneaux Hy. writing master, Clifton rd
Galpin Joseph, plasterer, Okehampton st
Gardner G. H. flour factor, 139 Fore street
Gibbs Sarah, gardener, Moreton road
Gill George, butcher, 27 Sidwell street
Goodridge Mr George, 9 Brook green ter
Greenwood R. lodgings, 9 Upr. Eaton pl
Griffiths Wm. baker, Preston street
Guichard Captain, E. 1 Albert terrace
Guppy— academy, Magdalen hill
Hare Gustavus, Esq. 7 Dix's field
Harvey M.A.& E. dressmakers, 79 South st
Hawkins Sarah, shopkeeper, Coombe street
Hawkins Mrs. lodgings, 3 Castle terrace
Heddington Captain R.N. *Bradford Hs*
Helmore Mr Wm. 4 Magdalen street
Henscough Mr R., Bouverie place
Herbert John, writing master, 56 South st
Hibberd J. druggist, 87 North street
Hobbs Henry, miller, Commercial road
Hook Joseph, hosier, Sidwell street
Hooper F. C. milliner, Broad street
Hooper Wm. printer, Alphington street
Hooper Amos, smith, Cowick street
Horsepool Mr Joseph, 2 Wellington place
Huish Mrs., St Leonard's Lawn
Jones Edw. grocer, 32 Sidwell street
Kennedy Geo. porter mercht. 21 South st
Knapman Wm. fruiterer, 217 High street
Lakin Mr Francis, 3 Hill's court
Lamb J. fruiterer, North Bridge
Langdon Isaac, vict. Globe Inn, Clifton rd
Lee Mrs. 2 Baring terrace
Lee Thomas, frame maker, 30 North street
Lock John, shoemaker, 47 Magdalen street
Lock F. jeweller, Cathedral yard
Lock Richard, saddler, West Quarter
Long Nicholas, jeweller, 59 Magdalen st
Luke Mr R., Mile end buildings
Luke Henry, Esq., 8 Colleton crescent
Mc' Arthur Mrs. academy, 5 Bystock ter
Mackay Captain, *Fair hill*
Maddock Silas, vict. Union, Waterbeer st
Maddocks Mrs M. 10 Dix's fields
Maddover & Easterbrook, milliners, 2 New
  Bridge street
Mallett James, shopkeeper, Sun street
Manley Mrs T , Berlin repy. Broadgate
Marriott Mrs S. A., Palace street
Martin Samuel, shopkeeper, Paris street
Mason James, master of *Workhouse*
Matthews John, coal dlr., Commercial rd
Maunder J. vict. Three Crowns, King st
May Genl., *Southernhay House*
May Thomas, shoemaker, 37 South street
Mc' Kinsey H. J., medicine dlr. 5 Paris st
Meanley Miss, 1 St Leonard's terrace

Mears Lieut. R.N. 6 Midway terrace
Monsley Mrs. 3 Prospect place
Moore John, livery stables, Sidwell street
Morris Wm. wheelwright, Commercial rd
Mortimer Wm. vict. Okehampton Inn,
  Okehampton road
Napier Mrs., Queen's square, Mt. Radford
Neame H. C., bookseller, 10 Paris street
Neville A. Esq. Bouverie place
Newton C. lodgings, Hill's court
Norrish Wm. brush maker, Paul street
Parminter Miss, Friars green
Penfound C. coach propr. 3 Summerland c
Penny Jph. & J. T. Esqrs. 8 and 9 Hr.
  Mount Radford terrace
Petherham Wm. Esq. Hill's court
Phillips James, brickmaker, Clifton road
Picketts Capt. R.N. 6 St James place
Pidsley Ann, confectioner, 7 Magdalen rd
Plowman & Brewster, haberdashers, 53
  High street
Pollard Edw. Esq. 1 Midway terrace
Pomeroy J.F. mattress mkr. 33 Russell st
Ponsford George, printer, North street
Potter Joseph, bacon factor, Paris street
Powney Capt. R.N. 4 Mount Radford cres
Pratt John, grocer, 122 Sidwell street
Pridham Eliza, draper, Magdalen street
Prowse John, pork butcher, Coombe street
Pullmann Philip, clothes dlr. West street
Raddon Wm. vict. Union, Okehampton st
Radford Mr. 11 Hill's court
Rainey Mrs. 6 Lower Mount Radford ter
Reed R. H. baker, Brook green
Reynolds Robert, pipe maker, Cheeke st
Richards John, builder, 6 Paris street
Rudler R. vict. Golden Eagle, Bartw. st
Salter Aaron, butcher, 123 Sidwell street
Sanders Wm. shopkeeper, 4 Hart's row
Shoebrooke Wm. tailor, North bridge
Shooter Edwin, grocer, South street
Skelton Mr. 4 Victoria terrace
Snook Wm. carpenter, 39 Paris street
Snow John, shopkeeper, Magdalen street
Southard G. plumber, Summerland street
Splatt Wm. wood dlr. 26 Paris street
Spratt Wm. tinner, Waterbeer street
Steel C. school, 16 Hart's row
Stokes R. grocer, Cowick street
Stone John, Esq. 1 St James' place
Strong James, baker, 96 Fore street
Stump Thomas, brickmaker, Clifton road
Sugg N. coal dealer, Colyton buildings
Sugg Nathl. beerhouse, Albert place
Sweetland Agnes, dairy, 27 Paris street
Sweetland Miss, Magdalen road
Symes Miss, 2 Hill's court
Symes F. S. baker, Crediton road
Symons J. mariner, 8 Wearfield place
Taylor J. B. Esq. 23 Dix's field
Teed Mr Robert, Jeffery's row
Thomas John, eating-house, 155 Sidwell st
Thomas Wm. fishmonger, Coombe street
Thorp Mrs. 14 Radnor place
Tidcombe Mrs. 4 Midway terrace
Townsend G. engraver, Little Queen st
Travis Mr H. D. 13 Radnor place
Treleaven M. school, *Larkbeare*
Trend John, wheelwright, Commercial rd
Tucker Eliz. milliner, Upr. Paul street
Uzzell Mr. road surveyor, Old Tiv. road
Verney Sarah, poulterer, Magdalen road

Walford Mr. railway clerk, Bystock ter
Ward Thomas, lodgings, 4 Upper Eaton pl
Warren Mrs C. milliner, Northernhay pl
Watson Thos. scalemaker, 9 New bridge st
Webb Miss, 3 Radnor place
Westcott Jas. hairdresser, Paul street
Western John, gardener, David's hill
White Miss, 9 New North terrace
White Alfred, baker, 44 Russell street
Whyand Peter, plasterer, King street
Williams Thomas, Esq. Alphington road
Williams R. builder, Bartholomew road
Williams Wm. plasterer, Stepcote hill
Willmett Mr James, 5 Friar's walk
Wills & Co. vesta lamp depôt, Cathl. yd
Wish Philip, fruiterer, Goldsmith street
Woodhouse Thomas, Esq. Alphington Cross
Woodman S. milliner, Cathedral yard
Wright M. A. dressmaker, Mary's yard
Yeates Mrs. lodgings, David's hill
Yelland Wm. tailor, 12 Holloway street
Youle John G. 2 Hr. Summerland place

EXETER MAGISTRATES.
Omitted at Page 70.
Sanders Edw. Andrew, Esq. *(mayor)*
Bastard Richard, Esq.
Maunders Samuel, Esq.
Sercombe John Clampit, Esq.
NEW PREBENDARIES.—(See p. 81.)
Rev N. Oxenham, *(vice Leslie)*
Rev H. Brown, *(vice Cornish)*
EXETER CORPORATION, (See p. 70.)
(Changes in November, 1849.)
MAYOR, Edw. A. Sanders, Esq. (also elected *alderman, vice* E D. Worthy, Esq.)
COUNCILLORS, Jph. Cuthbertson and Wm. Davey, *vice* Floud and Brunskill) Jno. Laidman, *(vice* Trewman ;) Josiah Rogers, *(vice* Bastard ;) and Edw. James, *(vice* Hertzel)
Sheriff, Wm. D. Moore
BEAFORD, *(add to page* 756.)
Ashton Thos. grocer, and Mr Wm.
Hammett Hy. blacksmith
Heard Arthur, plumber and seedsman
Heard John, timber merchant, &c
Heard Robert, vict. and gunsmith
Heard Wm. blacksmith
Marshall Wm. maltster, &c.
Snell Wm. maltster and miller
Weeks Wm. butcher
Westcott John, grocer and schoolmaster
Westcott Wm. vict. Globe
Wood Rev Chas., B.A. *Rectory*

FARMERS.
Arnold John
Leverton Wm.
Snell Thomas
Snell Mrs
Webber Nicholas
SHOEMAKERS.
Ashland Wm.
Isaac Thomas
Mippill John

REWE AND UP-EXE.
(Directory to be added to Page 201.)
Bishop Wm. rope and twine maker
Clatworthy Benjamin, mason, &c.
Frost Thomas, sexton, &c.
Haydon Thomas, farmer
Lipscombe John, shopkeeper
Littlejohn George, blacksmith
May R. farmer, ‖ Pester Rd. carpenter
Strangways Rev Hy. Fox, M.A., rector of Rewe and West Grinstead, *Rectory*
Taverner Thomas, farmer
Ware George, farmer

Whiddon Henry, parish clerk
Whipple Wm. farmer
White Joseph, grocer, Post-Office

INSTOW DIRECTORY.
(For Instow History, see page 747.)
*Marked * are at the Quay.*
Bale John, butcher
*Body John, beer seller
*Bradstock Rev. R. T., M.A.
*Chater George, surgeon
*Greening Wm. gent
Hulme Edward, Esq., *Worlington Hs*
*Lane Thomas, vict. Marine Hotel
Lang Capt. John, *Bellevista Cottage*
Lloyd Rev. A. F. *Rectory*
*Lock John, blacksmith
Lock Thos. and Son, surveyors, *Fern Hs*
Mallett John, gent. *Marine Cottage*
*Nation Wm. butcher
*Palmer Rev. Septimus, M.A.
*Powleslaud Wm. vict. Hotel
Priest John, tax collector
Puckford Capt. James, R.N. *Bar View*
Taylor John B. gent. ‖ Prestacott Mr
Torr Henry, gent. *Wood Villa*
Winch Wm. builder, &c.

FARMERS.
Bale James
Bellew John
Hancock John
Joslin James
Joslin John
Kitson Henry
Lock George
SHOPKEEPERS.
*Lane Elizabeth
*Mogridge Richa.
*Pidler Alex.
Winch Gertrude
LODINGS.
*Beara George
*Beara John
*Delve Wm.
*Fishley S. B.
*Goman Wm.
*Huxtable Wm.
Macey Wm.
Marshall Wm.
Onslow Cyril
Otley Louisa
Ryland Mary
Sanders Fredk.
Snell Charles
Tanner Hannah
Walker Letitia
Withecombe John
Withecombe Rd.
Young Wm. (and bath proprietor)

Pages.   ERRATA.
74, Leofric 12th, not 6th Bishop
265, J. P. Bellew, not Bellow
303, Tiverton Hundred, 24,000 acres
326, Hockworthy, not *worty*
351, Bishop Coleridge died Dec., 1849
367, The monuments and altar piece here noticed are in *Widworthy Church,* not at *Honiton*
391, W. Beadon, Esq., is building a handsome mansion at Wyke, called *Otterhead*
429, *Brixham,* add Wm. H. Wills, draper, &c.
463, *Ashburton and South Devon Geological and Mineralogical Society* was established in 1850. It has a museum, and Robert Palk & Hy. Caunter are its secretaries
499, Rev. Richd. Antrem, M.A., incbt. of Slaptoa, *(vice* Rev. T. G. Dickenson)
508, *Totnes,* add Messrs. Chas. Edwards and T. C. Kelk, attorneys
538, *Blatchford* House, not Blackford
571, Rev. Saml. Badcock was ordained *by* Bishop Ross, (not Bishop of Ross)
663, Weston Peverell, (not Western)
664, *Compton Gifford,* add Geo. Boughton Kingdon, Esq., & *Sir Jas. J. Gordon Bre-*

mer, K.C.B. The small tithes have been commuted for £160 a year to the Vicar of Charles, and £65 to the Vicar of St. Andrew's, Plymouth

767, *Buckland Filleigh*, add Joseph Risdon, gent

769, LANGTREE CHARITIES: The *Church*

Lands comprise 14A. and 5 houses, let for £35. The *Church and Poor's Land* (13A.) is let for £11, of which two-thirds belong to the poor, who have also 8A., left by Rt. Phipps in 1676, and the interest of £30, left by H. Futts and G. Gilbert

---

LIFTON HUNDRED, continued from page 804.

DUNTERTON, a small scattered parish, in the Tamar valley, 7½ miles N.W. by W. of Tavistock, has only 212 souls, and 1161 acres of land, including *Eastacott* hamlet. Arthur Kelly, Esq., is lord of the manor, and owner of most of the soil. The *Church* (All Saints,) is an ancient edifice, mostly in the decorated style, with a fine tower and three bells. In Chapel field are the remains of a chantry chapel, converted into a cowhouse. The Rev N. T. W. Royse is patron and incumbent of the *rectory*, valued in K.B. at £8. 7s. 1d., and having a good residence, and 70½A. of glebe. The tithes were commuted in 1842, for £210 per annum. In the valley is a fine *waterfall*, flowing to the Tamar over a rocky precipice 100 feet high. *Directory:*—Rev. Nathnl. Thos. W. Royse, *Rectory;* John Reath, *shopkeeper;* and James Fitze, Wm. Harris, Wm. Lark, John and Rd. Mason, Johanna Reath, and John Spear, *farmers.*

LAMERTON, a scattered village, 3 miles N.W. of Tavistock, has in its parish 1288 souls, and 6788 acres of land, including the small hamlets of *Ottery, Chaddlehanger, North Brentor,* and *Hilltown.* The manors and owners are—*Lamerton,* Earl Fortescue; *Ottery,* Duke of Bedford; *Willestrew,* J. Carpenter, Esq.; and *Collacombe,* Sir W. P. Call, Bart. Collacombe Barton, rebuilt in the reign of Elizabeth, was for many generations the chief seat of the Tremayne family, but is now a farm house. In one of the rooms is a large transom window, in 18 compartments, containing 3200 panes of glass. In the parish are several neat villas, and many scattered farm houses. A great part of the soil belongs to the Rev. W. Gill, of *Venn House,* and J. H. Clobery, John James, W. Weekes, and Henry Terrell, Esqrs., and several smaller owners. The *Church* (St. Peter,) is a large structure, with an embattled tower and six bells. Among its monuments is one to the memory of Thomas Tremayne, Esq., his wife, and sixteen children. Two of their eight sons were twins, and so exactly resembled each other, that even in manhood they could not be distinguished one from the other, even by their parents and friends. Their affections and propensities were the same, and they were both killed in the wars at Newhaven, in France, in 1564. The *vicarage,* valued in K.B. at £13. 2s. 1d., and in 1831 at £445, is in the patronage of J. H. Tremayne, Esq., and incumbency of the Rev. Edw. Carlyon, who has 26A. of glebe, and a good residence, erected in 1845. The tithes were commuted in 1840, the vicarial for £397, and the rectorial for £310. 16s. 11d. per annum. Of the latter, £157. 10s. belongs to R. Eales, Esq., and the remainder to 21 smaller impropriators. There is a small Chapel of Ease at North Brentor, built in 1825; and a small dissenting chapel in the village. The poor have £20 a year from Tremayne's charity, as noticed with Coryton, and here is a *Parish School,* erected by subscription in 1823. *Marked* 1 *are at North Brentor;* 2, *at Ottery; and* 3, *at Hilltown.*

Carlyon Rev Edward, *Vicarage*
Clemo John, vict. Bedford Arms
Clobery John Herring, Esq. *West Langstone*
Cowland Mrs. *Camplehay*
Geake John V. S. vict. Blacksmiths' Arms
Gill Rev Wm. *Venn House*
Hornbrook Mrs. *Chaddlehanger*
Hortop John, butcher, *Hill top*
Hortop Wm. jun. vict. Fortescue Arms
Irvine Rev G. M. curate
James John, Esq. *East Langstone*
Morgan Mrs. *Belle Grove*
Pengelly John, auctioneer and surveyor
Percy John, schoolmr., regr., asst. overseer, and agent to Alfred Life Office
Spry Jas. cattle dealer, *Chaddlehouse*
Terrell Henry, Esq. *Ottery Park*
Weekes Walter, Esq. *Hurlditch*
Willesford H. B., Esq., Woodman's Well

BLACKSMITHS.
Bennett Wm.
Box J., *Chip shop*
Brown Charles
2 Roskilly Isaac

BOOT & SHOE MKRS.
Northcote James
1 Rice Edward
3 Swailes Samuel
Tucker Joseph

CARPENTERS.
Arscott Thomas
Bate Arthur
Broad John
Gloyn John & jun
2 Hawkins John
Jury Wm.
1 Rice John
Rice Roger
1 Rice Stephen
1 Rice Thomas

FARMERS.
(* *are Owners.*)
Brook Wm.
Brown Wm.
2 Burrow Richard
Colmer Thomas
*Cundy Daniel
*Doidge Richard
Down John, *Fursdon*
Eastcott John
Ellis Richard
Fuge Samuel, *Hall*
Eggins Thomas
2 Gribble Wm.

Gribble John
3 Hortop Wm.
Hutchings Holnd.
Kinsman Wm.
Lethbridge Js.&Jno.
Major Thomas
Norrington Fredk.
Percy Wm.
3 Rawlins Mr
1 Rice John
3 Rickard Thomas
*Roskilly Thomas
*Rowe Rd. & jun
Sly Samuel
1 Squire Thomas
1 Squire Wm.
Watkins David
2 Weekes Thomas
Wilcocks Joseph
3 Williams Wm.

MASONS.
Botterell John
Botterell Thomas
Doidge Wm.
Hardy Richard

LIFTON HUNDRED. (OKEHAMPTON.)

20

MILLERS.	Sly Eml. & Saml.	Geake John S. V.	TAILORS.
Lewis James	SHOPKEEPERS.	Gloyne John	Hooper Wm.
Symons Philippa	1 Bickle John	Hardy Richard	Pomery John
SAWYERS.	Botterell John	1 Tapson John	POST, &c., from Ta-
Palmer Charles	2 Dinner Susan	2 Vinning Betsy	vistock.

OKEHAMPTON, or *Oakhampton*, is a small but busy *market town*, and ancient *borough*, which gives name to a large *union, deanery,* and *polling and county court districts*; and is picturesquely seated near the northern extremity of Dartmoor Forest, in the valley of the river *Okement*, which is formed here by the confluence of two moorland streams, called the East and West Okement, which unite below the East and West Bridges, the former of which was rebuilt in 1841, and the latter in 1831. The town is on the high road from Falmouth to Exeter, 22 miles W. by N. of the latter; 16 miles N.N.E. of Tavistock, 12 miles N.W. of Moreton-Hampstead, and 194 miles W. by S. of London. Its large *parish* had 1430 inhabitants in 1801, 2055 in 1831, and 2194 in 1841, and extends over 9552 acres of land, including the scattered hamlets of *Chicecott, Brightley, Lower Fatherford, Meldon,* and KIGBEAR, the latter of which includes *Southcott, Maddaford, Nethercott,* and *Croft* farms, &c., and comprises about 1400 acres, all in Black Torrington Hundred. The parish extends several miles round the town, and includes several large commons and moorland tracts, containing *slate, limestone,* and *granite.* There is a very superior quarry of the latter at Meldon. Near *Cranmere Pool,* among the rude and mountainous tors and hills, and the deep rocky glens of Dartmoor, about six miles south of Okehampton, seven rivers have their sources, namely, the *East and West Okement,* which unite below the town; the *Taw, Teign, Dart, Tavy,* and *Lyd.* (See page 44.) In Domesday, the town is called *Ockmenton,* from the river, and is described as having a castle, four burgesses, and a market; and as being the head of a great *barony* or *honor,* which was given by William the Conqueror to Baldwin de Sap, or de Brioniis. Richard de Redvers, or Rivers, Earl of Devon, obtained the *Barony of Okehampton* from William II., and in the thirteenth century it passed to the Courtenays, (Earls of Devon, &c.,) as noticed with the account of that noble and ancient family, at pages 32 and 33. After the death of Edward Courtenay, Earl of Devon, in 1556, without issue, the baronial estates were divided among four co-heiresses, who married into the families of Arundell, Trethurfe, Mohun, and Trelawny. Their shares afterwards passed to various other families; and the parish now belongs to A. B. Savile, J. M. Woollcombe, H. Hawkes, J. C. Luxmoore, and Jas. Crotch, Esqrs.; the Rev. C. T. C. Luxmoore, Sir R. R. Vyvyan, and many smaller owners. Mr. Luxmoore is lord of the manors of *Halstock and Meldon* and that of *Kigbear* belongs to J. G. Newton, Esq. Albany Bourchier Savile, Esq., is lord of the manor, and owner of *Oaklands* a large and handsome mansion in the Grecian style, built about 30 years ago, on the north side of the town, in a finely wooded lawn. On the summit and declivities of a high rocky mound, in the valley of the West Okement, and at the feet of the lofty hills of Dartmoor, about half a mile S. W. of the town, are the venerable ivy-clad ruins of *Okehampton Castle,* which was long the seat and fortress of its powerful Barons, who held 92 manors in fee, and had here a numerous retinue. The declivities of the mound are thickly clothed with foliage, and on its lofty summit rise the massy mouldering walls of the keep, some fragments of which are much higher than the rest, and appear ready to fall on the assault of the next boisterous tempest from the neighbouring wilds of Dartmoor; but owing to the durable quality of the cement, they may long withstand the fury of the elements. There are still remains of the centre gate, the moat, the base court, and the chapel. The extensive area occupied by the ruins, the solidity of their structure, and the advantages of the situation, prove that this fortress, before it was dismantled, in 1539, must have been of great strength and importance. The site of the castle has recently been purchased by Sir R. R. Vyvyan, Bart. The *Park,* which surrounds the castle and extends nearly three miles along the southern side of the West Okement valley, contains about 1600 acres, and belongs to the Rev. C. T. C. Luxmoore, but is leased to J. Luxmoore, Esq. It was disparked and alienated by Henry VIII., at the instance of Sir Rd. Pollard, but is said to have abounded in fine oak trees till the latter part of the last century. During the *civil wars,* Okehampton was occasionally occupied by the contending parties, but was seldom more than a temporary station. Prince Maurice was here with 2000 troops in 1644 from July 2nd to the 19th; and the King was here on the 29th. Sir Richd. Grenville was quartered here in Dec., 1645, with a considerable force, but he suddenly left the town on the approach of Sir Thomas Fairfax, who was here again in March, 1646. In the 20th of Edward I., Hugh de Courtenay, then lord of the barony of Okehampton, gave to the Portreeve and Commonalty about 300 acres of land, near the town, to be used by the burghers and inhabitants of the borough as a *common pasture,* in satisfaction of the rights which they had previously exercised in the castle park. About 40 years ago, the lord of the manor claimed the sole right of pasturage on this common during the Summer half of the year, and restricted the burgesses to the Winter half. The common is now being enclosed, and five-sixths of it have been allotted to the lord of the manor, and the remainder to the landowners and inhabitants of the borough, after selling 39A. 3R. 15P., for £1011, to pay the enclosure expenses. The portion belonging to the landowners and inhabitants will be let, and the rents applied to public uses. The *Borough* comprises a circuit round the town of about a mile in diameter. By pre_

OKEHAMPTON BOROUGH.

21

scription and feudal charters, the burgesses enjoyed a market and many important rights, from an early period, under the government of a portreeve; but the borough was not incorporated till 1623, when James I. granted it *a charter*, which vested the government in a *mayor, eight principal burgesses, and eight assistants*, with a recorder, town clerk, and other officers; and directed that the mayor should also be chosen portreeve,—thus uniting, in the same person, the feudal and corporate offices. This charter was confirmed and enlarged by another granted by Charles II. in 1684. The latter is still the governing charter, as the borough is not included in the Municipal Reform Act of 1835, though it was disfranchised by the Parliamentary Reform Act of 1832. It first sent two members to Parliament on the 28th of Edward I., but after the 7th of Edward II., it ceased to return representatives till 1640, when the privilege was restored, and was regularly exercised till 1832. The right of election was in the freeholders and freemen, who numbered about 180. The mayor is chosen yearly by the corporate body from two burgesses nominated by the late mayor; and the mayor, the late mayor, and the recorder, are justices of the peace, and hold general quarter sessions for the borough, but the court of pleas has been long disused. The mayor and burgesses are lords of borough, and have a guildhall, a small prison, and a share of the rents of the "Common Lands, as afterwards noticed. The Corporate Body and Officers are as follow:—H. R. Colling, Esq., *mayor;* H. C. Millett, H. R. Colling, J. Carpenter, G Lacey, and John and Jas. Crotch, Esqrs., *principal burgesses;* Rev. H. Hutton and J. W. Thorne, A. B. Savile, J. Lacey, H. Hawkes, and J. M. Burd, *assistants;* the Rev. H. B. Wrey, *recorder;* Hy. Hawkes, *town clerk;* Jph. Sprague and Jph. Moore, *serjeants at mace;* and Thos. Brown, *town crier.* The County Court, for all the parishes in Okehampton Union, is held at the Guildhall on every fourth Friday, and Mr. P. Pearce, of Newton-Abbot, is the *clerk;* Mr. H. Hawkes, *assistant clerk;* and J. H. Hawkes, high bailiff. The town was formerly engaged in the manufacture of serges and other coarse woollens. It has been much improved during the last 30 years. The present commodious market buildings were erected in 1826, when the old shambles were removed from the street. The *market*, held every Saturday, is extensively supplied, and great quantities of agricultural produce are bought here for the markets of Exeter, Plymouth, &c. Here are also large *cattle fairs* on the 2nd Tuesday after March 11th; on the 2nd Thursday in May; on the Thursday after July 5th and August 5th; on the Tuesday after Sept. 11th; and on the Wednesday after October 11th. Here is a *great market* on the Saturday before, and a *giglet*, or pleasure fair, on the Saturday after Christmas day. At *Brightley*, in this parish, was a small *abbey*, founded by Richd. de Rivers, Earl of Devon, but afterwards removed by his sister to Ford, near Thorncombe. On the site is an ancient house, and the remains of a chapel. The *Parish Church* (All Saints,) stands on a bold eminence, nearly half a mile west of the town, and was destroyed by fire, except the tower, on the 13th of Feb., 1842. It was rebuilt soon afterwards, at the cost of about £3500, and is a spacious and handsome structure, in the perpendicular style. The tower contains six bells, and has crocketted pinnacles. A. B. Savile, Esq., is patron of the *vicarage*, valued in K.B. at £20, and in 1831 at £450. The Rev. J. Downall, M.A., is the incumbent, and has 230a. of glebe, and a good modern residence in the Tudor style. The tithes were commuted in 1839, the vicarial for £370, and the rectorial for £271 per annum. A. B. E. Holdsworth, Esq., is impropriator of the latter. *St. James' Chapel* is an ancient building in the town, and was founded as a chantry, but was given to the Corporation by one of the Courtenay family. Divine service is performed in it occasionally by a chaplain appointed by the Corporation. Here is a neat *Independent Chapel*, erected in 1822, and a *Wesleyan Chapel*, built in 1841. Here are *National and Infant Schools*, established in 1837 and 1848, and a literary society with a library, commenced in 1834.

The *Parish and Church Lands* comprise 8a. and 3 houses, which had belonged to a chantry, and were purchased at the Reformation. The *Common Lands*, mostly acquired at the same time, and in the same manner, are vested in trust for the poor and the general benefit of the borough and parish. They comprise about 84 acres and four houses, &c., mostly let at low rents, in consideration of fines paid by the lessees. Half of the clear income is carried to the churchwardens' accounts, and the other half belongs to the Corporation, except 40s. a year for the poor parishioners, who have also the following charities; viz., the rent of 90a. of moorland, at Blackdown, left by *Walter Holditch*, in 1485; and about £21 per annum arising from the *benefactions* of Rd. Brock, R. Harragroe, Mary Field, J. Buckle, A. Palmer, and H. Macey. In 1713,.*John Northmore* left for the poor of Okehampton and South Tawton, a farm of 45a., at Drewsteignton, now let for about £32 a year. The *Almshouses* in Castle lane, for two poor people, were rebuilt in 1848, and were founded in 1588, by *Richard Brock*, and endowed with a field of 1a. 31p. They have also the interest of £20 given by several donors. The *Wester Almshouse*, a small old building, has no endowment. *Joan Stone*, in the 2nd of Richard III., left a farm of 150a. at Lower Westacott, for repairing the bridges and highways. The rents and fines are paid to the Corporation, who repair the bridges and roads out of the rents and profits of the ancient town and borough lands. Okehampton Union is described at page 799.

The Post-Office is at Mr. Richard Crotch's, and the mail is despatched to Exeter, London, &c., at 5 min. before 6 eveng., and to Cornwall, &c., at 5 min. before 7 morning.

444

Bestall Rev. W. S. (Wesleyan)
Bond Mr Wm. || Carpenter Miss
Bradshaw Rev Samuel, *Oaklands*
Burd John Marsh, solicitor
Carpenter John, timber merchant
Colling Henry Robson, solicitor
Crotch Jas., Esq. *Queen's foreign messenger*
Downall Rev John, M.A., *Vicarage*
Drew Henry, contractor
Eastman Peter Wm cooper
Evely Wm. veterinary surgeon
Fryer Merlin, solicitor
Gibbings Richard, relieving officer
Gould Geo. sen. & jun. surveyors, *Northcott*
Gower Rt. F. agt. to *National Provincial Bank of England*
Hawkes Henry, solr. town clerk, &c.
Holland Rt. gent || Gilbert G. P.
Jackson Rev Wm. (Independent)
Lake Mr John || Lewis Mrs
Landick Mr Samuel || March Wm.
Luxmoore Mrs || Walsh Captain
Millett Hannibal Curnow, Esq.
Newcombe Thomas, fellmonger
Painter Wm. plasterer
Paltridge Peter, master of *Workhouse*
Seymour Mary, lace, &c. dealer
Seymour Chas. clerk to *Savings' Bank*
Sparrow Rd. rope and bag maker

FIRE AND LIFE OFFICE AGENTS.
City of London, Thomas Chaming
Clerical and Medical, E. Newcombe
English and Scottish, M. Fryer
Farmers, W. Ashley
Globe, Hy. R. Colling
Legal and Commercial, Henry Newton
Star, Richard Jessop
Sun, P. W. Eastman
United Kingdom, C. Seymour
West of England, G. Lacey

INNS & TAVERNS.
Exeter Inn, Stephen Hole
Fountain, John Hucker
George, Robert Drew
King's Arms, Charity Frost
London Inn, John Ball, (*posting*)
New Inn, Samuel Gillard
Old Post Boy, John Hockaday
Plume of Feathers, John Kennard
Red Lion, Richard Rich
Star, John Jope
White Hart, John Crotch, (*posting*)

ACADEMIES.
Chaming Thomas
Friend John
Harris Jane
Lillicrap Mary
Sprague Joseph

BAKERS.
Pitts Jn ||Yeo Eliz.

BLACKSMITHS.
Hooper Thomas
Mallins Thos.
Moore Wm.
Pike Samuel
Paltridge Thos.
Paltridge Wm.

BOOKSELLERS.
SimmonsThs.&Eliz
Townsend John

BOOT & SHOE MKRS.
Brook John

Brown Thomas
Harris John
Heanes Wm.
Osborne James
Palmer John
Sampson Wm.
Westcott John
Williams Wm.

BUTCHERS.
Clark John
Leach George
Perry Richard

CARPENTERS.
Ceely Joseph
Coombe Wm.
Lillycrap Rd.
Lillycrap Edw.
Lovell Robert
Moore Joseph
Osborne James

Paltridge Wm.

CHEMISTS & DGTS.
Lacey George
Lake Ebenz.
Newcombe Eml.
Newcombe J. L.

CORN MILLERS.
Kemp Samuel
Lake John

CURRIERS, &c.
Ashley Wm.
Newcombe John
Sampson Robert

EATING HOUSES.
Coombes Simon
Crocker James
Perry Richard

FARMERS.
(* are Owners, & † in *Kigbear hamlet.*)
*Ball John
Ball Richard
†Banbury Charles
†Banbury John
*†Bevan James
†Bevan Robert
†Bevan John
Blackmore Henry
Blatchford Wm.
Bolt John, *Halstk.*
Britton George
*Brooks Robert
Chastey Mr
Coombe George
Coombe Wm.
Davey John
*†Davey Thomas
Ellis James
Endacott John
*Frost John
Gale Geo. *Chicecot*
Gard John, *Youldch*
Gloyne A. *Halstock*
Hodge John, *Moorgt*
Howard F. *Glendon*
Jackman Robert
Jackman Samuel
†Jones Squire
Knapman E. & A.
*Luxmoore John C. *Estrayer Park*
Newcombe John
†Newcombe Rd.
Palmer Johanna
Palmer Samuel
Pellow John
Rich Samuel
*†Shobrook John
*†Shobrook Jonas
*†Smale Wm.
*Smith Richard
Spray Matthew
†Squire George
Stanley James
*Watts Thomas
†Westlake Richard
Wills George

GROCERS.
Heanes Wm.
Lacey Geo. & wine & spirit mercht
Lake Ebenezer

Newcombe Eml.
Newcombe John L.
Seymour AndrewR.

HAIRDRESSERS.
Blatchford Joseph
Coombe James

IRONMONGERS.
Jessop Rd. *tinner*
Seymour Wm.
Tutcher John

L. & W. DRAPERS.
Knapman Wm. and Smith Charles
Newton Henry
Paddon Wm.
Treliving Wm.
Yeo Wm.

MILLINERS.
Bickle Jane
Lewis E. & S.
Josling Lucta.
Sampson M. A.

PAINTERS, &c.
Moore Wm.
Northam John
Palmer John

SADDLERS.
Hewitt Wm.
Webber John

SHOPKEEPERS.
Ballamy John
Blathford Joseph
Hammett Robert
Hewitt Alice
Platridge John

STONE MASONS.
Coombe Simon
Drew Henry
Earle Wm.
Harris Richard
Painter Thomas
Painter Wm.
Seldon Wm.

STRAWHAT MAKRS.
Jordan Rebecca
Paltridge John

SURGEONS.
Empson C. M.
Gunning H. J.
Hawkes Thos. C.

TAILORS.
Earle James
James George
Moore Wm.
Westcott Wm.
Yeo Wm.

TANNERS.
Ashley Wm.
Newcombe John

WATCHMAKERS.
Lee Wm.
Philip Richard

WHEELWRIGHTS.
Bassett John
Coombe Wm.
Holloway Hy.
Lillicrap Giles
Thorne John

COACHES, &c.
(*call at the Inns.*)
Mail to Exeter, 5.55

LIFTON HUNDRED.

| eveng. & to Fal- mouth, 6.55 mng. *Coaches and Busses* to Exeter, Corn- | wall, Barnstaple, Tavistock, & Ply- mouth, alternate days. | CARRIERStoExeter, Tavistock, &c., twice a week; and | Jewell & Hodge, Mon., Tu., Th., and Saturday |

SOURTON, a small village, on the north-western verge of Dartmoor, near the sources of the river Lew, five miles S.W. of Okehampton, has in its parish 732 souls, and 5018A. of land, including a large portion of open moorland, and the small hamlets of *Collaven, Lake, Southerleigh,* and many scattered houses. J. G. Newton, S. C. Hamlyn, and J. M. Woollcombe, Esqrs., are lords of the manor, and owners of most of the soil, and the rest belongs to the Rev. J. Woollcombe, John Gill, John Ball, and a few smaller owners. The *Church* (St. Thomas à Beckett,) is a small antique structure, with a tower and five fine toned bells, but the chancel was rebuilt in 1848, and has two stained glass windows. The curacy is annexed to Bridestowe rectory, and the tithes were commuted in 1846, for £258 per annum.

Ball Wm. shopkeeper
Crocker and Co. *quarry owners*
Dark Mary, vict., Seven Stars
Dark Wm. beer seller
Dawe John, quarry manager
Horn Richard, vict., New Inn
Rattenbury Hugh, shoemaker
Weeks Geo. & Baker Wm. *smiths*
Wordon Absalom, carpenters

FARMERS.
Allen Edw. *Combe*
Alford Rd., Rt., & Thos. *Southerleigh*
Ball Richard
Bray John, *Dowdon*
Bray Thomas
Brook John

Brook Joseph
Coombe Hy. & Rt.
Crocker Robert
Gay John, *Lake*
Gloyne Matthew
Gloyne Richard
Heathman Wm.
Hill James, *Lidon*
Horn Martha
Horn Richard
Jackman Richard
Lisle James

Millman Richard
Newcombe John
Nicholls James
Northcott James
Pellow Edward
Pellow Richard
Pellow Wm.
Rattenbury Hugh
Roberts Wm.
Squires Jonas
Vaudon Wm.
Watkins Emanuel

STOWFORD, a small village, in the valley of one of the tributary streams of the river Lyd, seven miles E.N.E. of Launceston, has in its parish 647 souls, and 2066 acres of land, including *Sprytown* hamlet, and many scattered houses. Hy. Blagrove, Esq., is lord of the manor of Milford, but that of Stowford belongs to Mrs. Harris, together with *Haine* and *Stone* estates, which have been held by the Harris family many genera- tions. She has a handsome seat here, called *Haine Castle*—a large quadrangular man- sion, in the castellated style, erected 40 years ago. The *Church* is a handsome structure, with a tower, six bells, and several monuments belonging to the Harris family, one of whom was master of the household to Geo. II. and III. The *rectory*, valued in K.B. at £11. 12s. 6d., and in 1831 at £270, is in the patronage and incumbency of the Rev. Jno. Wollocombe, M.A., who has 55A. 2R. 22P. of glebe, and a handsome residence. The *Parish Land* comprises a farm of 30A., and a wood of 6A., given by Mrs. Trist, in the 16th century, for the repairs of the church, and the surplus for the poor. The dividends of £300 three per cent. consols, purchased with the gift of *Margaret Doyle*, in 1791, are paid for schooling poor children.

Bickle John, shopkeeper & shoemaker
Bratton Mrs. *Issington*
Brown Ann, shopkeeper
Chagwin John, swine dealer
Ellis John, shopkeeper
Harris Mrs Eliz. *Haine Castle*
Perry Solomon, vict., Royal Oak
Rundle Wm. shopkeeper and carpenter
Scoffern Rt. beerhouse, *Portgate*
Oxman Arthur, carpenter, *Portgate*

Wollocombe Rev Jno., M.A., & Rev J. B. *Rectory*
CORN MILLERS.
Pedrick John
Spear Ralph. *Spry*
FARMERS.
Braund Arscott
Brown Charles
Combe John
Down Mr
Guscott Richard

Jackman John
Northcott Richard
Northcott Wm.
Perry Mrs
Rowe Thomas
Rundle Richard
Scoffern John D.
Woods Henry

SYDENHAM-DAMAREL, or *South Sydenham,* is a scattered parish, on the eastern side of the Tamar valley, from four to five miles W.N.W of Tavistock, containing 369 souls, and about 2200 acres of land. The Executors of the late John Carpenter, Esq., are lords of the manor, owners of a great part of the soil, and patrons of the *rectory,* valued in K.B. at £10. 6s. 8d., and in 1831 at £245. The Rev. C. E. Radclyffe, M.A., is the incumbent, and has 102A. of glebe, and a large residence. The tithes have been commuted for £165 per annum. The *Church* (St. Mary,) is a small fabric, in the perpendicular style, with a handsome tower, containing five bells. The poor have £20 a year from *Tremayne's Charity,* as noticed at page 801. Here is a small Bible Christian chapel, erected in 1832. H. Rundle, G. C. Bloye, J. S. Lethbridge, J. H. Gill, and Hy. Hoidge, have estates in the parish.

Bloye Mr G. C. ‖ Lethbridge J. S.
Bullivant Mr. mine agent
Burrow Richard, corn miller
Foot Matthew, vict., Horsebridge Inn
Hancock Natl. shopkeeper & carpenter
Pellow Wm. vict., New Inn

Radclyffe Rev Chas. Edw., M.A. *Rectory*
BLACKSMITHS.
Hearne James
Hooper John
FARMERS.
Amery James

Carpenter Richard
Cole Roger
Cole Wm. B.
Eastlake John
Freeman Richard

Harris John	Kerslake Robert	Ryalls Richard	Tapper James
Helson John	Pearn Robert	Sleeman Mr	Weeks Walter
Hoidge Henry	Reynolds John		

TAVY ST. MARY, or *Mary Tavy*, a scattered village in the Tavy valley, and on the western side of Dartmoor, 4 miles N.E. by N. of Tavistock, is chiefly inhabited by miners. Its parish contains 1552 souls, and 4180 acres of land, including about 2100A. of open moorland; the village of *Horndon;* the high moorland district of *Black Down*, and other parts of Dartmoor, where there are five valuable *copper, tin, and lead mines*, called *Wheal*, and *North, South,* and *East Wheal Friendship ;* and *Kingscott* and *Bedford.* Wheal Friendship has been worked half a century, and is the most profitable in the neighbourhood, except one of those named at page 624. John Buller, Esq., is lord of the manor, owner of a great part of the soil, and patron of the *rectory*, valued in K.B. at £14. 5s. 7½d., and in 1831 at £260. The Rev. Anthony Buller is the incumbent, and has 30A. 1R. 10P. of glebe, and a small Parsonage. The tithes were commuted in 1843, for £207. 10s. per annum. The *Church* is a small antique edifice, with a tower and three bells. Mrs. Carpenter and several smaller owners have estates in the parish, mostly freehold. The Bible Christians have one, and the Wesleyans two small chapels in the parish. The *Church Land* 2½A., is at Lidford. The National School was established in 1837. *Marked* 1 *are at Black Down ; and* 2, *at Horndon.*

Arthur Richard, National Schoolmaster	Lucas Thomas	Virgus John
1 Ball Richard, vict. Royal Standard	Maddock Wm.& jun	MINE AGENTS.
2 Ball Thomas, vict. New Inn	Maunder Jas.& Jph.	Barratt Alexander
Buller Rev Anthony, M.A. *Rectory*	Maunder Wm.	Harris James
Mitchell John, vict. Buller's Arms	Michell John	Williams Wm.
BOOT & SHOEMKRS.	Cole Elizbth., John,	Nicholls Mary	SHOPKEEPERS.
Hooper Wm.	Saml.,Ths.,&Wm.	Pearce Joseph	1 Crews Arthur
2 Newton Wm.	Daw Thos. & jun.	Perkins Christopher	1 Daw Wm.
2 Rayment Agts.	Doidge John	Reddicliffe John	1 Ferret John
CORN MILLERS.	Down John	Rich David	1 Nail Jane
Hoiles Charles	Floyd Richard	Richards James	1 Richards James
Virgus John	2 Floyd Wm.	Squires Thomas	Williams Wm.
FARMERS	Floyd John	Williams Wm.	TAILORS.
Arthur Jas. & Wm.	Fuge Samuel	Willing John	Gordon Wm.
Axford John	Goddard Messrs	MASONS.	Hurford John
Bennett Francis	Hill Henry	1 Daw Wm.	

THRUSHELTON, or *Thruselton*, is a scattered parish, 10 miles S.W. by W. of Oke-hampton, containing 628 souls, and 3714A. of land, generally having a heavy soil, resting on *clay, limestone,* and *manganese.* T. H. Tremayne, Esq., is lord of the manors of Thrushelton and Canonbarn, impropriator of the rectory, and patron of the *vicarage,* which is annexed to that of Mary Stowe. J. G. Newton and several smaller owners have estates here. The *Church* (St. George,) is a small structure, with a tower and five bells. The tithes were commuted in 1839, the rectorial for £130, and the vicarial for £109 per annum.

Davey Anthy. & Down Wm. carpenters	Horn John, *miller*	*Perry Wm.& John
Ellis Wm. blacksmith	Jeffery Wm.	Reynolds Mr
Frise Thomas, shoemaker	Kennard George	*Smith Philip
Parsons John, vict. New Inn, *Lew Down*	Mason Mr	*Soper Jane
Rice Roger, schoolmaster	*Northcott John	Tapson John
Yelland Wm. beer seller	*Northcott Roger	Taunton Peter
FARMERS.	Down Richard	*Page John & Thos.	Took John
(* *are Owners.*)	Frise Robert	*Palmer Thomas	Watkins Wm.
*Abell Henry	Hamley John, *Mills*	*Perry John S.	

VIRGINSTOWE, a small village, pleasantly situated in the valley of the Carey ri-vulet, 6½ miles N. by E. of Launceston, has in its parish 167 souls, and 1274A. 2R. 39P. of land. H. Hawkes, Esq., owns part of the soil, and the rest belongs to several smaller owners. The *Church* (St. Bridget,) is a small ancient dilapidated structure, which is about to give place to a new one, to be erected in the early lancet style, at the cost of about £500. The new church will have a bell gable, and 137 sittings, of which 83 will be free. The *rectory*, valued in K.B. at £5. 6s. 8d., and in 1831 at £103, is in the pa-tronage of the Lord Chancellor, and incumbency of the Rev. Ponsford Cann, B.A., who built the handsome Rectory House in 1845, supports the schools, and is a liberal contri-butor to the new church, to which Mrs. Morrison, of Yeo Dale, has presented a valuable silver-gilt service of communion plate. The glebe is 56A. 11P., and the tithes have been commuted for £119 per annum.

Cann Rev Ponsford, B.A. rector, and in-cumbent of Broadwoodwidger, *Rectory*	FARMERS.	*Hoidge Thomas
	(* *are Owners.*)	Meathrell Richard
Berribell Samuel, shoemaker	Baskerville Wm.	*Rockey Wm.
Rockey John, shopkeeper	*Braund Lewis	*Veale Wm.
Rowland Humphrey, smith and vict. Hare and Hounds	Croker John	*Vickary John
	*Fry John	

GENERAL HISTORY

AND

DESCRIPTION

OF THE

COUNTY OF DEVON.

DEVONSHIRE, the largest county in England, except Yorkshire, and the most western except Cornwall, ranks among the first in agricultural importance, and the sixth in amount of population. It has mines of copper, tin, lead, and iron ores; inexhaustible quarries of durable granite, slate, lime, building stone, marble, &c.; and is one of the oldest seats of the lace and coarse woollen manufactures, of which it still retains a considerable share, though greatly reduced since last century, by the machinery and factories of the midland and northern counties. Occupying the whole breadth of the central portion of that great south-western peninsula of the British Island, which juts out between the Bristol and English Channels, and having more than 150 miles of sea coast, and some fine navigable rivers and broad estuaries, Devonshire is one of the most important maritime counties in the kingdom. It has many sea ports, spacious harbours, and noble bays, and the great *naval station*, Plymouth and Devonport, is at its south-western angle, adjoining Cornwall. On its coast are many handsome and delightful *bathing places*, the principal of which are Torquay, Teignmouth, Exmouth, Sidmouth, Dawlish, and Budleigh Salterton, on the south-east coast, celebrated for their mild and genial climates; and Ilfracombe on the north coast. It comprises 30 market towns, including nine parliamentary boroughs, and its large and handsome capital—the city of Exeter, which is a county of itself. In picturesque beauties, embracing all the associations of hill and dale, wood and water, fertile valleys, elegant mansions, with sylvan parks and pleasure grounds; lofty moorland hills and dells, and extensive land and marine views, it yields to no county in England. In its greatest length and breadth it extends about 70 miles east and west and north and south; and though of an irregular figure, it may be said to occupy (if we include its large bays,) nearly all the area of a circle 70 miles in diameter, lying between the parallels of 50 deg. 12 min. and 51 deg. 14 min. north latitude; and 3 degrees and 4 deg. 30 min. west longitude. It is traversed in a south-westerly direction by the Bristol and Exeter and South Devon *Railways*, which have branches to Tiverton, Crediton, and Torquay; but the Taw Valley line and some other projected railways are not yet made, though acts were obtained for their construction a few years ago. The boundaries of Devon are Somersetshire and part of Dorsetshire on the north-east; the Bristol Channel on the north; the river Tamar, which divides it from

B

Cornwall, on the west; and the English Channel on the south and south-east, where its *coast line* is more than 100 miles in extent, and is beautifully diversified and broken by numerous bays, estuaries, creeks, promontories, and headlands; presenting in many places high rocky cliffs, fine sandy shores, pretty towns, villages, and villas, and busy ports and fishing stations. The north coast, including the large semi-circular sweep of Barnstaple Bay, is more than 50 miles in extent. The county is in the *Diocese of Exeter, Province of Canterbury,* and *Western Circuit,* and comprises 533,460 inhabitants, and about 1,700,000 *acres of land,* or 2493 *square miles,* as will be seen in the following Statistical Summary of its 32 *Hundreds, &c.* [LUNDY ISLAND, a detached member of Devon, is noticed at page 565.]

SUMMARY OF DEVONSHIRE, SHEWING THE POPULATION OF THE HUNDREDS, &c., IN 1841, AND THEIR TERRITORIAL EXTENT.

Hundreds.	Acres.	Population.	Hundreds.	Acres.	Population.
*Axminster	52,547 ..	15,197	*Ottery St. Mary.	9,944 ..	4,194
Bampton	30,000 ..	6,990	*Plympton......	32,230 ..	10,722
Black Torrington	141,600 ..	21,351	*Roborough ..	57,870 ..	12,169
Braunton	65,830 ..	24,694	Shebbear	79,200 ..	21,741
*Budleigh, (East)	52,341 ..	22,001	Sherwill........	45,790 ..	4,643
Budleigh, (West)	52,341 ..	3,372	*Stanborough ...	61,890 ..	15,633
*Cliston........	19,552 ..	3,871	*Tavistock ...	23,790 ..	7,697
*Coleridge......	51,470 ..	20,987	Tawton,(North) } with Winkleigh }	65,300 ..	13,955
*Colyton	31,382 ..	8,176	*Teignbridge....	58,454 ..	14,708
Crediton	36,924 ..	12,055	Tiverton	24,000 ..	10,770
*Ermington	51,610 ..	10,949	Witheridge	80,034 ..	10,805
*Exminster	45,189 ..	18,412	*Wonford	87,516 ..	30,101
Fremington	33,350 ..	9,631	BOROUGHS.		
Halberton	14,000 ..	3,021	*Exeter (City of)..	4,000 ..	31,312
Hartland	30,360 ..	4,966	*Plymouth ....}	2,300 ..	36,527
Hayridge	48,858 ..	13,783	*Devonport ..}		43,532
*Haytor........	61,256 ..	28,702			
Hemyock	28,000 ..	6,089			
*Lifton........	136,350 ..	16,020	Total....	1,684,208	533,460
Molton, (South)..	67,930 ..	15,100			

☞ The Hundreds are divided into PETTY SESSIONAL DIVISIONS, as shewn with the lists of Magistrates, and with the descriptions of the Hundreds. The County is divided into 25 UNIONS, which are described with the parishes from which they are named, and it is shewn with each Hundred to what Unions its Parishes belong. The Unions generally coincide with the COUNTY COURT DISTRICTS.

＊ PARLIAMENTARY DIVISIONS, &c.—The 16 Hundreds and 2 Boroughs marked thus ＊ are in the *Southern Division of the County,* which includes also Exeter Castle, *but the City of Exeter is a county of itself.* All the other 16 Hundreds are in the *Northern Division of Devon,* which has its *chief place of election* at South Molton, and has *polling places* also at Collumpton, Tiverton, Linton, Ilfracombe, Barnstaple, Bideford, Torrington, Holsworthy, Hatherleigh, Chulmleigh, and Crediton. For the *Southern Division,* Exeter is the principal place of election, and its other *polling places* are Newton Abbot, Totnes, Dartmouth, Kingsbridge, Plymouth, Tavistock, Okehampton, and Honiton. Each Division has *two members of parliament,* as also has the *City of Exeter,* and each of the following

BOROUGHS, viz., *Plymouth, Devonport, Barnstaple, Honiton, Tavistock, Tiverton*, and *Totnes*. The Boroughs of *Ashburton* and *Dartmouth* each send one, making the total number of 22 members sent from this county to the House of Commons. The boroughs of *Plympton, Okehampton*, and *Beer-Alston*, in Devon, were disfranchised by the *Reform Act* of 1832, previous to which this county sent 26 members.

COUNTY VOTERS.—There are in the county about 8000 *freeholders*, and a large number of lease and copyholders. The largest number of freeholders polled for the whole county before 1832, was in 1818, when 4190 voted for Lord Ebrington; 3830 for E. P. Bastard, Esq.; and 3814 for Sir T. D. Acland, Bart. The number of electors registered for the county in 1837, was 18,432; of whom 12,561 were for the *Southern Division*, and 7871 for the *Northern Division*. Their present MEMBERS OF PARLIAMENT are Sir T. D. Acland, Bart., and L. W. Buck, Esq., for the *Northern Division;* and Sir J. B. Y. Buller, Bart., and Sir R. Lopes, Bart., for the *Southern Division*.

POPULATION, HOUSES, &c.—Of the 533,460 *inhabitants* at the last census, 252,760 were *males*, and 280,700 *females*, living in 94,704 *houses*, besides which there were in the county 6129 *unoccupied houses*, and 901 building, when the census was taken, on the 7th of June, 1841, when there were in the county 51,058 persons born elsewhere. Of the persons *above* 20 *years of age*, 131,975 were males, and 158,927 females. In the year 1801, Devon had only 343,001 souls, but in 1811, they had increased to 383,308; in 1821, to 439,040; in 1831, to 494,478; and in 1841, to 533,460, living in 588 *parishes, chapelries, and extra-parochial places*. The total number of parishes in the county is 465, exclusive of the *new district parishes* recently established. In 1831, the population consisted of 103,277 *families*, 36,150 of whom were chiefly employed in *agriculture*, 33,880 chiefly in *trade, manufacture, or handicraft;* and 33,247 otherwise employed, or living on their property without trade or profession.

ASSESSMENTS, RENTAL, &c.—The annual rental of the *land* in Devon assessed to the property tax in 1811, was £1,217,547, but the annual value of *real property*, (land, buildings, &c.,) was assessed to the same tax in 1815, at £1,897,515. The *parochial assessments* of the county in 1823, amounted to £227,425, of which £175,412 was levied on *land;* £47,461 on *dwelling-houses;* £2624 on *mills and factories;* and £1927 on *manorial profits*. In 1803 the parochial assessments amounted to £179,359, of which £148,565 was expended on the poor. In 1821, these assessments amounted to £272,939, of which £234,097 was expended on the poor. In 1839, after the formation of the large *unions*, and the erection of extensive *workhouses*, the sums collected in poor rates in the county amounted to £214,500. The *County Rates* are levied in Devon on a valuation made under a special act of parliament passed some years ago. They amounted in 1800, to £7031; in 1810, to £23,159; in 1830, to £12,783; in 1838, to £18,459; and in 1849, to upwards of £24,000, exclusive of *Exeter*, and the *boroughs having separate quarter sessions*, viz., *Barnstaple, Bideford, Dartmouth, Plymouth, Devonport, Tiverton, and South Molton*—the latter of which is not a parliamentary borough. The quarter sessions for the county are all held at Exeter, where two *assizes* are held yearly for the county, and two for the city. (See page 62.)

ANCIENT HISTORY.—Devon was called *Dunan* by the Cornish Britons; *Deuffneynt* by the Welsh; and *Devnascyre* by the Anglo-Saxons. It is supposed that it was inhabited at a very remote period, and that its inhabitants had commercial transactions in *tin, &c.,*

B 2

with the Phœnicians and Greeks.   Polwhele says that its aborigines were the *Danmonii;* but Whitaker supposes the latter were the Belgic invaders, and that the first inhabitants were the *Cimbri,* some of whom, after the invasion of the Belgæ from Gaul, emigrated to Ireland, and others continued in the north-west parts of Devonshire. Cæsar tells us that when he landed in Britain, he found the Belgæ occupying the sea coast; but Richard of Cirencester says the *Cimbri* were on the north, and the *Danmonii* on the south coast of Devon. The county was included with Cornwall, under the name of *Danmonium,* which is supposed to be derived from the Phœnician words *dan* or *dun,* a hill; and *moina,* mines; or from Welsh words signifying *deep valleys.* Under the Roman domination, Devon was included in that large and important division of the island called *Britannia Prima;* and by the Saxons it was made part of the kingdom of *Wessex,* and so continued till the incorporation of the seven Saxon Kingdoms into one monarchy, in the time of Egbert; as will be seen at pages 52 to 59, where most of the momentous events relating to the general history of Devon, are necessarily incorporated with the history of the city of Exeter.   There has been nothing peculiar in the government of Devonshire, except that of the *Stannary Laws,* which have been in force from a very early period in the *mining districts.*   The "STANNARY PARLIAMENTS" were anciently held in the open air, on an elevated spot called *Crockentor,* in Dartmoor.   Polwhele, who wrote about 1795, says that the president's chair, the jurors' seats, &c., cut in the rude stone, remained entire nearly till that period, though it had been customary for a very long time only to open the commission and swear in the jury on the site of the ancient court, and then to adjourn to the court house of one of the *stannary towns,* viz., Ashburton, Chagford, Plympton, and Tavistock. The *stannary prison* was a miserable dungeon at Lidford Castle. The custom of opening the court at Crockerntor, has been many years disused.

Until the invasion of *Julius Cæsar,* 55 years before the birth of Christ, the history of Britain is almost a blank, though the Phœnicians of Cadiz are supposed to have traded with Devon and Cornwall for tin, &c., some centuries before the Christian era. The *Ancient Britons,* in the south of England, had made some little progress towards civilization when *Cæsar* invaded the island.   They were divided into various tribes and nations, and their religion, which formed part of their free monarchial government, was druidical. The BRITISH DRUIDS exercised their utmost authority in opposing the usurpation of the Roman invaders, who, fired with equal resentment, determined to secure themselves by exterminating the Druidic Order.   In ancient times, Devonshire produced greater quantities of *tin* than Cornwall, and the method of *mining* was then of the simplest description, by "*shoding and streaming.*"   There are numerous stream works on Dartmoor and its vicinity, which have been forsaken for ages.   In the parishes of Monaton, Kingsteignton, and Teigngrace, are many old tin works of this kind.   That the *Druids* abounded in Devonshire, and were conversant particularly with *Dartmoor Forest* and its neighbourhood, is evident from the *crom-*

lechs, logan-stones, rock basins, stone pillars, circles, cairns, rocking stones, rude bridges, &c., still to be seen in the wild solitudes of the forest, and in the surrounding parishes of Drewsteignton, Manaton, Okehampton, &c. (See page 190.) The *religious and civil jurisdiction of the Druids* prevailed all over Britain. They dispensed justice; not under any written code of laws, but on what they professed to be equitable principles—all their verdicts being determined by such sense as the assembled delegates entertained of impartial justice, and on discordance of opinion in the congress, appeal was made to the Arch-Druid, whose sentence was decisive. Their religious ceremonies were few, and nearly in unison with those of the ancient Hebrews. They worshipped on high places and in deep groves; and were not so much addicted to idolatry as some authors have asserted, but adored the God of nature, and rendered him praise on the yearly succession of the seasons, which they kept as solemn festivals. Though they dealt largely in allegory and symbolical representations, they practised but little priestcraft, and held not the ignorance of their votaries in the bonds of superstition; but they clearly explained the mysteries and symbols used in their ceremonies, to the initiated. To remove from the people all possibility of sophistry and innovation, their maxims of justice were taught orally; and the sons of chief personages were disciples in their ethic schools, where the rules of moral life were inculcated as the foundation of human wisdom. They studied medicine and the virtue of plants, of which the *misletoe* was their chief specific; and they held nothing so sacred as the misletoe of the oak, which they gathered with great pomp and ceremony on a certain day, appointed for their greatest festival. In their civil government, capital offenders were sentenced to death, and publicly sacrificed on the altars of their temples; whilst those convicted of minor crimes were excluded from public worship, and excommunicated from all civil and religious benefits, till they had washed out, with the tears of repentance, the stains with which their guilt had branded them. Julius Cæsar said the Druids inculcated the immortality and transmigration of the soul, and discoursed with youth much about the heavenly bodies. Great numbers of the Druids were massacred by the Romans in the unsuccessful revolt of the Britons under Queen Boadicea, and from that period their power and splendour rapidly disappeared. The wild solitudes of *Dartmoor* are the great store-houses of Druidical and other British remains in Devon, and it is even conjectured that the ancient oaks of Wistman's or Wiseman's wood, near Bairdown, or the *hill of Bards*, amidst the gigantic tors and the rude British remains of Dartmoor Forest, are the "posterity" of a Druidical grove. This extensive forest was no doubt one of the last retreats of the Druids of Danmonia, and it was always their favourite place of resort. *Ancient British Roads* ran from Exmouth to Woodbury, and thence to Taunton in Somersetshire; from Exeter to Molland, from Crediton to Haldon, from Exeter to Okehampton, and from Seaton to Molland. In the ancient tin streams in and near Dartmoor, various *celts* and *Roman coins, rings, brooches, &c.*, have been found. Antique bronze wristlets were found some years ago, on the wrists of a skeleton, dug up in

the earthwork near Lower St. Columb; and near the remains of the Phœnician smelting houses was found a block of Jew's tin, much corroded, and betraying marks of such great antiquity, that it is supposed to be the most ancient in existence.

As noticed at page 52, the ROMANS had their chief station in this county at Exeter, from which they had roads diverging mostly in the lines of the *British track ways.* The principal of these passed through the whole length of Devonshire from north-east to south-west, and was called *Ikeneld street.* It entered this county from Dorsetshire, a little east of Axminster, whence it proceeded by Shute hill, Dalwood-down, Honiton, &c., to the large entrenchment at *Hembury Fort.* (See page 294.) From the latter it passed by Colestock, Talewater, Tallaton Common, and Larkbeare to Stretway-head, where it is still known by the name of the Old Taunton road. It crossed the river at Exeter, a little below Exe Bridge, and went over Haldon hill, near Ugbrooke, where there is a strong British camp. Below Newton Abbot it crossed the Teign by a ford still called *Hacknieldway.* After leaving another British camp on its left, it passed over Ford common to Totnes, which was a station of the ancient Britons. This ancient road was joined at Streetway-head by that from Exmouth, which passed through the great camp at Woodbury. Owing to local circumstances, antiquarians have found much difficulty in tracing the Roman roads, and fixing the sites of the stations in this county; and their opinions are so much at variance, that we shall dismiss the subject by referring the reader to the histories of those towns and parishes where there are remains or traces of them.

Though vestiges of numerous *fortifications* and *encampments* shew that Devon was a seat of warfare at a very early period, the earliest military transaction on record is the defeat of the Britons, in 614, by *Cynegils*, King of the West Saxons. The *Danes* having made frequent descents upon the coast, at last settled themselves in Exeter, but were besieged by *Alfred the Great*, and compelled to a truce. In the ensuing year they landed on the northern coast, and were defeated, with the loss of their favourite standard—the raven. In 894, they attempted to besiege Exeter, but withdrew on the approach of Alfred. In 1001 they were equally unsuccessful in their attack upon that city, but pillaged the surrounding country and retired with the spoil. Subsequently, however, they gained possession, and nearly destroyed it. In 1067, Exeter stood a regular siege before it surrendered to *William the Conqueror.* On the accession of Wm. Rufus, it was laid waste by the partizans of Robert, Duke of Normandy. During the *civil wars* between the houses of York and Lancaster, Devonshire was much disturbed; though no battle was fought within its limits. In 1497, Perkin Warbeck besieged Exeter, but the siege being raised by the Earl of Devon, Warbeck proceeded to Taunton. When the civil wars between Charles I. and the Parliament commenced, this county was controlled by committees, and the majority of the inhabitants were attached to the Parliament. Plymouth was fortified by the townsmen against the royalists. Exeter was garrisoned by the parliamentarians, and a cavalry body, raised in the

county, was stationed at Fitzford, near Tavistock. After the defeat of the parliamentarians, a cessation of hostilities was agreed on ; but the treaty was soon broken off, and the county again disturbed by internal broils. In 1644, the Earl of Essex fixed his head quarters at Tiverton, and having secured Barnstaple for the Parliament, marched into Cornwall, and was followed by the King. In October, Ilfracombe and Barnstaple surrendered to the royal forces. In 1645, the clubmen of Devon declared for the Parliament, and from this time the royalists experienced great reverses. In the midst of their disasters, Sir Thomas Fairfax, commander-in-chief of the parliamentarian army, entered the county, and soon reduced every town and fortress. He took Exeter, after a long siege, in April, 1646. Pursuing his victorious career, he stormed the church and castle of Tiverton, and attacked and defeated Lord Hopeton's army at Torrington. This victory appears to have given the death blow to the royalists' power in the west, and the last garrison which held out for the King was Charles-fort, at Salcombe-Regis. The latest event of great national importance, which took place in Devonshire, was the landing of *William, Prince of Orange,* atTorbay, in 1688, preparatory to the "*glorious revolution*" which placed him upon the throne. *(See pages* 52 *to* 60.)

NORMAN CONQUEST:—No sooner was William the Conqueror seated on the throne of England, than he shewed that his policy was to root out the Anglo-Saxon nobility, and to degrade the native inhabitants of the humbler classes to the rank of miserable slaves; though in this work he was obstinately opposed in some parts of the kingdom, especially in the north. Conscious of the detestation in which he was held, he entertained perpetual jealousy of the English. He built and garrisoned stong castles, to keep them in awe ; and in the wantonness of his power, obliged them to extinguish their fires and candles every evening at the ringing of a bell called the *curfew.* He also caused a survey to be made of all the lands in the kingdom, the register of which is called *Domesday Book*, and was finished in 1081, after a labour of six years, on the model of the Book of Winchester, compiled by order of Alfred the Great. Throughout all time this book will be held in estimation, as it specifies the extent of the land in each district; the state it was in, whether meadow, pasture, wood, or arable ; the name of the proprietor ; the tenure by which it was held ; and the value at which it was estimated. It afforded the Conqueror an exact knowledge of his own land and revenue, while the rights of his subjects, in disputed cases, were settled by it ; and to this day it serves to show what manor is, and what is not, *ancient demesne.* This valuable manuscript is still preserved in the Chapter House, at Westminster Abbey ; and copies of it were printed in the 40th of George III., for the use of the members of both Houses of Parliament, and the public libraries in the kingdom. In Devon, as in other parts of the kingdom, the Conqueror dispossessed the Saxons, and after appropriating part of their manors and estates to himself and family, he gave the rest to his Norman friends and followers, especially such as had distinguished themselves in clearing with their swords his way to the throne.

From DOMESDAY BOOK we find that in Devonshire the King then held 78 *manors ;* the Bishop, 24 ; Jeffrey, Bishop of Constance, 91 ; Robert, Earl of Moreton, 82 ; Baldwin, the Sheriff. 181 ; Judhael de Totenais, or Totnes, 107 ; Wm. Capra, 44 ; Wm. de Faleise, 18 ; Wm. de Poilgi, 21 ; Walter de Douay, 28 ; Walter de Claville, 31 ; Goscelm, 27 ; Robert de Albemarle, 17 ; Robert Bastard, 9 ; Ralph Paganel, 10 ; Ralph de Pomerei, 54 ; Ruald Adobed, 30 ; Tetbald Fitz-Berner, 28 ; Alured Brito, 22 ; Odo Fitz-Gamelin, 24 ; Godbold Balistarius, 14 ; Nichls. Archibalistarius, 11 ; Wm. Hostiarius, 10 ; Godwin, 11 ; and Colvin, 8. The two latter were *King's thanes,* who, with 15 others, had 47 manors divided among them. The total number of manors in the county, as enumerated in Domesday Survey, are 1112, and among the owners at that period are many smaller proprietors, and ten churches, owning from one to six or eight manors each ; but Tavistock church had 14, and Buckfastleigh church 12 ; and four manors were held by the three Saxon ladies, Godeva, Alveva, and Alfhilla. The greater part of the manors were held by under tenants, who rendered suit and service to the lords paramount. The chief landed property of the county was divided soon after the conquest into several great BARONIES, namely, *Oke-hampton, Plympton, Totnes, Barnstaple, Dartington, Bradninch, Bampton, Harberton, Berry-Pomeroy,* the *Bishop of Exeter's,* and the *Abbot of Tavistock's.* There does not exist any document to prove that any estates in the county remain in possession of de-scendants of the persons who held them at Domesday Survey ; but it is not improbable that some of the ancient families, who, accord-ing to the custom of that period, took their names from the places of their residence, in the reign of King John, or that of Henry III., may have inherited their estates in direct descent from the Ralphs, Rogers, Walters, Williams, &c., who were sub-tenants in the reign of Wm. the Conqueror, under Baldwin the Sheriff, and other great lords paramount. In order to secure their newly acquired posses-sions, the Norman Barons and Chiefs built on their respective estates " strong and magnificent CASTLES, which might at once secure them-selves, and keep the conquered English in awe." The largest of these castles were in the great baronies named above. Of some of these, as well as of several smaller fortresses in various parts of the county, there are still interesting remains.

EARLS OF DEVON.—*Richard de Redvers,* or *Rivers,* who obtained the great barony of Okehampton from Wm. II., was created *Earl of Devon* by Henry I., and the title was held by his descendants till the death of Bald-win, the eighth **earl,** in 1262, when his sister and heiress, *Isabel de Redvers,* succeeded as *Countess* of Devon. She married Wm. de Fortibus, Earl of Albemarle, and left only a daughter, who died without issue, in 1293. *Hugh Courtenay, the sixth Baron and first Viscount Courtenay, of Powderham Castle,* being descended from the sister of Baldwin de Redvers, was created Earl of Devon, in 1335, and died in 1340. Thomas, the sixth Earl, of the Courtenay family, was attainted and beheaded in 1461, when all his honours were forfeited. *Humphrey Stafford,* Baron Stafford of Suthwicke, was cre-ated Earl of Devon, in May, 1469, but was beheaded in the August follow-ing, when the title again became extinct ; but it was restored to the Courte-nays in 1485, when Edward Courtenay, grandson of Hugh, the third earl,

was created Earl of Devon. He died in 1509, and was succeeded by his grandson, *Henry*, who was created Marquis of Exeter, in 1525, but being attainted and beheaded in 1539, all his honours became forfeited. His son, *Edward*, was restored in blood and honours, after suffering a long imprisonment in the Tower, and was created Earl of Devon, in 1553, but dying without issue, in 1556, the title again became extinct. In 1603, *Charles Blount*, eighth Baron Mountjoy, was created Earl of Devon, but dying without lawful issue, the earldom for the sixth time became extinct. It was not revived till 1831, when *Wm. Courtenay, Viscount Courtenay, the late Earl of Devon*, established his claim to the earldom, by the decision of the House of Lords, as heir of Edward, who was created Earl of Devon, in 1553. He succeeded as Viscout Courtenay, in 1788, and died in 1835, when he was succeeded by his nephew, the present *Rt. Hon. Wm. Courtenay*, EARL OF DEVON and VISCOUNT COURTENAY, who was born in 1777, and was eldest son of the late Rt. Rev. Henry Reginald Courtenay, D.D., who was *Bishop of Exeter* in the early part of the present century. The Earl resides at *Powderham Castle*, the ancient seat of his family, (see page 412;) and his eldest son, *Viscount Courtenay*, resides at the beautiful marine residence called the *Moult*, near Salcombe. (See page 531.) The ancient *family of Courtenay* took their name from the town of Courtenay, in France. Reginald, the immediate ancestor of the English branch, came to England with Henry II., in 1151, and having married the heiress of Robert de Abrincis, hereditary sheriff of Devon, Baron of Okehampton, and governor of Exeter Castle, his eldest son succeeded to those honours, and married a daughter (and eventually heiress,) of Wm. de Redvers, Earl of Devon. Reginald was *Baron Courtenay*, by tenure, in the reign of Richard I., and one of his descendants was created *Viscount Courtenay*, in 1762. Though they have suffered many reverses of fortune, the Courtenays have for many ages been a numerous, wealthy, and highly distinguished family in Devon. *Wm. Courtenay*, a distinguished prelate of the 14th century, was *Archbishop of Canterbury* from 1381 till his death, in 1396. *Richard Courtenay, LL.D.*, was *Bishop of Norwich* from 1413 till 1415, and like his uncle, the archbishop, was a violent opponent of Wickliffe's followers. *Peter Courtenay, D.C.L.*, became *Bishop of Winchester*, in 1478, and died in 1492. He and the principal members of his family were zealous partisans of the Lancastrians, and are said to have been present with the Earl of Richmond, at the Battle of Bosworth Field. The title of DUKE OF DEVONSHIRE has been held by the *Cavendish family* since 1694, and that of *Earl of Devonshire* since 1618, though they have no other connexion with the county. His Grace the present Duke of Devonshire resides at *Chatsworth House*, the splendid "*Palace of the Peak*," in Derbyshire.

The NOBILITY resident in or connected with Devonshire are, the Earl of Devon, as already noticed ; the *Duke of Somerset*, owner of Berry-Pomeroy Castle, (see page 423;) the *Duke of Bedford*, who has large estates in the county, and an occasional seat at Endsleigh, near Tavistock ; the *Duke of Northumberland*, who owns Werrington House, and has an estate in that neighbourhood ; the *Earl of Mount Edgcumbe*, of Mount Edgcumbe, near Plymouth ; the *Earl of Macclesfield*, who has estates at Buckfastleigh, &c.; *Earl Fortescue*, of Castle Hill, near South Molton, now Lord Lieutenant of the county; the *Earl of Morley*, of Saltram, near Plymouth ; *Viscount Sidmouth*, of Upottery Manor House ; *Viscount Exmouth*, of Canon-Teign House ; *Baron Clinton*, who has an occasional seat at Huish, near Hatherleigh ; *Baron Clifford*, of Ugbrook Park, (see p. 398;) *Baron Poltimore*, of Poltimore and North Molton ; *Baron Ashburton*, who takes his

title from the town of Ashburton; *Lord Cranstoun*, owner of Sandridge, which was the seat of the late Lord Ashburton; *Baron Teignmouth*, an Irish Peer, whose title was taken from Teignmouth, in Devon, in 1797; *Lord Kinsale*, of Ringrone, near Salcombe; and *Viscount Torrington*, who takes his title from Torrington, in Devon; as the *Marquis of Exeter* does from the capital of the county. The late *Lord Rolle*, of Bicton House, died in 1842, without issue, as noticed at page 218, and this title, like many others which formerly existed in the county, is now extinct.

The 27 BARONETS of Devonshire are *Prideaux*, of Netherton Hall; *Wrey*, of Tawstock House; *Pole*, of Shute; *Northcote*, of Pynes; *Chichester*, of Youlston; *Davie*, of Creedy Park; *Acland*, of Killerton House and Fairfield; *Carew*, of Haccomb; *Rogers*, of Blatchford; *Duntze*, of Payford, and formerly of Rockbeare; *Baker*, of Loventor, in the parish of Berry Pomeroy; *Palk*, of Haldon House; *Buller*, of Lupton; *Kennaway*, of Escot House; *Williams*, of Clovelly Court; *Milman*, of Woodland; *Lethbridge*, of Sandhill, Somerset; *Lopes*, of Maristow House; *Louis*, of Cadwell House; *Duckworth*, of Weir House, Topsham; *Perring*, formerly of Membland; *Drake*, of Nutwell Court; *Newman*, of Mamhead; *Chichester*, of Arlington; *Elton*, of Widworthy Court; *Seale*, of Mount Boone; and *Wheler*, of Torrington. These and the extinct *baronetcies* of the county are noticed in the parishes where their present or former seats are situated.

ASPECT, SOIL, AND AGRICULTURE.

The *Surface of Devonshire* is mostly of a very unequal and undulating character, the land opening up into a succession of small valleys, clothed with verdure, and within the sheltered recesses of which ample opportunities are afforded for careful and successful farming. Yet the rich luxuriance of the soil, and the soft and pleasing varieties of the general scenery, are not always maintained, nor, even in Devonshire, is the climate everywhere mild. In many places the land is of a less kindly nature, especially as we leave the green valleys and approach the great moorland wastes of Dartmoor, &c., which rise in lofty elevations, and are swept by cold and cheerless winds. Owing to the great variety of climate and soil, a system of farming has arisen in the county, which combines nearly every branch of practical agriculture. Dairy and tillage farming form the principal feature of this system, but the cultivation of orchards, the irrigation of meadows, and the breeding and feeding of stock, are also extensively pursued. These do not form separate occupations, but are generally combined in each farm, and carried out as the convenience of the farmer and the resources of the land suggest. Perhaps a mixed system of agriculture like this may appear little calculated to attain that degree of successful development which is generally supposed to follow the concentration of industry within those boundaries which the division of labour suggests, but such does not appear to be the practical result. *Devon cattle, cream,* and *cider* are all equally famous, and of late years the practice of agriculture in all its branches, has made great progress in the county; with but little assistance from the great land owners, who have, however, during the last two years, made some advances towards the permanent improvement of their estates. During the last 20 years, the rent of land in the county is said to have been increased one-third; though many of the farmers complain that they are often saddled with the expense of keeping in repair the most inferior description of farm buildings, and that their crops are robbed by the great abundance of large trees growing in the hedgerows. The *farmers* of Devon are divided into two classes, one consisting of men with small holdings, little elevated above the condition of labourers; and the other of men holding large farms, and who,

being educated as well as practical agriculturists, have been gradually introducing improved methods of developing the resources of the soil. In this way, though an immense arrear of useful and profitable labour still remains to be performed, draining has been introduced, and is now struggling into general use; the levelling of the hedgerows makes some progress; an increased breadth of meadow irrigation has been secured; the value of artificial manures has begun to be generally recognised; and the breeding of *Devon cattle*, one of the most graceful and shapely kind of the species in this island, has been brought to a high state of perfection. As a further illustration of the progress which agriculture has been making here, we may state that, in one parish in North Devon, there are now 800 acres of green crop raised where there were only 80 acres eight years ago. Formerly *leases for life* were very common here, having been granted generally by necessitous landlords for nominal rents, and the value of the land at about 18 years' purchase. Of late, leases for lives have been discountenanced, and in their stead have been generally substituted *leases for years*. For large farms, these are usually from seven to ten years in duration; and for small farms, six years, with a break at the end of three years, which, if not taken advantage of, extends the term three years more. The improvements in agriculture throughout the county are contemporaneous with the change from the old relations between landlord and tenant to the new; and, though the terms of the leases for years are generally complained of as much too short, they are infinitely preferable to the tenancies from year to year, which are so prevalent in other parts of England. The rent of land in Devon appears high, compared with that of many other counties, but perhaps the increase is due to the greater productiveness of the soil, and the mildness and salubrity of the climate. Over so large a tract of country, with such varieties of soil, situation, and other influences, farms let at very different rents; but we find that within a circle of three miles round Exeter, where there is a fine deep soil, well adapted for the growth of corn and green crops, rents range from 30s. to 50s. per acre; and the local burdens, or "out-goings," as they are called, amount to about one-third more. The *poor rates* vary exceedingly in some of the parishes; and *tithes* form a subject of much complaint among farmers, on the ground that the averages which regulate them are taken from the prices of seven years, instead of a more limited period.

The Devonshire tenant, is at once a dairy farmer, a breeder or feeder of cattle, sheep, and pigs; and a grower of corn and cider; and this variety of occupation, arising naturally from the character of the climate and soil of the county, has given him a tone of intelligence and activity which is looked for in vain in other parts of the kingdom, where a monotonous routine narrows the intellect of the dairyman. *Farms* here are generally of moderate size; for although some farmers hold 700 or 800 acres in several separate farms, the great majority run from 50 or 60 to 200 or 250 acres. *Farm buildings* are often found collected in a village; the housing of four adjoining farms being sometimes inconveniently placed at their point of junction. The buildings are of every variety of character, from the antique and dilapidated, to the more modern and convenient. On badly managed estates, the farmer is often bound to uphold in repair the most ricketty old mud and wooden thatched houses, at a cost to himself of 10 per cent. on the rental of a small farm. The better class of farm buildings are generally in the form of a square, close all round, and entered on the south side through a large arched door, under the granary. Immediately opposite is the barn, cider cellar, &c., which usually occupy one side of the square, having the corn rick yard behind. Two sides are for the accom-

modation of cattle, the back walls being built close up to the eaves; but the front is in two stories, supported on strong posts, and open from the ground to the eaves; the lower story occupied by cattle; the upper kept as a store for their provender. The cows are usually kept in loose boxes; the fattening cattle generally tied by the neck. The fourth side of the square embraces the farm stable and waggon shed. The houses are generally conveniently situated outside the square; and many of them, on the estates of the Duke of Bedford, and other wealthy and liberal landowners, have lately been rebuilt, or enlarged and improved. The larger farm-houses, many of which are fine old mansions, formerly occupied by the lords of the manors, are provincially called *Bartons*. The *soil* is of various character; good turnip and barley land, of deep friable texture, are met with in continuous succession, and from these the cultivator reaps the best returns. The *system of husbandry* followed is the alternate one, varied by allowing the land to rest one or more years in grass, as may be thought best by the farmer. There is nothing particular in the management of the arable land of this large county, but it is generally well and deeply tilled, not very heavily manured, but managed, on the whole, where the tenants have sufficient capital, with much skill and sagacity. Two-horse ploughs are universal, and light carts and waggons. Oxen are occasionally used in the plough, two young ones and two old ones being yoked together. They are fed very cheaply, and will plough an acre per day. Sixteen to twenty-four bushels of wheat per acre may be reckoned an average produce for South Devon, and thirty-two bushels of barley. Stubble turnips are occasionally taken; but the general practice is, a bare winter fallow in preparation for a root crop. In many districts of South Devon, the soil and climate are admirably adapted for crops of early potatoes, to be followed by turnips; or for producing crops of rye, winter vetches, &c., for spring feed. The *dairy management* in Devonshire is justly celebrated; the perfect cleanliness and freshness of the dairies forming a marked contrast with those of many other counties. Fresh *butter, clouted cream*, and *junkets*, are the products of the dairies, and great quantities of these delicious luxuries are sent to all the towns and bathing places of the county, and to London and other distant markets. The value of *watered meadows* is highly appreciated by the Devonshire farmers, advantage being taken of every little stream to increase the produce of the land. The warmth of the numerous valleys is highly favourable to rapid growth, and their declivities afford a cheap and convenient means of laying on the water. The expense of cutting the gutters is about £2 per acre, and the annual cost of keeping open the water courses and laying on the water is about 5s. per acre. The increased produce is fully 100 per cent.; but this depends chiefly on the quality of the water applied, which is found to vary extremely. The *cider orchard* is another source of income to the Devonshire farmer, the value of which has decreased nearly a half within the last twenty years. An orchard produces 10 to 15 hogsheads an acre, the selling price of which at present is 25s. to 30s. a hogshead, and the cost of preparing it 3s. to 5s. As much as 150 hogsheads are produced on some farms, half of which is consumed by the farm labourers. The *wages* of labourers vary from 7s. to 8s. and 9s. per week, with three pints or two quarts of cider daily, the men bringing in every morning their wooden bottle to receive their day's allowance. Task work is now much encouraged, and affords better wages to the industrious. The *cottages* of the labourers are many of them constructed of red earth, mixed with straw, commonly called *cobb*, and covered with reeds or straw thatch. When rough cast and kept dry, these kind of dwellings are very durable, the walls being generally from fourteen inches to two feet in thick-

ness. The chief *corn markets* in the county are Exeter, Tavistock, Totnes, Kingsbridge, Plymouth, and Barnstaple. The *Devonshire Agricultural Society* was instituted in 1791, for the improvement of the soils and the vegetable and animal produce of the county; and there are now in various parts of the county about twenty other *Agricultural Societies*, and nearly as many *Farmers' Clubs*, having for their objects, improvements in the cultivation of the soil and the breeding of stock; and the encouragement of skill, industry, and economy among the labouring poor.

In some parts of the county, considerable attention is paid to the breeding of *sheep*. The established breed, reared chiefly on Dartmoor and Exmoor, is the middle woolled class, bearing a strong resemblance to the Dorsets; but many other kinds are also reared. The total stock is estimated at about 700,000, of which about 200,000 produce heavy fleeces of long wool. But the extensive pasture lands are most generally appropriated to the purposes of the dairy and the fattening of the *North Devon Cattle*, a very fine breed, with wide spreading horns, and of an uniformly light brown colour. This breed, for working and for fattening, is allowed to be one of the most perfect in the kingdom; but they are not much esteemed for the dairy. The native breed of *horses* is very small, and resembles the Welsh and Highland breeds of cattle, but all the improved breeds of cattle, sheep, and horses, from various parts of the country, are to be found here. Among the natural vegetable productions of this county is the beautiful *scarlet lichen* of Dartmoor, formerly extensively used as a dye for cloth, and in the manufacture of orchal.

The *soils* of Devon are extremely various, and may generally be characterised according to the rock, or stratified substances which they cover, as granatic, slatery, calcareous, arenaceous, argillaceous, gravelly, and loamy. The poorest is the soil covering the granite of Dartmoor, which has also the disadvantage of a cold wet climate. That which lies on the slate district is more or less fertile, and fit for all purposes of agriculture. The most uniformly fertile soils are in the red sandstone district; but the richest are those occurring in contiguity with limestone or greenstone rocks, in many parts of the slate district; especially in that beautiful southern district, commonly called the *South Hams* and sometimes the " *Garden of Devon*," and having for its natural boundaries Dartmoor and the heights of Chudleigh on the north; the river Plym on the west; Torbay and Start Bay on the east; and Bigbury Bay and other parts of the coast of the English Channel, on the south. The red colour which characterises the best soils, both in the South Hams and the eastern division of the county, and which seems to be so closely connected with the principle of fertility, proceeds from an abundant mixture of iron, in a highly oxidated state. The soil of that part of the South Hams which is bounded by the Erme and Dart rivers, is generally a rich friable loam, of a hazel nut brown colour, mostly on a substratum of slate; but that east of the Dart as far as Torbay, is richer and redder, and generally on a substratum of marble rock. There are extensive tracts of rich meadow and arable lands in the valleys of the Exe, Taw, Teign, Otter, and other rivers. The Vale of the Exe, commonly called the *Vale of Exeter*, has in its northern parts an irregular billowy surface, presenting eminences of considerable magnitude; but its central and more southern parts preserve the vale character. Its northern boundaries are the hills that range from Clanaborough, by Halberton and Uffculm, to *Blackdown*, a dreary mountainous ridge, which, with its contiguous branches, skirts the eastern side of the vale. On the south-east it is bounded by the heights of Sidmouth, East-Down, and Woodbury; and on the west by the mountainous ridge of Haldon, and the undulating

eminences that stretch towards Bow-Nymet. This vale is one of the most fertile parts of the county, and its most prevalent soils are strong red loam, shillet, or foliated clay, intersected with veins of ironstone, and a mixture of sand and gravel.   North of Hatherleigh and Holsworthy, and eastward to Chumleigh, Bradninch, &c., the soil is chiefly clay; but north of this is a gravelly district adjoining both sides of Dartmoor.   Towards Hartland Point, there is much clay and moorland; a vein of black soil runs through Filleigh and Swimbridge; and a narrow vein of red soil from North Molton to Challacombe.   The rich red soil of the South Hams, which is of great depth, is sometimes worked as marl pits, and used most beneficially as manure for the poorer lands.   The chief manures are lime and sea sand. Limestone is got in various parts of the county, and extensively burnt in kilns on the banks of the navigable canals and rivers.

The *Climate* of Devonshire is so mild on the southern coast that, in flourishing gardens, orange and lemon trees, myrtles, &c., grow in the open air, with little shelter during the winter.   The laurels and bays of Devon are held to be the most beautiful evergreens in the world.   Broad leaved myrtle trees have grown here to the height of 30 feet, with branches spreading nearly from the roots, where the stalk or trunk was from $1\frac{1}{2}$ to 2 feet in circumference.   Swallows have been seen feeding their young in the latter part of Sept.; and martins flying, during mild weather, at Christmas.   The mean annual temperature, from eleven years' observation, was found to be 52 deg. 5 min.   But from its advanced position in the ocean, the climate of Devon is unquestionably a moist one, especially in the vicinity of the mountainous districts, where the air is often cold and damp.   Even the mild south-eastern parts of the county are often pervaded by the "*Devon-shire drizzle*," which is a rain so light as to deposit itself as a thick dew, attended by a grey cloudy sky; but these drizzles seldom continue for an entire day, and the accompanying warm temperature takes from them the usual injurious effects of damp weather in colder climates.   Indeed, the climate of Devon is considered by medical men to be so healthy and auspicious to invalids, that a residence within its bounds is generally advised, in preference even to Lisbon or the South of France.   Epidemics occasionally prevail, and in 1849 the *cholera* was very fatal at Plymouth, Devonport, and some other places.

DARTMOOR FOREST, the wildest and bleakest part of Devon, is an extensive and elevated tract of heath, morass, rocky tors and crags, and lofty moorland hills and dells,—stretching about thirty miles in length from north to south, and 14 from east to west.   The towns of Okehampton, Tavistock, and Moreton-Hampstead are near its borders, and it extends southward to within a few miles of Plymouth.   It comprises about 200,000 acres, of which 53,000 acres, in the central and most dreary part, are in Lidford parish.   It belongs mostly to the *Prince of Wales*, as part of the Duchy of Cornwall, but the outskirts and part of the hills are appendant to the surrounding manors, many of which have likewise the prescriptive right of common on the Forest, on paying an inconsiderable sum annually to the Duchy, under the name of *Venville* (fen field) money.   The Duchy, however, possesses the right of stocking the forest by *agistment*, and for this purpose much of it is leased in districts to various persons, who pasture the stock of the neighbouring parishes at low rates.   During the last 30 years, many thousand acres of its outskirts, belonging to adjacent parishes, have been enclosed and cultivated, and other extensive tracts have been planted; but the central part, comprising more than 60,000 acres, is still nearly in a state of nature, and many of its eminences rise to the altitude of from 1500 to 1800 feet.   On approaching this mountainous tract, the eye is bewildered by an extensive waste, exhibiting gigantic tors, large surfaces covered with vast masses of scattered granite, and immense rocks, which seem to have been precipitated from the steep declivities into the valleys.   These huge and craggy fragments are spread confusedly over the ground, and have been compared to the ponderous masses ejected by volcanoes; to the enormous ruins of formidable castles; and to the wrecks of mountains torn piecemeal by the raging elements.   Few places are really less known, and few are more deserving of attention than Dartmoor; and though a large portion of the high road which crosses it, presents an unvaried scene of solitariness and desolation, yet to those who pursue their investigations beyond the

ordinary beaten track, much will be found to delight the artist, the poet, and the antiquary. The peculiar characteristics of Dartmoor are derived from the granite tors, which are found piled mass upon mass, mostly upon the summits of its numerous heights; and the wild impetuosity of its numerous streams, which dash through narrow channels, between craggy hills and cliffs, and give rise to many of the larger and smaller rivers of the county. The numerous remains of rude stone *altars, circles, obelisks, logans,* and *cromlechs* scattered over the moor, and the names still attached to many of the tors, such as Bel-tor, Mis-tor, Ham-tor, &c., shew that it was one of the most favoured haunts of the Druids. From its lofty elevation, it is peculiarly the region of mists, storms, and tempests. The peaks of its mighty tors stand up many hundred feet above its lofty hills, and intercepting the moisture of the clouds, cause great quantities of rain to fall in and around the moor. The mist comes on at times so sudden and dense, that those who are overtaken in it, out of the beaten track, are sometimes lost, and even the moor men have great difficulty in regaining their habitations. But the climate is considered healthy, and it is said that persons born and bred here seldom or never die of pulmonary consumption. There are now but few trees on Dartmoor, except the lonely wood of Wistman, but immense trunks of oak and other trees have often been dug up in the peaty bogs and marshes in many of the romantic dells, as well as on some of the higher table lands. The peat is got extensively for fuel, and the heaths and commons afford good pasturage for sheep and cattle during summer. The delicacy and flavour imparted to the flesh of the sheep by the sweet herbage of the moor is so highly prized, that Dartmoor mutton is sent to London and other distant markets. *Wistman*, or *Wiseman's Wood*, is about a mile north of Two Bridges, on a lofty and steep acclivity rising from the western bank of the river Dart, opposite Bairdown. It is supposed to have been one of the sacred groves of the Druids. The ascent to it is strewn all over with immense masses of granite, partly covered by a grove of dwarf oaks, so stunted in their growth by sweeping winds, that few are more than ten or twelve feet high, though their branches spread far and wide, and are twisted in the most fantastic manner, and in some places festooned with ivy, and other creeping plants. Their trunks and arms are embedded in a thick covering of velvet moss, and the view down the valley from some of the bare rocks is truly sublime. *Crockerntor*, celebrated as the place where the ancient stannary parliaments were held, is about a mile from Two Bridges. On the summit of this tor, the chief miners of Devon were formerly obliged to meet, and hold the stannary court, as noticed at page 28. On entering the moor from Newton Abbot, is *Haytor*, and the extensive granite works noticed at page 473. In ancient times it was called *Solar-tor*, being dedicated by the Druids to the worship of the sun. On the top of the loftiest peak is one of the rock basins found in many of the granite-crowned tors of Dartmoor. Looking hence into the wild solitude of the forest, are seen dark masses of granite piled on either side; huge blocks of the same, scattered on the brows of the hills; and in the distance are seen tor upon tor, each capped with irregular masses of granite, assuming the most grotesque forms. But turning his back to the moor, the spectator sees a magnificent panorama of one of the loveliest and most fertile parts of Devon;—the Teign flowing at his feet through a rich and beautiful valley, the Exe opening out its wide estuary towards the ocean; and, in the extreme distance, the blue waters of the channel, with the noble outline of shore from Berry-Head to the coast of Dorsetshire. The secluded and romantic vale of Lustleigh, the *Cleave, Becky Falls, Hountor, &c.*, are noticed at pages 475-'6, and the cromlechs, rocking-stone, and other druidical remains, near *Drewsteignton*, at page 190. Some of the streams in the heart of the forest are crossed by ancient *British Bridges*, of the most primitive construction, each consisting of several piers, composed of massive pieces of granite rock, placed one above another, and each pier connected with the neighbouring one by an enormous slab of moorstone; thus forming a solid footway, which has borne for ages the rush of winter torrents, and the shock of time. On the road to Tavistock, the neighbourhood of *Merrivale Bridge* affords a rich field for the exploration of the antiquary, being literally strewed with Celtic remains, cromlechs, track-ways, circles, and other vestiges of Druidism. *Vixen Tor* is a most picturesque object, and the tall granite crags which crown its lofty summit, resemble a castellated tower, frowning over the valleys beneath.

A little south of the high road, about 7 miles east of Tavistock, is the wildly secluded hamlet of *Tor Royal*, or PRINCE TOWN, and the extensive, but now ruinous and deserted DARTMOOR PRISON OF WAR, which was erected in 1808-9, for the residence of *prisoners of war*, of whom it had often from 5000 to 10,000, guarded by from 300 to 500 soldiers. During the latter part of last century, the late Mr. Gullet, and the late Mr. Bray, of Tavistock, made great improvements in this part of Dartmoor, bringing some portions into cultivation and planting others. The late Sir Francis Buller purchased *Prince Hall* estate of Mr. Gullet, greatly improved it, and made it his occasional residence. But the greatest improver of Dartmoor was the late *Sir Thomas Tyrwhitt, Bart.*, who was seated at Tor Royal, and was for some time Lord Warden of the Stannaries and M.P. for Plymouth. It was through his suggestion that government erected the *war prison* here, for the accommodation of the numerous French and American prisoners, who had till then crowded the prison ships of Plymouth. This prison consisted of five rectangular buildings, each 300 feet long and 50 broad, with two stories for the hammocks of more than 1500 prisoners, and a large loft above for exercise in inclement wea-

ther. There were two other spacious buildings, one used as the hospital, and the other as the quarters of the petty officers. Adjoining the prison was the *Governor's House*, and other buildings necessary for the civil establishment; and at the distance of a quarter of a mile were *Barracks* for about 500 soldiers. The space between the walls of the prison formed a military road round the whole. On this the guard paraded. The sentinels were posted on platforms commanding a complete view of the prison; and some idea of its extent may be formed from the circumstance of the watch-word being a quarter of an hour in passing round. The lofty walls which surrounded all the buildings formed a circle nearly a mile in circumference, enclosing an area of nearly 30 acres. The great iron gate on the western side is arched over with immense blocks of granite, on which is engraved the appropriate inscription, "*Parcere Subjectis.*" Opposite this is a large reservoir, from which the prison was supplied with excellent water, obtained by a diversion of part of the river Walkham. Connected with the prison was a neat *Chapel*, built by the prisoners, and opened in 1813. It is still used as a chapel of ease for *Dartmoor Quarter* of Lidford Parish, in which Prince Town is situated, at the distance of ten miles S.E. of the mother church. During the war there were two large inns near the prison, and they still remain,—one of them being the *Duchy Hotel*, which was honoured by a visit from Prince Albert during his visit to Plymouth in 1846. A considerable number of tradesmen, necessary to supply the wants of so large a population, settled in the vicinity, besides the proprietors of the public bake-houses, slaughter-houses, and brewery; and a market was held in the prison every week-day, to which produce was brought from Tavistock, Moreton, Chagford, &c. Many of the prisoners had prize money to receive from their own country, and others obtained money by the manufacture of various ornamental or useful articles, which they sold to the market people. Some of the prisoners also kept stores, and were trusted with stocks to the amount of from £20 to £30. In reference to these stores, the French are said to have been "*very honest*," but the Americans "*great rogues.*" No. 4 prison was assigned entirely to *blacks*, on account of the dislike with which they were regarded by the other American prisoners. Oil lamps were placed at the corners of the prison buildings, and also on the walls, and were kept burning during the night. Some of the prisoners used to contrive to be supplied with a composition metal for the manufacture of base coin; and they managed to make in their hammocks 1s. 6d. and 3s. pieces, and even forged Bank of England and Local Bank Notes, which they passed off either in the prison market or through the medium of some of the soldiers, several of whom were transported for that offence. The French are said to have been much more orderly than the American prisoners, many of whom were really Englishmen. Attempts were often made by men of both parties to escape by undermining the walls, and they were sometimes successful. In April, 1815, an erroneous notion having got among the prisoners that peace had been proclaimed, a great number of the Americans made an attempt to escape at the time their dinners were served out; but the guard was immediately called in, and quelled the disturbance, after killing seven and wounding 35 others. After the termination of the war, this extensive prison, and most of the private dwellings in the neighbourhood, became unoccupied; but some of the houses were again tenanted after the commencement of the *railway*, or *tram-road*, which extends from Prince Town to Plymouth, and was constructed under acts passed in 1819, 1820, and 1821, for the purpose of affording an easy transit for the produce of the immense *granite quarries* of this part of Dartmoor, as well as for bringing up lime and other manure for the improvement of the land on either side, and coal, &c., for domestic use. Many plans have been suggested for appropriating the extensive prison to some useful purpose, either as a School of Industry, or an Establishment for Convicts, but these proposals have never been brought to maturity. Of late years it has fallen into a complete state of decay, proclaiming by its desolate and prostrate condition that a state of war no longer calls for its aid. At the present time, when the tide of emigration is flowing so rapidly from the British shores, it would, no doubt, be highly beneficial if Prince Albert, associated as he is with the Duchy of Cornwall,— to which this large portion of the Forest of Dartmoor belongs,—would institute a commission to devise a scheme, not only for the occupation of the prison, but for the cultivation of the vast moors which surround it. *Dartmoor* was fixed on as the subject of the first *prize poem* by the Royal Literary Society, established in 1821; and the prize was adjudged to Mrs. Hemans. It is supposed to have been a royal forest, attached to the manor of Lidford, in the time of William the Conqueror. In 1238, the castle of Lidford and Dartmoor Chase, or Forest, were granted by Henry III. to his brother Richard, Earl of Cornwall, and they were afterwards permanently united to the Duchy of Cornwall.

STRATA, QUARRIES, &c.—From the confused intermixture of the strata in Devonshire, the operation of earthquakes and volcanoes is strikingly apparent. *Granite* occupies the central and most elevated portions of the county, including all Dartmoor and the large district around it. Immense quantities of this durable stone are sent to Teignmouth and Plymouth for exportation to London and other distant places. Specimens of the red granite are exceedingly beautiful when polished. Laminated *schistus* is

common to almost all parts of the county. *Slate* occupies an extensive surface in the northern, southern, and eastern parts of the county. *Transition limestone* occurs in many detached parts of the county, but principally between Torbay and Plymouth; the whole coast between these points being composed of this rock. This limestone is extensively got both for agricultural and building purposes. Beautifully veined *marble* is worked near Torquay, Babbicombe, &c., into mantle-pieces, tablets, pillars, vases, and a variety of ornamental articles. (See pages 437 and 445.) *Red sandstone* occupies the district around Exeter, and most of the country around the hills of Haldon and Woodbury, as far as Torbay and Sidmouth. In some places it is sufficiently hard to serve as a durable building stone. The *green-sand formation* presents, on the confines of this county and Dorsetshire, many outlying masses forming considerable hills. *Coal* of very peculiar nature is obtained in the extensive peaty flat called Bovey-Heathfield, which was anciently covered by the tides. (See page 469.) The origin of this "*Bovey-Coal*" has occasioned much discussion among geologists; and is supposed to consist of an imperfectly carbonized wood, analagous to oak and other trees. The coal strata alternate with those of clay, to the depth of about 70 feet. This coal is used in the neighbouring pottery, and also by the poor, and makes as strong a fire as oaken billets. Kerwan says it consists of the wood of a submerged forest, penetrated with petrol or bitumen, and frequently containing pyrites, alum, and vitriol. *Pyrites* are obtained in various parts of the county, and are not unfrequently found in globular balls of different sizes. The fine *potters' clay*, near King's Teignton, &c., is extensively got for the Staffordshire and other potteries, where it is used in the manufacture of china. A bed of *pipe clay*, so impregnated with iron as to be fit only for making pipes, runs under the beds of potters' clay, lying east of the Bovey coal strata. White quartz and sand are found under this; and in various parts of the county are heterogeneous formations, intermixed with those already named.

MINES AND ORES.—Devonshire participates in the celebrity of Cornwall as a great mining district, producing *copper, tin, lead, and other metals.* Though its mining operations are now greatly inferior to those of Cornwall, they were in early times much more extensive, for we find that in 1213, the duty on tin payable to the Earl of Cornwall, was farmed at £200 for Devon, and only at 200 marks for Cornwall. The scale was turned in 1479, when the Earl's mining dues were £166.9s.5½d. for Devon, and £1620.17s.11d. for Cornwall. In 1838, previous to the abolition of the tin coinage duties, they amounted to £193.2s.10½d. for Devon, and £14,762.4s.10¾d. for Cornwall; but it must be observed that the duchy dues on Cornish tin were 4s. per cwt., and on Devonshire tin only 1s. 6d. The tin coined (or smelted and assayed) at Morwell-ham, in 1838, consisted of 82 blocks of grain or stream tin, and 674 blocks of common tin, each weighing about 3¼ cwt. In 1838, the tin coinage duties were commuted. The Phœnicians traded with this part of Britain for tin before the invasion of the Romans; and there are still to be seen in this county vestiges of the Phœnician smelting-houses, called by the miners Jews' Houses. Remains of ancient stream works are found in Dartmoor, and in all parts of the granite district, where the tin, copper, &c., are chiefly found. Although the tin works of Devon were mostly abandoned after the Cornwall mines became productive, some of the old *tin, copper, and lead mines* have been re-worked, and several new ones opened during the present century, as noticed at pages 188, 190, 192, 462, 468, 471, 529, 585, 603, 609, and 624, where it will be seen that portions of *silver* are extracted from some of the ores, and that *gold* has been occasionally found. (See page 610.) The richest and most profitable copper mine

in the county is he Devonshire Great Consols, or *Wheal Maria*, noticed at page 624. The metallic veins, or lodes, in general consist of crystalized ores, apparantly precipitated from water which had held them in solution; or of larger deposits in the *faults* or dislocations in the various strata, produced probably by volcanic action. The *argentiferous lead-lodes* of Combemartin, occur in beds immediately below the slate, and those of Beer-Alston cut through the slate, and are partly calcareous. Granite, or its modification, elvan, occurs near the copper and tin ores; and *lead, antimony, manganese, iron,* and *zinc,* are found at a distance from the granite or elvan. The great stanniferous district in Devon is Dartmoor, where the granite rock itself is sometimes impregnated with metal. North of the Tavistock mines are the lodes of Wheal Betsey and Lidford; and to the south are the argentiferous lead mines of Beer-Alston, where the metalliferous country runs south-west into Cornwall. Valuable manganese mines have been worked east of Dartmoor, at Doddiscombsleigh and Ashton; and fine *iron ore* is got near Ilsington, Brixham, and Hennock, (see pages 425 and 471,) and in some other parts of the county. About Bideford is some *clay-iron ore* mixed with *anthracite.* The ores of manganese and antimony are chiefly found in those portions of the *grauwacke,* which are associated with the *trappean rocks.* In 1811, there appears to have been only seven copper mines open in the county, and the number of tons which they respectively produced in that year were—Wheal Friendship, 110; Wheal Crebor, 1308; Crowndale, 863; East Crowndale, 913; Ding-Dong, 250; Wheal Hope, 6; and Wheal Hockworthy, 10 tons. At page 624, it will be seen that a large mine near Tavistock, now yields about 1350 tons of copper ore per month. In 1785, the lead mines in Devon yielded 6500 ounces of *silver;* but about 20 years ago, Wheal-Betsey mine alone yielded about 5000 ounces per ann. *Magnetic iron ore* of good quality has been worked near South Brent, and a piece of it was found to move a needle placed at the distance of nine feet. Various other mineral substances, such as cobalt, arsenic, yellow ochre, &c., are found in the county.

ORGANIC REMAINS.—The transition limestone, or marble rock, at Torquay, contains several species of *madrepores, turbinoliæ, flustra, orthoceræ, producti crinoidea,* &c. The strata of lias, which extend from Lyme Regis into Devonshire, contain the remains of *Icthyosaurus* and *Plesiosaurus,* two genera of animals related to the lizard family. The same strata also contain the remains of fish and *crustacea,* and abound in shells, chiefly of the genera *plagiostorna, gryphea, nautilus,* and *ammonites.* They also contain four species of pentacrinites, viz., *caput medusæ, briareus, subangularis,* and *basaltiformis.* The green sand strata of Blackdown and Haldon are very rich in shells of *mollusca;* which, in the former places occur, changed into a delicate hydrophanous calcedony, and in the latter, into an opaque red or yellow jasper, frequently imbedded in a matrix of green chert. Mr. James Parkinson and Mr. J. Sowerby describe the following species from Blackdown:—Trigonia *eccentrica, dædalea, spinosa, sinuata, alæformis, rudis, affinis;* Cuculia *glabra, decussata, carinata, fibrosa;* Cardium *hillanum, proboscideum, unbonatum;* Venus *plana, angulata, castrensis;* Chama *plicata;* Pecten *quadriscostata, quinquecostata;* Corbula *gigantea, lævigata;* Auricula *incrassata;* Hamites *spinulosum;* Nucula *margaritacea;* Ammonites *goodhalli;* Natica *canrena;* and two species of Rostellariæ. There occur also various species of *Turbo, Murex, Cerithium, Nautilus,* &c., and a highly interesting species of *Alcyonium.* The chalk at Beer contains the remains of a variety of *Pentacrinites, Caput Medusæ, Terebratulæ, Pectens,* &c. On Haldon, and in the flinty strata of its vicinity, the *echinus* is frequently found; *tubipores* have been met with near Newton Abbot, and

shells of various species at Hembury Fort; many of the latter bearing a perfect resemblance to some of the kinds brought from the West Indies. At Chapel-Farm, in Cruwys-Morchard, there was found some years ago a great quantity of remarkable substances, called *fossil bacon*. They were found on digging a pond; and at the depth of 12 feet, several perfect bodies of hogs were found, reduced to the colour and substance of Egyptian mummies. The bones of the *elephant, hyæna*, and other large animals, have been found in *Kent's Hole*, near Babbicombe, and in other caverns and cavities of the limestone rock, in various parts of the county.

Mineral Waters are very numerous in Devon, and are chiefly of the chalybeate kind, but none of them are now in medicinal repute. The strongest springs of this description rise at Gubb's Well, near Cleave; at Bella-Marsh, near King's Teignton; and at Bampton. That at the latter place is said to be more strongly impregnated with iron than any other in the county. Springs near Totnes, and at Brook, near Tavistock, and at St. Sidwell's, near Exeter, were formerly much resorted to for their medicinal virtues. At Ashburton, and near the Dart, are springs saturated with ochre. A pool in one of the Bovey coal pits is warm, and covered with an ochreous incrustation. Ley-well, at Brixham, formerly ebbed and flowed, but has been cut through and destroyed; and there was a pond of the same nature at Tidwell, near Otterton.

MANUFACTURES.—Devon has long been celebrated for its *woollen and lace manufactures;* one or the other of which was formerly to be found in most parts of the county, but both have greatly declined here during the present century, owing to the amazing extension of machinery and the factory system, in the Midland and Northern Counties, which have nearly annihilated these branches of industry in their primitive seats, where the old domestic system was adhered to. There are still several large woollen mills and several thousand looms in different parts of the county, employed in making *serges, blankets*, and other *coarse woollen cloths.* Cloth was woven at Exeter and Chudleigh in the reign of Edward I. Dartmoor wool, however, was at that time exported; but Edward III. prohibited the exportation of wool, and encouraged the immigration of foreign weavers, many of whom settled in this county. In the 15th century, *friezes, Tavistocks*, or western dozens, and other sorts of coarse cloths, were exported by the Devonshire merchants to Brittany. In the reign of Edward IV., an Italian taught the English the art of weaving *kerseys;* and in the early part of the 16th century, "Devonshire kerseys," were an important article of commerce to the Levant. The woollen manufacture was greatly extended here in the reign of Elizabeth, as noticed at page 63, and continued to flourish till the close of last century. The market for wool and cloths, which had been long at Crediton, was removed to Exeter, in 1538. Totnes produced a sort of coarse cloth, called Pynn-whites, not made elsewhere. Crediton was famous for fine spinning. Barnstaple and Torrington furnished *bayes, fryzadoes*, &c., and Pilton, cottons and lining, "so coarse a stuffe, that there was a *væ* (a woe) pronounced against them in these words:—Woe unto you, ye Piltonians, that make cloth without wool." Many other places contributed to the great Exeter mart, which ranked next Leeds in 1759, and exported no fewer than 330,414 pieces of cloth, in 1768, but its trade suffered considerably during the American war. In 1789, the East India Company bought here 121,000 pieces of serges, &c.; of which 600 pieces of broads were made at Crediton, and the rest chiefly at Ashburton, Tavistock, Modbury, North Tawton, and Newton Bushel. While they had the monopoly of the tea trade, they were enabled to force their serges or long ells, on the Chinese in exchange, and they were induced to do this on several occasions, at the request of govern-

ment, in order to relieve the weavers and manufacturers of this country in times of distress. From 1795 to 1805, this company annually purchased here from 250,000 to 300,000 pieces. In 1838, there were still in the county 39 *woollen mills*, and more than 3000 looms employed in weaving serges. Of the latter there were in and around Ashburton, 660 ; Okehampton, 530 ; Collumpton, 500 ; Buckfastleigh, 700 ; Exeter, 300 ; Totnes, 230 ; South and North Molton, 200 ; Crediton and North Tawton, 150 ; and Tavistock, 100. The manufacture of *blankets* has been introduced into Devonshire since the expiration of the East India Company's trading monopoly, and many of the women of Devon, previously employed in weaving serges, have since been employed in glove making, &c. Since the repeal of the prohibition to export English wool, great quantities have been exported from Devonshire, chiefly to France, for the manufacture of finer articles than serges. In 1838, there were in Devon three *flax mills* and three silk mills. The latter are at Church Stanton, Aylesbeer, and Ottery St. Mary, and employ upwards of 400 hands. From 1755 till 1835, there was a celebrated *carpet manufactory* at Axminster. (See page 357.) *Bone* or *thread lace*, commonly called *Honiton lace*, is extensively made in the town and neighbourhood of Honiton, and in many other parts of the county, and gives employment to many thousand women and children, as noticed at page 364. At Tiverton and Barnstaple are two extensive *lace factories*, employed in making bobbin-net, &c. (See page 308.) The former was established in 1815, and the latter in 1822. Blond lace is also made here, and there are in the county several potteries, many large malting and tanning establishments, several large foundries and machine works, &c., &c.

RIVERS.—In Dartmoor, the great headland of Devon, some of its principal and many of its smaller rivers have their sources ; all radiating from within the circuit of a few miles, on this central fountain head, and flowing down the slopes of its high summits to almost every point in the compass. Of the most important of these, the *Dart*, so termed from the rapidity of its course, (and hence the name Dartmoor,) runs south-east from Okement hill, in a winding course to Totnes ; and after a course of about 35 miles, gradually widens into a deep navigable estuary, and falls into the English Channel at Dartmouth haven. Its course is tidal for $10\frac{1}{2}$ miles. The *East and West Okement*, though they rise near the same hill as the Dart, take an opposite course, and unite at Okehampton, whence the stream runs northward to the *Torridge*, a large river which rises in the north-west angle of the county, and after taking a very tortuous course, flows past Torrington to Bideford, where it becomes navigable for large vessels ; and after a course of 45 miles, issues into an estuary at Barnstaple Bay, common to it and the Taw. Its course is tidal for about 15 miles. The *Taw* rises in Dartmoor, and flows northward past Chulmleigh, where it meets the Little Dart, and then, pursuing a north-west course, receives various tributary streams, among which is the Mole, from Exmoor and South Molton ; and after a course of about 45 miles, flows, by Barnstaple, into the Bristol Channel, through the same estuary as the Torridge. It is tidal in its course for $11\frac{1}{2}$ miles, and large vessels come up to Barnstaple. The *Tavy* rises in the centre of Dartmoor, and flows past Tavistock, to the *Tamar*, a large river which rises near the north-western extremity of the county, and flows southward to Plymouth Sound, forming, with a few slight exceptions, the boundary of Devon and Cornwall, in its course of nearly fifty miles, in which it is navigable to Launceston, whence a canal extends northward in the valley to Bude Haven, with a branch to Holsworthy, &c. There is also a canal from the Tamar to Tavistock. The *Teign* originates from two branches,

called the East and West Teign, both rising in the most elevated district of Dartmoor. The former is the main branch, and flows eastward between the Dart and the Exe, from Chagford to Dunsford, and thence southward to Chudleigh, below which it receives the West Teign, or the Wrey. Passing southward to Newton Bushel, the Teign turns eastward, and runs in a fine estuary to Teignmouth, about five miles below, where its waters are lost in the English Channel. The *Plym* rises in Dartmoor, and runs southward to Plymouth, in a course of about 15 miles. It mingles its waters with those of the Tamar, in Plymouth Sound. The *Erme* and the *Aven*, between the Plym and the Dart, are also considerable rivers, rising in Dartmoor, and flowing southward to the English Channel. The *Exe*, as noticed at pages 63-'4, has its sources in the forest of Exmoor, in Somersetshire, within a few miles of the Bristol Channel, and about 36 miles N. by W. of Exeter, to which it flows in a sinuous course, by Dulverton and Tiverton. It flows from Exeter to Topsham, where it expands into a noble estuary, extending nearly six miles, to Exmouth, where it falls into the English Channel. It is navigable for ships to Topsham, and from thence there is a broad and deep canal to Exeter. The whole course of the Exe, including all its windings, is about seventy miles. Its principal tributaries are the *Batham*, *Loman*, *Creedy*, *Clist*, *Culme*, and *Kenn*. The *Batham*, rising near Clayhanger, falls into the Exe about a mile below Bampton. The *Loman*, rising in Somersetshire, passes by Up Lowman and Craze Lowman, and falls into the Exe at Tiverton. The *Creedy*, which rises near Cruwys-Morchard, passes near Crediton, Newton St. Cyres, &c., and falls into the Exe, near Cowley Bridge. The *Clist*, after passing through the six parishes to which it gives name, falls into the Exe, at Topsham. The *Culme*, rising in Somersetshire, passes Church Stanton and Hemiock, through Culmstock and Uffculme, near Collumpton and Stoke Canon, and falls into the Exe, near Cowley Bridge. The *Kenn* rises near Dunchidiock, and running by Kenford and Kenn, falls into the Exe, between Kenton and Powderham. The little river *Yeo* falls into the Creedy, near Crediton. The *Axe* rises in Dorsetshire, and near Ford Abbey becomes for a while the boundary of the two counties; thence it runs to Axminster, and after passing between Colyton and Musbury, falls into the sea between Seaton and Axmouth. The smaller rivers *Yarty* and *Coly* fall into the Axe. The *Otter* rises in Somersetshire, near Otterford, and flows thence to Up-Ottery, Honiton, Ottery St. Mary, and Otterton, below which it opens into a short but broad estuary, which terminates in the English Channel, near Budleigh-Salterton. The small river *Sid* rises near Sidbury, and passing through Sidford, falls into the sea at Sidmouth. The *Harburn*, rising on the edge of Dartmoor, runs near Harberton, and falls into the Dart, near Ashprington. The small rivers which fall into the Tamar are the *Wick*, *Derle*, *Deer*, *Cary*, *Claw*, *Lyd*, and *Tavy*, on the western side of the county. The little river *Waldron*, which rises near Bradworthy, runs near Sutcombe and Milton Damerel, and falls into the Torridge, near Bradford. The *Little Dart* rises near Rackenford, and passing near Witheridge, Worlington, and Chulmleigh, falls into the Taw below the latter place. The small river *Bray* rises near Parracombe, and passing East Buckland, King's Nympton, &c., falls into the Taw, near Newnham Bridge. The *Lyn* rises on Exmoor, and after a course of ten miles, falls into the Bristol Channel, near Linton.

Navigable Rivers, Creeks, and Canals.—The Exe is navigable for large vessels up to Topsham, whence there is a canal for sloops and barges up to Exeter. The Teign is navigable to Newton Bushel, between which and King's Teignton it is joined by the Teigngrace Canal. The Dart is navigable from Dartmouth to Totnes. A fine estuary runs inland about five

miles, from *Salcombe to Kingsbridge*, and is navigable for sloops and barges. This estuary has several navigable creeks, branching from either side, and affording the adjacent parishes the means of importing lime, sand, and other manures, and of exporting their produce. The Yealm is navigable for sloops and small brigs, to Kitley Quay. The Tamar is navigable to New Quay, 24 miles from Plymouth, for vessels of 130 to 140 tons; and up to Morwellham Quay, for vessels of 200 tons. The Plym is navigable at Catwater, near its mouth, for men of war; and vessels of 40 or 50 tons go up as far as Crabtree. The Torridge becomes navigable for boats at Wear Gifford, and for ships of large burthen at Bideford. The Taw is navigable to Barnstaple, for vessels of 140 tons; and up to New Bridge for small craft; but large vessels can anchor within three or four miles of Barnstaple. *Exeter Canal* is noticed at page 64; and the *Grand Western Canal*, at page 305. The latter was intended to pass through a great part of Devon, but only extends to Tiverton. In 1792, an Act of Parliament was passed for making the *Stover Canal*, from the Railway of Haytor Granite Works, near Bovey Tracey, to the Teign, near Newton Abbot; with a collateral cut to *Chudleigh.* The former was finished in 1794, but the latter not till 1843. (See pages 398 and 455.) The *Tavistock Canal*, to Morwellham Quay, on the Tamar, was constructed under the powers of an act passed in 1803, but was not completed till 1817, as noticed at page 624. In 1819, an Act of Parliament was obtained for making the *Bude Canal*, from Bude Haven, on the Cornish coast, to the Tamar Valley, and thence eastward to Thornbury, &c., in Devon; and southward, down the valley, to Launceston. At Burmsdon, a branch of this canal proceeds to Moreton Mill, and to a large reservoir on Longford moor; and from Veale a branch extends to Vorworthy. There are inclined planes, and a tunnel of considerable length, in its route to Thornbury. One of its chief objects is to facilitate the introduction of Welsh coal into Devon.

FISHERIES.—Great quantities of *salmon* and *salmon-trout* are taken in the principal rivers of Devon; but those taken in the Exe and Dart are the most esteemed. *Salmon-peal* is found in the Tavy, Tamar, Erme, Dart, Mole, and Otter; and *lamprey* in the Exe and Mole. The Salmon-Weir in the Tavy, near Buckland Abbey, is a work of considerable magnitude, thrown across the river in a part where two projecting rocks serve as buttresses to the masonry, which is built somewhat arch-wise, to resist the pressure of the waters in times of flood, when they collect from the slopes of Dartmoor, and rush down with great impetuosity. Turbot, plaice, soles, whiting, mullet, mackerel, pilchards, gurnet, flounders, herrings, sprats, crabs, lobsters, and other fish abound in the Channels opposite both coasts. *Brixham*, in Torbay, is the largest fishing port in Devon, as noticed at page 425, and after it ranks Plymouth, Teignmouth, Lympstone, Topsham, Dartmouth, Salcombe, and Ilfracombe. There are extensive *oyster beds* at Starcross, Newton-Ferrers, Lympstone, and Topsham. The *torpedo*, or electric ray, has occasionally been taken in Torbay and the river Dart. The *opah*, or king-fish, is very rare, but one was taken at Brixham, in 1772, weighing 140 lbs., and its flesh "looked and tasted like beef." The sepia, or *cuttle fish*, is frequently taken in nets by fishermen off Teignmouth and Slapton Sands. Dartmouth, Teignmouth, Torquay, Bideford, Topsham, and Plymouth, formerly sent many vessels to the *Newfoundland fishery*, but that trade has considerably declined, and only the three first named places are now partially engaged in it.

ROADS.—The highway returns show an extent of roads in Devon far greater than that of any other county in England, except Yorkshire. In the three years ending October, 1814, the turnpike roads and paved streets were estimated at 776 miles; and all other highways, for wheeled carriages, at 5936 miles; the total expenditure on which was £44,658. In 1836, there were in the county 29 turnpike trusts, the total income of which was £62,024. 6s. 1d., of which £11,187. 4s. 4d. was expended on improvements. In 1839, the expenditure on 6898 miles of highway was £37,356. The great roads which cross the county from Somerset and Dorset, to Cornwall, meet at Exeter. The roads which radiate from that city and the principal

towns in the county, and the cross roads interlacing them, are very numerous. From the high fences and narrowness of many of the roads, together with the perpetual recurrence of hills and valleys, all extensive prospects are often shut out, but on the tops of the hills, and where there are no enclosures, there are many delightful views over the beautiful vales and coasts in their vicinity. Devonshire abounds in all parts with the best materials for the formation of good roads, and for keeping them in good repair. The principal roads are generally in excellent condition; but many of the others are narrow, with high banks and hedges, and have the disadvantage of frequent steep ascents, even where they might have been easily carried along the sides of the hills, or through the valleys, with but little loss in distance, and a great saving in labour, and the wear and tear of carriages.

RAILWAYS.—There are in the county two old railways, or *tram roads,* on which waggons are drawn by horses. One of these is the Dartmoor and Plymouth Railway, which extends about 18 miles southward from the extensive *granite quarries,* near Prince Town, in Dartmoor. It was made under an act passed in 1819, and amended by two other acts, passed in 1820 and 1821. It has a short branch to the lime works at Catdown, and to Sutton Pool, at Plymouth. The other mineral line is on the other side of Dartmoor, and extends about six miles, from *Haytor Granite Works* to the Stover Canal. By means of this tram road and canal, immense quantities of granite are carried down to Teignmouth, for exportation; and coal, manure, &c., are taken up for the use of the neighbourhood. Devon is now crossed in a south-westerly direction, by the BRISTOL AND EXETER and the SOUTH DEVON RAILWAYS, which form a continuous line for the transit of passengers and goods, and have *Stations* in this county at Tiverton Road, Collumpton, Hele, Exeter, St. Thomas's, Starcross, Dawlish, Teignmouth, Newton Abbot, Totnes, Brent, Kingsbridge Road, Ivybridge, Plympton, and Plymouth. There are also branch railways to *Tiverton, Torquay,* and *Crediton,* but the latter is not yet opened. Other branches are projected, as well as a line to cross the county in a north-west direction, from Crediton to Barnstaple and Bideford, under the name of the *Taw Vale Railway.* A few miles at each end of the latter have been constructed, but owing to the depressed state of railway property, many years may elapse before this line and the contemplated branches are completed. The projected line from Exeter to Topsham and Exmouth is not yet made, as stated at pages 59 and 178; and the *Cornwall Railway,* intended to pass from Plymouth to Falmouth, is still to commence, though an act was obtained for making it a few years ago. By means of the South Devon and Bristol and Exeter lines, and the *Great Western Railway,*—extending from London to Bristol,—Devonshire is connected with the great net work of railways, now traversing Britain in almost every direction.

[LISTS of COUNTY MAGISTRATES and PUBLIC OFFICERS are inserted at preceding pages.]

TABLE SHEWING THE DISTANCES OF TOWNS IN DEVON

FROM EACH OTHER AND FROM LONDON.

The Italics shew the Market Days, and the square where the respective Towns meet, the distance from each other.

> Modbury, Chulmleigh, Hatherleigh, Holsworth, Plympton, Bampton, and other *small towns*, are not included.

Market Towns.	London.																											Market Day
Ashburton	192½																											*Ashburton, Sat.*
Axminster	147¼	44																										*Axminster, Fri.*
Barnstaple	192	50	57																									*Barnstaple, Fri.*
Bideford	200	47	64	9																								*Bideford, Tue. and Sat.*
Brixham	202	18	54	68	64																							*Brixham, Tue. and Sat.*
Chudleigh	181	10	34	47	44	24																						*Chudleigh, Sat.*
Crediton	175	24	33	30	38	38	17																					*Crediton, Sat.*
Collumpton	161	32	20	36	34	42	20	16																				*Collumpton, Sat.*
Dartmouth	204	18	56	68	65	5	22	40	42																			*Dartmouth, Fri.*
Exeter	172	19	25	40	42	30	9	8	12	31																		*Exeter, Tue., Fri., and Sat.*
Exmouth	167	32	26	51	55	40	22	21	22	41	12																	*Exmouth, Sat.*
Honiton	156	35	9	46	49	46	25	24	10	47	16	18																*Honiton, Sat.*
Ilfracombe	202	60	66	10	18	78	57	40	46	78	50	61	56															*Ilfracombe, Sat.*
Kingsbridge	205	20	60	70	67	17	26	42	47	12	34	44	51	80														*Kingsbridge, Sat.*
Moreton Hampstead	185	12	37	39	36	30	12	12	24	29	12	25	28	49	31													*Moreton-Hampstead, Sat.*
Newton-Abbot	187	7	40	51	48	14	6	23	16	15	28	31	61	20	12													*Newton-Abbot and Bushel, Wed.*
Okehampton	194	22	47	29	24	40	20	18	34	40	22	35	38	39	43	12	24											*Okehampton, Sat.*
Ottery St. Mary	162	31	15	46	48	42	21	20	10	43	12	12	6	56	46	24	27	34										*Ottery St. Mary, Thurs.*
Plymouth	215	24	68	57	52	32	34	45	56	28	44	54	59	67	20	29	30	55										*Plymouth, Mon., Thu., and Sat.*
Sidmouth	158	34	16	52	57	45	24	23	16	46	15	10	9	62	49	27	30	87	6	58								*Sidmouth, Sat.*
South Molton	181	42	44	11	18	57	37	20	24	58	27	40	34	22	62	31	43	26	54	38	45							*South Molton, Sat.*
Tavistock	206	20	57	44	39	30	34	45	35	33	46	49	55	28	16	45	14	48	42	28	16	45						*Tavistock, Fri.*
Teignmouth	187	15	42	56	55	18	8	23	29	22	14	25	32	65	27	20	7	31	29	39	32	43	35					*Teignmouth, Sat.*
Tiverton	168	33	25	31	36	44	23	12	6	43	15	27	15	41	48	24	29	80	16	58	21	18	42	30				*Tiverton, Tue. and Sat.*
Torquay	207	12	46	60	58	9	12	29	33	12	21	31	37	69	21	19	7	33	31	36	49	32	8	35				*Torquay, Tue. and Fri.*
Torrington	196	40	59	10	6	58	38	28	39	58	36	49	49	21	61	28	40	18	48	46	51	16	34	47	34	49		*Torrington, Sat.*
Totnes	205	8	48	58	55	10	14	30	35	10	24	34	34	68	11	19	8	30	35	22	38	53	30	16	37	9	48	*Totnes, Sat.*

HISTORY

OF THE

CITY AND COUNTY OF THE CITY

OF

EXETER.

EXETER, though the capital of Devonshire, is a *City and County of itself*, locally situated in Wonford Hundred, and in the Southern Parliamentary Division of the county of Devon. It is the seat of the *Diocese of Exeter*, and has been styled "the emporium and principal ornament of the West,"—having a magnificent cathedral and many other fine specimens of ancient as well as modern architecture; and still retaining a large share of local commerce, and some remains of its formerly extensive *woollen manufacture*. It is a *port* for sea borne vessels of three to four hundred tons burthen; having a *ship canal*, communicating with the *river Exe*, which flows close to the city, and at Topsham, about four miles below, expands into an *estuary* about a mile in breadth, and thence pursues its course to the English Channel, at Exmouth, about nine miles S.E. of the city. Exeter has now nearly 40,000 inhabitants, though it had only about 18,000 in 1801. The Bristol and Exeter and the South Devon lines connect it with the great net-work of *Railways* which now traverse Great Britain in all directions; and excellent Turnpike roads diverge from it on all sides. It is delightfully seated on the north-eastern bank of the river Exe, in 50 deg. 45 min. north latitude, and in 3 deg. 35 min. west longitude; being 173 miles W.S.W. of London by road, and 194 by railway. It is about 9 miles from the English Channel; 44 miles N.E. of Plymouth; 15 miles S. of Tiverton; 32 miles N. of Dartmouth; 40 miles S.E. by S. of Barnstaple; 25 miles S.W. by S. of Wellington; 26 miles E. of Lyme Regis; and about 80 miles S.W. of Bath and Bristol. The elevated situation of the city promotes its cleanliness and ventilation, whilst its antiquity, its enchanting neighbourhood, its proximity to the sea, its abundantly supplied markets, its continual supply of amusements, and its railway accommodation, render it a favourite place of resort to the nobility and gentry, as well as to the invalid.

The *Municipal Limits of the City and County of the City of Exeter*, comprise an area of about 4000 acres, divided into the 23 parishes, &c., enumerated in the following list; but the *Parliamentary Limits* were extended by the Reform Act of 1832, so as to comprise all the suburbs in the three adjacent parishes of St. Thomas, St. Leonard, and Heavitree;—thus encreasing the County of the City to about 6000 acres, which entitle the owners to vote only for the city members, and not for the parliamentary re-

presentatives of the county of Devon. Within these limits there are now about 40,000 inhabitants, many houses having been built in the city and suburbs since 1841, when their total POPULATION was 37,231, consisting of 16,167 *males*, and 21,064 *females*, living in about 6000 *houses*, besides which there were about 600 empty and 130 building, when the census was taken in that year. The population within the Municipal Limits in 1841 amounted to 31,312 souls, consisting of 13,836 males and 17,476 females, living in 5122 houses, besides which there were 450 empty houses and 67 building. Of this population, 7608 males and 10,793 females were upwards of 20 years of age ; and 4548 of the inhabitants were returned as not having been born in the city, or in Devonshire. Exeter has more than doubled its population during the last fifty years. Its total number of inhabitants at four decennial periods of the parliamentary census was,—17,398 in 1801; 18,896 in 1811; 23,479 in 1821 ; and 28,201 in 1831. *The following enumeration of the 23 parishes, &c., within the Municipal Limits of the City and County of the City of Exeter, shews the Population of each, in* 1841. These 23 parishes, &c., have been *incorporated for the support of their poor* since 1699, as noticed at a subsequent page. For the election of *Aldermen* they are divided into *East, West, North* and *South Wards ;* and for the election of *Councillors,* into SIX WARDS, called *St. David's, St. Mary Major's, St. Paul's, St. Petrock's, St. Sidwell's,* and *Trinity.*

PARISHES, &c.	Population.	PARISHES.	Population.
2 Allhallows, Goldsmith st. parish	360	4 St. Mary Arches .....parish	651
4 Allhallows on the Walls, parish	866	1 St. Mary Major ....parish	3429
1 Bedford Circus, *(precinct & chap.)*	119	3 St. Mary Steps ....parish	1256
2 Bradninch ....*(precinct)*	55	4 St. Olave.............parish	912
2 Castle Yard,§..*(extra-parochial)*	7	2 St. Pancras ....parish	364
1 Cathedral Close ....*(precinct)*	684	2 St. Paul ....parish	1337
2 St. David,* ....parish	3508	1 St. Petrock...........parish	261
3 St. Edmund ....parish	1595	1 St. Sidwell,* ....parish	9154
3 St. George the Martyr ..parish	685	1 St. Stephen ....parish	477
3 St. John ....parish	500	1 Trinity (Holy)* ......parish	3796
2 St. Kerrian............parish	401		
2 St. Lawrence,* ....parish	641	*Total*†	31,312
1 St. Martin ....parish	254		

☞ Those marked 1 are in the *East Ward ;* 2, in the *North Ward ;* 3, in the *South Ward ;* and 4, in the *West Ward.*

* The return of St. David's parish included 110 persons in *Devon County Gaol;* 155 in *Devon County House of Correction ;* 62 in *Exeter City Prison ;* and 81 in the *Cavalry Barracks.* That of St. Lawrence included 40 persons in *St. John's Hospital.* That of St. Sidwell included 315 persons in *Exeter Workhouse.* The return of Holy Trinity parish included 196 persons in *Devon and Exeter Hospital;* five houses and 12 persons in an extra-parochial place called *No Man's Land;* and 35 persons in the *Female Penitentiary.* The *Parochial District of St. James* has been taken out of St. Sidwell's parish.

§ The *Castle* is in the jurisdiction of the County of Devon.

† The PARLIAMENTARY LIMITS OF EXETER include also large portions of the suburban parishes of *St. Thomas the Apostle, St. Leonard,* and *Heavitree,* in Wonford Hundred; and their *total population,* in 1841, amounted to 37,231 souls, embracing 5919 of the 8478 inhabitants of these three parishes. The return of Heavitree parish included 234 soldiers in the *Artillery Barracks.* St. Leonard's parish includes the pleasant modern suburbs of *Mount Radford,* &c., where many houses have been built since 1831, and are chiefly occupied by the families of naval and military men. The return of the parish of St. Thomas included 225 persons in *St. Thomas's Union Workhouse;* 59 in the *Lunatic Asylum ;* and 47 in the *Sheriff's Ward,* or *Debtors' Prison for the County.* The returns of the parishes of Holy Trinity and St. Thomas, included 70 persons in *boats and barges.*

☞ The *Annual Value* of the lands and buildings in Exeter was assessed to to the property tax, in 1815, at £54,330; but they are now rated to the poor at the yearly value of £130,246.

The CITY rises with a bold aspect on the north-eastern side of the river Exe, and was formerly enclosed with *Walls and Gates,* but in modern times it extended itself far beyond these ancient limits, which now only circumscribe the central parts of it. The Gates and Towers in the City Walls were taken down at various periods for the improvement of the thoroughfares, but many large portions of the Walls still remain. *North-Gate* was taken down in 1769; *East-Gate,* in 1784; *West-Gate* and *Quay-Gate,* in 1815; *South-Gate,* in 1819; and *Broad-Gate,* in 1825. A statue of Henry VII., which graced the East-Gate, now decorates the front of a house in High street. The space within the Walls is in the form of an irregular parallelogram, about 900 yards long and 500 broad, and having the Castle hill at the north-east angle, overlooking the city, which has from this point a declivity to every part of the Walls. The principal streets,—High street and Fore street,—run in a continuous line through the longest diameter, and are intersected by North street street and South street, at right angles, thus dividing the old part of the city into four equal portions. To the north-east, the populous and handsome suburb of St. Sidwell extends nearly a mile from the Walls, and includes Longbrook street, St. Sidwell street, Paris street, Summerland, Blackboy road, Dix's field, &c. Beyond these, are suburbs in Heavitree parish. Beyond the south-eastern side of the Walls, are the suburbs of St. Leonard's, Holloway street, Magdalen street, Mount Radford, and many handsome villas and neat houses. Mount Radford was formerly the park and seat of John Baring, Esq. On the north-west, another suburb extends to St. David's hill and the Railway Station. On the south-west, below the Walls, are the suburbs of Exe Island, New Bridge street, Commercial road, &c. Beyond Exe Bridge, is the suburb of St. Thomas, including Cowick street, Okehampton road, Alphington street, the Canal Basin, &c. The length of the city and suburbs, taken from St. Thomas's, through Fore street, High street, and St. Sidwell's, to the Blackboy road, measures more than a mile and a half; and the breadth, taken from St David's Church to St. Leonard's, through North street and South street, is about a mile. Being situated on a hill among hills, Exeter has a high character for salubrity, cleanliness, and picturesque scenery. It is seen to great advantage from Exwick hill, on the north-west, where there is a beautiful prospect,—the low grounds through which winds the Exe in its sinuous course, are in front; with the rich foliage of the Northernhay elms crowning the ramparts of the Castle hill, whence, too, may be obtained a delightful view of the surrounding country;—the numerous churches and other buildings of the city spreading gradually from the river, till they are surmounted by the towers of the venerable Cathedral;— while the distant hills and the heights of Haldon, with their bold and swelling outlines, terminate the landscape.

ANCIENT HISTORY :—Exeter is a city of great antiquity; for, though its origin cannot be clearly ascertained, there is sufficient evi-

dence to induce a belief that it was a settlement of the Britons long before the Roman invasion. By Geoffrey of Monmouth, it is called *Caer-Penhuelgoit*, which, in the language of the ancient Britons, signifies the Prosperous Chief City of the Wood. Among its other ancient appellations, are *Caer-Isc* and *Caer-Rydh*,—the former from its situation on the river Isc or Exe ; and the latter from the red colour of the soil round the castle. These names would not have been given to it, if it had been of Roman origin ; and though Camden imagines that it was not built in the time of Vespasian, by whom Geoffrey affirms it to have been taken, the circumstance of its being ranked, by Richard of Cirencester, amongst stipendiary cities, strongly militates against his opinion,—as the Romans would neither have suffered it to become tributary, nor to receive wages, if it had not existed previous to their making it a station. Many other circumstances might be adduced, in confirmation of Exeter having been originally settled by the Britons ; and it seems equally probable that it was anciently regarded as the capital of *Danmonium*, which comprised Devon and Cornwall. It was then called *Isca Danmoniorum*, but Ptolemy afterwards styled it " *Isca with the Legio Secunda Augusta.*" It was necessary that the country from which the Romans were to derive their greatest revenue from metals, &c., should be well guarded, and as we hear of no revolts against the Roman power in this part of the island, it may be concluded that the resident troops were in sufficient numbers to prevent insurrection ; and consequently that a considerable portion of the Second Augustan Legion remained here for a long period. Another circumstance in proof of the residence of this legion at Exeter, is the ancient tradition that it was once honoured by the Romans with the name of *Augusta*. In the Itinerary of Antoninus, it is called *Isca Danmoniorum*, and is the most westerly station noticed by that historian ; but from the Iters of Ptolomy and Richard of Cirencester, from the remains of Roman roads over and around Haldon hills, and from the vestiges of ancient ways through Drewsteignton to Okehampton, Dartmoor, &c., it is apparent that various principal roads ran westward from this city, and that the Romans must have had exploratory, if not permanent, stations beyond it. Some writers have asserted that there are no remains to prove that Exeter was a Roman station. On this it may be remarked, that the destruction made by the inroads of the Saxons and Danes ; the building of religious houses, for the foundation of which and for their cemeteries, the old remains must have been removed ; the erection of new walls, and the digging anew the ditches around the city by Athelstan , and, in fine, the rebuilding the whole town, after its total destruction by *Sueno*, or *Sweyne*, king of Denmark, in 1003, must all have contributed to a change, and even to the destruction of the Roman buildings. Many Roman remains have, however, been found here ; and even Roman coins have been discovered in the walls. Among other convincing proofs of the Roman residence in this city, may be mentioned five *Penates*, or *Household Gods*, discovered here in 1778, with other antiquities. These Penates are of bronze, and were found in digging a cellar in High street, at the

corner of Broad gate. One was a figure of Ceres; two were small statues of Mercury; another represented Mars; and the fifth was supposed to represent Apollo. They were found lying among a large quantity of oyster shells, and the fragments of two *urns*,—one highly · glazed and adorned with handsome borders and human figures, executed in relief. On digging the foundations of a house on the opposite side of the street in 1776, some remains of a tesselated pavement were discovered, with a few Roman medals, one of them a *Trajan*, in large brass. How long Exeter retained its name of *Isca Danmoniorum* is uncertain, though it seems probable that it fell into disuse soon after the Romans quitted the Island; about which time it appears to have been re-occupied by the Britons, who had preserved their independence by retiring to the wilds of Cornwall. They did not, however, continue its masters many years; for Cerdic, the founder of the Saxon kingdom of Wessex, having greatly extended his possessions, either by conquest or intrigue, included most of Devon within his dominions; and at length Exeter became subjugated to the Saxons, who gave it the name of *Exan-Cestre*, which, through the various modifications of *Exceaster*, *Excester*, &c., has been softened into *Exeter*. In early times, the city was often besieged, but the greatest calamities it experienced were inflicted by the Danes, who, in the reign of *Alfred the Great*, in violation of a solemn treaty, surprised and routed the king's horsemen, and mounting their steeds, rode to Exeter, and remained there for the winter. Alfred being now fully aware that nothing could preserve his kingdom but a brave resistance, collected all his forces and invested Exeter by land; while a fleet, manned chiefly by Frisian pirates, in his employ, blocked up the harbour. This fleet having defeated a Danish squadron, which was bringing a reinforcement to the besieged, the latter capitulated, and agreed to evacuate not only this city, but all the territories of the West Saxons.

Between the period of the death of Alfred and the reign of Athelstan, the Western Britons recovered possession of Exeter; but the latter monarch drove them beyond the Tamar, and they were never afterwards able successfully to oppose the Saxon arms. Athelstan, to secure his conquests, enclosed Exeter with a wall of hewn stone, defended by towers, and under his auspices, says Malmsbury, " It became such a place of trade, that it abounded with opulence." When Sweyne, king of Denmark, landed in England in 1003, to avenge the general massacre committed on his countrymen in the preceding year, by order of king Ethelred, Exeter became the first sacrifice to his vengeance. Though bravely defended during two months, the city was at last delivered up, through the treachery of Hugh, its Norman governor; and its inhabitants were put to the sword without mercy, and most of its buildings destroyed by fire. It is said to have lain in ruins till the reign of Canute, who took it into his favour and protection. Edward the Confessor was at Exeter with his queen, Edith, in 1050. *William the Conqueror* was scarcely seated on his throne, when the citizens of Exeter, impatient of the Norman yoke, rebelled against him, and made every possible preparation for defence. The king, on receiving information of their proceedings,

marched towards Exeter with his army, accompanied by some of
the chief English nobility.   Certain leading men of the city hastened to the king's camp, besought his pardon, and having promised
fealty, and that they would receive him with open gates, gave such
hostages as he required.   Notwithstanding this, when they returned
to their fellow citizens, they found them resolved upon an obstinate
resistance.   The king, hearing of this breach of promise, rode forward with 500 horse, and finding the gates shut and the walls and
towers manned with a great force, he gave orders for his army to
advance, and caused the eyes of one of the hostages to be put out
before the city gates.   The citizens defended the place with the utmost bravery for several days ; but were at length obliged to capi-
tulate, and throw themselves on the king's mercy.   Having pros-
trated themselves before the Conqueror, they obtained a free pardon, with protection from plunder.   To prevent future rebellion,
the Conqueror ordered a strong *Castle* to be built, and left Baldwin
de Moles and other select knights, in command of the city.   Two
years after this, the Saxons again attempted to possess themselves
of the city, but the citizens, mindful of their opposition to the Norman Conqueror in 1067, shut the gates against them.   The king
sent forces to their relief, and the Saxons were defeated with great
slaughter.
    Soon after King Stephen's usurpation, Exeter was garrisoned for
the Empress Matilda, by Baldwin de Rivers, Earl of Devon ; but
on the arrival of the King with a great army, he was joyfully received by the citizens.   The Earl was obliged to shut himself up in
the castle with his Countess, his children, and all his adherents ;
among whom were some of the most distinguished young men of the
realm.   In this stronghold they made a most obstinate defence, and
held it three months, though the besieging army availed themselves
of all the military engines then in use, and succeeded so far as to
take the barbican by assault, and to batter down the bridge which
communicated with the city.   They were at length obliged to capi-
tulate for want of water, but the Earl escaped to the Isle of Wight,
where he was soon after taken, and banished.   When Stephen left
Exeter, he committed the custody of the castle and the county to his
brother, Henry de Blois, Bishop of Winchester.   Henry II. granted
the citizens several privileges, as a reward for their attachment to
his mother, the Empress Matilda, and gave them the custody of the
castle.   During the reign of John, Robert de Courtenay was governor
of Exeter, but Henry III. gave the government of the city and
castle to Peter de Rivaux.   Edward I. and his Queen kept their
Christmas here in 1285, and were entertained fifteen days at the
Black Friary.   Izacke relates, that during their residence here the
murder of the precentor, Walter de Lechlade, was investigated ; and
that the late mayor, who had borne that office eight years, and four
others, were condemned to death.   In 1357, Edward the Black
Prince, having gained the memorable battle of Poictiers, landed on
his return, at Plymouth, whence, coming to Exeter with his royal
prisoners, (the King of France and his youngest son,) was received
with great demonstrations of joy; and he and his two captives were

sumptuously entertained for three days. Henry VI. was eight days at the Bishop's palace, in 1451, and in the contest between him and Edward IV. for the Crown, Exeter again became the scene of hostilities; but the dangers to which it was exposed were averted by the prudent conduct of the Mayor and other citizens, in 1469. At that period of the long continued wars between the *Houses of York and Lancaster*, the Duchess of Clarence, Lord Dinham, Lord Fitz-Warren, and other distinguished partizans of Henry VI., with many fighting men, were blockaded at Exeter, by the Yorkists under Sir Wm. Courtenay; but after twelve days, the blockade was discontinued, through the mediation of some of the canons of the cathedral, and the mayor. The battle of Losecote, in Lincolnshire, ensued in 1470, and the Duke of Clarence and the Earl of Warwick fled to Exeter, where they were entertained by the Bishop, till a ship was got ready at Dartmouth, to take them to Calais. They had only just escaped when the King arrived at Exeter with a numerous army. In 1471, previous to the battle of Tewksbury, the Lancasterians of Devon and Cornwall, under the command of Sir John Arundel and Sir Hugh Courtenay, mustered at Exeter, whence they marched to the fatal field. Some time after this, Edward IV., with his Queen and the infant Prince, visited Exeter, and at his departure, presented the Mayor with a sword, to be carried before him and his successors on all public occasions. A strong party was formed in the west of England, against the usurpation of Richard III., in 1483, but their hopes were for a time frustrated by the execution of the Duke of Buckingham; and a Special Commission was sent down to Torrington, under which the Marquis of Dorset, Bishop Courtenay, and others of the Courtenay family were outlawed. Sir Thos. St. Leger, the King's brother-in-law, and Thomas Rame, Esq., were condemned and beheaded at Exeter. Richard himself having made a progress into the west on this occasion, came to Exeter and was presented with a purse of 200 nobles.

The next siege of Exeter was in the time of Henry VII., when *Perkin Warbeck*, pretending to the Crown, and asserting himself to be Richard Duke of York, son of Edward IV., landed in Cornwall, and marched to this city, at the head of about 6000 men. He commenced a vigorous siege, but was repulsed in several assaults, and at last compelled to raise the siege. The conduct of the citizens during this siege, so conciliated the favour of *Henry VII.*, that on his visit to the city, shortly after the flight of Perkin Warbeck, he bestowed on them great commendations, granted them a new charter, and gave them the sword he then wore, as a testimony of his good-will. Some of the ringleaders of the rebellion were executed upon Southern Hay; and others received a free pardon, after being brought before the King with halters about their necks. The Princess Catherine of Arragon, having landed at Plymouth, in 1501, rested several days at Exeter, on her way to London. In 1536, Exeter was made a county of itself, as will be seen at a subsequent page. The *Reformation in religion* and the suppression of the *Monasteries*, in the reign of Henry VIII., and during the regency of his infant son and successor, Edward VI., caused much discontent

among the poor; and insurrections broke out in various parts of the kingdom, especially during the year 1549, when the nobility and gentry began to enclose the monastic lands, which had been divided amongst them. The poor had long enjoyed considerable benefit from these estates, as well as the right of pasturage on the commons and wastes. The insurgents of Devon being assembled in considerable numbers, encompassed Exeter on the 2nd of July, 1549, but the city was bravely and successfully defended by the inhabitants. The assailants burned the gates, and after attempting to scale the walls, tried to destroy them by mining, but without success; they then attempted to starve the citizens by a blockade. The besieged, though reduced to great distress, and obliged to eat horse flesh, and other loathsome viands, held out till they were relieved by the forces under Lord John Russell, who completely routed the rebels at Clist Heath, on the 5th of August, and entered the city on the following day. The magistrates, in gratitude for their deliverance, appointed the 6th of August to be kept annually as a day of thanksgiving; and the Lord Protector sent a letter in the King's name, thanking the citizens for their courage and fidelity. As a more substantial reward, the King, with the advice of the Privy Council, granted the Corporation the valuable manor of *Exe Island*, for the better maintenance of the city, with license also to take out of the woods of Cotledge and Perridge, wood sufficient for repairing the mills belonging to the said manor. In January, 1554, Sir Peter and Sir Gawen Carew, Sir Thomas Dennis, and others, being up in arms to oppose King Philip's coming to England, are said to have taken possession of the city and castle of Exeter. *Don Antonio*, the deposed King of Portugal, was liberally entertained with his whole retinue in 1584, by Jno. Davy, Esq., the then mayor. A terrible sickness broke out at the Assizes, in 1586, when Sir B. Drake, one of the Judges, and several of the magistrates, and jurymen, died of the distemper. Queen Elizabeth sent the citizens a letter of thanks for their zealous exertions against the Spaniards, in 1588, and granted them the motto of *semper fidelis*, to be borne in the city arms. In 1531, the *Rev. T. Bennett, M.A.*, was burnt to death at Liverydole, near Exeter, for *heresy*, though he was a learned and pious divine. In the last year of Queen Mary, (1557,) *Agnes Prest* was burnt to death on Southernhay, for denying the real presence in the sacrament.

At the commencement of the CIVIL WARS of the 17th century, when brother fought against brother, and father against son, the Earl of Bedford, being Lord Lieutenant of the county of Devon, and attached to the cause of the Parliament, repaired to Exeter, disarmed the loyal citizens, garrisoned the city, and planted ordnance upon the walls. When he quitted Exeter, he gave the government of it to the Earl of Stamford. After the loss of the battle of Stratton, in which the latter Earl had the chief command, he hastened to Exeter, with the news of his defeat, and, expecting a siege, destroyed all the houses in the suburbs, and ordered the trees on the walls and in the Northern and Southern Hays to be cut down. After the capture of Bristol, (July 24th, 1643,) Sir John Berkeley was sent by Charles I. to take the command in Devonshire, and to take mea-

sures for blockading Exeter. About the middle of the following month, Prince Maurice came with his army before Exeter, and found Sir John Berkeley besieging the city, with his guards close to the gates. The siege continued till after the loss of the Parliamentary garrisons upon the north coast, when the Earl of Stamford was induced to surrender. Sir John Berkeley was then made governor of Exeter, to the great joy of the major part of the citizens, who are said to have been zealous royalists. Exeter being regarded as a place of great security, the Queen, then far advanced in pregnancy, was sent there, and was joyfully received by the citizens, who conducted her to Bedford House, which had been fitted for her reception, and where she gave birth to the *Princess Henrietta Maria*, afterwards Duchess of Orleans. The Corporation voted the Queen a present of £200. On the approach of the Earl of Essex with his army, on his march westward, her Majesty left Exeter for Falmouth, and embarked for France. The Earl, however, made no attempt on this city, which was visited by the King, and the Prince of Wales, on the 26th of July, 1644, and the former was entertained at Bedford House, and the latter at the Deanery. On their arrival, the Corporation presented the King with £500, and the Prince with £100. After his successful expedition into Cornwall, the King returned to Exeter for one night, (September 17th,) and then proceeded to Oxford. The Prince was in Exeter in August and September, 1645. After the battle of Naseby, Sir Thomas Fairfax was sent as general into the west. Although the reduction of Exeter was one of the chief objects of the expedition, the general did not immediately besiege it, but placed garrisons in several of the neighbouring villages and gentlemen's seats, by which the city was greatly distressed. In the spring of 1646, Exeter was closely invested; and after a struggle of some weeks duration, Sir John Berkeley, the governor, was obliged to surrender the city on the 9th of April. One of the articles of capitulation was that the infant, Princess Henrietta Maria, and her household, should have liberty to remove to any part of England or Wales. Most of these articles are said to have been shamefully violated. The cathedral was defaced by the parliamentary soldiers, the painted glass destroyed, and the fabric divided into two places of worship, one for Presbyterians and the other for Independents; the chapter-house was turned into a stable; and the Bishop's Palace, the Deanery, and the Canon's houses, into barracks. Sir Thomas Fairfax, at the head of his army, entered Exeter on the 14th of April, and stayed till the 18th, when he left it in charge of Colonel Hammond, and one of the regiments raised by Col. Shapcote, Col. Weare, and Col. Frye. The unfortunate king surrendered in the same year, and was beheaded in 1649, when *Oliver Cromwell* began to give the reins to his ambition, and lost his early principles of liberty in the unbounded stretch of power which lay before him. In 1655, John Penruddock and Hugh Grove, Esq., were beheaded at Exeter Castle for having taken arms against the Commonwealth; and several gentlemen were hanged for the same offence at the common place of execution. The *restoration of Charles II.* was hailed at Exeter with much enthusiasm,

and when he was proclaimed on the 11th of May, 1660, the three conduits of the city were supplied with claret. The Corporation presented a piece of plate, of the value of £500, to the King; one of £300 to the Queen-Mother; and one of £200 to the Princess Henrietta Maria, who was born in the city. In 1670, Charles II., having been to see the new citadel at Plymouth, visited this city on his return, and lodged at the Deanery. On this occasion he promised the Corporation a portrait of his sister, Henrietta Maria, then Duchess of Orleans. This valuable picture was sent down the next year, and now hangs in the Guildhall. At the GLORIOUS REVOLUTION of 1688, Exeter was the scene of some interesting transactions. *William Prince of Orange*, having landed at Torbay on the 5th of November, rode on the 7th to Ford House, near Newton-Abbot. On the 8th, Lord Mordaunt, with Dr. Burnet, (afterwards Bishop of Salisbury,) came to Exeter with a troop of horse. The mayor, Sir Thos. Jefford, who had recently been knighted and elected to that office by the mandate of King James, ordered the gates to be closed against them; but the porter not being able to resist, reluctantly opened them, and soldiers continued to enter the city nearly all the day. On the 9th, the Prince of Orange entered the city with a most magnificent cavalcade, followed by the remainder of his army. The Prince was welcomed with loud acclamations, and conducted to the Deanery, where he kept his court, after offering up thanksgivings in the Cathedral for his safe arrival. Dr. Burnet read the Prince's declaration. At first, the neighbouring gentry, intimidated by the recent cruelties of Judge Jefferies, and the fate of the rash followers of the late Duke of Monmouth, showed much reluctance in declaring in his favour; and it is said he had some thoughts of abandoning his designs; but being emboldened by the arrival of Lord Colchester with some of the king's troops, the gentlemen of Devon joined the Prince's standard, and entered into an association for the defence of the Protestant religion, and for the maintenance of government and the liberties of the people, as established by Magna Charta. This instrument was signed in the Cathedral on the 17th; and on the 21st the Prince of Orange left Exeter on his march to London; leaving Sir Edward Seymour governor of the city. In the *Prince's cavalcade*, when he entered Exeter, were " the Earl of Macclesfield, with 200 horsemen, most of them English nobles and gentlemen, on Flanders' steeds, in bright armour; 200 negroes attendant, wearing embroidered caps, with white fur and plumes of feathers; 200 Finlanders, clothed in beavers' skins, with black armour and broad swords; 50 gentlemen and as many pages, to support the Prince's standard; 50 led horses, with two grooms to each; two state coaches; the Prince on a milk-white horse, in a complete suit of bright armour, a plume of white ostrich feathers on his head; 42 running footmen by his side; 200 gentlemen and pages on horseback; 300 Swiss guards; 500 volunteers, with two led horses each; the Prince's guards, 600 armed cap-a-pie; the remainder of the army, with 50 waggons laden with cash; and 120 pieces of cannon."

On October 18th, 1738, the Duke of Marlborough came to review the troops at Exeter, and was entertained by the Corporation. In 1779, the combined fleet appeared off Plymouth, and the numerous French prisoners then at that port were marched to Exeter, and guarded in the County Bridewell by a volunteer regiment, raised at this alarming period. In August, 1789, this city was honoured with a visit by George III., his Queen, and three Princesses. This royal visit was lampooned by Dr. Walcot, in his usual Pindaric humour, and in the dialect of Devonshire, his native county. The present Queen Dowager visited Exeter August 16th, 1845. During the alarms of French invasion, in 1798 and 1803, active measures were taken for securing and fortifying Exeter. In the early part of the late wars, large *Cavalry and Artillery Barracks* were erected here by Government; the former occupying an extensive oblong area on the north side of the city, and the latter pleasantly situated in the south-eastern suburbs, within the bounds of Heavitree parish. In the latter part of last, and early part of the present century, Exeter displayed its royalty and patriotism by forming several companies of *Volunteers*, both horse and foot. Many of the citizens at the same time joined the three regiments of *Devonshire Militia*, who were sent to various parts of the kingdom for internal defence, at the time when nearly all the troops of the line were abroad. For more than a year, in 1812-13, the South Devonshire Militia were stationed at Sheffield, where they were much esteemed for their orderly conduct, and proficiency in military tactics.

In 1796 and 1800-1, the high price of bread caused several riots in Exeter; and the ringleader of the mob in the former year was afterwards hung. Owing to the scarcity and dearness of provisions, there was a serious food riot in the city, on May 14th, 1847, when nine of the ringleaders were captured. The coronation and marriage of her present Majesty, Queen Victoria, were severally observed here with great demonstrations of loyalty, and the poor were regaled with old English fare. The opening of the *Bristol and Exeter Railway*, on May 1st, 1844, was kept as a general holiday, and a splendid *déjeûner-à-la-fourchette* took place at the Railway Station, where assembled thousands witnessed the arrival of the first train. This line has cost about £2,000,000. The *South Devon Railway* was opened to Laira on May 5th, 1848, and to Plymouth in April, 1849. It cost about £1,900,000. The atmospheric principle was tried for a short time on part of this line, at a loss to the proprietors of about £350,000. Other *Railways* have recently been opened from Exeter to Crediton, Topsham, Exmouth, &c. The *Railway Stations* for passengers and goods are very commodious, and are noticed at a subsequent page, with the public conveyances. The Dowager Queen Adelaide, accompanied by her sister, the Duchess of Leiningen, Prince Edward, and the two Princesses of Saxe Weimar, the Earl of Derby, Earl Howe, &c., arrived in Exeter, at the Clarence Hotel, August 16th, 1845, and stayed till the Monday following, when they proceeded to Powderham, Mamhead, Torquay, &c.

Though the locality of Exeter is peculiarly healthy, it has at various periods suffered severely from *plagues* and other fatal epidemics. It is said to have increased greatly in population in the reign of Athelstan, by the influx of strangers ; but in the Domesday Survey, 48 houses which had paid taxes are stated to have been then in ruins. The city was visited by famine and pestilence in 1234, and the two following years. Fatal pestilences are recorded to have happened in 1378, 1438, 1479, 1503, 1546, 1551, 1569, and 1586. The plague was very fatal here in 1590, 1603, and 1625, but the city appears to have escaped the great plague in 1665. The small pox was very prevalent here in 1777, when, out of 1850 cases, there were 285 deaths. That dreadful scourge, *Asiatic Cholera,* visited this city in July, 1832, but was much less virulent here than at many other places, the number of deaths resulting from it being only 40. The same awful malady made dreadful ravages at Plymouth, Devonport, and many other parts of the kingdom in 1849, but was only slightly felt in this city, where many *sanatory improvements* have been effected since 1832, as appears from the recent Report of the Health of Towns Commission, and from a History of the Cholera of 1832, published by Dr. Shapter, in 1849. In 1832, the city was very badly drained, and scantily supplied with water, but now, as Dr. Shapter says in his valuable work, " the drainage is comprehensive and efficient ; water gushing at all points yields its ample supply ; those attending the markets have covered buildings ; in St. Sidwell's a new church and schools cover the ground where the clothes of those dying of the pestilence were destroyed, and a new parish has been created in obedience to the wants of the people ; a pleasure park occupies the ground which was first devoted to the burial of those dying of the Cholera ; a spacious cemetery without the walls has relieved the former overcrowded grounds, which are now closed and planted; while in one of them a monument, erected over the last Cholera patient there buried, is a church—a parish church, the advantages of which had been denied to the inhabitants for nearly two hundred years."

The CASTLE of Exeter stood in the highest part of the city, within the north-east angle of the city walls, as noticed at page 51, From the colour of the soil of the bold eminence on which it stood, it obtained the name of *Rougemont Castle*. When Richard III. visited it in 1413, he commended it highly, both for its strength and beauty of situation ; but on being told it was called *Rougemont*, he mistook the name for *Richmond* and suddenly grew sad, saying that the end of his days approached ; a prophecy having declared that he would not long survive the sight of Richmond. After its surrender to General Fairfax, in 1646, this once formidable castle ceased to be a military fortress, and all its towers and battlements were destroyed. There are now but few remains of the building, its site being mostly occupied by the Devon Assize Hall and Sessions House. The governor's house, the old chapel, sallyport, &c., were taken down about 1773 ; but the lofty entrance *gateway*, with a circular arch, and finely mantled with ivy, is still to be seen in the beautiful gardens of Rougemont Lodge, formed on the site of the castle fosse, and com-

manding delightful prospects. There are still extensive remains of the boundary walls of the castle enclosure, which comprised a large area, and had a small collegiate chapel, which was dedicated to the Holy Trinity, and was taken down about 1782. Notwithstanding the general opinion of modern writers, that *Exeter Castle* was of more remote origin, and had been the residence of the West-Saxon Kings, we find no authority in history to countenance that opinion. The first building worthy of the name of castle is recorded to have been built by King Athelstan, and to have been destroyed by the Danes in 1003. As noticed at page 54. William the Conquerer, selected Rougemont as the site of a larger and more strongly fortified castle than had ever existed at Exeter, and gave the superintendence of its erection, and its future custody to *Baldwin de Moles* or *de Briöniis*, the husband of his niece Albreda. Baldwin was at the same time made heriditary sheriff of Devonshire, and after completing the castle, it became his place of residence. His son Richard died without issue, and this castle was granted to *Richard de Redvers or Rivers*, who had married a daughter of Baldwin de Moles, and was created *Earl of Devon* by Henry I. On the death of Isabel de Redvers, sister and heir of the 8th Earl, in 1293, the castle and honour of Exeter passed to Henry Courtenay, the 6th *Baron Courtenay*, who was created Earl of Devon in 1335. The Courtenays held the earldom, with a few short intermissions, till 1556, and it has lately been restored to them. (See Powderham Castle.) The title of Duke of Exeter was first conferred in 1397, on *John Holland*, who was 3rd son of the Earl of Kent, and was beheaded in 1400. *Thomas Beaufort*, natural son of John of Gaunt, Duke of Lancaster, was created Duke of Exeter in 1416, but on his death, without issue, in 1426, the title became extinct. In 1443 it was conferred on the son of the first duke, John Holland, Lord High Admiral, who was succeeded in 1446 by his son Henry, who was attainted in 1461, when the dukedom was forfeited. In 1525, Henry Courtenay, the 17th Earl of Devon, was created Marquis of Exeter, but he was attainted and beheaded in 1539. His son, Edward, was restored in blood and honours in 1553, but dying without issue in 1556, the title became extinct. In 1605, *Thomas Cecil*, 2nd Baron Burghley, was created Earl of Exeter, and in 1801, Henry Cecil, the 10th Earl of this family, was raised to the dignity of Marquis of Exeter, now enjoyed by his son, *Brownlow Cecil*, the present Marquis, who resides at Burghley House, near Stamford, Lincolnshire.

In 1232, Exeter Castle, as well as many others, was seized by Henry III, who gave it to his younger brother, Richard, *Earl of Cornwall*. In 1286, Edward I. granted it to Matthew Fitzjohn for life ; but it continued nevertheless, chiefly in the Earls of Cornwall ; and, in 1337, when Edward, the eldest son of King Edward III. was created *Duke of Cornwall*, this castle, with a small district adjoining, was made part of the duchy, which has been ever since vested in the heir apparent to the Crown, who becomes Duke of Cornwall immediately after his birth, and who has always been created *Prince of Wales*. In 1397, there being then no Duke of Cornwall, Richard II. made John Holland, the first Duke of Exeter, governor of this

Castle, in which he is said to have had a fine mansion. In 1711, an act of parliament was passed, enabling Queen Anne to grant a lease of Exeter Castle for 99 years, for the use of the county of Devon. It is probable that the castle had been used for county purposes long before that period; indeed the gaol is said to have been removed there from Bicton, in 1518.

DEVON ASSIZE HALL AND SESSIONS HOUSE, commonly called " *The Castle*," form a spacious and handsome building, on the north side of the Castle yard, on the site of the old county prison and courts of justice. This structure was erected in 1773-'4, but has undergone frequent alterations and some enlargements, to make it suitable for the augmented business of the county. It is faced with Portland stone, and contains two commodious courts, a grand jury room, magistrates' room, &c. In the crown-bar-court is a large painting presented to the county by the artist, Mr. Brokedon, and representing " The Judgment of Daniel." The judges on the western circuit hold the assizes here twice a year for Devonshire; and at the Guildhall twice a year for the city. Petty Sessions are held here every Friday, before the county magistrates, who also hold here quarter sessions, &c., at the usual periods. County meetings and election meetings for the Southern Parliamentary Division of Devonshire, are held in the front of the building, in the Castle yard, which is extra-parochial. On the Eastern side of the Session House the visitor may ascend to a very pleasant walk on the city walls, overlooking Northernhay. Beyond the latter are the DEVON COUNTY GAOL AND BRIDEWELL, occupying a pleasant situation in St. David's parish. These prisons comprise extensive ranges of brick buildings, with large yards, &c., enclosed within a strong and lofty boundary wall. The Gaol was commenced in 1796, and the Bridewell in 1807. They have accommodations for about 300 prisoners, and there are often as many as 100 in the *Gaol* and 150 in the *Bridewell or House of Correction*. Several judicious alterations were made a few years ago, so as to admit of a better classification of the prisoners, many of whom are employed on the treadmill and in other laborious occupations. The SHERIFF'S WARD or *County Gaol for Debtors*, is in the suburban parish of St. Thomas, on the opposite side of the river Exe. It is a large brick building, and has accommodations for about ninety debtors, but has seldom half that number of inmates. It was erected about 1820, at the expense of the county, and has a large yard for the recreation of the inmates. The gaolers, and other *public officers of Devonshire*, are enumerated after the list of *County Magistrates*, at a preceding page.

Danes' Castle, is a small circular earth work, in the northern suburbs of the city, near the County Gaol. Mr. Shortt pronounces it to have been an out-post of the Roman garrison of Exeter, and in corroboration of this opinion he evidences the number of broken urns, coins, &c., found near it, a few years ago, in cutting a road. The aggar or vallum of this little earth work is now very imperfect, but on one side of it there is still a fosse 28 feet wide and 4½ deep.

MANUFACTURES, &c.—It is said that there were two mints in Exeter in the reigns of Athelstan and King John; and it certainly

was one of the six places in which mints were established by Wm. III., in 1696. The silver coined here at the latter period has the letter E under the King's bust, and the mint is said to have been then in Hele's Hospital. The *Woollen Manufacture* existed here at an early period, and was much increased in the reigns of Henry VIII. and Elizabeth. There were fulling mills here in the time of Edward I., and in 1535 the wool market for this part of England was removed hither from Crediton. The weavers and fullers of Exeter were subsequently united to the merchant adventures, who were incorporated by Queen Elizabeth, in 1559, under a governor and four consuls. Under the auspices of this Queen great numbers of *Dutch, Flemish and other cloth workers*, who had fled from the religious persecutions of the Duke of Alva, settled in this and other parts of England, and brought with them their arts and their industry. After this period the Exeter merchants, chiefly Germans, Swiss and French, considerably increased their exports of woollen goods to Germany, Spain, Portugal, Switzerland, &c. In the reign of James I. the trade of this city was still further augmented, and woollen goods were then exported to Italy, Turkey, and the Levant. In 1676 eight out of ten of the citizens are said to have been engaged in the woollen trade, and upwards of £50,000 worth of goods were sold here weekly. In 1750 no fewer than 302,760 pieces of woollen cloth were exported hence to foreign countries, and the total annual value of the exports, including cloth, wool, corn, hides, &c., in this year, was estimated at one million sterling. The manufacture of *serges* was then flourishing here ; but a great part of them were sent *white* to London, to be there dyed and finished. For a long period the East India Company purchased here about £300,000 worth of serges, &c., yearly. When the ports of the Continent were shut against English good by Napoleon, the woollen trade of Exeter sustained serious injury, and it has continued to decline since the general peace ; the manufacturers here, and in other parts of the West of England, not having emulated those of Yorkshire in the introduction of improved machinery, and the erection of large mills and factories. In 1822 the manufactures of this city and its immediate neighbourhood employed only about 350 hands, and consisted chiefly of serges and other coarse cloths, for making which there are now only three factories, one at Exwick, and the other two in Exe Island, but nearly all the woollen goods made in the county for foreign markets are exported from Exeter, which has also a large share of *general commerce* and many mercantile houses, some of them extensively engaged in the foreign and coasting trades. Here are several large iron foundries, corn mills, paper mills, malt kilns, breweries, and tanneries ; and many coal, corn, wool, timber, wine, spirit, drug and grocery, &c. merchants.

The PORT OF EXETER extends about 26 miles along the coast of the English Channel, from Axmouth to Teignmouth, and includes the navigations of the rivers Exe, Teign, Otter, Sid, and Axe. The RIVER EXE, from which the city takes its name, has its sources in the forest of Exmoor, in Somersetshire, within six miles of the Bristol Channel, and about 36 miles N. by W. of Exeter. It flows in a very sinuous course, eastward to Dul-

verton, and thence southward to Tiverton, Exeter, Topsham, and the Eng-lish Channel. Its principal *tributary streams* are the small rivers Barle, Batherm, Loman, Culme, Creedy, and Clist. At Topsham, about four miles below Exeter, it suddenly widens its stream to more than a mile in breadth, and becomes navigable for ships of considerable burthen. An-ciently, vessels of good size had been accustomed to pass up the river to Exeter Bridge, and the tide flowed beyond the city; but in 1284, Isabella de Redvers, Countess of Devon, erected a lofty *wear* across the bed of the river, near Topsham, which from her is called *Countess Wear*. This obstruc-tion stopped both the shipping and the fish, to the great damage of the city and neighbourhood. It was satisfactorily shewn, by an inquisition taken at Exeter, in 1290, in a complaint preferred by the citizens, that the course of the river Exe, from the Checkstone at its mouth, to Exeter Bridge, was ori-ginally the property of the Crown; that the city of Exeter was also an ap-purtenance of the Crown; that Henry III. had granted the same to his brother, Richard, Earl of Cornwall; that the citizens held the fee-farm of the said city of Richard aforesaid, as they had holden it formerly of the Crown, by the yearly payment of £39. 15s. 3d.; that in virtue of such grant, and of ancient custom, the Exe water belongs to the said city, as far down as the port of Exmouth; and that the right of fishing and using the water is common to all. A verdict was recorded in favour of the city; but, not-withstanding this triumph of reason and justice, the navigation to Exeter was further impeded by the Countess's heir and successor, Hugh Courte-nay, Earl of Devon. He built a quay at Topsham, the general receiving place of the city's customs, and his bailiffs obstructed the city's sergeants in the execution of their right of searching vessels. The citizens very fre-quently preferred complaints against these encroachments; but owing to the confusion of the times, and the overwhelming influence of the Courtenay family, they could not accomplish the removal of the wear, though they maintained their right to the tolls. The tides, therefore, only reached Topsham, which belonged to the Earl of Devon, and became exceedingly flourishing. To provide a remedy for these ancient grievances, an act of parliament was obtained in the reign of Henry VIII., to cut a water-course or CANAL, from Topsham to Exeter. This "new work or haven," imperfect and inefficient as it was, still ranks its designer, *John Trewe*, an engineer of Glamorganshire, amongst the very first projectors of inland navigation. The expense of the undertaking amounted to about £5000. Charles II. made Exeter a royal port; and in 1675, an act was obtained, to enable the Corporation to widen and improve the canal. In 1699, they had expended nearly £20,000 in this work; but further improvements were suggested and adopted till 1725, when the port was considered to be finished, though only comparatively small vessels could get up to Exeter. In 1825, the Corpora-tion, deeming further improvements necessary, employed Mr. James Green, an able engineer, to considerably deepen the channel of the canal, and to extend it down to Turf, a deeper part of the tideway, where there is now a sea-lock 120 feet long, and 30 wide. The canal is now more than five miles in length, and 15 feet in depth, and runs along the western side of the river. The entrance is deep enough to admit vessels drawing ten feet water, even at neap tides, when there is not water enough for them to pro-ceed to Topsham. Any vessels (except steam packets,) which can pass the bar at Exmouth—that is, any drawing from 12 to 14 feet water—are ena-bled to proceed at once to Exeter. Two of the larger sailing vessels are also now enabled to pass easily abreast along the canal. Vessels which draw too much water to cross the bar, lie in *bight* at Exmouth, and dis-charge their cargoes into lighters, for Topsham or Exeter. The BASIN, or

floating dock, on the western side of the Exe, opposite the quay at Exeter, was opened in 1830, and is 917 feet long, and 18 deep. It is 110½ feet in width for more than two-thirds of its length, and the rest 90 feet. There are 18 *pilots* at Exmouth, who cruise at sea in four pilot boats. They are licensed by the Trinity Board at this port, as also are six *river pilots*, who reside at Topsham. The late Municipal Commissioners, in 1834, found that the old Corporation of Exeter had incurred a debt of £100,000 in improving the canal, and that this enormous expenditure was a subject of much complaint on the part of the city merchants, who said that the excessive tolls then paid bore a large proportion to the freight; sometimes as much as a quarter part for the freight on a coasting voyage. Since the introduction of railway competition, these tolls have been much reduced. Steam packets do not often come up to Exeter, and the first that arrived there was the *Alert*, which came to the quay on Sept. 20th, 1840. Here are Bonding Warehouses for all foreign goods except tobacco; but the latter can be bonded here, if sent coastwise for home consumption or ships' stores. The RAILWAYS are noticed at page 59. The gross receipts of *customs duty* collected at this port, in 1838, was £84,496; and in 1839, £90,081. The *excise duties* collected in this district amounted in 1838 to £70,710; and in 1839, to £80,460. The CUSTOM HOUSE is on the Quay; and the *Inland Revenue Office*, formerly called the Excise Office, is in South street. The POST OFFICE, STAMP OFFICE, and *Bankruptcy Court*, occupy a commodious and elegant building in Queen street, erected in 1849, by Messrs. W. H. and W. W. Hooper. Mr. P. Measor is the *postmaster;* and M. Kennaway, Esq., is *distributor of stamps* for Devonshire and Exeter.

MARKETS AND FAIRS.—From the richness of the soil of the surrounding country, Exeter has long been noted for the cheapness and plentiful supply of its markets, which are held by prescription, and were formerly held on Monday, Wednesday, and Friday. The principal market is now held on Friday, and is esteemed the largest in the West of England for all kinds of provisions. It is well supplied with corn and cattle, and there are also provision markets on Tuesday and Saturday. A " *Great Market*," for cattle, &c., is held on the second Friday of every month ; and here are four FAIRS for cattle and merchandise, held annually, on the third Wednesdays in February, May, and July, and the second Wednesday in December. The Corporation are owners of the markets, and have power to alter the fairdays, which they have done on several occasions. Henry I. granted to St. Nicholas's Priory, a fair to be held on St. Nicholas's day, (Dec. 1st,,) and the moiety of an ancient fair called *Crollditch*, now *Lammas fair*, which was held on Southernhay green till 1793. The latter is the fair which in Edward the First's time was said to be held by prescription, and continued four days. Both moieties of this fair were purchased by the Corporation some centuries ago. A fair at the feast of St. Mary Magdalen, which had belonged to the Leper's Hospital, was granted to the Corporation in 1463. They obtained an act of parliament in 1820, empowering them to remove the markets from the public streets, &c.; and to raise money by subscription, for the construction of two covered *Market Places*, which were not commenced till fifteen years afterwards, and are equal in design and accommodation to those in London. The WESTERN MARKET, in Fore street, was built in 1835, '6, and is open for all commodities, but is principally used for the sale of butchers' meat, corn, seed, leather, and wool. It has a central avenue, 71 feet long and 31½ broad; and a market hall, 157 feet by 91, comprising a nave and aisles, with arcades springing from piers of granite. The nave rises above the aisles by a second tier of minor arches, through which light and air are admitted ; and the roof is formed with circular ribs,

all exposed to view. Adjoining the hall is the Market House Inn, which has a large Exchange, with approaches from within and without the market. The walls are of stone and brick, and the use of timber is avoided as much as possible, by the substitution of iron. The EASTERN MARKET, in Queen street, was not opened till July, 1838, though the first stone was laid April 8th, 1835. It is a handsome and substantial building, of Cornish granite and Bath stone, in the Doric order, and is 230 feet long, and 165 broad, exclusive of the entrance from Paul street. Great attention has been paid to the free admission of light and air. The shops and stalls for the sale of various commodities, except fish, are distributed over the area of the general market. In the centre, is an avenue of granite pilasters, occupied by stalls for the sale of fruit and vegetables. The fish market is separated from the rest of the market by a covered colonnade round its four sides, and in its centre is a fountain, for keeping the temperature as cool as possible. The fish shops have marble slabs, with tubes for the distribution of water. The total cost of the Eastern and Western Markets was £88,220. Mr. Chas. Fowler was architect of the latter, and also superintended the erection of the former, from the design of the late Mr. George Dymond. The *Cattle Market* has been removed to Bonhay, on the banks of the river, near Exe Bridge, and is well supplied every Friday. In the city are five highly respectable *Banking Houses,* and many large and commodious *Inns, Hotels, and Public-Houses,* as well as many well furnished private *Boarding and Lodging Houses.* In the suburbs, many genteel houses are let furnished, at from £60 to £140 per annum.

BRIDGES.—The old bridge over the Exe had twelve arches, and was built about 1250, by subscription ; but Walter Gerves, who was the largest contributor, and left lands for its maintenance, was considered its founder. It was nearly swept away by a great flood in 1449, when an indulgence was granted by Bishop Lacy, in aid of its reparation. In 1769, an act of Parliament was obtained for building a new bridge, a little higher up the river, and for selling the bridgelands. The first stone was laid in 1770, and the work was in great forwardness in 1775, when it was destroyed by a flood. The work was recommenced, in 1776, by laying the first stone of the present EXE BRIDGE, which was opened in 1778, when the old one was pulled down. It is an elegant stone structure of three arches, and cost about £20,000, including the expense of the unfinished fabric, which was washed down in 1775. A smaller bridge crosses an arm of the river, to the little island of Shilhay, and beyond the north wall of the city is the IRON BRIDGE which crosses the small stream called Longbrook, and the deep hollow between North street and St. David's hill. This bridge, or viaduct, was erected by the Improvement Commissioners, at the cost of £3500. It was cast at Worcester, and has six arches, each 40 feet in span, with a roadway 24 feet wide. Its total length, including the masonry, is 800 feet.

IMPROVEMENTS.—From the period of the decline of the woollen manufacture in Exeter, may be dated the commencement of that spirit of improvement, in widening and making new streets, and removing those obstructions in the public thoroughfares, which, while it tended so much to make the city a place of genteel residence, opened new channels for the industry of the inhabitants. Four *Acts of Parliament* were obtained in the 1st, 46th, and 50th of George III., and the 2nd of Wm. IV., for better and more effectually *paving, lighting, cleansing, watching,* and otherwise improving the City and County of the City of Exeter. The *Improvement Commissioners* incorporated by these acts, comprise the Dean and Chapter, six members of the Town Council, and about sixty persons elected for the respective parishes, &c. These commissioners have expended large sums

annually during the last half century in improving the city and suburbs, and they are empowered to raise money by levying rates upon the inhabitants. The following are their officers :—Mark Kennaway, Esq., *clerk;* Mr. Thos. Whitaker, *surveyor;* Messrs. Henry Vatcher and S. B. Hodgson, *collectors ;* and Thomas Doble, *messenger.*

WATER WORKS were erected in Exeter many years ago, but the supply of the pure beverage of nature did not keep pace with the great increase in houses and population during the present century, till the construction of the present works, by the *Water Company,* which was formed in 1833, with a capital of £30,000, since increased to £45,750, in £25 shares, now selling at more than £10 premium. They completed their works in 1834-5, and by means of a powerful engine, worked by two water-wheels (equal to forty horses' power,) they propel an ample supply of good water from a clear and unpolluted part of the river Exe, about three miles above the city, into a large *Reservoir,* on the hill, near the County Gaol. This reservoir is at an elevation of 400 feet, and is about 200 feet square by 17 deep, and capable of holding 5000 hogsheads, or 315,000 gallons. Connected with it are more than twelve miles of iron pipes, branching out through every street, &c., in the city and suburbs, and supplying the inhabitants with about 7000 hogsheads of water daily. They also supply the public baths and several *jets d'eau* on the public promenades. The Company's offices are in Bedford circus, and Mr. Wm. Tompson is their *clerk.* Formerly the inhabitants were chiefly supplied with water by pumps and wells in the town, and from several springs on the hills about a mile distant, whence it was brought in leaden pipes to several fountains or conduits, erected in the principal streets. One of these, called the Great Conduit, or the *Conduit at Quatrefois,* or *Carfois,* was rebuilt in 1461, and stood in the centre of the city, at the junction of the four principal streets; but it was taken down in 1778, when a new conduit was erected in High street. Another was built in South street, in 1799, and there is one in Mary Arches street, erected in 1839, at the sole expense of J. Golsworthy, Esq. The Conduit in Milk street, which supplies the Western Market and the neighbourhood, has three cisterns, which will hold 100 hogsheads of water, enclosed in a brick building, and conveyed in pipes to an obelisk of granite.

The GAS WORKS on Exe Island, from which the city and suburbs are brilliantly illuminated, rank among the earliest provincial establishments of the kind in England. They are the property of the Exeter Gas Light and Coke Company, established in 1815, by Act of Parliament, with a capital of £45,000, raised in £25 shares, now worth from £35 to £40 each. The city was first lit with gas in 1817, and since then the works have been considerably enlarged. Richard Williams, jun., is the *clerk and manager.* Though the charges to consumers are moderate, and the quality good, both the Water and Gas Works are lucrative investments, for the yearly profits on the laid-out capitals, generally amount to 10 per cent. on the former, and 8 per cent. on the latter.

MUNICIPAL CORPORATION.

Exeter has, from time immemorial, enjoyed many privileges and immunities. At the Norman survey it was found to be exempt from paying taxes. Since then it has received many charters and grants, from different monarchs. Henry I. confirmed its prescriptive privileges, which were further confirmed by Henry II. and Richd. I. In the time of King John, " Isabel, his consort, held Exeter in dower, with a fair thereunto belonging." In the third year of this

monarch, the burgesses paid a fine of 110 marks for a confirmation
of their charters; and about the same time (A.D. 1200,) the city,
which had previously been governed by *port-reeves* and *bailiffs*, was
incorporated, and had a *mayor* for its chief officer, though the corporation claimed it to be so by prescription. In the reign of Edward
I., the citizens pleaded that their city was an *ancient demesne*, and
that they held it in fee-farm of the crown, at the yearly rent of £39.
15s. 3d. To support this claim, they referred to the charter of
Henry III., made to his brother Richard, whereby they further
claimed *return of writs, a gallows, pillory, &c.*, and a fair of four days
besides three weekly markets, which liberties they certified they had
enjoyed since the time of the Conquest, "upon which they were
allowed." Hy. VII. gave the citizens a sword and cap of maintenance,
and granted them a charter in 1497, which recognizes a *mayor*, 4
bailiffs, 24 *common council-men*, and 4 *serjeants-at-mace;* and settles
the mode of their election. A recorder and town clerk are also
mentioned in this charter. In 1627, Charles I. confirmed the city
charters, and granted many additional privileges. In 1683, this
charter was surrendered to Charles II., who granted a new one in
the following year, under which the corporation was made to consist
of a mayor, 8 aldermen, 15 common council-men, a recorder, &c. In
1770, George III. granted the city a confirmatory charter, and instituted some new regulations for the administration of justice in
the city. Henry VIII. constituted Exeter a distinct *county of itself*,
thus rendering it independent of Devon, of which it is nevertheless
the capital. This privilege was confirmed by Act of Parliament
in the reign of Edward VI. Originally the limits of the city and
county of the city were not the same, but they were afterwards
made co-extensive, except for certain purposes. The *Parliamentary
limits* were extended by the Reform Act of 1832, as already noticed
at page 49. Exeter is said to have been one of the first cities that
sent representatives to Parliament; and it certainly has returned
two members regularly since the time of Edward I. Before 1832,
the right of election was in the freemen and resident freeholders, of
whom there were about 1200. The number of names on the register in 1836 was 3488, of whom 460 were *freemen*, 952 *freeholders*,
and 2076 occupiers of houses of the yearly value of £10 or upwards;
but as many of these were entered in two or more parishes, as occupiers and owners, as well as in the list of freemen, the total number
of *voters* was only about 2800, as it still remains. The sheriff is the
returning officer, and the present *Members of Parliament* for the
city and county of the city are Sir J. T. B. Duckworth, Bart., and
Edward Divett, Esq. Exeter Castle is a polling place, and the
principal place of election for the Southern Division of Devon,
though the city, being a county of itself, is not a part of that
division.

By the *Municipal Reform Act* of 1835, Exeter has been divided
into six wards, and placed under the government of a *Town Council*,
consisting of a mayor, 12 aldermen, and 36 councillors, with a recorder, town clerk, and other officers, and a number of borough
magistrates. The latter are appointed by the Lord Chancellor, who,

in February, 1849, issued a new *commission of the peace* for the city. The style of the corporate body is still the Mayor, Bailiffs, and Commonalty of the city of Exeter, and the city is comprehended in Schedule A of the Municipal Reform Act, among the boroughs in which the old municipal boundaries are to be retained, until altered by Parliament. The *Provost Court*, the *Mayor's Court*, the *Sheriff's Court*, and the *Court of Requests* were the four civil courts held by the members of the old corporation. The court of requests was established by an act of the 13th of George III., and was held every Tuesday, for the recovery of debts under 40s., but it has lately given place to the COUNTY COURT, established a few years ago, under the Small Debts Act, for *Exeter District*, which comprises not only the city and county of the city, but also all the 49 parishes in St. Thomas's Union. This court is held at the Castle several times a month. Being a county of itself, Exeter has separate assizes and courts of quarter sessions. The recorder is judge of the *Provost Court*, which has cognizance in all real or personal actions to any amount, arising within the limits of the ancient glacis without the walls. The mayor and provosts, or bailiffs, hold the *Mayor's Court*, which has a concurrent jurisdiction with the above in personal actions. In this court the masters and wardens of the 13 *trading companies* of the old corporation were sworn in. Eleven of these companies, in the order of their foundation, are as follows :—Merchants, Tailors, Cordwainers, Brewers, Cappers, Hatters and Haberdashers, Weavers and Tuckers, Skinners and Glovers, Smiths and Cutlers, Coopers and Helliers, Butchers, and Bakers. The net *income* of the corporation for 1839 was £12,882 ; and their principal items of expenditure in the same year were, " principal paid off, and interest, &c., £7392 ; on public works, repairs, &c., £1569 ; on police and constables, £1215 ; administration of justice, prosecutions, &c., £533 ; and on the gaol, maintenance of prisoners, &c., £513. The *borough expenditure* for the half-year ending Michaelmas, 1849, was £1897. The heavy debt transferred by the Old to the New Corporation in 1835, has been considerably reduced, and much property which the former had long held, as trustees, for charitable uses, has been restored by the present Town Council, as will be seen at subsequent pages.

The GUILDHALL is a spacious structure, in High street, remarkable for the massiveness and variety of its architecture. The upper story, which projects beyond the line of houses in the street, is supported by an arcade of heavy moorstone columns. Beyond the vestibule is a lofty and spacious common hall, with an arched roof, supported by grotesque figures of beasts. The city assizes, sessions, &c., are held in this extensive court room, and its walls are wainscotted, with carved mouldings. In the cornices are a number of small shields, with the arms of England, France, the city, and the different incorporated trades, and also of various mayors and recorders. At the upper end are the magistrates' bench and two jury galleries, and from the centre is suspended a brass chandelier. The walls are decorated with many valuable portraits, among which are General Monk and the Princess Henrietta Maria, by *Vandyke;* George II., Chief Justice Pratt, John Tuckfield, Esq., founder of an

hospital here ; J. R. Walters, Esq., M.P. ; Benjamin Heath, Esq.; Henry Blackall, Esq., (three times mayor ;) and Alderman Phillips. Above stairs are the grand jury room, council chamber, and other apartments.   The Guildhall has, from time immemorial, occupied the same site, and was rebuilt in 1464.   A chapel, dedicated to St. George and St. John the Baptist, stood in front, and is supposed to have been taken down in 1593, when that part of the hall which projects into the street was erected.   The building was thoroughly repaired and beautified in 1720.

The CITY PRISON is pleasantly situated without the walls, at the junction of Queen street and Northernhay street.   It was erected in 1819, and has since undergone some judicious alterations, but it still does not admit of a complete system of classification.   It is in three divisions, called the debtors' ward, the felons prison, and the bridewell, or house of correction ; and comprises 36 cells, 7 wards, 8 day-rooms, and 6 airing yards, all enclosed by a lofty outer wall. It has room for about 80 inmates, but its average number is about 50.   Previous to its erection, the old City Prison was in South st., attached to the ancient South Gate.   The annual expense of maintaining this prison establishment is about £730, of which about £250 is repaid by government for the maintenance of prisoners and removal of convicts, and £293 is for salaries.   It is in contemplation either to enlarge and alter this, or to erect a new city prison, on the plan of the model prison at Pentonville ; or otherwise to arrange for the reception of the city prisoners in the *Devon County Gaol and Bridewell.*

CORPORATION AND OFFICERS—1848-9.

Mayor, Christopher Arden, Esq. (elected 9th November, 1848.)
Recorder, Francis Newman Rogers, Esq., Barrister-at-Law.
Deputy Judge of the Provost Court, George Granville Kekewich, Esq.
Registrar of ditto, John Gidley.

JUSTICES OF THE PEACE.

Thos. Foster Barham, Esq.	Geo. Chaplin Holroyd, Esq.	Patrick Miller, Esq.
John Carew, Esq.	Henry Hooper, Esq.	Richd. Lewin Pennell, Esq.
Daniel Bishop Davy, Esq.	Wm. Kennaway, Esq.	Thomas Shapter, Esq.
John Harris, Esq.	Samuel Kingdon, Esq.	Edward Woolmer, Esq.

ALDERMEN.

Christopher Arden, Esq.	Wm. Hooper, Esq.	Thomas Shapter, Esq.
Wm. Hobson Furlong, Esq.	Wm. Wills Hooper, Esq.	Chas. Henry Turner, Esq.
John Harris, Esq.	Wm. Page Kingdon, Esq.	Edward Woolmer, Esq.
Henry Lake Hirtzel, Esq.	Wm. Kingdon, Esq.	Thos. Dewdney Worthy, Esq.

COUNCILLORS.

1. ST. PAUL'S WARD.	3. TRINITY WARD.	5. ST. SIDWELL'S WARD.
Wm. Richards.	George Sercombe.	Robert Taylor.
Robert John Trewman.	Frederick D. L. Hirtzel.	Samuel Segar Bastard.
Frederick Franklin.	Richard Bastard.	Henry Hooper.
John Porter.	James Nicholls.	John Cockram.
Thomas Edward Drake	John Evomy Norman.	Henry Wilcocks Hooper.
John Burrington.	John Plimsaul Nicholls.	Wm. Land.
2. ST. MARY MAJOR WARD.	**4. ST. PETROCK WARD.**	**6 ST. DAVID'S WARD.**
Stephen Brunskill.	George Ferris.	John Toby, sen.
Thomas Floud.	James Carrall Wilcocks.	Charles Force.
Edwin Force.	Samuel Davies.	Charles Brutton.
Charles Richards.	John Trehane.	Wm. Denis Moore.
Wm. Piper.	George Du Chemin.	John Carew.
Joseph Sayell.	Thomas Latimer.	Peter Lisson.

The two first on the list in each ward go out of office in November, 1849.

Revising Assessors, George William Turner and John Toby, jun.
Auditors, Richard Holwell and Thomas Besley.
Auditor appointed by the Mayor, Henry Wilcocks Hooper, Esq.
Clerk of the Peace and Town Clerk, John Gidley, Esq.
Treasurer, Hugh Myddleton Ellicombe, Esq.
Coroner for the City and County of Exeter, John Warren, Esq.
Clerk to the Magistrates, Henry Downe Barton.
Sheriff, Thomas Floud: *Under-Sheriff*, Henry Wilcocks Hooper.
Chaplain to the City Prison, Rev. Charles Worthy.
Governor and Matron of ditto, John George Gully and Mrs. Ann Gully.
Superintendent of Police, David Steele || *High Constable*, William Morgan.
Inspector of Weights and Measures, Mr. Thomas Rodd.
Sergeants, Wm. Morgan, Wm. Howard, John Ginham, Henry Lascelles.
Staff-bearers, Frederick Woolcott, Thos. Vaughan, Wm. Stuckes.
Inspectors of Police, Frederick Woolcott, William Stuckes, William Joslin, James Ellicombe, and Wm. Fulford. (There are 20 policemen.)

CONSERVATORS OF THE RIVER EXE:—S. Mortimer, W. Kennaway, W. Kingdon, D. B. Davy, R. Bastard, J. C. Wilcocks, J. Golsworthy, and W. H. Furlong, Esqrs.

The BANKRUPTCY COURT at Exeter has jurisdiction all over Devon, Cornwall, and the Western Division of Somerset, and in all places in Dorset, more than 100 miles from London, excepting Poole, Wimborne, Blandford, Sturminster, and Shaftesbury. M. B. Bere, Esq., is the *commissioner;* J. Carew, Esq., *registrar;* Messrs. H. L. Hirtzel and F. Hernaman, *official assignees;* and John Bullivant, *messenger.*

The COUNTY COURT for Exeter District is noticed at page 69. It sits at the Castle on the Friday and Saturday after the second Monday of each month, and sometimes fortnightly, if required. Mr. John Daw, of 13, Bedford circus, is the *clerk*, and Mr. Robert Collings is the *high bailiff.* John Tyrell, Esq., is *judge* of this and all the other county courts in East Devon, and James Terreil, Esq. is the *treasurer.*

In order to obtain a summons, it is necessary that the plaintiff should apply at the office of the clerk of the Court, and furnish the name, residence, trade, or profession of himself and defendant, and the amount and nature of his demand. If the amount be above £5, the plaintiff must furnish as many copies of particulars of his demand as there are defendants, with an additional copy to file. At the time of taking out the summons, the plaintiff must pay the fees of the Court. The fees of the Court for summonses within the distance of one mile, are as table annexed :—

—	Not excdg. £1.	Not excdg. £2.	Not excdg. £5.	Not excdg. £10.	Exceeding £10.	
					Cont.	Tort.
Fund Fee.	....	6d.	1s. in the Pound.	1s. in the Pound.	1s. in the Pound.	1s. in the Pound.
Summons.	9d.	1s. 4d.	2s. 6d.	4s. 10d.	7s.	8s.
Beyond one mile, the above with the following additional mileage :—						
—	2d. per mile.	2d. per mile.	3d. per mile.	4d. per mile.	4d. per mile.	4d. per mile.

REVENUE OFFICERS.

Customs' Establishment at the Port of Exeter. (See page 63.) H. L. Greaves, Esq., *collector;* A. Stewart, Esq., *comptroller and landing surveyor;* and Mr. H. P. Wright, *landing waiter and searcher.* The creeks belonging to the port, and the landing waiters stationed at them, are—*Topsham*, Mr. George England; *Exmouth*, Mr. Robert Gallop; and *Teignmouth*, Mr. L. M. Maxton. The *pilots* of the port are under the supervision of H. L. Grove, W. Wilking, and Wm. Ash, Esqrs., who are sub-commissioners of pilotage, appointed by the Trinity Board.

The *Inland Revenue Officers* for Exeter district are—William Schofield, Esq., *collector;* John Jarman, *clerk;* Henry Druller, *permit writer;* John

Furse and Joseph Allen, *supervisors;* and several district officers. The STAMP OFFICE is in Queen street, and Mark Kennaway, Esq., is distributor for Exeter and the county of Devon. Mr. E. Martin is the deputy distributor. Mr. Henry Lascelles is inspector of hawkers' licenses.

ECCLESIASTICAL HISTORY.

It is said by Hooker, that Exeter, from its having abounded with religious houses in the time of the early Saxon kings, was called *Monkton*, and that Athelstan changed its name to *Exanceaster.* In an old poem, the city is made to speak as follows :—

" The ground of my first Ancestry
  Is worn out through Antiquity;
  Caeriske the Britains did me name,
  And *Monkton*, Saxons did me fame ;
	" Till of the river running by
	  Exeter icleped became I :
	  Seven times besieged mightily,
	  Mine Enemies to flight put I."

Of its MONASTIC INSTITUTIONS there are now but few vestiges. Three of them were situated in the Cathedral close, and one of these was a nunnery, which occupied the site of the Dean's House and College of Vicars. King Ethered founded a priory here about A.D. 868; and in 932, Athelstan founded a *Benedictine Abbey*, which was dedicated to *St. Mary and St. Peter*, and stood on the site of the Cathedral. The latter was scarcely completed when it was deserted for fear of the Danes, but it was restored by King Edgar in 969. The monks were again obliged to leave it in 1003, when Sweyne, King of Denmark, ravaged the country. It was restored by Canute about 1019, and is said to have had among its precious relics, part of Christ's garment, some of the hair of the Virgin Mary, and some of St. Peter's beard. On the removal of the Bishop's See from Crediton to Exeter, this abbey was given by Edward the Confessor to the Bishop and his successors, and its walls were incorporated into the structure of the Cathedral then founded. The abbot and monks were removed to Westminster. *St. Nicholas' Priory*, which stood in Mint lane, was founded by the Abbot of Battle, to whom William the Conqueror had given the chapel of St Olave in this city. King John was a great benefactor to this Benedictine priory, which was valued at £147. 12s. per ann. at the dissolution, in 1545, when its site was granted to Sir Thomas Dennis, who sold it to the Corporation, who disposed of it in lots before the end of the 17th century. The most remarkable remains of the priory is a crypt, with massive Saxon arches, which has long been used as a kitchen. The Catholic Chapel and Priest's House stand on part of the site, and when they were erected in 1792, mutilated pieces of carved mouldings and monuments were found in digging the foundations. The *Grey or Franciscan Friary*, which stood originally near the priory of St. Nicholas, was founded about 1240, but was removed, about 1300, to a place outside the city walls, beyond the South gate, given by John Gerves. The church of the first convent was standing so late as 1434, and its site was granted to the Corporation in 1507. The site of the friary was granted at the dissolution to Humphrey Rolle, and it afterwards passed to the Colleton and Graves families. Colleton crescent occupies part of the site. The *Black or Dominican Friary*, which stood in the extra parochial precinct called Bedford Circus, was supposed to have been

founded by Bishop Blondy about 1250. Its church became the burial place of the Ralegh, Martyn, Calwoodley, and other distinguished families. At the dissolution, Henry VIII. granted this friary to John Lord Russell, who converted it into a town residence for his family; and after they became Earls of Bedford, it acquired the name of *Bedford House.* In this mansion, the Russells received many illustrious visitors, as already noticed. Having been long neglected by the family, it was divided into tenements, which were taken down in 1773. Two ranges of houses, &c., forming a circus, occupy the site of this house and its once beautiful gardens. *Cowick Priory*, in St. Thomas's parish, was a cell of Benedictine monks, given by Wm. Fitz-Baldwin in the reign of Henry II. to the abbey of Bec-Harlewin. It was suppressed by Henry V., with other alien priories; but was refounded by his successor. In 1451, it was given to King's College, but Edward IV. gave it to Tavistock Abbey, with which it passed to John Lord Russell, at the dissolution. Some remains of the priory may be seen in a farmhouse, standing near its site, and still retaining a few fragments of stained glass in its windows. *Polesloe Priory*, in the eastern suburbs of Exeter, but in Heavitree parish, was founded for Benedictine nuns, by Wm. Lord Briwere, or Brewer, in or before the reign of Richard I. It was suppressed in 1538, when its revenues were valued at £164. 8s. 11d. per annum. It was granted in 1541 to Sir George Carew, and afterwards passed to the Champernowne, Petre, Izaac, and Parker families. The crumbling remains of this nunnery now form an indifferent farm house and out buildings. On the same side of the city was *St. James's Priory*, which was founded in 1146 by Baldwin de Rivers, as a cell to the Cluniac abbey of St. Martin, near Paris. It had only a prior and four monks, and was suppressed by Henry VI., who gave it to King's College, Cambridge. Scarcely a vestige of the building is now to be seen, though Chapple says the barn and part of the priory-house were standing in 1735. The *Chapel of St. Ann*, with an adjoining almshouse, at the junction of St. Sidwell street and Black Boy road, was founded at an unknown date as a hermitage or hospital. After the dissolution it was purchased by Oliver and George Mainwaring, and converted into an almshouse for eight poor people, in trust with the Dean and Chapter. The chapel is only about 15 feet in length and breadth, but has a handsome perpendicular window of three lights, with a piscina, and a canopied niche on each side of it. Within the Castle precincts stood the *Collegiate Chapel of the Holy Trinity*, founded by Ralph Avenell, in the reign of Stephen. It had four prebendaries called Cliston Hayes, Ash Clist, Cutton, and Carswell. Divine service was performed in it at the assizes till it was taken down, about 1782. It will be seen at subsequent pages that those charitable institutions, *St. John's Hospital, Magdalen Hospital*, and *Wynard's Hospital*, were established on the ruins of ancient religious houses. In the front of a modern house at the corner of North street stands the ancient wooden statue of " *Father Peter,*" reading a book and treading on Paganism. This figure is as large as life, and is in a crouching posture, as in its original situation it had the appearance of

D

supporting the angle of a very ancient house, long since taken down. It then held a church in the right hand, and besides the book in the left, it had two keys suspended on the fourth and fifth fingers, but these are broken off. An ancient building in Water-beer street, which was pulled down in 1803, was supposed to have been the remains of the first Christian church in Exeter.

DIOCESE OF EXETER:—After its partial subjugation by the Saxons, and the conversion of that people to Christianity, Devonshire became subordinate to the *Bishop of Wessex*, and so continued until 703, when it was deemed expedient to divide Wessex into two Sees. On that division, Sherborne in Dorsetshire was made the seat of the new bishopric, which comprehended Devonshire; but on the subdivision of the See of Sherborne, in the year 910, Devonshire was constituted an independent diocese, and Aidolf, its first bishop, fixed his See at *Crediton*. About the year 1040, the Bishopric of Cornwall, which had its cathedral at St. Germain's, was united to that of Devonshire, at the solicitation of Bishop Livingus, whose successor *Leofric*, the sixth Bishop of Crediton, was chancellor and chaplain to Edward the Confessor. This saintly king, by a charter granted in 1050, consolidated the pontifical chair at Exeter, in the church of the abbey of the Blessed Virgin and St. Peter, as already noticed. The king being present in person translated the Benedictine monks to Westminster, and enthroned *Leofric*, the first Bishop of Exeter, with much ceremony. Being thus established in his new See, and having a grant of the three monasteries which stood in the Close, Leofric began the erection of the Cathedral, which was finished by succeeding prelates, after the lapse of many ages. From the first establishment of the See at Exeter, 62 BISHOPS have presided over it. The most eminent of these were *Leofric*, who was Lord Chancellor of England; *Bartholomew Iscanus*, a native of Exeter; *Walter Stapledon*, who was Lord High Treasurer of England and founder of Exeter College, Oxford, and was murdered by the rebels in 1327; *Bishop Grandisson*, a learned writer and founder of a college at St. Mary Ottery; *Bishop Brantingham*, who was Lord High Treasurer; *Bishop Stafford*, who was Lord Privy Seal, and completed the foundation of Exeter College; *Bishop Neville*, remarkable for being made a bishop before he was 25 years of age, and Lord Chancellor before he was 28; *Bishop Fox*, several times ambassador to foreign courts, and one of the founders of Corpus Christi College, Oxford, in conjunction with *Bishop Oldham*, then bishop of Winchester, but afterwards translated to Exeter; *Bishop Coverdale*, the translator of the Bible; *Bishop Alleigh*, author of the "Poor Man's Library," and other works; *Bishop Woolton*, author of the "Scholar's Manual," and other popular works; the pious *Bishop Hall*, afterwards translated to Norwich; *Bishop Sparrow*, author of the Rationale on the Common Prayer; *Sir Jonathan Trelawney*, one of the seven bishops imprisoned in 1684; the *Hon. Geo. Pelham*, who was translated to Lincoln in 1820; and *Dr. Wm. Cary*, the late bishop, who was succeeded in 1830 by the *Rt. Rev. Henry Phillpotts, D.D.*, the present bishop of Exeter, who is also a

prebendary of Durham, and formerly held the rich rectory of Stanhope, which was valued in 1831 at £4848, and this bishopric at only £2713 per annum. The latter has lately been augmented by the Ecclesiastical Commissioners to about £5000 per annum. Bishop Brewer appointed the first dean about 1231, previous to which the 24 prebendaries were presided over by the precentor. There are four priest vicars and eight lay vicars, besides choristers, &c. An ancient almshouse for 12 poor men and 12 poor women, called *Fratres Calendarum*, was converted into a college for the vicars choral, by Bishop Grandisson, about the middle of the 16th century. The bishops are said to have had thirteen houses, besides the *Palace*, at Exeter. The latter was embattled by Bishop Quivil in 1289, and Bishop Stapledon had license in 1321 to fortify the Palace, and to surround the Close with a wall of stone. There was formerly a prison connected with the Palace for "convicted and scandalous clergymen." During Cromwell's usurpation, the Palace was sold to a sugar-refiner, who carried on his business there till the Restoration, after which it was repaired at a great expense by Bishop Ward. Among the ancient customs of Exeter Cathedral, was that of riding in procession on the vigil of St. Peter; and also that of electing a *Boy Bishop* out of the choristers, on St. Nicholas' day.

The Diocese of Exeter is divided into four ARCHDEACONRIES, one of which is *Cornwall*, which includes nearly all that county, together with the Scilly Isles; and is divided into eight Deaneries. The other three Archdeaconries are *Exeter, Totnes,* and *Barnstaple,* which comprise all Devonshire, except three parishes which are in Cornwall Archdeaconry, and some others which are peculiar jurisdictions of the bishop, the Dean and Chapter, &c. The DEANERIES, in the *Archdeaconry of Exeter*, are Aylesbeare, Cadbury, Christianity or Exeter; Dunkeswell, Dunsford, Honiton, Kenne, Plymtree, and Tiverton. Those in the *Archdeaconry of Totnes* are Holsworthy, Ipplepen, Moreton, Okehampton, Tamerton, Tavistock, Totton or Totnes, and Woodleigh. Those in the *Archdeaconry of Barnstaple* are Barum or Barnstaple, Chumleigh, Hartland, Sherwill, South Molton, and Torrington. The *number of benefices* in the diocese returned to the commissioners in 1831, inclusive of sinecure rectories, but exclusive of benefices annexed to other preferments, was 613, besides 16 not returned. The number of *parishes* in Devon is 465, and in Cornwall 203, but in some of them there are *chapelries* and *parochial districts.* Several of the latter have been recently created and provided with new churches, in the populous parts of Devon. The aggregate amount of the gross yearly incomes of *incumbents* in 613 of the returned benefices in 1831 was £194,181, making the average gross income of each £316; but the total net income was stated at £174,275, and the average individual net income at £284. The total number of *curates* in the diocese in the same year was 323, and the stipends paid them amounted only to £28,759, averging only £89 per annum each. At the same time, there were in the diocese two benefices worth from £1000 to £1300 per annum; 60 worth from £500 to £1000; and 247 not yielding £200 each. The rectorial tithes of about 160 parishes in the dio-

cese are in the hands of lay impropriators, and those of nearly
100 other parishes are in the appropriation of clerical dignitaries,
Deans and Chapters, Colleges, &c. The total amount of the average
gross yearly income of the bishop, for the three years ending Dec.,
1831, was £3147, but the net income was only £2713, including
the profits of ecclesiastical preferments annexed to the See, viz., the
rectory of Shobrooke, a prebend in Durham, and the treasurership
of, and a prebend in, Exeter Cathedral. " The revenues of this
bishopric," says Tanner, " were valued in the 26th of Henry VIII.
at £1566. 14s. 6d. per annum ; but so much was shortly after taken
from it, that they have long been rated at £500 only." The net
common revenues of the DEAN AND CHAPTER were valued in the
time of Henry VIII. at £1132. 18s. 11d. per annum, and in 1831 at
£7352, besides £754 appropriated to the Custos & College of Vicars
Choral. There are 24 *Canons and Prebendaries*, of whom nine are
Canons Residentiary, the dean being one. The prebendaries not
being Canons Residentiary, receive fixed payments of £20 per ann.
each. The nine *Canons Residentiary* receive each a fixed yearly
payment of £69. 5s., and divide among them the surplus net revenue, after payment of all stipends and allowances. The three *Archdeacons* of Devonshire are paid the annual sum of £135 among
them. The *Lecturer* has a fixed stipend of £30 out of the revenues.
The average sum, divided annually among the nine Canon Residentiary, in the years 1829, '30, and '31, was £5983. There are
houses assigned for the residence of the Dean, the Precentor, and
the Chancellor, and three others for Residentiaries, all of whom are
bound respectively to keep their houses in repair. There are separate revenues belonging to the Dean, Sub-dean, Precentor, Chancellor, and Treasurer, amounting to about £300 per annum, exclusive of fines paid on the renewal of leases. These fines belong
solely to the Precentor and the Dean, and the former derives from
them about £300, and the latter about £60 a year. The *Corporation of the Custos and College of Vicars Choral*, consists of four
Priest-Vicars, of whom one is dean's vicar and sub-treasurer, and
another custos of the college. They divide the net revenues among
them. They have houses in the Close, but being unfit for the residence of clergymen, they let them to lay tenants. There are in
the cathedral choir eight *lay-vicars* and five *secondaries*, (one of
whom is organist,) and ten choristers. A tenth part of all fines,
payable to the Dean and Chapter and the Vicars Choral, have (by
ancient custom,) been set apart for the reparation of the Cathedral,
which is now in a sound state.

The CATHEDRAL, which is dedicated to *St. Peter*, stands in a
spacious close, and is a venerable and magnificent structure, which
ranks as the chief ornament of Exeter, and is highly interesting to
the admirer of ancient architecture. As noticed at page 74, the
original cathedral was but a small fabric, formed about the year
1050, out of the conventual church of the Benedictine Abbey.
This Saxon structure, of which there are now no apparent remains,
gave place in A.D. 1111, during the prelacy of Bishop Warelwast,
to the commencement of the second, or Norman edifice. That pre-

late is recorded to have built the two existing towers, under which the transepts were afterwards formed. The cathedral suffered much during the siege of Exeter by King Stephen, but was repaired by several succeeding bishops. The honor of commencing the third or present Cathedral, belongs to Bishop Quivil, who was installed in 1280, but he made portions of the old edifice subservient to the grand design of the new one. The lower parts of the two ponderous Norman towers were converted into transepts, and the beautiful Lady Chapel, and that of St. Gabriel, built by Bishops Bruere, Blondy, and Bronescombe, were retained. Several successors of Quivil continued the work, according to the plan designed by him, and it was finally completed, with the exception of the internal decorations, and the Chapter House, by Bishop Grandisson, in 1360. Nothing can exceed the beauty of many parts of this cathedral, but on the whole it is not so satisfactory, for the unusual position of the towers renders the want of some lofty central feature very apparent, whether the building be viewed from the Close or the City. The ground on the north-east side of it has lately been drained, and lowered, so as to lay bare the plinth, which had been covered for ages ; and within these few years several mean buildings which stood near it have been removed, so that the exterior can now be tolerably well seen. It is built in the form of a cross, but the arms are very short, owing to the transepts been formed under the towers. The entire length of the building, including the Lady Chapel, is 408 feet ; the length of the of the transepts 140 feet, and the height of the towers 145 feet. The towers are Norman, and similar in size and general appearance, but they display varieties in their ornaments. Their surfaces are covered with blank arcades and other Norman ornaments, and there are square turrets and vanes at the four corners of each, rising several feet above the embattled parapets. The rest of the Cathedral is in the decorated style of English architecture ; and the numerous windows, with their flowing tracery, are amongst the finest examples of that rich style. Between the windows are bold flying buttresses, with crocketted pinnacles. The roof, which is of very high pitch, is covered with lead, and crowned by a fleur-de-lis ridge ornament. The most striking portion of the exterior is the WEST FRONT, which is unlike those of all other Cathedrals, and is surpassed by none of them in beauty. The lower part of this front is adorned with a rich screen, extending beyond the walls of the aisles, and rising to about a third of the height of the central pediment. This elegant screen has three door-ways, and its entire surface is occupied by canopied niches, containing statues of apostles, kings, bishops, crusaders, &c. The second story is formed by the west wall of the nave, and contains the large and noble west window, the arch of which is filled with the richest flowing tracery. On each side of this window are decorated arcades. The upper story, which recedes somewhat behind the second story, is formed by the gable of the nave, and has a smaller window of the same character. The statues and other ornamental work have lately been carefully restored, so that this magnificent façade is now seen in a nearly perfect condition.

The *interior of the Cathedral* is far more imposing than the exte-

rior. It comprises a spacious nave, with two aisles; a chapel at the north-west angle, a porch on the north side; a transept, from which two chapels open on the east; a choir, with two aisles, from which two chapels branch off near the middle, and several others at the east end, which is terminated by the Lady Chapel. The *Nave* is grand and spacious,—its lofty arch vaulting, covered with a profusion of bold ribs and elaborate bosses, exquisitely finished, attracts and leads the eye from one extremity of the church to the other, and will not fail to strike the stranger with its sublime and imposing effect. The subdivisions next merit attention, and command admiration; they consist of seven high and broad arches on each side, resting on clustered columns, with a low triforium above, and that crowded by a series of large florid windows. On the north side of the nave, projecting from the clerestory, is that singular example of ancient art, called the Minstrel's Gallery. It rises from a bracket cornice, and displays in front a series of twelve quatrefoil-headed niches, in which stand as many figures of angels, playing upon musical instruments of different kinds. There are galleries extending round the whole and communicating with each other. Two noble and elegant windows adorn this cathedral,—one at the east and the other at the west end, both of which are particularly admired for the beauty of the tracery and rich colour of the painted glass. Wooden gates of a peculiar but handsome pattern, separate the aisles of the choir from the transept; whilst the choir itself is divided from it by a *screen* or *rood loft* of most exquisite design; probably constructed in the reign of Edward III. The upper part has a modern finishing, and includes a range of thirteen paintings in oil upon stone, in arched compartments, representing the Creation, Adam and Eve, the Deluge, Moses dividing the Red Sea, the Destruction of Solomon's Temple, Building of the Second Temple, the Angel appearing to Zacharias, the Nativity, the Baptism of Christ, Taking down from the Cross, the Resurrection, the Ascension, and the Descent of the Holy Ghost. On a gallery, over the entrance of this screen, stands the *organ*, which is one of the largest and most powerful of the kind in the kingdom. It was built by John Loosemore, in 1665, and its scale ranges from *G. G. to D. in alt.* Its total number of pipes is 1496. In the north tower is a curious clock made in the reign of Edward III.; and the *great bell*, which weighs 12,500lbs, and is the heaviest bell in England, except Great Tom of Christ Church, Oxford, which weighs seven tons six cwt. and that at Lincoln, which weighs five tons eight cwt. In the south tower are *eleven bells*, ten of which are rung in peal, and form the largest and heaviest set in the kingdom, the tenor weighing 2000lbs more than any other of that denomination in this country. In the nave is a handsome stone font, given by Canon Bartholomew, in 1843, and executed by Mr. S. Rowe.

On entering the *Choir*, the stranger will feel the force of the description of the Rev. Dr. Oliver, where he says " The mind is enchanted with the exquisite richness of the noble east window, with the splendid episcopal throne, that towers in airy state to the vaulting, and seems to despise the modern desks and seats around it: and

as the spectator advances to the sanctuary, he will acknowledge that the three stalls on the right are unrivalled in beauty and delicacy of sculpture." The *throne* is of oak, about 52 feet in height, and its canopy is composed of pointed arches, columns, niches, pinnacles, and foliated ornaments, tastefully and delicately carved, rising in a pyramidical form, and finishing in a series of ascending spires. It was erected by bishop Bothe, in the year 1470. During the Commonwealth it was taken down and concealed, but replaced at the Restoration, and now remains as perfect as when first erected. The pulpit, opposite the bishop's throne, constructed in 1650, is an elegant piece of workmanship. The stone altar screen in the choir is a modern work by Mr. John Kendall, of Exeter, in 1819. It is in the pointed style of the fourteenth century, and composed of seven divisions, which are separated from each other by receding buttresses, surmounted by pinnacles, and supported by columns. The centre, over the altar, is enriched by a canopy entwined with ivy, combining the rose, thistle, and shamrock. The height of the centre is 21 feet, and length of the entire screen 41 feet. The fine old monuments existing in this Cathedral are numerous, and especially worthy the stranger's attention. We cannot do more than enumerate some of the principal, and point out their situation. In the choir, is a splendid monument of bishop Stapledon, who was murdered in 1326, and chaste and elegant altar tombs of bishops Marshall and Lacy, the former died in 1206, the latter in 1455. In a recess in the north aisle of the choir is a sepulchral memorial, representing a full length skeleton, lying on its winding sheet. Nearer the Lady Chapel, in the same aisle, is the statue of an armed knight, commonly supposed to be to the memory of Sir Richard Stapledon, the bishop's brother. In the chapel of St. Mary Magdalen, on the north of Lady Chapel, is the sumptuous tomb of bishop Stafford, who died in 1419. In the chapel of St. Gabriel, stands the stately monument of bishop Bronescombe, the founder of the chapel, who died in 1280. In this chapel also, are two fine specimens of modern art; one is an exquisite piece of sculpture, by Sir Francis Chantrey, and has a full length statue, in white marble, representing *Northcote*, the painter, who died in 1831. The other is by Flaxman, in memory of Lieutenant General Simcoe, who died in 1806. In the Lady Chapel are three monuments of early bishops, supposed to be those of Bartholomew Iscanus, Simon de Apulia, and Quivil. In the south choir are the effigies of two crusaders, one of whom is said to have been of the Chichester family, and the other represents Humphrey de Bohun, Earl of Hereford. Most of the chapels contain monuments, and the open screens, which separate them from the body of the Cathedral, are in several instances of exquisite beauty and delicacy. The *Chapter House* is said to have been built in the 15th century by bishops Lacy and Bothe, but the lower part of it appears to be much older. It is a handsome oblong structure, with an oak roof, in richly ornamented pannels. In it is arranged the *Cathedral Library*, which was formerly kept in the Lady Chapel, and contains about 8000 volumes, among which are many valuable and scarce books, and some genuine Saxon manuscripts. The *cloisters* of the Cathedral were sold to the

city, and converted into a serge market, during the Commonwealth, when the whole of the sacred pile " suffered grievously from puritanical wrath." Before the year 1547 there were 21 *chantries* in the Cathedral, founded by the Bishops and others, but they were all dissolved at the Reformation, and their lands and revenues given or sold to laymen.

The CLOSE, or *Cathedral yard*, comprises a large extra-parochial area, finely shaded with trees, and having many neat houses, &c., besides those occupied by the dignitaries of the church. In the 14th century it was enclosed by walls and had seven gates, but they were taken down many years ago. The BISHOP'S PALACE, which has extensive gardens, has been thoroughly renovated, and mostly rebuilt since 1845, in the Tudor style, at the cost of about £4000, of which £3400 was given by the Ecclesiastical Commissioners, who have recently augmented the Bishop's yearly income from about £2700 to about £5000. The old Palace was a very irregular building, which was erected at various periods, and was considerably reduced in size in the reign of Elizabeth, owing to the diminished revenues of the Bishop after the Reformation. In 1647 it was sold to the Corporation, who conveyed it in 1650, to the Governor's of St. John's Hospital, who leased it to a sugar baker. After the Restoration of Charles II., it was purchased by Bishop Ward, who repaired it and made it habitable. When altered and improved by Bishop Cary, in 1821, some of the troughs, &c. of the sugar refinery were discovered. It is now an extensive and elegant mansion, and has a very beautiful Tudor window, removed from Elyot's House, in St. Petrock's parish, and richly ornamented with carved tilting-shields, &c. A private covered passage leads from the Palace to the Cathedral; and the gardens are bounded on the south by a portion of the ancient wall of the city, on which is a terrace walk. Near the Palace Lodge is the DEANERY, a commodious mansion, which stands on the site of an Augustine Nunnery. Near it is COLLEGE HALL, an old chantry of the Vicars Choral, which has recently been restored and decorated, and is now occupied by the *Architectural Society*. This edifice is of the 14th century, and contains some fine specimens of wooden carved work, and some old portraits of the early bishops. The hall is now hung round with drawings, models of fonts, and other designs, chiefly ecclesiastical subjects, by some of the members of the society, which was established in 1841, for the promotion and cultivation of a correct taste in church architecture. The following are the—

DIGNITARIES OF THE DIOCESE OF EXETER.

MEMBERS OF THE CATHEDRAL, OFFICERS OF THE SEE, ECCLESIASTICAL COURTS, &c., WITH THE DATES OF THEIR APPOINTMENTS.

BISHOP:—The Right Rev. Henry Phillpotts, D.D., (Prebendary of Durham,) 1830.
DEAN:—The Very Rev. Thomas Hill Lowe, A.M., (Prebendary and Canon,) 1839.

CANONS RESIDENTIARY —

The Lord Bishop of the Diocese, Treasurer, Canon, and Prebendary, 1830.
Rev. George Martin, A.M., Second Canon and Prebendary, 1815.
Rev. John R⸺ers, A.M., Third Canon, 1820, Prebendary, 1808.
Rev. John ⸺ll, D.D., Fourth Canon, 1824, Prebendary, 1823.
Rev. John Bartholomew, A.M., Canon, 1840, Prebendary, 1821.
Rev. John Moore Stevens, A.M., Canon, 1842, Prebendary, 1821.
Rev. Richard Stephens, Sub-Dean, 1840.

Rev. William John Phillpotts, A.M., Precentor and Prebendary, 1840.
Chancellor of the Cathedral, Rev. E. C. Harington, A.M., 1847.
Chancellor of the Diocese, Rev. George Martin, A.M., 1820.

ARCHDEACONS:—
Ven. John M. Stevens, A.M., Archdeacon of Exeter, 1820.
Ven. William John Phillpotts, A.M., Archdeacon of Cornwall, 1845.
Ven. Robert Hurrell Froude, A.M., Archdeacon of Totnes, 1820.
Ven. John Bartholomew, A.M., Archdeacon of Barnstable, 1847.

PREBENDARIES:—

Hon. and Rev. Henry Leslie, A.M.	1809	Rev. Peter Johnson, A.M.	1843
Rev. Richard Ellicombe, A.M.	1813	,, Charles Lyne, A M.	1843
,, John Pomeroy Gilbert, A.M.	1815	,, Richard Luney, A.M.	1843
,, Robert Holdsworth, A.M.	1824	,, Robert Scott, A.M.	1845
,, James Duke Coleridge, LL.D.	1825	,, EdwardCharlesHarington,A.M.	1845
,, Thomas Scott Smyth, A.M.	1829	,, Joseph Dornford	1847
,, George Hole, A.M.	1842	,, William Molesworth	1849
,, George James Cornish, A.M.	1843		

Convocation Clerks: *For the Chapter,* The Rev. George Martin. *For the Clergy,* Rev. James Duke Coleridge, LL.D., and Rev. George James Cornish, A.M.
Examining Chaplain to the Lord Bishop, Rev. Henry Woollcombe.
Secretary to the Bishop, Chapter Clerk, and Receiver, Ralph Barnes, Esq.

PRIEST-VICARS:—
Rev. George Max. Slatter, B.D., Sub-Treasurer and Dean's Vicar ... 1817
Rev. Joseph Corfe, A.M., Custos 1836
Rev. Thomas Henry Knight 1843
Rev. Jas. Hen. Scuddamore Burr.... 1845

Organist, Sub-Chanter, and Informator Puerorum, Alfred Angel, 1842.

LAY-VICARS:—

LAY-VICARS:—				DEPUTY:—	
John Risdon	1803	Geo. W. Branscombe	1843	R. W. Wyllie	1844
William Spark	1819	James Ingham	1843	VERGERS:—	
John Kemp	1830	SECONDARIES:—		Henry Winsor	1836
Samuel Avent	1834	The Organist	1842	James Godbeer	1845
Frederick Calway	1842	Thos. Price Turner	1820	DOG-WHIPPER:—	
Abraham S. Hexter	1842	George Risdon	1834	Charles Reynolds.	
		John Hooker	1844		

Surveyor to the Chapter, R. S. Cornish.

EPISCOPAL PRINCIPAL REGISTRY OF EXETER.—Registrar, Rev. William Arnold Walpole Keppel; Deputy, Ralph Barnes, Esq., Exeter.

CONSISTORIAL COURT OF THE BISHOP OF EXETER.—Registrar, Mr. Charles Henry Turner, Exeter; Keeper of the Chancellor's Seal, Mr. Edwin Force, Exeter; Deputy Apparitor, Mr. G. Way, Exeter.

CONSISTORY COURT OF THE DEAN AND CHAPTER.—Official, The Very Rev. the Dean; Registrar, Charles Hamilton, Esq.

PECULIAR COURT OF THE DEAN.—Registrar, Mr. Ralph Sanders, Exeter.

PECULIAR COURT OF THE CUSTOS AND COLLEGE OF VICARS.—Registrar, Mr. John Geare, Exeter.

CONSISTORIAL ARCHIDIACONAL COURT OF EXETER.—Official, Rev. Henry Nicholls, A.M.; Registrars, Henry Rycroft, Esq., Theodore Bowens, Esq.; Deputy, Mr. E. L. Kemp, Exeter; Apparitor, Mr. Edward Bennett Crabhe, Exeter.

CONSISTORIAL ARCHIDIACONAL COURT OF CORNWALL.—Registrar, ———; Deputy, Mr. Preston Wallis, Bodmin.

CONSISTORIAL ARCHIDIACONAL COURT OF BARNSTAPLE.—Official, Rev. H. Luxmoore, Barnstaple; Registrar, Mr. Ralph Sanders, Exeter; Deputy, Mr. C. E. Palmer, Barnstaple.

CONSISTORIAL ARCHIDIACONAL COURT OF TOTNES.—Official, ———; Registrar, Samuel Barnes, Esq.; Deputy, Mr. George Farwell, Totnes.

ROYAL PECULIAR OF ST. BURYAN, CORNWALL.—Registrar, Mr. Francis Paynter.

PARISH CHURCHES.

As noticed at page 50, there are in the city and county of the city of Exeter, nineteen parishes and three precincts, besides the Castle; and in the suburbs are the three parishes of St. Leonard, St. Thomas, and Heavitree. In the city and suburbs are 21 parish churches and several episcopal chapels. Most of them are small, and possess but little architectural beauty, except those that have been erected or rebuilt during the present century. It is said that there were formerly 32 churches here, and that 12 of them were sold in 1658, when seven were purchased by the Governors of St. John's Hospital. It will be seen with the parochial charities at subsequent pages, that

land and buildings have been vested at various periods for the reparation of some of the parish churches, of which the following is a brief description, with the patrons and incumbents of the benefices.

Allhallows Church, in *Goldsmith street*, is a small antique fabric, which was disused from 1720 till 1822, when it was re-opened for public worship, after being thoroughly repaired. It has a wooden belfry and one bell. Its *rectory*, valued in K.B. at £6. 4s. 7d., and in 1831 at £66, is in the gift of the Dean and Chapter, and incumbency of the Rev. T. Coldridge.

Allhallows-on-the-Walls is a handsome structure of perpendicular architecture, which was finished and consecrated in Sept. 1845, except the tower, which was not commenced till 1849, when the south window of the chancel was enriched with stained glass, in memory of the late Mr. and Mrs. Cornish. The roof is open, and supported by circular ribs; and the east window is of beautiful stained glass, representing the four Evangelists, &c. The communion plate was presented by Canon Rogers, and the altar-cloth was the gift of the Hon. Mrs. Ford. The total cost of the building was about £3500, and at the time of its erection the parish had been about a century without a church, the ruins of the old one, which stood in Fore street, being cleared away about 1777, when the present Exe Bridge was built. The new church stands in *Old Bartholomew Burial Ground*, which was opened on St. Bartholomew's day, 1637, and was the principal place of interment for the city till the opening of the New Cemetery, on the other side of the city wall, in 1837. The *rectory*, valued in K.B. at £5. 4s. 9½d., and in 1831 at only £19, is in the gift of the Dean and Chapter, and incumbency of the Rev. S. U. B. Lee, M.A. The *tower* is not yet completed.

Bedford Chapel, in the precinct called *Bedford Circus*, is a neat brick building, which was erected in 1831-'2, at the cost of £4400, of which £2000 was raised in £50 shares, and the remainder by voluntary contributions. The interior has three aisles, three galleries, and about 1000 sittings, of which 300 are free. The front has three entrances, and over the centre door is a portico, supported on Tuscan pillars. The bell hangs in a small turret. The *perpetual curacy*, valued at £136, is in the patronage of trustees, and incumbency of the Rev. W. Jackson, M.A.

St. David's Church occupies a beautiful situation on St. David's hill, in the northern suburbs of the city. The ancient church was pulled down in 1816, when the erection of the present fabric was commenced, but it was considerably enlarged in 1839. It is chiefly in the Roman style, with a Doric portico, and a round tower, containing six bells. It has a spacious burial ground; and its large parish includes the City and County Prisons, the Cavalry Barracks, Northernhay, the Railway Station, the manor of Duryards, and many neat houses. It is said to have been anciently a chapelry to Heavitree, and to have had a chapel near the river, dedicated to St. Clement. The benefice is a *perpetual curacy*, worth about £280 per annum; but in 1850 it will be augmented with the great tithes, (£150 per ann.,) by gift of the Dean and Chapter. The latter are

patrons, and the Rev. C. C. Bartholomew is the incumbent. Until recently, the Vicar of Heavitree was patron.

St. Edmund's Church, in Edmund street, on the western side of the city, was rebuilt in 1834, at the cost of £2000. It is a plain cemented structure, with a tower containing a fine peal of eight bells. It has a handsome stone altar screen, given by Lord Rolle. When the old bridge over the Exe was standing near it, the ancient church was commonly called St. Edmund on the Bridge; and in some deeds it is styled the Chantry on the Bridge. The *rectory*, valued in K.B. at £10. 6s. 8d., and in 1831 at £196, was formerly in the gift of the Corporation, but G. Hyde, Esq., is now patron, and the Rev. Owen Owen, M.A., incumbent.

St. John's Church, Fore street hill, is a very ancient cemented structure, the tower of which has a peal of six bells, and a clock with two faces projecting into the street. The interior was beautified and fitted with galleries in 1843, when the *Church of St. George the Martyr* was taken down for the improvement of South street, and its parish united with St. John's. Here are several neat monuments, some of which were removed from St. George's, as also were five of the bells. The *rectory* of St. John's, valued in K.B. at £18, and that of St. George's, valued in K.B. at £9. 13s. 8d., are now consolidated, and worth about £300 per annum. The Lord Chancellor is patron, and the Rev. J. M. Collyns, M.A., incumbent.

St. John's Chapel belongs to St. John's Hospital, as afterwards noticed. The church service is performed in it twice every Sunday, and there is regular service every Sunday evening in the *Chapel at Wynard's Hospital.*

St. James' Church, in the north-eastern suburbs, has been made the mother church of a *parochial district*, separated from St. Sidwell's parish in 1838; but the privilege of solemnizing marriages, baptisms, and burials was not given to it till 1842; and its burial ground was not consecrated till 1846. Its district parish comprises about 4000 souls. It was consecrated as a chapel of ease on Nov. 26th, 1836, and was built at the cost of £3722, raised by subscription, except £500 given by the Church Building Society. It is in the modern Gothic style, and has 1200 sittings, of which 600 are free. The interior is neat, and the east window contains a large figure of St. James, in beautifully painted glass, given by Mrs. Wilkinson. The pulpit is richly carved, and is said to have been captured in a Spanish vessel, in the reign of Elizabeth. It was presented to the church by the Dean and Chapter. National Schools, for 250 children of this district parish, were built in 1845, at the cost of £778, of which £200 was granted by Government, and £150 was given by the National Society. The benefice is a *perpetual curacy,* in the patronage of the Vicar of Heavitree, and incumbency of the Rev. P. Carlyon, M.A., who derives his income from the pew rents and customary fees.

St. Kerrian's Church, in North street, is a small, ancient, dilapidated building, which has not been used for divine service during the present century. Its *rectory* is consolidated with that of St. Petrock, and the joint benefices are valued in K.B. at £5. 18s. 6½d.,

and are now worth only about £150 per annum. The Dean and Chapter are patrons, and the Rev. Joseph Corfe, M.A., incumbent.

St. Lawrence's Church, in High street, is a neat plastered structure, with a tower and one bell. It was repaired and newly seated in 1847, at the cost of about £600. It has a handsomely carved oak screen, and a curious painted altar-piece, in the pseudo-classic style, with emblems of the Mosaic covenants. Over the principal entrance is a small statue of Queen Elizabeth, which formerly ornamented a conduit that stood in the middle of the street. Its parish had anciently two chapels, dedicated to St. Bartholomew and the Holy Trinity. The *rectory*, valued at £135, is in the patronage of the Lord Chancellor, and incumbency of the Rev. W. G. Heathman, B.A.

St. Martin's Church, in the Cathedral yard, is a small antique fabric, said to have been consecrated in 1065. It has a tower and one bell, and contains a few ancient monuments. Its parish had a chapel dedicated to St. Peter, but it was disused before 1265. The *rectory*, valued in K.B. at £8. 14s. 6d., and in 1831 at only £77, is in the patronage of the Dean and Chapter, and incumbency of the Rev. M. Tucker, M.A.

St. Mary Arches' Church, in the street to which it gives name, is a spacious edifice, with a tower and three bells. The nave and aisles are separated by massive pillars, evidently of great antiquity, but the building has undergone many repairs and alterations. The interior is neatly fitted up, and contains many handsome monuments, principally of mayors of Exeter. The tomb of Thos. Walker, who died in 1628, has kneeling effigies of himself and wife. The *rectory*, valued in K.B. at £10, and in 1831 at £187, is in the patronage of the Bishop of Exeter, and incumbency of the Rev. J. J. Rowe.

St. Mary Major's Church, in the Cathedral yard, is a very ancient fabric, especially the tower, which is of Saxon origin. Over the north entrance is a small tablet, representing St. Lawrence in a state of Martyrdom, on a gridiron. The nave is separated from the chancel by a handsomely carved rood screen; and the front of the gallery is ornamented with round-headed arches, and a row of figures of angels, &c. The church was re-seated in 1816, and contains numerous monumental inscriptions, both ancient and modern. The *rectory*, valued in K.B. at £15. 14s. 9½d., and in 1831 at £150, is in the gift of the Dean and Chapter, and incumbency of the Rev. J. F. Turner.

St. Mary Steps' Church is in West street, at the foot of Stepcote hill, adjoining the site of the West gate, through which the city was formerly entered by a flight of steps. It is a small ancient fabric, and in its tower is a *curious clock*, over the dial of which are three small figures;—the centre one representing Henry VIII., in a sitting posture, bends forward every time the clock strikes; and the other two are in military costume, with javelins in their right hands, and in their left small hammers, with which they alternately strike the quarters on two small bells beneath their feet. These figures are vulgarly called Matthew the miller and his two sons, from the circumstance of an old miller, who formerly lived in the neighbour-

hood, and passed the clock punctually at stated times.   There are four bells in the tower, and the church has a handsome pulpit, a very ancient font, and a neat altar piece.   The *rectory*, valued in K.B. at £8. 6s. 8d., and in 1831 at £180, was in the gift of Dr. Carwithen, but is now in the patronage and incumbency of the Rev. Thomas A. Melhuish.

St. Olave's Church, in Fore street, is of great antiquity.   It was appropriated by William the Conqueror to Battle Abbey, and the benefice being of small value, was many years without an incumbent, and the church shut up.   Being in this state, the use of it was granted, after the edict of Nantes, to the *French Refugees*, many of whom settled here as cloth makers, &c.   Divine service was performed here for their accommodation, in the French language, till 1758, when the church was shut up again, and the interior went to decay.   After being thoroughly repaired, and enlarged by the addition of an adjoining building, the church was re-opened in 1815. The vaulted roof is supported by six massive pillars, which, like the tower, are evidently Saxon. The *rectory*, valued in K.B. at £7. 13s. 4d., and in 1832 at £92, is in the patronage of the Lord Chancellor, and incumbency of the Rev. C. R. Roper, M.A.

St Pancras' Church, in Pancras lane, is a small plain building, only 46½ feet by 16.   It was shut up for many years, but after being repaired, it was re-opened in 1830.   On the floor are some memorials of the Kelly family.   The *rectory*, valued at only £43, is in the gift of the Dean and Chapter, and is now enjoyed by the Rev. E. W. T. Chave, M.A.

St. Paul's Church, in Paul street, near the Cathedral yard, which is a handsome structure, was rebuilt in the latter part of the 17th century.   It contains a fine painted window with a full length figure of St. Paul.   It has also several handsome monuments, and an ancient oval font, of black marble, The tower has a clock and one bell.   The *rectory*, valued in K.B. at £8. 2s. 6d., and in 1831 at £174, is in the gift of the Dean and Chapter, and incumbency of the Rev. R. B. Kinsman, M.A., who is also rural dean.

St. Petrock's Church, in High street, near the Cathedral yard, was rebuilt in 1829, and is so closely surrounded with houses that the only part of it visible from the street is the tower with its projecting clock.   The sacramental plate is very superb, and comprises two cups dated 1572 and 1640, and two flagons, dated 1692.   In the tower are six bells.   The *rectory* is consolidated with that of St. Kerrian.   St. Petrock was one of the early propagators of christianity, and gave name to Petrockstowe, in Devonshire.

St. Sidwell's Church stands without the Walls, in the northeastern part of the city, and from its populous parish the new district parish of St. James, has been lately taken, as noticed at page 83. The original church was a very ancient fabric, dedicated to *St. Stativola, or Sidwell*, a virgin, who is said to have been beheaded with a scythe, about the year 740, and to have been buried here.   It was rebuilt in 1812 and '13, at the cost of more than £2200, except the tower, which was repaired and surmounted by a handsome octagonal spire, in 1823, at the cost of about £500.   It is now a beautiful

edifice in the pointed style, and in its lofty tower are eight musical bells, hung in 1768. The interior consists of a chancel, and a nave, with two side aisles, neatly pewed and having three large galleries. It will seat more than a thousand hearers, and the nave and aisles are separated by the clustered columns of the original church, supporting six arches, studded with rosettes. Each capital is divided into eight compartments, four containing angels supporting shields, and the other four small figures of St. Sidwell. The east window is enriched with a beautiful representation of the Ascension, in painted glass. The pulpit is richly carved, and supported by flying arches rising from four buttresses. The font is octagonal, and large enough for immersion. The organ is a fine toned instrument, and in the church are several handsome monuments. St. Sidwell's parish was anciently parcel of the parish of Heavitree, though it has always formed part of the county of the city of Exeter. It includes *Hill's court*, which was for many generations the seat of the Hill family, but is now a street with many neat houses. It also comprises all the handsome suburbs extending eastward from St. Sidwell street to the Workhouse, Polesloe Park, &c. In the church register are records of great ravages of the plague, in 1625, and an entry of the burial of Richard Wilkins, who was executed for *witchcraft* in 1610. The benefice is a *perpetual curacy*, valued in 1831 at £252. It is in the patronage of the Vicar of Heavitree, and incumbency of the Rev. Fras. Courtenay, M.A.

St. Stephen's Church, in High street, was a very ancient structure; but having been desecrated and made a garrison in 1657, it was rebuilt in 1664. The interior was completely altered in 1826, and has now a neat appearance. The tower has three bells, and is crowned by an octagon turret. The *rectory*, valued in K.B. at £7. 17s. 3½d., and in 1831 at only £85, is in the patronage of the Bishop of Exeter, and incumbency of the Rev. J. T. Toye, M.A.

Holy Trinity Church, in South street, adjoining the site of the South gate, was rebuilt in 1820, at the cost of £7295. It is a spacious Gothic fabric, with a turret containing a clock and bell. The body is separated from the entrance by a neat screen, and contains several handsome monuments. It has about 1000 sittings, of which nearly 100 are free. The *rectory*, valued in K.B. at £11. 6s. 4d., and in 1831 at £177, is in the gift of the Dean and Chapter, and is now enjoyed by the Rev. G. H. O. Shield, M.A.

CHURCHES AND PARISHES IN THE SUBURBS.

St. Leonard's Church occupies an elevated and pleasant situation at Mount Radford, on the south side of Exeter, and has in its parish several handsome villas and rows of houses, and the Deaf and Dumb Institution. The old church was very ancient, but the present fabric, which occupies its site, is a handsome Grecian structure, which was erected in 1833, and has a lofty portico over the principal entrance, supported by two massive columns. It cost about £1400, but was enlarged in 1843, at an additional expense of about £800, of which £500 was given by Sir Thos. Baring, Bart., who owns most of the parish, and whose family were formerly seated at

Larkbear and Mount Radford House, the former of which was for many ages the seat of the Hulls ; and the latter was built in the 16th century by Matthew Radford, Esq., and was made a garrison in the siege of 1643, when three pieces of ordnance were planted in it by the Parliamentary Governor of Exeter. It was afterwards a royal garrison, and was surrendered to Sir Thomas Fairfax, in 1646. The church was fortified at the same unhappy period, and suffered much during the last siege. The *rectory*, valued in K.B. at £4. 19s. 4½d., and in 1831 at £195, is in the patronage of the Executors of S. Wills, Esq., and incumbency of the Rev. G. W. B. Wills, M.A. The parish comprises only 80 acres, and 1129 souls, and is all in the Parliamentary Borough of Exeter.

St. Thomas the Apostle's is an extensive parish on the western side of the river Exe, connected with Exeter by Exe Bridge, and containing about 3700 acres of land, 4301 inhabitants ; the populous suburbs of Cowick street, Okehampton street, Alphington street, &c. ; the hamlets of *Exwick and Oldridge*, about a mile N.N.W. of the city ; many scattered houses ; and several mills It is crossed by the South Devon Railway, which has a small station near Cowick street. *St. Thomas's Union*, with its large Workhouse ; and the Lunatic Asylum, called *St. Thomas's Hospital*, are noticed at subsequent pages, as also are the charities belonging to this parish. J. W. Buller, Esq., is lord of the *manors of Cowick* and *Hayes*, and also of *Exwick and Barley* ; Sir J. S. G. Sawle, Bart., owns the manor of *Bowhill ;* and Thomas Northmore, Esq., owns *Cleave*, which has a pleasant mansion commanding a fine view over Exeter. *Franklands* belongs to the Jones family, and *Oldridge* to the Yardley and other families. *Floyer Hayes*, was the seat of the ancient family of Floyer from the time of the Conquest till last century. It was held by the service that when the lord paramount, (the Earl of Devon,) should come to Exe Island, the owner should come with a napkin, a pitcher of wine, and a silver cup, and offer his lordship to drink. *Cowick Priory*, is already noticed at page 73, but no traces of it are now extant. The populous parts of the parish of St. Thomas are included in the Parliamentary limits of the city of Exeter. The parish Church, in Cowick street, is a large ancient structure, which was enlarged in 1828, and has a tower and six bells. It has a handsome painted window, and contains some neat monuments, one of which is from the chisel of John Bacon, Esq., in memory of his daughter, Mrs. Medley, wife of the Bishop of Fredericton, formerly vicar of this parish. J. W. Buller, Esq., is impropriator of the rectorial tithes, and also patron of the *vicarage*, valued in K.B. at £11. 2s. 8½d., and in 1831 at £237, and now enjoyed by the Rev. Wm. Hy. Howard, M.A., who has a good parsonage house, and is also incumbent of *Exwick and Oldridge Chapels*, the latter of which was valued in 1831 at £60, and was rebuilt in 1789, by the late Jas. Buller, Esq. Exwick Chapel, dedicated to St. Andrew, is a neat modern building in the style which the Camden Society wished to introduce. It was consecrated September 26th, 1842, and was built by subscription, aided with a grant of £500 from the Church Building Society. It has a small turret and one bell, and its interior de-

corations are superb. The altar is of stone, the seats are open, and the rafters and cornices are covered with inscriptions, chiefly texts of Scripture. The Rev. T. R. Dickinson, M.A., is the curate. Ex-WICK is a considerable village on the banks of the Exe, 1 mile N.N.W. of Exeter, and has a woollen manufactory, a large corn mill, and a paper mill.

HEAVITREE PARISH, on the eastern side of Exeter, and partly within the parliamentary boundary of the city, contains 3469A. of land, and 3048 inhabitants. It comprises the Artillery Barracks, Regent Park, Baring Crescent, Polesloe, Richmond Grove, Mont le Grand, Bicton Place, and other eastern suburbs of the city, and the small villages of EAST and SOUTH WONFORD, and WHIPTON, at the distance of from one to two miles. The *village of Heavitree*, one mile E. of Exeter, has many neat houses, and is said to have de-rived its name from having been formerly the place of execution for the city. The *manor of Wonford*, which anciently gave name to this parish, and still gives name to the hundred, was part of the de-mesne of the crown in the reign of Edward the Confessor. It was given by Henry I. to Geoffrey de Mandeville, and afterwards passed to the Montacute, Courtenay, and other families. Sir Thomas Baring is now lord of this manor, but a great part of the parish belongs to other proprietors. Lord Poltimore is lord of the manor of *Wippen or Whipton*, which has been held for a long period by his family—the Bampfyldes. *St. Loyes* is the pleasant seat and property of Pitman Jones, Esq., and near it is the decayed chapel of *St. Eliguis*, or St. Loyes, which has long been used as a stable. South Wonford House belongs to Francis Spicer, Esq., and Ring-well Manor to Genl. Sir D. Ximenes. *Polesloe and St. James's Priories* stood in this parish, and are noticed at page 73. The PARISH CHURCH, dedicated to St. Michael, was rebuilt in 1845-'6, at the cost of about £3000, raised by subscription, and a grant of £500 from the Church Building Society. It was consecrated Aug. 1st, 1846, and is a neat structure of mixed architecture, with a tower of four bells. The Dean and Chapter of Exeter are appro-priators of the great tithes, and patrons of the *Vicarage*, which is in their peculiar jurisdiction, and was valued in 1831 at £641, and in K.B., (1535,) at £34. 3s. 4d. The Rev. A. Atherley, M.A., is the incumbent, and has a good residence, and six acres of glebe. The great tithes are held by several lessees, and both they and the small tithes were commuted in 1842. The *parish school* was rebuilt in 1840, and is attended by 140 children. The Wesleyans have a small chapel in the village, and the parish has several chari-ties, as afterwards noticed.

The NEW CEMETERY, which occupies nearly five acres of hilly ground, on the north side of the city wall, between Bartholomew street and Exe street, was purchased by the Exeter Improvement Commissioners in 1834, and divided into two portions, one for Dissenters, and the other for members of the Established Church. The latter was consecrated by the Bishop, on the 24th August, 1837. The whole of the ground is laid out in walks, and planted with flowers and shrubs. Its hilly nature affords room, by a series of arches and catacombs on the upper side, for the interment of

22,000 coffins, and, by building, at any future period, additional arches on the lower parts, space will be obtained for 10,000 more. Upwards of 500 interments take place here yearly, and the total cost of the cemetery has been about £5000. At the head of this beautiful burial ground is a terrace walk, on the top of a long portion of the city wall, on the other side of which is the Old Bartholomew Burial Ground, and the new church of Allhallows on the Walls—(see p. 82.)

The FREE CHURCH, or CHRIST CHURCH, in Southernhay, is the property of a gentleman, and is not within the pale of the Established Church, though its services are conducted in a similar manner. It was opened in 1846, and cost about £5000. It is in the Roman style, with a turret and bell. The interior has three aisles and three galleries, and will seat 1000 persons. The whole has a chaste appearance, and the east window is enriched with painted glass. The Rev. A. L. Mitchell is the minister.

The ROMAN CATHOLIC CHAPEL, in Mint lane, is a very neat building, erected in 1791-'2, on part of the site of *St. Nicholas's Priory*, as noticed at page 72. The interior is handsomely fitted up, and has a good organ. The *Rev. Geo. Oliver, D.D.*, has held the pastoral office here for many years, and, in 1821, published a valuable History of Exeter, compiled from original documents, the corporation records, the Bishop's registers, &c. In conjunction with P. Jones, Esq., he edited " *Westcote's View of Devonshire in* 1630," which was not published till 1845.

DISSENTING CHAPELS :—Besides the numerous episcopal places of worship, and the two last named, there are in the city and suburbs thirteen other places of religious worship. The UNITARIAN CHAPEL, called " *George's Meeting*," is a large handsome building, in South street. It was erected by Presbyterians, in 1760, and has an endowment of about £200 per annum, from landed property, chiefly in Polesloe. Its congregation have the chief management of the Protestant Dissenters' Charity School, afterwards noticed ; and also support a School of Industry, in Rack street, and an Evening Ragged School. The chapel will seat about 1000 hearers, and the Rev. Thomas Hincks is the minister. In the early part of last century, a great controversy arose among the dissenters of Exeter, which spread over a large portion of the kingdom, and gave rise to numerous pamphlets. The point in controversy was the doctrine of the Trinity, and two of the Presbyterian ministers here embraced the Unitarianism, and opened a meeting house in Mint lane. The congregations were afterwards united by that eminent divine, *Micaiah Towgood*, who died here in 1792, in the 92nd year of his age. The INDEPENDENT CHAPEL, in Castle street, was built in 1796, on the site of the old County Gaol, and was enlarged a few years ago. Attached to it is a small burial ground, and a school, built in 1832. The *Independent Chapel*, at *Grosvenor place*, is a small neat building, with a turret and bell. It was built in 1835, at the cost of about £1200, and is now under the ministry of the Rev. N. Hellings. The TABERNACLE, in Coombe street, belongs to the *Calvinists*, and was built in 1772, by the Rev. H. Tanner. Here are three BAPTIST CHAPELS, and that in *South street* was rebuilt in 1822, on the site of the oldest dissenting chapel in Exeter. The Rev. Geo. Gould is its minister. That in *Bartholomew street* was built by the Rev. G. Baring, in 1817, and was reseated in 1845. It has room for 1000 hearers, and is now under the ministry of the Rev. J. Bigwood. *Zoar Chapel*, in Longbrook street, is a small building, erected in 1841. It belongs to the Particular Baptists. The WESLEYANS have two chapels here ; one in the *Mint*, erected in 1812, and considerably enlarged a few years ago ; and the other in *St. Sidwell street*, erected in 1836. Schools are attached to both. The *Primitive Me-*

thodists occupy an old chapel in Musgrave alley, which was built by Inde-
dendents. The FRIENDS' MEETING HOUSE, in Friar's walk, is a neat substantial structure, built in 1835. The PLYMOUTH BRETHREN have a chapel
in Northernhay street, built by Sir Alexander Campbell, in 1839. The
interior is plain, and in the centre is a long table, at which the speakers
stand. In Mary Arches street is a JEWS' SYNAGOGUE, which was erected in
1764, and enlarged and beautified in 1838.

RELIGIOUS INSTITUTIONS are as liberally supported in Exeter as in
any other place in the kingdom, both by members of the Established
Church and Dissenters. The *Diocesan Association of the Society for the
Promotion of Christian Knowledge*, was established as early as 1699; and
the *Auxiliary Bible Society* in 1809. Here are also,—a Ladies' Branch, and
a Naval and Military Bible Societies; as well as Missionary, Tract, Pastoral Aid, and other societies, for the promotion of religion both at home and
abroad.

LITERARY INSTITUTIONS.

The city of Exeter has several large and valuable public libraries, and
various societies for the cultivation of literature, philosophy, and the arts
and sciences; and they are liberally supported both by the citizens and the
gentry of the surrounding country.

DEVON and EXETER INSTITUTION, in the Cathedral yard, was
established, in 1813, by a number of gentlemen of the city and neighbourhood, for the promotion of science, literature, and the arts. It occupies a
spacious building, handsomely fitted up. The large *reading room* is well
supplied with modern publications, newspapers, magazines, &c., and the
library comprises about 15,000 volumes in the various departments of
literature. The *museum*, in the galleries, contains numerous specimens
illustrative of natural history; an extensive herbarium of British plants;
and a fine collection of Devonshire mosses. The institution is supported
by 224 proprietary shareholders, who subscribe £2 each per annum. J.
Sillifant, Esq., is *president*; the Rev. J. Huish and J. Harris, Esq., are *vice-
presidents*; T. G. Norris, Esq., *treasurer*; Saml. Barnes, Esq., *honorary
secretary*; and Mr. John Squance, *librarian*.

The ATHENÆUM, in Bedford circus, is a large and handsome building, erected in 1835, by a society now consisting of 53 shareholders, each
entitled to a free ticket to the lectures; and seven original holders of double
shares, each entitled to two such transferable tickets, and a free personal
admission to all lectures. The pricipal part of the building comprises a
semi-circular *theatre* or lecture room, capable of seating nearly 400
hearers, and often used by the various literary societies of the city for public
lectures, discussions, &c. Dr. Miller is secretary to the proprietors.

EXETER PHILOSOPHICAL SOCIETY, was established in 1835, and meets
at the Athenæum on the first Monday of every month during the session,
when papers are read, and the subjects discussed. Mr. H. U. Janson is
the secretary and curator.

EXETER LITERARY SOCIETY, at the Athenæum, was established in 1841,
and has a reading room, a weekly lecture, and classes for instruction in
French, Latin, Drawing, &c. It has about 550 members, and a library of
more than 1300 volumes. Gentlemen pay 12s., and ladies 6s., per annum.
J. Sillifant, Esq., is *president*; and Mr. F. Channon, *secretary*.

The SCIENTIFIC and LITERARY INSTITUTION was established in 1844,
and holds its lectures, &c., generally at the Athenæum, and sometimes at the
Church Music Room. It has classes for German, French, Latin, Drawing, &c. Gentlemen pay 12s., and ladies 8s., per annum, and connected

with it is the GENERAL LIBRARY, which comprises about 1900 volumes, at the society's rooms, 43, High street. Lord Courtenay, M.P., is the *president*.

The PUBLIC SELECT LIBRARY, at 247, High street, was commenced in 1807, and now contains about 6000 volumes. Mr. Wm. Drewe is the *secretary*, and Mr. Wm. Balle the *librarian*.

The POLYTECHNIC INSTITUTION was established in 1847, solely by the zealous exertions of Mr. S. R. Ridgway, of *Magdalen House Academy*, where his students, and the citizens generally, are admitted gratuitously to the lectures, and where there is a highly interesting *museum*, illustrative of natural history, and a fine collection of antiquarian relics, models, drawings, paintings, &c.; as well as a variety of apparatus, for the exemplification of electricity, pneumatics, optics, chemistry, &c., &c. A good library is attached to the lecture room, and a botanic garden is in process of formation.

The *Cathedral Library*, now deposited in the Chapter House, contains about 8000 volumes, including many ancient manuscripts, and a folio edition of Cæsar, printed in 1471, and in good preservation.

The MEDICAL LIBRARY, at the Devon and Exeter Hospital, and the LAW LIBRARY, at the Athenæum, were established in 1833, and have large collections of works in their respective branches of literature.

Here is a *Botanical and Horticultural Society*, which was established in 1829, and holds periodical exhibitions of fruits, flowers, vegetables, &c. It has rooms and a good library at 263, High street; and is supported by a long list of annual subscribers. Sir R. Lopes, Bart., is president; Thos. Wm. Gray, secretary; and Mrs. Spreat, librarian. *Devon Agricultural Society*, formed here in 1831, has its rooms at 197, High street. It holds periodical exhibitions of live stock, &c., in the Castle yard, and gives prizes for the encouragement of agricultural labourers in habits of industry, cleanliness, and economy. Mr. Rt. Dymond is the secretary.

Five weekly NEWSPAPERS are published in Exeter, as will be seen with their names and proprietors in the subjoined Directory. One of them, *Woolmer's Exeter and Plymouth Gazette*, was established sixty years ago, and the others during the present century. Two other journals, called the *Alfred* and the *Exeter News*, were formerly published here. *Almanacks and Pocket Books*, adapted for the county of Devon, and some other periodical publications, are printed here. NEWS ROOMS are attached to several of the literary institutions, as already noticed, and there are others at some of the inns. *Mount Radford College School* was founded in 1826, in the commodious house which was formerly the residence of Judge Doderidge.

WORTHIES.—Among the *eminent men* who were born or flourished at Exeter may be enumerated—*Bartholomew Iscanus*, bishop of Exeter, who wrote the life of Guy, Earl of Warwick; *Josephus Iscanus**, who was born here about the close of the 12th century, and is styled by Wharton " the miracle of his age in classical compositions;" *Baldwin, Archbishop of Canterbury*, the patron of Geraldus Cambrensis; *Stephen Langton*, Archbishop of Canterbury and Cardinal; *John Hooker*, who was born here in 1524, and wrote a History of Exeter and many other valuable works; *Sir Wm. Petre*, a distinguished statesman, who was secretary and privy councillor to Henry VIII., Edward VI., and to Queens Mary and Elizabeth; *Sir Thos. Bodley*, the great patron of learning, who was born here in 1544, and founded that extensive and valuable collection of books and manuscripts at Oxford University, called the *Bodleian Library*, to which he left a yearly income for the

* His poem on the Trojan War has often been reprinted in Germany, under the name of *Cornelius Nepos*. He wrote his *Antiocheis* after attending Richard I. to the Holy Land.

purchase of books, the support of the librarian, &c.; *Wm. Tucker*, dean of Lichfield, who wrote upon the king's evil, &c., and was born about 1550; *Wm. Martyn*, recorder and historian of Exeter, born about 1562; *Dr. Barkham*, dean of Bocking, a learned antiquary, whose heraldic and historic works came before the public in the 16th century, under the names of Gwillim and Speed; *Sir Simon Baskerville*, an eminent physician and anatomist, born in 1573; *Wm. Hakewill*, a learned lawyer, who wrote on the liberty of the subject; his brother, *Dr. George Hakewill*, author of a popular work on the "Providence of God," and sometime chaplain to Prince Charles; *John Reinolds*, author of "God's Revenge against Murder," &c.; *Sir Wm. Morice*, secretary of state to Charles II.; *Matthew Locke*, the celebrated musical composer; *Thomas Long*, a controversial writer among the Separatists, in the 17th century; *Sir Peter King*, the son of a grocer at Exeter, and nephew of the great Locke, was born here in 1669, and became a learned lawyer and statesman, and was Lord Chancellor of England from 1725 till his death in 1733; *Sir Bartholomew Shower*, an eminent lawyer and reporter; his brother, *John Shower*, a learned dissenting minister, and author of several religious treatises, born 1657; *Thomas Yalden*, the poet, born 1671; *Simon Ockley*, the learned orientalist, and author of a History of the Saracens, born 1678; *Dr. Richard Walker*, author of the "Sufferings of the Clergy;" *Dr. John Foster*, a dissenting minister, who was complimented by Pope for his pulpit oratory, and wrote a defence of the Christian Revelation against Tindall; *Andrew Brice*, the printer, who published a Topographical Dictionary; *William Jackson*, an eminent musical composer, who died in 1808, and has a monument in St. Stephen's Church; *Samuel Walker* and *Richard Hole*, two learned divines; the late Chief Justice, *Sir Vicary Gibbs*; *Nicholas Hilliard*, a painter, in the reign of Elizabeth; *Charles Hopkins*, a dramatic writer, son of the Bishop of Derry, born 1664; *Tom Durfey*, a celebrated dramatic writer of the 17th century; *Eustace Budgell*, an eminent writer of last century, and a contributor to the Spectator, said to have been born at St. Thomas's, about 1685; and *Robert Pullein*, who, in the reign of Henry I., acquired great fame by his lectures on the Scriptures at Oxford, and was reputed the reviver of learning in that university. *Dr. Musgrave*, the antiquary, and *Dr. Downman*, the poet, resided several years at Exeter, as practising physicians. *Richard Hooker*, the learned author of the "Ecclesiastical Polity," was a native of Wonford; and *Sir Arthur Ducke*, author of the Life of Archbishop Chichele, was born at Heavitree, and was an eminent civilian in the reign Charles I.

JOANNA SOUTHCOTT, sometimes called the *Exeter Prophetess*, was the greatest of all the religious fanatics and impostors of the present century. She resided many years in this city, but is said to have been born at Gittisham; and she was certainly baptised at Ottery St. Mary in 1750, as appears from the parish register. She proclaimed herself here as a prophetess early in 1800, and afterwards removed to London, where she died in December, 1814, to the utter consternation of her deluded followers, who amounted to many thousands, in various parts of the kingdom, and had been led to believe that she was immortal, and was about to give birth to the promised *Shiloh*, under whom they were promised a patriarchal existence upon earth of at least a thousand years. To raise money, under the guise of ensuring them the full enjoyment of this *millennium*, she visited her ignorant proselytes in the populous parts of the kingdom in 1803, and subsequent years, and distributed among them her "*celestial seals*." At one time she promised her foolish followers a miraculous translation to the New Jerusalem, and hundreds of them gave up their employments, and dis-

tributed their goods and chattels among their unbelieving relations and neighbours, on the eve of their expected journey. This failing, she impiously declared that the promised land was at home, and that she was about to give birth to Shiloh, for whose reception a splendid gilt cradle was subscribed for, and exhibited to the gaze of the credulous and curious at a small sum per head. Her enthusiastic adherents were generally among the most vulgar and illiterate, though some of them were people of property, and one of them was George Turner, a Leeds merchant, who, in 1809, published an appeal to the public in defence of Joanna Southcott, her believers, and her *Book of Wonders*, which extends through several volumes. Even after the death of herself and many of her " *sealed faithful*," hundreds still lived in her " *light*," believing her to be "'not dead, but translated." Some of them and their descendants may still be recognised under the name of *Israelites*, and by their whity-brown hats, and the full growth of that dignifying ornament, the beard.

Notwithstanding the great exertions which have been made for the education of the poor, and the immense sums of money which have been expended in the erection of public schools during the present century, the most impudent pretenders to supernatural revelation and the science of astrology still find votaries, therefore we need not wonder when we read of the blind credulity and infatuation which existed in past centuries. So late as 1646, three poor friendless old women from Bideford were condemned and executed at Exeter, for the supposed crime of *witchcraft*, as also was Richard Wilkins, in 1610. They were not the last of the many victims who suffered capital punishment under this delusion in different parts of the kingdom; but happily the repeal of all the statutes relating to *witchcraft and demonology*, about half a century ago, removed from our criminal code the reproach which these ridiculous enactments cast upon the legislature. Yet it has been said that there never was a period when the lower orders of people in this kingdom " were more credulous, more easily imposed upon, or more generally duped, by the specious arts of daring deceivers, than in this very age ;" witness the astrological nonsense still circulated in one of our almanacs; the " *wise-men*" and the *fortune tellers* still finding employment among the ignorant; the many Mormonites, or Latter-Day Saints, lately gone or expecting to go to the supposed land of promise in America; and the numerous other quackeries and impositions which still disgrace humanity, and cast a slur upon the intelligence of the 19th century.

PLACES OF AMUSEMENT, &c.

The THEATRE, near Bedford Circus and Southernhay, is a commodious building, with a handsome stone front. Except the latter, it was destroyed by fire in 1820, and soon afterwards rebuilt. At the Hotel in the Close is an Assembly Room, which was the only room for such purpose in the city before 1820, when the ROYAL SUBSCRIPTION ROOMS, opposite the New London Inn, were erected at a great expense. The *Ball Room* in this large and elegant building is 92 feet by 41, and 40 in height. It is tastefully fitted up, and lighted by a handsome dome. The building also contains tea-rooms and other suitable accommodations for balls, assemblies, concerts, exhibitions, &c., and is now the property of Miss Congdon. The orchestra has a large organ-case, but the organ has not yet been inserted. Behind Fore street is the *Devon and Exeter Hall*, a large and handsome room, built by Mr. N. Tuckett, for public meetings,

concerts, &c.   The Athenæum, as already noticed, has a spacious room, used for public lectures, &c., by several of the Literary Institutions.   Attached to some of the latter are museums, libraries, and news-rooms.   *Exeter Oratorio Society* holds several performances yearly in the Royal Subscription Rooms, and possesses much vocal and instrumental talent, as also do several other musical societies, and the cathedral choir.

The PUBLIC BATHS at Upper Southernhay were opened in 1821, and comprise cold, hot, plunge, shower, vapour, medicated, and fumigated baths.   They are the property of Mr. E. W. Jackson, and a portion of the building is appropriated during summer to an exhibition of paintings, models, &c., arranged under the direction of the *Society for the Study and Encouragement of Art*.   The baths are supplied from the city water-works.

PUBLIC WALKS, &c.—As already noticed, the city and suburbs present a delightful diversity of public walks and picturesque scenery, in which are seen many interesting buildings of ancient and modern date, and many handsome villas and rows of genteel houses, with tasteful gardens, shrubberies, woody lawns, &c.   NORTHERNHAY, which extends round the northern and eastern sides of the Castle precincts, was distinguished, many years ago, as one of the finest public walks in England, and after being long neglected, it was restored, in 1845, by subscription, at the cost of about £700.   Two new lodges were erected, and new serpentine walks were laid out, and tastefully planted in those parts where many of the fine old elms had been cut down in former years.   The FRIARS' WALK is an ancient public promenade, now much obscured by buildings, but near it is Colleton crescent, where the river and canal, the shipping, the rich foliage of the surrounding country, and the elevated and distant hills, combine in producing a most pleasing landscape. About four acres of land, called *Bury Meadows*, near the New North road, was opened as a place of recreation for the public in 1846. With the permission of the proprietor (J. Abbott, Esq.,) many pleasure parties from Exeter often visit FORDLANDS, near Ide, about 2½ miles west of the city.   These romantic grounds, from their sylvan shades, gleaming lakes, rustic arbours, and devious, ever-winding paths, might be appropriately denominated Fairy-land.   The house itself is not a showy mansion, but the grounds are so fancifully laid out, as to attract the attention of numerous visitors.   Tea parties are accommodated in the neighbourhood, and numberless are the summer jaunts to this sequestered labyrinth of shady bowers and sylvan walks.   Charming strolls may be taken on all sides of the city, and extensive views may be had from Pennsylvania Hill ; Montpelier ; the site of Danes Castle, near the County Gaol and Cavalry Barracks ; and other eminences.   *Tea Gardens* are numerous in the neighbourhood, and at them may be obtained in perfection those preparations of milk called *Junket and Devonshire Cream.*

SPORTING AND FISHING.—To the lovers of field sports the neighbourhood of Exeter offers many attractions.   Within ten or fifteen miles, several packs of hounds are kept. To the angler, the different streams in the vicinity give excellent fishing—on the Exe, from

Cowley bridge upwards; on the Culme, branching off from the Exe at Stoke Canon; on the Creedy, another stream joining the Exe, near Cowley bridge; on the Teign, from Dunsford bridge; and on the Clist, near Sidmouth road. Anglers are sometimes allowed to fish in the canal by permission of the Town Council. The *Exe Fishing Association* was established in 1844, and Mr. S. B. Hodgson is its secretary. Exe River is noted for fine trout and a variety of smaller fish.

EXETER CHARITIES.

The stream which flows from the fountain of charity, for the solace of the indigent and infirm poor, and for the education and religious and moral training of poor children, is as copious at Exeter as at any other town in the kingdom. In various parts of the city are endowed almshouses for about 120 aged poor; and many public schools, where several thousand children receive instruction, either gratuitously, or for small weekly payments. At the Blue Boys' and Blue Maids' Schools, 34 of the children are also clothed and maintained; and several hundreds are provided with clothing from the funds of the Episcopal, the Protestant Dissenters', and other Charity Schools. The poor citizens, both generally and in their respective parishes, are relieved several times a year by distributions of money, clothing, coals, &c., arising from property that has been bequeathed by numerous donors, for charitable uses. The enquiry into the *Endowed Charities* of Exeter, occupy about 300 folio pages of the late *Parliamentary Commissioners' Reports*, printed between 1815 and 1839, and of which the following pages comprise the substance. The income of all the city charities, so far as they came under the cognizance of these Commissioners, may be estimated at upwards of £6000 per annum. Those under the control of the COR-PORATION, (commonly called the Chamber of Exeter,) were transferred, in 1836, to upwards of thirty CHARITY TRUSTEES, many of whom are also city magistrates, aldermen, or councillors. These trustees are divided into *two lists*, one for the management of the *General Charities*, and the other having the control of the *Church Charities*. The yearly income derived from the former charities, in 1837, was about £1500, and from the latter, about £3000, of which £1276 was the income of St. John's Hospital, and the Grammar and Blue Schools. The Parliamentary Commissioners found that most of the charity estates were let on leases for lives, at considerably less than half the yearly value, in consideration of fines paid to the old Corporation for granting and renewing the leases. These fines are far from being equivalent to the loss in rents; and the late Commissioners found much difficulty in their endeavours to distinguish the Charity from the Corporation Property,—the "Chamber" having for many ages strangely intermixed the accounts of several charities with the municipal receipts and expenditure, as will be seen at subsequent pages. Besides the endowed schools and hospitals, and the numerous benefactions for the relief of the poor, here are many *Charitable Institutions*, supported chiefly by voluntary subscriptions and donations, and some of these are in posses-

sion of large estates and funded property, derived from the bequests of former benefactors. These comprise many public schools; the Devon and Exeter Hospital, for the sick and infirm poor; an excellent Lunatic Asylum; Schools for the Blind and the Deaf and Dumb; a Dispensary, an Eye Infirmary; Clothing and Lying-in Charities, &c., &c.

CHARITY TRUSTEES. (*Appointed in* 1836.)

CHURCH CHARITIES.—Rev. Arthur Atherley, Ralph Barnes, George Braund, John Clench, James Golsworthy, General Gage, John Hall, Henry Hooper, Charles Hubbard, William Kennaway, William Kingdon, Rev. Thomas Hill Lowe, Patrick Miller, J. J. Tanner.—*Clerk and Receiver*, J. Daw, Solicitor, 13, Bedford Circus. The charities under their management comprise St. John's Hospital, the Free Grammar and Blue Schools, and some others.

GENERAL CHARITIES.—William Cole, John Carslake, John Hull Terrell, William Hooper, Samuel Mortimer, John Harris, William Lee, Patrick Miller, Kent Kingdon, Thomas Foster Barham, Rev. George Oliver, D.D., Samuel Kingdon, Jas. Golsworthy, Henry Lake Hirtzel, and Geo. Braund.—*Clerk*, James Terrell, Solicitor, Bartholomew yard.—*Surveyor*, R. B. Best, New North road. The charities under their management comprise all the Almshouses, Benefactions, &c., vested with the Corporation, except those classed under the name of Church Charities.

ST. JOHN'S HOSPITAL AND FREE GRAMMAR AND BLUE SCHOOLS.

ST. JOHN'S HOSPITAL.—An Hospital, under this name, was founded in the 23rd of Henry III., by Gilbert and John Long, for for five priests, nine boys, and twelve poor almsmen; and continued till the latter end of the reign of Henry VIII., when it was suppressed, along with the smaller religious houses. The origin of the present establishment was as follows :—In 1629, the Widow and Son of *Hugh Crossing*, alderman and merchant of Exeter, agreeable to his charitable intention, granted to thirteen trustees, and their heirs, the house and precinct of the late dissolved Hospital of St. John, and the church of the said late Hospital, and various other buildings, lands, &c., to be employed for an hospital in setting the poor to work. In the same indenture, made between the mayor and corporation of Exeter, and the aforesaid grantors, it is recited that £350 had been given to the Corporation by Thomas Walker, Eliz. Dowrich, and Walter Barough, in trust for the foundation of a *Free Grammar School*, which the Corporation agreed to establish in part of the hospital church. In 1637, the hospital was *incorporated* by Charles I., " for the relief, setting on work, and education in good learning and otherwise, of poor children of Exeter; also, for the maintenance of aged poor people inhabiting there, and not able to work." The mayor, recorder, aldermen, and common council of Exeter, were constituted governors of the charity, and vested with power to establish a *Free Grammar School* and a *Free English School*. For supporting the latter, £500, left by *Elizabeth Jourdaine*, was ordered to be appropriated. Numerous legacies and gifts were afterwards received by the governors for the support of the hospital and schools; and the *property of the charity* now comprises about 1170 acres of land, and many houses and other buildings, in the manors of Clist St. Lawrence and Clist Gerrard; a farm of 179 acres in Teignharvey; 55A. 12P. in Bovey-Travey; 26A. 28P. in Newton-Ferrers; and about forty houses, cottages, and tenements in the city of Exeter. This property was estimated, in 1821, at the

clear yearly value of about £4500; but it was held by about ninety lessees, at small *reserved rents* amounting to only about £700 a year, besides which, the charity receives occasionally large sums for fines and heriots, paid by the lessees on the renewal of leases, held for lives. More than half of the income is derived from the manors of Clist St. Lawrence and Gerrard, and other property, given by ELIZE HELE, Esq., in 1632, for charitable uses, and appropriated by his executors for the education and maintenance of poor children, except £32 per annum for two lecturers at Exeter College, Oxford. The average annual *expenditure* of the charity, from 1815 to 1820, was about £900, including the salaries paid to the masters of the Grammar and Blue Schools, and of a school at Moreton Hampstead. At the time of granting the letters patent of Chas. I., it seems to have been intended that a part of the building should be allotted for the habitation of aged or impotent poor persons; but that intention has never been carried into effect. The establishment consists only of the Chapel and the Free Grammar and Blue Schools. Divine service is performed twice on Sundays, in the ancient *Chapel*, by the master of the Free Grammar School, and the boys of both schools attend. Seats are reserved for the trustees; and the master of the Grammar School has the privilege of letting the other seats, which produce about £40 a year. This is the only remuneration which he receives for the duty performed by him at the chapel. The hospital buildings are extensive, and part of them are very old, but in good repair. Several rooms in the Hospital, formerly used as the Cloth Fair, are now let as retail shops.

The FREE GRAMMAR SCHOOL, in High street, was established by the citizens of Exeter a few years before the date of the charter of Charles I.; and in 1633, certain statutes and ordinances were made by the Mayor and Common Council for its government. The first appointment of a master does not appear. The earliest that is found in the "Act Book," is in 1648, when a master was elected by the Governors of St. John's Hospital, who was to receive £30 per annum, and to have the occupation of a house, and part of the garden behind the Hospital; for which he was to instruct freely all such scholars as should be admitted into the school, being the sons of freemen and inhabitants of the city or county of the city of Exeter. At present, only the sons of freemen are considered to be entitled to a free education, and it is necessary that they should be appointed by the Governors. The free scholars receive a classical education in common with the other boys; but very few applications have been made of late years for the admission of such scholars, the number being seldom more than two or three. The sons of all inhabitants of the city or county of Exeter are entitled to be admitted as day scholars, at a moderate expense, the master being restricted from charging or receiving more for their instruction than six guineas each per ann. The number of day boys is usually about 60. The master is allowed to take *boarders;* and with the intention of enabling him to accommodate a large number of them, a commodious house was built, adjoining the Hospital, in 1776-'7, at the cost of £1700. The Rev. Wm. Mills, D.D., is the head-master,

and has a salary of £40 from the trustees. He pays all the assistant masters, and the pupils are prepared for the universities, the learned professions, and commercial pursuits. The school is in high repute, and it and the Blue School and St. John's Hospital are under the management of the Church List of Charity Trustees, who appoint the Governors yearly, out of their own body. There are eighteen EXHIBITIONS at the two Universities, for boys from Exeter Free Grammar School. Four boys from this school are entitled to Exhibitions of £8 per annum, at Exeter College, Oxford, pursuant to the bequest of *Robert Vilvayne, M.D.*, in 1660. Two other boys from this school are entitled to exhibitions of £8 per annum, from *Sir John Acland's Charity*, as afterwards noticed. In 1745, the *Rev. Lewis Stephens, D.D.*, left £3000 to be vested with the Corporation, (after the death of three annuitants,) and applied for ever towards the support of six exhibitioners in the Universities, from this school, two to be natives of the city, two natives of Devonshire, and two natives of Cornwall. In 1821, this charity consisted of £7200 three per cent. Consols; and there are now six exhibitioners, each receiving £36 per annum. The other exhibitions are three of £20 each, founded by the *Rev. Dr. Reynolds*, at Exeter College, Oxford; one of £32, for the son of a freeman at either of the Universities, founded by the late *John James Stephens, Esq.*, of Lisbon; and two of £20 per annum each, at St. John's College, Cambridge, founded by the late *R. S. Vidal, Esq.* In the city and suburbs are several large and well conducted *Boarding and Day Schools*, for young ladies and gentlemen. One of these private establishments is the "College School," at Mount Radford, conducted by the Rev. C. R. Roper, M.A.

The BLUE SCHOOL, where 30 poor boys are lodged, boarded, clothed, and educated, and where 86 others receive gratuitous instruction, occupies the chief part of *St. John's Hospital*. The scholars here were formerly under the care of the master of the hospital, who received an allowance for providing them with food and clothing, and of a writing master, who received a salary for instructing them. In 1812, these two offices were united. The master is appointed by the Governors, and receives from them a salary of £150 a year, for the education of the Blue Boys, and 86 day scholars appointed by the trustees. He has also an allowance of £15 a year for each of the 30 Blue Boys, in consideration of which he furnishes them with board, lodging, washing, and part clothing. The rest of their clothing, and their bedding, books, stationery, &c., are provided out of the hospital funds. The boys are admitted from seven to ten years of age, and are allowed to stay till they are 14. They are taught reading, writing, arithmetic, English grammar, geography, &c.; and each of them is entitled to a premium of £10, on being bound apprentice, if a proper master can be found. Of the 30 boys on the foundation, 16 are admitted on account of *Hele's gift*, two on *Keate's gift*, two on *Gandy's gift*, one on *Newcombe's gift*, and nine on account of *Crossing's* and *Worth's gifts*, and other benefactions. They are appointed by the Governors, from the city and county of Exeter, with the exception of those for whom a specific

mode of nomination is pointed out by the donors. Five of those admitted on account of Hele's gift are selected from the children of poor parents of Devonshire, who never resided in Exeter or Plymouth;—the poor boys of Clist St. Lawrence, Broad-Clist, or Bovey, to have the preference. The two boys admitted on account of Gandy's gift are selected from the parish of St. Paul, and two others are chosen from the parish of St. Mary Major, on account of Keate's gift. One of the boys is nominated by the heir of the late Robert L. Newcombe, who, in 1773, in fulfilment of the intentions of his father, (John Newcombe,) granted for the support and education of one poor boy, three houses in High street, now let for £120 a year. *Abel Worth, Esq.*, who died in 1821, left £3000, four per cent. annuities, to this school.

HELE'S BOYS' SCHOOL, is a neat building, in New North road, built in 1848-'9, at the cost of about £1000, paid by the Charity Trustees, out of funds belonging chiefly to *Elize Hele's Charity*. It has been founded and endowed under her Majesty's warrant. The boys are instructed in reading, writing, arithmetic, mathematics, English grammar, history, &c., and in the rudiments of Latin. Those under ten years old pay 21s., and those above that age, 42s. per annum each. The master has one-half of these payments, and also £80 a year from the trustees, of whom the following is a list:— Sir J. T. B. Duckworth; J. W. Buller, Esq.; the Rev. G. Martin; the Rev. J. M. Stevens; and John Tyrrel, Samuel Barnes, Mark Kennaway, Jph. Sayell, Edw. Woolmer, and E. A. Sanders, Esqrs. They intend to erect a good house for the master.

The BLUE MAIDS' HOSPITAL, or *Hele's Hospital*, where four poor girls are maintained and educated, was founded pursuant to the will of *Elize Hele, Esq.*, whose executors settled for its foundation *Bovey Mills*, and directed that £1500 should be raised for the same purpose out of the fines received on granting leases of the lands and tenements granted by them to St. John's Hospital, agreeable to the charitable intentions of the same donor. This £1500 is supposed to have been laid out in erecting the hospital, and purchasing an adjacent tenement. In 1660, *Robert Vilvayne* gave certain premises in Exe Island, and directed that out of the rents £32 per annum should be applied towards the support of four exhibitioners at Exeter College, Oxford, and that the residue of the yearly proceeds should be applied to the use of this hospital. In consideration of a fine of £262. 10s., this property was let, in 1801, on a 99 years lease, for only £15. 15s. per annum; consequently, the hospital does not derive any benefit from it. Among other gifts to this hospital, we find £100, given by *John Mayne*; £200 by *Gilbert Keate*, in 1656; £100 by *Edmund Prideaux*, and various benefactions of smaller amounts. In 1821, the sum of £1636. 19s., belonging to the hospital, was vested with the Corporation of Exeter, at four per cent. interest; but the Charity Commissioners recommended that it should be invested in government securities. The hospital stands in St. Mary Arches street, and is under the government of the Trustees of the Church Charities. It is calculated for a much larger number of girls than have for many years been admitted.

The greater part of it is in the occupation of the schoolmistress, who has also the use of a large garden, and is allowed to take lodgers and day scholars. She has a yearly salary of £10 for teaching the four Blue Girls, and is allowed £8 per annum each, for providing them with board and washing. They are clothed out of the funds of the charity. Part of the hospital is let for about £15 a year, and Bovey Mills now yield about £50 per annum to this charity. The four girls are admitted at the ages of 7 to 10 years, and discharged at 14 years old, when they are bound apprentices, with premiums of £4, or placed as servants in respectable families.

Wotton's and Glass's Charity School, formerly occupied part of the Blue Maid's Hospital, but is now amalgamated with the *National School, in Bartholomew street*, where 50 children are admitted, in consideration of the following bequests. In 1689, *Wm. Wotton* gave to the feoffees of St. Mary Arches parish lands, a farm of 36½A., at Cullompton, in trust, for the payment of £10 a year for the poor of Blackauton, and for the application of the rest of the yearly proceeds in schooling poor children of the city of Exeter, and in buying them Bibles and other books. The farm is let for £76, of which £66 is applied in *schooling and clothing* about 30 boys of St. Mary Arches and other city parishes. Fifteen other boys are taught free, pursuant to the will of *Thomas Glass, M.D.*, who, in 1784, left £150, secured at four per cent. interest, on the Exeter turnpikes, for the education of poor children of the parishes of St. Mary Arches, St. Olave, and Allhallows-on-the-Walls.

The EPISCOPAL CHARITY SCHOOLS, in St. Paul's parish, where 180 boys and 130 girls are educated and partly clothed, were established in 1709, under the patronage of Dr. Blackall, then Bishop of Exeter. They were originally supported by voluntary subscriptions, and by collections made at the cathedral and the churches of the city. The present schools, with houses for the master and mistress, were built in 1817, at the cost of £1600, exclusive of £910 paid for the land. On the opening of the new schools, in 1818, the Madras system was introduced, and the number of scholars was increased from 200 to 250, and they have since been increased to 310. The boys are taught reading, writing, arithmetic, &c.; and the girls, also, knitting and sewing. They are appointed by the trustees and annual subscribers of 21s., from the parishes of the city, and that of St. Thomas. The boys are admitted at 9, and remain till 14; and the girls are admitted at eight, and remain till 13 years of age. Children of parents of all religious denominations are admitted; but so long as they remain, they are required to attend the service of the Church of England only. They are conducted on Sundays to four of the city churches, and are supplied with clothing, at the cost of about £500 per annum. The master has £100, and the mistress £35 per annum; and they have each an assistant, who has £35 a year. The average *annual income* of this useful charity is about £900, of which about £360 arises from land and buildings in the city, and a farm of 131A. at Ottery St. Mary; £160 from funded property, and £90 from annual subscriptions. For the management of the charity, the Bishop of Exeter and all the Dignitaries of the

Cathedral, the Mayor and Justices of the city, and the incumbents of each of the parishes of the city, and county of the city, and of the parish of St. Thomas, are trustees *ex officio*. All benefactors to the amount of £21, and all subscribers to the amount of £2. 2s., or upwards, per annum, are trustees. In 1712, *Wm. Ekins* left, out of land, &c., in and near the city, a yearly rent of £50, towards the support of these schools, and directed that part of it should be applied in teaching mathematics. Among the other donations towards the maintenance of the schools, are the following :—A house and garden, left by the *Rev. John Newte*, in 1715, and now let for £17.12s.10d. a year; £200 left by *Walter Rolf*, in 1718 ; six houses and 13A. of land, in and near Hills-court, given by *Samuel Daniel*, in 1738, and now let for about £120 a year ; numerous *legacies*, to the amount of about £12,000 ; and *benefactions*, amounting to more than £2500. Rolf's and other legacies, to the amount of £1170, were laid out in the purchase of a *farm* of 131 acres, in the parish of Ottery St. Mary, now let for £150 a year, subject to deductions for repairs and taxes. The charity has also £15 a year out of the workhouse land, left by *Mary Trelawney ;* and £20 a year, left by *Eliz. Tuckfield.* The funded property belonging to them now consists of £4797 three per cent. Consols, and £512. 8s. 6d. South Sea Annuities. Part of the Consols were purchased with the clear proceeds of a legacy of £6000, four per cent. Annuities, left to these schools by *Abel Worth, Esq.*, in 1821. This liberal donor was a native of this neighbourhood, and became a wealthy merchant in London, after residing some time at Lisbon.

The LADIES' CHARITY SCHOOL, in Castle street, was established in 1804, by a society of ladies, for the improvement of the female poor of Exeter. It is managed by a committee, and supported by annual subscriptions, for the education and clothing of forty girls, who are admitted at the age of six, and discharged at fourteen years old. They are instructed in reading, the church catechism, sewing, knitting, marking, &c.

BEDFORD CHAPEL SCHOOL, in Chapel street, Bedford circus, was established in 1835, for the purpose of preparing girls for domestic servitude. Thirty girls are admitted at the age of ten, and kept under tuition till they are fit to go into respectable situations. They each pay 2d. per week to the clothing fund ; and such of them as behave well, are provided with clothes on going into service. The school is under the control of a committee of ladies. The Rev. W. Jackson is *president ;* and Mrs. J. Bingham, *secretary.*

NATIONAL SCHOOLS.—The *Devon and Exeter Central and Exeter National Schools* afford instruction on the national system to about 430 boys and 270 girls, who pay from 1d. to 2d. each per week, except about 50 who are taught free, in consideration of Wotton and Glass's Charity, as noticed at page 100. The Central Schools, in Magdalen street, are attended by about 230 boys and 160 girls, and were established in 1814. The others, distinguished as *Exeter National Schools*, are in Bartholomew street, and were established in 1834. The latter are attended by about 200 boys and 110 girls. These large schools are supported by annual subscriptions, dona-

tions, collections at the churches, and the small payments of the scholars. The teachers of these and the other public schools will be seen in the list of academies at a subsequent page. The Revs. C. Worthy and S. Lee are the *secretaries*, and the Rev. J. F. Turner is the *treasurer*. There are National Schools in St. James's, St. Sidwell's, and some other of the city parishes. Devon and Exeter INFANT SCHOOL, in Bartholomew street, was established in 1825, and is attended by 170 children. In the city and suburbs are other Infant Schools supported by the church, and also several supported by Dissenters.

EXETER DIOCESAN BOARD OF EDUCATION was instituted in 1838, for the purpose of improving the system of education in Church of England Schools, through the medium of well-trained teachers, and an efficient system of inspection. The Board consists of the Bishop, the Dean and Chapter, and 150 of the nobility, clergy, and gentry of Devon and Cornwall. The *Training Schools*, for teachers of both sexes, are in the Close, and are under the superintendence of a *clerical principal*, (the Rev. George Martin, B.D.,) and a master and mistress. Since 1840, upwards of 50 young men and about 20 young women have been trained here for the management of schools, and many schoolmasters have been admitted for improvement. The Rev. E. C. Harington, M.A., is *secretary* to the *Diocesan Board*, and the Rev. F. Courtenay to the Exeter Local Board. The Diocese is divided into 16 districts, each having a local board.

There are in Exeter many SUNDAY SCHOOLS attached to the churches and chapels, and attended by several thousand children. The *Church Sunday Schools* were commenced in 1816, and the Revs. T. Coldridge and S. Lee are the secretaries.

The PROTESTANT DISSENTERS' CHARITY SCHOOL was established by subscription about 1770, and now occupies a house and premises in Paris street, which were purchased in 1789, and had previously belonged to an academy for the instruction of young men designed for the ministry among Dissenters. It affords instruction to about 80 boys and 40 girls, and provides part of them with clothing. It is free from sectarian bias, and is conducted on the system of the Irish National Board of Education. It derives about £100 per ann. from donations and annual subscriptions, and is chiefly under the control of Unitarians.

The BRITISH SCHOOLS, in Coombe street, were established in 1845, and are attended by about 300 children, who are instructed on the system of the British and Foreign School Society. The schools are supported by voluntary subscriptions and the small payments of the children. The Rev. John Bigwood is *secretary*, and the schools are in three departments for boys, girls, and infants. The WESLEYAN DAY SCHOOL, in the Mint, was opened in 1846, and has about 100 scholars. It was built at the cost of about £1200, and is conducted on the Glasgow system.

The WEST OF ENGLAND INSTITUTION, for the instruction of the *Deaf and Dumb Children* of the counties of Devon, Cornwall, Somerset, and Dorset, was founded in 1826, and occupies a handsome building in the Egyptian style, pleasantly situated on the south

side of Topsham road, and commanding a picturesque view over the vale of the Exe, as far as Haldon Hills. It is supported by voluntary contributions and the payments on behalf of the pupils, who are in three *classes*, viz., the *poor*, who each pay about 3s. per week; the *intermediate class*, who each pay £20 per annum; and the *private pupils*, who each pay £50 a year. The foundation scholars who partake of the benefits of the charity usually number about 30 boys and 20 girls. They are admitted between the ages of 7 and 12, and may remain till 15. They are instructed in reading, writing, arithmetic, drawing, &c. The girls are taught needlework, knitting, &c., and the boys are instructed in various trades, such as tailoring, shoemaking, gardening, printing, &c. There is also a fund for apprenticing some of them on leaving the institution. All subscribers of one guinea or upwards, or donors of £10. 10s. or upwards, are governors of the institution; and subscribers of two guineas are members of the committee of management. Among the *legacies* bequeathed to it are £2000, left by Nathl. Gundry, Esq.; £100 each by Mrs. Webber, Wm. Tonkins, Lord de Dunstaville, and Miss Luke; and £200 by R. Sanders, Esq. The last report shews a long list of subscriptions and donations, and notices the gift of £100 by Miss Meyrick, of Bath, to the apprentice fund. Visitors will be pleased with an inspection of this interesting institution, which is open on Tuesdays and Fridays between 12 and 1 for that purpose. The Rev. Dr. Troyte is the president; Capt. T. L. Lewis is the honorary secretary; Major J. R. Godfrey is the honorary treasurer; and Dr. W. R. and Mrs. Scott are the *master and matron*. Messrs. W. Matthews and S. A. Gilder are the *assistants*, and Mr. Jeffery is the *drawing master*.

The *West of England Institution for the Instruction and Employment of the Blind* was established in 1838, and removed to its present building, on St. David's hill, in 1843. It is supported by subscriptions, donations, and the payments for board of pupils. There are usually about 17 inmates, and all of them are taught to read and make baskets; and some of them are taught music, mat making, and worsted work. Visitors will be highly gratified on seeing the course of instruction pursued, and the works of ingenuity completed and in progress at this school for the blind. The Rev. W. Jackson is *chaplain*; the Rev. M. Tucker *secretary*; and Mr. G. H. Harvey, *honorary musical instructor*. Mrs. Sar. Eliz. Friend is the *superintendent*, and Mr. Dean and Susan Nicholls are teachers of *basket work*.

DEVON AND EXETER HOSPITAL is an extensive brick building in Southernhay, and was founded in 1741 for the relief of the sick and lame poor, both as in and out patients. This benevolent institution is one of the largest and oldest county hospitals in the kingdom. In 1643 and 1656, James Tucker and Thos. Ford, Esqrs., left £350 towards the foundation of such a charity. What they ineffectually attempted was carried into effect on a more enlarged scale in 1741, by the zealous exertions of Dr. Clarke, then Dean of Exeter. Through his indefatigable industry and the generous contributions of the nobility, clergy, and gentry of the city and

county, this truly charitable work was promptly begun and rapidly accomplished. The first stone was laid August 27th, 1741, and in January, 1743, the hospital was opened with 30 beds, but it was enlarged in 1748, 1753, 1762, and 1790, and has now about 200 beds for the reception of patients. The total cost of the building and furniture has been upwards of £7000. The funded property now belonging to the charity amounts to £29,620, which yields an annual income of £946. It derives also about £3000 per annum from yearly subscriptions, donations, collections at churches, and other sources. John Tuckfield, Esq., one of the city representatives in Parliament, was one of the principal benefactors, and gave the site of the Hospital. There are usually more than 170 in-patients, and about 800 out-patients participate annually in the benefits of this eminently useful charity. The total number of patients admitted since its foundation is about 120,000, including more than 30,000 admitted for accidents. Annual subscribers and benefactors recommend patients, according to the amount of their contributions. R. J. Marker, Esq., is *president;* the Rev. Chancellor Harington, *vice-president;* M. B. Bere and Hy. Collins-Splatt, Esqrs., *treasurers;* Rev. W. Hockin, *chaplain;* Mr. W. Clapp, *house surgeon and apothecary;* Mrs. Helms, *matron;* and Mr. Edwin Force, *secretary.* The medical gentlemen who lend their aid gratuitously are Drs. Miller, Granger, Pennell, and Shapter, *physicians*, and Messrs. Harris, James, De-la-Garde, and Edye, *surgeons.* A fancy fair, held for the benefit of this hospital in the summer of 1849, yielded a clear profit of £1600.

The DISPENSARY, in Queen street, was established in 1818, but the neat and substantial building which it now occupies was erected in 1840-'1. The total cost of the new building, including the ground, furniture, &c., was about £2400. This useful charity supplies the poor of the city and suburbs with medicine and surgical aid as out-patients, and is supported by voluntary contributions. It has about 2400 patients yearly; and its annual income is about £700, arising chiefly from annual subscriptions. Sir J. T. B. Duckworth, Bart., is the *president*, and Edw. Woolmer, Esq., *vice-president.* Mr. Saml. Hele is the resident *dispenser and secretary*, and the medical gentlemen who attend gratuitously are Drs. Miller, Pennell, Barham, Hulme, Elliott, Shapter, Blackall, Miles, and Granger, *physicians;* and Messrs. Kingdon, Tucker, Webb, Kempe, Amory, Harris, Barnes, and James, *surgeons.* A HOMŒOPATHIC DISPENSARY has recently been established here. The HUMANE SOCIETY was instituted in 1790 for the purpose of restoring suspended animation in those who are apparently dead by drowning. Mr. Edwin Force is the *secretary;* Wm. Lee, *treasurer;* and W. P. Kingdon, *registrar.*

The WEST OF ENGLAND EYE INFIRMARY, in Magdalen street, was founded in 1808, for the cure of diseases in the eye, and is supported by annual subscriptions, donations, and the dividends of £3574 consols, purchased at various periods with benefactions and savings of income. It has generally from 200 to 300 patients, and the total number admitted since the opening of the Infirmary in 1808, amounts to more than 27,000, of whom about 25,500 were cured,

and the rest benefited. Of those cured, about 440 had been blind from cataract, and 82 of them had been in darkness from birth or infancy. Sir H. R. F. Davie, Bart., is *president;* the Rev. J. Bartholomew, *vice-president;* and Mr. Thos. Morrish, *secretary.* Messrs. De-la-Garde, Edye, and Barnes, are the *surgeons,* and Dr. Blackall is the *consulting physician.*

St. Thomas's Hospital, near Exeter, is a *Lunatic Asylum,* in the suburban parish of St. Thomas. It was founded in 1801, when Bowhill House was purchased for its use at the expense of about £2650, including the cost of the furniture and repairs. Above £9000 has since been laid out in additional buildings and furniture. This institution, for the safe keeping and medical treatment of those afflicted with the worst of human maladies, was founded long before the County of Devon Lunatic Asylum at Exminster. From its foundation in 1801, to Lady day, 1848, the number of patients admitted was 1461, of whom 759 had been discharged as cured. The hospital is an extensive building, standing on rising ground, in a salubrious situation. The rooms are spacious and well ventilated, and the windows command extensive views of the surrounding country. The gardens and airing grounds are extensive, and there are five in-door galleries, two of which are 112 feet long and 8 broad, and one of the others is 119 feet long and 8 broad. These galleries and the other arrangements admit of a convenient and satisfactory classification of the patients. The affairs of the hospital are under the immediate direction and control of the Governors and Treasurer, and it has attached to it two Physicians, a Chaplain, a Resident Medical Superintendent, a Consulting Surgeon, a Matron, and nine Female and five Male Attendants. The general management permits of amusements and means of moral and intellectual improvement; and those Patients who may safely be trusted without the walls, are permitted to visit their friends, and to take walks and drives in the neighbourhood. Whilst enjoying the retirement and quiet of a private asylum, this hospital is really a public institution, subject to the inspection and supervision of the Commissioners in Lunacy, but not under the control of the County Magistrates. The expenses are defrayed, in a great measure, by the board of the patients, whose friends can afford to pay for their maintenance, the amount of which is about £1500 per annum. This is aided by the interest of benefactions and legacies, and by annual donations and subscriptions. Thos. Wm. Gray, Esq., is *treasurer;* W. D. Kingdon, M.D., *resident medical superintendent;* Miss Augusta Brutton, *matron;* and the Rev. J. F. Turner, *chaplain.* P. Miller and T. Shapter are the *physicians,* and C. K. Webb is the *consulting surgeon.*

Devon and Exeter Female Penitentiary, near the Holloway, was established in 1819, and in the following year a house was purchased for it, at the cost of £1400, and fitted up for the reception of about 50 penitents. Its object is to afford an asylum to those unfortunate females who, having deviated from the paths of virtue, are desirous of being restored to their proper station in society, by religious instruction and the formation of moral and industrious habits. It has been the means of plucking many brands from the burning,

and of solacing many parents by reclaiming their unhappy daughters from the lowest haunts of vice and degradation. It is supported by subscriptions and donations. The Bishop is *patron;* Rev. J. I. Holmes, *chaplain;* Jph. Sheppard, *treasurer;* Jph. Chapman, *secretary;* John Blackall, *physician;* S. Barnes, *surgeon;* E. P. Pridham, *apothecary;* and Mrs. Moyse, *matron.*

DEVON AND EXETER REFUGE *for the instruction and employment of Discharged Prisoners,* is at Lawn Lodge, Sidwell street, and was established in 1835. It has generally from 15 to 20 inmates, and is supported by subscription. J. Milford, Esq., is *treasurer;* John Palk, *secretary;* and Mrs. Jones, *matron.*

ALMSHOUSES.

The following almshouses and charities, unless otherwise expressed, are vested in trust with the Corporation, and were formerly under the management of one of the members of the " Chamber," called the warden of the poor, but are now under the control of the *General Charity Trustees.* (See page 96.)

The TEN CELLS, in Preston street, are almshouses for ten poor widows, and were built by *Simon Grendon,* who, in 1406, endowed them with 4A. 2R. 8P. of land in St. Sidwell parish, called Culverlands. They have since been endowed with other land and buildings by the following donors, viz. :—*Alice Heyth,* in 1556; *Wm. Buckenam,* in 1563; *David Hensley,* in 1566; *Wm. Herne,* in 1562; and *John Baker,* in 1603. The property thus acquired is worth about £280 per annum, but is let for only about £30, on leases for lives, on the renewal of which large fines are levied. From the latter source, the trustees held £400 in 1821. The ten almspeople have also a share of the charities of *Mrs. Tuckfield, Richard Lant,* and *Thos. Cook,* as afterwards noticed. Their various allowances amount to about 5s. per week per head; and they have gowns and shifts yearly from the charity of *Mrs. Joan Tuckfield,* who, in 1567, left two houses in Fore street, to provide gowns and shifts and 5s. yearly for 12 poor women. These houses have been improperly leased for 1000 years, at nominal rents, in consideration of £530 paid in two fines to the Corporation. The ten almspeople have 4s. 8d. yearly, from the charity of *David Hensley.*

WM. HURST'S ALMSHOUSES for 12 poor men, comprise a row of 12 tenements, with a small garden to each. They are situated in Paris street, and were built in 1821, in lieu of as many old decayed almshouses, which stood without the East gate, and were built and endowed by *Wm. Hurst,* in 1567. The endowment consists of various houses and building sites in the parishes of St. David and St. Sidwell, now let on leases, at rents amounting to about £130 per annum, besides which the charity has the interest of about £1000, held by the Corporation, and derived from fines paid on the renewal of leases, &c. The twelve almspeople have each a weekly stipend of 4s. 6d., and occasional allowances of coals. They are allowed to have their wives with them, and when a married man dies, his widow is sometimes permitted to remain in the same house till her death. The Devon and Exeter Subscription Rooms (built

in 1821,) stand upon part of the hospital land, which is held on lease, at the yearly rent of £60. These rooms form a handsome public building, standing on the site of the old Bristol Inn, and their original proprietors pulled down the old, and built the present almshouses, pursuant to the terms of their lease.

PALMER'S ALMSHOUSES, in Magdalen street, consist of four tenements, with gardens, inhabited by as many poor widows, who each receive 2s. weekly, and other occasional assistance from Thomas Cook's gift, as afterwards noticed. They were founded in 1487, by John Palmer, who endowed them with two houses, a cottage and garden, &c., in Trinity parish, now worth £112 per annum, though let on leases for lives at small reserved rents, amounting to only £2. 13s. 4d., but subject to fines on every renewal of the leases.

BONVILLE'S AND LANT'S ALMSHOUSES, in Bartholomew street:—In 1408, *Sir Wm. Bonville, Knight,* left several tenements in Exeter, and 300 marks, for the endowment of an hospital for 12 poor people. In 1675, *Richard Lant* left a farm of 68A. 1R. 1P., at Buckland, in Dorsetshire, for the benefit of the poor in these almshouses and in the Ten Cells. The old almshouses went to ruin about 1700, and the present almshouses, near the North gate, were built in 1764, at the cost of £746, derived from the savings of income. The farm left by Mr. Lant is now let for about £100 per annum. The only other property belonging to the almshouses in 1821 was about £1500, mostly in the hands of the Corporation. The 12 almspeople here receive 3s. 6d. each per week, and those in the Ten Cells have £2 per lunar month divided among them.

ATWILL'S ALMSHOUSES, in New North road, are neat stone dwellings on an elevated site. In 1588, *Lawrence Atwill* left about 320 acres of land, and several houses, &c., in the parishes of St. Thomas, Whitstone, and Uffculme, to the Corporation of Exeter, upon trust to apply the yearly profits thereof in setting the poor to work. As the charitable intentions of the testator could not be strictly or beneficially carried into effect, a new scheme was sanctioned by the Court of Chancery in 1771, directing that in future the rents and profits of the charity estate should be applied in the erection and support of almshouses for the reception of poor aged *woollen weavers,* &c., of the city, who should be provided with looms, &c., and small weekly stipends. Accordingly 12 almshouses were built in 1772. In consequence of the increased income of the charity, these almshouses were enlarged in 1815, at the cost of £425; and again in 1839, at the cost of £160. They are now occupied by 24 almspeople, who are provided with coals in winter; but only 16 of them have weekly stipends of 2s. 6d. each, and none of them are provided with looms. The charity estate is let to fifteen tenants, at rents amounting to about £250 per annum, and large sums are occasionally received for the renewal of leases and the sale of timber.

DAVYE'S ALMSHOUSES, for two married couples and two single women or men, are in Bartholomew street, and were founded by *John Davye,* who endowed them, in the 42nd Elizabeth, with a yearly rent-charge of £16 out of the rectory of Mariansleigh; 6s. 6d. yearly out of the George Inn; and with five tenements, worth £30

a year, but let for only £6, in consideration of £200 paid in fines on the renewal of the leases. Including the dividends of £232. 1s. 6d., Navy five per cent. stock, the annual income of the almshouses is £33. 4s. 8d., from which about 2s. 6d. per week is paid to the occupants of each of the four tenements.

LETHBRIDGE'S ALMSHOUSES for six poor people are in St. James' street, and were founded by *Chpr. Lethbridge*, who endowed them, in 1669, with £15. 12s. yearly out of two houses, and about 18A. of land, worth about £100 per annum, but they were let, about 1790, on leases for lives, at rents amounting only to £12. 1s., in consideration of £510 paid in fines. This property is held by the Corporation, subject to the above-named annuity for division among the six almspeople, who have also £7. 14s. yearly from the charity of *John Lethbridge*, who left £216 to the Corporation, upon trust that they should pay that annuity and also the following yearly sums, viz., 10s. to the poor debtors in the city prison, and 50s. towards the maintenance of poor boys in St. John's Hospital. The six almspeople have each a weekly stipend of 1s. 6d. The surplus rents and profits of the property derived from Chpr. Lethbridge's Will, after paying for the repairs of the almshouses, &c., belongs to St. John's Hospital.

MAGDALEN HOSPITAL, in Magdalen street, was founded at an early period, for the reception of leprous persons, and its endowment was augmented by a charter of the Bishop of Exeter, about 1170. It now consists of an ancient building, containing eight rooms, occupied by as many poor persons, and of a more modern building of six rooms, divided into three houses, occupied by three poor people and their families. The eleven almspeople are selected from the poor inhabitants of Exeter, men or women, married or single; but preference is given to such as are afflicted with scrofula. They have 3s. per week each from the original endowment, and the interest of £1500, derived from fines paid on renewing the leases of the hospital lands and tenements, which are now let to 33 tenants for about £50 per annum. They have also 2s. per week each from the dividends of £2100 three per cent. consols, left by *Thos. Cooke*, in 1810, as afterwards noticed.

FLAYE'S ALMSHOUSES, in St. Paul's parish, were founded and endowed by *Thos. Flaye*, in 1634, and enlarged and further endowed by his widow, *Elizabeth Flaye*, in 1667, for the reception of six poor widows, two of them to be the *widows of clergymen*. The property belonging to the charity comprises three houses and about eight acres of land, let for more than £100 per annum, of which about £30 is expended for repairs, &c., and the rest is divided among the almspeople, at the rate of about 6s. per week to each of the two clergymen's widows, and 3s. to each of the other four widows.

MOOR'S ALMSHOUSES, on the east side of Exe bridge, are three old tenements, which were built by John Moor and Barthmw. Fortescue, for the residence of poor people, but there is no endowment either for the inmates or repairs. *Livery Dole Almshouses* are in Heavitree parish, as afterwards noticed.

WYNARD'S HOSPITAL, in Magdalen street, was built by *William*

Wynard, in 1436, on the site of an ancient building, called *God's House*, without the South gate of the city, for the residence of a priest and twelve infirm poor people, for whose support he left two yearly rent-charges of £40 and £50, out of his estates, vested with twelve trustees and the Mayor of Exeter; the latter of whom, for the time being, is appointed as special visitor by the founder. The hospital and many adjacent houses were destroyed during the sieges of the city in the civil wars of the 17th century; and in 1654, a bill was filed in Chancery by the mayor and bailiffs of the city, against the owner of the founder's estates, who, after nearly four years' litigation, was compelled to rebuild the hospital, and to charge his property with the weekly payment of 2s. to each of the 12 almspeople, and with £12 per annum for equal division among them. He was also obliged to charge his estates with the maintenance and reparation of the hospital and chapel, and with the payment of the yearly salary of £6. 13s. 4d. to the chaplain for reading prayers to the almspeople, who are chosen from among poor decayed tradesmen. Eight of them are to be poor men of the city, appointed by the Mayor and Aldermen, and the other four are to be poor men of Devonshire or Somersetshire, appointed by Mark Kennaway, Esq., the owner of the founder's estates, who has lately repaired and beautified the *Chapel*, in which divine service is performed every Sunday evening. The Rev. Geo. Hy. O. Shield, M.A., is the *chaplain*.

VARIOUS BENEFACTIONS vested with the Corporation, and now under the control of the General Charity Trustees:— In 1556, GRIFFITH AMERIDETH left £1. 18s. per annum, to be applied in finding shrouds for criminals executed at *Ringswell;* but since the erection of the new gaol *executions* have taken place there, and no shrouds have been provided from this fund. In 1567, ELIZABETH BUCKENAM left a house in St. Petrock's parish, then let for £2. 16s. 8d. per annum, in trust to pay 14s. 2d. yearly to each of the parishes of St. Lawrence, St. Paul, Holy Trinity, and Allhallows-on-the-Walls, for five poor householders of each parish. This house is now worth £30 a year, but was let in 1800, on lease for their lives, at £3. 1s. per annum, in consideration of a fine of £360. In 1568, MRS. JOAN TUCKFIELD, left three houses, then worth £6 a year, in trust for the distribution of 50 dozen penny loaves on Christmas eve, and the same quantity on Easter-eve, among the poor of the city and suburbs; and to divide the remaining 20s. among the mayor and officers for their trouble. These houses were let in 1821, for £66. 13s. 4d. per annum, and it is supposed that the donor intended the poor to have the clear yearly profits. For distribution among the poor citizens, CHRISTIANA CHAPMAN, in 1470, left a yearly rent charge of £5 out of land in Westgate quarter. In 1821, the Parliamentary Commissioners found that there was upwards of £2000 owing by the Corporation to Hurst's, Heyth's, Grendon's, Buckenam's and Palmer's charities, arising chiefly from fines received on the renewal of leases, and unapplied rents, &c. In 1598, LAWRENCE SELDON, left a cottage and 26 acres of land at Sowton, in trust for the *weekly distribution* of 2s. 6d. in bread and meat among the prisoner's in the gaol, Sheriff's Ward and Counter of Exeter; and the following sums weekly in bread among the poor of the parishes specified, 1s. in each of the parishes of St. Mary-the-More, Holy Trinity and St. Sidwell; 8d. in St. Thomas's; 6d. in St. Lawreuce's; 4d. in Sowton; and 6d. among the prisoners in the High Gaol. The property is worth about £35 a year, but was let in 1798 for 99 years, at the annual rent

of £5. 5s., 'in consideration of a fine of £500, lent to the Corporation.

CALWODELEY'S GIFT :—By letters patent of the 12th of Henry VII., we find that Thomas Calwodeley granted to the mayor, bailiffs, and commonalty, his manor of *Awliscombe*, to provide for the payment of two fee-farm rents, and the relief of poor citizens and inhabitants of Exeter. The property thus granted to the Corporation, comprises eleven houses and about 207 acres of land, let on leases for lives, at low rents amounting to only £7. 8s. 8d. per annum; but from 1758 to 1801, £2177 was paid by the tenants for the renewal of leases. The Council of Exeter pays two *fee-farm rents*, one of £20. 15s. 4d., to Earl Somers, but it is not known whether these are or are not the rents alluded in Thomas Calwodeley's grant. The rents, fines, and other profits of the manor are carried to the general account of the Corporation; no portion of them has ever been applied to any specific uses. *Poor Debtors* in the City Prison have the following *weekly sums* divided among them in *bread*,—6d. left by *Hester Reed*; 1s. given by *Francis Pengelley*; and 1s. supposed to be derived from Hoydon's gift. They have several small annual sums from other charities.

SIR THOMAS WHITE'S LOAN FUND.—In 1556, Sir Thomas White gave £2000 to the Corporation of Bristol, on condition that they should purchase an estate, and out of the rents, pay yearly the sum of £104, in succession to one of 24 cities and towns named in the deed, one of which is Exeter. Of each annual payment, the donor directed £100 to be lent in sums of £25 each to four young men, "of honest fame," free of interest, for ten years; and the remaining £4 to be divided among the trustees for their trouble. The Corporation of Exeter have now received £1248, in twelve periodical payments, at intervals of 24 years. A large portion of this money has been lost or misappropriated.

NICHOLAS SPICER, in 1609, vested with the Corporation of Exeter a farm of about 106 acres of land in Halberton parish, in trust, after making certain annual payments for charitable and other uses, that they should [apply the remainder of the yearly proceeds in *loans* of £10 to £20 each to poor industrious and honest citizens. The charity estate is worth upwards of £200 per annum. In 1811, an information was filed in the Court of Chancery, charging the Corporation with having in their hands large sums of money belonging to this charity; amounting, as appeared by the report of the Master of the Rolls, in 1821, to no less than £3211, exclusive of interest. The Corporation appealed against this report, and the case was not finally settled till a few years ago, when a *new scheme* was approved by the court for the future application of the funds of the charity. Out of the income, the founder directed the following yearly sums to be paid, viz., 20s. for distribution in bread among the poor citizens; 10s. for repairing the church of St. Mary Arches; 40s. for a public lamp in the city; 6s. 8d. to the night bellman; and 10s. towards repairing Halberton church.

In 1599, PETER BLUNDELL left £900 in trust with the Corporation, to be *lent* yearly in sums of £20, to 25 poor honest men of Exeter, and 20 of Tiverton, at two per cent. per annum interest, which latter the Corporation were to have for their trouble. In 1815, the £900 was reduced by losses to about £240, then held by the Corporation at four per cent interest, there being no persons willing to borrow the sums of £20 on bonds, renewable every year. *Joan Tuckfield, Joan Cleveland*, and ten other donors left £980 to be lent to poor men, but the whole of it is lost, or was appropriated by the Corporation, many years ago, together with £3300 left by *John Peryam*, and eleven other donors, for *loans and other charitable uses.*

SIR JOHN ACLAND, in the 13th of James I., granted the rectory of Churchstowe to feoffees, in trust, to pay £75. 8s. per annum for weekly distribu-

tions in bread, in 27 parishes ; £23. 6s. 8d. yearly to the vicar of Church-stowe, and £16 yearly to two exhibitioners at Exeter College, Oxford. The rectory has often yielded a clear annual profit of £320 ; and in 1821, there was a balance of unapplied income, amounting to about £1300, held by the Corporation. The two Exeter parishes participating in this charity are St. Thomas's and St. Lawrence's, the former having 52s. and the latter 26s. yearly, for weekly distributions of bread.

REBECCA BOROUGH, in 1649, granted £30 a year out of Naddir estate, in Whitstone, to be given in sums of £3 to £5, to poor deserving citizens, who have never received parochial relief. This charity is subject to the yearly payment of £2. 3s. 9d. for land tax. Six poor widows of the city have £5 yearly from the Corporation as the interest of £100, left by CATHE-RINE GIFFORD, in 1665. Four poor men of the city are entitled to 21s. 8d. per annum, given by QUEEN ELIZABETH, out of the crown rent, paid by St. John's Hospital.

THOMAS FLOUD, Esq., one of the aldermen, gave to the trustees of Rebecca Borough's gift, £50 vested in the Exeter turnpikes, at four per cent. interest; and directed them to apply the yearly proceeds in the relief of one poor man above 30, and under 60 years of age.

JOHN MARTYN, in 1669, left £400 to the Corporation, in trust, to apply the yearly proceeds in *apprenticing poor boys* of the city. The greater part of this legacy was laid out in the purchase of land and tenements in Exe Island, now worth £78 a year, but let on leases at reserved rents, amount-ing only to £8. 10s. 2d., in consequence of fines paid on renewal of leases, from which source there was £500 belonging to the charity in 1821. An apprentice fee of £20 is given yearly, and about every third year, two are given.

THOMAS COOKE, in 1810, left to the Corporation the following sums of three per cent. consols, in trust to divide the dividends yearly among the poor of the almshouses, named with each sum, viz., £2100 to Magdalen Hospital ; £1750 to the almshouses called the Ten Cells; and £700 to Palmer's Almshouses.

For a WEEKLY LECTURE on Sundays, in such church in Exeter as may be thought most beneficial, £400 was vested with the Corporation by the *Rev. Lawrence Bodley, D.D.,* in 1615, and £200 by *Thos. Mogridge,* in 1617. These legacies were laid out in 1631, in the purchase of the impro-priate rectory and parsonage of Hennock, and the advowson of the vicarage of that parish. The rectory now yields a clear yearly income of about £100 per annum, which is paid by the Corporation to a Sunday evening lecturer.

The *Society for the relief of Poor Clergymen, their Widows, and Orphans,* in the Archdeaconry of Exeter, expends a large sum annually in these charitable objects, and is supported chiefly by annual subscriptions and donations. Mr. Chas. Henry Turner is the *secretary.* There are similar societies in each of the Archdeaconries of Totnes, Barnstaple, and Cornwall.

Tailors' Company Trusts.—In 1568, *Joan Tuckfield* left to the Corpora-tion of the Tailors' Company, in Exeter, all her lands and tenements in the parish of St. Paul, on condition that they should distribute 6s. 8d. yearly among the poor of the Ten Cells and Magdalen Almshouses, and the pri-soners in the City and County Gaols ; and that they should repair the walls of the burial ground of Ringswell, formerly the place of execution. The Tailors' Company consists of a master, head warden, three under wardens, and twelve assistants. They hold their *Hall* in Goldsmith street, and several houses and gardens adjoining it, under Mrs. Tuckfield's will; and they also receive £6s. 6s. per annum from the city Corporation, for distri-

bution among the poor freemen of the company, or their widows and children. This annuity is supposed to be paid as the interest of £300, left by Mrs. Tuckfield, for the purpose of being lent on bond to needy tradesmen. A yearly rent charge of £2. 8s., left by *Amniel Knight*, out of land at Upton-Pyne, is distributed in shirts and shifts among twelve poor freemen of this company, or their widows and relations

The Incorporated *Company of Weavers, Fullers, and Shearmen*, who received their first charter in 1490, have the management of the following charities for the benefit of the poor freemen of the company. In 1676, *John Pince* gave an annuity of 20s. out of a house at Topsham, to be bestowed in hose and shoes for four poor freemen. Another yearly rent charge of 20s., left by *Humphrey Bowden*, in 1678, out of a tenement in St. Mary Arches parish, is divided among poor widows and children of freemen; as also is one of 40s., out of the Star Inn, left by *John Reed*, in 1687. An estate called ROWE'S BARN, comprising 27A. 1R. 16P., now let for about £50 a year, was purchased by the company in 1730, for £733, which arose as follows:—£550 given by *Andrew Jeffery*; £60 by *Augustin Drake*, in 1642; £50 by *Henry Newcombe*, in 1693; £10 by *Wm. Marker*; £20 by *Nicholas Munckley*; and £43 from the company's stock. In consideration of Jeffery's gift, £4 is paid yearly to the dissenting minister of Ford chapel, in Stokenham parish, and about £33 is expended in providing coats, hats, shirts, stockings, and shoes, for 14 poor freemen of the company, and six poor parishioners of Ottery and Stokenham. The rest of the clear yearly income from Rowe's Barn estate, is distributed in money, shoes, &c., to poor freemen, or their widows and children. The rent of a farm, called *Chilleton*, in Aveton-Gifford parish, comprising 20A. 2R. 39P., let for £30, is applied in apprenticing the sons of poor freemen of the company, pursuant to the will of *Thos. Crispin*, dated 1689. A premium of £5 is given with each boy; and those who can produce a certificate of good behaviour from their masters, are presented with £5 at the end of their apprenticeships. The company meet at TUCKERS' HALL, Fore street, on the last Thursday in August and the 5th of November, when a distribution of the several charities takes place. Being now used by two Lodges of Freemasons, their hall is commonly called the TUCKERS' AND MASONIC HALL. It was anciently a chapel, and has recently been restored and embellished by the Freemasons, but it is still used occasionally by the Company of Weavers, &c., who, till lately, supported a school in it for the sons of freemen. The members of this company elect a *master*, and *senior and junior wardens* yearly. Mr. H. M. Ellicombe is their *clerk*, and Mr. Wm. Doeg is the *beadle*.

PHIPPS'S GIFT consists of a yearly rent charge of £30, out of land and houses, left by *Robt. Phipps*, in 1676, in trust for the relief of ten poor tradesmen of Exeter, who do not receive parochial aid. S. Kingdon, B. P. Pope, Jas. Terrell, and S. M. Cox, Esqrs., are the trustees.

POTTER'S GIFT.—In 1694, Thomas Potter left £600, to be laid out in land, and the yearly profits thereof to be distributed among eight tuckers and weavers of Exeter, not receiving parochial relief. The land purchased consists of 52A. 2R. 10P. in Ottery St. Mary, and 10A. 2R. 30P. at Farringdon, now let for £107 a year. The Rev. W. R. Ellicombe and H. M. Ellicombe, Jas. Creswell, Thos. Snow, and Henry Collins-Splatt, Esqs., are the *trustees*, and divide the clear income of the charity yearly among eight persons, who are or have been employed in the woollen trade, which flourished here till the close of last century, but is now nearly extinct. No person is allowed to receive the charity oftener than once in five years.

PENGELLY'S GIFT.—In 1700, Fras. Pengelly gave for charitable uses the

Dolphin Inn and two adjoining houses, which were sold in 1806 for £650, which was laid out in the purchase of £1095. 19s. 6d. three per Cent. Consols, still standing in the names of the six trustees. Out of the dividends £20 is divided yearly, in equal shares, among ten poor people, preference being given to such as are related to the donor or his wife. Out of the remainder the following yearly payments are made, viz., £6. 6s. is paid for educating six or seven poor boys; £3. 3s. to the Devon and Exeter Hospital; and £2. 12s. to the poor prisoners in the city gaol.

The *Society for the Relief of the Sober and Industrious Poor*, was established in 1799. It relieves its objects by the sale of coal in winter at reduced prices. B. P. Pope, Esq., is treasurer, and John Mortimer, of Bartholomew street, is the store keeper. The RELIEF SOCIETY was formed in 1838, in lieu of the old Mendicity Society, for the relief of travelling poor and residents. Mr. W. Sparkes, of 16, Bartholomew street, is the registering clerk. The BLANKET SOCIETY was established in 1817, for supplying the destitute poor with blankets. The depôt is at Mr. C. Pridham's, Magdalen street; and Miss Dacres is the secretary. The LYING-IN-CHARITY was instituted in 1808, and, during the year 1848, no fewer than 163 poor women partook of its benefits. Several medical gentlemen lend their aid gratuitously, and two midwives are employed by the society. Miss Canterbury, of 48, Holloway street, is the *matron*; and Mr. A. Kempe is the *secretary*. The CLOTHING AND DORCAS SOCIETIES supply the poor with articles of clothing, at greatly reduced prices. Mrs. F. Truscott is secretary of the former, (established in 1833,) and Mrs. Mackintosh of the latter, which was commenced in 1840. The STRANGERS' FRIEND SOCIETY was established about 44 years ago, for the purpose of visiting and relieving the destitute poor at their own habitations. Mr. Thomas Snow is the treasurer, and Mr. Thomas Foster secretary. Here are several other societies supported by voluntary subscriptions for the relief of the indigent poor of the city, and the following is a brief statement of the *Church and Parish Lands, and the various Charitable Funds, &c., belonging separately to the different Parishes.*

ALLHALLOWS, GOLDSMITH STREET.—The *Church Lands* comprise 2A. 22P. at East Teignmouth, and 1A. 2R. 12P. in St. David's parish, which were given in 1451 and 1527 by Richard Attehole and John Yeo, and are now let for about £22 per annum. The poor parishioners have 6d. in bread weekly, from Sir J. Acland's charity.

ALLHALLOWS ON THE WALLS.—The ancient parish church, and some of the adjoining buildings, were taken down in 1770, by the Commissioners of the Act for rebuilding and repairing Exe bridge, who pay £6 per annum to this parish in consideration of two tenements which belonged to the church and poor, and were taken down at the same time. In 1602, *Richd. Bevys* left 20s. a year to be given to a poor maiden on her marriage, provided she has lived in service in the parish during the two preceding years. The poor have a weekly distribution of 1s. 6d. worth of bread from *Sir J. Acland's* and *Hester Reed's Charities*. They have also 30s. in two rent charges, left by Nowell Pearse and Christian Wills.

ST DAVID'S.—For distribution in bread, the poor parishioners have the interest of £100, left by *John Jordaine*, in 1775, secured on the tolls of the Leskeard turnpike; and also 20s. a year from *Tooker's Gift*, noticed with the parish of St. Mary Major.

ST. EDMUND'S.—The *Parish Lands, &c.*, which have been vested in trust from an early period, comprise various tenements, let to nine lessees, at reserved rents, amounting to £32, but subject to fines on renewal of the leases. The feoffees have also £850 Navy five per cent. stock, purchased with money derived from fines, and £100 in two deeds poll of the Exeter

turnpikes, obtained from the sale of a house, which was taken down when Exe bridge was rebuilt. The income is all applied in the service of the church, except 20s. per annum, which is distributed in weekly doles of bread among the poor, as also are the three following yearly rent charges, viz., £4 left by *John Gubbs*, in 1670, out of a house in Exe Island; 20s. left by *Jph. Pince*, in 1689, out of the land now held by the Gas Company; and 10s. left by *Matthew Axe*, out of a house in Frog lane. In 1767, £80 received as arrears of Gubbs's rent charge, and £18 from the parish stock were laid out in the purchase of £112. 10s. old South Sea annuities, the dividends of which are distributed among the poor parishioners, in sums of 2s. 6d. to each. The deserving poor not receiving parochial relief have the rent of 3A. of land in St. Leonard's parish, purchased with £150 left by *Rebecca Leach*, in 1713, and now let for about £13 per annum. Four poor widows have the dividends of £81. 19s. 8d. three per Cent. consols, purchased with £50 left by *John Dewdney Worthy*, in 1797.

St. George-the-Martyr's.—The poor of this parish have 13 penny loaves every Sunday, from a rent-charge of 52s., left by *Richd. Shilston*, in 1645, out of a house at the bottom of Fore street hill. They have also the following yearly sums, viz.: 6s. 8d. left by the above-named donor; 3s. 4d., by *John Baker*; 20s., by *Thos. Gist*; 20s., left by *Johanna Cole*; and 20s., by *Iseat Peachy*.

Heavitree.—The Parish Lands, &c., which were mostly purchased with poor's money, in the 16th and 17th centuries, comprise about 40 acres, and a house and other buildings, let for £63 per annum; and the *Church House*, occupied by paupers. There is a considerable quantity of timber on part of the parish land called *St. Loyes*. Out of the clear income, £5 is paid for schooling poor children, and the rest is distributed in money and clothing among the poor parishioners. *Ducke's Almshouses* consist of four dwellings, built in 1603, by *Richd. Ducke*, who endowed them with a yearly rent-charge of 26s., out of the marsh in Clist St. Mary's. The almspeople have also the rent of the Parish Field, (1½A.,) let for £1. 6s. 8d. The *Livery Dole Almshouses* were rebuilt in 1849, and contain ten distinct dwellings for as many poor women, and a house for the chaplain. Attached to them is an acre of garden ground, and a small chapel. They were founded in 1591, by *Sir Robt. Dennis*, and are endowed with a yearly rent-charge of £45, out of Whitechurch Farm, in the parish of Winterbourne. Of this annuity the chaplain receives £9, and the remaining £36 is divided in equal portions of £3. 12s. to each of the almspeople, who are appointed by Lord Rolle, from the poor women of this or any other parish. The poor of Heavitree have the dividends of £55. 10s. 10d. four per cent. stock, purchased with £50 left by *Wenman Nutt*, in 1800. They have also the interest of about £250, derived from the bequest of *Ann Serle*, in 1810.

St. John's.—The *Church Land* consists of 1½A., let for £7. The churchwardens have also 6s. a year out of houses in Fore street hill. The poor parishioners have five annuities, viz., 20s. left by *Richd. Bevys*, in 1602; 10s., left by *Nowell Pearse*, in 1704; £2. 4s. 8d., from £76. 5s. 5d. stock, purchased with £50 left by *Henry Bate*, in 1811; 12s. as interest of £20 left by *Edw. Bartlett*, in 1778; and £3. 6s., as interest of £71 given by four donors, and expended by the churchwardens in the purchase of a cellar, which they let with an adjoining cellar, for £4. 4s. per annum.' In Friernhay lane is a small *Almshouse*, for six poor aged women, founded by *Alice Brooking*, in 1680. It is repaired by Mr. White, the owner of adjoining premises, but has no endowment for the inmates.

St. Kerrian's *Church Lands*, given by Richd. Foldhay and Jno. Wilford,

in 1416-'7, now comprise several tenements and an acre of garden ground, let for £3. 3s., subject to fines on the renewal of the leases.

St. Lawrence's.—The churchwardens have a house, garden, and a field of 2 acres, in Northgate, given by *Michael Dennys* and *Richard Wagott*, in 1478; and a house in High street, given by *Wm. Grigge*, in 1587. They are let for only £4. 12s. per annum, which is applied with the church rates, together with the sums levied in fines on the renewal of the leases. The *poor* have a yearly rent-charge of £16 out of a cottage and 16A. of land at Whitstone, derived from £100 left by Judge Jermin, John Jermin, Thomas Willing, and Peter Risden. For weekly distributions of bread, they have the interest of £25, left by *Robt. Dawe*, in 1735; and £2. 12s. yearly from the charities of Sir John Acland and Lawrence Seldon. They have also 20s. worth of bread, from the interest of £20 left by *Nicholas Abell*, in 1742. Five poor widows have 13s. 4d. yearly from Eliz. Buckenam's charity.

St. Mary Arches.—The *Church Lands, &c.*, given by John Taylor, Gilbert Kirkeby, and Gervase Luyshant, in the reigns of Henry VII. and VIII., now comprise several tenements, let to six lessees, at small reserved rents, amounting to £8. 7s. 8d. per annum; to which is added 11s. 8d. derived from four chief rents; and also 10s. a year from Nicholas Spicer's charity. The yearly income is expended in the service of the church, as also are the fines received on the renewal of the leases. This parish participates largely in the benefits of *Wotton's and Glass's Charity School*, as already noticed at page 100. A house and stable, left by *Richd. Poyntell*, in 1611, for the poor of this parish, were let in 1806, for 99 years, at 20s. per annum, in consideration of a fine of £138, which was laid out in the purchase of £215 three per cent. Consols. The income of this and C. and J. Lethbridge's charities is dispensed in a weekly distribution of 5s. 8d. in bread. *Chpr. Lethbridge*, in 1669, left to the poor a yearly rent-charge of £3. 0s. 8d., out of a house in Fore street. To this gift are added the dividends of £90 Old South Sea Annuities, purchased with about 50 years' arrears of the rent-charge; and the dividends of £60 in the same stock, purchased with £52 left by *John Lethbridge*, in 1701. A yearly rent-charge of 20s. was left by *Richard Bevys*, in 1602, to be given to poor maidens of this parish, on their marriage. The *Parsonage House* was given by *Joan Tucker*, in 1709, for the residence of the rector or his curate, charged with the yearly payment of £1. 12s., for a weekly distribution of 1s. worth of bread every Sunday, among the poor parishioners; who have also a yearly rent-charge of 20s. out of an estate, called Star Barton, in Brampford-Speke parish, supposed to have been left by *Chas. Watts*, in 1722; and the dividends of £25. 12s. 2d. five per cent. stock, left by *Joseph Green*, in 1807.

St. Mary Major.—The *Parish Lands, &c.*, comprise six houses, a large warehouse, 2A. 1R. 9P. of land, and five small chief rents. They yield only about £25 per annum, but fines are levied on the renewal of the 99 years' leases. Of the sums derived from fines, £330 was laid out in new seating the church, in 1816-'17; and in 1811, £100 was paid to the rector, to assist him in obtaining Queen Anne's Bounty for his benefice. Out of the rents, the feoffees pay £10 as an annual salary to the organist; £4. 10s. to the three following charities; and they apply the remainder in the service of the church. In 1686, *Roger Endibrook* left a clear yearly rent of £5 out of his tenements here, for distribution among the poor not receiving parochial relief. This annuity is distributed in bread and beef, at Christmas; as also are the five undermentioned yearly sums, viz., £3 from part of the parish land, purchased with £50 arising from arrears of the above-named rent-charge; 30s., as interest of £30 left by *John Martyn* and *Thos. Southcombe*, and laid out in the parish land; 20s., left by *John Peter*, in 1576, out of

the great tithes of Cornworthy; and 20s., left by *Thos. Tooker*, in 1640, out of Culver Park and other land in St. Sidwell's and St. David's parishes. The poor of this parish have 2s. worth of bread weekly from *Seldon's and Acland's Charities;* and 3s. worth weekly from three annuities of 52s. each, left by *John Reed*, in 1680, out of the Star Inn; by *Chas. Cunningham*, in 1685, out of a house on Bell hill; and by *Samuel Daniel*, in 1738, out of property given by him to the Episcopal Charity Schools. This parish is entitled, under *Gilbert Keate's* gift, to have two boys maintained in St. John's Hospital, and two girls in the Blue Maids' Hospital.

ST. MARY STEPS.—The *Parish Lands, &c.*, comprise five houses, and several tenements, gardens, &c., let for about £44 a year, on long leases. After deducting for repairs, &c., the net income is applied in the service of the church. The property has been held by the parish officers from an early period, and part of it, consisting of two cottages and gardens on Stepcote hill, was left by *Felicia Selman*, in 1462. Four poor women have the use of a house rent-free, and the dividends of £175 Old South Sea Annuities, which arose from the gift of *James Slade*, in 1769. For distribution in bread, the poor have an annuity of 20s., left by *Nicholas Evans*, in 1618, out of a foundry in Ewin's lane; and another of 20s., left by *Thos. Gist*, out of tenements on Stepcote hill.

ST. OLAVE.—The parish has two houses, which are now let for about £20 a year, and have been vested from time immemorial for the use of the church. Some land which had been long held for the same use, was sold for £290, which was laid out in repairing the *Church*, which after being shut up many years, was re-opened in 1815. In 1602, *Richd. Bevys* left an annuity of 20s., to be paid on her marriage to a maid servant of this parish. The poor have 16s. yearly out of the poor rates, as the interest of £20, left by *James Atkins*, in 1730.

ST. PAUL.—This *Parish* has held, from time immemorial, for the use of the *church and poor*, three houses and several tenements, with gardens, &c., now let for about £13 per annum. In respect of *Henry Gandy's gift*, this parish sends two poor boys to be maintained and educated at the Blue School, in St. John's Hospital. For distribution in bread, at Christmas, &c., the poor parishioners have the following yearly doles, viz.:—£3, left by *Thos. Binford*, in 1780, out of an estate here; 25s. as interest of £25, left by *John Pillet;* and 30s., paid out of a plot of building ground, which was purchased with £50, left by *John York*, in 1707. For distribution in shirts and shifts, they have £1. 7s. yearly, left by *Paul Phillips*, in 1714; and 20s. yearly, as the interest of £20, left by *Mary Pillet*.

ST. PETROCK.—The *Parish Lands, &c.*, comprise about five acres, and ten houses and cottages, now let for about £85 per annum; and two *almshouses*, occupied by two poor women. The property was mostly derived in the 15th century, from various donors, and the rents are applied chiefly towards the payment of the churchwardens' expenses. In 1799, £100 paid in fines by the lessees of part of the property, was laid out with a sum from Queen Anne's Bounty, in purchasing a field called Marsh Barton, for the augmentation of the rectory. The two women in the almshouses have £4 a year, as the interest of £100, left by Wm. Pitfield, in 1794, and now vested in the Exeter turnpikes.

ST. SIDWELL.—The *Parish Lands, &c.*, comprise about 15 acres, and 22 houses and cottages, let at small reserved rents, amounting to only £14. 4s. per annum, but subject to large fines paid on the renewal of the leases. This property has been vested in trust from an early period, for the use of the church and poor. The greater part of the income derived from rent and fines is applied in the service of the *Church*. (See page 85.) In 1771, the

feoffees laid out more than £400 upon the church bells; and in 1803, they erected an organ and a gallery, at the cost of £265. The rent of 3A. 3R. 30P. of land, called Summerlands, and let for about £20 a year, is applied in apprenticing poor children, pursuant to the gift of *Chpr. Sandford*, in 1689; except £2. 10s., which is yearly distributed among the most needy poor, as the interest of £50, left by *Ann Baker*, in 1689. Near the church are four *Almshouses* for four poor widows, founded by *John Webb*, who endowed them in 1676, with about 5½ acres of land, let for £30 a year. The almswomen have also a yearly rent-charge of 20s., out of three fields at the top of St. Sidwell street, left by an unknown donor. In 1717, *John Moffatt* left £100 for the benefit of the poor, and it was laid out in 1733 and '41, in the purchase of 2¼A. of land, now let for about £17 a year, of which £5 is given to ten poor people not receiving parochial relief, and the remainder is distributed in sums of 2s 6d. each to other poor parishioners. The poor have 4s. worth of bread weekly, from four yearly rent-charges of 52s. each, left by *Lawrence Seldon*, *Sir John Acland*, *John Cheeke*, and *Ralph Herman*. An annuity of 9s., left by *Wm. Chapple*, in 1729, is given in as much linen as will make two shirts or shifts. The poor have also, in linen and money, £4. 5s. yearly, arising from four annuities, left by *Thomas Tooker*, *Thos. Smalridge*, and *Thos. and Hester Bussel*. They have likewise £21 per annum, as the interest of £420, paid by the Dean and Chapter, in 1630, as arrears of charity money, and vested with the Corporation. *St. Ann's Almshouses*, with a small antique chapel adjoining, was formerly an hermitage or ancient hospital, as noticed at page 73, but is now the asylum of eight poor persons, who receive 2s. 6d. each, weekly, from the Dean and Chapter.

ST. STEPHEN.—In 1654, the *Countess of Pembroke* gave to this parish 4½A. of land near St. Ann's chapel, then worth £12 a year; in trust, to apply £10 thereof in apprenticing a poor boy or girl yearly, and to distribute the remainder in sums of 2s. each among the poor parishioners. This land is now let for about £30 a year, and there is now £150 three per cent. consols belonging to the charity, purchased with money derived from the sale of timber on the land, and from unapplied income. In 1662, *George Potter* left £500 towards rebuilding the *church*, and a house for the use and residence of the successive rectors. The house is worth £20 a year, and is in King's alley. In 1672, *John King* left £125 in trust, that the interest should be paid yearly to the rector for preaching a sermon on the last Saturday in each month. This legacy was laid out in the purchase of £152. 12s. 2d., three per cent. consols. The poor parishioners have the dividends of £65. 13s. 11d. three per cent. consols, purchased with £50 left by *James Green*, in 1807. They have also the interest of £10 left by *Thos. Vigurs*, at an unknown date.

ST. THOMAS THE APOSTLE.—This is one of the suburban parishes of Exeter, in Wonford Hundred, partly within the parliamentary, but not included in the municipal limits of the city. The two *Church Houses* are occupied rent free, by paupers, and stand on the site of two houses, which were destroyed with the church, during the civil wars of the 17th century. A house, given by the *Rev. Walter Battyn*, in 1564, for the repairs of the church, was rebuilt by the parish after the civil wars, and was occupied by the Vicar till 1801, when it was let for 99 years, at the yearly rent of 10s., in consideration of a fine of £280, which with £105, raised by a parish rate, was given to the then Vicar, (Rev. J. B. Copplestone,) towards the erection of the present *Vicarage House*, which cost more £1000. The poor parishioners have 8d. weekly, left by *Lawrence Seldon*, and 12d. weekly left by *Sir J. Acland*, for distribution of bread. In 1635, *Bartholomew Berry,*

left a house and half an acre of land, in trust, to pay 20s. yearly for two sermons, and to divide the residue of the rents among the poor. The house was rebuilt after the civil wars, and is now worth £25 a year. An annuity of £10 left by *Wm. Gould, Sen. and Jun.*, in 1632 and 1642, out of the Barton of Hayes, is paid to a *schoolmaster*, for teaching 24 poor children. The poor have £4 a year out of the same estate, left by Wm. Gould, Senior. Two annuities are paid out of the Barton of Cowick, pursuant to the will of *Robert Pate, Sen. and Jun.*, viz., 20s. for the poor, and 30s. to a *school-mistress*, for teaching four poor children. The poor have also the dividends of £150 three per cent. consols left by *Elizabeth Painter*, and two annuities of 20s. each left by *John Peter*, in 1570, and *Nicholas Evans*, in 1618.

HOLY TRINITY.—The churchwardens have a cottage, stable, and 1A. 33P. of land, given by *Robert Were*, in 1465, and now let for only 20s. a year but a fine is levied on every renewal of the lease. The Lamb and Flag public house, was purchased in 1684, for £65, given by *William and John Mathew, Hy. Fitzwilliams, and Alice Hele*, two-thirds for the use of the church, and one-third for the poor. In 1817, this house was sold for £160, which was invested in the purchase of £190. 18s. three per cent. reduced annuities. The churchwardens have also three annuities amounting to £1. 12s., left by *Hy. Fitzwilliams, Margt. Parker*, and *John Palmer*. The poor parishioners have 2s. worth of bread weekly from *Seldon's and Ac-land's Gifts;* and five poor widows have a share of *Eliz. Buckenam's Charity*, as already noticed. They have also the following *yearly doles*, viz., 15s. in two rent-charges left by *John Hance*, in 1625;—20s. out of two closes, left in 1629, by *Roger Selsby ;* 20s. out of a house in Exe Island, left in 1629, by *Wm. Mathew ;*—52s. for a weekly distribution of 1s. worth of bread, left by *John Cheeke*, in 1678 ; £4 out of a house in Southernhay, left by *Thomas Facy*, in 1700, for distributions of shirts and shifts ;—£5. 13s. 4d. from £190 three per cent. consols, purchased with £100 left by *Sarah Spry*, in 1788, for similar distributions; and 10s. left by *Alex. Pope*, in 1816, out of three houses in the Mint. The sum of £163. 6s. 4d., left to the poor by *James and Thomas Clutterbuck, and Ann Baker*, was laid out in 1696, in the purchase of two fields, which were sold in 1799, for £1500 three per cent. reduced annuities. The yearly dividends of this stock, (£44. 16s. 4d.,) are received by the Churchwardens, and carried to their general account, out of which they pay yearly £4 to four poor parish-ioners, and £2 for apprentice fees, as the gifts of J. and T. Clutterbuck ; and £2. 10s. for distribution among the poor at Easter, as the gift of Ann Baker. The residue of the dividends is applied in such manner as the trustees think most beneficial to the poor.

PROVIDENT INSTITUTIONS.

DEVON AND EXETER SAVINGS' BANK, in Bedford circus, was estab-lished in 1815, for the safe and beneficial investment of the savings of the humbler classes. The large and handsome building which it now occupies, was completed in 1839, at a considerable expense, paid out of the surplus fund. The principal office, or banking room, is 60 feet long and from 40 to 60 broad, and is very lofty. The building comprises also residences for the actuary and cashier, a board room, and other offices. The whole is warmed by hot water, heated by stoves on the basement floor, and passed through copper pipes into each compartment. The operations of this Savings' Bank extend over a very large portion of the county of Devon, by means of more than 130 *Branches*. It is under the direction of 48

trustees, and upwards of 260 *managers ;* and the amount of its deposits is only exceeded by one other Savings' Bank in the kingdom. The sum which it had invested in the Bank of England, on the 20th of Nov., 1848, including a year's interest, was £987,075.17s.5d., belonging to about 30,000 depositors, and a number of Friendly and Charitable Societies. The total sum which it had then received on 88,123 accounts, during the 33 years of its existence, amounted to £3,717,827; and the sums withdrawn and interest paid during the same period, amounted to £2,760,427. This institution is empowered, under the provisions of the 3rd of William IV., cap. 14, to grant *Government Annuities,* immediate or deferred, for life, or for a certain term of years; and the sum of £58,487, has been invested by it in the purchase of annuities of from £4 to £30 each, payable half yearly. A husband and wife are both eligible to hold an annuity of the highest amount. Copies of the regulations, with lists of the trustees, managers, branches, &c., may be obtained at the Bank, on application to Mr. Wm. Lee, the *actuary.*

The *West of England Fire and Life Insurance Company* was established in 1807; and empowered by act of Parliament, in 1813. It has a subscribed capital of £600,000, in £100 shares, of which £45.16s.6d. is paid. Its chief office is a large and elegant building at 237, High street, erected in 1833. The façade of this edifice is of Portland stone, and is about 50 feet wide and 26 high. It has a portico in the centre surmounted by a pedestal, on which stands a figure of King Alfred. Behind this is a large building, erected in 1820, and containing an excellent board room, and the secretary's residence. This provident institution ranks among the principal insurance companies of Europe, and has a large establishment in London, and agencies in Paris, Edinburgh, Dublin, and almost every town in the kingdom. In 1847, it paid no less than £42,856 as duty on fire insurance. Earl Fortescue, Earl Morley, Lord Clifford, Sir T. D. Acland, Bart., Edward Divett, Esq., M.P., and S. T. Kekewich, Esq., are the *trustees;* W. M. Praed, Esq., is the *president;* and Mr. Charles Lewis is the *secretary.* The London office is at 20, Bridge street, Blackfriars.

The *Western Provident Association* was established here in May, 1848, for the purpose of assuring to the industrious classes of both sexes, in return for their small monthly contributions,—weekly stipends and medical aid, during sickness and old age; also payments of £5 to £100 at death;—and endowments of from £5 to £50 for children. This mutual assurance society affords to the tradesmen and the working classes all the benefits, without any of the risks and evils of the old Benefit and Friendly Societies. Its rules are enrolled under the act of Parliament relating to such institutions, and its tables have been most carefully calculated by that eminent *statist*—Mr. Neison. The benefits of the association may be extended by the Board to any part of the West of England, by the formation of *Branches*, with the assistance of Local Committees; and any existing Benefit Society may be incorporated with it, on equitable terms . During the first ten months of its existence 663 members enrolled themselves as subsbribers for 857 assurances, and

their number has since been greatly augmented. *Branches* have been formed at *Plymouth, Devonport, Crediton, Torquay, Ashburton, Bovey-Tracey, Teignmouth, Exmouth, Ottery St. Mary, Leskeard,* and other places in Devon, Cornwall, Somerset, &c., Viscount Ebrington, M.P., is *president,* and some of the principal gentry of the city and neighbourhood are the *vice-presidents and trustees.* Mr. Chas. Hill is the *secretary,* and the office of the Association is at the Athenæum, Bedford circus, and is open daily from 10 till 4, and on Tuesday and Saturday evenings from 6 to 8 o'clock.

The *National Loan Fund Life Assurance and Deferred Annuity Society* has a branch office at 59, High street, and upwards of 70 *Fire and Life Insurance Companies* have agencies here, as will be seen in the subjoined Directory. The *Western Annuity Society* was established in 1831, and Mr. W. D. Moore, of 59, High street, is its secretary. Mr. Thomas May is manager of the *1st, 2nd, and 3rd Exeter Benefit Investment Societies,* established in 1845, '6, and '7. These societies consist of many hundred holders of £120 shares, to be raised by monthly contributions of 10s. per share, and lent out on security of freehold or leasehold property. Mr. Thos. W. Gray is solicitor to the *Devon and Exeter Benefit Building and Investment Society,* established in 1847, and Messrs. Walkey and Truscott are solicitors to the *Second Economic Benefit Building Society,* established in 1848. J. H. Terrell and Mr. Fryer are solicitors to *Exeter and St. Thomas's Benefit Investment Society,* founded in 1848. Mr. E. A. Copleston is secretary to the *Western Agricultural and General Benefit Society.* The Earl of Devon is chairman, and Mr. John Bowring, secretary, of *St. Thomas's District Loan Society,* which was established in 1839, and meets every Friday at 2 o'clock, in the Agricultural Rooms, 197, High street. Mr. Thomas May is secretary to the *West of England and South Wales Land Drainage and Inclosure Company,* established in 1844, and incorporated by act of Parliament in 1848. The object of this Company is to afford to landowners and occupiers increased facilities for draining and improving their land in the most scientific and effectual manner, or by the advance of capital for that purpose, to be repaid by instalments. Among the other provident institutions in Exeter are several Friendly Societies and Lodges of Freemasons, Odd Fellows, and other Secret Orders. The *Masonic Lodges,* (Nos. 46 and 129,) are open on the 2nd and last Thursdays of every month at the *Tucker's and Masonic Hall,* as already noticed at page 112.

EXETER WORKHOUSE :—In 1699, an Act of Parliament passed for erecting hospitals and workhouses for the poor of the 23 parishes, &c., of the City and County of the City of Exeter; under which a large Workhouse was built in the parish of St. Sidwell. Since 1704, the CORPORATION OF THE POOR, instituted by this Act, have been in receipt of most of an annuity of £40, left by the *Rev. John Bury,* in 1667, for the support of a workhouse for the poor of the parish of St. Sidwell. As part of this annuity they receive £30 yearly out of land at Netherstover, and £3 from a cottage at Broadnymet; but £8. 8s. per annum charged by the donor on a tenement called Rock, now held by the Dean and Chapter, has not

been paid for many years. In 1700, the site of the Workhouse, and 17 acres of land adjoining, were conveyed to the Governor and Guardians of the Poor, subject to a yearly rent-charge of £30, one-half of which belongs to Sir T. Lethbridge, and the other half was left to the Episcopal Charity Schools by Mrs. Mary Trelawny. Part of this land is occupied as the Workhouse garden, brick-yard, &c., and the rest is let for about £106 per annum, and chiefly occupied as nurseries, gardens, and the building sites of two rows of houses called Summerland place and terrace. The Corporation of the Poor derive also about £50 a year as the rents of a house and the Bury Meadows, of which four-fifths were left by *Sir Edward Seaward*, in 1703, and the remaining fifth by *Margery Gould*, at a subsequent date. About four acres of *Bury Meadows* were laid out as a public promenade for the inhabitants in 1846. The *Workhouse* has been enlarged at various periods, and comprises several extensive ranges of brick buildings, in which are accommodations for about 550 paupers, but it has seldom more than 400 inmates. It is pleasantly situated in the eastern suburbs of the city, and is surrounded by gardens and handsome houses. Behind it is a large *brick and tile yard*, in which many of the able-bodied paupers are employed. The 23 parishes, &c. of the city and county of the city of Exeter, are still *incorporated for the support of their poor*, under the local act of 1699, and they form a *Superintendent Registrar's District*, under the general registration act. The numerous and valuable charitable funds, which are periodically distributed among the indigent of Exeter, tend materially to lighten the burden of the city *poor rates,* which seldom exceed £10,000 per annum, and in 1838 only amounted to £7500. Under the act of 1699, the Mayor and 12 Aldermen are *Guardians of the Poor (ex officio,)* and about 40 others are elected for life by the ratepayers of the four wards. The following is a list of the Guardians and officers of the

CORPORATION OF THE POOR OF THE CITY OF EXETER.

Wm. Hooper, Esq., *Governor ;* Joseph Cuthbertson, Esq., *Deputy Governor ;* Wm. Lee, Esq., *Treasurer ;* the Mayor and Twelve Aldermen ; and Messrs. W. P. Kingdon, M. Franklin, J. Pearse, R. Taylor, E. Woolmer, M. Kennaway, J. Golsworthy, T. Balle, John Dymond, Samuel Mortimer, Samuel Maunder, Henry Hooper, George Maunder, George Bradford, Joseph Sayell, Christopher Arden, Wm. Nation, John Dinham Osborn, Wm. Hobson Furlong, H. Lake Hirtzel, W. Richards, James Luke Knight, Charles Davy, George Ferris, T. E. Drake, J. H. Gasking, R. S. Cornish, J. Pinn, J. C. Wilcocks, W. Drewe, J. P. Nichols, J. C. Sercombe, J. Sheppard, R. Pain, T. Salter, John Ware, and Joseph Moxon. *Chaplain,* Rev. Theodore Coldridge. *Solicitor,* Chas. Brutton, Esq. *Auditor,* John Tyrrell, Esq. *Clerk,* Mr. Robert Hake. Office, New Buildings, Castle st. *Medical Officers,* Messrs. F. H. Warren, Arthur Kempe, J. S. Perkins, and A. J. Cumming. *Head Beadle,* Mr. John Shears ; *Beadle,* Mr. John Sparkes ; *Assistant Beadle,* George Couch. *Schoolmaster and Mistress,* Mr. J. Fryer and Miss A. J. Thompson. *Foreman of the Brick and Tile Yard,* Mr. Robert Sparke.

*Commissioners for Controlling the Expenditure of the Corporation of the Poor :—*Messrs. Paul Measor, Thomas Besley, George Braund, Thomas Merchant, John S. Gard, John Hill, Rev. G. M. Slatter, Messrs. J. Northam, R. B. Best, C. K. Webb, W. Lang, W. Land, N. W. Tanner, W. H. Farrant, W. Tombs, W. Pepperell, Ralph Sanders, and George Weedon.

REGISTRARS:—James Terrell, Esq., is *Superintendent Registrar of Births, Deaths, and Marriages;* and Mr. Edward H. Roberts is his deputy. Messrs. Charles Hill and John Porter are *Registrars of Marriages.* The following are the REGISTRARS OF BIRTHS AND DEATHS, viz., Mr. S. M. Cox for St. David's District, and Mr. F. G. Farrant for St. Sidwell's District. Mr. R. B. Best is *deputy* to the *former,* and Mr. S. Hooker to the latter.

ST. THOMAS'S UNION, though none of it is within the municipal limits of Exeter, includes those populous suburbs of the city in the parishes of St. Thomas the Apostle, St. Leonard, and Heavitree, as well as 46 other parishes in Wonford and adjacent hundreds. It was formed under the New Poor Law, in 1836. Its 49 parishes comprise an area of about 126,510 acres, and contained in 1841 a *population* of 46,467 souls, of whom 21,671 were males, and 24,796 females. The total number of *Houses* in the Union in 1841 was 9735, of which 616 were unoccupied, and 147 building. Its total *expenditure* on the poor in the year ending March, 1848, was £22,728, including £2605 paid to the county rates. The number of paupers relieved in each quarter of the same year averaged 4571, of whom 350 were in-door poor. The UNION WORKHOUSE is a large stone building in St. Thomas's parishes, and was erected in 1837, at the cost of about £11,000, including the purchase of 3½ acres of land. It has accommodations for 450 paupers, and the rooms are spacious and well ventilated. The *Guardians* meet every Friday at eleven o'clock, and the Earl of Devon is chairman, and S. T. Kekewich, Esq., and the Rev. A. Atherley are vice-chairmen. The *Board* consists of 42 *ex officio*, and 61 elected Guardians. Messrs. J. G. Bidwill and J. Bowring are *joint clerks of the Union;* and the former is also *superintendent registrar*, and the latter *deputy sup. regr.* Mr. and Mrs. Hodge are *master and matron* of the Workhouse; the Rev. E. Bartlett is the *chaplain;* and Mr. and Mrs. Dunn are teachers of the schools. Sixteen surgeons are employed for the Union, and one for the Workhouse. Messrs. John Trenchard, of Exmouth, and James Lyddon, of St. Thomas's, are *registrars of marriages*, and the following is a

LIST OF PARISHES IN ST. THOMAS'S UNION,

With Notes referring to the subjoined List of Relieving Officers and Registrars of Births and Deaths.

Alphington ....D 7	Doddiscombs-	Kenton ....A 3	Sowton ....C 4
Ashton.........A 10	leigh........A 10	Littleham ....B 2	St Leonard's....D 6
Ashcombe......A 3	Dunchideock ...A 7	Lympstone .....B 2	St Thomas's ....D 1
Aylesbeare .....B 8	Dunsford ....A 7	Mamhead ......A 3	St Mary's Clist..C 4
Bicton..........B 5	East Budleigh ...B 5	Nether-Exe ....C 6	St George's Clist.B 4
BrampfordSpeke D 1	Exminster......B 3	Otterton ....B 5	Stoke Canon ....C 6
Broadclist ......C 9	Farringdon .....C 8	Pinhoe..........C 6	TedburnStMary..A 7
Bridford ....A 10	Heavitree.......D 6	Poltimore ......C 6	Topsham ....B 4
Christow........A 10	HolcombeBurnellA7	Powderham.....A 3	Upton Pyne ....D 1
Clist Hydon ......C 9	Honiton's Clist...C 4	Rewe ....C 6	Whimple ....C 9
ClistStLawrence.C 9	Huxham.........C 6	Rockbeare ......C 8	Whitstone......A 1
Clist Raleigh ...B 5	Ide ....D 7	Shillingford St	Whithycombe-
	Kenn...........A 3	George ....A 7	Raleigh ....B 2
			Woodbury ......B 8

☞ *All these Parishes are in the jurisdiction of the County Court, held at Exeter.*

RELIEVING OFFICERS:—Mr. Badcock, of Kennford, for all the parishes marked A; Mr. Edward Southcott, of Topsham, for those marked B; Mr. Henry W. Austin, of Broadclist, for those marked C; and Mr. Christopher Saunders, of Heavitree, for those marked D.

REGISTRARS OF BIRTHS AND DEATHS:—Mr. Benison, of St. Thomas's, for all the parishes marked 1; Mr. Land, of Exmouth, for those marked 2; Mr. Collyns, of Kenton, for 3; Mr. Tothill, of Topsham, for 4; Mr. Kendall, of Budleigh-Salterton, for 5; Mr. Madden, of Heavitree, for 6; Mr. Cheeseworth, of Dunsford, for 7; Mr. Lindsay, of Woodbury, for 8; Mr. Austin, of Broadclist, for 9; and Mr. Hamlyn, of Christow, for those marked 10.

LIST OF STREETS, &c. IN EXETER,

With References to their respective Situations.

Adelaide pl., Sidwell st
Albert place, Rock st
Albert street, Clifton rd
Albert ter., Mount Radf
Albion ter., Mount Radf
Albion pl.,OldTivertn.rd
Alphington street and road, St Thomas's
Anchor lane, Exe island
Austwick terrace, Alphington road
Baker's court, Sidwell st
Bampfylde st., High st
Baring crescent & place, Magdalen road
Barnfield, Southernhay
Barrack rd., Longbrk. st
Bartholomew street and terrace, North street
Bear street, South street
Beauverie place, Magdalen hill
Bedford chambers,Bamfylde street
Bedford circus, High st
Bedford street, High st
Bellair pl., Mt. Radford
Belmont pl., Clifton rd
Bellvue, Mount Radford
Black Boy rd., Sidwell st
Bicton place, Heavitree
Blackaller wear, Exe st
Bystock ter., Barrack rd
Bonhay, Exe bridge
Bradninch place& buildings, Gandy street
Bridge street, Fore st
Broadgate, High street
Brook-green terrace, St James' road
Brunswick pl., Paris st
Buller pl., Longbrook st
Castle st. & yd., High st
Castle ter., New North rd
Cathedral close, High st
Catherine st., High st
Cattle mkt., New Bridge street
Chapple's court,North st

Cemetery, Exe street
Cheeke street, Paris st
Chichester place, Southernhay street
Church street, St Sidwell's and Heavitree
City road, Exe bridge
Claremont ter., Mt. Radf
Clarence pl.,BlackBoyrd
Clifton road and street, Summerland street
Clifton place,StSidwell's
Close, Cathedral yard
Cobourg pl.,BlackBoyrd
Coaver, Matford lane
Colleton cres., Friarsgt
Colleton ter.,Hollowayst
Commercial road, New Bridge street
Coombe st., South st
CountyGaol,NewNth. rd
Cowick st., St Thomas's
CowleyBridge, 2 milesN.
Cricklepit lane, West st
Cross lane, Black Boy rd
Custom-house lane and quay, Commercial rd
DanesCastle, Barrack rd
Deanerypl.,Cathedral yd
Dix's field, Southernhay
Duke's place, Fore st
EasternMarket,Queen st
Eaton place, Paris st
Eldon place,Hill's court
Edmund street, West st
Egypt lane, High street
Ewing street, West st
Elmfield pl., St David's
Exe bdg., New Bridge st
Exe island, New Bdg. st
Exe street, Iron bridge
Exwick, St Thomas's
Fore street, High street
Friar's gate, road and walk, Holloway st
Friernhay st., Fore st
Frog st., New Bridge st
Gandy street, High st
George street, South st

George's pl.,BlackBoyrd
Goldsmith st., High st
Grosvenor pl., Sidwell st
Guinea street, South st
Hart's row, Northernhay
Hamptonbuildgs.,Black Boy road
Hampton pl., Alphington road
Harris place, Paris st
Head Wear, Exe street
Haven banks,Cattle mkt
Heavitree road, Summerland
High street, Fore street
Hill's ct., Longbrook st
Hiram pl., Blk. Boy rd
Holloway st., South st
Homefield pl., Heavitree
Hopping's buildings, Black Boy road
Iron bridge, North st
James st. &ter., South st
Jeffery's row, Sidwell st
John street, Fore street and Clifton road
Kerrian's pl., North st
King's alley, High st
King street, Fore st
KingWm. ter., Sidwell st
Lansdowne terrace, Holloway street
Larkbeare, Holloway st
Lawrence court, High st
Leonard's quay,Coml.rd
Lewis's bldngs., Paris st
Little Silver terrace,New North road
Limekiln ln., StLeond.'s
Longbrook street and terrace, High street
Maddock's row, Fore st
Magdalen street and road, South street
Manston ter., Magdln.st
Market street, Fore st
Martin street, High st
Mary-Arches st., Fore st

Matford terrace, place, and lane, St Leonard's
Melbourne street and place, Holloway st
Midway ter., Heavitree rd
Milk street, Fore street
Mint street, Fore st
Mont-le-Grand, Heavitree road
Montpelier, St David's
Mount Radford, Magdalen road
Mulgrave place, Mount Radford
Musgrave alley, High st
Nelson pl., Spiller st
New Bridge st., Fore st
New Buildings, Gandy st
New road, Barracks
New North road and terrace, Longbrook st
North Bridge, St David's hill
North lane, Heavitree
North rd., St David's hill
North street, High st
North ter., New North rd
Northernhay, Castle
Northernhay st., Iron bdg
Nosworthyrow, Sidwellst
Oakfield st., Heavitree
Okehampton street, St Thomas's
Painter's row, St Thos.'s
Palace street, South st
Pancras lane, North st
Penleonard pl., Magd.st
Paragon pl., South st
Paris st., St Sidwell st
Park place, Hill's court and Mount Radford
Park terrace, Heavitree
Paul street, North st
Pavilion pl., Holloway st
Peamore ter., Sidwell st
Pennsylvania terrace, St James's road
Plantation buidings, Clifton road

Polesloe Park, &c., Black Boy road
Poltimore place, Southernhay
Post-office st., Bedford st
Pound ln., St David's st
Powhay, Bonhay
Preston st. & pl., West st
Prospect place, Rack street & Black Boy rd
Quay, West street
Quay ln. & hill, South st
Queen street, High st
Queen's sq., Mt Radford
Queen's ter., New Nth. rd
Rack street, West st
Radnor place, Friar's rd
Railway Station, St David's hill
RedCow st., StDvd.'s hill
RegentPrk., Heavitree rd
Richmond pl., Mt. Radf
Richmond grove, Heavitree road
Rockfield pl., Barrack rd
Rougemont, Castle st
Russell ter., New Nth. rd
Russell street, Paris st
Saddler's lane, Exe islnd
Salem pl., St Sidwell st
Salutary place & mount, Clifton rd., Heavitree
Sandford st., Clifton rd
Shilhay, Commercial rd
Silver street and terrace, New North road
Sivell place, Heavitree
Smythen st., Fore st
South street, High st
Southernhay, South st
Spiller street, Paris st
Square (The,) High st
St Ann's ter., Sidwell st
St David's hill, road, and terrace, Iron bridge
St James's pl., rd., & ter., Old Tiverton road
St John's ter., Sidwell st
St Lawrence's, High st

St Leonard's place, cres., and ter., Mt. Radford
St Leonard's, Hollowayst
St Mary Steps, West st
St Olave's sq., Fore st
St Petrock's, High st
St Sidwell ter., Longbrook street
St Sidwell st., High st
St Thomas st., Exe bdg
Stafford ter., Heavitree
Stepcote hill, King st
Stephen st., High st
Summerland pl., Paris st
Summerland st., ter., and cres., St Sidwell's st
Sun street, South st
Sydney pl., Alphingtn. rd
Tiverton rd., St Dvd.'s hl
Tiverton old road, StSidwell street
Topsham rd., StLeond.'s
Trinity st., South st
Tudor st., New Bridge st
Union road, Victoria ter
Union terrace, Paris st
Verney pl., Sidwell st
Victoria pl., Topsham rd
Victoria ter., Mt.Radford and Union road
Water lane, West st
Waterbeer st., North st
Well lane, St James's rd
West st. & gate, Fore st
Wellington place, Black Boy road
Weir-field pl., StLeond.'s
Western (or Lower) Market, Fore street
Whipton, Heavitree
Windsor terrace, Summerland street
Wonford (E.&S.) Heavitree
Workhouse lane, Heavitree road
York street and buildings, St Sidwell st

EXETER DIRECTORY,

Including the Parishes of HEAVITREE, ST. LEONARD, *and* ST. THOMAS, *in the Suburbs of the City and County of the City of Exeter.*

The CONTRACTIONS *used are such as will be readily understood, being chiefly the usual abbreviations of Christian Names, and ct. for court; bdg., bridge; bldgs., buildings; cir., circus; cres., crescent; ln., lane; rd., road; st., street; pl., place; ter., terrace; H., Heavitree; and Mtd., for Mount Radford.*

The following MISCELLANY comprises the addresses of *Gentry, Clergy, Partners in Firms, and others* not arranged in the subjoined Classification of Trades and Professions, to which an *Alphabetical Index* is prefixed. This Index, in conjunction with the "Miscellany," affords all the advantages of a complete Alphabetical Directory of the City and Suburbs.

Abbott Mrs Har., St Leonard's lawn
Abbott John White, Esq. 32 Southernhay place
Acton Mrs. 2 York buildings
Adams Chas. Esq., 2 Midway ter
Adams Misses My.& Har., Midway ter
Aggassiz Capt. J. C. C. 7 StJames' pl
Allen Jph. supervisor, George's pl
Anderson Geo. gent. 5 Belmont pl
Angel Alfred, organist, Close
Anstey Thomas, clerk, North street
Anthony Rd. comss. agt. St John's ter
Arden Miss Ann, 2 Devonshire pl
Arden Chpr. Esq. *Marypole Villa*
Arden Major George, and Mr Wm. *Sungum Villa*, Pennsylvania road
Arden Miss Mary, 43 Magdalen st
Armistead Jno. gent. 5 New North ter
Arscott Mr Robert, Southernhay
Arscott Miss Maria, 1 Hill's court
Arthur Misses, Barnfield place
Ash Mrs Mary, Grosvenor place
Ash Mr George, Park place, H
Ashbee Rt. railway supt. St Dvd's hill
Atkins Miss Eliz. Cowick street
Atherley Rev Arthur, M.A. vicar of *Heavitree*
Avent Mrs. 16 St Sidwell street
Avery Mrs. 8 Park place
Aysh Richd. gent. St. David's hill
Bacon John, Esq. and Rev Thomas, 1 Upper Mount Radford terrace
Bailey Mrs Eliz. 2 Bystock terrace
Baker Andw. Clement, editor of the *Western Luminary*, 2 Salem pl
Baker Miss, Park place, Heavitree
Baker Mr James, Paul street
Baker John Harris, sec. to Building and Investment Soc. 59 High st

Baker Mrs H. 1 Bellair place
Bale John, solr's clerk, 3 Silver ter
Ball Archls. fish hook mkr.105Fore st
Ball Miss E. W. 15 Dix's field
Balle Mr Thomas, Cowick fields
Bamber Mrs Jane, 6 Weirfield pl
Banfill Thos. wharfinger, Quay
Baring Miss Mgt. 7 H. Summerld. pl
Barker Mrs Jane, 10 Belmont pl
Barker Mr John Fisher, Park ter. H
Barker Miss Sus. 11 Albert ter. Mtd
Barnes Misses A. & E. 6 Burnfield
Barnes Ralph, Esq. solr. and Misses Hanh. & Augusta, *Bellair House*
Barnes Wm. Esq. banker, *MatfordHs*
Baron Mr James, Alphington road
Barrett Capt. Wm. 4 Weirfield pl
Bartholomew Rev Chpr. C. incbt. of St David's, St. David's hill
Bartholomew Mrs. 12 Belmont pl
Bartlett Rev Edward, chaplain of St Thomas's Union, *Abbeville*
Bartlett Mrs Jane, 15 Paragon pl
Bartlett Miss Mary, 9 York bldgs
Barton Mrs Jane, Bartholomew st
Bastow Nichs. traveller, Salem pl
Bastard Saml. Segar, gent. 9 Higher Summerland place
Bastard Richard, gent. *Friars*
Bastard Segar, mercht. St James's st
Bate Capt. James, Claremont grove
Batt Hy. Pitt, agent, Friar's walk
Batt Mrs S. lodgings, Deanery pl
Batt Thos. railway clerk, St Thomas's
Baugh Rear-Admiral Thomas F. 3 Upper Mount Radford terrace
Bayley Lieut.Chas.B.13Mt.Radfd. ter
Bayley Hy. sedan ownr. Waterbeer st
Bean Mr John, East Wonford

Beddoes Rev B., Bartholomew ter
Belcher George, clerk, 22 High st
Beer Mrs. 9 Radnor place
Beer Mr John, *East Wonford*
Beer Mr Wm., Topsham road
Bellerby James, printer, &c. (Trewman and Co.) 3 Matford terrace
Bellew Mrs P. L. P., St David's hill
Benison W. N. regr. of B. and D. for St Thomas's, Exe bridge
Benn Richard, farmer, *Whipton*
Bennett Chas. clerk, Friar's road
Bennett Henry, draper; h 223 High st
Bent Mrs Fanny, York buildings
Bere Montague Baker, Esq. comssr. of bankruptcy, *Barley House*
Berkeley Capt. F. H. 17 Dix's field
Besley Wm. gent. 11 York terrace
Besley Wm. Hy. surgeon; h *Bradninch*
Betfield Mrs., Homefield place, H
Biden Thos. clerk, 1 Weirfield pl
Bidwill Jno. Green, gent. Alphington rd
Bidwill Jph. Geo. sharebroker, supt. regr. & joint clerk of St Thomas's Union, Bedford cir; h *Felix Well*
Bignell Mrs Eliz. 6 St Leonard's ter
Bigwood Rev John, (Bapt.) Union rd
Bingham Capt. John, R.N. 13 Dix's fd
Bingley Mr Richard, *South Wonford*
Birchill Mr George, 2 James' terrace
Bird Mrs Sophia, *Heavitree*
Bishop of Exeter, The Right Rev Henry Phillpotts, D.D. *The Palace*
Bishop Mrs Frances, Mount Radford
Bishop Wm. Richard, solr. &c. 19 Bedford circus
Blackburn Rev Peter, M.A. 6 Clifton pl
Blake Barnett, editor of the *Gazette*, 3 Okehampton terrace
Blake Mr Saml. 6 Park place, Mtd
Blanchard Mrs Ann, 9 Lr. Mt. Radfd. ter
Blatch John, gent. 18 Dix's field
Bletchley Mrs Maria, Friar's road
Blunden Mr Jas. 6 Summerland hill
Blunt Mrs and Misses, *Heavitree*
Bodley Chas. ship owner, 43 South st
Bond Alfred Majoribanks, Esq. *East Wonford*
Bond Mrs. 4 Colleton crescent
Bond John, butler, 12 Sivell place
Bond Mrs Mary, Park place, H
Booth Miss P. 15 Radnor place
Bowcher Wm. sedan onr. Trinity st
Bowden David, Burymeadow keeper
Bowden Mr John, 1 Longbrook ter

Bowden Mrs Sarah, 3 Hampton bldgs
Bowring Mr Charles, Larkbeare
Bowring John, joint clerk, and dep. registrar of St Thomas's Union; h 6 Radnor place
Box Rev Hy. Adderley, B.A., curate of Heavitree: h Mont-le-Grand
Boycott Mrs Sarah, Painter's row
Boyde Mrs L., Manston terrace, H
Boyde Mr Peter, 9 Baring cres. H
Boyde Mr Wm., Homefield pl. H
Braddick Mr Thos. 143 Sidwell st
Bradley Geo. engineer, Bartw. yard
Brake John, Chas. & Wm. wine, &c. merchts; h 25 Holloway street
Branscombe George Wm., lay vicar, Melbourne place
Branston Capt. John, 6 Albert ter
Braund Mr James, Cowick field
Braund Mr John, South lawn
Braund Mr George, Clifton place
Bremridge Mrs E. H. *Penrose Villa*
Brewer Mrs My., Richmond grove, H
Brewer Mr H. 1 Upper Eaton pl
Brewster Henry Lewis, tassel, button, and fancy trimming manufacturer, 3 Catherine street
Bristow Rev Jno. (Indpt.) 4 St Jas.' pl
Britton Geo. lodgings, 2 Upr. Eaton pl
Broad Josiah, clerk, 4 Colleton ter
Brock Wm. draper; h 177 Fore st
Brock Mrs Agnes, 4 New North ter
Brome Mr Chas. J. B. *Regent Park*
Brook Mrs. 4 Hill's buildings
Brook Wm. coms. agt. 7 Salutary pl
Brooking T. F. & Co. carriers, Mkt. st
Brown Lieut. E. L., (R.N.) 3 Devonshire place
Brown James Armitage, ironfounder; house Alphington road
Brown Rd. lodgings, 15 Lr. Eaton pl
Brown J. broker, Smythen street
Browning Mrs Car. 10 Hampton bldgs
Brunton John, travlr. O. Tiverton rd
Brutton Mrs Augusta, matron, St Thomas's Hospital
Brutton Mrs Mrgt. 7 East Southernhay
Brutton Capt. John, R.N. 6 Albert ter
Buckingham Mrs Ann, 12 Salutary pl
Buckingham Wm. solicitor; h 12 Southernhay place
Budge Rev Edw., B.A. rector of Bratton Clovelly, Magdalen hill
Bullock Miss Har. 4 Northernhay pl

Bullivant Mr John, messenger to Ct. of Bankruptcy, 10 Radnor place

Bulpin Mr Rd. 1 Sivell place, H

Burch Thomas, keeper of Sheriff's Ward prison, Cowick street

Burcher Rd. clerk, 6 Hill's court

Burne Rev Chas., M.A. chaplain to the Workhouse, 2 Manston ter. H

Burnett Mr John, Cathedral yard

Burr Rev. James Henry Scudamore, priest vicar, 3 Colleton crescent

Butland Elias, gent. New North rd

Byne Mrs My. Fras. 8 Baring cres

Calamy Michl. gent. 4 Baring cres

Calway Fredk. lay vicar, Okehptn. rd

Campbell Major, Magdalen hill

Campion Thomas, Esq. comssr. for taking special bail, Holloway st

Cann Mrs Margy. and Edward G. 2 Bicton place, *Heavitree*

Cann Hy. mathl. teacher, Friar's walk

Cann Wm. clerk to West of England Fire and Life Insurance Co. 237 High st; h 5 Chichester place

Cansley Thos. thatcher, Sandygt. H

Canterbury Miss, matron of Lying-in Charity, 48 Holloway street

Cardew Miss Mary, Radnor place

Cardew Mrs., Higher Mt. Radfd. ter.

Carew John, Esq. regr. of Court of Bankruptcy, St David's hill

Carew Miss Eliz. 20 Southernhay

Carew Miss, 20 Southernhay place

Carlyon Rev Php., M.A. incumbent of St. James's, Sidwell street

Carrol Mr James, New North road

Carne Mrs Mtda. 2 St Sidwell ter.

Carter Jas. ironmonger, 158 Fore st.

Carter Wm. draper, 157 Fore street

Carter Miss Betty, 14 Verney place

Cartwright Mrs G. Northernhay pl.

Carwithen Rev G. T. 8 Southnhay. pl.

Cathcart Miss, 17 Higher Mt. Rd. tr.

Cawsey T. A. gent. Marlpool cottage

Chadwick Mr Jas. jun. Alphington rd

Chafy Mrs Emma, Park terrace

Chamberlain Rt. H. gent. St Dd.'s hl

Champion Thos. Esq. *Duryard Hs.*

Chancellor Chas. clerk, St David's hl

Channing Rbt. gent. St David's hill

Channing Mr Wm. sen. Black Boy rd

Chaplin Mr Jno. Homefield pl. H

Charlton Harriet and John, *bleachers*, Okehampton street

Charmes Mr. Topsham road

Chave Rev Edw. Wm. Tanner, M.A. rector of St Pancras, 25 Dix's fld

Churchill Miss F. 3 St Leonard's pl

Clampitt Rd. W. gent. St Thomas st

Clapp Mrs Susan, 9 Salutary place

Clark John, bank clerk, Cowick st

Clark Mr John, *East Wonford*

Clarke Mrs Mary Ann, Peamore street

Clarence Mrs Eliz. Bicton place H

Cleghorn Lieut. G. Cowick street

Cleife J. P. Esq. 4 Prospect place

Clench John, railway sec. 14 Bedford circus; h Mont-le-Grand

Clifford Mrs Emma, 1 North terrace

Clifford Mrs Harriet, Parker's well

Cockram Jno. gent. 5 Summerland hl

Coldridge Rev Theodore, M.A. rector of Allhallows, Goldsmith st; h 46 Magdalen street

Cole Miss Catherine, New North rd

Cole Miss, 1 Albert terrace

Cole Mrs Mary, 2 Longbrook ter

Cole Wm. governor of County Prison, New North road

Collings Mr P. Longbrook street

Collins Chas. clerk, 4 St James's ter

Collins H. G. H. clerk, Okehampton rd

Collins Robt. bailiff of County Court, Post Office street

Collins-Splatt Hy. Esq. banker, East Southernhay

Collyns Rev John Martyn, M.A. rector of St John's and St George's, *Crossmead*

Collyns Misses, 20 Dix's field

Colson John, paper hanging dealer, 211 High street

Colson John Worthy, draper; h 3 Baring Crescent, H

Comer Mrs Mary, Mount Radford

Commin Thos. spirit mert. &c; h 3 Park pl; Thos; h 94 North street

Congdon Miss My. Ann, propr. of the Subsptn. Rooms, 13 Northernhay pl

Conway Fdk. lay vicar, Okehptn. rd

Cook Mrs Eliz. Okehampton road

Cook Fdk. clerk, 8 North terrace

Cooke John, carrier, Quay hill

Coombe Mr Wm. Pavilion place

Coombe Mrs. Mount Radford

Copp Chas. gent. Stafford ter. H

Copp Wm. Esq. *Park House*

Copp Wm. draper; h 206 High st

Corfe Rev Jpb. M.A. priest, vicar, & rector of St Kerrian & St Petrock, Old Tiverton road
Cornish Elijah Wm. glass cutter & blower, West street
Cornish R. Stribling, bldr. Hill's ct
Cornish R. gent. 3 Manston ter. H
Cotton Mrs Sarah, 6 Devonshire pl
Cotton Mr Fras. 23 Northernhay
Couch Geo. asst. beadle, *Workhouse*
Couche Wm. Esq. Pensylvania road
Courtney Rev Fras. M.A. incbt. of St Sidwell's, Southernhay
Cousins Mr Har. 80 St Sidwell st
Cousins Isaac, school, Coombe st
Cousins John, gent. Mount Radford
Cowley Arnold Jas. clk. Poltimore sq
Cowley Chas. F. clerk, St David's hl
Cox Mrs Eliza K. 1 Baring cres. H
Cox Mrs., St James's place
Cox Mr John, Park pl. H
Cox Mr. Wm. 7 Paris street
Crabb Jph. Wm. gent. *East Wonford*
Crabbe Edw. Bennett, *apparitor*, 15 Sivell place
Craigie Col. Edm. 14 Victoria ter
Cragg Miss Phœbe, 6 St Sidwell st
Cresswell Geo. Hy. Esq. surveyor of Post Offices, 7 Baring pl. H
Cresswell Jas. Esq. 7 Magdalen st
Cresswell Miss Maria, 2 Bouverie pl
Crester Mrs. Belmont Cottage
Creyke Rev Robt. 4 Salutary place
Cridland Augs. travr. 16 Salem pl
Crispeigny C. Esq. 6 Baring place
Crofts Mr Hy. St Mary's yard
Cross C. Esq. *Middle Duryard*
Cross Mrs E. Homefield pl. H
Crowther P. Wyatt, Esq. *Baring Ldg*
Cubitt Mrs Hanh. 7 St James' place
Cumming Arthur Jas. surgeon; h 5 Upper Southernhay street
Cumming Hugh, gent. St David's hl
Cumming Mrs Eliz. 5 Albion place
Cunningham Mrs A. M. Victoria ter
Curry Saml. clerk, 3 Lit. Silver ter
Curtis Miss Ann, Cowick street
Cusack Mrs. 3 Baring place
Cuthbertson Mr Jph. sen. 16 Paris st
Cutler Miss, Pennsylvania
Cutliffe Mrs Eliz. 15 Upr. Mt. Radfd
Cutliffe Mrs Mary, 2 St James's pl
Dacie John, gent. St David's hill
Dacres Mrs Hannah, St David's hill
Dalton John, lapidary, 48 Holloway

Damerel Mr Wm. Prospect place
Daniel Mrs Mary C. 10 Albion pl. H
Darke Miss Eliz. Bartholomew ter
Darke Mr. Robt. Old Tiverton road
Davies Danl. tea dlr ; h Verney pl
Davies Miss C. 4 Summerland cres
Davies Saml. tea dlr; h Cathedral yd
Davies Mr Wm. 9 Silver terrace
Davis Mr Chas. Bellair pl
Davy Chas. currier ; h Mount Radfd.
Davy Francis, hemp and iron mert. Palace st. and *Topsham*
Davy Joseph, gent. Heavitree
Dawdady Mrs Ann, Sivell pl. H
Dawson S.T.gent. Mizpeh cot. St Sid.
Day Mrs. 4 Clifton place
Dean Rd. clerk, 5 Pavilion place
DeHaviland Mrs. 4 Southernhay pl
Delamain Mrs. 2 Richmond Grove
Delaney M. horse breaker, Paris st
Dennis Mrs. *Polesloe Park*
Densham Mr Thos. Black Boy road
Denty Mrs Col. 6 Higher Mt. Radfd.
Dicker Hy. organ bldr. Gandy st
Dickinson Rev T. Rutherford, M.A. curate of St Thomas's, *Beaufort hs*
Dinham John, grocer; h 104 Fore st
Discombe Mr W. Prospect place
Divett Mrs My. Ann, *Claremont Grv.*
Doble Thos. messenger, Barthlmw. st
Dodd Miss My. Eliz. 14 Bedford cir.
Dodley Chas. ship onr. Friar's rd
Doeg Wm. beadle, *Tucker's Hall*
Dommett Abm. lodgings, 5 North ter
Donellon Mrs. 6 Eaton place
Doran Mrs., Higher Mt. Radford ter
Doveton Mrs. Mary, 4 Belmont pl
Down Miss, lodgings, Barnfield
Downe Mrs. Grgna. 66 South street
Downe Geo. bank clerk, Friar's road
Drake Mr Jno. 3 Lr. Summerland pl
Drake Mrs. 9 Colleton terrace
Draper Mr Wm. 174 St Sidwell st
Drewe Wm. wine mert; h 64 South st
Drewe Edw. Simcoe, Esq; h *Honiton*
Druller H. permit writer, James st
Dryden Jno. travlr. 10 Sivell place
Du'Chemin Mr. Geo. 8 Bartholw. ter
Duckworth Sir John Thos. B. Bart. M.P. *Weir House, Topsham*
Duffield Thos. clerk, 13 Magdalen st
Duffield Wm. clerk, Albion place
Dunley Mrs. lodgings, 12 Prospect tr
Dunn T. W., school, St Thos.'s Wks.
Dyer Saml. corn mert. 241 High st

Dymond Mrs A. *Combe Leonard*
Dymond John, Esq. bank manager, St Mary's yard
Dymond Mr John, 5 Albion place
Dymond Mrs Hanh. 15 Radnor place
Dymond Wm. ldgns. 47 Magdalen st
Eales R. Esq. Queen's sq. Mt Rdfrd.
Eales Wm. Venetian blind maker, 2 Summerland street
Eardley Thos. dairyman, Heavitree
Earle Mrs Mary, 4 St Ann's terrace
Edger Wm. draper; h 62 High st
Edwards Mrs Mary, 62 Magdalen st
Edwards Chas. ferryman, Quay
Ellicombe Rev Richd. M.A., prebendary and rector of *Alphington*
Ellicombe Hugh Myddleton, solr. & city treasurer; h Union road
Ellicombe John Bradford, solicitor; h 4 Southernhay street
Elliott Abm. clerk, 7 Ltle Silver ter
Elliott C. sheriff's officer, 8 King William terrace
Elliott H. lodgings, 2 Southernhay st
Elliott Mrs. St David's terrace
Esworthy Mr Benjmn. Clifton road
Evans Geo. gent. Claremont terrace
Evans Mrs Mary, 3 St James's pl
Eveleigh F. R. engraver; h 19Mgd.st
Farrant Mr Hy. 2 Longbrook street
Farrington Mrs. South Lawn
Fernandez Mrs Sarah, Topsham rd
Ferreira G. A. gent. *Bellevue*, Mtfd
Ferris Mr Geo. 166 Fore street
Fitze Miss Mary, 2 North terrace
Fitzgerald Miss A. Upper Mt. Rdfrd
Fletcher Jas. carrier, Cowick st
Flood Samuel Cphr. Esq., comssr. of Bankruptcy, 8 Dix's field
Flood John, sexton, St Sidwell's
Flood Sml. crier, St. Sidwell st
Floud Mrs Ann, Matford terrace
Follett J. mert; h 15 Southernhay pl
Forbes Capt Wm. Richmond Grove
Forbes Mrs E. Prospect cottage
Force Reginald, clerk, Friar's rd
Ford Dnl. & Co. carriers, 19 South st
Ford Rev James, *Southlands H*
Ford Jas. cooper; h 30 Holloway st
Ford Rd. Esq. *Heavitree House*
Ford Hy. Melhuish, solicitor, &c; h Southernhay place
Ford Wm. F. clerk, 3 Longbrook ter
Forord Mrs Eliz. Cathedral yard
Foster Mrs Susan, 4 Baring pl. H

Foster Thos. cooper, Holloway st
Francis Jas. gent. Painter's row
Francis Mr Wm. 13 Salutary place
Franklin Mrs C. 10 Mont-le-Grnd. H
French Mr J. D. 2 St Ann's terrace
Friend Mrs Sarah Eliz. supt. Blind Instn., St David's hill
Frise Rd. P. lithogr; h Palace st
Fryer John, draper; h 155 Fore st
Fryer Josiah, Workhouse School
Fryer Thos. Northernhay keeper
Fulford Capt Wm. R.A. 1 Bystock tr
Furse John, supervisor, 86 South st
Furse Mrs. and Miss, Alphington rd
Gale Wm. traveller, *Exwick*
Gale Mr Robert, Mount peasant
Gale Chas. lodgings, 2 North ter
Galpin Mr Thos. 13 Salem place
Galway Mrs Jane, 3 Hampden pl
Gambles Mrs My. Ann, Park ter. H
Gard Edw. woollen mrt; h Castle st
Gard Rd. Somers, Esq., *Rougemont Lodge*
Gard Mrs Agnes, Brandninch pl
Gard Mrs Sar. & Miss, St. David's hill
Gardner J. A. gent., Cowick street
Gardner Mr Wm., Belmonte pl
Garland Wm. book agent, 4 Sivell pl
Garton Jno. ironmgr; h 25 North st
Geare John, solr; h Bedford street
Gichard Capt. Edw. 1 Albert ter., Mtd
Gifford Miss H. *Parker's Well House*
Gill John, city crier, Barthlmw. st
Gingham Jno. serj. at mace, Police off
Glendenning R. gent. St. David's hill
Gliddon Mrs Carln. 42 Southernhay
Glyde Mrs Rachel, Brandninch bldgs
Glyde Miss Sar. 5 York buildings
Godbeer Jno. Edw. verger, Close
Godfrey Major J. R. 5 Pennsylvania
Godfrey Rd. sexton, Heavitree
Godfrey Wm. clerk, 1 Little Silver st
Golsworthy Jas. Esq. Priory place
Gordon Chas. Esq. *Heavitree House*
Gould J. B. ins. agent, &c. Palace gt
Gould Mr Wm. 3 Hiram place
Gowings Mr. Jno., Magdalen road
Gould Rev Geo. (Bapt.) Friars
Gould Geo. M. school, 271 High st
Gould J. B. secry. to the Provident Clerks' Association, High street
Gould Mr Wm. 3 Hiram place
Granger Rev Thomas, Maddocks row
Grantham Wm. clerk, Russell ter
Gray Mr Rt., Alphington road

F 3

Gray Mrs A. 7 Hampton pl
Green Edw. draper; h Mont le Grand
Gregory Mrs Jane, Cowick street
Gregory Wm. sub-post, *Exwick*
Gregory Capt. Ts., R.N., Black boy rd
Greig Mrs. 6 Lr. Summerland pl
Grendle Mrs Jane, Up. Mount Radfd
Griffin Capt. Jas., Alphington road
Griffiths Rd. J. sub-post, Magdln. hl
Groom Mrs Ann, Queen's square
Grose Rev John,(Wesln.) 15 Verney pl
Grove Capt. Hy. Leslie, R.N., colr. of
    customs; h 26 Southernhay
Gullett Misses, Cathedral yard
Gully Jno. Geo. gov. *City Prison*
Guppy Mrs Maria, 2 Regent park, H
Haddington Mr. 3 Prospect place
Haggerston Capt. John, 2 Baring pl
Hake Robt. clerk to corporation of the
    poor, New bldgs; h 40 Bartw. st
Hall Lieut. Genl. G.J., *Elmfield hse*
Hall Mr Chas., Cowick street
Hall Mr Wm. 1 Baring place
Hallett Mr Richd. 6 Albion place, H
Halls John, tea dlr; h 9 Hills court
Halls Wm. tea dlr; h 1 High street
Halstaff Mr Saml. 12 Brookgn. ter
Ham Jas. druggist; h 187 High st
Ham Mrs., Maddock's row
Hancock Mr Fras. S., Pavilion pl
Harding Miss Mary, Magdalen st
Harding Chpr. gent. Marypool villa
Harding Wm. guard, 5 Brook green
Harding Lt. Col. Wm. *West Park villa*
Harper Mrs Eliz. 1 Devonshire pl
Harrington Rev Edwd. Chas., M.A.,
    Chancellor of the Cathedral, 27
    Southernhay
Harris Edw. draper; h 62 High st
Harris Misses A. & D. 2 Magdln. hill
Harrison Lieut. Col. J. C., Mount Rad-
    ford Park
Hart Mrs Ann, 14 Hill's court
Hart Mrs Jane, Hill's court
Hart Rev John Alphington road
Hart Mr John, Albion pl. H
Hart Thos. gent., *Stokehill*, H
Hartley Thos. gent. 2 Victoria ter
Hartnoll Thos. comssr. for taking spe-
    cial bail, ins. agent, &c. 59 High st;
    h Alphington rd
Harvey H. D. clerk, 8 Dix's field
Harvey Mr Jas. 7 Weirfields
Harvey Rev Saml. 19 Dix's field
Haswell Rev J. P. (Wes.) Verney pl

Havill Jas. W. tmp. hotel, &c. 91 Fore st
Hawke Mrs. 5 St James' terrace
Hawke Miss Grace, Cowick street
Hawke Richd. carrier, Waterbeer st
Hawkins John, street paver, 50 Bar-
    tholomew street
Haydon G. H. agent, Paris street
Haydon Mr Saml., Homefield pl. H
Hayman Mrs My. 5 St Sidwell st
Haynes Mrs Lucy, Hill's court
Hazeland Miss, 8 Albion pl. H
Heacock J. file cutter, Sidwell street
Head J. lodgings, Martin street
Head Robt. Thos. solicitor; h *Briars,
    Alphington*
Heard Mr Chas., Rougemont Cottage
Heard Mrs Eliz., St David's hill
Heathman Rev Wm. Grendon, B.A.
    rector of St Lawrence's, 11 Clifton rd
Hedgeland Misses, Magdalen hill
Heinzelman Mrs. A. M., Summerld. hl
Hele Saml. apothecary, Dispensary
Hellins Rev Wm. Brook, chapln. to
    County Prisons; h Pennsylvania
Hellings Rev Nchs. (Indpt.) Clifton pl
Helmore Thos. draper; h 157 Fore st
Helms Mrs. matron, Devon&Ex.Hospl
Henning Edw. gent. 5 Weirfield pl
Herbert Lieut-Genl. Dennis, 17 Sa-
    lutary place, H
Hern Mr Owen, 1 Hiram place
Hernaman Fras. official assignee of
    Court of Bnktcy., Upper Paul st; h
    Hill's court
Hewett Mr. John, *Heavitree*
Hewett Lieut. Thos., R.N., Cowick st
Hexter Thos. lodgings, 6 Silver ter
Hickey Jas. drill mr. 38 Clifton st
Higgins Thos. agent, Coombe street
Higgs Mr John S. 7 Park place
Higgs Capt. Wm. Hy., R.N., *Est. Wonfd*
Hill Mrs Ann, 28 Dix's field
Hill Chas. sec. to Western Provident
    Asstn. & regr. of marriages, Bed-
    ford circus; h Priory cottage
Hill Mr John, 4 Victoria ter. H
Hill Miss Mary, 28 Dix's fields
Hill Wm. B. gent. Mount pleasant
Hinckes Chas. grocer; h Friar's walk
Hincks Rev Thos. (Unitarian) 14
    Mont-le-Grand
Hirtzel Frdk. Dashwood Lake, wine
    mert. &c; h James street
Hirtzel Fdk. T. wine mert; h James st

Hirtzel Hy. Lake, official assignee of Ct. of Bankrptcy., Upper Paul st; h Colleton cres.

Hitchcock Jas. agent to Pickford & Co., Sun st; h Pavilion pl

Hitchcock My. comb mkr. Stepcote hl

Hitt Thos. gent. Upper Mt. Radford

Hoblyn Mrs. & Misses, *Hill House*

Hockin Rev Wm. chaplain to Devon & Ex. Hospital, 18 Salutary place

Hodge Jas. master of St Thos's Workhs

Hodge Miss, 5 Magdalen hill

Hodge Maria, lodgings, 9 Sidwell st

Hodgson Saml. Butler, colr. of rates, Gandy street

Hoffnung Rev Saml. *Jewish rabbi*, 12 Paragon place

Holman Mr Jas. 6 Grosvenor place

Holmes Rev Jas. Ivory, M.A. chaplain to Penitentiary, Baring crescent

Holmes Wm. clerk, 7 Colleton ter

Holroyd Geo. Chaplin, Esq. bank manager; 18 Southernhay place

Holwill Richd. gent. 10 Salutary pl

Hooper Hy. builder, Mnt. Radford

Hooper Hy. Wilcocks, Esq. solr; h Manston terrace

Hooper Jas. clerk, Friar's road

Hooper John Smith, clerk, 4 St Jas.' ter

Hooper Rd., mail contr. 8 Albion pl

Hooper Wm. builder; h David's hill

Hooper Wm. Wills, builder; h Mount Radford

Hooper Wm. gent. 4 Manston ter

Hopping Mrs Agnes, Mount Radford

Hore Mrs Mary, Alphington road

Horndon Misses, 2 St Leonard's ter

Houghton Mr Geo. Hampton bldgs

Howard Wm. serj. at mace, Northrnhay

Howard Rev Wm. Hy., M.A. vicar of St Thomas's, Cowick street

Howe Mrs Amelia, 34 Paris street

Howell Mr Geo., *Heavitree*

Howell Mrs. lodgings, Prospect pl

Hudson Mrs., *Crossmead*, St Thos's

Hughes J. lodgings, 16 Lwr. Eaton pl

Hughes Hy. ironmgr; h 158 Fore st

Hugo Capt. Geo., R.N., 3 Cowick st

Huish Rev John, 21 Dix's field

Hulme Capt. John L., 7, Dix's field

Hunt Geo. church clerk, *South Wonfd*

Hunt Miss Mary Ann, David's hill

Hurst John, scale beam & coffee mill mfr., Paul st

Hussey J. Esq., Manston terrace

Hutchings Mr John, railway inspector, Crediton road

Hutchinson Mrs Har. 9 North terrace

Hutton Mrs. 4 Radnor place

Huxham Frdk. & Chas. ironfounders; h Alphington road

Huxham John, clerk, 7 Longbrook ter

Huxham Geo. clerk, 3 Pavilion pl

Hyett Mrs. brewer; h Summerland cres

Hyett Edwin, brewer; h 2 Windsor ter

Hyett Mr F. A., Church street

Ingham Jas. lay vicar, 2 Weirfields

Ingle Rev John, B.A. curate of St Olaves's, 2 Friar's walk

Ireland Mr John, Cowick st

Jackson Edw. Wm. coach bldr. auctioneer, & bath propr., Upr. Southernhay

Jackson Genl. Geo. 10 Baring cres

Jackson Mr John, Hoppings bldgs

Jackson Mrs Isbla. Mt. Radford park

Jackson Rev Wm. M.A. incbt. of Bedford chapel, 2 Pennsylvania ter

Jacobs Mr Jph. 7 Albion pl. H

James Edw. oil, &c. dlr; h Exe islnd

James Mr Philip, 7 North terrace

James Mrs Chltte. 5 Midway ter

Janson Hy. U. gent. 6 Pennsylvania ter

Jarman John, inland revenue clerk, 86 South street

Jarvis Ambrose P. ironmngr. &c; h Exe view

Jeffery E. artist, 8 East Southernhay

Jeffery Capt. R. barrackmr. Topsham rd

Jenkins Mrs., Park place, H

Jennings Mrs Ann, Poltimore place

Jervis John, Esq., Heavitree road

Jerwood Jas. Esq. 9 Dix's field

Jess Mrs Eliz. Victoria ter. Mrd

Jewell J. waiter, Paris street

Johnson Mrs., Victoria ter. Pvna

Johnson Wm. gent. Salutary mt. H

Jonas Benj. watchmaker's tool dlr. 3 Bartholomew street

Jones Mrs Ann, 4 Brook green ter

Jones Mrs Sarah, 6 Sidwell st

Jones Mrs. 10 Verney place

Jones Pitman, Esq., *St Loyes, East Wonford*

Jones Wm. gardener, Well lane

Jones Wm. Luxmore, gent. St Jas' vla

Joslin John, lodggs. 8 Bystock ter

Joslin & Quick, warehousemen and straw plat mfrs. 8 Queen street

Joslin John Parson; h 8 Queen st

Julian Jno. gent. Mount Radford
Kekewich Geo. Granville, Esq. barrister, 6 Summerland hill
Kekewich Saml. Trehawk, Esq., *Peamr*
Kelly Miss Eliz. 4 Sidwell terrace
Kemp John, lay vicar, Stoke hill
Kemp Mrs. 3 Colleton terrace
Kendall Wm. wln. drapr; h 215 High st
Kennaway Mark, solr., under-sheriff, & stamp distr. Queen st; h Pennsylvania
Kennedy Mrs D. 4 Pennsylvania
Kennier Richd. gent. Heavitree rd
Kenyon Mrs Sus., St. David's hill
Kersteman H. G. Esq. 8 Colleton cres
King Mr George, Black Boy street
King Jas. M. bank cashier, 30 High st
King W. H. C. vesta lamp maker, 45 Magdalen street
Kingdon Mrs Sus. St David's hill
Kingdon Mr Saml. and Wm., New North road
Kingdon Miss A., Hill's court
Kingdon Jane & Son, paper stainers and carpet, &c. dlrs. 180 Fore st
Kingdon Kent, paper stainer ; house New North road
Kingdon Wm. Dashwood, M.D., St. Thomas's Hospital
Kingwell Mr John, Matford ter
Kingwell Mr A. 1 Weirfield place
Kinsman Rev Richd. Byrn, M.A. rural dean and rector of St Paul's, 3 New North terrace
Kitson Fdk. solr ; h 16 Southernhay
Knight Mr J. L., Lower Southernhay
Knight Rev Thos. Henry, B.A. priest vicar, Magdalen street
Knight John, bill poster, Smythen st
Lake Mrs Jane, Black Boy road
Lake Mrs Elizabeth, Friars
Laking Mrs. 3 Hiram place
Land Miss Mary Ann, 4 Hill's court
Land Mr John, King William ter
Lane Miss Eliz., Cowick street
Lane Mrs Sarah, 7 Bouverie place
Langdon Miss, Crossmead
Larkworthy Mrs. 4 Landsdowne ter
Lascelles A. billiards, Sumrld. cres
Lascelles Hy. inspector of licenses, Bartholomew street
Lathy Mrs Caroline, Hopping's pl
Lawless Mrs Cath. 157 Sidwell st
Lawson Miss My. Ann, St Leonard's
Lea Wm. D. clerk, Rosemary cotg

Leak Mr R. L. 1 Summerland hill
Lee Miss Eliz. 4 H. Summerland pl
Lee Mr Edw., Black Boy road
Lee Rev Sackville, U.B., M.A. rector of Allhallows on the Walls, 18 Southernhay place
Lee Miss Sus. Grace, 2 Matford ter
Lee Wm. actuary of Savings' Bank, 21 Bedford circus
Leigh Mr Edw. M. 5 Lr. Sumrld. pl
Lemon Hy. bank clerk, Friars' road
Lendon Robt. gent. Cowick street
Lendon Mr Saml. *Well Park House*
Lenwood Mrs Georgiana, Heavitree
Lester Alf. solr ; h Rose villa, Pvna
Letchworth Thos. Esq. Alphington rd
Lethbridge Mrs Jane, 4 Upr. Mt.Rad
Lewis Miss A., Palace street
Lewis Chas. sec. to West of England Insurance Co. 237 High street
Lewis Rev Geo. Tucker, chaplain to County Lunatic Asylum, *Exminster*
Lewis John, glove mkr. Cowick st
Lewis Jane, engraver ; h 19 Magd. st
Lewis Capt. Thos. Locke, R.E., *Ibsley cottage*, Pennsylvania
Ley Edw. bill poster, Upr. Paul st
Liddon Mrs A. P., Cowick street
Lightfoot Lieut., recruiting officer
Linscott John, pawnbkr. St John's st
Lindsey Mr Robt. 10 Midway ter
Lock Mr John, Park place, Heavitree
Long Mr Saml., Northernhay st
Loram Jas. blacking maker, Mint
Loram Mr Robt. Friars' road
Lott Mrs Ann, Cobourg place
Lovesey Rd. Esq. 5 Mt. Radford ter
Lowe Very Rev Ths. Hill, A.M. *dean of Exeter*, Deanery
Loxton Chas. lessee of market tolls, North road
Lucombe Mrs Frances, Close
Ludlow Saml. gent. 14 Clifton pl
Lutley Saml. B. hop mert. Mt. Radfd
Macdonald Mrs Car., Friars' road
McKeag Jas. schoolr. Paris street
Mackintosh Miss Sus. 2 Queen's sq
Mackintosh Mr Rd. 10 Dix's field
Major Miss Ann, Melbourne place
Mallow Mrs. 1 Mount Radford cres
Maltby Miss, 7 Radnor place
Manlagh Miss Margt. 8 Baring pl
Manley Mr Robt., Verney place
Manley John, store keeper, *Castle*
Manley John, gent. *Belle vue*

Manley Wm. Hy. clerk, Cowick st
Manning Miss Lydia, 6 Baring pl
Mardon My. lodgings, Chicester pl
Marker Jas. lithographer, Palace st
Marks Mr Wm. 3 St Ann's terrace
Marsh Jas. gent. Alphington road
Martin Rev Geo., B.D. chancellor of the diocese, vicar of Harberton, &c. Cathedral yard
Martin Rev Edw. Wm., M.A. curate, 112 St Sidwell street
Martin Misses H. & R. St Leond.'s ter
Martin Edwin, clerk, Bampfylde st
Martin Geo. tax colr. St John's st
Martin My. lodgings, Chichester pl
Martyn Mr Anthy., Cowick street
Martyn Rev John Waddon, M.A., chaplain of the County Prison, 13 Albert terrace
Matthews Mr Henry, 3 Peamore ter
Maunder Mr Robt. 13 St Sidwell's
May Mr Geo. 4 Longbrook terrace
May Geo. Hy. Esq. Baring place, H
May Major Jph. M. 4 Lower Mount Radford ter
May John, clerk, 2 Ltl. Silver ter
May Mr Thomas, Bear street
May Thos. sharebkr. and sec. to West of Eng. and S. Wales Draining Co. &c. 9 Bedfd. cir; h Northernhay Hs
Mayes Wm. last maker, Preston st
Maynard Edw. Cross, assay master, Bartholomew terrace
Mayne Joseph, road contractor, Okehampton road
Measor Paul, postmaster, Bedford st; house 4 Bedford circus
Medland Mr Rd. 3 St Leonard's ter
Melhuish Rev Thos. Abm. (S.C.L.) rector of St Mary Steps, Alphington road
Melhuish Sml. farmer, *South Wonford*
Merchant Mr Thomas, North st
Merivale Mrs Annie, *Cowley bridge*
Meyrick Lieut. Genl. Geo. *Southernhay House*
Miles Rd. Esq., Seville cottage, Mtd
Miles Wm. Esq., 12 Dix's field
Milford John and Fdk. Esqrs. bankers, *Coaver House*, Topsham rd
Miller Lady, *Cleave House, Exwick*
Miller Mr John, 3 North terrace
Miller Mr Robt. 5 Albion place, H
Mills Mrs Jane, Okehampton st

Mills Rev. Wm., D.D. head master of Grammar School, 1 High street
Mitchell Rev A. L. incbt. of Christ Church, Southernhay
Mitchell John, solr; h Southernhay
Mitchell Saml. gent. Upr. Mt. Radfd
Mitchell Wm. cattle dlr. Cowick st
Molland Mrs Eliz. 11 Salutary pl
Monteith Miss Margt. 8 Baring pl
Moresby Mrs H. M., Lr. Mt. Radfd. ter
Morgan J. cashier, Commercial rd
Morgan Mrs Sar., Mt. Ratford ter
Morgan Wm. high constable and sheriff's officer, 6 Bartholomew st
Morrish Mrs Eliz. 4 North terrace
Mortimer Sml. gent. 6 Maddock's rw
Mortimore Miss L. Albert terrace
Moxon Rd. comss. agt. 5 Windsor ter
Moyse Mrs. matron, Penitentiary
Mudge J. E. supt. of water works, Warren cottage
Mugford Miss Sar. 13 Sivell pl. H
Murch Mr Thos. *South Wonford*
Nares Mrs Eliz. 5 Baring place, H
Nation Wm. Esq. 25 Southernhay pl
Neilson Mrs J. P. 5 Longbrook st
Nevett Miss, Clifton place
Newberry Mr W. M., Devonshire pl
Newcombe D. G. fireman, North rd
Newman Geo. post off. clk. Albion pl
Newman Thos. ditto, 11 Sivell pl. H
Newton Rt. ginger br. Goldsmith st
Nias Jph. S. gent. Belmont place
Nicholls Mr John, 6 Buller place
Nicholls Mr Jas., Bartholomew st
Nicholson Mr Geo., Radnor place
Norman John Evomy, Esq, brewer; house Sydney place
Norman Mr R. C. 3 Victoria ter
Norrish Mrs., Queen's square
Nosworthy Mr Mattw. 2 Dix's field
Nosworthy Thos. gent. 24 Dix's field
Nutcombe Miss Frances, Close
Ocock Wm. farmer, Painter's row
Odgers Rev Jas. Commercial road
Oliver Rev Geo., D.D. (Cath.) Mint
Opie Wm. wine mert; h 26 Dix's field
Orchard Mr Chas., St James's st
Owen Mr Thos., Salutary place
Owen Rev Owen, M.A. rector of St Edmund's, Lr. Mount Radford ter
Oxenham Mrs. 29 Southernhay pl
Pain Mr Rd. 8 Lr. Summerland pl
Palmer Thos. excise, 2 Wellgton. pl
Park Edw. coal agt. Railway Station

Parker Sir Chas. Cphr. Bart. *Fair Hl*
Parker Mrs Cath. Hampton bldgs
Parker Jp. gent. 10 Lr. Mt. Radfd. ter
Parkin Mrs. 4 Hampton buildings
Parsons Sar. midwife, Sidwell st
Parsons Mr Wm., Salutary mount
Partridge MrWm. B., Brook green
Pasmore Jas. draper; h 73 High st
Patch Mrs Emma, 16 Upr. Mt. Radfd
Patch Miss Louisa, 3 Southernhay st
Patterson Lieut. General Sir Wm., K.C.H. Baring place
Patterson Mr Wm. 2 Colleton ter
Pattinson Rt. clerk, Victoria terrace
Payne Mrs. 154 St Sidwell's
Pearce Mr Edw. 13 Clifton road
Pearce Mr John, St George's place
Pearce Mr Saml. Old Tiverton road
Pearse Mr Edw., Black Boy road
Pearse Mrs Eliz., Cowick street
Pearse Mr J., Prospect place
Pearse Jas. draper; h 2 Hiram pl
Pearse Jas. jun. draper, *Elm Grove*
Pearse Mrs., Colleton terrace
Pearse John Mortimer, draftsman, Albion place
Pearse Wm. draper; h 171 Fore st
Pearse Wm. clerk, Canal basin
Pedlar Capt. Chas., R.N. Friars' rd
Pellew Mrs My. 5 Hampton place
Pengilley Thos. lodgings, 9 Salem pl
Pennell Mrs Cath., Park place
Penn MrsMy.Garland,154 Sidwell st
Penn Mrs Susan, Magdalen hill
Perkins Rt. tripe dresser, Ewing st
Perkins Misses, Melbourne place
Perriam Mr. Geo. 22 Magdalen st
Petherbridge Jas. farmer, *East Wonfd*
Petherick Rev John, 11 Radnor
Pettle Mrs H., Alphington road
Phillips Mr John, Old Tiverton road
Phillips Mrs Mary, 7 St Ann's ter
Phillips MrWm.15Lr.Mt.Radford ter
Phillips Mr Wm. 15 Salem place
Phillpotts Rt. Rev Henry,DD. *Bishop of Exeter*, The Palace
Phillpotts Rev Wm. John, M.A. *precentor*, Close
Pickard Mr John, 4 Albion pl. H
Pickford and Co. carriers, Sun street, (James Hitchcock, *agent*)
Pigot Captain, Cowick street
Pike Mary Ann, lodgs. 2 Hill's ct
Pike Richard, clerk, 1 Queen's ter
Pile Mrs Mary, *Heavitree*

Pilgrim MrEdw.Trapp,Magdalen hill
Pim Mr Joseph, Commercial road
Pim Mr Wm. Cowick terrace
Pim Mrs Elizabeth, Alphington rd
Pinhay Mr Robt. 10 Albert ter. Mtd
Pinhay Misses, 2 Albert ter. Mtd
Pinn Mr Joseph, Commercial road
Pitts James, solr; h Black Boy st
Platel Mr Henry, 10 Salem place
Pollard Mr T. B. Alphington road
Polson Mrs Gna. 33 Sothernhay
Pook Mrs. 4 Grosvenor place
Poole Henry, lodgs. 7 Bystock ter
Pope Mr Bartw. P. Claremont ter
Pollard Thos. B. gent. Alphington rd
Pollett John, clerk, 15 Harris place
Porter Rev Chas. B.D. Alphington rd
Porter John, grocer; h 91 North st
PotterRd.P.ship&boat bldr.Haven bk
Powning Mr John, 27 South street
Poynter James, draper, St Sidwell st
Prater Mr Wm. 7 Salem place
Pratt Mrs. *Combe Leonard*
Pratt Thos. gent. Stafford ter. H
Presswell Mr Wm. 5 Hill's court
Priaulx Mr Joshua, 3 Barnfield
Price Captain, 10 Lower Eaton pl
Price Chas. W. lodgings, 23 Dix's fd
Priddy Mr Robert, 8 Friar's walk
Pridham Peter, rate colr. Sidwell st
Pridham Jph. excise offr. Cowick st
Prince Mr Henry, Belmont place
Prinsep Mrs H. 14 Albert terrace
Prout Mr James, 2 Sivell place, H
Puddicombe Mrs Eliz. 2 Belmont pl
Quick Hy. warehsman; h 8 Queen st
Quick Mr John Paul, 5 Okehptn. ter
Quick Jas. Walter, travr. Okehptn. rd
Radcliffe Rev John Wm. curate of St Sidwell's, Mount Radford terrace
Radcliffe Misses, Waterloo Cottage
Radford Benj. T. Esq. Montpelier
Radford John Geo. solr; h *Sidmouth*
Radford Elizabeth, servants' register office, Goldsmith street
Rea Miss Eliza, 4 Bystock terrace
Redwood Rt. ironfounder; h Bonhay
Reece Mr John, 6 Belmont place
Reece Mrs Eliz. 6 Lansdowne ter
Reed Mrs Ann, Stokeland villa
Reed Mrs Isabella, 2 Victoria ter
Reed Jas., auctioneer, &c ; h*Wonford*
Reed John, clerk, 6 St Ann's ter
Reeves Edw. lodgings, Pavilion pl
Rendle J. violin tchr. St John's ter

Rew Henry, farmer, *Whipton Barton*
Rew John, farmer, *Exwick Barton*
Rew John, gent. Pennsylvania
Rew Wm. farmer, East Wonford
ReynoldsChs. dogwhipper, Cathedral
Reynolds Mr Zacharias, 10 St Jas. pl
Richards Genl. Alfd. 3 Summerld. hl
Richards John, salt dealer, Quay hill
Richards Mrs Har. 5 St Ann's ter
Richards Mr Richd. sen. Haven bank
RichardsRd.ship owner,&c.Friar's rd
Richárds Mrs S., Black Boy road
Richards Mrs Mary, Park pl., Mtd
Rickard Hercules, clerk, 2 Park pl
Ridge Mr James, Cathedral yard
Ridgewey John, tea dlr ; h 1 High st
Ridgway Simon Radford, classical
  schl.&PolytechnicInst.*Magdln.Hs*
Rippon Mr John D., Well lane
Rippon Mrs Ann, Poltimore place
Roberts Mr Evans, 10 Pavilion pl
Roberts Lady, Albert villa, Mtd
Roberts Jane, farmer, *Exwick*
Roberts Miss Susan, Queen's square
Roberts Wm. riding master, Paris st
RobinsonGeo. school,7 Melbourne pl
Rodd Miss Jane, 11 Southernhay
Rodd Thomas, inspector of weights
  and measures, St George's square
Rodd Mr Thos. Fras., Topsham rd
Rodier Jas. travlr. 7 Lr. Sumrld. pl
Rogers Capt. Hy. 9 Mont le Grand
Rogers Mrs Ann, Victoria terrace
Rogers Mr C. F. Magdalen road
Rogers Mrs Lucy, 3 Albion pl. H
Rogers Rev John, M.A. canon, Close
Rollo Capt. Robt. Rougemont cottage
Rookes Rev Charles, LL.B. rector of
  Nymet Rowland, Hill's court
Rookes Mrs J. 3 Poltimore terrace
Rookes Mrs Cath. Summerland hill
Rookes Wm. horse dlr. Heavitree rd
Roope MajorGen.Benj. 13Victoria ter
Roper Rev Chas.Rodwell, A.M. rector
  of St Olave's, Mount Radford
Roper Geo. post off. clerk, Sivell pl
Rose Charles, sexton, 7 Buller pl
Rose Edward H. deputy governor of
  County Prison, New North road
Rosebear Mrs Eliza, 8 Eaton place
Ross Mrs Lucy, 2 Summerland hill
Rosser Capt. Thos. R.N. Park ter. H
Rouse Miss M. 1 Eldon place
Rowe Jas. blacking mkr. Coombe st
Rowe Mrs Ann, St Olave square

Rowe Rev John James, rector of St
  Mary Arches, 8 Mont le Grand
Rowe Mr Wm. 8 Silver terrace
Ryde John Gabriel,gent.7 Baring cres
Sadler Mr James, 11 Belmont pl
Salisbury John,comb mkr.9 Bartw.st
Salter Eleanor Ann, religious tract
  depôt, Deanery place
Salter James, Esq. 3 Albert ter. Mtd
Salter Mr John, Homefield place, H
Salter Mr John, 15 Harris place
SalterThos.Upham,gent.*East Wonfd*
Sampson Thos. gent. 15 Salutary pl
Sanders Edw. A. Esq. banker, *Stoke-
  hill House, Heavitree*
Sanders Fredk. solr. 4 East Sthnhay
Sanders Mrs J. B. Friars
Sanders Mrs C. Black Boy road
Sanders Mr James, Northernhay st
Sanders Ralph, gent. 9 Colleton cres
Sanders Robt. gent. Crescent House
Sanders Robt. ship agent,&c. West st
SandersThos.C.wine mert; hGandy st
Sandford Thos. clerk, Painters' row
Sandys Mrs J. Hampton buildings
Savery John, draper ; h *Silverton*
Sayell Mr Joseph, 58 St Sidwell st
Scanes Miss Rachel, Cowick street
Scanes Miss Rose, 10 Summrld. st
Scanes Mr John, Upr. Mt. Radford
SchofieldWm. Esq. colr.of inland rev.
  Bartw. ter; office South st
Scott Daniel, nail mkr, Cowick st
Scott Rev Ralph, (Wes.) Salutary pl
Scott Mr John, 2 Albion place, H
Scott Dr Wm. R. and Mrs.,Deaf and
  Dumb Institution
Seaman Mrs Chltte. 12 St James' pl
Searle Mrs Jane, 2 Topsham road
Searle Mrs Lydia, 4 Magdalen hill
Searle Mr R. Cheeke street
Searle W. L. gent. Topsham road
Seaward Mrs Mary, 9 St James' pl
Seccombe RevWm.(Wes.) Salutarypl
Selley John, clerk, New North road
Serena Mrs Ann, Wellington place
Sercombe John Clampitt, merchant;
  h 7 Colleton crescent
Sercombe Mr John, Cowick fields
Shapter MrsMargt.12LrMt Radfd.ter
Sharland Mrs. 3 Albion terrace
Sharland Mr Jno. Wm. Peamore ter
Sharland Richd. clerk, Claremont ter
Shaw Captain James, 1 Palace st

Shears John, head beadle and relieving officer, 6 Nelson place

Shelford Mrs E. J. Claremont grove

Shelton Mr John, *Heavitree*

Shepherd Rt. clerk, Russell terrace

Sheppard Jph. wn. dpr. &c; h *Cowley Hs*

Shield Rev Geo. Hy. O., M.A. rector of Trinity, 3 Southernhay

Shipley Mrs Sarah, Well lane

Short Mrs Eliz. 1 Magdalen hill

Shortt Capt. W. T. P. 7 Midway ter

Shorto Edward, clerk to St Petrock's, Russell terrace

Shuttleworth Mrs Ann,12Victoria ter

Simms John, gent. Hopping's bldgs

Sison Mrs Eliza,11 Lr Mt Radford ter

Skinner Mrs E. 96 St Sidwell st

Slatter Rev Geo. Maximilian, B.D. dean's vicar and vicar of West Anstey, Close

Smale Thos. currier ; h Silver ter

Smith Captain F. St David's hill

Smith Miss Jane, 2 Salutary place

Smith Mrs Mary, 4 Albert ter. Mtd

Smith Mrs Phœbe, Grosvenor place

Smith Mrs. lodgings, Hill's bldgs

Smith Mr Richard, Waterbeer street

Smith Wm. Hewitt, clerk, Well lane

Smith Mr Wm. 9 Park place

Smallridge Mr Wm. Cowick street

Snell Mr Thos. Western, Chichester pl

Snell Mr John, Mont le Grand

Snow Thomas, wine merchant and banker ; h *Franklyn Hs*.St Thos.'s

Snow Ts.Maitland,banker,*Frnkln.Hs*

Snow Misses, Belmont House

Snow Mr Wm. *Heavitree*

Snow Wm. keeper, *Castle*

Somerville Capt. Jno.12Mont le Grand

Soper Henry, farmer, St Thomas's

Soper Mrs. 7 Poltimore terrace

Southard M thw. machine ruler,Bear st

Southcott Rd. lodgings, 12 Castle st

Sowton Miss, 3 Grosvenor place

Spark John, draper ; h *East Wonford*

Sparke Robt. brick mkr. Black Boy rd

Sparke Wm. ship owner, Verney pl

Sparkes Mr Hy.& Miss,Mont le Grand

Sparkes John, beadle and relieving officer, 3 Verney place

Sparkes Thomas Truslade, gent. 3 Magdalen hill

Sparkes Wm. drilling master, Paul st

Spence Mrs Ann, 6 North terrace

pence Mr Ralph, *Duryard Wood*

Sprague John, cane worker, Rack st

Sprague Mrs Mary, St Sidwell ter

Spreat Mr Wm. 263 High street

Squance John, librarian, Cathedral yd

Squire Mr Wm. Lr Summerland pl

Stabback Miss Hannah, Sivell place

Stabback Mrs Julia, St David's hill

Stabback George, clerk, Palace st

Stamp Thos. block mkr. Comrcl. rd

Stanley Capt. Wm. P., Mt Radford ter

Stanley Mrs Mary, Black Boy road

Stark Mrs Ann, Palace street

Starling Mr Wm., Clifton road

Steel Mrs Ann, Cobourg place

Steel Dd. supt. of police, Northernhay

Steer Chas. Wm.Esq. *Spring Lawn,H*

Stephens John, Esq. Stafford ter. *H*

Stephens Rev Richd. M.A. sub-dean ; house *Holcombe Burnell*

Stevens Ven John Moore, A.M. archdeacon of Exeter, Close & *Otterton*

Stewart Arthur, comptroller of customs, Stafford terrace, *Heavitree*

Stirling Major, Clifton House

Stocker Mrs E. F. 4 Verney place

Stocker Robert, travlr. 3 Salem pl

Stone Mr Charles, St James' place

Stone John, lodgings, 5 Sidwell st

Stopps Mrs D., New North road

Stott Rev Ralph, (Wes.) 6 Salutary pl

Street Mrs D., Sivell place, H.

Stringer Mr T., Belmont place

Stritch Mrs Janet, 11 Bedford circus

Strong J. carrier, Commercial road

Strong Wm. bone crusher, Bonhay

Sutton Rev Adoniah Schuyler, curate of St James', Salutary place

Sutton John, waiter, 2 Poltimore pl

Swale Mr David, *South Wonford*

Swale Mr R., Prospect pl., Tops. rd

Sweetman Wm. Esq. *Weir Cliff cottg*

Symons Miss Priscilla, Black boy rd

Tabor Miss Martha, Hampton bldgs

Tanner Capt Thos., R.N., Sumlnd. pl

Tapley James, 7 Verney place

Taylor Mr Fredk. and Mrs Mary, 2 Groveland villa, Mount Radford

Taylor Mr George, 1 Albion place, H

Taylor Mr Robt. 17 Verney place

Teddy Mrs. 3 Mount pleasant

Teague Rd. reporter, 236 High st

Templer Mrs Chatte. 16 Dix's field

Templer J. W. gent. Mount Radford

Terrell Mrs Eliz. 3 Magdalen hill

Testy Mr Rt. Jph. 4 Hampton place

Thacker Robt. Pearson, printer and joint propr. of the *Gazette ;* house 12 Dix's field

Thomas Mrs Eliz. 1 St. James' ter

Thomas Mr John, Lr. Magdalen st

Thomas Jas. B. clerk, Cowick street

Thomas Mrs Sarah, Hill's court

Thompson Mrs Chatte. 1 Castle ter

Thompson Col. Thos., Black boy rd

Thompson Miss L. J. 3 Victoria ter

Thornton John, gent. 5 Sivell pl., H

Threlkeld D. gent. Vic. ter., Mag. rd

Tibbs Jph. draper ; h Alphington rd

Tighe Mrs Maria, 3 Belmont place

Tilman Mrs Mary, 6 Hampton blgs

Timewell Jas. R. clerk, St. David's ter

Tinling Rev Edwd. Douglas, M.A., government inspector of schools, 30 Southernhay place

Toby Mr John, sen. 10 York buildgs

Toby Mr Thos., Lower North street

Todderick Mrs Julia, *Heavitree*

Toll Mrs Ann, 43 Southernhay place

Tolley Mr John, 10 Paris street

Tolley John, blacking mfr. Clifton rd

TombsWm. Esq. bank mgr.83 Fore st

Tomlinson Mr John, *Whipton*

TompsonWm. clerk to the Water Co., Bedford circus ; h 2 Queen's ter

Tonar John, linen and carpet warehouse, 266 High street

Toose Lewis Edw. gent. Tiverton rd

Tothill Mr Rd., Salutary place, H

Townsend John, flock makr. West st

Townsend Wm. clerk, Friars' walk

Toye Mrs Ann, 3 East Southernhay

Toye Rev Jph. Thps., M.A., rector of St Stephen's, Victoria ter., Mtd

Tozer Mrs Rebecca, Leonard's quay

Traer Wm. lodgs. 41 Southernhay pl

Traer Mr Wm. 6 York buildings

Treble John Richd. medicine vendor, Bartholomew street

Treffry Geo. tea dlr ; h 168 Fore st

Treffry Thos. do ; h St Olave's sq

Treffry Mr Saml., St Olave's square

Trefusis Mrs Eliz. 6 Southernhay st

Trehane Mr Spn., Bartholomew st

Tremlett Mrs My. 9 Albert ter., Mtd

Trew Miss Eliza, 1 Clarence place

Trewman Robt. John, printer, &c ; h 11 Salutary place, H

Trimble Jno. pawnbkr ; h Cowick st

Tripp Capt.Jno. Upton, R.N., Mount Radford

Trobridge James T. 7 Silver terrace

Truscott Geo. Fdk. solr ; h Deanery pl

Tucker Rev Chas., M.A., 2 Baring cr

Tucker Geo. drapr ; h New North ter

Tucker Miss Har. 8 Hr. Sumlnd. pl

Tucker Rev Marwood, M.A., rector of St Martin's, 4 St Leonard's place

Tucker Michl. grcr ; h Melbourne pl

Tucker Walter, gent. 9 Belmont pl

Tucker Mr Wm. 11 Albion place, H

Tucker Wm. bank clk. Matford ter

Tuckett Jas. and Son, herbal doctors, Botanic Hall, 44 Bartholomew st

Tuckett Nichs. concentrated manure manfr. &c. Commercial road

Turner Rev John Fisher, rector of St Mary Major, Colleton crescent

Turner Rd. Esq., Fair hill, Mt.Rad

Turner Mrs My. Upper Mt. Radford

Turner Mrs D., St Sidwell's terrace

Tyrrell John, barrister and judge of County Court, 42 Magdalen street

Upjohn Mr John, Cowick street

Vanstone Rt. corn dealer, Gandy st

Vatcher Hy. colr. of rates & sharebroker, 3 Bedford street

Venn Henry Clement, solicitor ; h Bellevue villa, Mount Radford

Venton Mrs Margt.37 Bartholomew st

Vigers Mr John, Albion place

Viscick Mrs. Homefield place, H

Vosper Mrs Eliz. 149 St Sidwell st

Wager and Smale, carriers, Queen st

Wager Charles ; house Queen street

Wake Richd. Esq., Heavitree road

Walkey Mrs Catherine, St. David's hl

Walkey Joseph Elliott Collyns, solicitor ; house *Ide*

Wallis Lieut. Jas., R.N., 11 Albion pl

Walters Chas. clerk, Salutary place

Ward Mrs J. 2 Claremont terrace

Ward Mrs Lydia, 3 Paragon place

Ward Richd. gent. Alphington road

Wardrobe Mrs., *South Wonford*

Ware Mr. 4 St Leonard's terrace

Warr Mr John Hood, Hill's court

Warren Mrs. Port view, Mt. Radford

Warren Rev Geo. 7 Mont-le-Grand

Warren John, solr. and city coroner; h 2 Bradninch buildings

Warren Samuel Hobson, solicitor ; h 2 Bradninch buildings

Warren Geo. tripe dlr. Goldsmith st

Watson Mrs L., St David's hill

Watts Geo. tax assessor, Mt. Radfd.

Way John, draper; h 155 Fore st
Webb Mrs Isabella, Salutary place, H
Webber F. upholstress, New buildgs
Webber Geo. farmer, *Little Cleave*
Webber Miss Jane, 5 Magdalen hill
Webber Richd. farmer, Sandygate, H
Wedderburn Alex. inspectr. of mail coaches, 14 Longbrook street
Weedon Mr Geo., Bartholomew st
Weedon Mrs Mary, 19 Bartholomew st
Welch Joseph, surveyor of taxes, 4 Park place
Wellington Mr J., Melbourne terrace
Were Mrs Margaret, 3 Southernhay
West Mr Jas. Topsham road
Westcott Mrs. lodgings, Friar's walk
Wescott Mrs. midwife, Exe Island
Wharton Benj. traveller, Silver ter
Wheler Jas. gent. 7 Eaton place
Whitchurch Wm. W. gent. Salutary pl
White Edw. gent. Okehampton road
White Chas. lodgings, 15 Castle st
Whitlock Mrs Amelia, 12 Verney pl
Whitton Mary, upholstress, Mint
Whitton Mrs Eliza, 44 Paris street
Widdicombe Hy. mariner, Comcl. rd
Wilcocks J. M., gent. *Spurbarn*
Wilcocks Jas. M. grocer; h Barth.yd
Wilcocks Jno. C. drpr; h 1 Colleton c
Wilkey Mr J. F.. Richmond villa
Wilkey John, travelr. Claremont ter
Wilkinson Mrs My. 5 St James' pl
Williams Mr Edwin, Paul street
Williams Mrs and Misses, Larkbeare
Williams Capt. Jas., Alphington rd
Williams Major Jph. 12 Radnor pl
Williams Rd. jun. manager of Gas Works, Exe Island
Williamson Miss, 7 Windsor terrace
Wills Rev Geo. Wm. Burrow, M.A., rector of St Leonard's, Magdln. rd
Wills Misses M. & E. A., Richmd.pl
Wilson Mrs. Bartholomew terrace
Windeatt James, gent. Hill's court
Winslow Mrs Mary, 1 North terrace
Winsor Hy. verger, Nelson place
Winstanley Mrs My., Black boy rd
Wippell Mr Jph. and Rev Wm., St David's hill
Wolland Thos. B. gent. Salutary mt
Wolland Mrs Ann, *Heavitree*
Wolston Rev Thos. 7 Mt. Radfd. ter
Wood Mr Thos. 8 St James' place
Wood Wm. coachman, Pavilion place
Woodgate Wm. gold beater, North st
Woofe Mrs H., Black boy road
Woolcombe Mrs Eliz., St Leonard's ter
Woolcombe Rev Chas. W., Poltimore pl
Woolcombe Miss My. 6 Chichester pl
Woolley Mrs. lodgings, Bystock ter
Woolmer Edw. printer and joint proprietor of the *Gazette*; h 2 Barnfld
Wooster John, travlr. Alphington rd
Worthy Rev Chas. curate of St Paul's, and chap. of city prison, Bartholomew terrace
Worthy Mrs Eliz. 6 Hampton place
Wotton Ann, fur cleaner, Paul street
Wreford John, Esq. 5 Baring cres
Wreford Mrs C. 4 Friar's walk
Wrentmore Wm. gent. 8 Albert ter
Wrey Mrs Sophia, 7 Pennsylvania
Wright Fras. paper hanging dealer, &c. 14 Eaton place
Wright Hy. P. landing waiter, &c. 7 Lansdowne terrace
Wright Capt. John, R.N., Eldon pl
Wright Jas. coal agent, West street
Wyatt Mrs Mary, 5 Longbrook st
Yarde Mrs Ann, 4 New North road
Young John K. clerk, Hampton blgs
Zamoiske Rodolph, trvlr.Waterbeer st

INDEX TO PERSONS AND FIRMS

ARRANGED UNDER THE SUCCEEDING

CLASSIFICATION OF TRADES AND PROFESSIONS.

Channing Geo. 127;
Rd. 69; Wm 96,
114,127;W.&G.21
Channon Esha, 133
Chanter Jas. 117
Chaplin Wm. 93; &
Westburn, 123
Chapman John, 26,
82; Jph. 13, 62
Chapple Charles,69;
Edred, 21; Jas. 21;
John, 7, 26, 115;
Robert, 127
Charlton C. A.& E 1
Chave Samuel, 98
Chilcott John, 8
Chorley John, 14
Chown John, 26,142
Chudley John, 8
Clapp Benj. 8; Rd·
112; Samuel, 32;
Wm. 125
Clarence Emma, 1
Clark Jas. 21, 23,69,
121,131; Saml 62;
and Timewell, 85;
Thos.117: Wm.114
Clarke Jas. 69; Sml.
17, 50, 136
Clatworthy Louisa85
Cleeve Abm. 78,148;
Susanna, 118
Clement Henry, 98;
John, 69
Clifford Misses E. &
E. 1; Wm. 16
Clode Wm. 25
Clogg Ann,123; Jno.
107; Joseph, 107
Clynick John, 69
Cobley J. 142; Wm.1
Cockerom Sarah, 30
Cockren John, 24
Coffin Geo. 7, 126
Cole Geo. 72; Jane,
68; Rd. 8; Saml.
60; Wm. 114
Coleman Chs. F. 17;
Wm. 32
Collings Paul, 69,80;
Rt. 8; Wm. 21,114
Collins Ann M. 1;
Chas. 127; John,
123,124,143; Jph.
17, 31
Colmer Wm. 17
Colson & Spark, 78,
148; John, 120
Commin Jas. 38; S.
and T. 130, 145
Commins G. C. 127
Compton Stephen,69
Coneybeer S. 14, 69
Connett Jmh. 43; J.
69; Wm. 25, 69
Cook Frederick,7, 25
Coombe Eliz. 123;
Geo. 83; John, 36;
Saml. 114; W.117
Coombes John, 60
Coope Wm. 98

Cooper Geo. 45, 120
Copleston E. A. 6,52
Coplestone John, 8
Copp & Poynter, 78
Cornelius J. 70, 114
Cornish Rt. S. 126,
132;&Whitehead,
23
Cossins Richard, 26
Cosway John, 8
Cottrell Alfred, 127
Court Rebecca, 70
Courti Paul,135,141
CousinsIsc.1; Jno127
Cox Hy. 2; H. S.93;
John, 47; Rt. 24;
Saml. M. 6
Crabb Eliz. 17; Jas.
23; John, 26; Ts.
59,128; Wm. 17
Crabbe Wm. R. 6,52
Crang & Son, 26
Cresswell J.& Co. 84
Cridge Philip,69,144
Crocker John, 114
Crockett Wm. 145
Crocombe Wm. 69
Croft Wm. 17
Crook John, 69
Croome John, 31
Cross Chas. 141; Fs.
26; Geo. 15; Wm.
121, 145
Crouch John, 17;
James, 98
Cruickshank J.W.48
Cummings John, 17;
and Venton, 117
CunninghamChs. 64
Curson & Son, 16,76
CuthbertsonC.F.127;
Jph. 23; Wm.8,36
Dale Geo. 28; Eliz.
69; Wm. 98
Dalgleish Hy. 55,58
Damerel Jno. 52, 72
DancasterT.85;J.100
Daniel Wm. 127
Dann Wm. 8, 60
Darby Jas. 23, 32
Dare Thos. 69, 139
Darke Edw.24;Geo.
24; James, 24
Davey A.17; F.123;
Jn.17; Jno.&Sons,
93; Ths.121; Wm.
5, 14, 69, 90
Davidge J. 28; T. 17
Davies Mrs. 1; S. &
D. 60, 131; Wm.15
Davis Chtte. 85; H.
73; John, 18, 24;
M. 62; Robt. 85
Davy Chas. 32; Frs.
84; John, 8, 36;
My. 54; & Son,
77; Wm. 58; W.
and Son, 42
Davys Wm. 93, 100
Daw John, 6
Dawe Wm. 21, 23

DawsonR. H. & Co.
65, 145; Wm. 48,
126
Deacon and Co. 35
Dean John, 12, 17
Dear Thomas, 55
De la Garde P.C.125
Delaney Mattw. 80
Denham Daniel, 98
De Niceville M. 116
DenshamAaron,127;
Wm. 114
Dewdney Jno. S.88,
103; Rt. & Co.94;
Rd. 52; Rd. H. 60
Dey Thos. 93, 100
DickerH.P.92;Ths.8
Dickes Barthw. 145
Dilling Wm. 69
Dimond John, 8
Dingle D. 25; W. 78
Dipstale E. 93; J. 85
Discombe John, 43
Dobbs Chltte. 73
Dobel Jn.93; Jph.98
Doble Elizabeth, 17
Doeg E. L. 85
Dolbear Giles, 26
Doney Wm. 114
Down Geo. 127; My.
85; Rd. 81
Downe & Son,59,100
Downey John,65
Downing Wm. 14
Downman Mary, 85
Downs Anna M. 1
Drake Augsts. 99;
Edwin, 14, 140;
Geo. 55, 114; Geo.
Henry, 6, 52, 104;
My.85; Sarah, 55;
Thos.E. 6, 52, 104
Drayton & Sons, 16
DrewE.114;Jph.114
Drewe & Son, 145
Druller Caroline, 17
Dudley Henry, 3
Dunley John S. 17
Dunn A. S. &E.62;
Hanh. 83; Hy. 60
Dunsford M. L. &
R. 42A
Durant G. 101, 145
Duval Fras. 1, 105
Dyer S. 42, 83: Ths.
31, 60, 118, 127
Dymond Jno. 9; Rt.
48, 126; Wm. 47
Eagles Eliz. 122
Eales Hanh. 123;
Har. 85; Rd. 6
Eardley Thos. 43
East Henry, 43
EasterbrookWm.127
Easterling Thos. 32
Easton J. 121
Ebbles Jno. L. 60
Edbrook Wm. 29
Eddy George, 69
Edelstein J. W. 60,
134

Edye John, 125
Edger & Harris, 78
Edger Wm. 131
Edwards Fras. 17;
Eliz. 57; J. H.
27; Rd. 17; W.69
Ekers Wm. 108
Ellett Wm. 39, 69
Ellicombe H. M. &
J. B. 6, 104
Elliott Wm. Hy. 99
Ellis Betty, 122;
Fdk. 105; Hy. &
Sons, 115, 141;
John, 26
Elson Henry T. 8
Elston E. 181; W. 55
Elworthy Ann, 69;
Eliza,85; Fredk.
69; Geo. 127
Emery Fras. 30
Endacott Edw. 60;
Geo. 23, 69, 82;
Saml. 8; Wm. 56
England Hy. 8; J.
24; My. Ann,123;
Wm. 24
Escott Wm. 108
Esworthy Hy. 69;
Thos. 69; Wm. 43
Evans Alfd.&Co.45,
120; Chas. 127;
Edwin. 144; Jno.
98; Saml. 17,114;
Wm. 17; S. E. &
L. 85
Eveleigh John, 55,
60; Eliz. 85; Wm.
23, 55
Every Rd. & Son, 6
Facey Hugh, 23
Fagan Charles, 47
FarrantFredk.G.125
Farthing John, 44
Featherstone Eliz.
114; Wm. C. 79,
103, 120
Ferenbatch Jph. &
Co. 141
FergusonWm.27,70
Ferris E.B.42;F.127
Fewins Wm. 1
Fey John, 27
Finnimore Eliz.123;
Wm. 127,141
Fisher J. 28; Rt. 23
Fitze A. 136; J. 16
Fitzgerald J. B. 78
Fitzpatrick Thos. 17
Fixott James, 99
FletcherJ.102;R.47
Flewellin Saml. 17
Flood Jno.17; Nichs.
56; Noah, 127;
Wm. 127
Flond Thomas, 6
Folland W. J. 141
Follett & Co. 84, 132
Follett John, 37
Foote S. B. 60, 130

Mitchell Eliza, 1; & Ford, 6; Hy. 17; John, 127; Pris. 85; My. 85; Thos 60, 93; Thos. & Co. 116; Wm. 69

Mogridge W. K. 89, 110

Monkley Wm. 139

Moody Chas. 17, 24

Moon John, 60

Moore Ann, 69; Geo. A. 7, 52, 67, 68; Jno. 23, 26, 69; Saml. 69, 114; Wm. 60; W. D. 6, 52

Morgan James, 43; Thomas, 22, 95

Morrish S. and O. 1; T. 65

Mortimer John, 14, 22; Roger, 14; Wm. 22, 112

Mortimore John, 95; Thos. 69; Wm. 8, 40, 112

Morton M. 69; W. 23

Moschrisker F. A. 105

Moss Saml. 21, 24, 117; Thos. J. 62

Mountstephens J 85

Moxey A. and W. 1; John, 17

Moxley John, 58

Moxon Jph. 69; Jno. 69

Mudge P. P. 105

Mugford Gilbt. 8; Jas. 17; Philip, 69

Mullens John Dl. 127

Munk Wm. 72

Murch Jas. 101, 145; Sarah, 36

Myers James, 28

Napper James, 35

Narraway Henry, 93

Neale Thomas, 69

Neck Wm. 60, 101

Nethercott Henry, 17

Newberry Robt. 114; W. 43

Newcombe Ann, 123; Danl. 114; John, 39; Sarah and Co. 30

Newman Car. 62, 68; John Francis, 105

Newton Wm. 8

Nex Wm. 142

Nicholls Eliz. 85; Jno. 17, 25; J.P. 25, 56; Sus. 12

Nightingale Rt. 62, 78

Nobbs Robert, 69

Norcombe Jas. 78, 148

Norman Abm. 12; & Co. 19, 82; Fras. 12; Geo. 35, 83; Jno. 12, 14; Wm. 12

Norris Thomas Geo. 125; Wm. 93

Norris & Redway, 35

Norrish John, 35

Northam James, 71, 72, 86; Wm. 144

Northcott Henry, 17

Norton J. 8; Wm. 103

Northway Rd. 114

Nosworthy Wm. 114; Ellen, 1

Nott Wm. 24, 89

Nurton David, 42A

Ocock John, 114

Odam George, 98

Oliver John, 24

Oman Elizabeth, 123

Orchard Chtte. 1; Jno. 24; Wm. 2

Osborn Geo. & Son, 53, 136, 143; Hy. 143; Jas. 61; John, 39; J. D. 30; Wm. 61, 143

Osment E. 25; J. 115

Otton Joseph, 126

Owen George, 31

Oxley Edw. 99

Paddon T. J. 75

Page Eliz. 69

Pain Rd. 69: Jane 24

Palk John, 31, 52

Palmer Peter, 69: Rt. 100: Sar. 114: Thos. 8: Wm. 8, 24, 36

Pannell John, 24: Wm. 23, 26

Parish Jno. 22: R. 117

Park James, 131

Parker Btw. 43: John B. 125: Mary, 118: Wm. 59

Parkin, Isaac, 69

Parnell James, 69

Parr Jno. 60: Jas. 114

Parratt J. & W. 23

Parson George, 29

Parsons John Hy. 33, 69: John King, 33

Partridge J. 17: W. 17

Pasmore and Savery, 78, 148: John, 35: Thos. 139: Wm. 55

Pates George, 31, 52, 60: Charles, 125

Patey Margaret, 1

Paul A 1: E.W. 6, 52

Payne John, 142

Paynter Car. 122

Pear George, 47

Pearse Brothers, 72: Eliz. 1: Edw. 31: & Sons, 78: Geo. 66, 80: Jas. 148: Wm. & Co. 78

Pedrick Wm. 80

Pelzer Miss J. 148

Pembroke Hy. 17

Penberthy Isaac, 55: James, 55

Pengilley Robert, 20

Pennell Rd. L. 99

Penney Thomas, 114

Pentecost M. 1: Rd. 93

Pepperell Wm. 23

Perkins Ann, 114: Grace, 24: Jno. 99A: J. S. 125: S. S. 125

Perry Edw. 28, 69: Jas. 127: Wm. 24

Perryman Mary, 114

Persac E. 105

Peters Edw. 60, 74: Jas. 74, 137: Robt. 146: Richard, 74

Petherick John Wm. 6: Chas. John, 93

Petherbridge J. 147

Phillips Adam, 127: John, 20: Sus. 60

Pike Har. 83, 123: E.R. 123: Geo. 88A, 127: Thomas, 127: Wm. 69

Piller Robert, 60

Pillman Richd. 138: Wm. 64

Pim John, 49

Pinder Thos. 1: Rd. & Co. 32, 64, 127

Pinn Jas. 32, 127: Jno. 17, 23: Thos. 26, 115

Pinney Wm. 105

Piper Wm. 98

Pippett Chas. 62, 68

Pitt Geo. & Thos. 60

Pleace Jonth. 144

Please Charlotte, 1

Plowman Geo. H. 148

Pollard W. 28: W. C. 103

Pomeroy G. 54: H. 114

Ponsford Jermh. 24: Jas. 17: Jph. 58

Poole Sml. 46: Ths. 80

Pope Ephm. 60: Hy. 58, 89: John, 8, 17, 64: John W. 6: Jno. and Son, 117

Portbury John, 17

Porter & Hinckes, 60, 84: Wm. 25

Potter Geo. 55, 114: John, 83: Robt. 28

Powlesland Robert, 33, 69

Powning Ambrs. 46

Pratt Joseph, 69

Presswell C. & C. B. 127: Frances, 85: Wm. 30

Price Chas. 30: Jph. 98

Prickman Tzn. 17

Pridham Chas. 7, 23, 93, 100: Edw. P. 125: Maria, 8: Thos. 114, 144: Wm. 42

Pring Wm. 88A

Prinn Jane, 85

Priston John, 26; Wm. 24, 26

Prout Wm. 8, 114

Pryor Joseph, 139

Pulman Jno. 14: Jas. 53, 143

Punchard Wm. 114

Purkis John, 4

Putt Philip, 114

Pye Edw. R. 135: Geo. 134: K. J. 107

Pyne Sarah, 22, 95

Quick John, 108: Ths. 98: Wm. 93

Quicke T. & T. R. & E. 1

Rabjohns Wm. 114

Radcliffe Wm. 17

Raddon Jno. 62: Har. 85: Lsa. 122: Pp. 68, 78: Thos. 62, 78, 123

Radford L. 122: R. 80

Radmore John, 141

Raiscott Robert, 125

Ramson Jn. L. 60, 105

Ramster Wm. 109

Ranney Hy. S. 31, 52

Rawling Chas. 6: W. 2, 28

Raymond Wm. 69

Reddaway Rd. 21: M. 123

Red John, 117

Reed John, 8, 108; John & Edw. 19, 60, 82: Thos. 8: and Warren, 7, 126: Wm. 114

Reeves & Linscott, 96

Rendle John, 105

Renouf John, 107

Rew Jas. 42: Jas. & Son, 129: Rt. 129

Reynolds Chas. 117: Chtte. 123: Rd. 117: Robert, 25, 133

Rice John, 8, 127, 144: Jph. F. 98: Michl. 105: Thomas, 93

Rich E 60: W. 23, 26

Richards Chas. 6, 17, 52: Fras. 39: John, 26, 68, 108: Mary, 85: Rd. 35, 84: Thos. 17: Wm. 28, 82

Rickard Emma, 1: H. 141: John, 141: Sidney, 115

Ridge Jas. 33: Jph. 127: Jph. Dnl. 78, 127: Thos. 26: Wm. 127

Ridgewey, Halls, & Co. 60, 130, 145

Ridgway S. R. & J. 1: Thomas, 114

Ringwell Wm. 93

Ripley Edwin, 75, 79

Rippon George, 127: T. 55

Risdon George, 127: Chas. 79: John, 78: Sarah, 47

Roach Samuel, 69

Roberts Chas. 93: E. H. 6; Hy. 8: Jno. 17, 55, 93: Joseph, 8: Mary, 54: Rd. 35: Sar. 85: Wm.

Tremlett E. N. & Co. 94 : H. P. 15 : J. 4
Trethewey Rd. 70
Trewman R. J. and Co. 88
Trick Sarah, 85
Trickey R. 17, 127 : Jas. 71
Trimble J. 23 : Son & Brooking, 96
Tripp Robt. 112
Trist A. 27 : J. 98
Trix John, 31
Troake Benj. 18
Trobridge J. T. 52 : J. 60
Trowt Rt. 60 : J. 58
Truscott G. F. 52 : J 13 A'
Tuck Sarah, 85
Tucker Edw. 27 : C. 60 : Chas. 81 : Ed. 4, 93 : F. W. 4 : H. 85 : Jas. 35, 55 : J. 17, 25, 55, 56, 125 : J. T. 52 : M. 55 : Thos. 43, 69, 144 : Wm. 69, W. B. 27
Tuckett C. 86, 142 : N. 84, 116, 132 : Thos. 32
Tuckwell Hy. 78
Turnbull J. W. 68, 114
Turner C. H. 6, 104 : Cht. 8 : Edw. 69 : Eliz. 1 : Geo. 58 : G. W. 6 : John, 21, 25, 78, 114 : T. P. 105 : Wm. 17
Turpin Wm. 114
Twiggs E. 25 : J. 39
Twitchen Jno. 117
Tyrrell John, 10
Underhay Wm. 129
Underhill H. 43 : T. 17 : Wm. 14, 67
Upjohn R. & J. 141
Upright Hy. 8 : J. 41
Vanstone J. 58 : J. 60
Vatcher Hy. 112
Vaughan D. L. 16

Veitch J. & Son, 89
Venn Jas. 69
Veysey Wm. 64, 68
Vicary Jno. 18, 127 : Jph. 18
Vicker Wm. 17
Vigers Joseph, 83
Vinnicembe Ann, 1 : J. P. 16, 87, 105
Visick Robt. G. 31
Vowler Benj. 17
Voysey Wm. 8, 25
Wager & Smale, 80
Walker Jno. 49 : J. 36 : Rd. 36
Walkey S. 125 : and Truscott, 6
Wallis Jno. 1 : H. J. 16, 52 : Rt. 127
Walters F. L. 117
Wannell Susan, 55
Ward Joel H. 132 : John, 17 : Jph. 8, 36 : J. & Son, 33 : Rt. 35 : Thos. 25 : Wm. 17
Ware Ann, 24, 28 ; G. 69 : Jno. 7, 23 : Moses, 132 ; S. 40
Warr Robt. 8
Warren C. J. 93 : F. H. 125 : John, 23, 24, 46 : J. & Son, 6 : M. 85 : R. 114 : S. 93 : Wm. 24, 127
Waters A. H. 85
Watts G. A. E. 6
Way John, 43
Wayborn James, 69
Waymouth Thos. 24
Webb Hy. 48 : B. J. 125 : C. K. 125
Webber Geo. 69 : J. 26, 72, 105 : R. 17, 138 : Wm. 17, 55, 98, 127, 138
Webster Edward 60
Weeks J. 17, 58, 70
Welch Jno. 22, 109 : W. 17
Wellacott John, 127
Wellington Thos. 43

Welsford H. H. 16, 103
Welsman Geo. 25
West Benj. 27 : J. 137 ; Wm. 17
Westbeare J. 17, 127
Westcott Thomas, 17
Western Abm. 55 : Jno. 80 : Jas. 35 : Sus. 85 : T. 24, 47
Westlake Geo. 117 : J. 32 : M. 85 ; R. J. 60, 130 : W. 114
Wheaton A. & M. A. 16
Whitaker Thos. 126
White Chas. 127 : J. H. 117 : H. 60 : J. 35 ; J. J. 23, 26 : L. 123 ; Jph. 93 : Thos. 80, 114 : T. D. 15
Whitehead A. 3, 48
Whitford Mrs F. 93
Whitlock N. 132
Whitmarsh T. W. 16
Whitton Wm. 127
Whyburn G. 70, 83
Wickett R. T. 8
Widger John, 8
Widgery Wm. 60
Wilcocks and Brock, 25, 78 : Dinham, 60, 130 : Henry, 17
Wilkins M. 1
Wilkinson W. J. P. 145 : R. C. 65, 101
Willesford F. G. 8. 6
Willey E. 127 : E. W. 135 : Elias, 17 : J. 17, 93, 117 : S. 30, 114
Williams C. F. 4, 52, 105 : E. 125 : J. L. & C. 1 : T. 98 : T. E. 101, 145 : W. 125
Wills E. 117 : John 8, 23, 24 : Wm. 7, 23, 24, 49, 128
Wilson G. 117 : Jas. 114, 121 ; John, 25

Winsor S. 93 : Hy. 136
Wippell G. 58, 72 : Jph. 52, 149
Wish Wm. 55
Withycombe Hy. 105
Wolland John, 138 ; Eliz. & Son, 138
Wood E. 122, 123 : Eliz. 69 : G. D. 105 : Sar. 114 ; T. 17 ; Wm. 47
Woodbridge W. 41
Woodbury J. 14 ; W. 17
Woodhouse R. 61
Woodley Saml. 114
Woodman Frar. 85 : S. & D. R. 33 : W. 125
Woodward F. 85
Woolcott G. 18 : B. 67
Woosley J. W. 17
Woolmer & Thacker, 88 : E. & Co. 103
Wootton Ann, 57
Worth E. 15 ; P. E. 1
Worthy T. & R. 149
Worton J. P. 49, 79
Wotton Mary, 1
Wrayford Geo. 114
Wreford Eliz. 85 : R. 17, 70 : R. 6, 42 : S. 78 : Wm. 72
Wrentmore Mrs 1
Wright C. 29 ; Fras. 23 ; Jas. 43 ; Jane, 85 ; Rt. 35 : W. 8
Wrighton Wm. 31
Wyatt E. 141 ; G. 55
Wyser Thos. 17
Wyllie R. W. 105 : W. 127
Yelland P. 80
Yendall Jacob, 93 ; J. 114 : John, 17
Yeo Wm. 69
Yeomans Wm. 17
Yerbury Rd. 31
Youlden W. 1 : W. 24
Young Wm. 8

CLASSIFICATION OF TRADES & PROFESSIONS.

☞ *The figures in the preceding INDEX refer to those attached in parenthesis to the various HEADS OF TRADES AND PROFESSIONS, and shew under which the Address of any Person or Firm may be found.*

(1) ACADEMIES AND SCHOOLS.
*Marked * take Boarders.*

*Ashworth Mary, 12 Baring crescent
Babbage Ellen, 7 South street
*Ball Caroline, 14 Dix's field
Barton Mary, Bartholomew street
Batten Jane, 22 Bartholomew street

Beadon Thos. 115 St Sidwell street
Bedford Chapel School, Mrs. Holmes
Bennett Matthew, Okehampton st
*Bennett Rachel, 3 Homefield place
Blackmore Louisa, St Sidwell street
Blue Boys' School, St John's Hospital, High st ; Geo. Masters Gould

G

Blue Maids' School, Mary Arches street; Eliza Mitchell

*Bonter Annie, 2 Hampton place

*Bremridge Mrs Frs., Salutary mnt

British School, Coombe st; Isaac Cousins, Mary Akrill, and Caroline Harris

Brock George, Cowick street

Campbell Mrs. Park place, Heavitree

Canterbury Eliza, 48 Holloway st

*Charlton Cath., Ann and Elizabeth, 21 Magdalen street

*Clarence Emma, Bicton place

Clifford Misses, 1 North terrace

Cobley Wm. 127 St Sidwell street

College School, Mt. Radford House, Rev C. R. Roper, M.A., and Rev J. Ingle, B.A.

Collins Ann M., Cowick street

Davies Mrs. 8 Silver terrace

Devon and Exeter Central National Schools, Magdalen st; Geo. Robinson and Mary Wilkins

Diocesan Training Schools, Cathedral yard; Rev G. Martin, B.D. *principal;* and Chas. Long & Miss Wilkins, *teachers*

Downs Anna Maria, Barnfield

Episcopal Charity Schools, Paul st; Thos. Pinder and Charlotte Please

Fewins Wm. 7 Windsor terrace

Free Grammar School, High street; Rev Wm. Mills, D.D., *head master;* Rev Chas. Worthy, A.B., *second master;* H. Cann, *mathl. mr;* and F. Duval, *French master*

Frost Mary Ann, 66 Magdalen street

Gattey Miss, 43 St Sidwell street

*Goodridge Geo. Hy., Victoria terrace

*Hake Misses, 38 Southernhay

*Halloran Chas. F., Regent Park, H

Harvey Mary, Longbrook street

Hele's Boys' School, New North road

Helmore Miss, *Larkbeare*

Hill Abm. S., Hampton place

Infant Schools, Wm. and My. Ann Moxey, Bartw. st; & Eliz. Hawke, Cowick street

*Johns Sar. M. 20 Holloway street

Johns Jemima, 77 Paris street

*Knox Mary Ann, 3 Crescent row

Ladies' Charity, Castle st; My. Harris

*Lethbridge Mary, Bradninch place

Marker James H., Maddock's row

*Martin Rev Edw. W., M.A., 112 Sidwell street

*Morrish Sophia and Ophelia, East Southernhay

National Schools, John Fryer and Cath. Taylor, *Bartholomew st;* Jno. and Chtte. Tootel, *St Thomas's School,* Cowick st; and Saml. and Eliz. Stockman, Heavitree

Nosworthy Ellen, 10 St Sidwell st

Orchard Charlotte, 46 Russell street

Patey Margaret, Radnor place

Pearse Eliz. 13 Northernhay street

Pentecost Mary, St Sidwell street

Protestant Dissenters' Charity, Paris st; James and Jane McKeag

*Quicke Thos. & T. R., *King's Lodge*

*Quicke Elizabeth, *King's Lodge*

Refuge for Discharged Prisoners, Lawn lodge; Mrs Jones, *matron*

*Rickard Emma, Cowick street

Ridgway James, New buildings

*Ridgway Simon Radford, *Magdalen House*

Rowe Robert, Cheeke street

Sampson Samuel, West street

Saunders Sarah, 2 Verney place

Sharland Mary, 5 Bradninch place

*Smith Mrs S. 3 Pennsylvania ter

*Smale Harriet, 18 Northernhay st

Sparkes Henry, 4 Mont-le-Grand, H

Stephens Fdk. Y., Bartholomew yd

Stocker Elizabeth, 4 Verney place

Stone John, Pancras lane

Tanner Mary, 173 St Sidwell street

*Templeton Jas., M.A., St David's hill

Thorne Miss, Paris street

Townsend Mary, Friar's walk

*Turner Eliz. 2 Lansdowne terrace

*Vinnicombe Ann, Bradninch place

West of Engd. Instn. for the Blind, David's hill, Mrs Friend, supintdt

West of England Deaf and Dumb Instn., Topsham road, Dr. Wm. Robson and Mrs Scott

Wesleyan School, John Wallis and Miss F. S. Taylor, Mint

*Williams Jane, Louisa and Caroline, *Larkbeare*

*Worth P. E. 5 Grosvenor place

Wotton Mary, 7 Bradninch place

*Wrentmore Mrs., Bartholomew ter

Youlden Walter, North street

(2) ACCOUNTANTS.

Cox Henry, Harris place

Hill Charles, Bedford circus
Hill Wm. Hy. Brown, Cathedral yard
Hodgson Saml. Butler, 12 Gandy st
Martin George, 3 St John's terrace
Orchard Wm., Bedford street
Rawling Wm. 15 Northernhay street
Sellers H. W., Woodbine villa
Steel Richard, 4 Paris street
Syms Philip, Bartholomew street
Tilbury John Southey, Albion place
Tapper Wm., Colleton crescent
(3) ARCHITECTS, &c.
Ashworth Edward, 263 High street
Best Robt. Brown, Queen street road
Dudley Henry, 45 Holloway street
Hayward John, Cathedral yard
HedgelandChas., Mt. Radford terrace
Julian Geo. Hanson, city surveyor,
9 Friars' walk
Mackintosh David, 11 Verney place
Southwood Samuel Rd., Castle street
Whitehead Arthur, 136 Fore street
(4) ARTISTS.
(*See also Professors.*)
Beer Robt. (*on glass,*) 42 Barthmw. st
Bristow Robert, Clifton road
Garland Robert T., Heavitree
Gendall John, Cathedral yard
Hake Wm. 115 St Sidwell street
Leakey James, 9 East Southernhay
Mardon Samuel, Mint
Purkis John, Summerland street
Photographic Portrait Rooms, 3
Castle terrace, Mr J. Jury
Traies Wm., East Southernhay
Tremlett James, 6 Paris street
Tucker Edwin, 73 St Sidwell street
Tucker Frederick W., Mint lane
Williams Chas. Fredk. 2 Palace st
(5) ARTISTS' COLOURMEN.
Davey Wm. 144 Fore street hill
Thomas G. P. P. & Co. 168 Fore st
(6) ATTORNEYS.
Marked * *are Comssrs. for taking ac-
kngmts. of married women ; and* +
are notaries public.
(*See also Conveyancers & Proctors.*)
Abraham Rd. Thos. 3 Castle street;
house Stafford terrace
Adney Rd. L., Hill's court
Atkins Lionel Daniel, Clifton place
*+Barnes Ralph, (chapter clerk,
bishop's sec. & dep. regr.) Palace
gate; house *Bellair House*

Barton Henry Downe, (clerk to city
magistrates,) 28 Southernhay pl
Benison Wm. Marks, 3 New Bridge
Bishop & Pitts, 19 Bedford circus
Bremridge Thos. Julius, Cathedral
yd ; h Penrose Villa, Heavitree
Brutton Chas. (mr. ex. in Chancery)
1 Northernhay place
Bussell John, Bedford street
*Campion Rd. Crudge,1Bedford cres
Carter Fdk. Roger, Black Boy road
Copleston Edw. Arthur,10 Queen st;
house *Newhays*, St Thomas's
Cox Samuel Molland, 22 Lower
Northenhay
Crabbe Wm. Richd., Deanery place
Daw John, (clerk to county court,)
13 Bedford circus; h Upper Mtd
Drake Geo. Henry, Upr. Paul street
*Drake Thos. Edw. (clerk to magis-
trates of Wonford Div.) New bldgs
Eales Richard, (clerk of the peace,)
Castle
Eales Rd. jun. Upper Paul street
*Ellicombe Hugh M. and John B. 4
Southernhay street
Every Rd. & Son, Bampfylde street
Floud Thomas, 5 Bedford circus
+Force Edwin, (clerk to comssrs. of
income tax,) Deanery place
Friend James Walter, 5 North street
Fryer Merlin, Cowick street
Fulford Robert, 87 South street
Furlong and Tucker, Northernhay
*Geare, Mountford and Geare, 2
Bedford street
*Gidley John, (town clerk, &c.) 15
Bedford street
Gray Thos. Wm. 4 North Bridge
Grove Geo. Wilson, Post office st
Hartnoll Thos. Wm., Close
Head & Venn, Bartholomew square
Hooper Hy. Wilcocks, (under sheriff
for city,) 12 Bedford circus; h
Manston terrace
Jones Winslow, Deanery place
Julian John, Mount Radford
+Kemp Edw. Louis, (dep. regr. of
Archdecnry., &c.,) Cathedral yard
*Kennaway and Buckingham, 12
Southernhay place
Laidman John, Bedford circus
Lambert Wm., Close
Lester and Radford, Bampfylde st
Luke Geo. Ponsford, Musgrave's aly

Mitchell and Ford, 25 Southernhay p
Moore Wm. Denis, 59 High street;
  h Portland villa
Paul and James, Close
*Paul Edm.Wm. (county treasurer,)
  Close
Petherick Jno. Wm. 3 Bedford st
Pope John Woodford, Deanery place
Pope John, 7 North terrace
Rawling Charles, 14 Hart's row
Richards Charles, 8 Bedford circus
Roberts Edw. Hunt, (dep. sup. regr.)
  171 Fore street; h Exe Villa
Sanders and Kitson, Palace gate
Sanders Saml. Harford, Deanery pl
Stogdon John, Gandy street
Strong Wm., Exe Island House
Tanner Wm. Hy., 17 Bedford circus
*Terrell John Hull, Martin street
Terrell Jas. (supt. regr.) Bartw. st
Toby John, jun. Castle street; house
  10 York buildings
*†Turner Chas. Hy., Cathedral yard
Turner Geo. Wm. (mr. ex. in Chan-
  cery, &c.) 14 Castle street
Walkey and Truscott, 37 Upper
  Southernhay
*Warren John and Son, 2 Bradninch
  buildings
Watts Geo. Augus. Everit, Bedfd. st
Willesford Fras. Eugenio Scoble, 11
  Castle street
Wreford Robt., Close; h *Alphington*

(7) AUCTIONEERS, &c.

Back Wm., Paris street
Barrett Samuel, Cathedral yard
Burch John, 97 St Sidwell street
Chapple John, 19 High street
Coffin Geo. 1 Square, & Castle st
Cook Fredk., Southernhay street
Force Chas. 106 St Sidwell street
Force Henry, 93 North street
Hussey Thomas and Son, *Waybrook*
Jackson Edw. Wm., Upr. Southnhay
Moore Geo. Augustus, 71 Paris st
Pridham Chas. 27 Magdalen street
Reed and Warren, *Wonford Cottage*
Rowe Joseph Coplestone, Smythen st
Taylor Robert, 17 Verney place
Ware John, 11 Paris street
Wills Wm. 5 North Bridge

(8) BAKERS.

Baker John, 16 Catherine street
Barrett Matthew, Frog street
Barrett Samuel, Cathedral yard

Beckett Wm., Alphington street
Beedle Catherine, 19 Magdalen at
Beedle Thomas, West street
Bell Sarah, 1 Lower North street
Bickford Martha, Okehampton st
Birkett Wm., Alphington road
Blackmore John C. 10 Longbrook st
Bodley Edwin, G. 40 South street
Buckland Geo. 112 Fore street
Butland Henry, Clifton road
Cann John, 90 North street
Carpenter Geo., Stepcote hill
Case Wm., Black Boy road
Chilcott John, Cowick street
Chudley John, Coombe street
Clapp Benjamin, Catherine street
Cole Richard, Heavitree
Collings Rt. 45 Russell street
Coplestone John, St David's hill
Cosway John, Brook green terrace
Cuthbertson Wm. 57 South street
Dann Wm. 20 New Bridge street
Davy John, 8 Magdalen road
Dicker Thomas, Clifton road
Dimond John, Cowick street
Elson Hy. Taylor, Summerland st
Endacott Samuel, 33 Holloway st
England Hy., St David's hill
Force Charles, 106 St Sidwell street
Ford Henry, 37 St Sidwell street
Ford James, 152 Fore street
Gasking John Hannaford, Harts' row
Gay Frederick, 101 St Sidwell street
Goodridge Rd. M. 96 St Sidwell st
Gregory Thos. 5 St David's hill
Gribble Wm., Preston street
Harris Ann, 126 St Sidwell street
Hawker Hy. 56 St Sidwell street
Henley Henry, Melbourne street
Holcombe Wm. Market street
Hooper Wm. 171 St Sidwell street
Herwill Jas. 162 St Sidwell street
Hoskins Wm., Rack street
Jarman John, Heavitree
Jones Thomas, 97 Fore street
Kay Quintin R., Cowick street
Kelland John, 11 Bartholomew st
Kenwood Thomas, 39 South street
Laskey John, 74 Paris street
Lee Elizabeth, Elmfield place
Lee Richard, Alphington road
Madge Benjamin, Preston street
Manley George, 4 Gandy street
Marchant John, Goldsmith street
Marles Wm. 49 St Sidwell street

Maunder Wm. 110 St Sidwell street
Mortimer Wm., Frog street
Middleweek Geo. Magdalen street
Mugford Gilbert, Lime Kilns
Newton Wm., King William terrace
Norton John, Waterbeer street
Palmer Thomas, 6 Cowick street
Palmer Wm. 148 St Sidwell street
Pope John, Exe Island
Pridham Maria, Black Boy road
Prout Wm., Coombe street
Reed John, 34 Holloway street
Reed Thomas, *Exwick*
Rice John, St Sidwell street
Roberts Henry, West street
Roberts Joseph, Oakfield street, H
Russell Henry, *Heavitree*
Salter Geo. B., Smythen street
Salter Thomas, 253 High street
Salter Wm., West quarter
Saunders Wm. 172 St Sidwell st
Scott Thomas, Waterbeer street
Snell John Gregory, 17 South st
Stacey John, 10 Northernhay street
Stocker Joseph, 36 Paris street
Taverner Robt. 150 Fore street
Taylor Hy. Elson, 11 Summerland st
Turner Charlotte, 14 Paris street
Voysey Wm., Holloway street
Upright Henry, Cowick street
Warr Robert, 2 New Bridge street
Ward Joseph, 5 Queen street
Widger John, Mary Arches street
Wills John, Cowick street
Wright Wm., Paul street
Young Wm., Heavitree

(9) BANKERS.
City Bank, (Milford, Snow, & Co.) Cathedral yard, (draw on Robarts, Curtis, and Co.)
Devon and Cornwall Banking Co. Cathedral yard, (on Hanbury and and Co.;) John Dymond, *manager*
Exeter Bank, (Sanders & Co.) Cathedral yard, (on Barclay & Co.)
National Provincial Bank of England, Cathedral yard; G. C. Holroyd, *manager ;* (on Joint Stock Bank, Princess street, London)
West of England and South Wales District Bank, 83 Fore st; Wm. Tombs, *manager ;* (on Glyn & Co.)
Savings' Bank, (*Exeter and Devon,*) 21 Bedfd. circus; Wm. Lee, *actuary*

(10) BARRISTERS.
Bird Charles, 22 Dix's field
Jerwood James, 8 Dix's field
Kekewich Geo. Granville, (dep. judge of Provost Court,) 6 Summerld. pl
Sparkes Perry, Cathedral yard
Tyrrell Jno. (judge of County Court,) 42 Magdalen street

(11) BAROMETER, &c., MKRS.
Courti Paul, Market street
Ronchetti Edmund, Waterbeer st
Ronchetti Thos., Black Boy road
Ronchetti Thos., jun. Black Boy rd

(12) BASKET MAKERS.
Burrows Saml., Holloway street
Blind Institution, Mr Dean and Sus. Nicholls, teachers, St David's hill
Laskey Robert, Alphington road
Norman Abraham, Preston street
Norman Francis, Goldsmith street
Norman John, Cowick street
Norman Wm., St Sidwell street
Somerwill George, 111 Fore street

BEER HOUSES.
(See after Inns, &c.)

(13) BERLIN WOOL DLRS.
Chapman Joseph, 212 High street
Stabback Caroline, Palace street

(13A) BIRD, &c., PRESERVERS.
Atkins Wm. 33½ South street
Truscott James, 89 North street
Tucker Wm. 10 New Bridge street

(14) BLACKSMITHS.
Bartlett Noah, St Sidwell street
Borne John, Bear street
Capron Richard, North ln. Heavitree
Carnell Wm., Crediton road
Carpenter John, Magdalen street
Chorley John, Heavitree
Coneybeer Samuel, *Exwick*
Davey Wm. (& *coach,*) Coffin's pl
Drake Edwin, Paul street
Downing Wm., Paris street
Ford Joseph, *Cowley bridge*
Godbeer John, 75 St Sidwell st
Halfyard Mary A., *Whipton*
Hill Samuel, Cowick street
Hill James, Paris street
Johns Samuel, Westgate
Loram Henry, Commercial road
Mortimer J., Spiller's lane
Mortimer Roger, Bedford street
Norman John, Cowick street
Pulman John, Stepcote hill
Richards George, Commercial road

Sargent John, Stepcote hill
Seldon John, *Cowley bridge*
Tozer Saml. (and farrier,) Alphington street
Underhill Wm., Frog street
Woodbury John, *South Wonford*
(15) BOOKBINDERS.
*Marked * are Machine Rulers.*
Besley Henry, 76 South street
Brayley Wm., Little Queen street
Cross George, 14 High street
Davies Wm., Gandy street and New North road
Featherstone Wm. C. 246 High st
*Foweraker Jno. (account books,) 3 Castle street
*Gibbs Wm. 91 North street
*Hodge Henry, 5 High street
Spark Wm., Cathedral yard
Spreat John, 3 Summerland street
Stabback George, South street
Thomson David, 43 High street
Tremlett H. P., Chapple's court
White Thos. Danl., Bampfylde st; house 3 Crescent row
*Worth Edwin, James street
(16) BOOKSELLERS, &c.
(See also Printers and Stationers.)
Balle Wm. 247 High street
Besley Hy. (& publisher,) 76 South st
Clifford Wm. 23 High street
Curson and Son, (Mrs and George,) 17 High street
Drayton Sar. & Sons, (Wm. & Jno.) 201 High street
Fitze James, 39 and 226 High st
Glanville Andrew, (tract depôt,) 9 Bedford street
Holden Adam, 60 High street
Howe Thomas, 207 High street
Hunt Henry Fras. 111 Fore street
Jessep James, 31 St Sidwell street
Lambert Wm. 6 Salem place
Mack Margt. (sub post,) 92 Fore st
Roberts Wm. Robt. 197 High street
Roberts Wm. Thos. 265 High st
Shanly Wm. (Catholic,) Mint st
Spencer Robt. 94 St Sidwell street
Spreat Jane, 263 High street
Stone Robt. 10 New Bridge street
Thomson David, 43 High street
Vaughan Dennis L. (old,) 63 South st
Vinnicombe J. P. (music,) Northernhay place
Wallis Henry John, 245 High st

Welsford Harriet H., Paul street
Wheaton Alfred, 29 High street
Wheaton My. and Anne, 185 Fore st
Whitmarsh Thos. Webb, 7 High st
(17) BOOT & SHOE MAKERS.
Allen Henry, Lower North street
Arthur George, Bartholomew st
Avent Samuel, 123 Fore street
Babbage Edw. John, 7 South st
Babbage George, Heavitree
Bailey Joseph, Cowick street
Balkwill John, 34½ New Bridge st
Ballman James, 7 Paris street
Bartlett Samuel, Melbourne street
Bartlett Samuel, 23 Magdalen st
Beer Joel, Goldsmith street
Bennett Matthew, Okehampton st
Bickell John, Goldsmith street
Board Maria, 125 Fore street
Bolt Thomas, Pancras lane
Bowden John, *Exwick*
Brodie Thos. John, 91 South st
Brown Thos. 9 New Bridge street
Browning Rd. 11 Northernhay st
Burdon John, 134 Fore street
Burdon Wm. 42 Holloway street
Burge Wm. 16 Holloway street
Burnett John, Preston street
Burridge George, Bartholomew st
Burrington Samuel, 3 High street
Byne Samuel, Quay
Callaway Thos. 14 Alphington st
Camble Wm. 12 Market street
Cambridge Charles, Sidwell street
Cann James, *Whipton*
Carter John, Sun street
Caryl Wm., Lower North street
Champ Wm. 39 Magdalen street
Clarke Wm. 228 High street
Coleman Chas. Fredk., Mint street
Collins Joseph, Friernhay street
Colmer Wm., St David's hill
Crabb Elizabeth, Upper West street
Crabb Wm., Upper West street
Croft Wm., Cowick street
Crouch John, Paul street
Cummings John, St Sidwell street
Davey John, (and India rubber golash manufacturer,) Martin st
Davey Aaron, Heavitree
Davidge Thomas, Longbrook st
Dean John, Okehampton street
Doble Eliz. 40 Holloway street
Druller Caroline, 4 North street
Dunley John S. 4 Bartholomew st

East Samuel, 103 Fore street
Edwards Francis, Mint
Edwards Richard, Stepcote hill
Evans Samuel, Preston street
Evans Wm., Guinea street
Fitzpatrick Thos. 13 Paris street
Flewellin Samuel, 40 Russell st
Flood John, Summerland street
Fry John, 44 Paris street
Furse Thomas, 5 High street
Furse Wm., New bridge
Ganniclifft Geo. (and blacking, &c. manufacturer,) 41 South street
Glenn Samuel, 255 High street
Gilbert John Henry, Stepcote hill
Goldsworthy Saml., Oakfield st. H
Grant Charles, Cowick street
Grafton Wm., Black Boy road
Gribble Sus. 28 Holloway street
Hallam Wm., St David's hill
Handford John, 8 St David's hill
Hanssen John, 154 Fore street
Heath Edward, Silver place·
Herbert and Son, (Thos. and Geo.) 79 South street
Hill James, Cowick street
Hill John, 24 Sidwell street
Hill John, 127 Fore street
Hitt John C. 2 London Inn sqr
Holland John, Black Boy road
Hooper Edw. 140 St Sidwell st
Hore John, Paris street
Howe Wm., James street
Hutchins John, Summerland st
Huxham Richd. 155 St Sidwell st
Isaacs Wm., Bear street
Johns (Wm.) and Kendall (Saml.) 3 King's alley
Joslin Wm., Exe street
Kenshole Robert, 10 Paris street
Kenshole Samuel, Cowick street
Knight Charles, Smythen street
Land James, Alphington road
Landray Joseph, Exe island
Lake Charles, Commercial road
Langdon Robert, Paul street
Last Edward, *East Wonford*
Leat Joseph, 78 St Sidwell street
Lemon John, 18 South st
Lewis Thomas, 1 Paris street
Lovering Henry, West street
Manning James, 138 St Sidwell st
Manning Wm., Paul street
Martin John, Barrack road
Matthews Wm., New North street

Maunders John, 26 Paris street
Maunders Robert, St David's hill
May Mary, 37 South street
Middleweek Wm., 9 St David's hill
Miller Robert, Sunderland street
Mitchell Henry, Black Boy street
Moody Charles, 2 St Sidwell street
Moxey John, 20 New Bridge street
Mugford James, 8 Magdalen street
Nethercott Henry, Heavitree
Nicholls John, Upper West street
Northcott Henry, Mary Arches st
Partridge John, Black Boy road
Partridge Wm., John street
Pembroke Henry, 229 High street
Pinn John, Black Boy road
Ponsford James, Northernhay st
Pope John, Painter's row
Portbury John, 53 Bartholomew st
Prickman Tamazin, 5 North street
Radcliffe Wm. 2 Cowick street
Richards Chas., 75 South street
Richards Thos., Oakfield street, H
Roberts John, Clifton road
Rowe Henry, Coombe street
Salomon Samuel, 36 High street
Sellick Henry, Guinea street
Shepherd Wm., Nothernhay street
Snow John, Cowick street
Spingall John, Paris street
Srague Samuel, 2 Paris street
Stanlake Jno. Edw. C. 5 Summerld. st
Stocker Ann, Upper West street
Tapscott Alex., Goldsmith street
Tapscott Richard, Palace street
Taylor Thomas, Well lane
Tothill Thomas, Heavitree
Towill Edward, 32 Russell street
Tree Philip, 6 St John's terrace
Trickey Robert, Sun street
Tucker John, *Exwick*
Turner Wm., St Sidwell street
Underhill Thomas, Upper West st
Vickery Wm., Edmund street
Vowler Benj. 47 Russell street
Ward John, 5 Cowick street
Ward Wm. 48 Russell street
Webber Robt. ct 160 St Sidwell st
Webber Wm., Cowick street
Weeks John, Magdalen street
Welch Wm. 50 St Sidwell street
West Wm. 11 Magdalen street
Westbear James, 5 Paris street
Westcott Thomas, 43 St Sidwell st
Wilcocks Henry, 18 Magdalen st

Willey James, 61 St Sidwell street
Willey Elias, Friar's walk
Wood Thomas, Okehampton st
Woodbury Wm., Heavitree
Woosley John Walker, 2 Summrld. st
Wreford Richard, Coombe street
Wyser Thomas, Upper West st
Yendall John, Exe island
Yeomans Wm. 9 Northernhay st

(18) BRAZIERS & TINNERS.
(See also Ironmongers.)
Bright John, Lower North street
Broadmead John, 17 Catherine st
Broadmead Hy. 102 St Sidwell st
Davis John, Alphington road
Fouracres Eliza, Cowick street
Garton and Jarvis, 190 High st
Gaul Robert, 42 South street
Hayne Joseph, 40 St Sidwell st
Huxtable Thomas, Ewing street
Jones James, West street
Landray Richard, Stepcote street
Lethbridge Thomas, Paul street
Martin John, West street
Martin Saml. Wm., Holloway st
Spratt John Pike, 125 St Sidwell st
Troake Benjamin, Smythen street
Vicary Joseph, 88 South street
Vicary John, (gas meter manufacturer,) 123 Fore street
Woolcott George, Bartholomew st

(19) BREWERS.
Baker Elizabeth, Heavitree
Hyett Mary & Sons, New North rd
Norman & Co. City Brewery, Exe bdg
Reed John & Edw, Alphington st

(20) BRICK & TILE MAKERS.
Corporation of the Poor, Black Boy road ; Robt. Sparke, manager
Hooper W. H. and W. W., 14 Paris st
Hopping John, Cullompton road
Horrell Thomas, Black Boy road
Knowling George, 65 Magdalen st
Pengilley Robert, Park pl. Heavitree
Phillips John, Black Boy road

(21) BRICKLAYERS, &c.
(See also Builders, Slaters, &c.)
Bickell Wm., Heavitree
Burch Wm., Cowick street
Channing Wm. and Geo., Heavitree
Chapple Edred, St David's hill
Chapple James, 38 South street
Clark James, 18 Paris street
Collings Wm. 35 Russell street
Dawe Wm. 26 Holloway street

Friend Wm., Heavitree
Grant John, 36 St Sidwell street
Harvey Robert, Waterbeer street
Larcombe George, Well lane
Moss Saml. (and paver,) James st
Reddaway Richard, Exe island
Sanders Wm., Heavitree
Turner John, Preston street
Western Thomas, 40 Paris street

(22) BRUSH MKRS. & DLRS.
*Marked * are Patten Makers.*
*Bradbeer Jph. & Son, Exe bridge
Gubb Saml., St David's hill
*Marks John, 131 Fore street
*Morgan Thomas, 7 Paris street
Mortimer John, Paul street
Mortimer Wm. 80 Fore street
Parish John, Quay lane
*Pyne Sarah, 146 Fore street
Reddaway Nicholas, Exe island
Roleston George, 45 South street
*Tarbett Thomas, Edmund street
Welch John, King's alley

(23) BUILDERS.
*Marked * are also Undertakers.*
See also Carpenters, &c.
*Back Wm., Paris street
Bickell John, 133 St Sidwell st
*Blackmore Wm. (and house agent,) Larkbeare
Bond Thomas, Cowick street
Bradbeer Thomas, Weirfields
Canes Wm., Okehampton street
Clark James, 18 Paris street
Cornish and Whitehead, 136 Fore st
Crabb James, Commercial road
Cuthbertson Joseph, jun. 16 Paris st
Darby James, Upper Paul street
Dawe Wm. 26 Holloway street
Endacott George, 71 South street
Eveleigh Wm., Upper Paul street
Facey Hugh, York cottage
Fisher Robert, St David's hill
Force Charles, 106 St Sidwell st
Gattey Joseph, St Sidwell street
*Helmore Robert, Stepcote hill
*Hill John and Son, (Geo.) Bartholomew street ; h Little Silver ter
Hitt Henry, Heavitree
Hodge Chas. Jas., Alphington st
Hooper Wm. Hy. and Wm. Wills, 14 Paris street
*Huxtable Wm. 15 Magdalen st
Johns Henry, Lion's holt
Kenshole John, Heavitree

Kinsman Thomas, Palace street
*Knowling George, 65 Magdalen st
Langdon Waller, Albert street
Mason John, Holloway street
Moore John, *Exwick*
Morton Wm., Frog street
Pannell Wm. 18 Holloway street
Parratt J. and W. 9 Magdalen st
Pepperell Wm., Palace street
Pinn John, Melbourne place
Pridham Charles, Magdalen street
*Rich Wm., Alphington street
*Rowe Jph. Coplestone, Smythen st
Rowse John, 24 Paris street
Sanders Joseph, 153 St Sidwell st
Savill Henry, North ln. Heavitree
Scanes Thomas, Fore street hill
Scott John Ward, St David's hill
Southcott John, Cowick street
Southwood John, Cowick street
Stafford John, 24 Bartholomew st
*Stamp Wm. 20 Magdalen street
Stear John, 14 Holloway street
Stocker James, Cowick street
Stuckes John, St David's hill
Tozer Wm., John, and Rowland,
　13 North street
Trimble John, Regent Park, H
Twitchen John, Cowick street
Ware John, 12 Paris street
Warren John, 8 South street
White John James, Bartholomew st
Wills John, 9 Bartholomew street
Wills Wm. 5 North bridge
Wright Francis, 14 Eaton place
　(24) BUTCHERS.
*Marked * are Pork Butchers.*
Allen Eliz., Goldsmith street
Arundel Jas. 8 Summerland street
Bartrum Susan, Milk street
Batten Robert, 76 St Sidwell st
Batten Wm. 42 St Sidwell street
Beavis John, Smythen street
Beedell Thomas, Lower North st
Bidwell Thomas, Magdalen street
Bowden Robert, Sivell place, H
Bradford Ann, 145 St Sidwell st
*Brooks Wm. 141 St Sidwell st
Burnett Mary, Smythen street
Cann Wm. 89 South street
Chamberlain Thomas, 249 High st
Cockren John, Goldsmith street
Cox Robert, 108 Fore street
Darke Edward, Smythen street
Darke Jas. & Geo. 89 St Sidwell st

*Davis John, 60 South street
England James, 85 St Sidwell st
England Wm., Smythen street
*Fry Wm., Preston street
Gargatt John, Smythen street
Glass Elizabeth, Smythen street
Hallett John, Goldsmith street
Hallett Wm., Topsham road
Harvey Wm., Market street
Havill George Goldsmith st ; house
　South Wonford
*Hawkins John, Okehampton st
Hill George, 102 St Sidwell street
Hore John, Market street
Horn John, Summerland street
Howard John Charles, *Heavitree*
*Hucker Elizabeth, Paul street
Hucklebridge Thos., Alphington st
Kerswell James, West quarter
Knapman Edw. 20 St Sidwell st
Knapman Wm., Smythen street
Knowling Wm. 123 Sidwell street
Lake John, 10 South street
Lane John, 29 Paris street
Lane Wm. 34½ Holloway street
Lendon Frederick, 31 North st
*Lutley Thomasin, George street
Manley Charles, 97 St Sidwell st
Manley Thomas, Broad street
Masters George, Coombe street
Matthews John, 56 South street
Mayo Caroline, 6 New Bridge st
Mayo Isabella, 23 South street
Melhuish John, 3 New Bridge st
*Moody Charles, St Sidwell st
Moss Samuel, James street
Nott Wm., Exwick
Oliver John, Market street
Orchard John, Milk street
Paine Jane, 166 St Sidwell street
Palmer Wm., Alphington road
Pannell John, Cowick street
*Perkins Grace, Paul street
Perry Wm., Smythen street
Ponsford Jeremiah, 3 Paris street
Priston Wm., Cowick street
Salter Wm. 250 High street
Sellick Samuel, West quarter
Seward Robert, 8 New Bridge st
Slocombe Thomas, Market street
Slocombe Wm. 12 Paris street
Smale Grace, 8 South street
Smith Isaac, Sun street
Smith Wm. 90 North street
Spark Elizabeth, Milk street
　G 3

Symes W. S., Paul street
Trace John, Catherine street
Trace Thomas, 128 St Sidwell st
*Ware Ann, 49 South street
Warren John, 35 St Sidwell st
*Warren Wm., George street
Warren Wm., Goldsmith street
Waymouth Thomas, 36 Paris st
Wills John, 24 New Bridge st
Wills Wm., Edmund street
Youlden Wm. 46 South street

(25) CABINET MAKERS AND UPHOLSTERERS.

Badcock John, 5 Queen street
Bryett Wm. 2 Gandy street
Clode Wm. 167 St Sidwell street
Connett Wm., Magdalen street
Cook Frederick, Southernhay st
Dingle Daniel, 17 New Bridge street
Foster John, Duke's place
Gibbs Wm., College
Gordon Thomas, 15½ Holloway st
Gove John, 6 Milk street
Green Wm. ct 137 St Sidwell st
Guest Wm. 5 New Bridge street
Harding Charles, Trinity street
Isaac John, James street
James Theodore, 6 Queen street
Kerridge John, 13 Northernhay st
Kingdon Jane and Son (and paper stainers,) 180 Fore street
Langsford Wm. 128 Fore street
Letherby John, Cowick street
Marshall James, Exe island
Nicholls J. P. 21 New Bridge st
Nicholls John, 141 Fore street
Osment Edward, 75 Paris street
Porter Wm., Bear street
Reynolds Robert, 3 Paris street
Roberts Wm. 63 Magdalen street
Sellick Wm., Mary Arches street
Stamp Wm. 20 Magdalen street
Street Edward Henry, 8 Paris st
Tozer Wm., Jno. & Rowld.11 North st
Tucker John, Mary Arches street
Turner John, 15 Alphington st
Twiggs Edward, 134 Fore street
Voyser Wm., King street
Ward Thomas, Castle green
Welsman George, 12 Gandy street
Wilcocks and Brock, 177 Fore st
Wilson John, Cathedral yard

(26) CARPENTERS & JOINERS.
(See also Builders.)

Ashe John, West street

Babb Wm. 1 Park pl., St Sidwell's
Beavis John, 138 Sidwell street
Beedle Thomas, Albert street
Beer George, Topsham road
Bickell John, 133 St Sidwell st
Bond Peter, 62 South street
Bond Thomas, Cowick street
Borne Robt., Church st., St Sidwell's
Bradford Robert, James street
Brinsmead Hugh, St David's hill
Chapman John, 160 St Sidwell st
Chapple John, 64 St Sidwell street
Chown John, Cowick street
Cossins Richard, New buildings
Crabb John, Commercial road
Crang John and Son, 137 Fore st
Cross Francis, 161 St Sidwell st
Dolbear Giles, St Sidwell street
Ellis John, Preston street
Ford Ambrose, Lower North st
Gattey Joseph, 43 St Sidwell st
Gibbings John, 11 Longbrook st
Harris Thomas, Butcher's row
Helmore Robert, Stepcote hill
Hodge Charles Jas., Alphington st
Hutchings John, Exe street
Isaac George, Catherine street
Jellard John, Weirfield place
Jerman James, Exe street
Kenshole John, *Heavitree*
Kinsman T. 8 St Leonard's ter
Lamerton Thomas, Guinea street
Lucas John, Stepcote hill
Lucas Matthew, Stepcote hill
Moore John, *Exwick*
Pannell Wm. 18 Holloway street
Pinn Thomas, Black Boy road
Priston John, Friar's green
Priston Wm., Cowick street
Rich Wm., Alphington street
Richards John, Paris street
Ridge Thomas, 9 Pavilion place
Sanders Joseph, 153 St Sidwell st
Southwood John, Cowick street
Stuckes John, St David's hill
Thomas John, Friernhay street
Todd Charles, Musgrave's alley
Ward Thomas, Castle street
Webber George (boat builder,) Leonard's quay
White John James, Bartholomew st

(27) CARVERS & GILDERS.
Edwards John H. 31 Holloway st
Ferguson Wm. S. 26 St Sidwell st
Fey John, 20 Magdalen street

Gendall John, Cathedral yard
Gordon Edwin James, Friar's gate
Hall Wm., Castle street
Roper Edwin, Coombe street
Rowden John & Robert, 18 High st
Stamp Joseph, Bear street
Trist Anthony, Rack street
Tucker Edward, Little Queen st
Tucker Wm. B. 10 New Bridge st
West Benj. (frame mkr.) 22 Sidw. st

(28) CHEESE&BACON FACTORS.
Brooking Joseph, 29 South street
Brooking Wm. 33 North street
Brown Richard, St Sidwell street
Bryant Samuel, 28 New Bridge st
Carter Wm. (bacon,) Cowick st
Dale George, 4 New Bridge street
Davidge John, 86 Fore street
Fisher John, Paul street
Lendon Samuel, 114 Fore street
Luckes Thomas, 85 Fore street
Myers James, Black Boy road
Perry Edward, 42 South street
Pollard Wm. 3 Paris street
Potter Robert, Clifton road
Richards Wm., Guinea street
Southcott John, Smythen street
Toby Stephen, 5 and 6 South st
Ware Ann, 49 South street

(29) CHIMNEY SWEEPERS.
Edbrook Wm., Black Boy road
Franks John, Water lane
Howe John, Water lane
Luget James, 25 Paris street
Parson George, Water lane
Smith Henry, West street
Tomlinson James, 23 Paris street
Wright Charles, 165 St Sidwell st

(30) CHINA, GLASS, &c. DLRS.
Attwood Wm., Market place
Cockerom Sarah, 159 Fore street
Emery Frances, 90 Fore street
Ford John, 73 South street
French Richard, 2 Paris street
Hammott James, Pancras lane
Hunt Henry Francis, 111 Fore st
King George, 205 High street
Newcombe Sar. & Co., East market
Osborn John Dinham (and lamp,) 198 High street
Presswell Wm. 248 High street
Price Charles, 9 South street
Shooter Edwin, West street
Taylor Mary, Exe bridge
Willey Susan, 130 St Sidwell st

(31) CHEMISTS & DRUGSTS.
(See also Druggists, Wholesale.)
Brailey Charles, Heavitree
Bremridge Elias, 35 South street
Burge Samuel, 79 Fore street
Collins Joseph, 124 Fore street
Croome John, 47 High street
Dyer Thomas, 3 Cowick street
Froom Wm. J. (whols.) 11 North st
Gould Robert, Lower North street
Holman and Ham, 187 High st
Hooker Seraphin, 139 St Sidwell st
Huggins George, 210 High street
Husband & Co. (wholsl.) Waterbeerst
Knott Thomas (and soda water mfr.) 41 High street
Lang Isaac (and oilman,) 96 Fore st
Milton Wm. & Reuben, 66 High st
Owen Geo. (pharmactcl.) 2 Queen st
Palk John (Medical Hall,) 84 St Sidwell street, and Southernhay
Pates George, Upper West street
Pearse Edward, 169 Fore street
Ranney Henry Sargent, 259 High st
Stone John, 167 Fore street
Tanner Nicholas Wms. 246 High st
Tozer Richard John, 15 South st
Trehane James, 33 St Sidwell st
Trix John, 26 High street
Visick Robt. Goodyear, 224 High st
Wrighton Wm., Cowick street
Yerbury Richard, 1 Alphington st

(32) CLOTHES DEALERS.
(See also Tailors.)
Avent Wm. 119 Fore street
Bidgood Thomas, Edmund street
Clapp Samuel, Cowick street
Coleman Wm., Upper West street
Darby Joseph, Upper West street
Davy Charles, Upper West street
Easterling Thos., Upper West st
Guy Thomas, Upper West street
Hyam David, 193 High street
Marks Joseph, 113 Fore street
Pinder Richard & Co. 191 High st
Pinn James, Palace street
Sanders John, Upper West street
Sanders Robert, Upper West st
Silverston Israel, 107 Fore street
Stone Samuel, West street
*Strong George, 118 Fore street
Tucket Thomas, Lower North st
Westlake John, Upper West street

(33) COACH BUILDERS.
(And Harness Makers.)
Foster Charles, 50 Magdalen st
Franklin Frederick and George, 271
  High st. and 98 St Sidwell st
Fulford Thomas, Bampfylde st
Godbeer Robert, 10 Queen street
Gould Wm. and Son, Post Office st
Hayman Geo. & Co. 100 St Sidwell st
Jackson Edw. Wm., New North rd
Parsons John King, Alphington st
Parsons John Henry, Holloway st
Powlesland Robert, Frog street
Ridge James, jun. 11 Hill's court
Sellers John Alexander, Bedford st
Ward Joseph & Son, 41 Paris st
Woodman (Samuel) and Down (Rd.)
  8 Catherine street

(34) COACH LACE AND FRINGE
    MANUFACTURERS.
Brewster Hy. Lewis, 3 Catherine st
Goodridge Ths. Trist, 31 New Bridge st
Kingdon Francis, 24 High street

(35) COAL, &c. MERCHANTS.
Arthur John (dealer,) Coombe st
Ash Henry B .& Co., Quay, &*Star Cross*
Barratt Sarah, Preston street
Bastick Wm. Henry, Railway Station,
  Cowick street
Burrows James, King street
Caseley Wm., Black Boy road
Davis Robert, Heavitree
Dawson and Co., Railway Station
Densham Wm., Rack street
Deacon and Co., Railway Station
Foster Jane, Baker's ct., Sidwell st
Greenslade George, Rack street
Groves Wm., Waterbeer street
Hawkins Edward, Commercial rd
Hawkins Richard, 30 Russell st
Hellyer Philip, Coombe street
Holmes Wm., Commercial road
Hussey John, 152 St Sidwell st
Jackman John, Russell street
Jenkins John, Lower North street
Jones Benj. 3 Bartholomew street
Jones Abraham, Black Boy road
Kingdon John Eyre, Waterbeer st
Mear Wm., Quay
Napper James, Paul street
Norman George, 3 Summerland st
Norrish John, 38 Bartholomew st
Northern Coal Mining Co., Quay;
  Wm. Holmes, *manager*
Passmore John, 23 Paris street

Richards Rd., Quay; h 1 Lansdowne ter
Roberts Richard, Cowick street
Sanders John, 127 St Sidwell street
Scott Wm. 143 St Sidwell street
Snape James, Paul street
Squires George, Mary Arches st
Taylor Henry, Commercial road
Tucker James, Exe bridge
Ward Robert (and guano, bone-dust,
  &c. dealer,) Railway Station
Western James, Commercial road
West of England Coal Co., Railway
  Station
White John, 30 Magdalen street
Wright Robert, Commercial road

(36) CONFECTIONERS.
Anley Charlotte, 21 High street
Blackmore Mattw. Hy. 15 North st
Bodley Edwin G. 40 South street
Burge Ann, 30 South street
Burnell Wm. (cook,) 33 Paris st
Coombe John, Cowick street
Cuthbertson Wm. 57 South street
Davy John, 8 Magdalen road
Ford James, 152 Fore street
Frost Wm. 47 South street
Goodridge Richd. 96 St Sidwell st
Haycraft James, 3 North bridge
Helmore Mark, James street
Incledon James, 112 St Sidwell st
Jones Thomas, 97 Fore street
Kenwood Thomas, 39 South street
Mackay Hy. (and medicated lozenge
  manufacturer,) 11 Gandy street
Middleweek Geo. 29 Magdalen st
Murch Sarah (cook,) Broad street
Palmer Wm. 148 St Sidwell street
Salter Thomas, 253 High street
Sherry Wm., Alphington street
Snow John, Paul street
Snow Wm. 39 St Sidwell street
Walker Richard, Preston street
Ward Joseph, 5 Queen street

(37) CONSULS (VICE.)
Portugal, F. D. L. Hirtzel, James st
Prussia & Spain, J.C. Sercombe, Quay
Sweden & Norway, Jno. Follett, Shilhay
United States of America, J.H. Terrell,
  Martin street

(38) CONVEYANCERS.
(See also Attorneys.)
Commin James, Cathedral yard
Rawling Wm., Lower Northernhay
Sparkes Perry, Cathedral yard

(39) COOPERS.

Bond John, Cowick street
Bowden Joseph, 14 Bartholomew st
Ellett Wm., Cowick street
Ford & Foster, 30 Holloway street
Gard Wm., Sandygate, *Heavitree*
Labdon Jacob, 151 Fore street hill
Labdon Wm. S., Coombe street
Lewis John, Cowick street
Newcombe John, Castle square
Osborn John (wine,) Exe island
Richards Francis, Adelaide place
Saunders Wm., Preston street
Selley Robert, Sun street
Twiggs John, 44 St Sidwell street

(40) CORK CUTTERS.

Allen Thomas, Sun street
Mortimer Wm. 80 Fore street
Stockham John, Paul street
Tothill John, Cowick street
Ware Shadrach, Cowick street

(41) CORN MILLERS & DLRS.

Blackmore Jph., Powhay New Mill
Buckland George, Cricklepit, and
  112 Fore street
Carthew Oliver, *Exwick*
French John D., St Ann's terrace
French Wm. *Kenton Mills*,&1 Paris st
Hemens Sarah, Round Tree mill
Shore Thomas, *Exwick*
Strong James & Son, Powhay mills
Upright James, City mills
Woodbridge Wm. 124 Fore street

(42) CURRIERS &LTHR. CUTRS.

Branch Thomas, 117 Fore street
Burrington Frederick, 164 Fore st
Davy Wm. and Son, 33 South st
Dyer S., Goldsmith street
Ferris Edw. Bussell, 70 Sidwell st
Hearn Frederick, 32 New Bridge st
Hearn Samuel, 95 North street
Hill Richard (cutter,) 84 Fore st
Hookway Wm. 32 Bridge street
Hutchings Charlotte, Cowick st
Lendon Henry, Waterbeer street
Pridham Wm. 2 Mary Arches st
Rew James, 6 Castle street
Wreford Robert Wm., Coombe st

(42A) CUTLERS, AND TRUSS AND SURGICAL INST. MAKERS.

Dunsford Matw. Lichegary,165 Fore st
Dunsford Richard, 55 High street
Fouracres Edwin Geo., 2 South st
Nurton David, Alphington street

(43) DAIRYMEN.

Allen James, 4 King's alley
Alford E., Okehampton road
Ash Wm., Paris street
Beer R., Catherine street
Butland John, 8 Clifton road
Butland Nicholas, St James street
Canes Sarah, 22 St Sidwell street
Chalice John, *Cowley Barton*
Connett Jeremiah, Lower North st
Discombe John, Rack street
Eardley Thomas, Heavitree road
East Henry, Mint
Esworthy Wm., Salutary court
Fowler Samuel, 11 Russell street
Good Charles, Smythen street
Gray Frederick, Black Boy road
Hamlyn John, 6 Little Silver terrace
Harris Francis, New Mount Radford
Hill John, Albion place
Hodges James, Commercial road
Hook Thomas, Magdalen street
Honeywill Susan, West street
Kelley John, Okehampton street
Kent Mary, Barrack road
Knight Wm., King street
Luke Richard, Market street
Marley John, 2 Magdalen street
Martin John, North lane, H.
Martin Joseph, Cowick street
Matthews J., Topsham road
Mead Richard, Bartholomew street
Merivale Wm., Stepcote hill
Morgan James, Commercial road
Newberry Wm., Magdalen road
Parker Bartholomew, Cowick street
Perrell Wm., Mary Arches street
Satterley John, 5 Summerland st
Snow Susan, Coombe street
Snow Wm. 17 Longbrook street
Soper Wm., West street
Stamp Joseph, West street
Stoneman Joseph, Black Boy road
Stoneman Thomas, St Sitwell st
Taylor John, Preston street
Taylor Wm., Lower North street
Tothill Robert, North lane, H.
Treble John, Old Tiverton road
Tucker Thomas, Alphington st
Underhill Hugh, Alphington st
Way John, Paul street
Wellington Thomas, Cowick st
Wright James, St David's hill

(44) DENTISTS.

Cartwright Edward, 23 Dix's field

Farthing John, Upper Southernhay
Fox Robert Were, 7 Southernhay pl
Groves Brothers, 2 East Southernhay
Hele Samuel, Dispensary, Queen st
Huntley Henry Frederick, 11 High st
King Norman, 7 Bedford circus
King Edward John, Cathedral yard
Levander James, 2 Crescent row
Sheffield Thos., Palace gt; h Vic. ter
(45) DRUGGISTS. (*Wholesale.*)
Cooper George, 101 Fore street
Evans Alfred & Co. 98 Fore street;
house 6 Bystock terrace
Froom Wm. Jacobs, 11 North st
Holman and Ham, 187 High st
Husband Mattw. & Co., Waterbeer st
Lang Isaac, 95 Fore street
(46) DYERS, &c.
Ford John, 73 South street
Heathcote John H. 69 St Sidwell st
Poole Samuel, Exe island
Powning Ambrose T., Paul street
Salter Charles, 28 New Bridge st
Shapcott John, 25 Holloway street
Tibbs Eliz. 29 New Bridge street
Warren John, West street
(47) EATING HOUSES.
Alford Robert Wm., Goldsmith st
Avent E., Fish market
Bennett Wm. 74 St Sidwell street
Blacking Priscilla, 1 South street
Bowcher Wm. D. 2 Castle street
Brooks Thomas, 93 North street
Brown Elizabeth, Upper West st
Canes Sarah, 22 St Sidwell street
Cox John, Mary Arches street
Dymond Wm., Elmfield place
Fagan Charles, Coombe street
Fletcher Richard, 2 South street
Grant John, 35 St Sidwell street
Hurst John, Paul street
Ireland John, 66 St Sidwell street
Jenkins James, Cowick street
Johns Richard, Goldsmith street
Lake Mary, Higher Market
Mackenzie John, 3 Milk street
Maunder John, 4 Milk street
Pear George, 103 St Sidwell street
Risdon Sarah, 3 Milk street
Skinner Sarah, 21 North street
Skinner Samuel, 121 St Sidwell st
Snell Matilda, 91 South street
Stoneman Wm., Exe Bridge
Spratt Elizabeth, 34 South street
Western Thomas, Lower North st

Wood Wm., Sun street
(48) ENGINEERS. (CIVIL)
(*See Ironfounders and Surveyors.*)
Cruickshank John W., Cowick st
Dawson Wm. 7 Northernhay place
Dymond Robert, 10 Bedford Circus
Grant John, 12 Castle street
Taperell Nichs. & Son, 5 Queen st.
and 15 Albion place
Webb Henry, 9 Longbrook terrace
Whitehead Arthur, 136 Fore street
(49) ENGRAVERS, &c.
Angel Owen, 94 Fore street
Frise and Marker, 3 Palace gate
Jenkins Wm. 129 St Sidwell street
Lewis and Eveleigh, 18 Magdalen st
Pim Wm. Deanery place
Southard Mathw. (*printer,*) Bear st
Walker John, Upper Paul street
Willis Wm. 3 Waterbeer street
Worton James P., James street
(50) FANCY REPOSITORIES.
Clarke Samuel, 228 High street
Howe Thos. (*Bazaar,*) 207 High st
Levi Joseph, 179 Fore street
Spalding John, 32 High street
(51) FELLMONGERS.
Branch Thomas, Commercial road
Tanner James Jones, (and leather
dresser,) Westgate yard

(52) FIRE & LIFE OFFICE AGTS.
Agricultural Cattle and Atlas, C.
Richards, 8 Bedford circus
Alfred Life, G.F. Truscott, Bedford st
Alliance, E. A. Copleston, Queen st
Anchor Life, S. B. Hodgson, Gandy st
Argus Life, T. W. Gray, North bdg
Architects',Builders',&c. J. Mason, Qy
Australasia and Colonial Life, A.Hol-
den, High street
Britannia, G. H. Drake, Paul street
British, G. Bigwood, New Bridge st
British Guarantee, E. A. Copleston,
10 Queen street
Church of Engd.R.Dewdney,82Fore st
Clerical and Medical, T.E. Drake, jun.
New buildings
Commercial and Legal, J. Bannehr,
Bedford street
County and Provident, J. Gendall,
Cathedral yard
Defender, G. A. Moore, 71 Paris st
Eagle, C. Brutton, Northernhay
Economic Life, T.Higgins,Coombe st

Engineers', Masonic, &c. Life, A. and W. Tucker, 9 Bridge street
English and Scottish Law Life, M. Fryer, Cowick street
Equity and Law Life, M. Kennaway, 12 Southernhay place
Etonian Life, C.F.Williams, Palace st
European Life, H. M. and J. B. Ellicombe, Upper Southernhay
Experience Life,S.H.Sanders,Dnry.pl
Family Endowment,R.Hake,Brthw.pl
Farmers'&General,Ths.Hussey,Waybrook; and J. Bowring, High st
Freemasons' and General, E.W.Paul, Close; & Rt. Tripp,Bedford chmbrs
General, J. Rowse, Paris street
General Annuity,G.F.Truscott,Bdfdst
General Reversionary & Investment, C. Brutton, 1 Northernhay place
Globe, Wm. Lambert, jun. Close
Great Britain, J. Toby, Castle st
Gresham Life, T. D. White, Queen st
Guarantee Society, F.Sanford,5 Musgrave's alley
Guardian, J. Laidman, Bedford cir
Hand in Hand, W. Buckingham, Southernhay place
Imperial Fire, H. S. Ranney, High st
Imperial Life, W. Lambert, Close
Kent Mutual Fire, J. H. Heathcote, 69 St Sidwell street
Law Fire, H. W. Hooper, Bedford cir
Life Association of Scotland, J. T. Tucker, 3 Upper Paul street
London Assurnc. G.Pates, New Bdg.st
London Union, J.Damerel, Sidwell st
Medical & General Life, & Phœnix Fire, J. King, 30 High street
Medical, Legal,and General, E.Bremridge, South street
Medical Invalid, J. B. Ellicombe, 4 Southernhay street
Mercantile, J. Trehane, Fore street
Metropolitan Counties&General Life, May and Bidwill, Bedford circus
Mitre, J. T. Trobridge, Deanery pl
National Life, A. Kemp, Magdalen st
National Loan Fund, W. D. Moore, 59 High street
National Provident, &c. T. Sparkes, 11 Northernhay place
Norwich Equitable, Robert Fulford, 87 South street
Norwich Union,T.Hartnoll,59High st
Pelican, J. Stogdon, Gandy street

Phœnix, John Stogdon, Wm.Godfrey, and George Martin
Professional Life,W.R.Crabbe,Dny.pl
Provident Clerks',J.B.Gould,Palace gt
Royal Exchange, H D.Barton, Southernhay place
Royal Naval and Military, and East India, N. W. Tanner, High strect
Scottish Equitable, G. Treffry, 169 Fore street
Scottish Union,W.&R.Milton, High st
Solicitors'&Genl. J.W.Friend,North st
Standard, H. W. Hooper, Bedford cir
Star, J. M. Sercombe, Colleton ter
Sun, Bishop & Pitts, Bedford circus
Temperance Life, J. Bale, Silver ter
Tontine Life,T.Sanford,5 Musgv.alley
Universal, H. J. Wallis, High st
West of England (Fire and Life,) Chas. Lewis, sec. 337 High st
Western Life,T.J.Bremridge,Cthdl.yd
Western Annuity, W. D. Moore, 59 High street
Westminster Life, J. Palk, 84 St Sidwell st; & R. Force, 226 High st
Yorkshire, J. Wippell, High street
(53) FISHING TACKLE MKRS.
Bale Archelaus,(hook mfr.)105Fore st
Bowden Henry, 24 North street
Osborn Geo. & Son, 64 High st
Osborn Wm. W. 26 North street
Pulman Jas. (& fire wks.) Guinea st
(54) FISHMONGERS.
Bartlett Mary, New North rd. & Mkt
Davy Mary, 7 Martin street
Gregory Emanuel, Goldsmith st
Gregory Emanuel, jun. Fish market
Herbert George, 4 York place
Pomery George, Eastern market
Roberts Mary, Fish market
Sharland Thomas, Waterbeer st
(55) FRUITERERS AND GREEN GROCERS.
Andrews Elizabeth, 4 Catherine st
Ballman Ann & Eliz. 7 Paris st
Biggs Charles, St Sidwell street
Board Thomas, King street
Bodley Robert, Lower North street
Broadmead John, 17 Catherine st
Carlile Thomas, 6 Martin street
Chambers James, Goldsmith street
Dear Thomas, 22 South street
Drake George, Magdalen road
Drake Sarah, 23 Longbrook street
Elston Wm. 3 Paris street

Eveleigh Wm. West street
Eveleigh John, 31 South street
Gough Wm. Sun street
Gandy Jph. (& game dlr.)250 High st
Knapman Wm. 48 South street
Langworthy Wm. Owen's street
Lee Wm. Melbourne street
Lee Wm. Holloway street
Lotton Joshua, Preston street
Manning James, 138 High street
Marwood Margaret, 145 Fore street
Matthews Henry, Guinea street
Maunder John, Mary Arches street
Maunder Samuel, King street
Maunder John, 26 Paris street
Passmore Wm. 28 New Bridge st
Penberthy Jas. Frog street
Penberthy Isaac, 16 Magdalen street
Potter Geo. 11 St Sidwell street
Rippon Thomas, St Sidwell street
Roberts John, 10 Magdalen street
Sellick John, Guinea street
Sumpter Henry, Lower North street
Thomas Richard, West street
Taylor Thomas, George street
Tozer John, Alphington street
Tucker John Champ, New Bridge st
Tuck James, St David's hill
Tucker Mary, 73 Sidwell street
Wannell Susan, Upper West street
Webber Wm. 133 Fore street
Webber Wm. 30 St Sidwell street
Western Abm., Mary Arches street
Wish Wm. Goldsmith street
Wyatt George, 104 St Sidwell street

(56) FURNITURE BROKERS.
Berry Wm. Preston place
Endacott Wm. Stepcote hill
Flood Nicholas, Stepcote hill
Force Henry, 93 North street
Godolphin Wm. 81 South street
Greenslade Ebenezer, Lwr North st
Grigg Wm. 35 South street
Guest Wm. 5 New Bridge street
Langsford Wm. 128 Fore street
Lucas John, Stepcote hill
Lucas Matthew, Stepcote hill
Marwood James, 147 Fore street
Manning Wm. Smythen street
Nicholls John Plimsaul,21New Bdg.st
Strong Wm., Lower North street
Street Henry, 2 Musgrave's alley
Tucker John, 25 South street

(57) FURRIERS.
Allen and Hill, North street

Edwards Elizabeth, Duke's place
Hake Thomas, 93 Sidwell street
Hill Ann, Martin street
Ley Elizabeth, Cathedral yard
Wootton Ann, Paul street

(58) GARDENERS, &c.
(See also Nurserymen.)
Berry Daniel, Barrack road
Bryant Amos, Heavitree road
Bustard Arthur, Clifton road
Capron James, Heavitree
Dalgleish Henry, 43 South street
Davy Wm. (tea garden,) Exwick
Friend Wm. *Whipton*
Gibbs Mary, Alphington road
Hayman John A. Homefield pl. H
Haydon Matthew, Cowley Barton
James John, Hill's court Nursery
Jones Wm. Well lane
Kerswell Thomas, Moreton road
Kerswell John, Painter's row
Manley James, Heavitree
Matthews John, Plantation bldgs
Moxley John, New North road
Ponsford Joseph, Northernhay
Pope Henry, Dunsford road
Rudd Wm. 1 St Sidwell street
Sanger John, *Lower Duryard*
Sclater George, St David's hill
Sercombe John, East Southernhay
Simpson Wm., Black Boy road
Shepherd Wm., Old Tiverton road
Thorn John, Okehampton street
Tinker Wm. W., Colleton terrace
Townsend James, St David's hill
Tree Thomas, Black Boy road
Trout James, Holloway street
Turner George, Barrack road
Vanstone James, Exwick
Weeks J. (florist,) Union road
Wippell Geo. (tea garden,) *Cleave*
GLASS. *(See China, &c. Dealers.)*

(59) GLASS & LEAD MERTS.
Downe and Son, 66 South street
Gray Charlesworth Thos. (& paint,)
    2 Market street
James and Rosewall, *Exe Island*
King, Long,& Co. 40 Bartholomew yd
Parker Wm. 4 High st; h Friars
Thoms G. P. P. & Co. 168 Fore st

(60) GROCERS & TEA DEALERS.
*(Marked thus * are Wholesale.)*
Anning Richard, 176 Fore street
Bailey Richard, Black Boy road
Baker Mary Ann, Lower North street

Batterson Wm., Upper West street
Benyon John Wm. 38 South street
Biggs Charles, 168 St Sidwell st
Blackler Francis, 41 South street
Bovey Robert, Friars
Bremridge Elias, 35 South street
Brown Richard, 41 St Sidwell st
Bucksey John, 33 New Bridge st
Cole Samuel, 23 North street
*Commin Saml. & Thos. 92 North st
Coombes John, Clifton road
Crabb Thomas, 259 High street
Dann Wm. 20 New Bridge street
Davies Samuel & Daniel, 44 High st
*Dewdney Rd. Hatswell, 82 Fore st
Dunn Henry, Mount Radford cres
Dyer Thomas, 3 Cowick street
Ebbles John Lendon, Paul street
*Edelstein S. J. W., Preston street
Endacott Edw. 131 St Sidwell st
Eveleigh John, 31 South street
Foote Samuel Best, 6 Queen street
Fouraker James, 29 Holloway st
French Mary & Eliz. 9 Paris street
*Froom Wm. Jacob, 41 North street;
  h Hill's court
Gardner Henry G. & Co. 183 Fore st
Gitsham Samuel, 126 Fore street
Goldsworthy Francis, Holloway st
Gould Charles Spry, 40 High street
Hall Mary, Paul street
Haycraft James, 3 North Bridge
Hayne Joseph, 40 Sidwell street
Hayman Elizabeth, 4 Market st
Henley Henry, Melbourne street
Hodgkinson George, 236 High st
Holloway Wm., Lower North street
Hooker and Son, 7 Magdalen road
Hooker Seraphin, 139 St Sidwell st
Hooper Wm. 171 St Sidwell street
Huckvale Wm. 48 High street
Hutchinson Frank, Heavitree road
Jones Henry, 32 St Sidwell street
Jury John, 69 St Sidwell street
Lawrence Wm. 17 St Sidwell street
Lemon John, 18 South street
Lockyer John, Cowick street
Luckes Thomas, 199 High street
Madden Mary, Magdalen street
Manley Wm. 71 St Sidwell street
Manning Jane, 47 St Sidwell street
Matthews Wm. 24 Magdalen street
Mitchell Thomas. 29 North street
Moon John, 70 High street
Moore Wm. 139 Fore street

Neck Wm. 10 Paris street
Parr John, 51 St Sidwell street
Pates George, Fore street hill
Peters Edward, 32 South street
Phillips Susan, 235 High street
Piller Robert, Heavitree
Pitt George & Thomas, 204 High st
Pope Ephraim, 122 St Sidwell st
*Porter and Hinckes, 91 North st
Ramson John Luce, 28 North st
Reed John and Edw. Alphington st
Rich Elizabeth, 69 High street
*Ridgewey, Halls, & Co. 1 High st
Sanford Joseph, Catherine street
Smeath John, 25 Magdalen street
Snow Richard, Goldsmith street
Snow Wm. 39 St Sidwell street
Squire John, 5 Cowick street
Strowbridge Wm. 24 Holloway st
Toms Joseph, 119 St Sidwell st
Treffry Geo. & Thos. T. 169 Fore st
Trobridge John, St David's hill
Trowt Robert Pearse, 11 South st
Tucker Charlotte, 35 High street
Vanstone John, Commercial road
Webster Edward, 60 St Sidwell st
White Henry, 16 Alphington street
Westlake Rt. Jackman, 36 New Bdg. st
Widgery Wm. 10 Magdalen street
*Wilcocks & Dinham, 104 Fore st
(61) GUN & PISTOL MAKERS.
Harvey John & Son, (Wm. James,)
  68 South street
Hewson George, Cowick street
Osborn James, (dealer,) High st
Osborn Wm. (dealer,) 26 North st
Woodhouse Robert, Market street
(62) HABERDASHERS.
Barber Joseph, 10 Russell street
Bond Wm. 51 High street
Bowcher Eliz. & Ferris Ann, 20 High st
Chapman Joseph, 10 Russell street
Dunn Anna, Sophia, & Eliz. 8 North st
Hamlyn Wm. Mann, 86½ Fore st
Mallett John, 159 St Sidwell street
Maunder Robert, St Sidwell street
Moss Thomas J. 45 St Sidwell st
Newman Caroline, 230 High street
Nightingale Robert, 28 High street
Pippett Charles, 88 St Sidwell st
Raddon John, 52 High street
Raddon Thomas, 78 South street
Ross James & George, 227 High st
Spalding John, 32 High street

(63) HARDWAREMEN.

Clark Samuel, 228 High street
Courti Paul, Market street
Davis, Morris, & Hyman, 173 Fore st
Levi Joseph, 179 Fore street

(64) HAT DEALERS.

*(Marked * are Manufacturers.)*

Bale Henry, 213 High street
*Bisney Charles, 61 High street
Braund Henry, 67 High street
Brice Joseph, 88 North street
Burrington George, 81 Fore street
*Champion Henry Mattw.36 South st
*Cunningham Chas. N. Goldsmith st
George Wm. 37 High street
*Isaac George Christian, 87 Fore st
*Pillman Wm. 17 North street
Pinder Richard & Co. 191 High st
*Pope John, Bonhay
Titherley Charles, 5 High street
Veysey Wm. 49 High street

(65) HOP MERCHANTS.

Bastard W. S. and S. St James st
Dawson Richd. Hy. & Co. 8 North st
Downey John, Palace street
Kennaway George, 21 South street
Lutley & Brunt, (& seed,) 20 South st
Matthews & Opie, 27 Dix's field
Morrish Thomas, Martin street
Salter Thomas, Gandy street
Sercombe John C. & George, Quay
Smith Thomas, Waterbeer street
Traer Wm. 6 York buildings
Wilkinson Rt. Carne, 89 North st

(66) HORSE REPOSITORIES.

(See also Livery Stables.)

Pearse George, 2 Bedford street
Rogers J. and Son, 68 South street
Rooks Catherine, Heavitree road

(67) HOSIERY MANUFACTRS.

Back Henry, Upper Paul street
Moore Geo. Augustus, 71 Paris st
Taylor Robert, Sun street
Underhill Wm. Exe street
Woolcott Benjamin, George street

(68) HOSIERS AND GLOVERS.

(See also Linen Drapers, &c.)

Brown Wm. C. 6 North street
Chapman Joseph, 212 High street
Cole Jane, 100 Fore street
Gay George, 106 Fore street
Gay Wm. 251 High street
George Wm. 37 High street
Green John, (lace, &c.) 243 High st
Hamlyn Wm. M. 86½ Fore street

Mallett John, 159 St Sidwell street
Moore Geo. Augustus, 71 Paris st
Newman Caroline, 230 High street
Pippett Charles, 88 St Sidwell st
Raddon Philip, 91 North street
Richards John, 31 Magdalen street
Ross Jas.&Geo. (lace,&c.) 227 High st
Spalding John, (lace, &c.) 32 High st
Turnbull Jas. Wm. (glover,) Paris st
Veysey Wm. 49 High street

(69) HOTELS, INNS, & TAVERNS.

Acland Arms, Peter Lisson, Sidwell st
Acorn, Geo. Medland, 15 Magdalen st
Albion Hotel, Thomas Neale, 24 Southernhay
Anchor, Saml.Lovering,Castle square
Anchor, Elizabeth Page, Exe Island
Anchor, Wm. Gill, Paul street
Anchor, Wm. Russell, Alphington st
Antelope, Hy.Sheehan, 109 Sidwell st
Artillery Arms, Jas. Gill, Holloway st
Axminster Inn, Wm. Born, Paris st
BarleyMow,'Ths.Mortimore,Cowick st
Barnstaple Inn,Joseph Ireland,Lower North street
Bear, Stephen Compton, 9 South st
Bishop Blaize, Jas. Clarke, West qr
Boat Royal,Geo.Webber,Leonard's qy
Black-a-moor's Head, Wm. Yeo, Upper West street
Black Dog, Edw. Turner, Lr. North st
Black Horse, Peter Bond, 62 South st
BlackHorse,PaulCollings,Longbrk st
Black LionInn,John Stuckes,67Sth.st
Blue Ball, Wm. Symons, Sandy gt. H
BlueBoar,Thos.Bromell,10Magdln.st
Blue Boy, Wm. Spicer, West street
Bristol Inn, Anna Maria Spreat, 95 St Sidwell street
Britannia,Ths.Southwood, 4 South st
Bude Haven & Coml. Hotel, Saml. Southcott, *(posting,)* St Sidwell st
Bull Inn, Saml. Roach, Goldsmith st
Buller'sArms,Sml.Coneybeer,*Exwick*
Buller'sArms,Wm.Hele,75St Sdwll.st
Buller's Arms, Geo.Scott, Alphngtn.rd
Butcher's Arms, Eliz. Dale, Market st
Canteen, Wm. Connett, Barracks
Cattle Market Inn,Sar.Rudall,Bonhay
Clarence Royal Family Hotel, Sarah Street, Cathedral yard
Coach and Horses, Wm. Bickell, 135 St Sidwell street
Coach Makers' Arms, John Strong, Smythen street

Corn ExchangeTavern,Thomas Bury, Market street

Country House, Ann Elworthy, 14 Catherine street

Cowley Bridge Inn, Wm.Davey, *Cowley Bridge*

Crediton Inn,JohnGreenslade,Paul st

Crown& Sceptre,Wm.Tucker,North st

Custom House, Jno.Saunders,Quay gt

DevonportInn,GraceWare,121Fore st

Devonshire Arms,W.Love, Stephen st

Dolphin, John Born, Market street

Dove, Joseph Moxon, 37 South st

Duke of York, John Crook, 147 St Sidwell street

Eagle, John Martin, Barrack road

Eagle, Wm. Batten, 42 St Sidwell st

Elephant Inn, Philip Rattenbury, 93 North street

Falcon, Thos. Dare, Lower North st

FalmouthInn,Chs.Chapple,Cowick st

Firemen's Arms, John Sandsbury, Preston street

Fountain, James Venn, Quay steps

George and Dragon, George Ash, Black Boy road

Globe Inn, Thos. Dare,jun. Clifton rd

Globe Hotel, James Parnell Moxon, Cathedral yard

Golden Ball,Ann Moore,My Arches st

GoldenEagle,Thos.Tucker,51Bthw.st

Golden Fleece, Wm. Raymond, Smythen street

GoldenLion,Stphn.Hooper,Clifton rd

Greyhound, Edward Howe, Paris st

Half Moon Inn, Ann Stephens, 22 High street

Half Moon, James Wayborn,*Whipton*

Half-way House, John Connett, Tiverton road

Haven Bank Tavern, Robert Powlesland, Haven bank

HonitonInn,JohnHawkins,13Paris st

Horse and Groom, James Clarke, Salutary mount, Heavitree

Hour Glass, John Henry Parsons, Melbourne street

Jolly Sailor, Geo. Bissett, Quay

King Alfred,Jcb. Labdon, 151 Fore st

King Wm., John Thomas, Paul st

King Wm. IV., Geo. Townsend, West quarter

King's Arms,Chas. Holmes, Cowick st

King's Arms, Wm. Routley, 105 St Sidwell street

King's Arms, Peter Palmer, West st

King's Arms, Wm. Samuel Labdon, Coombe street

King's Head, Dd. Hele, 34 Sidwell st

Lamb Inn, Jno. Moore, *Exwick*

London Ale House, Samuel Moore, Mary Arches street

Market House, George Lee Tancock, Guinea street

Mermaid, John Clynick, Preston st

Moreton Inn,Jno.Southcott, Cowick st

New Golden Lion, R.Graddon, Mrkt. st

New Inn,Wm. Holmes, St David's hill

New Inn, Wm. Roberts, Catherine st

New London Inn, Jph. Pratt, (*posting*,) Northernhay place

New Mrkt. Inn,Ed.Perry,Waterbeer st

New Mount Radford Inn, Humphry Ley, Magdalen road

North Bridge, Sml. Gubb,StDavid's hl

North Devon Inn,Eliz. Taylor, Paul st

Oat Sheaf, Sar. Locke, 164 Fore st

Okehampton Inn, Fredk. Elworthy, Okehampton road

Old Bell, John Born, Edmund st

Old Golden Lion, Geo.Eddy,Guinea st

Pack Horse, W. Brownston, David's hl

Paper Makers' Arms, Philip Cridge, Exe street

Phœnix, Thos. Jones, Goldsmith st

Plume of Feathers, Wm. Edwards, North street

Plymouth Inn, P.Mugford, Alpngtn. st

Poltimore Inn, Wm. Mitchell, 65 St Sidwell street

Port Royal, Geo. Webber, St Leond.'s

Prince Albert, Eliz. Wood, Rack st

Prince Albert, T. Smith, Cowick st

Queen Adelaide, J. Hele, Haven bk

Queen Victoria, Isc. Parkin, Exe Ild

Queen Victoria, Geo. Endacott, 71 South street

Queen's Head,Wm.Crocombe,West st

Race Horse Inn, Jno. Clement, 36 Paris street

Railway Inn,'J.Hutchings, Crediton rd

Red Cow, John Gayler, Elmfield pl

Red Lion, Wm. Lovell, 18 Sidwell st

Ring of Bells, Hy. Esworthy, West st

Rising Sun,Ts.Esworthy,37 Russell st

Round Tree, Mary Morton, Frog st

Royal Artillery Arms, James Gill, Holloway street

Royal George, Wm. Pike, Quay gate

Royal Oak, Wm. Tothill, Heavitree

Sawyers' Arms, Ts. Tucker, Preston st
Sawyers' Arms, John Gibbs, Cowick st
Seven Stars' Inn, Mrs. Bragg, Okehampton road
Ship, Rt. Nobbs, Goldsmith street
Ship, Sar. Goodwin, 5 Martin street
Ship, Jas. Ash, Alphington road
Ship, Geo. Biggs, Heavitree
Smiths' Arms, Jph. Stocker, Waterbr. st
Star Hotel, My. Taylor, 109 Fore st
Sun, John Howard, Sun street
Swan, Nancy Melhuish, 11 Cowick st
Tailors' Arms, Hy. Harris, Preston st
Teignmouth Arms, W. Dilling, West st
Three Cranes, Rd. Pain, 74 South st
Three Crowns, Rd. Channing, King st
Three Tuns Inn, W. Keeth, 8 High st
Topsham Inn, William Johnson, 42 South street
Turk's Head, J. Sampson, 202 High st
Turk's Head, Wm. Ellett, Cowick st
Union, Geo. Sticklin, Okehampton st
Union, Thos. Collihole, Waterbeer st
Valiant Soldier, Ed. Leach Herbert, 34 Magdalen street
Victory Inn, Rt. Balkwill, 75 St Sdwl. st
Wheat Sheaf, John Ashe, Fore st
White Ball, Wm. Lee, My. Arches st
White Hart, Ts. Hex, 12 Alphington st
White Hart Inn, Mary Ann Summers, 54 South street
White Horse, Hy. Davis, 90 Sidwell st
White Lion, Jno. Moxon, 99 Sidwl. st
Windsor Castle, Wm. Smallridge, 11 Summerland street
Wind Mill, W. Southcott, 50 Hollwy. st

(70) BEERHOUSES.

Bambury John, *East Wonford*
Bickell John, 133 St Sidwell street
Bickell John, *South Wonford*
Bowden Thos., Cowick street
Boon William, Clifton road
Burrows James, King street
Cornelius John, 22 New Bridge st
Court Rebecca, Exe street
Ferguson William, Preston street
Hayman John, Rack street
Hill James, Black Boy road
Holton Wm., Well lane
Honeywill Wm., *South Wonford*
Hooke George, Mary Arches street
Hooper Mary, *South Wonford*
Ireland James, *High Hoopern*
Jarman Francis, 21 Longbrook st
Jarman John, *Cowley Bridge*

Lee Susanna, Frog street
Ronchetti Thos., Black Boy street
Rudall Elizabeth, Stepcote hill
Satterley Chpr., 156 St Sidwell st
Sherman Richard, West street
Skinner John, Heavitree
Wreford Richard, Coombe street
Whyburn Geo., Colleton buildings
Thomas John, Paul street
Trethewey Richd., Elmfield place
Weeks John, Union road

(71) IRON & BRASS FOUNDERS.
*(Marked * are Engineers, &c.)*
*Bodley Alfred, Commercial road
*Bodley Wm. Canute & Co. (stove grate, &c.) *Bonhay*
Bowden John, (brass,) Bartlmw. st
Downe & Son, (plumbers' brass, &c.) 66 South street
Garton & Jarvis, (hot water apparatus mfrs. to her Majesty,) 190 High st
Hooper Samuel, Maddocks row
*Huxhams & Brown, Commercial rd
Kerslake Thomas, 102 Fore street
*Martin John & Co., Engine bridge
*Northam Jas., Commercial road
Trickey Jas. (brass,) Pancras lane

(72) IRONMONGERS.
Broadmead John, Heavitree
Cole George, 244 High street
Damerel John, (& appraiser,) 62 St Sidwell street
Fouracres Eliza, 21 Paris street, and Cowick street
Gard Jno. Somers, 53 High street
Garton & Jarvis, 190 High street
Hayne Jph. 40 St Sidwell street
Hughes & Carter, 158 Fore street
Kerslake Thomas, 102 Fore street
Marshall Thos. 34 New Bridge st
Munk Wm. (*whols.*) 135 Fore street
Northam James, Commercial road
Pearse Brothers, 93 Fore street
Scott John, 42 St Sidwell street
Webber John, Pancras lane
Wippell George, 231 High street
Wreford Wm. 1 North Bridge

(73) LACE MAKERS.
(Honiton Point Lace Workers, &c.)
Bradbeer Eliz. 4 Northernhay row
Davis Hannah, Cathedral yard
Dobbs Charlotte E., Cathedral yard
Jessep Chtte. F. 31 St Sidwell street
Stewart My. & Sar., Magdalen hill

LAND SURVEYORS, &c.
(See Architects and Surveyors.)

(74) LATH RENDERS.
Hussey John, 152 St Sidwell street
Peters Edw. 14 Little Eaton place
Peters James, Waterbeer street
Peters Richard, Goldsmith street

(75) LAW STATIONERS.
Bannehr James, Bedford street
Paddon Theodore Jas. 48 Sidwell st
Ripley Edwin, 2 Castle st. & Gandy st
Sparkes Thos. 11 Northernhay place

(76) LIBRARIES.
Besley Thomas, 247 High street
Curson & Son, 17 High street
Medical Lib., Devon & Exeter Hospl
Devon and Exeter Instn., Cathedral yard; John Squance, *librarian*
Exeter General Library, at David Thomson's, 43 High street
Exeter Law Library, Bedford circus; Robert Fulford, *secretary*
Featherstone Wm. C. 246 High st
Fitze James, 39 High street
Horwill James, 162 St Sidwell street
Pomeroy Hannah, 46 Paris street
Public Select, 247 High street; Wm. Balle, *librarian*
Roberts Wm. Robt. 265, High street
Stone Robt. 10 New Bridge street

(77) LIME BURNERS.
Davy and Son, *Countess-Weir*
Hooper W. H. & W. W., Leonrd.'s qy

(78) LINEN DRAPERS, &c.
Bastard Wm. S. & S. *(whols.)* St Jas. st
Braund G. & J. *(whols.)* High street
Braund Henry, 67 High street
Brunt Eliz. & Cath. 19 New Bridge st
Burne Hy. & Co., 130 Fore street
Cleeve Abm. 71 High street
Colson & Spark, 34 High street
Copp & Poynter, 206 High street
Dingle Wm. 164 Fore street
Edger and Harris, 62 High street
Fitzgerald John Butler, (linen whs.) 25 High street
Fryer and Way, 155 Fore street
Gard E. & Co. *(whols.)* Castle street
Green and Bennett, 25 High street
Hall Mary, 12 South street
Hamlyn Wm. Mann, 86½ Fore street
Hearn James, 233 High street
Helmore & Carter, 157 Fore street
Hemley Geo. Wm., Heavitree
Hooker Robt. 134 St Sidwell street

Luxmore Wm. 7 Queen street
Mallett John, 159 St Sidwell street
Martin Geo. 107 St Sidwell street
May Wm. 4 Queen street
Nightingale Robert, 28 High street
Pasmore & Savery, *(whols.)* 73 High st
Pearse Wm. & Co. 196 High street
Pearse and Sons, 171 Fore street
Raddon Philip, 91 North street
Raddon Thomas, 78 South street
Ridge Jph. Daniel, 70 South street
Risdon John, 194 High street
Rowe Cphr. & Son, 184 Fore street
Taylor Saml. 269 High street
Tonar John, *(linen & carpet whs.)* 266 High street
Tuckwell Hy. 15 New Bridge street
Turner John, 152 Fore street
Wilcocks & Brock, 178 Fore street
Wreford Saml. 181 Fore street

(79) LITHOGRAPHERS.
Angel Owen, 94 Fore street
Bannehr James, Bedford street
Featherstone Wm. C. 246 High st
Frise & Marker, 3 Palace gate
Lewis & Eveleigh, 19 Magdalen st
Ripley Edwin, 2 Castle street
Risdon Charles, 5 Paris street
Smith Richard, Waterbeer street
Southard Matthew, Bear street
Spreat Wm. 229 High street
Townsend George, Deanery place
Worton James P., St James street

(80) LIVERY STABLEKEEPRS,
And Chaise, Fly, Hack Horse, &c. Owners.
Ashford Edward, Cowick street
Avery Samuel, Southernhay
Back Wm. 72 St Sidwell street
Bradford Richard, Southernhay
Carpenter Wm. H. 69 Paris street
Collings Paul, Longbrook street
Delany Matt. (riding mr.) Paris st
Harrap Saml. 9 Catherine street
Hurley John, Okehampton road
Knowles Job, Castle street
Lucas Geo. (fly owner,) St Sidwell st
May Richard, Bartholomew street
Pearse George, Bedford street
Pedrick Wm. Post-Office street
Poole Thomas, Southernhay
Radford Richd. 2, Bedford mews
Skinner Mary, St Sidwell street
Smallridge Wm. 11 Summerland st
Smale G. Holmes, 18 Northernhay st

Smith Wm., Magdalen street
Southcott Wm., Magdalen road
Trace John, Catherine street
Wager and Smale, Queen street
Western Jno., Baker's ct. Sidwell st.
White Thomas, Southernhay street
Yelland P., Friar's gate

(81) MACHINE MAKERS.
(See also Iron Founders.)
Down Rd. (thrashing) Mint street
Garton & Jarvis, (lathe,) 190 High st
Tucker Chas. (agrl.) Commercial rd

(82) MALTSTERS.
Barker Elizabeth, Heavitree
Brown Edward, Alphington road
Chapman John, Cowick street
Endacott Geo. 71 South street
Goodridge Wm., Heavitree
Harding Joseph, St David's hill
Luscombe Wm., Longbrook street
Mallett Ann, West quarter
Norman & Co., Commercial road
Reed Jno. & Edw. Alphington street
Richards Wm., St David's hill
Salter Thomas, Gandy street
Scott John, Black Boy road
Southcott George, Holloway street

(83) MARINE STORE DLRS.
(Rags, Old Ropes, &c.)
Avery Jesse, Upper West street
Avery Samuel, Commercial road
Coombe George, Coombe street
Dunn Hannah, Upper West street
Gibson John, Bartholomew street
Godbeer Wm., Cowick street
Hales James, Coombe street
Harris Wm., Paul street
Hayes John, 59 South street
Hearn Saml. 21 Magdalen street
Jewell Maurice, Sun street
Kerswell Thomas, Black Boy road
Milne James, Coombe street
Norman Geo., Summerland street
Potter John, King street
Tothill Robert, Cowick street
Vigers Joseph, Frog street
Whyburn Geo., Colleton buildings

(84) MERCHANTS.
Cresswell J. & Co., Magdalen street
Davy Fras. (iron, &c.) Palace st. &
  Topsham
Dyer Saml. (corn,) 241 High street
Follett & Co., Shilhay wharf
Francis Jas. (hide,) Painter's row
Higgins Thos. (corn, &c.) Coombe st

Langdon Jas. Hy. 2 Palace street
Porter & Hinckes, 91 North street
Norris & Redway, (corn, flour, &c.) Qy
Richards Richd. 7 Friar's walk
Sanders Wm. (hide, &c.) Exe island
Sercombe Jno. C. & George, Quay
Tuckett Nicholas, (manure, &c.) 161
  Fore street

(85) MILLINERS, &c.
*(Marked * Baby Linen, &c., Dlrs.)*
Ashelford Ann, 17 Paragon place
Barber Mary, 10 Russell street
Baple Caroline, Coombe street
Bartrum & Howard, 13 Castle street
Beer Sally & Mary, 3 High street
Best Eliz. 19 St Sidwell street
Bickford C. & A. 84 South street
*Bidlake & Nicholls, Cathedral yard
Bignell Ann, Mary Arches street
Blake and Beavis, 45 Paris street
Blamey Grace & Eliz. 20 Paris street
Bond Wm. 51 High street
Bowcher Eliz. and Ferris Ann, 20
  High street
Boyle Jane, 9 Summerland street
Bradford Eliz., C., L., & J.,22 Paris st
Brewer Frances, Commercial road
Brook Sarah, Castle street
Brunt Maria, 128 St Sidwell street
Bryett Frances, 2 Gandy street
Cambridge Mary Ann, St Sidwell st
Canes Mary, 123 Fore street
Carter Margaret, 19 Holloway street
Clark & Timewell, 18 Paris street
Clatworthy Louisa, 16 Holloway st
Dancaster T. 20 Holloway street
Davis Chtte. 52 St Sidwell street
Dipstale Mrs Jane, 11 High street
Doeg E. L. 20 Magdalen street
Down Mary, 18 Catherine street
Downman My. St James street
Drake Mary, 4 Melbourne place
Eales Har. 2 Summerland street
Elworthy Eliza, 16 Castle street
Evans S. E. & L. 228 High street
Eveleigh Eliz. Upper Paul street
Ford Mary, 5 Milk street
Foster Sar. 50 Magdalen street
French Matilda, 4 Buller place
Frost Louisa R. 36 Paris street
Godfrey Ann, 10 North street
Green Mrs J. 243 High street
Hardwick Ann, Mint
Haywood Ann, St Olave square
Hemens Sarah, Frog lane

Holt Mary, 9 Paris street
Holway Jane, 8 Paris street
Hutchings Emma, Poltimore place
Isaac M. A., Gandy street
Jackson Elizabeth, Heavitree
Jones Ann, Paul street
Kendall & Holburd, 245 High street
Kenton Eliz. J. 20 Magdalen street
Keys Eliz. 8 Bartholomew street
Lake Caroline, 2 Paris street
Lake Eliz. 148 Fore street
Lakeman Eliz., Upper Paul street
Lambert Misses, Cathedral yard
Leverton Ann, 17 Paris street
*Luxton My. Ann, 225 High street
Maddever Mary, 133 Fore street
Mayne Eliza, 45 High street
Maunder Mary, 3 Magdalen street
Meggs M. & F., Deanery place
Mitchell Mary, St Olave square
Mountstephens Jane, Alphington rd
Nicholls Eliz., Melbourne street
Pike Harriet, 71 St Sidwell street
Presswell Frances, Cathedral yard
Prinn Jane, James street
Raddon Harriet, 75 South street
Richards Mary, Sun street
Roberts Sarah, Cowick street
Sanders Eliz. 129 St Sidwell street
Sanders Mary, Heavitree
Scanes Eliz. 48 St Sidwell street
Searle Jane, Cathedral yard
Shepherd Elizabeth, Southernhay
Shute Eliz. 4 College row
Snell Mary Cook, 229 High street
*Spalding John, 32 High street
Southcott Ellen, Okehampton street
Stephens & Carter, 19 Holloway st
Sutton Eliz. & Eleanor, Cathedral yd
Taylor Walter Hy. 10 Northernhay pl
Tole Louisa, 17 Magdalen street
Townsend Ann, 30 South street
Tozer Sar. & Jane, Cathedral yard
Tucker Henrietta, 84½ Fore street
Tuck Sarah, 35 South street
Warren Mary, Gandy street
Waters Ann H., Upper Paul street
Woodman Frances, 8 Catherine st
Woodward Fanny, Catherine street
Wreford Eliz., Bartholomew street
Western Susan, St James street
Westlake Mary, Bedford street
Wright Jane, Holloway street
(86) MILLWRIGHTS.
Huxhams & Brown, Commercial rd

Northam James, Commercial road
Rogers Nicholas, Exe lane
Tuckett Charles, Commercial road
(87) MUSIC & INSTMT. DLRS.
Ashe Wm. John, 245 High street; h
Radnor place
Skinner Wm. 189 High street
Smith Doherty & Fdk. 257 High st
Vinnicombe John Pewtner, 14 Northernhay place
MUSIC TEACHERS.
(See Professors and Teachers.)
(88) NEWSPAPERS.
Devonshire Chronicle, (Tuesday,) Ts. Besley, 89 North street
Exeter and Plymouth Gazette, (Sat.) Woolmer & Thacker, 236 High st
Exeter Flying Post, (Thursday,) R. J. Trewman & Co. 226 High st
Western Luminary, (Tuesday,) J. S. Dewdney, 6 Bedford circus
Western Times, (Saturday,) Thomas Latimer, 143 Fore street
(88A) NEWS AGENTS.
Gibbs Wm. 91 North street
Havill James Webber, (& medicine vender,) 91 Fore street
Pike Geo. 39½ South street
Pring Wm. 67 St Sidwell street
Spreat Jane, 163 High street
(89) NURSERY & SEEDSMEN.
Addiscott Wm. & Son, Alphington rd
James John, Hill's court
Lucombe, Pince, & Co., Alphington rd
Mogridge Wm. Kerswell, 14 New Bridge street
Nott Wm. Alphington road
Pope Henry, Cowick street
Sclater & Son, (Chas. & Jas.) Summerland hill and Heavitree
Southwood Richard, Okehampton rd
Thorn John, Okehampton road
Veitch Jas. & Son, 54 High street and Topsham road
(90) OIL & COLOURMEN.
Davy Wm. 144 Fore street hill
Gray C. T. 2 Market street
James & Rosewall, Exe island
Tanner Jas. Jones, Westgate
Thomas J. L. & R. F. (oil,) 163 Fore street
Thoms G. P. P. & Co. 168 Fore st
(91) OPTICIANS.
Alexander Alex. 6 High street
Carter George, 252 High street

Ronchetti Edmund, Waterbeer st

(92) ORGAN BUILDRS. & PIANO FORTE, &c. MANFRS.

Brooking Hy., Upper Paul street
Dicker Hy. Philip, Gandy street
Mardon Jas., Chas., & Wm. (& violin, &c.) Mint

(93) PAINTERS & GLAZIERS.

*(Marked * are Paper Hangers.)*

Algar John, Upper Paul street
Ashby Arthur, (heraldic,) Cheeke st
Batten Ts. Belmont, 20 Barthlmw. st
Beer Robert, 42 Bartholomew street
Berridge Edward, 17 Holloway st
Bond Wm. (heraldic,) 5 Hill's bldgs
*Butcher Wm. 29 New Bridge street
*Bradley John, 129 Fore street
Bradley Wm. 159 Fore street
Chaplin Wm. 80 South street
Cox H. S. 4 Sandford street
Davey John & Sons (Chas.&Jno.jun.) 3 Southernhay street
Davys Wm. 18 Paris street
Dey Thomas, Guinea street
Dipstale Edward, Mint street
Dobel John, Heavitree
Godbeer James, St Stephen's str et
Gould John, 10 Cowick street
Gould Thos. 7 Alphington street
Gregory Charles, 3 Paris street
Harvey Danl. 112 St Sidwell street
Hucklebridge John, 70 Paris street
Hutchison Robert, Bear street
Johnston John, Stephen street
*Kerslake Cornls. 161 St Sidwell st
*Kingwell Jas. 52 Bartholomew st
*Kingwell Wm. 47 South street
Knight Richard, 26 South street
Langsford John, Commercial road
Marshall Thos. 34 New Bridge st
Mitchell Thos. 29 North street
Norraway Hy. 56 Magdalen street
Norris Wm. 7 North street
Norris Wm. jun., Friar's green
Pentecost Richd. 14 St Sidwell st
Petherick Chas. John, 9 Paris street
Pridham Charles, Magdalen street
Quick Wm. G. 151 Fore street
Rice Thomas, Waterbeer street
Ringwell Wm. 44 South street
Roberts Charles, Cowick street
Roberts John, 10 Magdalen street
Roper Fredk. 73 South street
Ronchetti Fredk. 1 Mount pleasant
Salter Thomas, 73 St Sidwell st

Taylor James Stayley, Bear street
Thoms G. P. P. & Co. 168 Fore st
Thorn Richard, Waterbeer street
Tucker Edwin, *(heraldic,)* 73 St Sidwell street
Warren Chas. Jas., Lower North st
Warren Samuel, 9 Paris street
*White Jph. 74 St Sidwell street
Whitford Mrs F. 67 Magdalen st
Willey James, 130 St Sidwell st
Winsor Samuel, 19 Paris street
Yendall Jacob, 17 North street

(94) PAPER MAKERS.

Dewdney Robt. & Co. *Trew's Weir*
Harris Charles, *Countess Weir*
Matthews George, *Exwick*
Matthews Richard, *Huxham*
Matthews and Martyn, *Huxham*
Tremlett E. N. & Co. *Head weir Mill*

(95) PATTEN & CLOG MKRS.

Bradbeer Jph. & Son, Exe bridge
Burdon James, St David's hill
Burdon Wm. 42 Holloway street
Marks John, 131 Fore street
Mayes Wm. *(last,)* Preston street
Mortimer John, Paul street
Morgan Thomas, *(last,)* 8 Paris st
Pyne Sarah, 146 Fore street
Roleston Joseph, Smythen street
Tarbett Thomas, Edmund street

(96) PAWNBROKERS.

Channing Wm. jun. 7 South street
Reeves & Linscott, St John's street
Trimble, Son, and Brooking, Gandy street and Mint street

(97) PEN CUTTERS & QUILL DRESSERS.

Jacobs Eml. & Co. 8 Market street
Jonas Benj. 3 Bartholomew street
Lazarus Dvd. (& pencil mfr.)Mkt. st

(98) PERFUMERS & HAIR DSRS.

Bedford Wm., Coombe street
Beaumont Charles, Preston street
Clement Henry, 24 Longbrook st
Chave Samuel, Theatre house
Coope Wm., Bedford street
Crouch James, 69 South street
Dale Wm. 9 New Bridge street
Denham Daniel, Goldsmith street
Dobel Joseph, Heavitree
Evans John, King street
Havill Jas. Webber, 91 Fore street
Hopekirk Robt. 42 High street
Isaac Wm., Market street
Jacombe Wm. 127 St Sidwell st

Lake John, St Sidwell street
Leat Thomas, 36 South street
Lewis Wm., Fore street
Lillycrop Thomas, Mary Arches st
Martin Joseph, 76½ Paris street
Odam George, 22 New Bridge st
Piper Wm. 334 High street
Price Joseph, Guinea street
Quick Thomas, Okehampton street
Quick Wm., Alphington street
Rice Joseph F., Guinea street
Rose Richard, 22 South street
Staddon Wm., Waterbeer street
Staddon Thomas, 77 St Sidwell st
Stocker John, 6 Catherine street
Stone Joseph, 264 High street
Tancock James, 30 North street
Tarrant John, Preston street
Taylor Robert, 26 Sidwell street
Trapnell Josias, 93 North street
Trist John, Edmund street
Webber Wm., Cowick street
Williams Thomas, Upper West st
(99) PHYSICIANS.
Barham Thos. Foster, Spring Lawn, Magdalen road
Blackall John, 13 Southernhay pl
Budd Samuel, 21 Southernhay pl
Drake Augustus, 27 Southernhay
Elliott Wm. H. 1 Bouverie place
Fixott James, 18 High street
Freer John, *Oakford House*
Gibbs H. L. 19 Southernhay place
Granger Frederick, Musgrave's alley
Guinness Arthur, 3 Dix's field
Hall Stephen, 4 Victoria ter. Mrd
Hall Wm. 12 Clifton place
Hulme Edward, 3 Chichester place
Kingdon W. D., St Thomas's Hospl
Lang Jeffery, Stafford terrace, H
Ludlow Samuel, 14 Clifton place
Makintosh Rd. Duncan, 11 Dix's fd
Massy Rd. Tuthill, 2 Upr. Southrnhy
Miles Erasmus Madox, Homefd. pl. H
Miller Patrick, Grove House, Mtd
Oxley Edward, 4 Salutary place
Pennell Rd. Lewin, 10 Castle st
Shapter Thomas, 1 Barnfield
(99A) PIANO TUNERS.
(*See Organ, &c., Builders.*)
Boone Thomas, Paris street
Brooking Henry, Upper Paul st
Guest John, Friar's road
Mardon Wm. (and maker,) Mint
Perkins John, 64 Magdalen street

Seymour I. W., 23 North street
Vinnicombe J. P., 14 Northernbay pl
(100) PLUMBERS & GLAZRS.
Dancaster John, 20 Holloway street
Davys Wm. 18 Paris street
Dey Thomas, Guinea street
Downe & Son, (& brass founders & engine makers,) 66 South street
Ford John, jun. St David's hill
Ford T. & Son, 3 Bartholomew st
Fouracres Eliza, 21 Paris street, and Cowick street
Gaul Robert, 42 South street
Hamers James, 2 Bartholomew st
Hooper Samuel, Maddock's row
Hucklebridge John, 70 Paris st
Palmer Robert, Mary Arches street
Pridham Charles, 27 Magdalen st
Rouse Richard, 43 Paris street
Scanes Eliz. (and gas fitter,) 48 St Sidwell street
Scanes Thomas, St Sidwell street
(101) PORTER & ALE MERTS.
Commin Samuel, 94, Fore street
Dawson Rd. Hy. & Co. 8 North st
Durant George, George street
Murch James, 87 South street
Neck Wm. (pale ale,) 10 Paris st
Sercombe Thomas, 16 New Bridge st
Trehane John, 78 Fore street
Wilkinson Robt. C. 89 North st
Williams Thos. Elson, 267 High st
(102) POULTERERS.
(* *are Game Dealers.*)
Andrews Eliz. 4 Catherine street
*Chamberlain Alice, Bedford street
Chambers James, Goldsmith street
Fletcher James, Cowick street
Hooper Henry, 97 North street
*Loram John, Mary Arches street
Sanders Thomas, Martin street
Southcott Richard, Bampfylde st
*Sparke Robert, 12 Martin street
Stevens Eliz., Catherine street
(103) PRINTERS. (*Letter-press.*)
(*See also Bookslrs. & Newspapers.*)
Balle Wm. 247 High street
Besley Thomas, 29 North street
Besley Henry, 76 South street
Dewdney Jno. Sweetland, 6 Bedfd. cir
Freeman Robert John, 220 High st; house Salutary mount
Featherstone Wm. C. 246 High st. and 1 Bedford street
Godfrey Wm. & Son, (Fdk.) 227 High st

H

Latimer Thomas, 143 Fore street
Norton Wm. ct 247 High street
Pollard Wm. Carss, 96 North st
Roberts Wm. 197 High street
Roberts Wm. Thos. 265 High street
Spencer Robert, 94 St Sidwell st
Stone Robert, 10 New Bridge street
Trewman Robt. Jno.&Co. 226 High st
Wallis Hy. John, 245 High street
Welsford Harriet H., Paul street
Woolmer Edw. and Co. 236 High st

(104) PROCTORS.
Barnes Ralph, Palace gate
Bishop and Pitts, 19 Bedford circus
Bremridge Thos. J., Cathedral yard
Brutton Charles, 1 Northernhay pl
Drake Geo. Henry, Upper Paul st
Drake Thomas E., New buildings
Ellicombe John B., Southernhay
Force Edwin, Deanery place
Ford Henry, 25 Southernhay place
Furlong Wm. H., Lower Northernhay
Geare John, 3 Bedford circus
Gidley John, 15 Bedford circus
Gray Thos. Wm. 4 North bridge
Hooper Hy. Wilcocks, 12 Bedford cir
Kemp Edw. Louis, Cathedral yard
Kitson Frederick, Palace gate
Turner Chas. Hy. (regr. of Consistory Court,) Cathedral yard

(105) PROFESSORS.
*Marked * are Teachers of Music; + Drawing; and ‡ Languages.*
*Angel Alfred, Cathedral yard
*Ashe Wm. John, 254 High street
*Carlile Rd. & Mrs. 8 Paris street
*Carpenter Edw. 3 Upper Eaton pl
*Carpenter Wm. 18 Northernhay st
+‡ De Niceville Mons. 4 Jeffery's rw
‡Duval Francis, 8 Lansdowne ter
+Ellis Fredk. 10 Bystock terrace
*Franklin H. 6 Colleton terrace
‡Galindo S., Black Boy road
Gurney Mrs and Miss, (dancing,) 9 Northernhay place
+Hake Wm. 115 St Sidwell street
+Halls Thomas, Heavitree
*Harvey Geo. H. 19 Dix's field
*Hexter Abrm. Soper, (lay vicar,) Cathedral yard
*Ingham Jas. (lay vicar,) 2 Weirfd. pl
+Jeffery Emanuel, 8 East Southrnhy
*Lambert Clara, Mary's yard
Mason Hubert, (dancing,) Longbrk. st

‡Moschzisker F. A. (German, French, and Hebrew,) Cowick street
*Mudge Parmenas Pearce, Lower Mount Radford terrace
*Newman John Fras. 230 High st
*Pelzer Miss C. J. (guitar, &c.) 6 Longbrook terrace
+‡Persac E., Woodbine cotg. North rd
*Pinney Wm. 3 Warren place
*Pye Kellow John, 6 Magdalen st
*Ramson J. L. (flute,) North st
*Rendle John, (violin,) 9 St John's ter
*Rice Michael, Trinity street
*Salter Wm. (organist,) Deanery pl
*Seymour Isaac Wm. 25 North st
*Shapcott Brothers, 26 Holloway st
*Smith D. and F. 257 High street
*Smyth Martha, 4 Cobourg place
*Turner Thomas Price, North st
*Vaughan D. L. 63 South street
*Vinnicombe J. P. 14 Northernhay pl
‡Thimm Hugo, 50 Sidwell street
Webber Jane, (dancing,) 21 South st
+Williams Chas. Fredk., Palace st
*Withycombe Hy. (guitar,) 12 Albion pl
*Wood George D. 12 Paris street
*Wyllie Rt. Wilson, Bartw. st & *Whipton*

(106) PUMP MAKERS.
(See also Plumbers, &c.)
Ley Humphrey, Magdalen road
Rouse Richard, 43 Paris street

(107) ROPE & TWINE MKRS.
Bowden John, Cowick street
Clogg Joshua, Cowick street
Clogg John, Cowick street
Hill James, Black Boy road
Renouf John, 32 Holloway street
Snow James, Black Boy road

(108) SADDLERS,
And Harness Makers.
Badcock Wm. 34 North street
Bolt Simon, Heavitree
Brewer James, Stepcote hill
Brown Charles, Cowick street
Brown John, 10 North street
Chalk John, 39 South street
Ekers Wm. 13 South street
Escott Wm. 156 Fore street
Franklin Fredk. & Geo. 271 High st
Hayman Geo. & Co. 100 St Sidwell st
Jackson Edw. Wm., Upr. Southrnhy
Quick John, Broad street
Reed John, Cathedral yard
Richards John, 137 St Sidwell st
Roper Alexander, Coombe street

Scott Wm. 166 Fore street
Sharland Thos. (& tawer,) Edmund
   street and Southernhay street
Smith James, 22 Holloway street
Toms John Ratcliffe, Bampfylde st;
   house Hiram place
   (109) SADDLE TREE MKRS.
Ramster Wm., Paul street
Welch John, 3 Albert street
   (110) SEEDSMEN.
   (See Gardeners & Nurserymen.)
Carter John, 7 Market street
Mogridge Wm. Kerswell, 14 New Bdg. st
Sercombe John C. & George, Quay
Thomas George, Market street
   SERGE MANUFACTURERS.
   (See Woollen Manufacrs.)
   (112) SHARE BROKERS.
Bannehr James, Bedford street
Clapp Richard, High street
Gliddon Geo. Robins, Bampfylde st
Higgins Thos., Bartholomew yard
Jury J. 3 Castle terrace
May and Bidwill, Bedford circus
Mortimer Wm. 3 York buildings
Sanford J. 3 Hill's buildings
Sanford Thomas, 5 Musgrave's alley;
   house St Sidwell's street
Tripp Robert, Bedford chambers
Vatcher Henry, 3 Bedford street
   (113) SHOE MERCERS.
Hanssen John, 154 High street
Joslin and Quick, Queen street
   (114) SHOPKEEPERS.
   (Grocery, Flour, &c., Dealers.)
Bailey Wm., Cowick street
Baker Jane, Coombe street
Bambury John, *East Wonford*
Bamsey John, Cowick street
Bastin George, 12 Paris street
Beard Wm., Summerland street
Bending John, Exe street
Berry George, Preston street
Bickham Wm. 10 Alphington street
Bickell John, South Wonford
Bond Thomas, Cowick street
Bowers John, 15 Holloway street
Braddon Wm., Coombe street
Bradford Lucy, 22 Paris street
Brannan Abraham, Black Boy road
Brewer Samuel, 14 Holloway street
Brice John, 8 Alphington street
Brown Richd. 41 St Sidwell street
Bunclerk John, Well lane
Burge Wm., Paul street

Burgoin Wm., Heavitree
Butland John, Exe street
Carter Wm., Bartholomew street
Casely Wm., Black Boy street
Channing Wm., Heavitree
Clark Wm., Rack street
Cole Wm., Heavitree
Collings Wm., Russell street
Coneybeer Samuel, Exwick
Coombe Samuel, Exe Island
Cornelius John, 23 New Bridge st
Crocker John, West street
Densham Wm., Rack street
Doney Wm., Edmund street
Drake George, Magdalen road
Drew Joseph, 132 St Sidwell street
Drew Edward, Edmund street
Evans Samuel, Stepcote hill
Featherstone Eliz., Preston place
Gill Wm., Smythen street
Godfrey Robert, North lane, H
Goldsworthy Francis, Melbourne st
Goveyer Jane, Preston street
Griffin Nicholas, Frog street
Griffin Thomas, Coombe street
Gully Mary, Coombe street
Hayman John, Rack street
Harris Maria, 19 Paris street
Harvey John, Oakfield street, H
Heal John, 160 St Sidwell street
Heard Robert, 4 Castle street
Herbert Richard, Cowick street
Hexter Ann, 164 St Sidwell street
Hill John, Melbourne street
Hitt Henry, Heavitree
Holloway Thomas, St David's hill
Holmes Charles, Alphington street
Hookway Samuel, Preston street
Hooper Edward, 140 St Sidwell st
Hooper Johanna, 10 Russell st
Hutchings Wm. 6 Alphington st
Hyde Joseph, Cowick street
James Philip, Mary Arches street
James Wm., Summerland street
Jarman Francis, 21 Longbrook st
Jarman John, 52 Russell street
Johnson John, 15 Clifton road
Johnson Sarah, Longbrook street
Jury Eliz. 14 Magdalen street
Knapman John, Mary Arches street
Knapman Mary, Preston street
Lee Sarah, 60 Magdalen street
Lee Wm., Cowick street
Luxton John, West street
Marsh Robert, Exe Island

Martin Charles, Paul street
Mason James, Preston street
Moore Samuel, Paul street
Newberry Robert, 27 St Sidwell st
Newcombe Daniel, Stephen's bow
Northway Richard, Mint
Nosworthy Wm., Gandy street
Ocock John, Okehampton street
Palmer Sarah, Waterbeer street
Parr James, Guinea street
Penny Thomas, Upper West street
Perkins Ann, Cowick street
Perryman Mary, 37 St Sidwell st
Pinn Thomas, Black Boy road
Pomeroy Hannah, 46 Paris street
Potter George, 11 St Sidwell street
Pridham Thomas, 8 Catherine st
Prout Wm., Clifton road
Punchard Wm., Coombe street
Putt Philip, Russell street
Rabjohns Wm., Goldsmith street
Reed Wm., Coombe street
Ridgway Thomas, West street
Roper Frederick, 73 South street
Rowden Wm., 76 Paris street
Rush Philippa, 78 Paris street
Saunders Edward, Mary Arches st
Selly Wm. C. 11 Holloway street
Sercombe John Ths. 13 Northrnhy pl
Shooter Edwin, West street
Smith Richard, Albert street
Squire John, Cowick street
Snow Roger, 24 St Sidwell street
Sellick John, Guinea street
Soper Wm., West street
Southard John, Summerland street
Stocker Joseph, Paris street
Stocker Richard, 7 Cowick street
Symons Henry, 28 Magdalen street
Thomas John, 83 South street
Tothill Wm., Heavitree
Tozer John, Alphington street
Turnbull Jas. Wm. 2 Paris street
Turner John, Preston street
Turpin Wm., St David's hill
Warren Richard, Summerland st
Westlake Wm., Cowick street
White Thomas, Paul street
Wilson James, 6 Sun street
Willey S , Bedford street
Woodley Samuel, Preston street
Wood Sarah, Upper West street
Wrayford George, Cowick street
Yendle James, Market street

(115) SILVERSMITHS AND
JEWELLERS.
(See also Watch, &c., Makers.)
Adams E. H.(goldsmith,) 38 High st
Avent Thomas, 126 Fore street
Byne Thomas, (working,) Mint lane
Chapple John, 19 High street
Ellis Henry & Son, 200 High street
Guest Thomas, 35 New Bridge st
Lake Henry, 214 High street
Lazarus Isaac, Northernhay place
Lazarus Moses, Lansdowne terrace
Osment John, (working,) Mint
Rickard Sidney, 19 Paris street
Sobey Wm. Rawlins, 1 Queen st
Silverston Israel, 107 Fore street
Stone John, 30 New Bridge street
Torr Eli, (working,) George street
(116) SLATE, &c., MERCHTS.
Beck Henry, Commercial road
Mason John, Commercial wharf
Mitchell Thos. & Co., Haven bank
Tuckett Nicholas, Commercial road
(117) SLATERS & PLASTRS.
Bennett Wm. 47 Paris street
Callaway John, 170 St Sidwell st
Channing George, Heavitree
Chanter James, 141 St Sidwell st
Chanter Joseph, St Sidwell street
Clark Thomas, Cowick street
Coombe Warwick, 26 Magdalen st
Cummings and Venton, Barthw. yd
Gibbons Nicholas, Mary Arches st
Gilpin James, Okehampton street
Gregory John, Preston street
Hawker Thos. Cowick street
Moss Samuel, James street
Parish Richard, Maddock's row
Pope Jno. & Son, 3 Holloway street
Red John, Lower North street
Reynolds Chas., St David's hill
Reynolds Richd., Silver street
Rowse John, 24 Paris street
Sanders Wm., Heavitree
Southard Rt. Summerland street
Selly Wm. Cobley, 11 Holloway
Tope James, James's terrace
Twitcher John, Cowick street
Walters Frs. Lovis, 11 Longbrke. st
Westlake George, Rack street
White John Henry, Preston place
Willey Josiah, St Sidwell street
SOLICITORS.
(See Attorneys.)

(118) SPIRIT DLRS. (Retail.)
(*See also Wine & Spirit Merchants.*)
Bond John, jun., 1 Cowick street
Bucknole John, jun., 4 Paris street
Cleeve Susanna, 203 High street
Dyer Thomas, 3 Cowick street
Elston Elias, 137 St Sidwell street
Mardon James, 34 South street
Matthews Thos. 86 St Sidwell street
Skinner Wm. 58 Bartholomew street
Parker Mary, Friar's gate
Suter Susanna, 77, South street

(119) STARCH MANFRS.
Brailey & Williams, 4 St Sidwell st
Thomas J. L. & R. F. (*and hair powder,*) 163 Fore street

(120) STATIONERS.
(*See also Booksellers, &c.*)
Besley Henry, 76 South street
Besley Thomas, 89 North street
Colson John, (& paper hanging dlr.) 211 High street
Cooper Geo. (paper ruler, &c.) 101 Fore street
Featherstone Wm. C., Bedford street
Evans A. & Co. (wholsl.) 98 Fore st
Jacobs Emanuel & Co. 9 Market st
Hayes John, 59 South street
Knight Samuel, 1 Summerland st
Mack Margaret, 92 Fore street
Sparks Thos. 11 Northernhay place
Spencer Rt. 94 St Sidwell street
Stone Robert, 10 New Bridge street
Thomson David, 43 High street

(121) STONE AND MARBLE MASONS.
Clark James, (undertaker and appraiser,) 18, Paris street
Cross Wm., George street
Davey Thomas, Upper Paul street
Easton John, (stone,) Friars
Mason John, Commercial Wharf
Rowe Simon, York st. St Sidwell's
Stephens James & Son, 116 Fore st
Wilson James, 12 Magdalen street

(122) STAY MAKERS.
Allen Harriet, Goldsmith street
Brown Sarah, Cowick street
Bale & Sweet, Paris street
Burdon Robert, 16 North street
Burdon Ann, St David's hill
Eagles Elizabeth, 15 Paris street
Ellis Betty, Mint street
Freeman Thos. C. 73 South street
Gower Ann, St Olave square

Hooper Mary, Paul street
King Eliz. C. 30 High street
Lear Eliz., Deanery place
Milford Mary Ann, Exe Island
Paynter Mrs Caroline, 256 High st
Raddon Louisa, New North road
Radford Louisa, 71 South street
Saunders Harriet, 48 Magdalen st
Soper Mary Ann, South street
Sprague Eliz. 26 New Bridge street
Wood Eliza, Gandy street

(123) STRAW HAT MAKERS.
Bickell Sarah, 133 St Sidwell st
Bickford Chltt. & Adld. 84 South st
Bowcher & Ferris, 20 High street
Blake & Beavis, 45 Paris street
Bond Wm. 51 High street
Callaway Thos. 14 Alphington st
Collins J. (platt warehs.) 7 Queen st
Chambers Eliz., Bartholomew street
Chaplin & Westburn, 4 Albert st
Clogg Ann, Cowick street
Coombe Elizabeth, 26 Magdalen st
Davey Francis, St. David's hill
Eales Hannah, Summerland street
England Mary Ann, Goldsmith st
Ferris Eleanor, 38 South street
Finnimore Elizabeth, Goldsmith st
Hobbs Eliz. and My. 48 Holloway st
Hutchings Frances, Goldsmith st
Jago Elizabeth, Cowick street
Joslin & Quick, (*platt mfs.*) Queen st
Lake Elizabeth, 148 Fore street
Lee Mary Ann, South street
Lock Catherine, St David's hill
Newcombe Ann, 134 Fore street
Osman Elizabeth, 2 Bonhay
Pike Harriet, 71 St Sidwell street
Pike Eliz. Reb., Holloway street
Raddon Thomas, 78 South street
Reddaway Mary, Paragon place
Reynolds Chtte. 129 St Sidwell st
Siequin Eliz. 3 Summerland street
Sprague Harriet, 2 Paris street
Smith Mary, 2 St Sidwell street
Street Elizabeth, 9 Longbrook street
White Leonora, West street
Wood Eliza, Gandy street

(125) SURGEONS.
Amory George, Palmertree, 6 East Southernhay
Arscott Robt. F. 7 Southernhay pl
Barnes Samuel, 5 Barn field
Besley and Cumming, 5 Upper Southernhay street

Caird Wm. 40 Southernhay place
Calder James, Cowick street
Campion John T. 2 High street
Clapp Wm. *Hospital*, Southernhay
De la Garde Philip Chilwell, 22 Southernhay place
Farrant Fdk. Granby, 1 York bldgs
Harris John and Son, (Jno. Wm.) 47 Southernhay place
James John Huddy, Chichester place
James Wm. W. 1 Bedford street
Kempe Arthur, 48 Magdalen street
Kingdon Wm. Page & Son, (Chas.) 153, Fore street
Land Thomas, Cowick street
Land Wm. 57 St Sidwell street
Lyddon James, (regr. of marriages for St Thos.'s) Exe Bridge
Madden Jas. Malachi, 13 Salutary mount, H
May Geo. H. 9 Baring place
Norris Thos. Geo. 46 Southernhay pl
Parker J. Battishill, Cathedral yard
Pates Charles, 5 Maddock's row
Perkins J. Steele, 65 South street
Perkins Saml. Steele, 118 St Sid. st
Pridham Edw. Parker, Colleton pl
Shaw Henry, 1 Palace street
Tucker John, 4 Chichester pl. H
Walkey Saml. 4 Southernhay place
Warren Fdk. Hobson, Upper Paul st
Webb Benjmn. Johnson, St David'shl
Webb Chas. Knighton, 6 Southnhy. pl
Williams Edwin, Paul street
Williams Wm. 10 Salutary Mnt. H
Woodman Wm. 16 Bedford circus

(126) SURVEYORS, *(Land, &c.)*
Ashworth Edwd. 263 High street
Best Robt. Brown, Queen street rd
Cornish Rt. S. (bldng.) 139 Fore st
Dawson Wm. 7 Northernhay place
Dymond Rt. 10 Bedford circus
Grant John, 12 Castle street
Hayward Jno. *(County,)*Cathedral yd
Helmore Wm. near *Cowley Bridge*
Hedgeland Chas. Mount Radford ter
Julian Geo. H. 9 Friar's walk
Otton Joseph, Cowick street
Southwood Saml. R., Castle street
Reed & Warren, *South Wonford*
Rowe Joseph C., Smythen street
Taperell N. & Son, 15 Albion place
Whitehead Arthur, 136 Fore street
Whitaker Thomas, *(city and county bridges,)* Hill's court

Winsor Henry, Nelson place

(127) TAILORS.
*(Marked * are Drapers also, and +
Clerical Robe Makers.)*
Adams E., Commercial road
Badcock John, Paris street
Baker Elijah, 13 Magdalen road
Bale Henry, 213 High street
Balson Thomas, North street
Bambury John, *East Wonford*
Bearn John, St George's square
Beavis Richard, Sivell place, H
* Bigwood Geo. 1 New Bridge street
Bolt Samuel, 52 St Sidwell street
* Bowcher Wm. D., Castle street
* Brunskill Stephen, 242 High st
* Channing Geo. 7 New Bridge st
Channing Wm., Heavitree
* Chapple Robt. 4 Martin street
* Collins Chas. 227 High street
Commins Geo. C. 7 New Bridge st
Cottrell Alfred, Mint street
Cousins John, 8 Bedford street
Cuthbertson C. F. 58 South street
* Daniel Wm., Bedford circus
Densham Aaron, 78, St Sidwell street
* Down Geo. 18 Catherine street
Dyer Thomas, 49 St Sidwell street
Easterbrook Wm., Paul street
* Elworthy George, 46 High street
* Evans Chas. 3 Gandy street
Ferris Fras. 129 St Sidwell street
Finnimore Wm., Goldsmith street
Flood Wm. 188 High street
Flood Noah, Church st. St Sidwell
* Fursman John, 8 Market street
* Force Hy. Geo. 30 High street
Gibbs John, 81 St Sidwell street
Glanville Thos. 4 Alphington street
Green John, 49 St Sidwell st
Gregory John, North street
Harris Henry, Park terrace, H
Heal John, 160, St Sidwell street
Heard Robert, 4 Castle street
Holmes Charles, Cowick street
Hutchings John, Bartholomew street
Hyam David, 193, High street
Kirk Geo. R., Exe Island
Knott George, 35 South street
Lamerton Wm., George street
Lawrence Wm. 17 St Sidwell street
* Leverton Wm. 17 Paris street
Luget Samuel, Cowick street
Mallett Jas. 15 Catherine street
* Manders & Tibbs, 33 High street

* Marker John, 8 South street
May Rd., Bartholomew street
Merricks Rd., Alphington street
Miller Richard, James street
Millman Wm., Preston street
Milne Geo. A. 58 South street
Mitchell John, Sidwell street
Mullens John Danl. 18 Paragon pl
Perry James, 28 Paris street
Phillips Adam, Heavitree
Pike George, 37 South street
Pike Thomas, Paul street
* Pinder Rd. & Co. 191 High street
* Pinn James, Palace street
Presswell Chas. & C. B., Cathedral yd
Rice John, Clifton street
Ridge Joseph, North street
* Ridge Jph. Danl. 70 South street
+* Ridge Wm. 16 High street
+ Rippon Geo. 2 Catherine street
Risden Geo. St. Mary's yard
Russell John, 51 St Sidwell street
* Sampson Hy. Fras. 5 High street
Scanes Wm., Adelaide place
* Searle Samuel, Cathedral yard
* Sercombe Thos. 14 South street
Sercombe Wm., Black Boy road
Smeath John, 25 Magdalen street
Smith James, Okehampton street
* Southwood James, 18 New Brdg. st
Southard James, 21 St Sidwell st
+* Sparke Edw. Bowden, 20 Paris st
* Staddon Samuel, Goldsmith street
* Stemson George, 18 Castle street
Stoneman Edward, Red Cow street
Strong George, 118 Fore street
* Tolley John, 5 High street
Trickey Robt., Harris place
Vicary John, Lower North street
Wallis Robert, 14 High street
* Warren Wm. 14 North street
Webber Wm. 30 St Sidwell street
Wellacott John, Exewick
Westbeare John, Trinity street
White Charles, Cowick street
Whitton Wm., Mint
Willey Edward, 61 St Sidwell st
Wrayford George, Cowick street
* Wyllie Wm. 270 High street
(128) TALLOW CHANDLERS.
Bedford Thomas, 99 Fore street
Brailey & Williams, 4 St Sidwell st
Crabb Ths. 259 High st; h Com. rd
Thomas Chas., Alpington street

Thomas Jas. Langdon, & Robt. Ford, (and soap mfrs., oil refiners, &c.) 163 Fore street
Wills Wm., Frog street
(129) TANNERS.
Branch Thomas, Commercial road; h Okehampton road
Francis Wm. 1 Painter's row
Rew James & Son, *Lion's holt*
Rew Robt. *Alphington*
Underhay Wm. *East Wonford* and Coombe street
Wippell Mrs J. *Alphington*
(130) TEA & COFFEE DLRS.
(*See also Grocers, &c.*)
Commin Saml. & Thos. 92 North st]
Davies Saml. & Danl. (wholesale,) 44 High street
Dawson Rd. Hy. & Co. (wholesale,) 8 North street
Foote Samuel B. 6 Queen street
Hodgkinson George, (London Tea Co.) 236 High street
Houghton James, Sun street
Huckvale Wm. (coffee roaster,) 48 High street
Jury John, 87 St Sidwell street
Ridgewey, Halls & Co. 1 High street
Treffry Geo. & Thos. 168 Fore street
Westlake Rt. J. 36 New Bridge street
Wilcocks & Dinham, (wholesale,) 104 Fore street
(131) TEA DLRS. & DRAPERS.
(*Travelling.*)
Barratt John, 39 Bartholomew st
Brown Saml. 14 Salem place
Clarke James, Alphington street
Edger Wm. 5 Paris street
Gale Charles, 2 North terrace
Glencross Wm., Longbrook street
Johnston James, Cowick street
Johnston John, Mint street
Johnston Thomas, Summerland st
Kennedy James, 1 Salem place
Mc.Lean John, 8 Russell street
Park James, 5 Salem place
Simpson Wm., Wellington place
(132) TIMBER MERCHANTS.
Brooking Wm., Painter's row
Cornish Rt. S. 139 Fore street
Follett and Co. (*importers*) Shilhay
Hichens Thos. and Co. Haven Bank; h Sidney place
Lawes Wm., Commercial road
Ley Humphrey, Magdalen road

Strong James & Son, Bonhay
Tuckett Nichls. Commercial road
Ward Joel Hayman, 16 Alphington st
Ware Moses, Commercial road
Whitlock Newman, Painter's row
(133) TOBACCO PIPE MKRS.
Channon Elisha, Rack street
Gill Ann, Cheeke street
Heath Ann, Hiram place
Jordan Robert, Black Boy road
Middleton Wm., Cricklepit lane
Reynolds Robert, Cheeke street
(134) TOBACCO & SNUFF MFRS.
Edelstein S. J. W. *(cigar,)* Preston st
Lloyd Richard, 76 Fore street
Pye George, *(snuff)* Gandy street
(135) TOBACCONISTS.
Courti Paul, Market street
Gascoigne C. 2 New London Inn sq
Lloyd Richard, 76 Fore street
Pye Edw. R. 229 High street
Sercombe Thos. 15 New Bridge st
Willey Edward Wm. 92 North street
(136) TOY DEALERS.
Brodie Thos. Jno., Cowick street
Clarke Samuel, 228 High street
Fitze Agnes, 13 High street
Hearn Charles, North street
Havill James Webber, 91 Fore st
Howe Thomas, *(Bazaar and Magic cave,)* 207 High street
Incledon James, 3 St Sidwell street
Osborne Geo. & Son, 64 High st
(137) TRUNK, &c. MAKERS.)
Barrett James, 4 High street
Glanville M., Mary Archers street
Glanville Wm., Paul street
Lemon Wm., Cowick street
Northam Jas. 75 St Sidwell street
Peters James, Waterbeer street
West J. *(and portmanteau,)* 4 High st
(138) TURNERS. *(Wood, &c.)*
Keys Thomas, Bartholomew street
Linscott Wm., Commercial road
Pillman Rd., Sun street
Shooter Edward, Friernhay street
Webber Robt., Waterbeer street
Wolland John, St Sidwell street
Wolland Eliza and Son, (Wm.) 5 Mary Arches street
(139) UMBRELLA MAKERS.
Dare Thomas, 22 South street
Limpenny Robt. 136 Fore street
Monkley Wm. St David's hill
Passmore Thos. 136 St Sidwell st

Pryor Jph. 195 High street
(140) VETERINARY SURGEONS.
Austin Joseph, Guinea street
Drake Edwin, Paul street
Hill James, 13 Paris street
Rogers Josias, 73 Paris street
Tozer Saml. *(farrier.)* Exe Bridge
(141) WATCH & CLOCK MKRS.
(See also Silversmiths, &c.)
Adams Edw. Hewish, 38 High street;
  h Salutary place
Bradford Wm., Mary Arches street
Broom John, 149 Fore street
Brown John & Anthony, 168 Fore st
Burrington John, 2 High street
Courti Paul, jun., 75 Fore street
Cross Charles, Paul street
Ellis Hy. and Sons, 200 High street
Ferenbach Jph. &Co.*(German clocks,)*
  2 Alphington street
Finnimore Wm., Exe Island
Folland Wm. John, 160 Fore street
Frost Wm. 4 Paris street
Harris Israel, 166 Fore street
Jonas B. *(tool, &c. dlr.)* 3 Bartw. st
Keys Joseph, James street
Lake Henry, 214 High street
Lear James, Deanery place
Lazarus Isaac, 12 Northernhay street
Lisle Wm. 27 New Bridge street
Rickard Hercules, 6 Paris street
Rickard Jno. 10 Austin st & Bdge. st
Ross Daniel, 31 High street
Smale John, Mary Arches street
Sobey Wm. Rawlins, 1 Queen street
Spieglehalder A. *(German clocks,)* 73
  South street
Stone John, 30 New Bridge street
Taylor Richard, Alphington street
Treadwin John, Cathedral yard
Upjohn Robt. and Jas. 16 South st
Wyatt Edward, Commercial road
(142) WHEELWRIGHTS.
(See also Coach Builders.)
Castle James, 20 South street
Chown John, Cowick street
Cobley John, Lower North street
Friend John, Commercial road
Harris Henry, Heavitree
Hill Wm., Commercial road
Hitt Wm., Sandygate, H
Nex Wm., Vineyards
Payne John, *Whipton*
Radmore John, Cowick street
Tuckett Charles, Commercial road

(143) WHIP MAKERS.
Bowden Henry, 24 North street
Collins John, 3 Paris street
Osborn Geo. & Son, 64 High street
Osborn Henry, Commercial road
Osborn Wm. 26 North street
Pulman James, Guinea street
Taylor Robt. 5 Alphington street
(144) WHITESMITHS, &c.
Allen James Clode, Goldsmith street
Bastin John, Commercial road
Beadon Samuel, Higher Paul street
Cridge Philip, Exe street
Evans Edwin, Bartholomew street
Fouraker James, Coffin place
Garton & Jarvis, 190 High street
Hawkins John, 13 Paris street
Hawkins Wm., Gandy street
Hubbard James, Okehampton road
Hurst Jno. (beam & mill,) Paul st
Northam Wm., Mary Arches street
Pleace Jonth. 138 St Sidwell street
Pridham Thomas, 9 Catherine street
Rice John, Cheeke street
Rowe James Horn, Quay lane
Sage Epaphras, (coach spring,) Summerland street
Shepherd Wm. 76 St Sidwell street
Tucker Thomas, Preston street
(145) WINE & SPIRIT MERTS.
(See also Spirit Dlrs.—Retail.)
Bennett & Co. Holloway street
Bastard Wm. S. & Son, St James st.
Berry John, Bedford street
Bowcher Elizabeth, 71 High street
Brake & Co., 25 Holloway street
Commin Samuel, 94 North street
Crockett Wm., Paul street
Cross Wm. 90 South street
Dawson Rd. Hy. & Co. 8 North st
Dickes Bartholomew, 28 South st
Drewe & Son, 64 South street
Durant George, George street
Hirtzel & Son, Bedford circus
Kennaway George, 21 South street
Kennaway Wm. & Co. Palace st; h Barnfield
Madge George, 10 High street
Maunder Wm., Bampfylde street
Matthews & Opie, 27 Dix's field

Murch James, 87 South street
Ridgewey, Halls & Co. 1 High street
Salter Thomas, Gandy street
Sercombe Thos. 16 New Bridge street
Sharland George, 30 Paris street
Shepherd Jph. & Co. (importers,) 87 Magdalen street
Smith Thomas, Waterbeer street
Snow, Sanders, and Co. Gandy street
Toby Thomas, 7 New Bridge street
Trehane John, 78 Fore street
Williams Thos. E. 267 High street
Wilkinson Wm. Jno. Platers, (& rectifier,) 89 North st; h East Wonford
(146) WIRE WORKERS.
Kerslake Thos. 102 Fore street
Peters Robert, Mary Arches street
Southwood Jph., Bartholomew st
(147) WOOL FACTORS, &c.
Gard and Co. Castle street
Maunder Brothers, Exe Island
Petherbridge J. (& corn,) Wonford
Rodier James, P., St David's hill
(148) WOOLLEN DRAPERS.
(See also Linen Drapers.)
Braund G. & J. (wholsl.) 52 High st
Braund Henry, 67 High street
Brunskill Stephen, 242 High street
Burne Henry & Co. 130 Fore street
Cleeve Abraham, 71 High street
Colson & Spark, 34 High street
Gard & Co. (wholesale,) Castle st
Manders & Tibbs, 33 High street
Norcombe Jas. 186 Fore street; h Salutary place
Pasmore & Savery, (wls.) 73 High st
Pearse Wm. & Co. 196 High street
Pearse Jas. & Sons, 171 Fore street
Plowman Geo. H., 14 High street
Sheppard, Kendall and Tucker, 215 High street
Wippell Jph. jun. (and church decorator,) 219 High street
(149) WOOLLEN MANFRS.
Hitchcock, Maunder, & Hitchcock, Exwick & South Molton
Maunder Brothers, Exe Island
Taylor, Robt. (worsted,) Sun street
Worthy Thos. & Rd. (yarn, worsted, and serges,) Exe Island

EXETER POST OFFICE.

The Post Office is in Queen street.—*Surveyor and Superintendent of Mail Coaches, &c.*, George Stow, Esq. *Surveyor of the West of England Post Offices,* Mr. Geo. Henry Creswell. *Post Master,* Mr. Paul Measor.

The Box closes half an hour before the departure of each mail, (with the exception of the London, before the dispatch of which it closes one hour,) 2d. is charged for the first quarter, and 3d. for the last. Money Orders granted and paid from ten till five.

There are RECEIVING BOXES at 92, Fore street, in St. Sidwell street, on St. David's hill, and in South street, Magdalen road, Cowick street, *Exwick*, and *Heavitree*.

Arrival and Departure of Mails, by Exeter time.

MAILS.	ARRIVAL. H. M.	DISPATCH. H. M.	MAILS.	ARRIVAL. H. M.	DISPATCH. H. M.
London	4 5 A.M.	8 30 P.M.	Exmouth	11 15 A.M.	5 5 A.M.
London Day Mail	5 30 P.M.		Ditto	7 25 P.M.	11 30 A.M.
Bristol	4 5 A.M.	2 40 P.M.	Bideford	2 0 P.M.	12 45 P.M.
Ditto	10 45 A.M.	8 30 P.M.	Bude	8 15 P.M.	4 20 P.M.
Plymouth	3 15 P.M.	3 30 A.M.	Southampton ..	9 30 A.M.	3 20 P.M.
Ditto	9 5 P.M.	11 25 A.M.	Moreton	7 40 P.M.	5 0 A.M.
Falmouth	8 30 A.M.	4 20 A.M.	Starcross	7 30 P.M.	5 10 A.M.
Ditto	5 45 P.M.	5 45 P.M.			

RAILWAY CONVEYANCE.

The RAILWAY STATION at the junction of the *Bristol and Exeter and the South Devon Railways*, is at the north western angle of the city suburbs, beyond St. David's hill. The *Bristol and Exeter line* was till lately leased to the proprietors of the Great Western Railway. It connects Exeter with that great net work of railways which now traverses Great Britain in all directions; and others are projected to Crediton, Topsham, Exmouth, &c. The *South Devon Railway* extends southward to Star Cross, Teignmouth, Newton Abbot, Totnes, and Plymouth, where it joins the Cornwall Railway. The principal stations in the route from Exeter to London are *Hele, Tiverton Junction, Wellington, Taunton, Bridgewater, Weston-super-Mare, Clevedon, Nailsea, Bristol, Bath, Swindon, Oxford, Reading, Slough,* and *Paddington.* Passenger trains leave from six to eight times a day to all parts, and Luggage trains twice a day. There is a small station in *St. Thomas's,* near Exe Bridge, for passengers travelling to and from the city on the South Devon Railway. *London Time,* which is kept at all the stations, is 11 minutes before Bath and Bristol, 14 minutes before Exeter, and 16 minutes before Plymouth. The *Receiving Offices for goods, &c.,* are at the New London Inn, Half Moon Inn, Acland Arms, and White Hart Inn; and at *Wayer and Smale's,* Queen street. *Omnibuses,* &c., attend the arrival and departure of every train, and convey passengers and luggage to and from all parts of the city. First-class passengers are allowed 112lbs. of *luggage,* and 2nd and 3rd class passengers only 60lbs. free of charge; all excess is charged for according to distance. Mr. Robert Ashbee is *station master* at the Bristol and Exeter Station, and Thomas Batt at the South Devon Station.

COACHES AND OMNIBUSES.

The Queen and Ruby Coaches, to *South Molton, Barnstaple, Ilfracombe, Torrington, Bideford,* &c., from the New London, Half Moon, and Crown and Sceptre Inns, daily, except Sunday, at 12 noon.

The Hero Royal Mail, to BIDEFORD, *via Crediton, Winkleigh,* and *Torrington,* from the above-named Inns daily, at half-past one afternoon.

The Era Coach, to *Topsham, Exmouth,* and *Budleigh-Salterton,* daily, from the New London Inn, at 8¼ morning. This coach goes on to *Sidmouth* every Monday, Wednesday, and Saturday.

The Royal Mail, from the Half Moon Inn, to DORCHESTER, *via Honiton,* Axminster, Charmouth, and Bridport, every day at 1½ afternoon.

The Cornet Coach, to *Dorchester, Southampton,* and *Weymouth,* daily except Sunday, at 10½ morning, *via Honiton* ; the Magnet, to *Honiton* and *Axminster* at 4 afternoon ; the Royal Day Mail, to *Falmouth, Penzance, &c., via Okehampton,* every Tuesday and Saturday aftn., at 3; all from the New London Inn.

OMNIBUSES, &c. :—To *Crediton,* daily, at 5 afternoon, from the Crown and Sceptre and Barnstaple Inns ; to *Exmouth,* every Tuesday and Friday, at 4½

afternoon, from the White Hart; to *Holsworthy, Hatherleigh,* and *North Tawton,* every Tues., Thurs., and Sat. mornings, at 9, from the Crown and Sceptre; to *Honiton,* every Tues. and Friday aftn., at 5, from the New London Inn; every Wed. and Friday aftn., at 5, from the White Lion; and every Saturday at 6 morng., from Mr. Fletcher's, Cowick street; to *Moreton-Hampstead,* every Mon., Tues., and Friday, at 4 aftn., from the Golden Ball; to *Ottery St. Mary,* every Tues. and Friday, at 4½ aftn., from the King's Arms; to *Sidmouth,* at 5 aftn., from the New London Inn; to *Tiverton,* every Tuesday morning, at 6, from Cowick street; and every Mon., Wed., and Friday, at 4 aftn., from the Crown and Sceptre, Black Horse, and Three Tuns Inns; to *Topsham,* three times a day, from the Bear, Dove, and Topsham Inns; to *Winkleigh, Dolton, &c.,* every Tues. and Friday aftn., at one, from the Crown and Sceptre; and to *Okehampton,* every Friday morning, at 6, from Mr. Fletcher's, Cowick street. Many of the Carriers convey passengers in Omnibuses, Vans, &c., and there are in the city many HACKNEY COACHES, which may be hired on the various stands, at the rate of 1s. per mile, or 2s. 6d. per hour.

CARRIERS BY RAILWAY, &c. *(Daily to all parts.)*

BENNETT AND Co., Waterbeer street, (Richard Hawke, *agent.*)
T. F. BROOKING AND Co., Market street.
D. FORD AND Co., 19, South street, by rails to all parts, and *Waggons* to *Okehampton* and all parts of *Cornwall,* daily; and to *Honiton, Bridport, Dorchester, Southampton,* &c., every Monday, Wednesday, and Friday.
PICKFORD AND Co., Sun street, to all parts, (James Hitchcock, *agent.*)
WAGER AND SMALE, Queen street, (agents to Railway Co.)

CARRIERS FROM EXETER,

With their times of departure, and the INNS where they attend.

ASHBURTON AND BUCKFASTLEIGH—*Ford & Co.* daily, South street; *Hext,* Tuesday and Friday, Dolphin.
AXMINSTER—*Ford & Co.* Mon. Wed. and Friday, South st; *Gill,* Tues. and Friday, White Hart; *Huxford,* Black Lion, Saturday, 9 A.M.
BAMPTON—*Vicary,* Friday, Elephant.
BARNSTAPLE, BIDEFORD, ILFRACOMBE, and all parts of North Devon—*Penfound, Pridham and Lake,* daily, at 3, Dolphin.
BARNSTAPLE—*T. Murch,* Tues. and Friday, at 4, Black Lions.
BEER—*Searle,* Frid. at 12, Dolphin.
BIDEFORD, TORRINGTON, &c.—*Penfound, Pridham, and Lake,* Tues. Thurs. and Saturday, at 4, Dolphin.
BISHOPSTEIGNTON—*Beal,* Friday, at 4, Black Lions.
BLACK TORRINGTON — *Larkworthy,* Friday, 4 P.M. Dolphin.
BODMIN—*Hodge,* Tues. and Friday, 5 P.M. Mermaid.
BOVEY TRACEY—*John Winsor,* Tues. and Friday, at 4, Black Lions.
BRADNINCH—*Vinnicombe,* Tues. and Friday, Acland Arms; *Mortimer,* Tues. and Friday, Golden Lion.
BRADWORTHY—*Robins,*Frid.4,Anchor.
BRIDPORT—*Gill,* Wed. and Saturday, 9 A.M. White Hart.

BRIXHAM—*J. Shears,* Tues. Thurs. and Sat. White Hart; *Balkwill,* every day (except Mon.) at 4, Black Lions.
BUDLEIGH SALTERTON—*Linsey,*Tues. and Friday,Dolphin; *Emanuel Harding,* Tues. and Friday, Dolphin; *J. Austin,* Tues. and Friday, New Golden Lion; *Tuck,* Mon. Wed. and Friday, 4 P.M. Black Lions.
BUDLEIGH—*Coombe,*daily,WhiteBall.
CHAGFORD—*Blanchard,* Tues. and Friday, Golden Ball; *Endacott,* Tues. and Friday.
CHAWLEIGH AND LAPFORD — *Bird,* Tuesday, Elephant.
CHAWLEIGH—*Herrell,* Tuesday and Friday, Falcon.
CHERITON FITZPAINE — *Channing,* Tues. and Friday, Plume of Feathers.
CHITTLEHAMPTON—*Woollcott,*Friday, Elephant.
CHUDLEIGH—*J. Gill,* every day,White Ball.
CHULMLEIGH—*Tucker,* Tuesday and Friday, at 4, Elephant.
COLYTON—*Newton,* Tues. and Friday, at 4, White Hart: *Bull,* Friday, 2 P.M. Mermaid yard.
COLYTON AND SEATON—*French,* Frid. at 4, White Hart; *Copp,* Tues. Thurs. and Saturday, at 9 A.M. Black Lions.

CREDITON—*J. Rudall*, every aftern. Barnstaple Inn; *Rudall*, every day, Crown and Sceptre; *Sprague*, daily, Elephant; *Browning*, Friday, Bull; *Coles*, daily, at 5, Falcon Inn.

CULLOMPTON—*Ellicott*, Friday, Acland Arms; *Bennett*, Friday, Dolphin; *Saunders*, Friday, Anchor.

CULMSTOCK—*R. Pook*, Tuesday, at 10, White Ball.

DAWLISH—*Ellis* and *Lake*, every day, at 4 P.M. Mermaid.

DOLTON—*Collihole*, Tuesday & Frid. at 1, Crown and Sceptre; *Folland*, Frid. Barnstaple Inn.

DREWSTEIGNTON—*Cann*, Tues. and Friday, Okehampton Inn.

DUNSTER, DULVERTON, &c.—*James Wake*, Wednesday, at 4, Black Lions.

DULVERTON, BAMPTON, & MINEHEAD—*James Harwood*, Mon. Wed. and Friday, White Hart.

EXBOURN—*J. Dart*, Friday, Falcon.

EXMOUTH—*Wood*, every afternoon, (except Thurs.) at 5, Black Lions; *J. Hayne*, every aftn. at 5, Dolphin; *Hayne* daily, Dolphin and Mermaid.

HATHERLEIGH—*Axford*, Friday, Anchor; *Ellicott*, Tues. Thurs. and Sat. at 9 a.m. Crown and sceptre; *Kemp*, Tues. and Sat. from Mermaid, at 9 a.m.

HOLSWORTHY, STRATTON, BUDE, &c. —*Gist*, Thurs. 9 a.m. Mermaid; *Adams*, Friday, 8 a.m. Black Lions.

INWARDLEIGH — *Huxtable*, 2 p.m. Anchor.

KILMINGTON, ILMINSTER, AND CHARD, *French*, Friday, White Hart

KINGSTEIGNTON, *Westaway*, Friday, 4 p.m. Mermaid.

LAUNCESTON, BODMIN, TRURO, &c.— *W. Hodge*, Tues. & Fri. 4 p.m. Mermaid

LYME—*Huxford*, 9 a.m. Black Lions.

LYMPSTONE—*Denning*, Mon. Wed. & Friday, White Hart

MORCHARD BISHOP—*Putt*, Tues. and Friday, at 4; *Salter*, Tues. and Friday, Plume of Feathers.

MORETON—*Lee*, Mon. Tues. & Friday, at 4, Golden Ball; *John Wecks*, Mon. Wed. and Friday, Mermaid yard.

NORTHMOLTON—*Prescott*, Friday, at the White Hart.

OKEHAMPTON—*Ford & Co*. Tues. and Friday, at 7, South st; *Jewell*, Tues. at 9, & Fri. at 4, Dolphin; *Mary Fanson*, Tues, 9 A.M. & Friday, 6 P.M. Mermaid.

OTTERTON AND WOODBURY—*Radford*, Tues. and Friday, New Golden Lion.

OTTERY—*Baker*, Tues. and Fri. at 4, Black Lions; *Pike*, Friday, Dolphin.

PETERSMARLAND—*Pincombe*, Friday, at 4, Elephant.

PUDDICOMBE—*White's* Spring Van, Friday, at 3, Barnstaple Inn.

ROBOROUGH—*J. Symons*, Friday, at 4, Elephant.

SHEBBEAR AND SHEEPWASH—*Wickett*, Friday, at 3, Black Lions; *Larkworthy*, Friday, Dolphin.

SIDBURY—*Barrett*, Frid. at 4, Dolphin.

SIDMOUTH—*Bole*, daily at 4, Blk.Lions.

SILVERTON—*Rawel*, Mon. Wed. and Friday, Bull.

SOUTHMOLTON—*T. Murch*, Tues. and Friday, at 4, Black Lions.

SOUTHZEAL—*Westaway*, Tues. Okehampton Inn.

SPREYTON—*Honeychurch*, Friday, at 2, Okehampton Inn.

STARCROSS—*Barton*, daily, Bull.

STRATTON, BUDE, HOLSWORTHY, &c.— *Adams*, Friday, at 9 A.M. Black Lions.

TAVISTOCK—*Ford*, daily; *Mary Fanson*, Tues. and Friday, at 4, Mermaid.

THORVERTON—*W. James*, Mon. and Friday, Bull.

TIVERTON—*Harwood*, Mon. Wed. & Friday, at 3, White Hart; *Methuish*, Tues. Thur. and Sat. at 4 P.M. Mermaid.

TOPSHAM—*Thorn*, every day, Topsham Inn; *Halfyard, Ponsford, & Dolling*, every day, from Mr Hookway's, currier, South street, and Black Horse.

TORRINGTON, BIDEFORD, &c. — *W. Handford*, Tues. Thurs. & Sat. morning, White Hart; *Penfound, Pridham, & Lake*, Tues. Thurs. & Sat. at 4, Dolphin.

WINKLEIGH—*G. Barry*, Sat. Anchor; *Collihole*, Tues. and Friday, at 1, Crown and Sceptre.

WITHERIDGE—*Southcott*, Friday, Elephant.

WOODBURY—*Barton*, Tues. & Friday, at 4, White Hart.

VESSELS TRADING TO & FROM EXETER & LONDON.

GROCER, R. Norman, 150 tons; SWIFT, — Popham, 106 tons; THAMES, Wm. Croft, 160 tons; UNION, R. Hore, 106 tons; DEVON, Richard Bence, 150 tons Commodore, W. Bence, 105 tons; ALICE, Geo. Widdecombe, 100 tons; JANE, Robt. Redman, 106 tons; FLEECE, Elias Croft, 160 tons; FAME, Thomas Stockham, 140 tons.   *Agents*:—Mr P. Palmer, Upper West street; Mr Anning, grocer, 174 Fore street; Mr J. L. Ramson, Upper North street; Messrs S. and

W. Kingdon, High street, Exeter; or in London, of Messrs Scovell, at Topping's Wharf; Mr Barber, Chamberlain's Wharf; and Mr T. Popham, Topsham. One of the above vessels leaves Exeter every Friday. A vessel clears from Topping's & Chamberlain's Wharfs, London, for Exeter & Topsham, every Thurs.

WONFORD HUNDRED,

Is in the *Southern Division* of Devonshire, and extends about 19 miles westward and 4 miles eastward from Exeter; completely encompassing that city, and adding a considerable population to its suburbs. (See page 50.) Exclusive of two distant detached members near Newton Abbot, it is about 23 miles in length from east to west, and varies from eight to four miles in breadth. It is bounded on the north by the Northern Division of the county, on the east by East Budleigh and Cliston Hundreds, on the south by Exminster and Teignbridge Hundreds; and on the west by the extensive mountainous moorland district of *Dartmoor Forest;* large portions of which, near Chagford, Gidleigh, Throwley and South Tawton, are within its limits. (See Lidford.) It is generally a fertile and picturesque district, traversed by the Exeter and Okehampton turnpike and other good roads, and extending down the river Exe to Topsham,—the shipping port of Exeter. It comprises 87,516 acres of land, and 31,000 inhabitants, and is divided into 33 *parishes* of which the following is an enumeration, shewing the territorial extent, and the population of each in 1841 :—

Parishes.	Acres.	Pop.	Parishes.	Acres.	Pop.
Alphington	2720	1286	+ Ogwell (East)	1249	356
Brampford Speke	1150	393	+ Ogwell (West)	1020	51
Bridford	4090	560	Pinhoe	1930	568
* Chagford	7492	1836	Poltimore	143	264
§ Cheriton-Bishop	5000	848	Rewe (part of)	990	181
Christow	3680	624	Sowton }	1360	167
+ Combeinteignhead	2217	425	Clist Satchfield tyth. }		215
* Drewsteignton }	6900	1134	* Spreyton	3606	404
* Teignholt ham. }		181	Stoke Canon	1217	490
Dunsford	6000	925	+ Stokeinteignhead	2250	591
* Gidleigh	2400	182	* Tawton South	6097	1871
+ Haccombe	290	14	Tedburn St. Mary	4433	867
Heavitree ¶	3290	3048	Thomas the Apostle St.	3780	4301
§ Hittisleigh	1155	199	* Throwleigh	1943	445
Holcombe Burnell	1890	306	Topsham	1521	3733
Huxham	830	150	Upton-Pyne	2210	512
Leonard (St.) ¶	80	1129	Whitstone	4046	670
+ Nicholas (St.)	580	1175			
			Total	87516	30101

☞ UNIONS:—Those marked * are in *Okehampton Union ;* † in *Newton-Abbot-Union ;* § in *Crediton Union ;* and the rest are in ST. THOMAS'S UNION. (See page 122.)

¶. The three parishes of *Heavitree, St. Leonard, and St. Thomas the Apostle,* are suburbs of Exeter, and all the populous parts of them are now comprised in the parliamentary limits of the city and county of the city of Exeter. (See page 50.) *Rewe* parish is partly in Haybridge Hundred, and Clist-Satchfield is partly in East Budleigh Hundred: Heavitree parish includes the hamlets of *Whipton and East and South Wonford,* and Exeter *Artillery Barracks.* (See page 88.) The parish of St. Nicholas includes *Shaldon,* a village with 538 souls at the mouth of the Teign. ST. THOMAS'S parish comprises the hamlets of *Oldridge and Exewick,* (see page 87,) a large Union Workhouse, a Lunatic Asylum, the Debtor's prison for the county, and Exeter Canal Basin. The Eastern half of the Hundred is in *Wonford Division,* for which *petty sessions* are held every Friday at Exeter Castle; and the western half of it is in *Crockernwell Division;* but its

detached members, comprising the parishes of East and West Ogwell, Haccombe, Combeinteignhead, Stokeinteignhead, and St. Nicholas's, are in Teignbridge Division. These and the other petty sessional divisions of the county are shewn on the Map of Devon accompanying this work, and the Magistrates and Clerks of each are enumerated at preceding pages.

ALPHINGTON, a neat and pleasant village on the western side of the river Exe, 1½ mile S. of Exeter, has in its parish 1286 inhabitants, and about 2700 acres of fertile land, traversed by the South Devon Railway and Exeter Ship Canal. It has *cattle fairs* on the first Wednesday after the 20th of June, and on the Wednesday after Michaelmas day. It was one of the principal quarters of Sir Thos. Fairfax's army, when he was blockading Exeter, in 1646. The Earl of Devon owns most of the soil, and is lord of the manor of Alphington, which was obtained by his family in the reign of Richard II., in exchange, from the Seagraves. *Matford,* formerly a seat of the Smith and other families, belongs to Sir L. V. Palk, and several smaller proprietors have estates and neat houses here. Risdon says a man named Stone died here at the age of 120 years, in the reign of Elizabeth. On July 2nd, 1760, by the sudden inundation of the rivulet which runs through the village to the Exe, upwards of 20 houses are said to have been thrown down, and the damage was computed at upwards of £1000. The *Church,* (St. Michael,) is a large antique fabric, with a tower and eight bells. The *rectory,* valued in K.B. at £34. 6s. 8d,, and in 1831 at £979, is in the deanery of Kenne. The Rev. Rd. Ellicombe, M.A., is patron and incumbent, and has a good Rectory House, on an eminence near the church. The glebe is 18A., and the tithes were commuted in 1841 for £990 per annum. The Church House, worth £20 a year, was built by the parish in the reign of Elizabeth, on land given by Wm. Courtenay Esq. The *Poor's Land* comprises about 21A. and a farm house at Holcombe Burnell, purchased in 1756, with money left by John Bliss and other donors. It is now let for £15 a year. The poor parishioners have also 30s. a year out of Matford estate, left by *Francis and Daniel Vinnicombe,* in 1675 ; and the dividends of £230 three per cent consols, purchased in 1784, with £110, left by *Edward Leach* and another donor. They have likewise the interest of £5 left by James Pitman. The *Poor Houses,* comprising four small cottages, occupied rent free by poor families, where purchased in 1675, with £45 given by various donors.

Bales John A. gent. || Abell Mrs
Brewer Thomas, *Natnl. Schoolmr.*
Browning John, gentleman
Browning Mrs and Misses
Brown Richard, corn miller
Buckley Jph. gent. *Alpington Cottage*
Copleston Edward Arthur, solr; h Newhayes (and Exeter)
Cotton Wm. gentleman
Cole Charles, carpenter and sexton
Davies Wm. plumber and glazier
Dorvill Hy. gent. *Laurel Cottage*
Downing James, road contractor
Ellicombe Rev. Richard, M.A. Rectory
Fisher Hy. pit sand dealer
Fry Richard, butcher
Gubb Lieut Geo. || Godwin Mr Thos
Hammond Thos. gent. *Mount Hs*
Hallett Geo. currier & leather cutter
Head Robt. Thos. solr; h *Briars*
Hill Thomas, gent. *Myrtle Cottage*
Howard J. road surveyor
Hussey Thos. and Son, (Edw. B.) auctioneers, *Waybrook*
Kekewich Samuel Trehawke, Esq. (magistrate,) *Peamore*
Knott John A. clerk and Mr. John
Lear Richard, saddler

Latchworth Thos. Esq. Alphgtn. Hs
Loram Wm. butcher || Lillies Mrs F
Luxmoore John C. Esq. (magistrate)
Mantle Mrs My. Ann, *Bridge Cottage*
Marsh James, gent. *Rock House*
Marker Wm. collector of taxes
Martin Mr Edwin || Pike J. thatcher
Pocknell Mrs A
Ponsford Luke, gent
Porter Rev. Charles, B.D.
Sharland John, gent. || Symons Mrs
Skinley Lieut. John, R.N.
Taylor Edward, basket maker
Toms Henry, cooper & parish clerk
Tuckett Mr John
Westcott John, mason, &c
Wilcocks Ebenezer, gent. *Rose Villa*
Wippell John, maltster
Woodman Thos. gent. *Cross*
Wreford Robt. solr. (and Exeter)
Wyse Misses, Louisa & Ellena
   INNS & PUBLIC HOUSES.
Admiral Vernon, Wm. Gover
Bell Inn, Thomas Langsford
Double Lock Inn, Thos. Pennyman
King William, Thomas Carpenter

BAKERS.
Tripp George
Wright Mary
   BLACKSMITHS.
Brewer James
Wright John
   BOOT&SHOE MKS.
Payne George
Rowe Rd. *beerhs.*
Sibley Charles
Symons Thomas
Stevens James
Woolsey John
   FARMERS.
Floyd Wm
Hedgman Drthy.
   Pole House
Hodge Rt.*Cudmr.*
Lear Robert
Loram Richard
Neck Wm.,*Matfd.*
Rowe Wm
Webber John
Wrey John
   SHOPKEEPERS.
Grant Robert

Herbert George
Langsford Jno.(&
  painter, &c)
Snell James
Stone Robert
   TANNERS.
Rew Robert
Wippell Mrs
   TAILORS.
Banks Wm
Elsworthy Geo.
Dobson John
Gibbon James
Sharland Peter
Stone John
   WHEELWRIGHTS.
Bastin Jph. (and
  machine mkr.)
Bastin Henry
Lovell & Parkin
Wright Thomas
POST OFFICE at J.
  Hele's, Letters
  desp. to Exeter
  7½ night

BRAMPFORD-SPEKE is a pleasant scattered village, in the vale of the river Exe, near the Bristol and Exeter Railway. Its parish contains 1150A. 2R. 30P., and 393 inhabitants, including the hamlet of COWLEY, which is separated from the rest of the parish by Upton-Pyne, and comprises about 500 acres, near *Cowley Bridge* and the confluence of the Creedy and Exe, two miles N. of Exeter. Near this bridge, are houses in the parishes of St. Thomas the Apostle and Upton Pyne. Sir S. H. Northcote, Bart., is lord of the manor of Brampford Speke; but a great part of the soil belongs to the Roberts, Blackall, and other families. It was anciently held by the family of *Espek*, or *Speke*, who appropriated the church in the reign of Stephen, to St. Nicholas's Priory, Exeter. It was purchased by its present lord in 1815, and had previously been held by the Pierce, Taylor, and Palk families. *Cowley* belongs chiefly to the Rev. W. H. Arundell, Dr. Blackall, and E. G. Roberts, Esq. It is supposed to have had a chapel, though there are no traces of such a building. The parish *Church* (St. Peter,) is an ancient structure, to which a north aisle was added in 1840. It has a substantial tower, containing five bells; and on its south side is an ancient chapel, or chantry, in which was formerly a monumental effigy of one of the Spekes. The *vicarage*, valued in K.B. at £10, and now worth £250 a year, was endowed in 1269 with the rectorial tithes of Cowley, now commuted for £63. 17s. 3d. per annum. In 1842, the rectorial tithes of Brampford Speke, which belong to the Bishop of Exeter, were commuted for £115. 13s., and the vicarial tithes for £132. 10s. per ann. The vicarage has 39A. of glebe, and is in the patronage of the Lord Chancellor, who in 1847 appointed the Rev. Geo. Cornelius

Gorham, B.D., to the benefice; but the Bishop of Exeter has refused to institute him to the living, in consequence of his not holding the doctrine of baptismal regeneration. The Rev. B. Houchen is now the curate and sequestrator. The church and poor have long held five tenements in St. Thomas's parish, which were let in 1800 for three lives, at the nominal rent of 10s., in consideration of a fine of £125, now invested in £136. 10s. four per cent. stock. MRS. MARY TUCKER, who died here in 1849, bequeathed no less than £12,200 stock to various charitable and public uses; among which are, £1000 for repairing and altering Brampford Speke church; £500 for the poor of this parish; £1100 for the poor and Infirmary of Barnstaple; £1000 to the Devon and Exeter Hospital; £300 to the Exeter Refuge for Destitute Women; £500 to the Blind Institution in Exeter; £200 to the Exeter Dispensary; and £300 to the Deaf and Dumb Asylum in Exeter. Among her other legacies are large sums to various religious societies, &c.

*Marked * are at Cowley, and the others in Brampford-Speke.*

Clement Miss || Fry Wm. sexton
Fursdon Geo., Esq. || Norburn Mrs
Greenaway George, blacksmith
Haffner John Frederick, gent
Humphrey John, carpenter & par. clk
*Mercer Col. Alex., *Cowley Cottage*
Mudge John, gentleman
*Sheppard Jph., Esq. *Cowley Place*

Staddon Henry, shoemaker
Veysey Robert, shoolmaster
Veysey Thos. vict. Agricultural Arms
FARMERS.
Carpenter John
Carter Joseph
*Challice John
*Cornish John
Elliott James

Beer George

*HelmoreWm.(& surveyor)
Salter C., *Woodrw*
Sharland Robt.
Veysey Thos.
Wippell Richd.

BRIDFORD is a village and parish, 9 miles S.W. by W. of Exeter, and 4 miles E. of Moreton Hampstead. It contains 560 souls, and 4090 acres of fertile land. The river Teign bounds the parish on the north and east, and has here two corn mills. Sir L. V. Palk is lord of the manor, but part of the soil belongs to the Northcote and other families. It was held in demesne by Joel de Totneis, at Domesday Survey, and afterwards passed to the Valletort, Champernowne, Leach, and other families. The ancient lords had the power of inflicting capital punishment. *Lapflode* estate was anciently held by a family of its own name. The *Church* (St. Thomas à Beckett,) is an ancient fabric, and its register commences in 1538, and contains notices of the insurrection in Devon and Cornwall in 1549. The *rectory*, valued in K.B. at £13. 15s., and in 1831 at £350, is in the gift of Sir L. V. Palk and incumbency of the Rev. Henry Palk. In 1706, Edward Hall left the yearly sums of 10s. for a sermon, 3s. for the poor, and 3s. 4d. to buy hassocks for the church. An annuity of 40s., left by John Stoke, is applied in relieving the poor, and buying sacramental bread and wine.

Bailey Eliz. vict. Harriers
Palk Rev Henry, rector of Bridford and Dunchideock
Taverner John, butcher and shopkpr
Whitter Rev Walrond, curate
ACADEMIES.
Branscombe Ths.

Wills John

BLACKSMITHS.
Adams John
Booley John
CARPENTERS.
BaileyGeo. parish clerk

Beer George

CORN MILLERS.
Dorman George,
Stone
Woodbridge Wm.

FARMERS.	*Lapflode*	*Smallridge Jno.,	Wolland Wm.
* *are Owners, & +*	Hemens Wm.	*Stone Farm*	
at Westcote.	Lamacroft John,	Smith John	MASONS.
*+Adams Nichls.	*Beaconton*	Tancock John	Rendle James
Beer Jonas	+Miller Thomas	*Tuckett Nichls.	Stamp Thomas
Bennett James,	Mudge Thomas,	Tuckett Wm.	
Swanford	*Lowtan*	Vooght Wm.	TAILORS.
*+Berry John	Parratt Septms.	*WillsWm. *Furze	Bearn John
Harvey Daniel,	Passmore John	*land*	Pike John

CHAGFORD is a small ancient town, on the eastern side of Dartmoor Forest, in the picturesque valley of the river Teign, 3¼ miles W.N.W. of Moreton Hampstead, and 15 miles W.S.W. of Exeter. Its parish comprises 7492 acres, of which 5732 acres are old enclosures and well cultivated; 1271 acres are in pasturage and tillage in Dartmoor; 359 acres are waste, and 129 acres in roads, &c. The gross estimated rental is £7654, and the rateable annual value £5656. The parish has many scattered farm houses, &c., and four corn mills on the Teign, and had 1836 inhabitants in 1841, but they have since decreased to about 1740, owing chiefly to the Woollen Factory here being closed in 1848. Chagford town has only about 1050 inhabitants. It was made one of the *Stannary* towns in 1328, and had a *stannary court,* for regulating the tin mining operations of Dartmoor, till about 60 years ago, when it was removed to Tavistock. The court-house fell down in 1618, and killed the steward and nine other persons. (See Dartmoor.) The town has a *market* on Saturday, for meat, vegetables, &c.; and four annual *cattle fairs,* held on the last Thursdays in March, September, and October, and the first Thursday in May. Sir John Berkeley attacked and dispersed some of the forces of parliament quartered here in 1643, and and in the action fell that accomplished poet Sidney Godolphin. The *manor* of Chagford belonged to Sir Hugh Chagford in the reign of Henry III. It was successively held by the Wilbery and Whyddon families, for many generations, and the latter were long seated at *Whyddon Park,* now the seat of E. S. Bayley, Esq., and consisting of an ancient mansion, and a woody park of 300 acres. John Coniam, Esq., who has a pleasant seat called *Way Barton,* is now lord of two-thirds of the manors of Chagford and Cotterew; and Nicholas Clampitt, of *Holy Street,* is lord of the other third. There are several other manors in the parish;—viz., *Prince's Manor,* belonging to the Duchy of Cornwall; *Shapleigh,* belonging to Mr. Maunder, of Exeter; and *Rushford,* belonging to the Hon. Newton Fellowes. The Earl of Devon, R. L. Berry, Esq., and many smaller owners, have estates in the parish. Rushford was an ancient seat of the Hoares; Holly Street formerly belonged to the Rowes and the Southmeads; and Way Barton was long the residence of the ancient family of Prous, or Prouz. The CHURCH (St. Michael,) is a large antique fabric, with an embattled tower and six bells. The *rectory,* valued in K.B. at £39. 0s. 10d., and in 1831 at £560, is in the patronage and incumbency of the Rev.Wm. Hames, who has about 99 acres of glebe, and a large Rectory House, built about twenty years ago, on a commanding eminence, encompassed

by higher hills. The tithes were commuted, in 1843, for £539.10s.1d. per annum. There are vestiges of ancient chapels at *Teigncombe* and *Great Weeke*, or *Wyke St. Mary*, and there was one at Rushford, but these places are now only farms. The *Church Lands, &c.*, have been vested from time immemorial for the use of the church, and comprise about four acres, with a right of common, let for £14; the *tolls* of the markets and fairs, let for about £10; and a house, let to the overseers for 20s., except the upper story, used as a school room. The dividends of £200, four per cent. stock, left by *John Weekes*, in 1790, are applied in schooling and apprenticing poor children. The poor have £5 a year out of Withecombe estate, left by *John Hunt*, in 1732. For distribution in bread, they have 27s. yearly from the churchwardens, as interest of money left by unknown donors. A congregation of Baptists was formed here in 1829; and the *Wesleyans* have a chapel in the town, which was leased to them for 21 years, at a nominal rent, by the late Mr. John Berry, in 1834. Here is also a small chapel, belonging to the *Bible Christians*, built in 1844.

Bayley Edwd. Seymour, Esq., *Whyddon Park*
Berry Richard Leach, gentleman
Coniam John, Esq. *Way Barton*
Coniam Mrs Susan and Miss Eliz.
Collard John, ironmonger & brazier
Courtier Mr Wm. *Westcote Cottage*
Hames Rev Wm., M.A. rector of Chagford and of *Ham*, Kent
Hunt Samuel, surgeon
Miles Thos. watch and clock maker
Murch George, wheelwright. ironmonger, and glass, &c. dealer
Pardon John, sexton
Penrose Thomas, mine agent, *Whitebury Cottage*
Thorn Richd. registrar & par. clerk

CORN MILLERS, &c.
Aggett Edward, *Holy street*
Collins James, *Batworthy*
Nicholls Joseph, *Sandy Park*
Torr Peter, *Rushford*

FARMERS. (* are Owners.)
Austin Wm. *Drewston*
Bennett John, *Teigncombe*
*Brock George, *Drewston*
*Brock John || Collins Wm.
Clampitt Gabriel, *Middlecote*
Clampitt Nicholas, *Holy street*
*Dicker John, *Drewston*
Dodd James || Ellis John
*Ellis John, *Westcote*
*Ellis Wm. *Great Wicke*
*Ellis Wm. *Stinial*
Endacott James, North hill

Ford John, South hill
Harvey George, *Cleeves*
*Harvey Humphrey, *Corrindon*
Harvey Humphrey, *Yadworthy*
Harvey John || Harvey Richard
*Harvey Robert, *Forder*
Harvey Wm. *Easton*
Hast Wm., Nattadon
Hellyer Richard, *Calla hole*
Hellyer Wm. *Masher-hole*
Holmes Alexander, *Easton*
Holmes George || Holmes Richard
*Hooper Henry, *Yelham*
Hooper Lydia, *Great Weeke*
Hooper John (survyr.) *Withecombe*
Hooper Wm. *Rushford*
Morris Wm. *Little Weeke*
Mortimore George, *Frenchbeer*
Northcote Thos. & Wm. *Teigncombe*
*Nosworthy Wm. *Broadhouse*
Nosworthy John, *Willan head*
*Perryman John, *Yeo*
*Rowe George and John, *Easton*
Rowe James, *Calla-hole*
Scott Henry || Scott John
Stanbury John, *Frenchbeer*
Stanbury Richard || Stanbury John
Strong Wm. & Wills Geo. *Waddicote*
Torr Peter || Thorn Richard
Webber George, *Whyddon Park*

INNS AND TAVERNS.
Bakers' Arms, Rd. Holmes, *wheelgt*
Globe Inn, Henry Gregory, *cooper*
King's Arms, John Hooper, *butcher*
Royal Oak, George Harvey, *butcher*

Ring of Bells, Richard Stanbury
Three Crowns, John Brock

BAKERS.
Heard My. Ann
Stone Ann

BLACKSMITHS.
Hill Samuel
Murch George
Stoneman Wm.
Stoneman W. jun
Stott John

BOOT&SHOE MKS.
Aggett James
Clampitt George
Gill George L.
Harvey John
Holman Robert
Lyddon Edward
Lyddon George
Scott Wm.

CARPENTERS.
Aggett John
Ball Thomas
BrimblecombeW.
Collins James
Luscombe John
Underhill Wm.
GROCERS & DPRS.
Gale Joseph
Gibbons Wm. (&
woolcomber)
Heard My. Ann
Morrish Wm.

Pearse Thomas
Pike James
Pratt Eliz.
SADDLERS.
BrailyJn||ThornJ
TAILORS.
Endicott Jeffry
Gilbert Wm.
Pike James
POST - OFFICE
at Eliz. Pratt's.
Letters via More-
ton Hampstead

CHERITON-BISHOP, or *South Cheriton*, a village on the Oke-hampton road, 9¼ miles W. of Exeter, and 6 miles S.W. of Crediton, has in its parish 848 souls, and about 5000 acres of land, of which 4719 acres are rateable. The gross rental is £4397. The parish has many scattered houses, and includes the hamlet of *Cheriton Cross*, and part of the village of CROCKERNWELL, which is partly in Drewsteignton parish, and gives name to a division for which *petty sessions* are held at the *Royal Hotel*, on the first Monday of every month. The Bishops of Exeter were formerly lords of Cheriton, but the manor was alienated in the reign of Henry VIII. Baldwin Fulford, Esq., is now lord of the manors of Eggbeare and Lamp-ford, which have been long held by his family, but a great part of the parish belongs to Dr. Pennell, the Rev. Wm. Ponsford, George Ponsford, Esq., Wm. Lambert, Esq., and many smaller freeholders. *Medland* was a seat of the Foulkes family, but the estate was sold in parcels some years ago. The parish *Church* (St. Mary,) has a tower and six bells, and contains some monuments of the Davy family. The *rectory*, valued in K.B. at £22. 13s. 4d., and in 1831 at £360, is in the patronage of the Bishop of Exeter, and incum-bency of the Rev. Wm. Mallock, B.D., who has an old thatched residence, and 53A. of glebe. The tithes were commuted in 1841 for £399 per ann. The *Church Lands*, &c., comprise about 4 acres and three houses, let for about £13 a year. The poor have the interest of £45, left by various donors, and a yearly rent-charge of 20s., left by *Wm. Strong*, in 1728, out of Blackpits estate, at Tedburn St. Mary. Here is a *National School*, and at Crockernwell is a small *Wesleyan Chapel*, built in 1847.

Marked 2 are at Cheriton Cross ; 3, at Crockernwell ; and the others at CHERITON-BISHOP, or where specified
Bean Felix, gent. *Venbridge House*
3 Bolt Robert, shopkeeper, *Post Office*
3 Endacott Henry, saddler
HarrisJohn, schoolmr.&asst. overseer
3 Langdon Wm. butcher
Mallock Rev Wm., B.D. *Rectory*
  FARMERS. (* *are Owners.*)
Bolt Robert, *Waterland*

Bolt Thomas, *Higher Mounson*
Brimblecombe Wm. *Honey ford*
Brook James, *Coxland*
2 Chudley Sar. || Gibbins Jonas
Finch Wm. *Hooperton*
*Gorwyn John, *Hole-farm*
*Gorwyn George, *Medland House*
Guscott Wm. *Furze Down*
3 Hamley Wm. || Hole Joseph
*Haydon John || Hole John
Haydon Samuel || *Haydon Wm.
*Haydon Wm. *Westford*

Hutchins Wm. *Westbeare*
Kemble Samuel, *Lower Mounson*
Kemble Robert, *Lewdon*
Kemble Wm. *Tillerton*
Leach Joseph, *Middle Eggbeare*
Pitts Daniel ‖ Sampson John
Seward John ‖ Snell Andrew
Wills George ‖ Wolland Moses
*Wreford Samuel, *Orchard Lake*
INNS AND TAVERNS.
3 Golden Lion, Wm. Langdon
2 New Inn, John Lias
Rest and be Thankful, John Hole
Ring of Bells, John Hole
3 Royal Hotel, Wm. Hamley

Royal Oak, Ann Browning
BLACKSMITHS.
2 Ashplant John
2 Davy Samuel
BOOT&SHOEMKRS
3 Bolt George
3 Preston Andw.
Smith Samuel
2 Townsend Geo.
CARPENTERS.
2 Browning Jas.
3 Chudley John
and Wm.

3 Fewins Samuel
(& wheelwgt)
Groves John
MASONS.
3 Ching Thos.
Tancock Geo.
Tancock Joseph
TAILORS.
Osborn John
3 Osborn Wm.
Post-Office at
Robert Bolt's,
Crockernwell

CHRISTOW, a straggling village on the western side of the river Teign, 9 miles S.W. of Exeter, and 4½ miles N.W. of Chudleigh, has in its parish 624 souls, and about 3600 acres of land. Viscount Exmouth owns a great part of the soil, and is lord of the manors of *Christow and Canon-Teign*, which were purchased by his father of W. Helyar, Esq., in 1812. L. Palk, Esq., and several smaller owners, have estates here. Both manors were held by abbeys in Normandy, and were granted at the Reformation to John, Lord Russell. Canon-Teign was successively the seat of the Berry, Gibbs, Gibbon, and Davy families, and was garrisoned for Charles I. in the civil wars, but was taken by Fairfax in December, 1645, and placed under the command of Colonel Okey, who afterwards suffered as one of the regicides. The *Church* (St. James) is a small ancient fabric, with a tower and six bells, and was appropriated to Bec Abbey, in Normandy, and afterwards to Tavistock Abbey. The great tithes were purchased by the landowners in 1812. The *vicarage*, valued in K.B. at £8. 6s. 8d., and in 1831 at £176, is in the gift of Viscount Exmouth, and incumbency of the Rev. Wm. Woolcombe, who has a neat residence, and £170 a year in lieu of tithes. *New Canon Teign House* is an occasional seat of Viscount Exmouth, and in its pleasure grounds is a beautiful waterfall. The *mine* in this parish, called Adams William, was opened about forty years ago, and was long worked for copper ore, manganese, &c. It is now sunk to the depth of 60 fathoms, and yields lead, from which a portion of silver is extracted, but it is not very prolific. A *Friendly Society* was established for this parish and neighbourhood in 1839. *John Stooke*, in 1691, left Smyth's Hay farm for charitable uses, &c., in this and other parishes. It comprises 26A., and is let for about £26 per annum. Out of this yearly income, the vicar of Christow receives about £11, and the poor have five 4d. loaves weekly. Of the remainder £5 belongs to the poor of Ashton, and £5 to the rector of Trusham.

Viscount Exmouth, *New Canon Teign House* (and Treverry, Cornwall)
Adams Jane, school and postmistress
Bowley John, blacksmith
Guscott Fras. cattle doctor & shopr

Dunrich Wm. vict. *Artichoke*
Hill Wm. surgeon
Norrish John, shoemaker
Price Wm. stone mason
Sandford Jno. vict. *Teign House Inn*

Scanes Edward, tailor
SmerdonHughJno. gent. *White'sFarm*
Toms Joseph, parish clerk
Woolcombe Rev Wm. *Vicarage*
Woon Bartholomew, shopkeeper
   FARMERS. (* *are Owners.*)
Adams Joseph, *Bowden*
*Adams Nathaniel, *Clampit*
Adams Nicholas, *Moor Barton*
*Archer Wm. *Seahill Farm*
Braddon Joseph Gray, *Newhyner*
*Delvebragg John, *Wells Farm*

Edwards John, *New House*
Endicott Samuel, *Orphan*
Gidley James, *Loomscroft*
*Hamlyn James, *Lower Bennah*
*Hamlyn Jno. (regr.) *HigherBennah*
Hemens Robert, *Court Farm*
*Lovies Thomas, *Kennick*
Oldrey Richard, *Canon-teign*
Peters Wm. *Water Well*
*Pinwill John, *Cleaps House*
Stranger Richard, *Shootimoor*

COMBEINTEIGNHEAD, (*Combe-in-Teign-Head,*) is a village and parish on the south side of the estuary of the river Teign, 3 miles E. of Newton-Abbot, and 10 miles N.E. by N. of Totnes. It is in the detached part of Wonford Hundred, and contains 425 souls, and 2217A. 1R. 8P. of land, including the hamlets of *Netherton, Rocombe,* and *Ringmore.* (See Shaldon.) The manor of Combe-in-Teign was long held by the Bourchiers, Earls of Bath, but was sold to 10 or 12 purchasers about 30 years ago, by their representative Sir Bourchier Wrey, Bart., who has also recently disposed of the advowson of the rectory. Lady Reynell, Sir W. P. Carew, W. Wilkin, Esq., and several other proprietors, have estates here. The remains of an ancient mansion, called *Buckland Baron,* are occupied by labourers. The estate attached to this house was anciently held by the Baron family, and passed to the Earl of Cavan, in right of his mother, who was heiress of the late Mr. Justice Gould. Part of the parish is in the manor of Haccombe. The *Church* is an ancient structure, with a tower and four bells, and the aisles are divided from the nave by octagonal pillars. The *rectory,* valued in K.B. at £32. 2s. 8½d., and in 1831 at £377, is in the patronage of J. W. Harding and W. Long, Esqrs., and incumbency of the Rev. John Wrey, M.A., who has a handsome residence in the Elizabethan style, erected in 1840. The glebe is 23A. 3R. 17P., and the tithes were commuted in 1842 for £358 per annum. An old *almshouse* for four poor families is supposed to have been founded by an ancestor of the Earl of Bath. The poor have two ancient rent-charges of 5s. and 2s. per annum. The dividends of £100 three cent. annuities, left by *Margaret Burgoyne* in 1789, are paid for the education of ten poor children, at the National School.

Barrett Jane, schoolmistress
Boden Miss Sus. || Dicker Mrs
Clynick John, sexton
Fowler John, baker
Garrett Samuel, mason
Honeywill George, cooper
Limpenny John, schoolr. *Netherton*
Metherell Wm. miller, Nethercott
Mortimer Mr W.||Underhay J. p. clk
Murgin Jas. vict. Boat House
Taverner Mary, shopkeeper
Wrey Rev John, M.A., Rectory

BLACKSMITHS.
Bulleid Wm.
Linscott Thos.
   SHOEMAKERS.
Newton Henry
Taverner John
   FARMERS.
(* *are Owners.*)
Ashford R. *Nethct*
Fowler Wm.
*Franklin John,
   Westborough

Heath Ts. *Nethct*
Hill John
*Lang Stephen,
   Gullmswell
Lovecraft Joshua
Rendell Robert
Rendell Wm.
   MARINERS.
Metherell Edw.
Sanders George
Ferris

DREWSTEIGNTON, a large village on the northern acclivity of Teign valley, 13 miles W. of Exeter, and 9 miles E. by S. of Oke-hampton, has in its parish 1315 souls, including 181 in the hamlet of TEIGNHOLT, which has several scattered farms, houses, &c. The parish also includes part of the village of *Crockernwell*, (see p. 187,) and contains 6938A. 1R. 22½P. of land, extending westward to the borders of Dartmoor. About 6506 acres are rateable, and the rest are roads, wastes, and river. The rateable annual value is £5406, and the gross rental £7285. The parish abounds in fine scenery of rocks and woods. *Drewsteignton Lime Rock Quarries* are worked extensively by Messrs. Ponsford and Co. and Jas. Pitts, Esq. This lime rock is of a dark blue colour, and contains manganese and white veins lying in alternate strata with schist, or black shell, much closer in texture and harder than the limestone beds, which vary from two to six feet in thickness, and dip regularly towards the north at an angle of 30 degrees. Petrifactions of marine shells, &c., are found at a depth of 100 to 200 feet. When the rock is well burnt, it produces a reddish brown lime, which is in great request for agricultural purposes, as well as for cement in masonry under water, &c. Drewsteignton has two annual fairs for cattle, &c., on the Thursday after Candlemas-day, and the Thursday after Trinity Sunday. In the reigns of Henry II. and Richard I., the *manor* was held by *Drogo*, or *Drewe de Teignton*. For many generations, it was held by the Carews, who sold it in lots in 1791. G. Ponsford, Esq., J. Pitts, Esq., and the Rev. W. Ponsford, are now lords of the manor, but a great part of the soil belongs to W. Lambert, Esq., John Pons-ford, Esq., Wm. Bragg, Esq., and several smaller freeholders. These gentlemen have neat and pleasant seats in different parts of the pa-rish. The late Rev. S. Pidsley owned *Drascombe* farm, on which a valuable *tin lode* was discovered and worked some years ago. This mine has recently been taken by a company of gentlemen at Bris-tol, and sunk to the depth of 34 fathoms, where excellent *copper ore* is found, as well as tin, with a mixture of silver. Mr. J. Luke, of Exeter, owns the barton or farm of *Shilston*. In the middle of an enclosure on this farm is a *Cromlech*, or druidical monument, con-sisting of three large upright stones, supporting a fourth, which is 12 feet long and 9 wide in the broadest part. The supporting stones are about 6 feet high, and all are rudely shaped moor stones. On the brink of the river Teign, at a short distance south of Shilston, is a remarkable *Logan or Rocking Stone*, but its motion is now scarcely perceptible. In a neighbouring part of Dartmoor, on the descent of a hill, are two curious *Circles*, supposed to be of Druidic origin, and each about 93 feet in diameter, but most of the stones are gone, or are deeply sunk in the mounds and vallums. Near them are also some traces of what has been called the *via sacra* or Druid-way, and it is supposed that this was the principal place of Druidical ceremony in the county. Some antiquaries say that *Drews-Teignton* had the first part of its name from this circumstance, but others, with more probability, derived it from Drogo or Drewe, its early Norman proprietor, before whose time the parish was merely called Teignton, from its situation on the river Teign. The *Church*

(St. Peter,) is a large Gothic structure, with an embattled tower and six bells. The east window has a beautiful representation of the Ascension in painted glass, given by the late rector, in 1825. The Messrs. Ponsford are patrons of the *rectory*, valued in K.B. at £40. 13. 4d., and in 1831 at £876. The Rev. Wm. Ponsford is the incumbent, and has 440A. of glebe, and a handsome brick residence, with a fine lawn, commanding picturesque views. The tithes were commuted in 1841 for £659. 17s. per annum. Here is a small National School. The *Parish Land, &c.*, comprise about 30 acres, two houses, seven cottages, &c., let for about £26, and seven cottages occupied rent free by paupers. They have been vested, from an early period, for the use of church and poor. For a weekly distribution of bread, the poor have £2. 12s. per annum, left by *Thos. Hall* in 1705, out of Venton estate. They have also £10 a year out of Hare Path estate, left by *Mary Ponsford* in 1817.

DREWSTEIGNTON.

Those Marked 1, are at Crockernwell; 2, Sandy Park; 3, Teignholt; and the rest in Drewsteignton Village, or 'where specified.

POST-OFFICE at Thomas Hooper's, *Whyddon-down.* Letters desp. at 10 mg. *via* Exeter, and 8 night. to Okehampton, &c.

Aggett John, manager of lime quarries, &c.
Bevens Jno. & Sons, masons & bldrs
Gorwyn Richd. L. Esq. *Higher Bridbrook*
1 Gregory Saml. & Sons, coopers
Hill John, farrier
Lambert Mrs E., *Broadmoor House*
Lambert Wm. Esq. *Wallon House*
Penrose John, copper mine agent
-Pitts Jas. Esq. lime quarry owner, *Newton House*
Ponsford and Co. proprietors of the Lime Rock quarry and kilns
Ponsford John, Esq. *East Ford Hs*
Ponsford Geo. Esq.||Skinner Mr W.
Ponsford Rev. Wm., *Rectory*
Smith John, parish clerk
Snell Saml. schoolr. and overseer
Stoneman John, road contractor
Walker Rev Fredk. J. curate
PUBLIC HOUSES.
New Inn, Wm. Smith
Post Office Inn, Thomas Hooper, *Whyddon-down*
2 Sandy Park Inn, Wm. Perrott
Beerhouses, Rd. Austin & Jno. Marks
FARMERS. (* *are Owners.*)
Blanchford Hy. || Blanchford Jas.

*Bragg Wm. Esq. Furlong
Bremridge John, *Martin's*
Brimblecombe John, *Davyland*
Brock John, *Great Tree*
Browning John Symons, *Hobhouse*
3 Clark Henry, *Westwood*
3 Clark Wm., *Tray-hill*
Dodd Mary, *East Fingle*
Drew James, *Red Lake*
3 Dunning John, *Wood Park*
Ellis Wm., *Great Shilston*
Ford John, *Wisdom*
3 Grendon John, *West Fursham*
Hellier Joseph, *West Ford*
Hole Wm., *Winscomb*, & Matw. *Stone*
Hole Wm., *Notton hole*
Jackson Alexander, *Furze down*
Kenshole Samuel, *Glebe land*
*Knapman Edward, *Tor hill*
Knapman Andrew, *Drascombe*
Lampey Geo. *Northill*||Lang Wm.
Lee Richard, *Swallow Tree*
3 Middlewick John, *Crayford*
3*Mortimer Charles, *Wood green*
Nickells Jas. miller, *Veet Mills*
Perrott Rd. and Wm., *Sandy Park*
Phillips Wm. miller, *Weir Mills*
Pitts Joseph, *Underdown*
Pike Samuel, *Venton*
Robins George, *Higher Pasford*
Seward Wm., *Greystone*
*Skinner John, *Burrow*
Smith Wm. (and cattle dealer)
*Strong Richard, *Narracott*
*Strong Jno. high constbl. *Combhall*
3 Violl John N., *East hills*
Wolland Rd., *Harepath & Preston*
Wolland Samuel, *Buracre*

BAKERS.	SHOEMAKERS.	CARPENTERS.	THATCHERS.
Blanchford Hy.	Bevens Richard	Langmead Wm.	Holman John
Marks John	Holman Wm.	Milton John	Holman Wm.
Langmead Wm.	Holman J.	Williams Geo.	WHEELWRIGHTS.
BLACKSMITHS.	Smith George	Williams Jas.	1 Fewvins Simon
1 Booth John	SHOPKEEPERS.	Williams John	Hooper Ts. *Whyd*
1 Groves John	Milford John	TAILORS.	2 Perrott Wm.
2 Nickels Wm.	Stanbury Eliz.	Cann Wm.	CARRIER *to Exe-*
Smith Jno. & Rbn.	Smith Wm.	Ponsford John	*ter,* Cann Sml.
	Williams Geo.		Tu. and Fri.

DUNSFORD, which gives name to a deanery, is a scattered
village and parish, on the northern acclivities of the picturesque
valley of the river Teign, from 7 to 8 miles W. by S. of Exeter. It
contains 925 souls, and about 6000 acres of land, including 72A. of
waste and water, and 350A. of woodland.   There are two corn-mills
on the river, and a *cattle fair* is held in the village, on the Monday
after Sept. 8th.   The soil is generally fertile, the surface rises in
bold swells, in some places richly diversified with flourishing woods,
and bare granite rocks.   Baldwin Fulford, Esq., is lord of the *manor
of Dunsford*, and Sir L. V. Palk is lord of *Little Dunsford* or *Sowton*
manor; but part of the soil belong J. S. Pitman, Esq., and several
smaller owners.   A *copper mine* was opened here in 1848, by B.
Fulford, Esq., of FULFORD HOUSE, a large square mansion, of the
Elizabethan age, in a finely wooded park of about 400 acres, stocked
with deer, and having a small lake.   This seat is about 8 miles W.
of Exeter, between Dunsford and Tedburn St. Mary, and the estate,
called *Great Fulford*, is partly in the latter parish.   The Fulfords
have possessed this estate since the reign of Richard I., and one of
them, Sir John Fulford, purchased the manor at the Reformation,
previous to which it had been held by the abbey of Canonleigh.
Sir Wm., Sir Baldwin, and Sir Amias de Fulford, distinguished
themselves in the Holy Land.   Another Sir Baldwin Fulford, having fought on the side of Henry VI. at Towton, was beheaded at
Hexham, in 1461.   His son Sir Thomas, was attainted in 1483, but
escaped, and was among those who assisted the Earl of Devon in
the relief of Exeter, when besieged by Perkin Warbeck, in 1497.
Col. Fras. Fulford, afterwards Sir Francis, garrisoned Fulford House
for King Charles, and his son was killed in his service.   Fulford
House was taken by Sir Thos. Fairfax, in December, 1645, and the
command given to Col. Okey, one of the regicides.   The mansion
contains some good family portraits, and a full length of Charles I.
The small manor of *Halstow*, in this parish, belongs to the priest-
vicars of Exeter; and that of *Cetley* (mostly woods) to King's College, Cambridge.   The barton of *Clifford* belongs to the Clifford
family.   The CHURCH (St. Mary) is a fine old structure, and contains some handsome monuments of the Fulfords.   The chancel
was mostly re-built in 1846, when a new organ was erected.   The
tower contains a clock, chimes, and six bells.   The *vicarage,* valued
in K.B. at £19. 10s., and in 1831 at £319, is in the gift of B.
Fulford, Esq., and incumbency of the Rev. Richard Stephens, M.A.,
of Holcombe Burnell.   In 1814, it was endowed with the tithes of

hay, and the great tithes of Fulford and Clifford. The *Vicarage House* is a neat and pleasant residence, commanding fine views of Teign valley, and the romantic woods and granite rocks which enclose the road to Moreton Hampstead. The glebe is 7A., and the tithes were commuted in 1841, for £613 per annum, of which £368 belongs to the vicar, £143. 19s. to B. Fulford, Esq.; £60. 12s. to the executors of the late Geo. Gregory, Esq.; £36. 1s. to James Pitman, Esq.; and £4. 8s. to Sir L. V. Palk. Here is a National School. The *Poor's Land* consists of 104A. of moor land, called *Cranbrook*, let for only about £25 per annum, and purchased mostly in 1707, with £220 given by Agnes Harrison, and Florence and Christopher Barrow; and partly in 1802, with £157, raised by subscription. The poor have also a yearly rent charge of 20s., left by *Nicholas Sperke*, in 1606, out of Sowton farm.

Cheesworth Chas. Nosworthy, schoolmaster, *Post-Office*
Cheesworth C. N. jun. registrar, &c
Day Saml. auctioneer, surveyor, and parish clerk
Froom Thos. Nield, surgeon
Fulford Baldwin, Esq., *Fulford Hs*
Hellier George, vict., Royal Oak
Helson Ts. edge-tool mfr., Iron Mills
James Hy. copper mine agent
May Mr John, *Farrants* || Pook Wm.
Southcombe Rev. J. L. Hamilton, B.A. curate, *Vicarage*
Winser John, vict., Half Moon

FARMERS (* *are Owners.*)
Ash Richard, *Langley*
*Berry Joseph, *Brook*
Bolley Geo. || Carnell Wm.
Carnell Rd. Norris, *Clifford Barton*
Cole Wm., *Mayne Farm*
Colbridge George, *Midwinter*
Day Samuel, *Culver Farm*
Dicker Wm., *Hole-land*
*Elsworthy Wm. || Elsworthy Geo.
Gossland Thos. || Jordan John
Gray Geo., *South Halstow*
*Jarvis Jeremiah, *Owlhole*
Lee Jas. || May Geo., *Farrants*
May Walter, *Sowton Barton*
Northcott Joseph, *Meadhay*
Paddon James, *Gillwell*
Phillips Wm., *Easton Boyland*
Pitts Henry, *North Ramridge*

Sanford Simon, *Pools*
Seward Benj. E. || Seward John
*Seward George, *Combes*
Seward Martin, *South Zeal*
Seward Wm., *Berry Barton*
Shears Robert || Shears Wm.
Short Mary || Short John
*Taverner John || Taverner Mary
*Tuckett Wm. || Taverner Wm.
Wills Ann || Wills Peter
Wills Joseph || Wills Thomas

BEER HOUSES.
Roleston Wm.
White Jane

BAKERS &SHOPRS.
Bond Wm.
Cox John
Rice Wm.
Shilston John

BLACKSMITHS.
Crispin James (& wheelwright)
Smallridge Jph.

BOOT & SHOEMRS.
Bolt Samuel
Parr James
Shears George
Taverner Saml.

BUTCHERS.
Hellier Francis
Hellier George

CARPENTERS.
Bright Wm.

Chaffe John
Guscott James
Sercombe Sl.&Jn.

MASONS.
Bond George
Hill George
Orchard Wm.
Sercombe Wm.

MILLERS.
Chaffe Geo. *Sowtn.*
Phillips J. *Dunsfd.*

TAILORS.
Rice John
Routley Robert

THATCHERS.
Connett James
Connett Wm.

POST-OFFICE at C. N. Cheesworth's. Letters desp. 7 mg. & 5 evng.

GIDLEIGH, or GIDLEY, a small scattered village, on the eastern declivities of Dartmoor Forest, near one of the tributary streams of the river Teign, 7½ S.E. of Okehampton, and 17 miles W. by S. of Exeter, has in its parish 182 souls, and 2435A. 3R. 30P. of land, more than half of which is open common, &c., in Dartmoor. It includes two small hamlets, called *Chapel* and *Forder*, and is

I

watered by the Teign and two of its tributaries, which have their sources a few miles westward, among the rude hills and dales of Dartmoor. The manor belonged, from the reign of Wm. the Conqueror till that of Edward II., to the ancient family of *Prouz* or *Prous*, who had a *castle* here, and an extensive park. Some remains of the castle keep are still standing, near the church. With the heiress of the Prouz family, the manor passed to the Mules; and from them it passed the Damarells. It afterwards passed to the Coad, Gidley, and Rattery families, and was purchased with the advowson, under a decree of the Court of Chancery, by the late Rev. Thomas Whipham. The Rev. Arthur Whipham, M.A., is the present *rector, patron*, and *lord of the manor*, and has a handsome modern seat in GIDLEIGH PARK, which comprises in its ancient boundaries an extensive tract of rocky ground, "fruitful only in rabbits, but curious from its singular appearance." A steep descent from the park to the river Teign, is studded by enormous rocky protuberances, whose level summits display many of the excavations called Rock-basins. The roaring stream at the bottom of this descent, the wooded front of the bold bank that rises on the opposite side, and the vast masses of rock on either hand, grey with moss, or dark with ivy, render this part of the park truly romantic. Mr. John Rowe, Mr. Wm. Brock, and several smaller owners have estates in the parish. In 1848, L. Prinsep, Esq., built a neat house and two towers on the highest hill in the parish. The *Church* (Holy Trinity,) is an antique structure, with a tower and four bells. Its fine old screen was cleansed and repaired in 1848. The *rectory*, valued in K.B. at £14. 19s., and in 1831 at £80, has 29A. 1R. 39P. of glebe, but the parsonage house is now only a cottage. The tithes were commuted in 1843 for £87. 10s. per annum. Two houses and 24A. of land have been vested from an early period, for the repairs of the church.

Finch Charles, parish clerk
Prinsep L. gentleman
Whipham Rev. Arthur, M.A., rector, *Gidleigh Park*
FARMERS.
Brock Wm., *Chapel*
Brunning Wm., *Moortown*
Endicott John, *Gidleigh Mill*
Endicott Wm., *Forder*
Rowe John || Newcombe John
Sampson Wm., *Greenaway*
Westcott Wm., *Bothery*

HACCOMBE, 3 miles E. by S. of Newton Abbot, is a small parish, or extra-parochial liberty, in the detached part of Wonford Hundred, south of the estuary of the Teign. It contains only 14 inhabitants, 290 acres of land, and two houses. It is the seat and property of *Sir Walter-Palk Carew, Bart.*, and has been held for many generations by his family, one of whom was created a baronet, in 1661. The present mansion, called *Haccombe House*, was built on the site of the ancient hall, about 45 years ago. It is a large plain building, standing in a well wooded lawn, at the bottom of a gradual descent, near the church, on the door of which two horse shoes were fastened, "in memory of one of the Carews, who won a wager of a manor of land, by swimming his horse a vast way into the sea, and back again." At Domesday Survey, the manor was held by Stephen de Haccombe, under Baldwin the Sheriff. It

passed successively to the Archdeacons and Courtenays. In the 13th century, it passed with the heiress of the latter to *Nicholas Lord Carew*, one of whose descendants, George Carew, was created Baron Carew and Earl of Totnes in 1625, but, dying without issue, in 1629, his titles became extinct. Another member of the family was created Lord Carew of Ireland, in 1834, and of the United Kingdom in 1838. Haccombe *Church* (St. Blaize,) is a small ivy clad structure, with a bell turret, and contains some ancient monuments of the Haccombe and Carew families. In 1821-'2, it was newly fitted with a handsome stone screen, stone pulpit, gothic altar piece, &c. Sir John L'Ercedekne, or Archdeacon, about the year 1341, founded in it a *college* or *archpresbytery*, consisting of an archpriest and five other priests, who lived together in community, and were endowed with the great tithes of Haccombe and of Quethiock, in Cornwall. These tithes now belong to the *rectory*, valued in K.B. at £25, and in 1831 at £253. Sir W. P. Carew, Bart., is the patron; the Rev. Thos. C. Carew, is the *incumbent;* and the Rev. Thos. Kitson, *curate*. The Rectory House is a small old building, occupied by labourers.

HEAVITREE is a suburban parish of Exeter, and partly within the parliamentary limits of that city, as already noticed at pages 88 and 114.

HITTISLEIGH is a hilly parish of scattered houses, about 8 miles W.S.W. of Crediton, and 13 miles W. by N. of Exeter. It contains 199 souls, and 1155A. 3R. 11P. of land. C. Calmady, Esq., is lord of the manor, which was anciently held by the Talbots, Londons, and Shilstons, but the soil is all freehold, and belongs to the Hole, Pedlar, Haydon, Gorwyn, Webber, and other families. The *Church* (St. Andrew,) has a tower and three bells, and was newly seated in 1839-'40, at the cost of £120. The *rectory*, valued in K.B. at £6. 2s. 1d., and in 1831 at £94, is in the gift of C. Calmady, Esq., and incumbency of the Rev. Richard Holland, M.A., of Spreyton. The glebe is 30A., and the parsonage house is a small building, erected about 12 years ago, on the site of the old one, which was destroyed by fire.

Gregory Jno., carpenter, parish clerk, and vict. Hunter's Arms
Manley Rev John, B.A. curate
Middlewick John, carpenter
Middlewick Joshua, shopkeeper
Ware Mr Daniel, *Beadon Down*

FARMERS. (* *are Owners*.)
*Gorwyn Geo. and James, *Midlake*
*Haydon Andrew ‖ *Haydon Wm.
*Hole John ‖ Newton Wm.
*Pedlar Richard ‖ Rowe Wm.
*Webber John, *Trenhay*

HOLCOMBE-BURNELL parish, about 4 miles W. by S. of Exeter, has 306 inhabitants, and 1836 acres of land. The houses are scattered, except in the village of LONGDOWN, which has only 14 dwellings, on the high road from Exeter to Moreton-Hampstead, and is partly in Dunsford and Alphington parishes. The soil belongs to James Pitman, Esq., the Rev. R. Stephens, Mr. R. Mortimore, and several smaller freeholders. At Domesday Survey it belonged to Tetbald Fitz-Berners, or Bernerii, and it passed to the Kawl, Dennis, Baker, Campernowne, and other families. *Culver House,* the handsome seat of the Rev. Richd. Stephens, sub-dean of

I 2

Exeter, was built by him in 1836, and is in the irregular Tuscan order of architecture. It is delightfully situated about 5 miles W. by S. of Exeter, and the high ground behind it has been very tastefully planted. *Perridge*, the romantically situated, and well wooded seat of Chas. Dormer, Esq., is a mansion and estate of 150A., adjoining this parish, but belonging to the parish of Kenn, from which it is distant 7 miles. This isolated estate is the property of the heirs of the late Henry L. Toll, Esq., and its inhabitants use Holcombe church. The old *manor house* of this parish is occupied by a farmer. It was formerly a large mansion, built by Sir Thos. Dennis, in the reign of Henry VIII. An ancient chapel, in an adjoining field, was taken down by Edw. Campernowne, Esq., in 1700. The *Church* (St. John,) was rebuilt, (all but the tower,) in 1843-'4, at the cost of £610. The tower has five bells, and in the chancel is a very handsome altar-tomb of Sir Thos. Dennis, who was lord chancellor, and an ancestor of the late Lord Rolle. The chancel is very neat, and on its south side are two sedilia, handsomely carved and inscribed to the memory of an aunt of the Rev. R. Stephens. The *vicarage,* valued in K.B. at £8. 9s. 2d., and in 1831 at £20, is endowed with all the tithes, which were commuted in 1842 for £145 per annum. The glebe comprises 100 acres of poor land, and the *Vicarage House* is a neat and pleasant mansion, built in 1838, at the cost of £1000, on a commanding eminence. The Rev. H. L. Houlditch, B.A., is the incumbent, and the *Prebendary of Holcombe,* in Wells Cathedral, has long held the patronage, but after the death of the present prebendary, the advowson will pass to the Bishop of Exeter. Here is a small school, and the poor parishioners have the interest of £5, left by the late Jas. Pitman, Esq.

(*Marked * are in Longdown.*)
*Bennett John, vict. Lamb
*Britton Thomas, carpenter
Dormer Charles, Esq. *Perridge*
Dymond John, parish clerk
*Honeywill Thomas, blacksmith
Houlditch Rev Henry Lovelace, B.A., *Vicarage*
Lightfoot My. Ann, schoolmistress
*Morrish Samuel, shoemaker
*Milford George, tailor
*Shapcote Wm. wheelwright

Stephens Rev Richd., M.A. sub-dean of Exeter and vicar of Dunsford, *Culver House*

FARMERS.
Branscombe Wm. *Rugg House*
Dymond Mrs W. *Lower Pitt*
Easton John || Grant Mr
Guscott John, *Noysland*
Harvey George || Kelly John
Honeywill Theophs. *East Hill*
Norrish Thos. || Mugford Mr. *Pitt*
Sanford Joseph. *Down's House*
Stanbury Thomas, *King's ford*

HUXHAM, a small parish, on the banks of the river Culm, 3½ miles N.N.E. of Exeter, has only 150 inhabitants, and 830 acres of land, mostly the property of Lord Poltimore, the lord of the manor, which was anciently held by the Huxham family, whose heiress carried it in marriage to an ancestor of its present owner, in the reign of Edward III. The *Church* is a small ancient structure, and the living is a *rectory*, annexed to that of Poltimore, in the incumbency of the Hon. and Rev. John Fortescue, M.A. The parsonage is a neat building occupied by the Rev. Thos. Bremridge Meluish, the *curate.* The other principal parishioners are Richard Matthews,

paper maker, Upper Mill; Charles Matthews and Richard Martyn, *paper makers*, Lower Mill; Edward Cyrl, *parish clerk;* and John Norris and Robert Rew, *farmers.*

ST. LEONARD'S PARISH is a suburb of Exeter, and has been added to the parliamentary borough of the City and County of the City, as already noticed. *See pages* 86 and 125.

ST. NICHOLAS' PARISH includes the large village of SHAL-DON, and most of the adjacent village of RINGMORE, on the south side of the mouth of the river Teign, opposite the sea port and bathing place of Teignmouth, 5½ miles E. of Newton-Abbot and Bushell. It comprises only 580 acres, but had 1175 inhabitants in 1841, including 538 in Shaldon hamlet, which has since greatly increased in population and buildings. The church stands in Ringmore, which is partly in the parish of Stokeinteignhead. St. Nicholas's parish has now about 1500 inhabitants, most of whom are in SHALDON, a handsome village and bathing place, picturesquely seated on the coast of the English channel, opposite Teignmouth, and partly under the lofty promontory of bold red rocks, called the *Ness.* Shaldon is connected with Teignmouth by a ferry, and also by the longest *Bridge* in England, which crosses the Teign by 35 arches, and is 1671 feet in length. (See Teignmouth.) Having a fine beach and much romantic senery in its vicinity, it has become a favourite sea bathing place, during the last twenty years, in which many neat and tasteful houses, &c., have been erected on the Green, on the Marine terrace, in Clifford place, and in Bridge street, as well as in the pleasant suburb of Ringmore. It has been much improved during the last five years, and has now many neat villas, and commodious lodging-houses; a small National School, a Baptist Chapel, built in 1815; and an Independent Chapel, erected in 1825. *St. Nicholas's Church*, from which the parish has its name, was rebuilt by the Carew family about 180 years ago, and stands in a picturesque situation, overlooking the estuary of the Teign, about half a mile W. of Shaldon. It is a small plastered building, with a tower containg one bell, and crowned by a short wooden spire. The *vicarage*, valued in K.B. at £8, and in 1831 at £128, is in the patronage of Lord Clifford, and incumbency of the Rev. R. Hutton, B.A. It has been augmented with Queen Anne's Bounty, and is said to have been formerly annexed to Haccombe. The *manor*, which was parcel of the barony of Okehampton, was held during many generations by the Carews, who sold it in 1671, to Lord Treasurer Clifford, an ancestor of Lord Clifford, the present owner, The poor parishioners have 10s. a year out of the parish rates, as interest of £10 left by Thomas Mudge, at an early period.

ST. NICHOLAS'S PARISH.
*Those marked * are in* RINGMORE, *and the others in* SHALDON.

POST-OFFICE at Andrew Denley's. Letters arrive 8 mng. and desp. 6 evening, *via* Teignmouth

Adams Mr Hy.|| Bartlett Mrs & Miss
Amery Thomas, farmer

Atcherley Rowland, M.D.||*Bere Mrs
Bartlett Mr Nicholas Adams
*Bennett Mrs My. || Bulley Miss
*Boden Wm. merchant, & Robt. gent
Bradford Robert, merchant
Brokensha Lieut. Saml., R.N. & Miss
Bulley Edward, boat builder
*Burton Hy. gent.|| Chandler Mrs E.

Chasty Chas. Heard, watch maker
Clapp Mr Gilbert || Cook Mrs Ann
*Collins James, gent.
*Copp Mrs Grace
Coryton Capt. Hy., R.N. *Platway*
Davis Mrs Hanh. || Crook Mr Wm.
Douglas Jno. Esq. *Lower Platway Hs*
Drew Wm. gent || Down Mr John
Farley Daniel, cooper
Fox Wm. gent. || Hall Mrs Jane
Good Hy. draper & spirit merchant
Gray Capt. Edward Evans, R.N.
Hall Mr Chas. || Haswell Mrs Ann
Hannaford Mr Geo., and Mr Peter
Harvey Mr John, and Mr Stephen
Heaviside James, gent. *Platway Hs*
Hele John Carrol, merchant
Holmes Wm. Henry, *Clifford House*
Hook Samuel, ship and boat builder
Howard Mrs Marian||Lawton MrGeo.
*Hutton Rev Rufus, B.A. *rector*
James William, painter, &c.
Lavis Richd. cabinet mkr. & upholstr
MacDougall Major Peter||*Noble Mrs
Nosworthy Thos. cabinet maker, &c.
O'Reilly Lieut. John, *The Den*
*OwenMrsThos.||Parker Mr Geo. Hy.
Parsons Robt. White, coal merchant
Pollard John, coal merchant
Pratt Thos. chemist and druggist
Redway Wm. rope maker and beerhs
*Rendle John, merchant
Rendle Miss E.
Richardson Lieut. Thomas L., R.A.
Rowe Mr Wm. || Satterley Mrs Eliz.
Sanders Mr Wm.|| Stevens Mr Robt.
Small Wm. Charles, surgeon
*StevensonMajorEd.|| SullockMissA.
*Sweeting Misses Margaret, & Selina
Travers Rev Chas. Henry, *curate*
Tuffnel Hon. Lady, *The Beach*
Wane Mr Richd.||Tucker Mrs Hannah
Warren Jph. tinner and ironmonger

White Mr Thomas, *Sea View House*
Wills Thos. farmer, *Triangle Green*
Wreford Rev Wm., Indpt. minister

INNS AND TAVERNS.

Adelaide Inn, John Townsend
Crown and Anchor, Robert Square
London Inn, Uriah Widdicombe

ACADEMIES.
(+*Boarding*.)
Beal Harriet
CleaveWm.&Mrs
+Hallaham Mary
+Pridham Jno.W.
    Teignbridge Hs
BAKERS.
Anning Richard
Cade Mary
Churchward Wm.
Elson Wm.
Full Joseph
BLACKSMITHS.
Churchward John
Short Benjamin
BOOT & SHOEMRS.
*Alward Samuel
Coysh Richard
Devonshire Robt.
Hoare James
Owen John
White John
Winsborrow Ths.
BUTCHERS.
White Gains
Wills Frdk.Thos.
JOINERS & BLDRS.
Bulley Abraham
Bulley Wm.
Prideaux Wm.
MASTER MARINRS.
Coysh John
Gowin Stephen
Harris Thomas

Hoskin Valentine
Lavis Robert
*Matthews Stpn.
Nicholls Wm.
Parker Wm.
Sanders Samuel
Sanders Thomas
*Stoggins Thos.
Whitway Chas.
MASONS & BLDRS.
Coulman Chas.
Madge Richard
Madge Thomas
Nicholls Wm.
Windeatt Geo.
Windeatt Wm. H.
MILLINERS.
Coysh Mrs J.
Lear Mary
Pridham Eliz.
Stevens Misses
Stoggins Mary
SHOPKEEPERS.
Harvey Charlotte
Morrish Sally
Murch Elizabeth
Strange Eliz.
Tucker Edw. (&
    horse letter)
Whiteway Jane
TAILORS.
Bovey Wm.
HammondWm.C.
Toms John

OGWELL (EAST) is a parish and scattered village, 1½ mile
S.W. of Newton Abbot, containing 1249 acres of land, and 356
inhabitants.   With the neighbouring parish of West Ogwell, it
forms a detached member of Wonford Hundred, in the deanery of
Ippleden.   The manor was held at the Domesday Survey by Wm.
Pictavensis, from whose family it afterwards passed to those of Malston, Stighull, and Reynell; but *Holbeame* estate was for some time
held by the Petre family.   General T. W. Taylor, C.B., is now lord
of the manor, owner of most of the parish, and patron of the *rectory*, valued in K.B. at £19. 3s. 1d., and in 1831 at £200.   The Rev.
F. J. Taylor is the incumbent, for whom a handsome new Rectory

House was built in 1849, on 26A. 2R. 21P. of land, which was obtained in 1848, in exchange for the old glebe land. The *Church* (St. Bartholomew,) is a small ancient structure, with a tower and three bells, and stands in a picturesque valley. At Grendon, in this parish, is an old *Almshouse*, for the residence of two poor families. In 1733, *Sir Richard Reynell* left 4A. of land, now let for £10, and directed the rent to be applied in repairing this almshouse and his family burial place, and in schooling poor children. The Rev. Edward Reynell, who died in 1663, was rector here, and published the Life of Lucy Lady Reynell, who founded the Almshouse, " Eugenia's Tears for Britain's Glory," and other works.

Elliott John, smith and wheelwright
Field Wm. vict. Jolly Sailor
Heath Catherine, schoolmistress
Hellings John, baker
Hockings Nicholas, corn miller
Matthews Jacob, parish clerk
Nichols John, blacksmith
Taylor Rev Fitzwilliam John, rector of East and West Ogwell, *Rectory*
Webber Joseph, sexton
Webber Richard, mason

FARMERS.

Ellis Robert Langley, *Hollins*
Gillard George || Langler Wm.
Parrott John || Rouse John
Rendell Richard || Rendell Wm.
Vooght John & Jph. || Vallance Dnl.

OGWELL (WEST) is a small parish adjoining East Ogwell, about two miles S.W. of Newton-Abbot. It has only 51 souls, and about 1000 acres of land, generally fertile, and finely undulated. At Domesday Survey the manor was held by Wm. Pictavensis, or Peytevin. It was sold by one of the Earls of Devon to the Reynell family, and is now the property of General Thos. Wm. Taylor, C.B., who is Lieut.-Governor of the Military College at Sandhurst, and has a handsome seat here, called OGWELL HOUSE, pleasantly situated in a small deer park, finely clothed with wood, and now occupied by H. C. B. Barton, Esq., and Mrs. Barton. The *Church* is a small plastered fabric, with a tower and three bells, and contains several neat monuments. The *rectory*, valued in K.B. at £7. 2s. 11d., and in 1831 at £127, is in the same patronage and incumbency as that of East Ogwell. The principal residents are, Henry Chas. Benyon Barton, Esq., and Mrs. R. L. Barton, *Ogwell House;* and John Harris, John Lethbridge, John Shapley, James Shepherd, and Geo. Wilcocks, *farmers.*

PINHOE, a pleasant village and parish, 2½ miles N.E. of Exeter, contains 568 souls, and about 1930 acres of land, generally fertile, and rising in bold undulations. On *Beacon Hill*, a commanding eminence near the village, are several neat houses. In 1001, King Ethelred's army was defeated here, with great slaughter, by the Danes, who burnt Pinhoe, Broad-Clist, and other neighbouring villages. The manor was part of the royal demense, and is described in Domesday Book as containing the vills or farms of Monkerton, Pinpound, Langaton, Herrington, and Wotton. It was successively held by the Vallibus, Multon, Strech, Cheney, Walgrave, Elwill, and other families. Lord Paltimore is now lord of the manor ; but a great part of the soil belongs to Sir Frederick H. H. Bathhurst, Lee Hanning Lee, Esq., the Rev. W. H. Arundell, and

a few smaller owners, mostly freeholders. The *Church* (St. Michael,) is an antique stone fabric, with an embattled tower, and four bells. The nave and chancel are separated by an old carved oak screen; and in the churchyard, opposite the porch, is a large stone cross, on a pedestal. The *vicarage*, valued in K.B. at £14. 13s. 4d., and in 1831 at £227, is in the patronage of the Bishop of Exeter, and incumbency of the Rev. John Bradford, M.A., who has a neat brick residence, on an eminence commánding a fine prospect of the surrounding country. The glebe is only one acre, and the vicarial tithes were commuted, in 1836, for £265 per annum. The Misses Arundell are lessees of the rectorial tithes, under the Dean and Chapter of Exeter. *John Reynolds*, a learned divine, and successful writer against the Roman Catholics, was born here about 1546. In 1655, £175 was given by *Grace Bampfield*, and other donors, and was laid out in the purchase of a house and 13 acres of land, at Broad Clist, now let for about £26 a year. Five-ninths of the rent of this estate belong to the poor of Pinhoe, and the rest to the poor of Stoke-Canon and Thorverton parishes. The poor of Pinhoe have £6 a year as the rent of two acres of land, left by *Humphrey Wilcocks*, in 1686; and £6. 18s. a year from £230. 8s. three per cent. consols, purchased with £180, left by *John Land*, in 1817. They have also two yearly rent-charges, viz., 30s. left by *John Sanders*, in 1729; and 40s., left by *Sir John Elwill.*

Bradford Rev John, M.A., *Vicarage*
Deacon Capt Hy. Chas., *Beacon Hill*
Morgan Miss Chtte. ‖ Stewart MrsR.
Osborne Rev Peter Mann, M.A.
Shirreff Clifford Esq., *Beacon Hill*
Rogers Thomas, blacksmith
Warren John, baker, &c

PUBLIC HOUSES.
Heart of Oak, Robt. Kitt, (joiner)
Old Black Horse, Mary Lympaney
Poltimore Arms, Charles Walters

BASKET MKRS.
Butt Christpr.
Patey John

BOOT&SHOE MKS.
Hamlyn Thos.

Lilland Wm.
Squire Wm.

COOPERS.
Southcott Robt.
Walters John

FARMERS.
AshfordJohnReynolds
Batten Rt.*butcher*
Beavis Joseph
Beavis Wm.
Besley John
Besley Wm.
Bradford Thos.
Bradford T. jun.
Clement Richd.
Greenway Jas.R.,
  Stoke Hill
Harris James
Hill Wm.
Jennings Oliver

Madge Joseph
Matthews Wm.
Muggleton Wm.
Pidsley John
Pidsley Mrs R.
Ralton Samuel
Squire Robert
Turner Mrs
Turner Wm.
Walters Charles

SHOPKEEPERS.
Bambury John
Bradford Thos.

TAILORS.
Austin John
Bambury John

POLTIMORE, a parish of scattered houses, 4 miles N.E. of Exeter, includes the small hamlet of RATSLOE, and contains 264 inhabitants, and 1430 acres of land, all the property and manor of Lord Poltimore, who resides occasionally at POLTIMORE HOUSE, a large square cemented mansion in a beautiful park, stocked with deer, and encompassed by verdant and well-wooded hills. His lordship has recently much improved both the mansion and the park, and considerably enlarged the latter. At Domesday Survey, the manor of Poltimore was held in demense by Haimerius de Arcis, but it soon afterwards passed to the Poltimores, who conveyed it in the reign of of Edward I. to Simon Lord Montacute, who sold it to Wm. Pointington, a canon of Exeter. The latter gave it to his pupil, *John*

Bampfylde, or *Baumfield*, an ancestor of its present owner. In 1641, John Bampfylde, Esq., was created a *baronet*, and the late Sir Charles Warwick Bampfylde was the fifth baronet of his family. The present *Rt. Hon. Sir George Warwick Bampfylde* was created BARON POLTIMORE in 1831, and is colonel of the North Devon Militia. He was born in 1786, and his eldest son, the *Hon. Augustus Fredk. George Warwick Bampfylde*, was born in 1837. He has another seat at Hardington Park, Somerset. Lord Goring, who had been quartered at Poltimore with 1500 horse, retired into Essex on the approach of Sir Thomas Fairfax, in October, 1645, when Poltimore House was garrisoned by the latter, with the consent of its owner. The treaty for the surrender of Exeter is said to have been opened here on the 3rd of April, 1646. Sir Coplestone Bampfylde was an active promoter of the restoration of Charles II., and was the first sheriff of Devon after the king's return. Two farms here formerly belonged to the prebendaries of *Cutton* and *Hayes*, in the small collegiate chapel which stood in Exeter Castle yard. The *Church* (St. Mary,) is an ancient cruciform structure, with a tower and six bells. It was built by John Bampfylde, who died in 1390, and gave the great bell, as appears by an inscription in the church. The *rectory*, valued in K.B. at £15. 15s. 5d., and in 1831 at £589, with that of Huxham annexed to it, is in the gift of Lord Poltimore, and incumbency of the Hon. and Rev. John Fortescue, M.A., who is also a canon of Worcester. The Rectory House is a neat cemented building, with tasteful grounds. Lady Poltimore supports a *school* here for 36 poor children. The *Almshouses* were founded and endowed for poor people, by *John Bampfylde*, in 1631, and enlarged for two additional almspeople, by the executors of *Sir R. W. Bampfylde*, who, in 1775, left for that purpose £200, now vested in £245. 7s. 11d. three per cent. reduced annuities. The original endowment consists of 4½ acres of land and two cottages, at Pinhoe, let for about £12 per annum. The rent and dividends are divided equally among the six almspeople. In 1797, *Mary Bradford* left £100, five per cent. annuities, in trust, that the yearly dividends should be distributed among the poor of Poltimore, except what was necessary for repairing the monument of her husband and daughter.

Lord Poltimore, *Poltimore House*
Fortescue Hon. & Rev John, *Rectory*
Adams Henry, blacksmith & par. clk
Capp Henry, farmer, *Cutton*
Carthew Arthur, carpenter
Franklin Thos. farmer, *Horn Hill*
Gould John, land agent, *Hayes*
Hughes Robert, gamekeeper
Pearce John, butcher, *Ratsloe*
Smith Chas. pork butcher, *Ratsloe*
Thomas Wm. carpenter, *Ratsloe*
Watts Catherine, schoolmistress
Wilcocks Thomas, sexton

REWE, a straggling village, on an eminence 5 miles N.N.E. of Exeter, has in its parish 301 souls, and 1340 acres of land, including UP EXE tything, which is in Exe valley, and in Hayridge Hundred, nearly two miles from the church, and contains 120 souls, and 370 acres. The parish is crossed by the Bristol and Exeter Railway. Before the reign of Edward III., the manor of Rew, or Rewe,

was held successively by the Villiers, Sachville, Causebeuf, Blakeford, Picot, and Tantifer families. It was afterwards held by the Chiseldons and Wadhams. The present lords of the manor are, the Earl of Ilchester and the Trustees of the late Earl of Egremont, the former having five, and the latter seven shares. They are patrons of the rectory in the same proportion; but part of the parish belongs to Sir T. D. Acland and a few smaller owners. The *Church* (St. Mary,) is a venerable structure, with a tower and five bells. It has a north transept, and a curious old screen. The *rectory*, valued in K.B. at £22. 4s. 2d., and in 1838 at £429, is enjoyed by the Rev. Henry Fox Strangways, M.A., who is also rector of West Grimstead, near Salisbury, and has here a handsome *Rectory House*, built in 1844, at the cost of £2500. The glebe is 48 acres, and the tithes were commuted in 1837 for £348 per annum. The poor have two yearly rent-charges of 20s. each, left by Emanuel and Nicholas Warren, in 1696 and 1700, out of Pale and Millhayes estates. They have also the interest of £50, left by *Joseph Steere*, in 1792. For the *Directory of Rewe and Up Exe*, see the appendix.

SOWTON, a small village and parish in the picturesque valley of the Clist rivulet, 3½ miles E. of Exeter, contains about 1360A., and 382 inhabitants, of whom 215 are in the village and tithing of CLIST SACHVILLE, which has also 71 inhabitants in Farringdon parish, on the opposite of the valley, in East Budleigh Hundred, and is sometimes called BISHOP'S CLIST, from its having been for some time the property and one of the seats of the Bishops of Exeter. John Garratt, Esq., owns most of the parish, and is lord of the manor of *Clist Sachville*, or *Bishop's Clist*, and *Sowton*, alias *Clist Fomeson*. The former was held by the Sachville family till the reign of Edw. I., when it was mortgaged to Bishop Bronscombe, who built a mansion here, and afterwards annexed the manor to the See of Exeter; but in the reign of Edward VI., it was given to the Earl of Bedford, from whom the mansion was called *Bedford House*, till the civil wars of the 17th century, when it was garrisoned and fortified by Sir Thos. Fairfax, during the blockade of Exeter. It is now called *Bishop's Court*, and is the seat and property of J. Garratt, Esq. The house is a commodious building, pleasantly situated on a commanding eminence, in a well-wooded park, on the east bank of the small river Clist, and was the seat of the late Lord Graves, who purchased the manor of the executors of Miss Beavis, in 1802. The manor of Sowton was long held by the Fomeson and Ash families, and was sold to the late Lord Graves by the heirs of Miss Salter, in 1800. The *Church* (St. Michael,) is a handsome structure of perpendicular architecture, with a tower and eight bells. It was erected on the site of the old one in 1844-5, at the cost of about £4700, and has an elegant stone pulpit, richly sculptured with figure of St. Michael, St. Paul, and the four evangelists. The east window is enriched with stained glass, and the living is a *rectory*, valued in K.B. at £11. 16s. 3d., and in 1831 at £245. The Bishop of Exeter is patron, and the Rev. Henry Sanders, M.A., is the incumbent, and has 18A. of glebe, and a neat residence. There is a small National School at Sowton, and another at *Clist Sachville*, or *Satchfield*, as it is some-

times called. The latter is connected with the parish of Clist St. Mary. Sowton has £3. 15s. yearly for schooling four children, from *Weare's Charity.* (See Clist Honiton.) The poor parishioners have three yearly doles, viz., 17s. 6d., left by Lawrence Seldon; 20s., left by John Forward, in 1699; and £4 as the interest of £100, left by various donors, and vested in the Exeter turnpike.

*Marked * are in Clist Sachville, and the others in Sowton.*

*Bambury Joseph, shopkeeper
*Burge Jas. roper||Batty Wm. sexton
*Burgoin Jas. steward and vict. Cat and Fiddle
*Cook John, blacksmith
*Coward John, tailor
*Dennis John, corn miller
Dunnett Mary, schoolmistress
Fogden Charles, gamekeeper
*Franklin Richd. shoemaker
*Garratt John, Esq. *Bishop's Court*
*Hayward Miss E. || Pring J. school
*Horn Hy. manager of brick & tile yd

*Langford Wm. wheelwright
*Manning Wm. blacksmith
Maunder Isaac, baker and vict. Half Moon
Sanders Rev Henry, M.A. *Rectory*
Shute John, shopkeeper
*Skinner Thos., *National schoolmr*
*Simonds Mr Thos.||Teed Miss E.
*Snell Geo. baker || Treel J. gardener
*Taylor John, maltster & vict. Maltsters' Arms

FARMERS.

*Dennis Wm.	Pidsley Richd.
Froom Robert	Pidsley Rd. jun
*Parsons Henry	Ware Thomas

SPREYTON is a village with several neat houses, on a lofty eminence, about 8 miles E. by N. of Okehampton, and 17 miles W. by N. of Exeter. Its parish contains 3600 acres of land, and 404 inhabitants. The manor was held, for a long period, by the Talbots, whose heiress carried it in marriage to the Kelly family in the reign of Henry VI. It was sold to various freeholders during the last century, and now belongs to Messrs. W. H. Battishull, W. C. Cann, G. L. Gowin, Jno. Norris, Geo. Cann, the Rev. G. Hole, the Rev. R. Holland, and a few smaller owners. *Fuidge House*, the seat of J. Norris, Esq., is a neat cemented structure, and is pleasantly situated, as also is *Barton*, the seat of W. H. Battishull, Esq. The *Church* (St. Michael,) is a plain structure, with a handsome tower, containing five bells, and commanding extensive views in which 30 parish churches are seen. The font is of granite, with some rude figures carved upon it. The screen was removed about 70 years ago, except a few fragments in the clerk's seat. The chancel is of later date than the nave and aisles, and has upon its roof a long Latin inscription, recording that it was rebuilt by Richd. Talbot, in 1451. The church is approached by an avenue of fine trees, and near the entrance is a venerable oak, the decaying trunk of which measures 40 feet in girth at the bottom. The benefice is a discharged *vicarage*, valued in K.B. at £10. 5s. 8d., and in 1831 at £135. The Rev. Richd. Holland, M.A., is patron and incumbent, and has held the living since 1802. He has a good residence, and 82A. of glebe. The small tithes were commuted in 1844 for £117. 10s. per annum, but the great tithes belong to the land owners, and were formerly appropriated to Tavistock Abbey. The poor parishioners have £3 a year, as the rent of a fourth part of Bush tenement, purchased with £45, given by unknown donors. They have also two annuities of 20s. each, left by Thos. Hoare and John Cann, but that left by the latter ceases in 1857.

Battishull Wm. Harrington, Esq. *Barton*
Battishull John, gent. *Wick*
Battishull John, surgeon
Cann Wm. C. gent. *Northbeer*
Dalve Henry, stone mason
Gowin Geo. Lambert, Esq.
Harvey John, carpenter
Holland Rev Richd., M.A. *Vicarage*
Honeychurch Wm. shopr. & carrier
Lavis Edward, schoolmaster
Martin Wm. butcher and vict. White Hart

Middlewick Joshua, shoemaker
Newton John, wheelgt. & My. shopr
Norris John, Esq. *Fuidge House*
Northcott Richd. sexton, &c.

BLACKSMITHS.
Hill Samuel
Vigers Wm.

FARMERS.
Cole John
Cole Wm.
Jackman Thos.
Martin Simon
Norris John, jun

Powlesland Saml.
Powlesland Wm.
Shopland Jas.
Vanstone John
Weeks John

TAILORS.
Honeychurch Ts.
Vigers Saml.

STOKE-CANON, a small village near the confluence of the rivers Exe and Culm, and near the Bristol and Exeter Railway, 4 miles N.E. by N. of Exeter, has in its parish 490 souls, and 1217 acres of land. The *manor* was given by King Athelstan to Exeter Cathedral, and still belongs to the Dean and Chapter, who also own a great part of the soil, and are appropriators of the tithes and patrons of the *perpetual curacy*, valued in 1831 at ·£221, and now enjoyed by the Rev. Wm. T. N. Penoyre, for whom the Rev. T. H. Knight, of Exeter, officiates. The *Church* (St. Mary,) was rebuilt about 1836, except the tower, at the cost of £1000. The interior is neatly fitted up, and the tower has a clock and four bells. In April, 1847, a hot cinder, blown from one of the railway engines, ignited the thatched roof of a row of cottages, and the fire spread till 24 dwellings, including the Parsonage House, were destroyed. The damage was about £10,000, half of which was recovered from the Railway Company. Six double cottages, in the Swiss style, were erected in 1848. A new Parsonage House and school are about to be built. R. Barnes, Esq., and several free and copy holders have estates in the parish. *Oakey* or *Oakhay*, now the residence of Mr. Chas. Cole, was long a seat of the Rodd family, and is held under the Dean and chapter by M. Parker, Esq. The poor parishioners have about £5. 15s. per annum for distribution in linen from *Grace Bampfylde's Charity*. (See Pinhoe.) They have also three other yearly doles, viz., 21s., left by *Richard Clarke*, in 1635, out of Bridwell estate; 40s. left by *Emanuel and Nicholas Warren*, out of land at Rewe; and 39s. 2d. from £65. 7s. 9d. three per cent. stock, purchased with £50, left by *J. D. Worthy*, in 1797.

Bond Rev John, M.A. rector of *Romansleigh*, &c.
Bonner Wm. baker
Bucknell Isaac, maltster & hop mert
Carnell Samuel, vict. King's Arms
Chamberlain Sarah, butcher
Cragg Eliz. boarding school
Crook Wm. tailor
Dewdney John, beerseller
Dewdney Wm. & Richd. paper mkrs
Elmore John, flax grower & butcher
Melhuish Rev Richard
Penoyre Rev Wm. Timy. Napleton, M.A. incumbent

Staddon Chas. shoemkr. & par. clk
Trimlett Wm. blacksmith
Webber Thos. wheelgt. and smith

FARMERS.
Ramsey Wm.
Barber Henry, *Bennett's*
Cole Chas., *Oakey*
Greenslade Pp.
Hodge John
Hunt John
Hill Chpr.

SHOEMAKERS.
Bonner Thos.
Greenway Thos.
Price Wm.

SHOPKEEPERS.
Frost Jno., *Post Office*
Richards John
Shildon John

STOKEINTEIGNHEAD, or *Stoke-in-Teign-head*, is a small village in a picturesque dell, about half a mile from the sea coast, one mile south of the estuary of Teign, and 4 miles E. of Newton Abbot. Its parish is one of the detached members of Wonford Hundred, and contains about 620 inhabitants, and 2250 acres of land, including the hamlets of *Gabwell* and *Rocombe*, and also part of *Ringmore*, a suburb of *Shaldon*, on the south side of the Teign, opposite the town of Teignmouth. (See page 197.) Saml. Trehawke Kekewich, Esq., is lord of the *manor*, formerly held by the Fitzpayne, Stowford, Speccot, Trehawke, and other families. Part of the parish belongs to the Trustees of the late Wm. Flamank, Elias Blackaller, J. and T. Rendell, Wm. Hearder, and several smaller proprietors. The farm, called *Teign-Harvey*, belongs to Elize Hele's Charity, Exeter. The *Church* (St. Andrew,) has a tower and four bells, and was repewed about 20 years ago. The *rectory*, valued in K.B. at £36. 15s. 10d., and in 1831 at £529, is in the patronage of the Bishop of Exeter, and incumbency of the Rev. J. N. Gould, B.A., who has nearly 38 acres of glebe and a commodious residence, on a pleasant acclivity, with tasteful grounds, which have lately been much improved. The tithes were commuted in 1842 for £429 per annum. Here is a *National School*, established in 1829. The *Church House* is let for about £10 a year, which is applied with the church rates. In 1741, *Gregory Andrews* left 30s. a year for schooling poor children, and for distributions of bread, &c. This annuity has been changed for another of the same amount, charged by the *Rev. Aaron Neck* on two meadows called Rocombe Gardens, which he also charged with £6. 10s. per annum for schooling poor children.

Marked + are in Ringmore; § in Rocombe; ‡ in Gabwell; and the rest in Stokeinteignhead village, or where specified.

Bartlett Hy. gent. || Millman Mr
Coryton Capt. Hy., *Platway House*
Fowler Jph. miller, *Charlycombe*
Gibbings John, wheelwright
Gould Rev John Nutcombe, B.A. *Rectory*
Hearder Wm. gent. *Rocombe*
+Hore Wm. & Mrs. *National School*
+Langley Wm. T. solicitor and agent to Globe Fire and Life Office
May Mr John and Mr Wm.
Nichols Geo. par. clk. & Jas. sexton
Pitts James, blacksmith
+Stockdale Wm. gent || Parsons Mrs
Webber Mrs Christiana
Winsborrow Wm. baker and vict. *Church House*

BOOT & SHOE MRS.
Pepperill Roger
Weymouth Wm.

BUTCHERS.
Adams Wm.
Prowse Richd.

FARMERS.
(* *are owners.*)
Adams Wm.
*Ager Edward
*Blackaller Elias, *Maidencombe*
Bond George
Bond Geo. jun.
Buckingham Ncs.

+Commins Rd.
Devonshire Saml.
+Hex Samuel
§Mitchelmore W.
Nichols Robert
§Nichols Wm.
*Rendell John
*‡Rendell Thos.
‡Tuckett Wm.
§Whiteaway Edw.
Whiteaway John, *Teign-Harvey*
+Wills Chas.
*‡Wills Joseph

TAWTON (SOUTH) is a compact village, pleasantly situated on the banks of the small river Taw, at the north end of Dartmoor Forest, four miles E. by S. of Okehampton, and 18½ miles W. of Exeter. Its parish contains 1871 inhabitants, and 6097½ acres of land, including 86A. of woods, 79A. of orchards, and 1574A. of open pasture and forest. It comprises the hamlets of *Itton, Tawgreen,*

Whyddon Down, Gooseford Week, Fulford, Ramsley, Dishcombe, and *South-Zeal*, extending from two miles S. to three N. by E. of the church. The parish also comprises many scattered farm-houses, &c., and its surface is picturesquely broken into hill and dale, rising boldly on the south-west to the heights of Dartmoor, where the Taw and other rivulets have their sources. H. A. Hoare, Esq., is the lord of the manor of *Black-hall ;* G. S. Fursdon, Esq., is lord of South-Zeal, and Wm. Damarel, Esq., is lord of Itton manor; but here are several smaller manors and estates, belonging to various owners. OXENHAM, the property and occasional seat of H. A. Hoare, Esq., belonged to the *Oxenham family* from the reign of Henry III. till 1814. This family resided here for many generations, and is remarkable for the *tradition of a bird,* which is said to have appeared to many of its members previously to their death. SOUTH-ZEAL is a straggling village, on the high road, half a mile S.E. of the church, and is described as a borough in ancient records, and as having a market and two fairs, granted in 1298 by Robt. de Tony, then lord of the manor. It has still a *cattle fair* on the Tuesday in the week after the festival of St. Thomas-a-Becket, (July 7th.) Its ancient chapel has been long used as a *school,* where 60 children are educated at the expense of H. A. Hoare, Esq., who has greatly improved the condition of the poor parishioners. *Itton,* or *Ilton Moor,* was enclosed in 1849. The *Parish Church* (St. Andrew,) is a large antique structure, with a tower and six bells. Among its ancient monuments is the effigy of a warrior in armour, supposed to represent one of the Wike, or Weeks family, who were long seated at North Wick. The *vicarage,* valued in K.B. at £10, and in 1831 at £150, is in the patronage of the Dean and Canons of Windsor, and incumbency of the Rev. Thomas Birkett. The former are also appropriators of the great tithes, now leased to H. A. Hoare, Esq. The vicar has a neat thatched residence, and 34A 3R. 21P of glebe. The tithes were commuted in 1844. The parish has three *Almshouses* for poor widows, founded by *Robert Burgoyne,* in 1656, and endowed with 1½A. of land, worth £5 a year. The poor parishioners have the following *yearly doles,*—30s. left by *Oliver Lang,* in 1654, out of Brushcombe close; about £15 from *John Northmore's Charity,* as noticed with Okehampton ; £5 left by *Wm. Oxenham,* out of Higher Cullaford estate; 5s. left by *John Dunning,* out of Scurhill's estate; and about £12 from 9½A. of land, called Derracombe field, purchased in 1730, with £80 given by *Wm. Battishull, Edw. Northmore,* and other donors.

Marked 1 are at Eastwick, 2 Dish-combe, 3 Itton, 4 Ramsley, 5 SOUTH-ZEAL, 6 Taw-Green, 7 North-Wick, 8 Whyddon Down, and the rest in SOUTH TAWTON village, or where specified.

5 Arscott Wm. butcher
Birkett Rev. Thomas, *Vicarage*
5 Crocker John, parish clerk
5 Crocker Thomas, mason

Hoare Hy. Arthur, Esq., *Oxenham Hs*
5 Perkins Wm. rope & twine maker
8 Powlesland John, beerhouse
2 Wannacott Geo. nurseryman
Watts Mr William
5 Yeo Jas. schoolmr. & asst. overseer

PUBLIC-HOUSES.

5 King's Arms, Wm. Knapman, *mltsr*
5 Lamb Inn, James Moore
5 London Inn, Wm. Pearce

5 Oxenham Arms, James Drew
Seven Stars, John Drew
5 Victoria, John Arscott
FARMERS. (* *are Owners.*)
7*Arnold Jno. || Ash Robert
3 Baker John || 7 Borne John
6*Brailey Wm. || 6 Cann Mark
2*Cann George || *Cann Wm.
2*Cann Philip || 2 Counter Joseph
Carnell Richard || Cooper Henry
5*Counter Wm. || Counter Robert
Cooper Wm. || *Curson Robert
5*Curson Wm. || 5 Curson Val.
*Cumming Robert, *Lovaton*
*Drew John || 2 Dunning Richard
*Fewins Mary, *Addiscott*
6*Finch John || Finch Charles
5 Finch Wm. || Gilland Richard
Hearn Samuel || 2 Hole Jane
8 Hole Wm. || 5 Jopa George
*Knapman Arthur, *Well*
*Knapman Dewes and George
5*Knapman Wm. and John
*Lee Mary || Lock Grace
Lethbridge Richard || Lethbridge Ts.
Merton Joseph, *Gooseford*
8 Moore Andw. || 5 Moore James
1*Moore John || 1*Moore Smn.
*Moore Wm., *Gooseford*

6 Patterson Jph. || Sampson Mary
Powlesland Geo. || Powlesland John
Powlesland Thos. || 3 Thorne Thos.
Soper Henry, *Black-hall*
Stoneman Chpr., *Wickington*
5*Wannacott Faithful

CORN MILLERS.
Bailey Wm., *Taw-green Mill*
Browning Wm., *Frog Mills*
2 Fewins Wm., *Tawton Mills*

BLACKSMITHS.
5 Beer John
8 Gove James
5 Finch Isaac
8 Finch John
Knapman Wm.

CARPENTERS.
5 Glanvill Thos.
5 Glanvill T. jun.
5 Tucker Eml. &
wheelwright

HUCKSTERS
And Carriers.
5 Cooper James
5 Powlesland Geo.
Westaway Geo.

SHOEMAKERS.
5 Counter Saml.
5 Jopa Andrew
5 Oudas Wm.

SHOPKEEPERS.
Curson Valantine
Finch Charles
5 Perkins Hugh
5 Wedlock Arthur

TAILORS.
5 Crocker Eml.
5 Edicott Thos.
POST from Exeter
& Okehampton
daily, and *Car-*
riers Tu. & Sat.
The *Post-Office*
is at South-Zeal

TEDBURN ST. MARY, a pleasant village on the Okehampton road, 7½ miles W. by N. of Exeter, has in its parish 867 souls and 4433 acres of land, generally fertile, and hilly. It has a *cattle fair*, on the Monday before Michaelmas day, and includes the hamlet of *Upcott*, and many scattered farm-houses. At Domesday Survey, *Tedbourne* (Teteborne) was held by Ralph de Pomerai, under Baldwin de Sap. It is now held by John Hippesley, Esq. The manors of *Hackworthy* and *Melhuish* were formerly held by families of their own names, and now belong to Baldwin Fulford, Esq., of *Fulford House*, which is noticed with Dunsford, at page 192. John Abbot, Esq., and several smaller owners have estates in the parish. The *Church* is an ancient structure, with a tower and six bells; and the *rectory*, valued in K.B. at £18. 6s. 3d., and in 1831 at £319, is in the patronage and incumbency of the Rev. Charles Burne, M.A., who has 38¼A. of glebe, and a good residence, finely embowered in wood. The tithes were commuted in 1838 for £410 per annum. For the repairs of the church, seven cottages and two houses, &c., have been vested with feoffees from an early period, and are now let for about £20 a year. Another house, vested in the same trust, is occupied by paupers. The poor parishioners have £10 a year, left by *Eliz. Tuckfield.* (See Crediton.) They have also the following small annuities, viz., £1. 11s. 4d. left by *Sir John Acland;* 10s. left by *Paul Triggs;* 10s. left by *James Lake;* 20s. left by *Wm. Strong;* and 24s. as interest of £30, given by Sir G. Chudleigh,

Agnes Westcott, and John Williams.   Here are *National Schools*
for both sexes.

Burne Rev. Chas. M.A., *rector*
Fulford B. Esq., *Fulford House*
Lake Wm. vict., King's Arms
Lambert Miss Mary
Langdon Jas. school & post master
Marchant Danl. vict., Red Lion
Orchard Wm. thatcher
Priston Andrew, saddler
Priston Wm. schoolmaster
Taverner Thomas, butcher
Trigg John, parish clerk
    FARMERS. (* *are at Hackworthy*.)
Arscott Wm., Great Torwood
Bastow John || *Batten John
Batten Thomas || Blandsford Wm.
Browning John || Cole John
Guscott John || Goss Thomas
Henley John, *Melhuish*
Hodge George, sen., *Huish*
Hodge George, jun., *Upcott*
Holman Thomas || Kelly Edward
Kemble James || Kemble Samuel
Lambert Mary || Langdon James
Ledger George || Lethbridge Hugh
May Thos. Taverner, *Duxhay*
May Wm. || Parr Wm.

Priston Henry, *Upcott*
Pike Geo. (& *auctioneer*,) South hill
Priston Samuel || Priston Wm.
Saffin Thomas, *Higher Town*
*Stanbury John || Stoneman John
Taverner John || Twiggs John
Twiggs Wm. || Wills Wm.
Whidburn Wm., *Haynse's*

BEERHOUSES.
Belworthy   John
    (& butcher)
Hodge Samuel
Linscott   George
    (& butcher)
BOOT & SHOEMKRS.
Marchant Wm.
Parr John
Taverner Thos.
BRICKLAYERS.
Davey Richard
Phillips John
BLACKSMITHS.
Lake John
Marchant John
CARPENTERS.
Baxter James

Beer Nathan
Laskey John
Lethbridge J.
Milford George
Orchard Thos.
Pook Henry
Priston John
SHOPKEEPERS.
Marchant Daniel
Wills Wm.
TAILORS.
Milford John
Morrish Wm.
Parsons Richard
POST-OFFICE.
Letters via Exeter
daily

ST. THOMAS-THE-APOSTLE is a parish forming a suburb of
Exeter, and partly within the Parliamentary limits of that city.
See pages 87, 117, and 122.

THROWLEIGH, or THROWLEY, is a small village, near a
rivulet at the foot of the north-eastern declivities of Dartmoor, 6½
miles E.S.E. of Okehampton, and 3 miles S.E. of South-Zeal. Its
parish contains 445 souls, and 1943A. 3R. 12P. of land, including
several farms, &c., bearing different names.   Mr. John Dunning is
lord of the manor of Throwleigh, but the greater part of the parish
belongs to R. D. Gay, Richard Herbert, John Underhill, the Rev.
A. Whipham, and several other freeholders.   The manor belonged
at an early period to the Ferrers, and after passing to many other
families, it was dismembered.   The *Church* is a stone fabric, with
a tower and five bells, and the living is a *rectory*, valued in K.B. at
£19. 6s. 10½d., and in 1831 at £222, in the patronage of the Lord
Chancellor.   The Rev. Wm. Herman Schwabe is the incumbent,
but is now abroad as a missionary.   The glebe is 49A. 3P., and the
tithes were commuted in 1840 for £178 per annum.   At *Providence Place*, on the south side of the parish, is a small chapel belonging to the *Bible Christians*, built in 1839, at the cost of about
£140, and having a small burial ground.   A house and garden have
been vested from an early period for the use of the church, and are
let for about £5. 10s. per annum.   The churchwardens have also
two annuities of 5s. each, left by John Dunning, and an unknown
donor.   The latter also left 5s. a year for the poor.

Brimblecombe Richard, carpenter
Coneybeer Rev. Wm. (Bible Chtn.)
Dodd Thomas, tailor
Endicott Jph. tailor & par. clerk
Gay Rd. Dunning, gent., *Providence pl*
Gidley George, cooper
Gidley George, shoemaker
Gidley Gustavus, vict., New Inn
Haggart James, thatcher & sexton
Hill Wm. schoolmaster
Osborn Daniel, vict., Star Inn
Whiddon Rev. Samuel, M.A. *curate*
BLACKSMITHS—Jas. Curson, Thos.
  Hill, and Wm. Murch
  FARMERS. (* *are Owners.*)
*Aysh John || Dicker John

*Coombe Wm. *corn miller*
*Dunning James, *Throwleigh*
*Dunning John, *Wonson*
*Dunning Wm., *Way*
Easterbrook John, *Row*
Endicott George, *Way*
Endicott John, *Murchington*
French George, *Langstone*
*Gay John Dunning, *Forder*
Gidley George, Royal Oak
*Gidley Richard, *Murchington*
Herbert Philip, *Walland Hill*
Lemon John, *Murchington*
*Moore Wm., *Langstone*
POST via South-Zeal and Chagford.

TOPSHAM is a small ancient market town, sea port, and fishing station, within the jurisdiction of the Port of Exeter, pleasantly situated about 4 miles S.E. of Exeter, on the east bank of the river Exe, which here receives the small river Clist, and suddenly expands into an estuary, about a mile broad and six in length, extending southward to the English Channel, at Exmouth. Its parish contains 3733 inhabitants and 1528A. 2P. of land, including the straggling village and chapelry district of COUNTESS-WEIR, or WEAR, on the east bank of the Exe, from 1 to 2 miles N.W. of the town. Topsham consists chiefly of one long street, extending north and south, and several short ones running east and west to the Exe and the Clist, which unite at the south end of the town, which projects into the broad estuary on the point of land called the Strand, whence the tides are seen rolling in majestic grandeur between a succession of the richest and most varied scenery, having the woods and Castle of Powderham on the west, and the pleasant village of Lympstone and many gentlemen's seats on the east. At the Strand the water flows near the houses, and the prospect is highly interesting, but a still more extensive view is commanded from the high cliff in the centre of the town, on which the church stands, and which is occupied as the churchyard. Before the construction of Exeter Ship Canal, and for some time afterwards, the business done at Topsham was very great, as noticed at page 64, where we have already noticed the erection of *Countess-Weir* across the bed of the Exe, and the long continued dispute between the Corporation of Exeter and the former lords of the manor of Topsham. Exeter Ship Canal now falls into the estuary by a spacious lock on the opposite side, at *Turf*, near the South Devon Railway ; but still Topsham enjoys a share of the coasting trade, and its merchants import timber and other produce from America and the Baltic. The quays and wharfs are spacious, and here are bonded warehouses for all foreign goods, except wine and spirits, East India goods, and tobacco. Here are three ship and boat building yards, a large paper mill, and several roperies and chain cable manufactories, &c. Topsham seemed doomed to decay, after the erection of the ship canal to Exeter, for which city it had previously been the shipping port. After languishing for a long

period a new spirit came over it a few years ago, and the town and its trade and commerce have recently been much improved. Many new buildings have sprung up in the town and neighbourhood, many of the shops and old dwellings have been much improved, and it is becoming a favourite place of resort for the invalid, and the care-worn citizen, seeking health or retirement. It has two good inns, several commodious taverns, many well stocked shops, and eleven fishing boats, employing about 100 men and boys in catching herrings, whitings, sprats, &c. Sprats are plentiful in the estuary, and no less than 100 tons of them were caught here from the 6th to the 13th of Nov. 1848. The *market*, held every Saturday, is well supplied with provisions, and here is a *fair*, for cattle, &c., on the Thursday after July 18th. Edward I. granted a charter for a market to Hugh de Courtenay Earl of Devon; and also confirmed a fair for three days at the festival of St. Margaret, which had been granted by Henry III., in 1257, to Baldwin de Redvers, the 8th Earl. The *manor* of Topsham was part of the ancient demesne of the Crown, and was held for a long period by the Earls of Devon. (See p. 61.) It was afterwards held by the De Courcy family, but the parish now belongs to various freeholders, some of whom have pleasant seats here. The fee-farm rent is vested in A. H. Hamilton, Esq., of the *Retreat*, a neat cemented villa, with tasteful grounds, formerly the residence of his late uncle, Sir Alex. Hamilton, Kt. The manor of *Weir Park*, or *Wear*, was anciently called Heneaton, Hineton, or Honiton Siege, and obtained its present name from the weir which was constructed by the Countess of Devon, as already noticed, and from which the hamlet is called *Countess Weir*. It belonged successively to the Bukenton, Bathonia, Medsted, and Holland families. It was a seat of a younger branch of the Hollands till the latter part of the 17th century. It was purchased in 1760, of the Rodds, by the Spicers, of Exeter, who sold it in 1804, to the late gallant admiral *Sir John Thomas Duckworth*, who greatly improved his handsome residence, called WEIR HOUSE, and was created a baronet in 1813. He died in 1817, and was succeeded by his son, the present *Sir John Thos. Buller Duckworth, Bart., M.P.*, one of the parliamentary representatives of the city of Exeter. The mansion stands on an eminence commanding delightful views, and contains a fine bust of the late Admiral. The ruins of the old seat of the Hollands are to be seen about a mile from the present mansion. The other principal proprietors who have seats in the parish are J. B. Cresswell, Esq., *Newcourt House;* Henry Seymour, Esq., of *Northbrook House*; G. F. Travers, Esq., of *Fairfield Lodge;* and Mrs. Mitchell, of *Newport House*. When Exeter was besieged by the King's forces in 1643, the Earl of Warwick, the parliamentary admiral, is said to have battered down a fort at Topsham, and killed 70 or 80 men. Sir Thomas Fairfax, with the parliamentary army, was quartered here in October, 1645. (See page 57.) The *Parish Church* (St. Margaret,) stands on the cliff overlooking the Exe, and is an old structure, containing two handsome monuments by Chantrey. One of them is in memory of the late Admiral Sir J. T. Duckworth, Bart., G.C.B. The bust on

this monument is an excellent likeness of the deceased, and below is a representation, in bas relief, of the naval engagement in which the brave admiral defeated the French fleet, at St. Domingo. The other is in memory of the Admiral's son, Colonel George Duckworth, who fell at the battle of Albuera, in 1811. The Dean and Chapter of Exeter are appropriators of the tithes and patrons of the *perpetual curacy*, which is in their jurisdiction, and was valued in 1831 at £227. The Rev. Henry Thorp, M.A., is the incumbent. The glebe comprises 36 acres and several houses, but the Parsonage is a mean building not occupied by the incumbent. Several tenements, let for £10. 15s., have been long vested for the repairs of the church. The appropriate tithes were commuted in 1842 for £445 per annum. *Countess Weir* hamlet, forming the north side of the parish of Topsham, was constituted a *chapelry district* by Order in Council, in 1844, under the provisions of an act of the 59th of George III. Its *Chapel* (St. Luke,) was built and endowed by subscription in 1837-'8. The building cost about £900, and the sum of £1500 was invested in the funds as the endowment, which was augmented, in 1840, with £200 of Queen Anne's Bounty, £100 given by the Dean and Chapter of Exeter, and £200 given by the Rev. Chas. Burne, B.C.L., who was the first incumbent, and gave £300 towards the foundation of the chapel. The benefice is a perpetual curacy, and was further endowed in 1846, by the appropriators, with £30 out of tithes of the parish. It is now enjoyed by the Rev. Robert Bartholomew, and is in the patronage of the incumbent of Topsham. The chapel is a plain neat building, with a cupola and one bell, and has 340 sittings, all free, except a few private pews, the rents of which are applied in aid of the clerk's and organist's salaries.

In Topsham are three chapels, one of which is an old *Presbyterian Meeting House*, now belonging to Unitarians. The *Independent Chapel*, in Victoria place, was erected in 1838-'9, in lieu of the old chapel, in High street, at the cost of about £1100. The *Wesleyan Chapel* is a small building, erected in 1818, at the cost of about £400. The Unitarian minister has about £10 year from several tenements left by John Greenfield, in 1734. The NATIONAL SCHOOL, in Monmouth street, is attended by about 150 children, of whom about 20 are taught entirely free, in consideration of a legacy of £300 left by *Joseph Somaster*, in 1767, and several small benefactions. The endowment arising from these sources now consists of Rushmore field, let for £12, and the dividends of £640 three per cent. consols. There is also a National School at Countess Weir. *Elliott's Free School*, for 13 poor children, was founded in 1768, by Saml. Elliott, who left £400 for that purpose, and the yearly sum of £1.11s. 6d., to the minister of the Presbyterian Chapel, for preaching two sermons on education. The *Infant School*, connected with the Independent Chapel, but open to all denominations, was established in 1847. *John Watkins*, about 1600, left for the poor of Topsham a house in Exeter, now the King's Head Inn. It is worth about £60 a year, but was let in 1796, for 99 years, at £12 per annum, in consideration of a fine of £80, which was laid out in the purchase of £150 four per cent. stock. The rent and dividends are divided

among the poor parishioners, at Christmas. In 1636, *John Shere* left three houses in trust to pay £4 yearly to the perpetual curate, and to divide the residue of the clear rents among the poor. They are now let for about £40 per annum. For apprenticing poor children, *Ann Collier*, in 1777, left £500 three per cent. consols. To this stock £25 was added in 1801, by gift of Mr. S. Dorrington. For distribution in bread the poor parishioners have the interest of £100 left by *Wm. Kennaway*, in 1792; the dividends of £83. 1s. 8d. three per cent. consols, left by *Wm. Short*, in 1801; and a yearly rent charge of £4 left by *Wm. Townson*, in 1810, out of several houses. Among the eminent men who were born at Topsham, are *Capt. Burgess, R.N.*, who was killed at the battle of Camperdown, and Sir Wm. W. Follett, the late Attorney General. In memory of the former there is a monument in St. Paul's Cathedral, erected at the national expense. Under the port of Exeter, a *custom house officer* and six *river pilots* are stationed here.

In the following DIRECTORY OF TOPSHAM, *those marked * are at* COUNTESS WEIR; 2, *in Fore street;* 3, *High street;* 4, *Monmouth street;* 5, *at the Quay;* 6, *in Passage lane;* 7, *in Shapter street;* 8, *on the Strand; and* 9, *in White street.*

The POST-OFFICE is at the Globe Inn. Letters are despatched, *via* Exeter, at 10½ mng. and 7½ evening. There is a sub-post-office at Wm. Ford's, Countess Weir.

Adams Mrs Elizabeth, Fore street
*Bartholomew Rev Robt., B.A., incbt
2 Bonkern John, china & glass dlr
3 Bowden Misses Eliz. and Mary
Bradley Mr Wm., Mount House
Brand Mr Nicholas, Broadway House
Breakspear Mrs Eliz., High street
Bristow Rev Jph. B. (Unitn.) Vic. pl
Brown John, parish clerk, Tract, &c. Depôt, High street
Carrington Mrs Eliz., Monmouth st
2 Carlile Wm. tax collector
7 Carter Lieut. Thos. Gilbert, R.N.
Clarke Miss Barbara, High street
Cocke Rev Fdk. and Mrs, Bridge hill
Cresswell John Bowden, Esq. *Newcourt House*
Cridland Rd., sexton, Church yard
Davy Francis, iron merchant, &c.
*Davy Robt. and Samuel, merchants
8 Dewdney Wm. Sweetland, gent.
Drew Mrs Hannah, Grove House
*Duckworth Sir John Thos. Buller, Bart., M.P., *Weir House*
3 Eales Mrs Ann, High street
*Englefield James, butler
Fletcher Rev Richard, (Indpt.) Rose Cottage, Victoria place
8 Foster Mr Wm. || 2 Francis Mrs
3 Gale Geo. sen., income tax collector
2 Gale Geo. wine and spirit mercht
Goodrich Mrs Sarah, Fore street
Hamilton Alx. Hamilton, Esq., *Retreat*
Hannaford Mrs Elizabeth, Strand
*Harris Chas. paper manfr. *Countess Weir Mills*
2 Hemer Mrs Fras. || 3 Hill Mrs G.
4 Hewson Capt. George, R.N.
2 Hodder Samuel, tallow chandler
6 Holman John, sen., surveyor to Lloyd's, and sec. of Exeter Shipping Company
Hooper Isaac, gent. Victoria place
2 Hoare Mrs Sar. || 3 Hoskins Miss
Hoskins Capt. Saml., R.N., *Strand*
Hurdle Mrs Mary, High street
Kemp Mr Edw. Lewis, Strand
4 Lambert Lieut. Charles, R.N.
Lang Mr Wm., Upper Shapter street
Langworthy Lieut. Jno., R.N., Strand
Lewin Lieut. Elisha, R.N., Strand
Lodge Mrs Judith, Strand
*McAdam Cphr., Esq., (road surveyor,) *Mount Weir House*
Mitchell Mrs My., *Newport House*
8 Owen Mr Thos. || 7 Markwell **Mrs**
8 Paine Mr Thos. || 5 Parker Mrs
Parkhouse John, cooper, High street
8 Paul Henry, traveller
4 Peters Misses Sarah and Lucinda

3 Plumb Curtis, gent. || Pine Mrs S.
3 PopeJno.Woodford, solr.(&Exeter)
8 Popham Mr Thos. || Rodd Mr T.
8 Pyle Rev Saml., M.A., asst. curate
7 Quarry Mrs Mary Ann
Ross Francis Wm. L., gent. High st
Row John, town crier, Fore street
8 Salmon Miss || 4 Salisbury Mrs J.
Seymour Hy., Esq. *Northbrook Hs*
7 Shepherd Mr Sml.||*Smart Jno. gent
Skinner John, wharfinger, Quay
4 Southcott Edward, relieving officer
Stephens Wm. saddler, High street
Stevens James, gent. Shapter street
Sweeting Rd. inland revenue officer
Thorn Wm. carrier, High street
8 Thorp Rev Hy., M.A., incumbent
Thorp Ths.R.gent.|| *Templeton Jno.
*TraversGeo.Fras.gent.*Fairfld.Lodge*
Troake Hy. accountant, High street
8 Trout Miss My. & Tucker Mrs Ann
Wallis Robt. private tutor, Strand
Wilcocks Mrs, Upper Shapter street
6 Willicott Edward, clerk
8 Wright Capt. Philip, R.N.

FIRE AND LIFE OFFICE AGENTS.
Atlas, Henry Troake, High street
Western Life, Wm. Carlile, High st
Widows' Life, John Ford, High st

INNS AND TAVERNS.
Bridge Inn, Philip Pyle, Bridge hill
Commercial, Wm. Parr, High street
*Countess Weir Inn, (empty)
*Country House, Wm. Ford, (post)
Globe Hotel, Mrs Harrison, (post office,) Fore street
4 Duke of Monmouth, George Henry P. Westcott
Half Moon, (empty,) High street
7 King's Head, John Please
8 Lighter Inn, Thos. Stancombe
Lord Nelson, Jas. Snell, High street
6 Passage House, Charles Hall
Salutation, Wm. Lake, Fore-street
Ship, Susan Gullock, Quay
Steam Packet, John Ellis, Quay

ACADEMIES.
(§ *Boarding, and*
+*National Schls.*)
8 Barrett Eliz.
+Boult Julia
2 Fare Wm.
4+Halfyard Hy.
2 Hart Mary
§Hill Ann,Vic. pl

8§Hookins Hy.
*+Hooper John
2 §Walters Hart. and Louisa
WhiteMy. (*Infnt*)
Willicott Thomas (*Charity*)Vic.p
BAKERS, &c.
2 Ford John

7 Giles James
3 Melhuish Wm.
5 Mugford Wm.
2 OsbornSaml.(& confectioner)
2 Pridham John
4SalisburyJno.H.
2 ScobleW.&Geo.
3 Toogood Hy.
3 Wilcocks John
BASKET MAKERS.
3 Bass Samuel
9 Crocker Thos.
3 Mann Thos.
BEERHOUSES.
3 Heales John
9 Pearce Henry
*Potter Robert
BLACKSMITHS.
Markd §areChain Mkrs.&Shipsmths
Harris John
Harris Wm.
6 § Holman and Walters
5§Jackson Hy.
8§LockThos.&Rd
5§Moore Ananias
3 Tapper John
6§Toby Samuel
3 Westcott Jph.
BOOKSELLERS,&c
2 Ford John
2 Pope George
BOOT&SHOE MKRS
2 Burgess Rd.
3 Francis Edwd.
3 Francis Wm.
*Hooper John
2 Hooper Wm.
2 Marks Wm.
4 Powell John
8 Redman Wm.
9 Rich Edward
2 Swain Robert
3 Underhill Wm.
2 Willicott Edwd.
BRICKLAYERS.
Carlile Edward
2 Carlile Wm.
4 Harswell Hy.
4 Havill Wm. Hy.
*Wills & Mitchell (and masons)

BUTCHERS.
2 Hayward John
3 Toogood Hy.
2 Tozer Richard
2 Walling Samp.
2 Walters Henry
2 Walters Thos.
CARPENTERS.
3 Boutcher John
3 Clapp George
2 Clapp Wm.
*Cloff Wm.
5 Ford Nelson
2 Francis John
2 Mitchell Ezekl.
3 Rowe John
4 Stamp Edw.
*Ugler Robert
COAL MERTS.
2 Bussell Robert
*Davy and Son
5 Gullock Susan
3 Harvey Thos.
3 Hurdle George
4 Periam Gilbert
DRUGGISTS.
2 Trevor Edwin
2 Troake Marler
FARMERS.
3 Bellamy Geo.
*Cleave Richard
3 Cole James
Tavendor John, *Newcourt*
*Wilcocks Wm.
FISH MERCHTS.
5 Andrews Geo.
2 BattiscombeJp.
FLY OWNERS.
8 Caseley Wm.
3 Ireland James
GARDENERS.
4 Downey Wm.
Matthews James
Matthews Wm.
7 Westcott John
GROCERS.
(§ *Drapers also.*)
2§Brown Wm.
2 Carlile William, (& auctioneer)
3§Elson George
2 Gould My. Ann
2 Holman Sarah
2 Ireland James

3 §Phillips Sus.
3 Pope George
2 §Parr Mary
2 Sweetland Jas.
3 White Edward
HAIR DRESSERS.
2 Rowe John
2 Tozer Wm.
IRONMONGERS.
3 Gubb William, (and *currier*)
3 Portbury Eliz.
MALTSTERS.
3 Gale Geo. sen.
2 Harrison Jno. S.
Jackson John, 2 Vietoria place
2 Lake Wm. *brewer*
Pyle Pp., Bdg. hill
MASTR. MARINERS.
4 Bartlett Edw.
2 Bence Wm. Hy.
2 Bence Wm.
4 Butt Wm.
5 Buttell Benj.
2 Croft Elias
2 Croft Wm.
4 Frost John
3 Holman Robt.
7 Hore James
7 Hore Richard
8 Periam Joseph
5 Salisbury Chas.
7 Salisbury Hy.
5 Symons John
3 Toogood Thos.
MAST & BLOCK MRS.
6 Holman and Walters

2 Row James
8 Row Wm. & John
5 Stamp Edm.
MERCHANTS.
2 Bence Wm.
*Davy and Son
6 Davy Danl. Bp.
4 Davy Francis
4 Periam Gilbert
MILLINERS.
2 Adams Alice
6 Buttell and Cridland
3 Hallett Mary
3 Harris Eliz.
2 Madge Eliza
3 Maddicks Ann
2 Periam Sar. G.
2 Phillips Sus.
2 White Sally
PAINTERS, PLUM., AND GLAZIERS.
3 Hodder Wm.
2 Ireland James
2 Pope Wm. H.
6 Williams Chas.
PILOTS.
Luxton Wm.
Pym Daniel
Pym Joseph
Pym Wm.
Wannell George
ROPE, TWINE, AND SACKING MFRS.
2 Follett & Co.
3 Manley James
3 Moore Edw.
3 Paine Thos.

SAILMAKERS.
6 Holman and Walters
6 Holman Jno. jun
5 Mitchell John
SHIP AND BOAT BUILDERS.
8 Bowden Thos.
6 Holman and Walters
7 Please John
SHIP OWNERS.
7 Bence Richard
2 Bence Wm.
*Davy and Son
8 Periam Joseph
8 Popham Thos.
4 Salisbury Jas.
SHOPKEEPERS.
3 Harris Richard
3 Harvey Thos.
2 Rew Susan
5 Sleep Jane
3 Underhill Wm.
*White Wm.
*Woodgate John
SURGEONS.
3 Fox Charles
5 McKee Alex.
3 Tothill Thomas Chas. (*regr.*)
2 Yarde Wm.
TAILORS.
Baker Zach.
2 Bolster James
2 Brown Harriet
3 Francis Thos. (& hatter & draper)
*Goveyer Hphy.

8 Halfyard Hy.
8 Harvey Thos.
5 Heddon Thos.
3 Irwin John
2 Martin Rt. (and hatter & drapr)
5 Osborne Robt.
Westcott James
TIMBER MERTS.
5 Cornish Robt.
6 Follett & Co.
TINNERS & BRAZS.
2 Baker George
3 Portbury Eliz.
3 West John
WATCHMAKRS. &c.
2 Manley Wm.
2 Salter Robert
2 Trevor John
WHEELWRIGHTS.
3 Harris Wm.
Westcott Joseph, Pound lane

OMNIBUSES
To Exeter 3 *times a day*, from Wm. Caseley's and Jas. Ireland's

CARRIERS
Wm. Thorn, to Exeter daily, and others from the Inns

VESSELS to London, &c. wkly

UPTON-PYNE is a straggling village on the north-east side of the vale of the small river Creedy, near its confluence with the Exe, and nearly 4 miles N. by W. of Exeter. Its parish extends to *Cowley Bridge*, and contains about 2200 acres of land, and 512 inhabitants. *Sir Stafford Henry Northcote, Bart.*, is lord of the manor, and owner of a great part of the soil, and resides at PYNES HOUSE, a commodious brick mansion, in a small but well-wooded park, commanding picturesque views. The manor belonged to the Pyne family as early as the reign of Henry I., and it afterwards passed to the Larders, Coplestons, and Staffords. The heiress of the latter carried it in marriage to the late Sir Henry Northcote, one of whose ancestors was created a *baronet* in 1641. An estate called Ley or Leigh, in this parish, belongs to the Roberts family, and here are several farms belonging to other proprietors. The

Church (St. Peter,) is an ancient structure, with a tower and five bells, and a south aisle was added to it about 14 years ago. An old monument has an effigy in armour, of one of the Larder family. Over the altar is a painting of the Lord's Supper, by an Italian artist, bought by one of the Stafford family. The *rectory*, valued in K.B. at £23. 6s. 8d., and in 1831 at £482, is in the patronage of Sir S. H. Northcote, Bart., and incumbency of the Rev. S. C. Northcote, M.A., who has a good residence and 90A. of glebe. The tithes were commuted, in 1837, for £400 per annum. The patron and rector support a National School, in the Churchyard; and the poor have the interest of £60, left by various donors, and the dividends of £141. 18s. three per cent. consols, purchased with £100, left by *Nicholas Williams*, in 1803.

Couch Abraham, blacksmith
Fursey Wm. shopkeeper
Freer John, M.D. *Oakford House*
Heard Eliz. *post-office*, Cowley bdg
Helmore Wm. land surveyor, &c., *Cowley Bridge*
Lamacraft Wm. assistant overseer, &c
Northcote Sir S. H., Bart. *Pynes Hs*
Northcote Henry Stafford, Esq., *ditto*
Northcote Rev Stafford C., M.A. *Rectory*
Perkins John, shoemaker
Perry Elizabeth, schoolmistress
Pitt Wm. vict. Horse and Groom
    CARPENTERS.
Bamsey Richard ‖ Bamsey George

Finch John ‖ Finch John, jun
Hogg Wm (and machine maker)
Smeedon Thomas (and wheelwright)
Webber John (and parish clerk)

    FARMERS. (* are Owners.)
Beedell Thomas (and butcher)
Pidsley Wm. *Ley* ‖ Finch Thos.
*Rew John, *Exe-weir Barton*
*Roberts Edmund Gay, Esq. *Firlake*
Sharland John (constable,) *Pearse's*
*Townsend Henry C. *Stevenstone*
*Turner Edward (sheep breeder,) *Naddircott*

WHITSTONE, or *Whitestone*, a scattered village, 3½ miles W.N.W. of Exeter, has in its parish 670 inhabitants, and 4046 acres of land, picturesquely broken into hill and dale. One of the hills commands extensive views, in which Exmouth, Honiton, and other distant places may be seen. The manor was anciently held by the Beaumont, Powderham, and Bohun families. It passed from the latter to the Courtenays, and is now held by the Earl of Devon, but a great part of the soil belongs to the executors of the late Thomas Sowdon (owners of *Whitstone House*,) the Rev. Nathaniel Cole, of South Brent, (owner of *Hurston House*,) J. W. Abbott, Esq., and several smaller freeholders. That part of the parish called *Halles-ford Ward* was formerly a manor, including *Naddir, Rohorn*, and other farms. *Sherewood*, at the west end of the parish, is an extra-parochial farm, belonging to Mrs. Floud. The *Church* (St. Catherine,) stands on a commanding eminence, and is an ancient structure, with a tower and four bells. The *rectory*, valued in K.B. at £19. 13s. 4d., and in 1831 at £707, is in the patronage and incumbency of the Rev. Charles Brown, M.A., who has a good residence, and 73A. 1R. 35P. of glebe. The tithes were commuted in 1839, for £616. 16s. per annum. The *Church House*, which had been vested from an early period for charitable uses, was rebuilt, in 1753, by *John Splatt*, and divided into apartments for the use of a school-master and five poor people. Mr. Splatt also gave two fields at

Heavitree, and directed the rents to be applied in repairing the building and supporting the inmates. These fields comprise 6A. 1R. 38P., and are let for about £26 a year, of which £20 is paid to the schoolmaster for teaching poor children. The poor parishioners have the dividends of £114. 10s. 9d. three per cent. consols, purchased with the gifts of *Ann Best, John Sowdon,* and others. They have also a yearly rent-charge of £3, left by *Thos. Sowdon,* in 1733, out of Higher Southway estate; and the dividends of £112. 7s. 3d. three-and-a-half per cent. consols, left in 1837, by Mrs Mary Brown, wife of the present rector.

Brown Rev Charles, M.A. *Rectory*
Gilpin Lawrence, Esq. *Sherewood*
Harris Saml. vict. Traveller's Rest
Hawkins John, blacksmith, *Naddir*
Newman Joseph, tailor
Pike Robert, wheelwright
Stocker Hannah, vict. Royal Oak
Stocker John, schoolmr. & par. clerk
Yarde Thos., Esq. *Whitstone House*

CARPENTERS.
Butlin Wm.
Carter J.

Mayne John
Pester George, *Hallesford*

FARMERS.
Baker Mark
Baxter Edward
Beer Peter
Bushell Wm.
Cheviton Richard
Cheviton Wm.
Harris Samuel
Hawkins Samuel
Hawkins Sarah
Isaac Wm.
Roberts Joseph

Salter Henry
Seward James
Seward W. *Naddir*
Taverner John
Tucker Robert

SHOEMAKERS.
Reed George
Liscombe Jermh.

POST-OFFICE at
John Stocker's.
Letters desp. 4 aft

EAST BUDLEIGH HUNDRED.

This Hundred is in the Southern Division of Devon, in the Archdeaconry of Exeter, and all in the Deanery of Aylesbeare, and in the Woodbury Petty Sessional Division; except Gittisham parish, which is in Honiton Deanery and Petty Sessional Division. It is about seven miles in breadth and extends more than ten miles in length along the sea cost from Exmouth to Salcombe-Regis, but Ottery St Mary, which lies within its limits, is a separate liberty. It is generally a fertile and picturesque district, and includes the *bathing places* of Exmouth, Sidmouth and Budleigh-Salterton. It is intersected by the rivers Otter and Sid, and bounded on the west by the broad estuary of the Exe. The following enumeration of its 24 *parishes and* 4 *hamlets, &c.,* shews their *territorial extent,* and their *population in* 1841 :—

Parishes, &c.	Acres.	Pop.
* Aylesbeare parish..	2948	433
* Newton Popfd. tyth.	524	549
* Bicton parish	1184	61
* Yettington ham....		137
* Budleigh East + par..	2620	2319
* Clist St George par..	1001	370
* Clist-Honiton par....	1760	467
* Clist St Mary par....	583	197
* Coylton Raleigh par...	3331	841
Dotton, *extra parochial*..	160	17
* Farringdon par....	1978	310
* Clist-Satchfd. part of		71
§ Gittisham parish	2067	376
§ Harpford parish	1518	305

Parishes, &c.	Acres.	Pop.
* Littleham parish ..	3011	273
* *Exmouth* part of ‡ ..		3654
* Lympstone parish ..	1790	999
* Otterton parish......	3500	1245
* Rockbeare parish....	2309	513
Salcombe Regis parish..	1909	525
§ Sidbury parish......	8222	1771
§ Sidmouth parish	1539	3309
§ Ven-Ottery parish ...	1200	134
* Withycombe Raleigh	1882	490
* *Exmouth* part of....		702
* Woodbury parish	7305	1933
Total	52,341	22,001

UNIONS :—Those marked * are in *St. Thomas's Union*, and those marked § in *Honiton Union*.

+ East Budleigh includes *Budleigh-Salterton* and Great and Little Knowle. Hamlets. *Clist-Satchfield* or *Sachville* is mostly in Sowton parish, Wonford Hundred.

‡ *Exmouth* town is mostly in Littleham, and partly in Withycombe Raleigh parish. It has now about 5500 inhabitants. *Petty Sessions* are held alternately at Woodbury and Exmouth.

AYLESBEARE is a small village on the eastern declivity of the bold range of hills between the vales of the Exe and the Otter, eight miles east of Exeter. Its parish contains 433 souls and 2948 acres of land, exclusive of NEWTON POPPLEFORD tithing and chapelry, which has 549 inhabitants and 524 acres of land, on the opposite side of the hills, in the vale of the Otter, where it has a good village and a stone bridge of three arches, 10 miles E. by S. of Exeter, and 3 miles S. of Ottery St Mary. Newton-Poppleford Bridge was built by the county in 1840, at the cost of £2500, and the village has two annual *cattle fairs*, held on Holy Thursday and the Wednesday after October 7th. The manor of Aylesbeare was long held by the Courtenays as part of the barony of Okehampton. After the attainder of Sir Francis Englefield, one moiety of it was granted to the Earl of Essex, who sold it to the tenants. The other moiety, with a great part of the parish, belongs to the Trustees of the late Lord Rolle. The vicar has a small manor here, and *Minchin Court*, with one moiety of the great tithes, belongs to the Rev. H. W. Marker. The other moiety of the latter belongs to the rector of Huxham. John Divett, Esq., John Praed, Esq., the Rev. Samuel Walker, and several smaller owners have freehold estates here. The parish *Church* (St Christopher,) is an ancient structure, with a tower and three bells, and the living is a discharged *vicarage*, valued in K.B. at £16. 2s. 4d. and in 1831 at £155. The Rev. H. W. Marker is patron, and the Rev. W. H. Carwithen, M.A. is the present vicar, and has a neat thatched residence, and 59A. of glebe. The tithes were commuted in 1841, for £143. 15s. 2d. to the vicar, and about £156 to the impropriators. The *Chapel of Ease* (St Mark,) at *Newton Poppleford*, is served by the vicar, and is said to have been founded as a chantry chapel by Edward III., about 1330. It is a stone fabric, with a Norman tower and one bell. The village of Newton has also a small *Independent Chapel*, built in 1816 ; and on the river bank is a *crape and silk factory*, which belongs to Hy. Elliott, Esq., but is now unoccupied. Many females here are employed in making *Honiton Lace*, and a child's cap of this beautiful material, was lately presented by one of the parishioners to Her Majesty, for one of the royal children. The Queen graciously accepted the present, and liberally rewarded the donor. The river Otter is celebrated for trout and other *fish*, and is a favourite resort for anglers. In 1696, Richard White left 30s. a year out of Porch House, for schooling six poor children. Two small schools, in the two villages, are supported chiefly by the patron, the vicar, and other contributors.

*Marked * are in Newton-Poppleford-
and the rest in Aylesbeare.*
Carwithen Rev Wm. Hy. M.A. *vicar*

* Carter Elias, vict. *Exeter Inn*
* Cooper Wm. mason & chapel clerk
* Coplestone Hy. vict. *Cannon Inn*

K

Berry John, thatcher ‖ Bolt Charles
Dennis Henry, vict. *Blue Anchor*
* Drake Mrs E. ‖ Ebden Mrs. school
Ham Wm. W. vict. *Half-way House*
Harris Wm. parish clerk, &c
Land Col. Samuel, *Rosemont*

BAKERS.
Hallett John
* Ham Nicholas
* Sage Robert

BLACKSMITHS.
* Ashford Chas.
Eveleigh George
Newbury Henry
Sanders John

BOOT&SHOE MRS.
* Bastin Jno. (&
  ironmonger)
* Darke John
* Fayter Wm
Quintance John
* Skinner Wm

FARMERS.
(‡ are owners.)

Allen Wm.
Bastin John
* Beer John
Bickley Mary
* Blackmore Jno.
Carter Thomas
Clarke John
‡ Dayman John
Ellicott Julian
* Fayter Wm.
* Hare Wm. sen
Hallett Abraham
Havill John
* Knowles Chas.
Nicks Francis
Reed Jas. (*Min-
  chin court.*)
Salter Charles

* Dean Wm. beerhouse keeper
* Lavis Wm. road contractor
Rowe Wilmot & Ann, schools
Sanford John, butcher
Sloman Mr. John
Smale Thomas, butcher
‡ Salter Samuel
Sanders Elizabeth
  Pottlehayes.
Simons Wm.
Sloman Jas. & Jno.
Street John
Stile James
‡ * Taylor John
‡ * Taylor Jtn.
Taylor Wm.
* Took John

GROCERS, &c.
* Hare Wm. (*and
  draper*)
* Hare Wm. jun.
  (*& drugst. &c.*)

SHOPKEEPERS.
Eveleigh Richd.

* Godfrey Susan
Gostage Chas. M.
* Mitchell Robt.
Tozer John

TAILORS.
* Ham John
* Hazzell Wm.
Tozer John
* Squire John

WHEELWRIGHTS.
Calverwell Anty.
Eveleigh George
Gooding Cyns.
* Ham Abm.
Pile James
* POST-OFFICE at
  W. Ham's, sen.
Lts. des. 3 aftn.

BICTON parish, on the west side of the river Otter, 4 miles W. S.W. of Sidmouth and 11 miles E.S.E. of Exeter, contains 1184 acres, and has only 198 inhabitants, of whom 137 are in YETTINGTON hamlet, on the high road, near the large and beautiful park of BICTON HOUSE, the seat of *Lady Rolle*, relict of the late *Lord Rolle*, who died in 1842, without issue, in the 86th year of his age. Henry, the first Lord Rolle, was created *Baron Rolle of Stevenstone*, in 1748, and died without issue in 1759, when the title became extinct. His nephew, *John Rolle*, the late Lord, was raised to the peerage by the same title in 1796, and was born at Hudscote, in 1756. He was twice married, but having no issue the title became extinct at his death, and his extensive estates became vested in Trustees, for the benefit of his widow and heirs. He was an active magistrate and statesman, and was Colonel of the South Devonshire Militia. In early life he was a zealous adherent of Mr. Pitt in parliament, and became the rallying point for the opposition wits and satirists of the time. He gave name to the famous " Rolliad," but in his private character, neither satire nor ridicule found anything which could be made the legitimate ground of attack; and in his public conduct he acted with a firmness and consistency not often equalled. He greatly improved Bicton House, which is a spacious brick mansion, standing in a large and pleasant park, plentifully stocked with fine trees, and abounding in deer. Lord Clinton and others, as *heirs and trustees of the late Lord Rolle*, are lords of the manor of Bicton, and owners of most of the parish. At Domesday Survey this *manor* was held by *Wm. Portitor*, by the service of keeping the *king's gaol* for the county of Devon. After passing to various families, it was purchased in the 16th century, of the Coplestons by *Sir Robert*

Dennis, who rebuilt the old mansion, enclosed a deer park, and made it his chief residence. His grand-daughter carried Bicton in marriage to *Sir Henry Rolle,* ancestor of the late Lord Rolle. The county gaol was removed from Bicton to Exeter, in 1518, but it was not till 1787, that the lord of Bicton was exonerated from the custody of the prisoners. The Rolles have another seat at Stevenstone, and were for a long period a numerous, wealthy, and distinguished family. *Sir Samuel and Sir Henry Rolle* were firm supporters of the parliamentary cause during the civil wars of the 17th century. The latter was appointed chief justice in 1648, and died in 1656. *Sir John Rolle, K.B.* was a zealous friend of Charles II., and made him large remittances during his exile. He was made Knight of the Bath at the Restoration. His grandson, *John Rolle, Esq.*, was offered an earldom in the reign of Queen Ann, but refused it. *Bicton Church,* (Holy Trinity,) is a small ancient structure, situated in a romantic spot, encircled by a beautiful screen of woods, in the lower part of the park, but it will be taken down after the completion of the handsome *new church,* now (1849,) erecting near it by Lady Rolle. In the former is an elegant monument of *Dennis Rolle, Esq.*, with effigies of himself and lady in statuary marble, richly habited. He died in 1638, aged 24, and was celebrated for his ready wit and the generosity of his disposition, and is noticed in a poetical epitaph written by Dr. Fuller, author of "The Worthies." The *rectory,* valued in K.B. at £12. 13s. 4d., and in 1831 at £220, is in the patronage of the Trustees of the late Lord Rolle, and incumbency of the Rev. G. H. Kempe, M.A., who has a neat residence, commanding a fine view of the coast and the ocean. The glebe is 50 acres, and the tithes were commuted in 1844 for £170. 16s. 11d. per annum. At Yettingham is a *Free School,* built in 1847, by Lady Rolle, in the Swiss style of architecture.

*Marked * are in Bicton, and the others in Yettington.*

* Lady Rolle, *Bicton House*
* Kempe Rev Geo. Hy. M.A. *Rectory*
* Barnes James, gardener
Gush John, carpenter & shopkeeper

Moxey Alice, schoolmistress
* Sanders Philip, farm bailiff
FARMERS.
Hallett John
Halse John
Hart Thomas
Lugg Charles
Pyne John
Pyne John, sen
Pyne Thomas

BUDLEIGH (EAST) is a straggling village in three parts, called Lower, Middle, and Higher, pleasantly situated near Bicton Park, in the vale of the Otter, about two miles from the sea, five miles W. S.W. of Sidmouth, and 10 miles S.E. by E. of Exeter. Its parish contains 2620 acres and 2319 souls, including the hamlets of *Great and Little Knowle*, about two miles S.S.W. of the pleasant and handsome little town and bathing place of BUDLEIGH SALTERTON, delightfully situated on the sea coast at the mouth of the estuary of the Otter, nearly three miles S. of East Budleigh, and four miles E. by N. of Exmouth. Like many other places on the coasts of Devon, Budleigh Salterton has risen from a few straggling fishing huts, into a fashionable watering place, during the present century. It is built along the bottom of a small picturesque valley, opening to the sea. The shops and inns form one principal street, and the lodging houses are mostly on the summit and sides of the hills on either side.

Through the middle of the main street runs a small brook, which is crossed by three wooden bridges, and gives a refreshing coolness to the air. The *beach*, which is composed chiefly of broad flat oval shaped pebbles, extends from Otterton point to Orcombe hill on the west, a distance of 2¼ miles; and affords incessant occupation and amusement to the curious and the lovers of natural history in seeking out the moss, agate, jasper, and other rich pebbles and petrifactions, with which it abounds. The cliffs rise in some places from 100 to more than 250 feet in height, and are occasionally broken into romantic caves and rocks. The terrace or marine parade, affords a delightful promenade, and in the vicinity are many pleasant walks and rides. There are hot and cold bath.; in the town, and bathing machines on the beach. Here is a coast guard, consisting of a lieutenant and eleven men; and mackerel and other fish are caught near the bar of the estuary. The town is within the limits of the port of Exeter, and has two circulating libraries and reading rooms; a neat *National School*, built by the late Lord Rolle, in 1842; a *Wesleyan Chapel*, erected in 1811, at the cost of £1700 by James Lackington, the late celebrated London bookseller; and a neat *church*, (Holy Trinity,) built in 1812-'13 at the cost of about £900, but enlarged in 1837, at the additional cost of £1100. The late Lord Rolle was the principal founder of this church or chapel of ease. *Great and Little Knowle* are suburbs of Budleigh-Salterton, and on Park terrace, in the latter hamlet, is a small *Baptist Chapel*, built in 1844, by subscription. *East Budleigh Church*, (All Saints,) is more than two miles N. of Salterton, and is an ancient structure, with a tower and five bells. The living is a discharged *vicarage*, valued in 1831 at £340, with the curacy of Budleigh-Salterton, and the perpetual curacy of Withycombe Rawleigh annexed to it; in the patronage of the Trustees of the late Lord Rolle, and incumbency of the Rev. Ambrose Stapleton, who has a neat thatched residence and two acres of glebe. In 1845, the vicarial tithes were commuted for £223, and the rectorial tithes for £346. 8s. per annum. The latter were formerly appropriated to Polesloe Priory, but are now in four equal shares, belonging to the Trustees of the late Lord Rolle and the James, Cockeram, and Lampriere families .In the village is an *Independent Chapel*, built in 1719, and enlarged in 1836. *Fairs* for pleasure and pedlery are held at East Budleigh on Easter Tuesday, and at Budleigh-Salterton on Whit-Tuesday. The Trustees of the late Lord Rolle own most of the parish, and are lords of the manors of Budleigh-Sion and Polstow, the latter of which was held by Polesloe Priory, and the former by St Michael's Abbey, in Normandy. *Tidwell*, a large brick mansion, was successively the seat of the Tidwell, St. Clere, and Arscott families, but is now unoccupied. There are several neat mansions in the parish, and on the river are four corn mills.

Poer Hayes or *Duke's Hayes* in this parish, was successively held by the ancient families of Poer and Duke. The large farm house on this estate, called *Hayes Barton*, is celebrated as the birth place of SIR WALTER RALEIGH, whose talents and undeserved fate have excited the admiration and regret of posterity. His father had a long lease of this estate, and he was

born here in 1552. Though his family was not wealthy, he was indulged in a liberal education, and was early distinguished at Oxford University for the vivacity of his genius and the variety of his attainments. He begun his career of glory at the age of 17, as one of the troop of a hundred young gentlemen, authorised by the Queen to volunteer their services in the cause of the Protestant Princes on the Continent. In 1578 he shared with William Prince of Orange the glory of delivering Holland from the yoke of Spain. In 1579, 1583, and subsequent years he was actively engaged in voyages of discovery. On his return, after the important discovery of Virginia, he received from the Queen the honour of Knighthood, accompanied with a grant of lands in Ireland, and the exclusive privilege of vending *wines* by retail throughout the kingdom. A fleet of seven sail, which he sent out to colonize Virginia, not only accomplished its mission, but his cousin, Sir Richd. Grenville, who commanded it, on the voyage home captured a Spanish prize, estimated at £50,000. In tracing the progress of Sir Walter through the rest of Elizabeth's reign, history records a series of brilliant actions and success. He was one of the most distinguished officers on board the fleet, which destroyed the Spanish Armada. On the death of Queen Elizabeth and the ascension of King James, Raleigh's sun set. That timid and contemptible monarch, destitute of talent himself, hated it in others, especially military merit. Sir Walter was soon marked out for destruction; though James, the better to conceal his designs, affected in the beginning to treat him with great kindness. The first step to his disgrace was his dismissal from the post of Captain of the Guards. A forged accusation was in the meantime prepared; and though no evidence was adduced of his having been engaged in any treasonable act whatever, he was brought in guilty, and condemned for high treason; but the dastardly court durst not proceed to execution; he was therefore reluctantly reprieved, and detained a close prisoner in the tower for nearly thirteen years. During this long imprisonment Sir Walter produced his "*History of the World*," a highly popular work, which displays the greatness of his mind, and is written in a pure, nervous, and majestic style. He was at length released, through the joint intercession of the Queen and Prince Henry, and the application of a douceur of £1500, given to a relative of James's minion, George Villiers. The events which befel him after his liberation are recorded at length in British history. A combination of unfortunate circumstances, some of them purposely contrived, prevented his bringing home the golden treasures he expected, after his fourth voyage to Guinea, and occasioned his ruin. Gondamor, the Spanish Ambassador, who hated him as the sworn foe of his nation, was loud in his complaints: and it was resolved therefore to sacrifice him to Spain, by calling him down to judgment on his former sentence, passed fifteen years before. Having received notice to prepare for death, he was taken out of bed in the hot fit of an ague, and being put to the bar, was asked why execution should not be awarded against him: he pleaded that the words in the King's commission, appointing him admiral in his last voyage, did of themselves imply a pardon; but he was not suffered to proceed: the warrant for his execution, which was ready signed and sealed, was read; and on the following day (October 29th, 1618,) he was conducted to the scaffold. He ascended the steps with a cheerful countenance, spoke in a firm and decided manner to the people; and, after inspecting the axe, laid his neck upon the block, and it was severed at two blows; "his body never shrinking or moving." Thus fell the brave Sir Walter Raleigh, in the 68th year of his age, a sacrifice to the despicable administration, and the resentment of a mean Prince. His head was conveyed away by his Lady, who survived him some time, and was buried at East Budleigh.

Two annuities of £7 for a lecture, and £2 for the poor, are paid to East Budleigh parish, from *Robert Drake's charity*. (See Littleham.) About 1607, *Richard Duke* gave a house and garden for the residence of poor parishioners. For beautifying the church, an annuity of £3, given by John Fowler, is paid out of Allgood's estate. The poor of this parish and Awliscombe, have a close of 4A. at Honiton, left by *George Pring* in 1735, and now let for about £14. The poor of East Budleigh have also two annuities, viz., 14s., left by Pp. Westcott, in 1624, and 11s. 8d. left by *Pp. Wotton*, in 1638.

In the following Directory, those marked 2 are in EAST BUDLEIGH; 3, *Great Knowle;* 4, *in Little Knowle; and all the rest in* BUDLEIGH SALTERTON, *or where specified.*

Adams Mrs Eliz. || 2 Adams Mr G.
2 Adams Rev George Dacres, curate
Algar John, clerk of Trinity Church
Barlow John, gent. Ivy Cottage
Birch Ann, sexton of Trinity Church
Chamberlain George, gentleman
4 Collins Rev Thomas (Baptist)
Coldridge Saml.Taylor, Esq. & Rev S.
2 Comins Rev John, B.A. curate
Couche General Edw., West terrace
3 Cowd Mrs Eliz. *Leeford House*
Cross Mrs Kate, Cliff terrace
Curry John, eating house
Dagworthy Mary Ann, lace maker
2 Daw Mr Jno. || Gibbs Ann, eatghs
Edwards Benedict, currier, &c
Elliott James, gent. West hill lodge
Elsworthy Thomas, gardener
Fouraker Edmond, hairdresser
3 French Joseph, cider merchant
HaffnerThos. Pitman, Esq. Temple hl
Halsey Ann, lace dealer, &c
Hayman Captain John
HaymanWm.lace mfr. (&*Woodbury*)
Hayman Mary Ann, lace maker
3 Hine John, Esq. *Leeford House*
Holder John Rose, gent. *Bushy Park*
Hole Lieut. Wm. (coast guard)
Jeffery Mrs Ann, Church terrace
Jones James, tinner and brazier
Kelly John, hatter, Fore street
Larking Charles, basket maker
Letton Sarah, bathing machine ownr
Lowe Miss Harriet || Mackie Mrs
Martin Henry, gent. Canton Cottage
2 Palmer John, parish clerk
Palmer MrThomas || ParsonsMrWm.
Patten Mary, staymaker
Portbury Mrs Har. || Pratt Mrs C.
Pover Roger, gunsmith
Pratt Rev Richard, B.A. curate

2 PriddleWm.&Thos.veterinary surgs
Roe Mr John || Stott Rev W. (*Wes.*)
Sanders Wm. beer seller
Smith Rt. lithographer & agt. to So.for Promoting Christian Knowledge
Smith Mr Rt. || 2 Starling Lieut. T.
Staddon Wm. lapidary
2 Stapleton RevAmbrose,B.A.vicar of East Budleigh & rector of Halwell
2 Stephens Capt Wm. K., R.N.
Stone Wm. Harry, Esq. *Oak Hill*
2 Teed John, sexton and beerseller
Teed Samuel, overseer & dep. regr.
Tetley Rev Wm. M. (*Independent*)
Thomson Mr John || Todd Mrs C.
Tidball Rev Thos., B.A. West ter
Torriano Wm. Edward, gent
2 Tucker Samuel, cooper
Turner James, hairdresser
Walters Mr Thos. || Wilson Mr Hy.
Wilcocks James C. gent. Castle Cotg
2 Wood Saml. gent || Williams Miss

INNS AND TAVERNS.
Feathers Inn, Abraham Freeman
King Wm. IV., Joseph Thorne
Rolle's Arms Hotel, Richard Morris
2 Queen Victoria, Mary Baker
2 William IV., Thomas Williams

FIRE AND LIFE OFFICE AGENTS.
Freemasons' & Genl., Herbert Scott
Globe Fire and Life, Samuel Teed
Norwich Union, Wm. Strickland
Provident & County, John Parsons
Star Fire and Life, John Casely
West of England, Robt. Williams

CORN MILLERS.
Franks Henry, *Dalditch Mill*
Rice Daniel, *Kersbrook*
Tedbury Daniel, *Thorn Mill*
Tedbury Joseph, *Town Mills*

ACADEMIES.
(* *Boarding.*)
Blatchford Tpa.
*ChudleighW.Hy
2 Copp Sophia
2*Hayden Fnces.
Palmer Rosa

Wescombe Chas.
*White Jas.&Mrs

BAKERS, &c.
Kerslake Walter
2 Lane Edward
3 MatthewsJetho.
Perriam George

Perriam Sarah
Pidsley Thomas
Tedbury Isaac

BLACKSMITHS.
2 Aunis Wm.
3 Bolt Joseph
Ellis James
Havill Richard
Humphreys Rt.
2 Jackson Fdk.

BOOKSELLERS, &c
Baker Wm.
Parsons John

BOOT & SHOE MRS.
3 French Saml.
Gibbs George
Gibbs John
Good Wm.
2 Helman Chas.
2 Lee Wm.
2 Palmer James
2 Patch Wm.
2 Potbury Thos.
Puddicombe Jno.
2 Steer Samuel
Stevens James
Trickey Wm.
Webber James

BUTCHERS.
2 Carter John
Dagworthy Saml.
2 Hallett Isaac
2 Patch Fredk.

CARPENTERS.
Clique Wm.
Cowd John
2 Dyer Wm.
Parker George
Parsons Robert
Smith Robt. jun.
Strickland Wm.
Thorne Wm. Hy.
Wesley Wm.
2 Williams Thos.

COAL DEALERS.
Hill George
Smith John

FARMERS.
Bastin Ann, *Tidwell*
2 Carter John
2 Carter Robert
Carter Tho. *Hayes*
3 Cocks John
3 Franks Henry
Glass George
2 Leat John
3 Leat Henry
2 May John
2 Mitchell Richd.
2 Patch Fredk.
3 Paul Reuben
Piles Jno. & Wm.
Kersbrook
Pyne Wm.
Sanders Wm. (& maltster)
Tedbury Daniel
3 Walters Wm.

FLY OWNERS.
Freeman Abrahm.
Horner Robert
Morris Richard
Salter John
Stone Herbert
Stone John

GROCERS & DPRS.
Hern Geo. Hy.
Perriam Ann
Perriam Geo. Chas
Phillips George
Scadding Mary
Southcott Eliz.
Scott Herbert
Stone John
2 Williams Alfred (and lace mfr.)
2 Williams Robt.

LINEN DRAPERS.
Gush My. Ann
Sprague Mary

LODGINGS.
Barnes Thomas
Bastin Wm.

Bence Mrs
Birch James
Brewer Thos. B.
Cox Robert
Farrant George
Freeman Abm.
Goss Eliz.
Goulett Arthur
Horner Richard
Knight Theophls.
Langdon F. W.
Maddock Jph.
Parsons John
Pile Michael
Pratt Richard
Salter Jas. B.
Thorne Wm. Hy.
Wood Wm.

MASONS, &c.
Barnes Robert
Barnes Thomas
Birch James

MILLINERS, &c.
Deem Eliz.
Gibbs Sophia
Horner Hannah
Langdon Mary
Leat H. & A.
Puddle Sarah
Nias Jane Mary
Smith Eliz.

PAINTERS AND PLUMBERS.
Carpenter John
Trickey Thos.
2 Williams John
Williams Saml.

SHOPKEEPERS.
2 Coombes Wm.
3 Cox Robert
2 French Patience
2 Tedbury Isaac

SURGEONS.
Kendall Walter (& registrar)
Musgrave Jsn.
Walker D. R. G.

TAILORS.
Algar John
Clode Fredk.
2 Cook Edward
2 Copp George
Gibbs Wm.
Pester Wm.

WATCHMAKERS.
Carpenter Wm.
Patch Robert

WHEELWRIGHTS.
2 Gale John
2 Patch John
2 Perriam John
2 Small John

POST-OFFICE at Jno. Parsons'. Letters desp. 5 evng. Money orders granted and paid. There is also a sub-post office at Mr John Palmer's, East Budleigh.

COACHES from the Rolles' Arms to Exeter, Sidmouth, &c. daily in summer, and three times a week in winter.

CARRIERS to Exeter, &c. Mon. Tues. Wed. & Friday:—Jas. Austin, Emanuel Harding, and Geo. Tuck.

CLIST ST. GEORGE, or *Clyst St. George*, a scattered village and parish, 1½ miles E. by N. of Topsham, and 4 miles S.E. of Exeter, has 370 inhabitants, and 1001 acres of land. It is the most southern of the six Clist parishes, in the valley of the small river Clist, or Clyst, which falls into the Exe at Topsham. J. B. Cresswell, Esq., is lord of the manor, which was anciently held by the Champernownes, who had a seat here; as also had the Sukespic, or Sokes-

pitch family. Alex. H. Hamilton, Esq., owns the estate which belonged to the latter, and the other principal owners are J. Daw and H. Porter, Esqrs. The *Church* (St. George,) is an ancient structure, with a tower and three bells. The *rectory*, valued in K.B. at £17. 16s. 8d., and in 1831 at £350, is in the patronage and incumbency of the Rev. R. W. Ellicombe, M.A., who has 8A. 1R. 18P. of glebe, and a large brick residence. The tithes were commuted in 1842 for £325 per annum. The *Free School* for 50 poor children is endowed with a house and 22A. 29P. of land at Woodbury and Ottery St. Mary, left in 1705 by *Lady Hannah Seaward*, relict of Sir Edward Seaward, Knight. The schoolmaster has also £3 a year from Weare's Charity. (See Clist Honiton.) The parish has also the following yearly sums, viz., 24s. for the poor, left by *George Gibbs* in 1721; and £5 for the poor, and 10s. for the clerk and sexton, left by *Rd. Pidsley* in 1799. *Clyst Agricultural Association* (for eighteen parishes,) has a numerous list of subscribers, and distributes yearly a great number of prizes for the encouragement of improvements in agriculture, and skill and industry among labourers and their families. Edward Divett, Esq., is president, and Mr. John Warren, of Wonford, honorary secretary of this useful society.

Baker George, shopkeeper
Bower James, blacksmith
Bradford James, tailor
Brown Jas. corn miller, Marsh mills
Chaplin Wm. shopkeeper
Clarke Rev Thomas, curate
Doveton Rev John Frederick, LL.B., *Carisfield*
Ellicombe RevWm.Rous, M.A. *Recty.*
Gove Eliz. vict. George & Dragon
Mawditt John, wheelwright
Palmer James, carpenter
Parr Samuel, Esq. *Knowle*
Potter John, shoemaker

Reed Wm. auctioneer (and Exeter)
Skinner Robert, par. clerk & schoolr
Stokes Wm. butcher
Voyser Thomas, shopkeeper
Warren Mr Thomas
Westcott Charles Alexander, artist

FARMERS.

Ellier John, Marsh Barton
May John, Hollin Bush
Page John (and butcher,) Clay pit
Pidsley Henry, Court
Roach Samuel, *Old Winslade*
Shiles John, Kennford
Warren Thomas, junior

CLIST HONITON, a village and parish on the east side of the river Clist, 4 miles E. by N. of Exeter, contains 467 souls, and 1760 acres of land. The Dean and Chapter of Exeter are lords of the manor, owners of most of the soil, impropriators of the great tithes, and patrons of the perpetual curacy, valued in 1831 at £146, and now enjoyed by the Rev. W. W. Bagnell, B.A., who has nearly 3A. of glebe, and £165 a year in lieu of tithes. The *Church* is a fine old structure, with a tower and six bells, and contains several monumental memorials of the Yarde, Short, and other families. In 1691, *Thos. Weare* left various rent-charges out of *Holbrook* estate for schooling poor children of this and other parishes. The annuity payable to this parish is £4. 10s.

Arscott Richd. vict. Coach & Horses
Ashford Mrs My. || Wm. shoemaker
Bagnell RevWm.Webber,B.A. incmbt
Barber Mr Jas. || Boys Mr Wm.
Bond Wm. vict. Duke of York
Boys Edwin T. veterinary surgeon

Chamberlain John, bricklayer
Chown Wm. cooper
Drake John, blacksmith
Fish James, shoemaker
Gould John, baker, *Post-Office*
Gould Thomas, gent. *Rectory House*

Palfrey John, parish clerk
Rider Sarah, grocer and beerseller
Smith Abm., Esq. *Treasurer's Bere*
Watkins Daniel, surgeon
Woolcott Robt. & Mrs. *boardg. school*
    FARMERS. | Baker Wm.
Arscott John | Down Richard

Mitchell Thos.
Newbury Wm.
Pile Samuel
Rew John
Reynolds Jno. (& butcher)
Salter Philip

Sanders Wm.
Walrond Benj. & Geo.*Gibb'sHayes*
West Richard
Westcott Thos.
Wish Edw. Richards, *Holbrook*

CLIST ST. MARY, a small parish and scattered village, 4 miles E.S.E. of Exeter, in the vale of the small river Clist, has only 197 souls, and 582A. 3R. 35P., of land, belonging to H. Porter, S. Barnes, J. Guitton, and Robt. Davy, Esqrs., Miss Pidsley, and a few smaller owners. *Winslade House*, a large stone mansion, on an eminence, with tasteful grounds, is the seat of Henry Porter, Esq., and has been greatly improved during the last seven years, at the cost of about £10,000. It has three beautiful terraces in front, and was formerly the seat of the Spicer and Porcher families. The *Church* (Virgin Mary,) is a cruciform structure, with a tower and three bells, and its chancel was rebuilt about 40 years ago. The *rectory*, valued in K.B. at £5. 1s. 3d., and in 1831 at £210, is in the patronage of Thomas Strong, Esq., and incumbency of the Rev. E. Strong, M.A., who has a good residence and 32A. 1R. 3P. of glebe. The tithes were commuted in 1838 for £155 per annum. *Wm. Tantezen*, at an early date, left for the repairs of the church a cottage, garden, and 4A. of land, now let for £8 per annum. An annuity of £3 is paid to this parish for schooling poor children, from *Weare's Charity*. (See Clist Honiton.) The poor have an annuity of 5s., out of Shear Meadow, left by *John Ceely;* and another of 16s., left by *George Gibbs*, in 1721, out of Ashmore estate. The parish has a small National School. This place was one of the chief scenes of the *rebellion* which happened in 1549, on account of the *reformation in religion*. An ancestor and namesake of Sir Walter Raleigh observing an old woman going to church with a string of beads in her hand, advised her to renounce all superstitious usages. The old woman so inflamed the minds of her neighbours by her representation of what had passed, that they broke out into open insurrection. Mr. Raleigh narrowly escaped with his life, and the disaffected having joined the rebels from other parishes, laid siege to Exeter; but after a long blockade, they were completely routed on *Clist Heath*, as noticed at page 56.

Bagg Wm. farmer, *Shepherd's*
Cook Thomas, saddler
Cox Wm. clerk,& Tapley Wm. sexton
Elms Henry, gardener
Manning Wm. blacksmith
Matthews Wm. corn mill, &c.
May Edward, shoemaker
Moore Richd. farmer, *Little Grindle*

Pidsley Miss Eliz. *Greensdale*
Porter Henry, Esq. *Winslade House*
Roach J. *Winslade Farm*
Strong Rev Edmond, M.A. rector of Clist St Mary, and Lympstone
Tidball Wm. & Eliz. *Nationl. School*
Wills Samuel, tailor
Zeal Wm. shopkeeper, *Post-Office*

COLYTON RAWLEIGH, or COLATON RALEIGH, a straggling village, on the west side of the Otter valley, 11 miles E. by S. of Exeter, and 3½ miles W. of Sidmouth, has in its parish 841 souls and 3331 acres of land, rising boldly from the valley, and including

the small hamlets of *Bystock, Blackbury, Great Grindle, Hawker-land, Kingston, Stoneyford, and Stowford,* extending from 1 to 3 miles N. and W. of the village. The manor of Colyton was conveyed by the heiress of the Chiltons to the Raleighs, in the reign of Henry III. The latter held it till the 16th century, and it afterwards passed to the Dukes, and from them to the Rolles. The Trustees of the late Lord Rolle now own a great part of the parish. The other principal proprietor of the parish is Edward Divett, Esq., M.P., of Bystock, a large and elegant white brick mansion, standing on a commanding eminence in a well wooded park, with beautiful gardens, shrubberies, &c., and a handsome lodge entrance. Mr. Divett is one of the representatives of Exeter in Parliament, and his estate here was formerly the seat and property of the Drakes, who sold it in 1742 to the Jacksons. The Dean of Exeter has a rectorial manor, and is impropriator of the great tithes, and patron of the *vicarage,* valued in K.B. at £16. 4s. 9½d., and in 1831 at £401. The Rev. Noel Lowe is the vicar, and has a pleasant residence and 42a. of glebe. The great tithes were commuted in 1842 for £324, and the small tithes for £270 per annum. J. Cutler, Esq., is lessee of the former. The *Church* (St. John,) is a large Gothic fabric, with an embattled tower and three bells. Several new pews were erected and a new chancel floor laid down in 1849. The Liber Regis mentions a chapel of St. Theobald in this parish, which had been demolished. The *Independents* have a small meeting-house here, built by Mr. W. Jarratt. The poor parishioners have the dividends of £230 old South Sea Annuities, purchased with benefaction money; and 40s. a year out of an estate belonging to the Rolles. The *National School* was built a few years ago, by the Rev. R. Greenwood, the late vicar.

Marked 2, are at Blackbury; 3, Great Grindle; 4, Kingston; 5, Stoneyford; 6, Stowford; and the rest in COLATON RALEIGH, *or where specified.*

Divett Edw., Esq., M.P. *Bystock*
Lowe Rev Noel, B.A. *Vicarage*
Austin Jas. Beal, veterinary surgeon, and vict. Brick Yard Tavern
Butter J. L. brick and tile maker, *Little Grindle*
Carter Hanh. gardener, & Sarah, sex.
Gooding E., & Skinner J. thatchers
Jarratt Wm. gent. *Kingston Cottage*
Law James, gardener, Bystock
Sellick Francis, vict. New Inn
Sellick Wm. parish clerk
White Wm. schoolmaster

BLACKSMITHS.
Matthews John
Pratt Charles
Toby Benedict
BOOT&SHOEMKRS
Dare John
Kettel Herman
Sellick Wm.
White Charles
White Wm.
FARMERS.
Ackland Cath.
4 Bolt Wm.
2 Brice Wm.
3 Butter John
5 Clapp Samuel
5 Cole Robert
6 Crook Charles
3 Knott Mrs.

5 Mingo John
4 Nugg Charles
4 Nugg John
4 Nugg Thomas
2 Sage Thomas
Searl John
6 Sellick John
TilkeMrsMy.Ann
3 Turner Mr
3 Ware Aaron
SHOPKEEPERS.
Elliott Thomas
Newton John
Newton John, jun
Pile Wm.
WHEELWGTS. &c.
Potter Thomas
Way Wm.
Way Wm. jun.

DOTTON, or DONITON, about 9 miles E.S.E. of Exeter, is an *extra-parochial* estate of 160 acres and 17 souls. It adjoins the parishes of Aylesbeare and Colaton Raleigh, and belongs to the trustees of the late Lord Rolle. It had a chapel till the 13th century,

and is now occupied by Wm. Pile, farmer; and Joel Carter, corn miller.

FARINGDON, or FARRINGDON, a small scattered village, 6 miles E. by S. of Exeter, has in its parish 1977A. 3R. 9P. of land, and 381 inhabitants, of whom 71 are in *Clist Sachville, or Satchfield tything*, which is mostly in Sowton parish, as noticed at page 202. At Domesday survey Faringdon was held by Fulcher Archibalistarius, or the chief bow bearer, and it was afterwards held for a long period by a family of its own name. The manors of Faringdon and Bishop's Clist, now belong to John Garratt, Esq., of *Bishop's Court;* but W. Cannop, Esq., occupies *Faringdon House*, a large cemented mansion with a handsome front, standing in a small park, and commanding extensive and beautiful views of the surrounding country. Bishop's Court is on the east side of the river Clist, and is noticed at page 202. The parish is bounded on the east by the hills which separate it from the Otter valley. The Rev. Wm. Rous Ellicombe, General Ellicombe, J. Lee, Esq., and several smaller owners have freehold estates here. The estate called *Crowley*, or Creely, was formerly held by St. James's Priory, Exeter, but is now the property of King's College, Cambridge. The *Church* has a tower and one bell, and the living is a *rectory*, valued in K.B. at £8. 8s. 1½d., and in 1831 at £262. The Bishop of Exeter is patron, and the Rev. C. H. Collyns, D.D., is the incumbent, and has a handsome residence and about 60 acres of glebe. The tithes were commuted in 1837. There was a chapel near Bishop's Court, dedicated to *St. Gabriel*, founded by Bishop Bronscombe, and to which Bishop Stapeldon annexed an hospital for twelve poor infirm clergymen. They were suppressed by Edward VI., but their revenues were given to the priest vicars of Exeter by Queen Elizabeth. Faringdon has £3 a year for schooling poor children from Weare's Charity. (See Clist Honiton.) The schoolmaster has also the interest of £56 left by *Walter Wotton*, in 1790, and the poor have the interest of £20 left by *John Hornbrook*. The schoolmaster's house was purchased about 1710, by subscription, together with £40 left by Walter Wotton.

Burgoin James, land agent and vict. Cat and Fiddle
Butter James Langdon, brick & tile maker, *Little Grindle*
Cannop Woodham, Esq. *Faringdon House*
Canterbury John, parish clerk
Collyns Rev Chas. Hy., D.D. *Rectory*
Culverwell Thomas, joiner
Fewins Wm. schoolmaster
Garratt John, Esq. *Bishop's Court*
Horn Henry, manager of the West of England Brick and Tile yard
Mildon Mr Wm. || Salter W. sexton

Smeath James, wheelwright
Tucker Benj. shoemaker & shopkpr
Wyatt Charles, butcher

BLACKSMITHS.
Dean Joseph
Skinner Joseph
Smith Wm.

FARMERS.
Bickley Samuel, *Upham*
Farrant John
Froom Robert
Hayman Henry

Hook John
Lane Geo. (and butcher)
Matthews Abm.
Pearce Philip S.
Reynolds John
Sanders James, *Benbow*
Sanders Joseph
Stokes Henry

GITTISHAM, a small straggling village on a picturesque declivity, near the source of the river Sid, about 3 miles from Ottery St. Mary and Honiton, and 14 miles E.N.E. of Exeter, has in its

parish 376 souls and 2067A. 2R. 5P. of land, rising in bold hills from
the Otter and Sid valleys. The knightly family of De Lumine held
the manor in the reign of Henry II., and it afterwards passed to the
Willingtons, Beaumonts, and the Putts. It passed from the late
Rev. Thos. Putt to the Rev. Henry Wm. Marker, the present lord of
the manor and owner of most of the parish, who has a pleasant seat
here called *Combe House*, a large stone mansion in the Elizabethan style, standing on a commanding eminence in a well wooded
park, overlooking the Otter valley. Thos. Putt, who resided here,
was created a baronet in 1666, but his son dying without issue in
1727, the title became extinct. The *Church* is an ancient structure,
with a tower and three bells, and contains some fine monuments
belonging to the Beaumont and Putt families. One of them has
kneeling effigies, and is in memory of Henry Beaumont, who died
in 1591. In the churchyard is a large elm tree, the hollow trunk of
which is 30 feet in circumference. The *rectory*, valued in K.B. at
£21. 8s. 11½d., and in 1831 at £320, is in the patronage of the Rev.
H. W. Marker, and incumbency of the Rev. Thomas John Marker,
M.A., who has a large residence with pleasant grounds, and 47A. 1R.
6P. of glebe, *Beaumont's Charity*, for the poor of this parish, was
derived from a legacy of £800 left by Henry Beaumont, Esq., in
1590 and now comprises several tenements, and 166A. of land, let
for about £144 per annum, and including Wampford farm and mills,
at King's Nympton. The net income is applied in weekly payments to the poor parishioners, who are not receiving parochial
relief. There are also two cottages belonging to the trust, occupied
rent free. For teaching 20 poor children the teacher of the *Parish
School* has £10 a year out of an estate here, left by *Sir Thos. Putt*,
in 1686.

Badcock John, vict. Nag's Head
Clare John Edw. gent. Eveleigh Cotg
Dimond John, tallow chandler
Hayman Wm. blacksmith
Knight Mrs. schoolmistress
Marker Rev Hy. Wm., B.A., *Combe H*
Marker Rev Thos. Jno., M.A. rector
  of Gittisham and Farway
Pring James, shoemaker
Putt Miss Amelia, *Pomeroy*
Sellars Wm. parish clerk

FARMERS.
Ashford John
Darby John
Isaacs Wm.
Madge Abraham
Madge Jno. *Curl-
ditch*
North Ann
Prouse Mary
Scovern John
Tucker John

Tucker Hy. *West-
cot*
Turner George
Walkem John
White Thomas
Wilmingham Jn.
Wilmingham Rt.
WHEELWRIGHTS.
Pile John
Tucker John
Tucker J. jun.

HARPFORD, a scattered village in the picturesque valley of the
small river Sid, 3½ miles N.W. by W. of Sidmouth, and 10½ miles
E. by S. of Exeter, has in its parish 305 souls and 1518 acres of
land, including the hamlets of *Bowd*, or Bowood, *Sotherton*, and
Burrow, each about a mile from the church. Harpford Wood contains about 400 acres, and exhibits some picturesque scenery formed
by the hills of Ottery and Sidmouth. The Trustees of the late Lord
Rolle are lords of the manor and owners of a great part of the
parish; and the rest belongs to the Rev. J. Sydenham, Henry Peppin, Miss L. H. Peppin, Mr. Thomas Stocker, and a few smaller
owners. The manor was anciently held by the noble family of Din-

ham, and their old mansion, now a farm-house, called Court Place, is traditionally said to have been the county gaol, before its removal to Bicton. The *Church* (St. Gregory,) is a venerable fabric, with a tower and three bells, and was appropriated in 1205 to the Abbey of St. Michael de Monte, and afterwards to Sion monastery. The *vicarage*, valued in K.B. at £18. 11s. 3d., and in 1831 at £239, with that of Venn-Ottery annexed to it, is in the patronage of the Trustees of the late Lord Rolle, and incumbency of the Rev. J. C. Fisher, M.A., who has a good residence, and 7A. 3R. 8P. of glebe. The vicarial tithes were commuted in 1840, for £146. 15s., and the great tithes for £130. 15s. per annum. The latter are now held by J. Lee Lee, Esq.

Acland Henry, gent. *Mnt. Pleasant*
Carter James, parish clerk
Fisher Rev Jno. Campbell, M.A., vicar
Maunder George, gentleman
Newton John, carpenter
Peppin Miss Lydia H. gentlewoman
Potbury Wm. vict. Bowd Inn
Russell Wm. sexton

FARMERS.
(* *at Bowd, and*
+ *at Burrow*.)
*Batten Wm.
Carter James
Carter John
Carter Joel

Holmes Wm.
+Parsons Robert
*Potbury John
*Potbury Wm.
*Pile Thomas
+Pring Henry

LITTLEHAM is a small straggling village on the sea coast, about one mile E. of Exmouth, and 13 miles S.E. by S. of Exeter. Its parish contains 3011 acres of land, and in 1841 had 3927 inhabitants, of whom 273 were in Littleham, and 3654 in the town of Exmouth, which is afterwards noticed. The manor of Littleham was anciently held by the Earls of Devon, and was given in 1122 to Sherbourn Abbey. After the dissolution it was granted to Sir Thomas Dennis. The Trustees of the late Lord Rolle are now lords of the manor, and owners of a great part of the parish, which is in the peculiar jurisdiction of the Dean and Chapter of Exeter, who are appropriators of the rectorial tithes and patrons of the *vicarage*, valued in K.B. at £15. 12s. 6d., and in 1831 at £191, with the curacy of Exmouth annexed to it. The Rev. Thomas Jas. Rocke, M.A., is the present vicar, and has a good modern residence and about 60A. of glebe. The rectorial tithes were commuted in 1842, for £383, and the vicarial for £112 per annum. The *Church* (St. Margaret,) is an ancient structure, with an embattled tower and four bells, and it and the burial ground contain many memorials of persons from remote parts of the kingdom, who died whilst resident at Exmouth. In the 16th century there was an ancient dilapidated chapel of St. Saviour at Chickstow in this parish. Mrs. Elizabeth Pratt, John D. Pratt, John Bastin, and several smaller owners have land and houses here.

Charities belonging to Littleham, Exmouth, &c.—In 1628, ROBT. DRAKE granted to feoffees in trust for charitable and public uses, in Littleham and other parishes, and for the relief of his poor relations, Perry's and Westcott's tenements, comprising 72A.; one half of the rents of 149A. of land and six houses, in Withycombe Rawleigh; and also the great tithes of that parish. The land, buildings, and tithes, belonging to this charity, now yield a clear annual income of about £350, which is applied as follows, according to the donor's intention:—Three yearly sums of £7 each are given to the vicars

of Littleham, Withycombe, and East Budleigh ; three annual sums of 40s. each are distributed among the poor of the said parishes ; £5 is applied in apprenticing poor children of Littleham and Withycombe ; and 20s. for repairing an almshouse in the latter parish. The surplus, amounting to about £300 per annum, is distributed among a large number of the *donor's poor relations*, except £8, which is given to the poor of the above-named parishes, instead of being expended in a feast for the trustees. In consideration of £100 left by HENRY PEARDON, in 1717, two annuities are paid out of Stafford's farm, at Withycombe, viz.,—18s. towards the repairs of Exmouth Chapel ; and £3. 4s. for the education of eight poor children. The sums of £250 given by SIR JOHN ELWELL, in 1724, and £50 given by his father, were invested in the purchase of £436. 13s. 7d. three per cent. consols. The dividends of this stock are applied for the education of poor children, for which purpose two-fifths belong to this parish, and three-fifths to East and West Teignmouth. The dividends of £184. 19s. 2d. three per cent. consols, purchased with £100 left by SARAH SPRY, in 1788, are distributed in linen among the poor of Littleham parish. The poor parishioners have also the interest of £10 left by *John Leslie, Lord Newark*, in 1818. The *National School*, built by the late Lord Rolle, at Exmouth, for 150 children, is endowed with about £23 a year, arising from the above-named charities and from £200 navy five per cents., given by the late Lady Rolle, in 1816. It is supported by subscription, and there is a small Sunday School at Littleham, built in 1844. In the latter year, BARTW. DAVEY FLOUD left £100 to the Churchwardens and Overseers of Littleham and Exmouth, in trust, to distribute the interest yearly in bread among the poor parishioners.

LITTLEHAM DIRECTORY.
(See also Exmouth.)

Davy and Son, lime burners and merchants, *Mare Lime Kilns*
Holder John Robt. gent. *Bushy Park*
Maunder Francis, blacksmith
Moon Mr Thos. ‖ Tillman Isaac, *sex.*
Partridge George, beerseller
Paull Thos. farmer and beerseller
Pratt Mrs Elizabeth, *Pratt's Hayes*

FARMERS.
Baker John
Barrett John
Bastin John, *West Down*
Blackmore Mary
Cockram Wm.
Crabb Joel
Liffton Wm.
Milton Samuel
Paull Zach.
Paull Zach. jun.
Pearse Wm.
Pratt John Drewe, *Pratt's Hayes*

EXMOUTH, 10 miles S.S.E. of Exeter, and about 167 W.S.W. of London, has its name from its situation at the mouth of the broad estuary of the river Exe, opposite Star Cross Railway Station, within the jurisdiction of the Port of Exeter. It is a market town, and one of the handsomest and most fashionable sea bathing places on the southern coast of Devonshire, and is mostly in the parish of *Littleham*, and partly in that of *Withycombe Rawleigh*. It has now about 5500 inhabitants, but had only 4356 in 1841, when 3654 were returned as being in the former, and 702 in the latter parish. Though it is one of the oldest and best frequented watering places in Devon, it was, about 150 years ago, only a small hamlet, occupied by fishermen. It was then brought into repute by one of the Judges of the Circuit, who retired hither to bathe, when in a very infirm state of health, and received great benefit. But we are told that in early times it was one of the principal ports of the county, and that, in the reign of Edward III. it sent two members to the Council of State, held at Westminster, and furnished 10 ships and 193 mariners for the expedition against Calais. This return, no doubt, included the ships and men furnished by Topsham and other places within the

present limits of the Port of Exeter. (See pages 63 and 71.) Hollinshed says there was a *Castle* here, to defend the entrance to the haven, and tradition affirms it to have stood on Gun Point, where some slight vestiges of embrasures may still be seen. The Earl of March sailed from Exmouth, in 1459. Exmouth Fort, then garrisoned for King Charles, was blockaded by the Parliamentarians, under Colonel Shapcote, in February, 1646, and was taken in the following month, with 19 pieces of cannon and a great quantity of arms and ammunition. (See page 56.) In 1814, the late Admiral *Sir Edward Pellew*, was created *Baron Exmouth*, of Canon-Teign; and in 1816, after his expedition to Algiers, he was raised to the dignity of *Viscount Exmouth*. He died in 1833, when the title descended to his eldest son, the present viscount, who resides at Treverry, in Cornwall. Until the early part of last century, the town of Exmouth consisted of a few straggling houses running down the side of the hill to the east, from the spot where the ancient chapel of the Holy Trinity stood, towards the Cross, and a few more towards the west, called the Strand. The sea at this time covered most of the ground on which the north-western part of the town is now built, and washed the base of the cliffs on the left hand side of the turnpike at the entrance to the town from Exeter. The first improvement, by which this ground was rescued from the sea, commenced by an embankment made by the late W. T. Hull, Esq., at the beginning of the present century. A number of neat houses, built near the Parade and Beacon, first gave Exmouth the name of a watering place, and led to the erection of the handsome buildings on the brow of the cliff, called Beacon hill. The manor of Littleham-cum-Exmouth has been long held by the Rolles, and the late Lord Rolle and his present surviving relict have been liberal patrons of the town. The commodious Church built in 1825, and the market house in 1830; the plantations and walks under the Beacon; the new sea wall; and most of the public improvements carried out during the last 20 years, have been at their suggestion and expense. The *Sea Wall* was begun in 1841 and completed in 1842, under the direction of John Smeaton, Esq. It is built of limestone, and extends 1800 feet in length by 22 in height. It contains 70,000 cubic feet of stone, and is protected by a row of piles 12 feet long. *Gas Works* were constructed in 1842; and the town is now abundantly supplied with pure soft water from the copious springs in the meadows at the top of the hills behind the town, where a new reservoir, covering 1½A. of ground, was constructed in 1847-'8, by J. Trenchard, Esq. Many neat houses have been built during the last four years, on Brunswick terrace, &c., and a square of handsome villas are now building round the large reservoir. Upwards of 40 houses were built here in 1848, and the town is still increasing. In the lower or old part of the town the streets are narrow and irregularly built, but all the modern parts are composed of terraces surmounted by good houses, mansions of considerable size, and villas, pleasantly detached, but so placed as to present to the spectator a continuous and unbroken neighbourhood. Many of these residences are in the permanent occupation of opulent families, and nearly the whole

command views which, for beauty and extent, are not surpassed in any part of England; indeed, the bay of this part of the English Channel is said to be inferior only to that of Naples. Louisa, Trefusis, and Beacon terraces, on Beacon hill; Adelaide terrace, on the Budleigh-Salterton road; and Church terrace, near the Church, are lined with large and handsome dwellings, mostly built within the last fifteen years. The aspect of the town is south-west, and its altitude above the sea and the estuary is sufficient for all the purposes of health and convenience. The promenades are numerous, but the principal is on Beacon hill, which is tastefully planted, and commands a charming view of the opposite shore of the noble estuary, studded with luxuriant woods and gentlemen's seats, and traversed by the South Devon Railway. Below the town is a gradually sloping sandy beach, enlivened on one side by the rolling sea; and adorned on the other by woody summits of unequal heights, barren rocks of various shapes, interspersed with craggy cliffs of fantastic forms, and embellished with tasteful plantations. The situation for bathing is excellent, the machines being within the bar, and well protected by hills from the north-east and south-east winds, Here is also a commodious *Bath House*, where warm, cold, fumigated, or vapour baths may be had on the shortest notice. In addition to the accommodation for numerous visitors of all classes at the private lodging-houses, here are several commodious inns and hotels. At the Globe Inn, near the Market place, is a large and elegant Assembly Room, where balls and concerts are held. The Public Rooms, on Beacon hill, comprise reading and billiard rooms, &c.; and there is a well supplied reading room in the *Albion Rooms*, on Sheppard's walk, in the centre of the town, as well as a lecture room, &c. The Coast Guard Station, near the sea wall, has dwellings for a lieutenant and 13 men; and on the Point is the station for the custom-house officers, consisting of a landing waiter and nine boatmen. Vessels take in pilots here for Topsham and Turf, the latter of which is the entrance to Exeter Canal. The *Bar* which contracts the entrance to the haven, consists of two shoals of sand, projecting from either side of the broad estuary. A great portion of the sand bank on the western side is called the Warren, and is now raised above high water level by means of the sea-mat weed, *(arundo arenaria,)* which retains the sand carried by the south winds. The gentlemen's seats and other objects of interest in the vicinity, are noticed in this volume with Withycombe-Rawleigh, Lympstone, Powderham, Mamhead, Bicton, and other neighbouring parishes, to which the walks and rides are beautifully diversified and picturesque. The soil round Exmouth is dry and well wooded, and the *climate* is so mild that winter seldom sets in till after Christmas, and does not often continue above six weeks; but, though deep snow is unknown, and severe frost uncommon, this part of the coast is not exempt from the piercing winds of March. The night air is generally dry and warm, and the skies during summer resemble those of Italy. Another circumstance of great importance to invalids, is the excellent medical aid which may always be procured here, from the vicinity of the town to Exeter, and the very frequent conveyances daily between the two

places. The *market*, held every Saturday, is well supplied with provisions, and there are also large supplies every Tuesday and Thursday. There are annual *fairs* on the 25th of April and 28th of October. The shops are numerous, and abundantly stocked. Mackerel, turbot, salmon, herrings, soles, whitings, crabs, lobsters, shrimps, and a great variety of other fish, are caught in the estuary and the adjacent parts of the coast, and give employment to a number of men and boys; while about 300 females are employed in making lace. *Petty Sessions* are held at the Globe Hotel every fourth Saturday, and Mr. H. C. Adams is clerk to the magistrates. The *Church* (Holy Trinity,) is a chapel of ease under the parish church of Littleham, and was erected by the late Lord Rolle, at the cost of £13,000, in 1824-'5. It is a handsome structure, in the perpendicular style, standing on the Beacon hill, and having a tower 104 feet high, containing a clock and one bell. The whole length of the building is 140 feet, and its breadth 84. The interior is handsomely fitted up, and has sittings for 1500 hearers. It has a fine toned organ, and over the altar table is a fine canopy of Beer stone, in the florid Gothic style, ornamented with crockets, pinnacles, &c. The *curacy* has a small endowment, given by the noble founder, and is annexed to the vicarage of Littleham. Until the erection of this church, Exmouth was without an episcopal place of worship; for though a small ancient chapel, dedicated to the Holy Trinity, was standing in 1412, all traces of it disappeared some centuries ago. *Glenorchy Chapel*, at the north end of the town, belongs to the *Independents*, and was built in 1800. The *Wesleyan Chapel*, on the Parade, was erected in 1845, in lieu of *Ebenezer Chapel*, near Bicton place, which was built in 1807, and is now occupied by Independents. The *Plymouth Brethren* have also a small chapel here, built in 1843, at the expense of W. H. Hull, Esq. The *National School*, (attended by about 200 children,) and the *Charities* belonging to Littleham-cum-Exmouth, are already noticed at page 229. Here is a *Mental Improvement Society*, which has a numerous list of members, and has frequent lectures at the Albion Rooms; and in the town are several Benefit Societies and institutions for the promotion of religion and the relief of the poor.

EXMOUTH DIRECTORY.

The POST-OFFICE is at Mr. Wm. Sheppard's, Albion place. Letters despatched at 9¼ morning and 6 evening; but the box closes half an hour before each departure. Money Orders granted and paid from 9 till six o'clock.

Acton Mrs F. Eliz., Adelaide place
Allever Mrs Eliz., *Sandbank Cotg*
Attwater Mrs Ann, 29 Bicton st
Axon Jas. farmer, South Town
Baker Wm. poulterer, Fore street
Barnes Mrs. 3 Trefusis terrace
Bastin Robt. farmer, 19 Beacon hill
Bellman Jph. livery stables, 1 Bicton place
Bickford Mr Thos. 1 Clarence rd
Birch Isaac. gent. Johnson's place
Bishop Mr Henry, Tower street
Black Major John, Beacon hill
Blackmore Edwin, town crier, 8 Staple's buildings
Blackmore Geo. par. clk. & registrar, Tract, &c., depôt, 6 Staples' bldgs

Blatchford Wm. bird, &c., preserver, Manchester street
Boles Rev Jas. Thos., M.A. curate, 7 Claremont terrace
Boles General Thos., *Carnford*
Bowey John, thatcher, Fore street
Bricknell Mr Charles, Parade
Bricknell Mr Samuel, 50 Bicton st
Browne Major Genl. Sir Hy., K.C.H. *Bronwylfa*
Browne Jonth. Esq. 5 Beacon hill
Buller Mrs Ann, 1 Louisa terrace
Burridge Thos. bath propr. Beach
Campbell Capt. Duncan, *Hermitage*
Carrington Sir Edwd., *Castle Park*
Champante — Esq. *Beaumont villa*
Clapson Rev Rd. (Indpt.) 3 Parade
Clerk Lieut. Fras. N., coast guard
Cobham Thos. Esq. *Marley Lodge*
Cole Wm. Cole, Esq. *Highfield Hs*
Colson Miss Sophia, Parade
Cosnett Thos. gent. *Lauristina Cotg*
Coventry Mr Thos. Wm. *Lion House*
Cowd Gilbert, Esq., *Leeford House*
Crutchett Anna Maria, upholstress, Chapel street
Crutchett My. staymkr. 41 Bicton st
Dallas Genl. Chas., *Trefusis House*
Daniel Mrs — 12 Beacon hill
Dansey Mrs Margt. 5 Claremont ter
Dashwood Miss Sophia, Trefusis ter
Davies Mrs Mary, Johnson's place
Denby Fras. artist, *Rill Cottage*
Dennis Mrs Maria, 5 Claremont ter
Eddy Mr John, 33 Bicton street
Elson Mrs., Bicton street
Fisher John, umbrella mkr. Bond st
Fitzmaurice Captain J. (R.N.) *The Point*
Floud Mrs Mary, 20 Beacon hill
Foote Capt. Hy. R., *Catch Castle*
Forrest Lady My. 7 Louisa terrace
Foster Jas. market clk. 3 Parker's pl
Gallop Rd. custom hs. officer, Point
George Wm. H. S. Esq. 6 Beacon hl
Gibbs Chas. E. Esq. 2 Trefusis ter
Gifford Chas. Esq. *Cliff's End Hs*
Gifford Mr Wm., North street
Gillies Mrs Jane, 4 Claremont ter
Gillum Major Wm., Adelaide terrace
Gulson Edw. Esq. assistant poor law commissioner, 3 Beacon hill
Hall Matilda, stay mkr. Parker's ln
Hall Rev Wm., M.A. 11 Beacon hill
Hallett Isaac, saddler, Exeter road

Halse Mr Thomas, Chapel street
Harding Mrs Mary, 7 Clarence st
Hather Mrs Ann, 29 Bicton street
Haward Mr Robt. 28 Bicton street
Hayne Geo. currier, &c. Fore street
Hill Miss My. Ann, *Riverbank*
Hill Rd. gent. 12 Claremont ter
Holden Capt. Robt. 3 Ormond ter
Holroyd Miss, Adelaide terrace
Holt Mr Robt. Henry, The Point
Horndon Rev John, 12 Bicton place
Hore Mrs Jane, boat owner, 12 Bicton street
Horsewell Mr John, Adelaide place
Howard Mr Robert, 28 Bicton pl
Hudson Mrs Lucy, 1 Claremont ter
Hull Wm. Hartop, Esq. *Marpool Hl*
Hunter Miss Louisa, 1 Bicton place
Hutchings Wm. coach builder, Parade
Inverarity Mrs Chtte. 14 Beacon hill
Jackson Mrs Fanny, 23 Beacon hill
Jarman Mrs Martha, Exeter road
Jeffreys Miss My. 8 Claremont ter
Johnson Mrs Harriet, North street
Lamplowe Mr Wm. Chas., North st
Laye Mrs gentlewoman, Louisa ter
Lee Rev W. J. T. curate, Exeter rd
Lloyd Major John, 6 Claremont ter
Louis Misses, 14 Claremont ter
Lunn Mrs My., Castle Park ter
McGillivary Mrs A. 2 Beacon hill
Maunder Wm. corn mert. 4 Bicton pl
Moresby Capt. Fairfax, *Beach*
Nesham Vice-Admiral Chpr. John Wm. 1 Bicton terrace
Newton Miss, North street
Nicks John, music professor, Parade
Nolloth Jph. vessel onr. 15 Bicton pl
Norman Miss Thirza, Fore street
Nowell Miss Ann, 4 Parker's place
Ord Mrs Margt. 9 Claremont ter
Palfrey Mrs., Baring place
Palin Mr John, 46 Bicton street
Parker Mr Arthur, 6 Parker's pl
Parker John, sail and rope maker, Tower street
Parker Mrs Jane, *Greenwood Cotg*
Parminter Miss, *A la Ronde*
Parsons Capt. Robt., Adelaide ter
Peak Mr Robt., Charles street
Penny Mrs., Exeter road
Penrose Rev John, M.A. 5 New rd
Pepperell Mrs Eliz., Fore street
Perriam Mrs Eliz., Chapel street
Perriam Mr John, *Australia Cotg*

Perring Miss Lucy, *Louisa House*
Perry Mrs and Misses, Johnson's pl
Perry Wm. slater, &c. South town
Pigott John, Esq. 2 Louisa ter
Plimsoll Mrs Hanh. 16 Bicton st
Potter Edw. tea dealer, Bond st
Prettyjohn John, 3 Claremont ter
Probert Mr John E. 10 Claremt. ter
Prout Misses, 14 Bicton place
Rake Isaac, policeman, 21 Bicton pl
Randle Mr John, 13 Beacon hill
Rashleigh Lady Ann, *Stanley Lodge*
Redway Rd. patent rope mkr. Point
Redway Thos. ship chandler, Windsor place
Reed Miss My. A. 2 Claremont ter
Rich Captain Edwin Ludlow, R.N. *Belle Vue House*
Roberts Mr Rd. 2 Parker's place
Rocke Rev Thos. Jas., M.A. *Vicarage*
Roden Saml. dairyman, Fore st
Salter Hy. gent. and Misses, Brunswick terrace
Scoble Geo. vessel owner, 8 Bicton st
Scott Alex. Innis, gent. 1 Trefusis ter
Scott Capt. Hy. Wm., Adelaide ter
Shearman Mr Wm. 3 Johnson's pl
Small Bartw. sweep, Back street
Southcott Hy. colr. 3 Stafford place
Spicer Wm. Fras. Esq. *Courtlands*
Sprague Mrs Eliza, 5 Parker's pl
Squire Robt. poulterer and game dlr. Queen street
Staple Mr Wm. 2 Parade
Stark Hy. B. piano tuner, Bicton st
Start John, chandler, Chapel st
Stewart Mrs Fanny, 3 North st
Stockman John, gunsmith, 38 Bicton street
Stogdon Mr Abm., *Rose Cottage*
Stowell Capt. Jonas, New road
Stupart Rear-Admiral Gustavus, 4 Bicton terrace
Symonds Capt. Thos. Edw., *Elm grv*
Teschemaker Ts. gent. 22 Beacon hl
Thorne John, saddler, Fore street
Tiller Wm. Hy. toll colr. Back st
Tobin Genl. Jph. 11 Claremont ter
Tottle Mr Joseph, River bank
Treatt Mr Rd. Court, 2 Bicton pl
Tupman Mr Wm. Henry, Strand
Usherwood Capt. Wm., Trefusis ter
Vinnicombe Geo. piano-forte maker, River bank
Walker Lieut. John, coast guard

Walrond Mr George, 1 Parade
Warren Miss Eliz. 7 Sheppard's wk
Ware Mr Gilbert, 12 Clarence road
Way Mr George, Parade
Webber Mrs., Gwydir place
Webber Mrs Ann, 30 Bicton street
Weeks Mrs Mary, *Woodbine Cottage*
Wellington Hy. Esq., *Montpelier Cotg*
Welsh Mrs Ann, 13 Claremont ter
Wightman Rev Chpr. (Indpt.) 31 Bicton street
Wilkinson Lieut. J. Js. 8 Clarence rd
Williams Geo. gent. 4 Ormond ter
Winsor Wm. Staple, surveyor, 2 Clarence road
Winsor Mr Philip, 49 Bicton st
Wood Wm. clog maker, &c. Bond st
Wright John, fishmonger, Market

ACADEMIES & SCHOOLS.
*Marked * take Boarders.*
Bartlett Robert, Tower street
*Clapson Margaret, Ormond ter
Hague Charlotte, Exeter road
Kinghorn Elizabeth, Bicton street
*Lendon Miss, (ladies')
Long Mary, Queen street
Mansfield James and Mrs., Strand
National School, Little Bicton place, Jno. Bannister & My. A. Osment
*Penrose Rev John, Louisa terrace
*Sharland Wm., Manor Hs. North st
White John, Wanhill row
Yarde John, Bicton place

ATTORNEYS.
Adams Henry C., Strand
Watts George A. E., Johnson's pl

AUCTIONEERS.
Crudge Thos. and Son, Parker's pl
Sheppard Wm., Albion place
Tupman George, Strand

BAKERS. (+ are Confectioners.)
Copp James, 5 Bicton street
Cook Wm., Parker's lane
Dyer John, Fore st; & Wm., Bond st
Ellis Thomas, Parker's place
Elson Henry, Chapel street
+Farncomb Henry, Strand
Halse Thomas, Chapel street
+Law Henry, Strand
Long Michael, Strand
Melhuish James, South town
Morey Robert Henry, Fore street
Perriam Wm., New town
+Setten John, Albion place
+Sheppard John, 3 Bicton street

Stevens James, Fore street
Thompson Richd. 47 Bicton st
+Walters Joseph, Chapel street
Ware Walter, Tower street

BASKET MAKERS.
Crocker George, Exeter road
Searle George, Fore street

BLACK & WHITE SMITHS.
Bartlett Wm., Back street
Blackmore Sl. & Sons, Staple's bldgs
Blackmore James, Chapel street
Blackmore James, jun. Bond st
Cruse Robert, Bird's court
Margrie Wm., Back street
Maunder Thomas, Exeter road
Webster John, Back lane

BOAT BUILDERS.
Dixon Thomas, Sea wall
Hayman John, 8 Parker's place
Hook George, The Point
Wishart James, The Point

BOOKSELLERS, PRINTERS, &c.
Bounsall Wm. M., Gwydir place
Spencer Chas. Wm. Hy., Strand

BOOT & SHOE MAKERS.
Acland John, Back street
Bricknell Wm., Queen street
Crocker George, Exeter road
Crofts George, Strand
Haynes Wm., Bond street
Higerty Edmund, 2 Bicton street
Higerty John, Parade
Knight George, Chapel street
Knight Wm., Strand
Lediart Maria, Strand
Matthews Wm., Charles street
Marchant Charles, Bond street
Polteridge James, Chapel street
Priddis Samuel, Bond street
Richards Robert, Bicton street
Pound John, Fore street
Salter Wm. (fly owner,) Strand
Searle Wm. (fly owner,) Fore st
Underhill Thomas, Strand
White Charles, The Cross
Winsor Thomas, Strand

BREWERS & MALTSTERS.
Courtney Clement, The Cross
Foster James, 3 Parker's place
Radford Mary, South town
Vine Emanuel, Tower street

BUILDERS.
Burridge Thomas, Beach
Benmore Thomas, Beacon hill
Branscombe Henry, Albion street

Burgin Herman, and Berlin wool
    dealer, Baring place
Cooper Robert, 6 Bicton street
Hall John, 43 Bicton street
Roberts Charles, Little Bicton pl
Winsor Wm. Staple, 2 Clarence road

BUTCHERS.
Anderson Richard, South town
Baker Charles, (pork,) Strand
Blake Wm. Pearse, Bond street
Cock George, The Cross
Dagworthy Samuel, Chapel street
Maeers John, Bond street
Patch Henry, Bond street
Webber Richard, Bond street

CABINET MAKERS.
Bence Edward, Chapel street
Crudge Thomas & Son, Parker's pl
Snow Samuel, 1 Bicton street
Stamp Wm., Strand
Turner Henry, Wellington place

CARPENTERS.
Branscombe John, 22 Bicton st
Cole Geo. Fredk., Wellington pl
Hall Wm., Exeter road
Ireland Solomon, 5 Bicton place
Litton Richard, 6 Bicton place
Sprague Richard, 22 Bicton place
Tozer John, Strand

CHEMISTS & DRUGGISTS.
Bickford Nicholas, Gwydir place
Carter John, Tower street
Thornton Samuel, Beacon hill
Walters Wm., Chapel street

COAL DEALERS.
Beavis Wm., Fore street
Carter John Lord, Exeter road
Copp Wm., Manchester street
Harris Edward, Chapel street
Parker Arthur and Co. Parker's pl
Pyne Geo. (and salt,) Manchester pl
Pyne John, 9 Bicton street
Reeves Horatio, Exeter road
Tupman Henry, 44 Bicton street
Wicking John, Strand

COACH BUILDERS.
Dennes John, Bicton street
Hutchings Wm., Parade

COFFEE & EATING HOUSES.
Churchhill Wm. Gilbert, (dyer,)
    Tower street
Hole James, Bond street
Luke Alexander, The Cross
Richards Wm., Bond street
Turner Henry, South town

COOPERS.
Jewell James, 7 Parker's place
Parker Joseph, Back street
Taylor George, Bird's court
FIRE & LIFE OFFICES.
Atlas, Wm. Sheppard, Albion place
County Fire and Provident Life, Crudge and Son, Parker's place
Imperial, W. Wills and Son, Strand
Medical Invalid, N. Bickford, Strand
West of England, H. C. Adams, Strand
Western Life, Crudge and Son, Parker's place
GREEN GROCERS, &c.
Marked + are Gardeners.
Dalley Henry, Parker's row
+Harris Wm. Thos. 42 Bicton st
+Jordan Wm., Bond street
Perry Joseph, Chapel street
+Tarn John, 27 Bicton street
Taylor Ann, Tower street
GROCERS & TEA DEALERS.
Marked + are Drapers also.
Batt Michael, Strand
Burrow John, The Cross
Horne Thomas, Bond street
+Long Mary Ann, 39 Bicton st
Nicks James Dane, Strand
Searle George, Fore street
+Southcott Sarah, Exeter road
Stockman Wm., Staple's buildings
Toop Joseph Samuel, Bond street
+Walters Wm., Chapel street
+Wicking John, Strand
Wishart James, Fore street
HAIR DRESSERS.
Litton John, Fore street
Potter John, Bond street
Potter John, jun.(& hatter,) Chapel st
Tolley Wm., The Cross
White George, Vicarage hill
INNS AND TAVERNS.
Anchor, Hy. Newberry, Tower street
Beacon Royal Hotel, Benj. Butter Bastin, 1 Beacon hill
Dolphin Inn, Eliz. Courtney, Cross
Exeter Inn, (empty,) Chapel street
Globe Hotel, Hy. Bastin, Strand
King's Arms, Jph. Fletcher, Fore st
London Inn, John Gifford, Union st
Marine Hotel,Hy.Bastin,19 Beaconhl
Maltsters', Emanuel Vine, Tower st
New Inn, Ann Taverner, South Town
North Country Inn, Tamasin Blake, Chapel street
Passage House,John Treble, Sea wall
Pilot, Robert Snell, Vicarage hill
Railway Inn, James Pound, Strand
Ship, Wm. Metherell, Chapel st
Volunteer, Wm. Norris, Bond street.
White Hart, John Toby, Fore st
BEERHOUSES.
Copp Wm., Quay
Harris Edward, Chapel street
Hayne Florence, Bond street
Haywood James, Fore street
Maypee Charles, George street
IRONMONGERS, &c.
Cooper Robt. 6 Bicton street
Plimsoll John, Strand
LACE MAKERS & DEALERS.
Copp Hannah, Parade
Drake Francis, Strand
Elliott Wm. 3 Clarence road
Moore Edward, Staple's buildings
Randle George, Strand
Southcott Sarah, Exeter road
Walker Eleanor, Wanhill row
Weeks Eliz. 22 Bicton place
LINEN & WOOLLEN DRAPERS.
Hayman Tryphena, 4 Parade
Rising Tilney, 1 Parker's place
Sawday Geo. Wm., The Cross
Sheppard Wm., Albion place
Staples Wm., Staple's buildings
Webber and Son, Strand
LODGING HOUSES.
(Many of the Tradesmen let Lodgs.)
Brindley Maria, Beacon hill
Burridge Thomas, Bath House
Copp Sarah, 4 Beacon hill
Gay Joseph, Sea wall
Hathur Eliz. 25 Bicton street
Hewings George, 11 Bicton place
Hewings Susan, 16 Beacon hill
Liffton John, 2 Ormond terrace
Martin Jane, Strand
Mildon Robert, 16 Bicton place
Nichols Susan, Parade
Perriam Ann, 19 Bicton place
Peak James, 12 Bicton place
StoneHerbert,(polisher,)20 Bicton pl
Taylor Sarah, 7 Bicton place
Toswell John, 8 Beacon hill
Tupman John, Cleveland place
Webber Mrs., Strand
West Simon, 8 Bicton place

MASONS & BRICKLAYERS.
Collings Thomas, 18 Bicton street
Collings Thomas, jun. 26 Bicton st
Cooper Robert, 6 Bicton street
Hyne Edw. (statuary,) 51 Bicton st
Hyne Henry, (statuary,) Strand
Koggle Wm., South town
Perry Wm. (& slater,) South town

MASTER MARINERS.
Bellman John, 35 Bicton street
Blundell John, 10 Bicton place
Burton Wm. Henry, Point
Carder Samuel, Albion street
Dixon John, 34 Bicton street
Down Wm., Albion street
Hore Wm. 32 Bicton street
Litton John, Albion street
Maypee Charles, George street
Mildon Robert, 16 Bicton place
Parker Arthur, 6 Parker's place
Parker Charles, Queen street
Parker Wm. 7 Bicton street
Perriam Henry, 4 Bicton street
Perriam John, 15 Bicton street
Phillips George, Chapel street
Richards Wm. 36 Bicton street
Shapter Thomas, Exeter road
Street John, 5 Parade
Tomlin John, 2 Cleveland place
Treatt John, 5 Parade
Tupman Charles, 3 Bicton place
Weeks George, Albion street
Weeks Samuel, Albion street
Widdicombe Wm. Albion street

MILLINERS & DRESS MKRS.
Bastin Sarah, Charles street
Batstone Hannah, Strand
Bishop Eliz., Tower street
Crofts Caroline, Strand
Ellis Caroline & Maria, Bond street
Francis Maria, Strand
Hall Sarah, Charles street
Hook Eliza, 23 Bicton place
Priddis Susan, Bond
Skinner Ann, Tower street
Titcher Louisa, Baring place
Tupman Sophia, Strand
Yarde Eliz., Baring place

PAINTERS, PLUMBERS, &c.
Blackmore & Sons, Staple's buildgs
Blackmore James, Chapel street
Hayne Walter, Exeter road
Sheppard Thomas, Wellington pl
Stamp Philip, Bond street
Wells Wm., Strand

Williams Thomas, George street

SHOPKEEPERS.
Berry Mary, Bond street
Coles Patience, Fore street
Cook Henry, Tower street
Culley Wm., Fore street
Dyer George, Chapel street
Hannaford Ann, Wellington place
Harding Jane, Fore street
Hayne Florence, Parade
Roberts Susan, South town
Sellers Ann, Vicarage hill
Smith George, Fore street
Snow Edward, Tower street
Walker Eleanor, Wanhill row
Ware Jane, Strand
Withall Richard, Strand
Yarde John, Baring place

STRAW HAT MAKERS.
Bartlett Mary Jane, Tower street
Crofts Caroline, Strand
Dixon Jane Dove, Back street
Davey Sarah, Charles street
Grace Charlotte, 45 Bicton street
Hallett Matilda, Ivy cottage
Mitchell Mary Jane, Adelaide place
Payne Mary, Exeter road
Peak Margaret, Parker's lane
Pincombe Sarah, Tower street
Skinner Ann, Tower street
Thompson Eliz., Chapel street
Winsor A., Strand
Wishart James, Fore street

SURGEONS.
Kane Wm., M.D., Beacon hill
Land Wm. Henry, Strand
Spettigue John, Bicton terrace
Ward Thos. Morris, Ormond ter
Waters Allan, 6 Louisa terrace

TAILORS.
(* are Drapers also.)
Best James, Fore street
*Bishop George, Strand
Elliott Wm., Bicton street
Grace Thomas, Fore street
*Grigg James, Strand
Knight Samuel, Chapel street
Liffton and Son, Strand
*Melluish James, Bond street
Redway Thos. (clothier,) Strand
Southcott Hy. (constable,) Fore st
Winter Chas. (clothier,) Chapel st
*Youldon John, The Cross

TINNERS AND BRAZIERS.
Howe John, Fore street

Littlejohn James, Tower street
Plimsoll John, Strand
TOY DEALERS.
Elston Mary, Strand
White George, Vicarage hill
WATCH & CLOCK MAKERS.
Carter Edward, Parade
Hill Wm. W. (& jeweller,) Strand
Maynard Wm., Staple's buildings
Nicks John, The Parade
Veals James, Wellington place
WHEELWRIGHTS.
Axon Wm., South town
Hensley Wm., Fore street
WINE & SPIRIT MERCHTS.
Bastin Henry and Benjamin Butter,
Wellington House

Langsford Thomas, Beacon hill

COACHES from the Globe Hotel
and London Inn, daily, to *Exeter,*
at 8½ morng. and 5 afternoon; and
to *Budleigh Salterton* at 10 mrng.

CARRIERS to *Exeter,* daily, Robt.
Hayne, Bond street; John Hayne,
Wanhill row; and James Wood,
Union street

RAILWAY.—The Ferry Boat takes
passengers, at 6d. each, to *Star-
Cross Station,* on the opposite side
of the estuary, whence trains run
to Exeter, Plymouth, &c.

LYMPSTONE, a pretty village, with several large and handsome houses, is pleasantly seated on the eastern bank of the broad estuary of the river Exe, about 2 miles N. by W. of Exmouth, and 8 miles S.S.E. of Exeter. It has in its parish 999 inhabitants, and 1866 acres of land, including *Sowden* hamlet, and rising picturesquely from the principal street, which extends on a level near the estuary. Leland describes Lympstone as a "pretty townlet," with a "great trade in shippes;" and it is still a very considerable fishing station, having about 60 small fishing boats, and large beds of oysters in the estuary, brought there to fatten, from the sea coast near Exmouth. The village may be considered as a suburb of the watering place of Exmouth, and has many commodious lodgings, for the accommodation of visitors, who throng here during the proper season. The manor, anciently called Leningston, was given by Henry I. to William, his steward. It afterwards passed to the Damarell, Dinham, Prideaux, Putt, and Heathfield families. It passed from the late Lord Heathfield to Sir Thomas F. E.-Drake, Bart., its present owner; but a great part of the parish belongs to Capt. Wright, Chas. Gifford, W. H. Hull, Wm. Spicer, W. H. Peters, and Thomas Porter, Esqrs., and a few smaller owners. The *Church* (St. Mary,) is a fine old structure, with an embattled tower, and five bells. It is said to have been rebuilt in 1409; but the nave, aisles, and chancel, have undergone many repairs and alterations. It was enlarged in 1830, and the east window was enriched with stained glass by the late rector. The beautiful altar-piece was given by Mrs. Wyatt, and the organ purchased by subscription in 1845. The *rectory,* valued in K.B. at £15. 13s. 4d., and in 1831 at £300, is in the patronage of Thomas Porter, Esq., and incumbency of the Rev. Edmond Strong, M.A., of Clist St. Mary. The Rectory House, occupied by the curate, is a neat residence. The glebe is 12A. 3R. 14P., and the tithes were commuted, in 1838, for £264 per annum. The *Unitarians* have a district chapel in the adjoining parish of Woodbury, built in 1774, and a small one at Lympstone, built in 1820, but the latter is now let to the *Wesleyans.* The poor of Lympstone have the dividends of £500, three per cent Consols, left by *Wm.*

Spicer, Esq., in 1848. A yearly rent-charge of £4 was left in 1727, by *Henry Metherell*, for schooling poor children of this parish. The interest of £20, left by *John Egerton*, in 1730, is paid for the same purpose; as also is £2. 13s. 4d., of the yearly dividends of £270, three per cent. Consols, left in 1818, by *Wakelin Welch*, who directed two-thirds of the income to be distributed in blankets among the poor. The *National Schools* form a neat building, erected in 1823, by the late Mrs. Eliz. Welch, relict of the last named donor. Mrs. Wyatt allows the mistress £24 a year; and the boys' school is supported partly by subscription. In 1829, *John Denning* left the dividends of £100, three per cent. Consols, towards the support of the Sunday school.

Adney Capt. John ‖ Lock Mrs
Bennett Henry B., *Metherell's*
Burch Jas. plumber, painter, &c
Burgmann Lady ‖ Claxton Mrs L.
Coventon Mr Wm., *Underhill*
Crespin Capt. Henry, R.N.
Fley Wm. cider merchant
Gardner Wm. mason
Hamlin Thos. lodgings, *Brook Cottg*
Harbottle Thos. R., *Sowden Villa*
Harris John, horse and fly letter
Hawker Ann, lodgings
Hilliker Eliza, milliner
Howell Elizabeth, staymaker
James Rev Wm. ‖ Kilner Mrs My.
Langdon Mary Ann, schoolmistress
Lefevre Belfield, M.D.
Lewin Lady Caroline
Linscott Thomas, corn miller and maltster, *Sowden*
Linscott Wm. corn miller
Moorshead Rev J. A., M.A., curate, *Rectory*
Newberry Wm. traveller
Palmer James, cooper
Pengilly Mrs ‖ Munhall Miss
Perry Mrs ‖ Pennell Philip, sexton
Peters Wm. Hy., Esq. *Harefield Hs*
Price Rees Charles, surgeon
Reynolds Mrs G. ‖ Powell Mrs
Rider Edw. druggist, wine and spirit merchant, and agent to Norwich Union Fire and Life Office
Shears Richard, master mariner
Squire Rev Edmd. (Unitn.) *Underhill*
Upcott Chas. Haynes, watchmaker
Venman John, stone mason
Williams Mrs. *Sowden House*
Williams Miss Mary Ann
Windover Edward, saddler
Wolland Saml. Thorne, schoolmr
Wolridge Capt. Wm., R.N., *Nutwell*

Wright Capt. Wm. Hy. & Miss Emily
Wyatt Mrs Henrietta, *Strawberry hill*

INNS AND TAVERNS.
Globe, Mary Ann Voysey
New Inn, John Stanton
Saddlers' Arms, Samuel Darby
Swan Inn, Wm. Linscott, corn dlr

BAKERS.
Linscott James
Taylor Thomas
Ware James

BLACKSMITHS.
Carter Francis
Hutchings John, (& wheelwght)
Jackson Henry
Marshall Wm.

BOOT & SHOE MKS.
Carslake Abrm.
Crabb Saml.
Hawkins Saml.
Hilliker James
Lacey Henry
Quick Thomas
Pyne Thomas
Saunders John
Silvester Fredk.
Upcott John

BUTCHERS.
Mitchell W. F.
Till Edward

CARPENTERS.
Coventon John
Searle Fras. Y.
Sivill John

COAL MERCHTS.
Skinner James
Widdicombe Ths.

FARMERS.
Bridle George
Cowd Wm.
Fley Richard

Hill Charles
Linscott Thos.
Manley Saml.
Mitchell Wm.
Neck John
Ridge Henry
Stamp Philip

GROCERS & DPRS.
Crabb Richd. (& parish clerk)
Parsons John
Searl Thos. Yarde (& spirit mert)

SHOPKEEPERS.
Blampin Jonas
Clapp John
Membury Saml.
Woodley Oliver

TAILORS.
Cowd John
Cowd Philip
Johnson Robt.
Membury Saml.

TINNERS, &c.
Edwards John
Shears Chpr.

POST-OFFICE
at Rd. Crabb's.
Letters desp. 10 mg. & 6¼ evg.

COACHES to *Exeter, &c.* dly
CARRIERS *to Exeter,* Denning
C. & Wood J. dly

OTTERTON, a long village, on the eastern bank of the river Otter, within a mile of the sea, and 11 miles S.E. by E. of Exeter, has in its parish 1245 souls, and 3500 acres of land, extending southward to the mouth of the Otter, and including the small hamlets of *Northmost-town, Pitson, Passford,* and *Pinn.* Many of the female inhabitants are employed in making Honiton lace; and two *fairs* are held here on the Wednesday in Easter week, and the Wednesday after October 10. King John founded here a *Priory* of four monks, subject to St. Michael's Abbey, in Normandy, and endowed it with the manors of Otterton, Sidmouth, and East Budleigh. These monks were to perform divine service, and to distribute 16s. worth of bread weekly among the poor. As an alien priory it was dissolved by Henry III., and given to Sion Abbey. At the dissolution, its yearly revenues were valued at £87. 10s., and granted to *Richd. Duke,* whose family was seated here till 1741. The Trustees of the late Lord Rolle are now lords of the manor of Otterton, owners of most of the parish, impropriators of the great tithes, and patrons of the *vicarage,* valued in K.B. at £22, and in 1831 at £314. The Ven. J. M. Stevens, M.A., is the *vicar,* and has a good residence, and 28A. of glebe. The vicarial tithes were commuted in 1846 for £336 per annum. The vicar is entitled to the tithes of beans and fish, all small tithes, and the lands called the Sanctuary. The *Church* (St. Michael,) is an ancient cruciform structure, with a tower and five bells. The transept was rebuilt by the late Lord Rolle, about ten years ago. There was anciently a chapel at a place called Hederland. The National and Infant Schools are chiefly supported by Lady Rolle, and £25 per annum left by the late Lord Rolle. For a monthly distribution of bread, the poor have £5 per annum from the Trustees of the late Lord Rolle, as interest of £100 left by *Henry Austin,* in 1701. They have also £5 yearly from the same Trustees, as interest of £100 left by *Richard Duke,* in 1745; and a yearly rent charge of 10s., left by a *Mr. Channon,* out of a field at Crediton. A house and garden, occupied by paupers, are supposed to have been purchased with £20, left by Anthony Isaack, in 1639.

Marked 2, are at Passford; 3, *Pinn;* 4, *Pitson;* 5, *Northmost-town;* and the rest in Otterton.

Grosse Wm. schoolmaster
Hallett Henry, carpenter, &c
Palmer John, vict., King's Arms
Sanders Sarah, schoolmistress
Stephens Jno. draper, (& Sidmouth)
Stevens Ven. John Moore, M.A. archdeacon of Exeter, & vicar of Otterton
Tidbury Thomas, saddler
Uglow John, corn miller

BAKERS.
Bridle James
Roberts Henry
BEERHOUSES.
Bastin Wm.

Pile Michael
BLACKSMITHS.
Gosling Wm.
Northcott Richd.
Patch Wm.

BOOT & SHOE MRS.
Hine John
Miller John
Patch Thomas
Pile John
Pile Michael
BUTCHERS.
Drake Robert
Harding Captain
FARMERS.
Bridle James
Bridle Robert
Bridle Wm.
Carter Thomas
5 Chown Robert
3 Drake Robert
Drake Wm.

4 Dyer Joel
Harding Charles
2 Halse Abm.
2 Halse Henry
3 Harding Richd.
Harding Wm.
Hayman Edward
Hayman Joel
3 Pile Thomas
Pile Samuel
2 Pile Wm.
3 Pile Wm.
5 Pile Wm.
Robins Richard
5 Rutter John
Skinner Jacob
Skinner Isaac

L

Tidbury Thomas	Hitt Henry	Pile Thomas	Till Robert
3 White Thos.	Northcott Richd.	Pinn Wm.	POST - OFFICE
2 White Thomas	Sanford Wm. (&	Sanford Thomas	at J. Palmer's.
SHOPKEEPERS.	par. clerk)	WHEELWRIGHTS.	Letters despd.
Bastin Michael	Till Robert	Baker John	4½ afternoon
Carter George	Wheeler Hannah	Patch Wm.	CARRIER, John
Hayman John	TAILORS.	Robins Sharman	Redford, to Ex-
Helling Agnes	Anger Francis	Robins Wm.	eter, Tu. & Fri.

ROCKBEARE, a small straggling village, six miles E.N.E. of Exeter, and five miles W. of Ottery St. Mary, has in its parish 513 souls, and 2309 acres of land, including the small village of *Marsh-Green*, more than 1½ mile S.E. of the church, and many scattered farms, &c. The soil is generally fertile, and the surface boldly undulated. The common, about 200A., was enclosed in 1849. In the reign of Edward III., the manor was given to Canonleigh Abbey, by the Countess of Gloucester. It was long the seat and property of the Sainthill family, of whom it was purchased by Thos. Porter, Esq., of Nutwell House, the present lord of the manor, and owner of a great part of the soil, and of *Rockbeare House*, which he rebuilt after purchasing the old mansion of Sir J. L. Duntze, Bart., whose father resided here. The present mansion is a handsome structure, with pleasant grounds, about a mile S.E. of the church. It is occupied by H. F. Bidgood, Esq., who has a large estate here, and whose family was long seated in a house near the church. *Westcott* is the seat and property of the Rev. John Elliott. Mrs. Ann and Mr. Edward Payne, and a few smaller owners have estates in the parish. The *Church* (St. Mary,) is an antique fabric, with a tower and five bells ; and in its burial ground is a monument in memory of Sir John and Lady Duntze, who died in 1795 and 1801. The Bishop of Exeter is appropriator of the rectory, and patron of the *vicarage*, valued in K.B. at £9, and in 1831 at £160. The Rev. Hy. Nicholls, M.A., is the incumbent, and has 21A. of glebe, and a good residence, built in 1833. The vicarial tithes were commuted in 1846 for £150 per annum. Here is a small *Independent chapel*, erected in 1840. The poor parishioners have the dividends of £97. 7s. 3d. three per cent. consols, purchased with money left by *John Stile*, and other donors. In 1702, *Lawrence Colesworthy* charged Allercombe estate with the yearly payment of £4, for schooling poor children, and 20s. for yearly distribution among 20 poor labouring men of this parish. *Radford Wild* charged Woodhouse estate with the yearly payment of 10s. for a sermon, and 15s. for the poor. The *Rev. Charles Bidgood* left 12s. a year, out of Farm estate, for a monthly distribution of bread among the poor.

Marked 2, are at Marsh Green ; 3, at Allercombe ; 4, at Southwood ; 5, at Upcott ; and the rest in Rockbeare, or where specified.

Bidgood Hy. F., Esq., *Rockbeare Hs*
Brooks Chas. vict., Bidgood Arms
2 Chown Charles, bricklayer
Clode John, shopkeeper
Elliott Rev. John, *Westcott*
Fursdon John, tailor

Leake Wm. wheelgt. & timber mert.
Nicholls Rev. Hy. M.A. vicar of Rockbeare and Peyhembury
Payne Mrs Ann, *Ford House*
Pearse Assa, wheelwright
2 Pratt George, blacksmith
Reed & Sparke, brick & tile makers
2 Stile John, bricklayer & builder
Toby Thomas, carpenter
Tripe Richard, baker

FARMERS.	5 Elliott Bridget	Pike Wm., *Copse*	Trickey James
Bastin Richard	2 Knowles Thos.	Pile Thomas	Tripe James
2 Bishop John	Marker Wm.	2 ReynoldsNichs.	2 Tuck Philip
2 Blackmore Jno.	4 Roberts John	Roberts John	SHOEMAKERS.
5 Carter Oliver	Page Jno. *butcher*	3 Skinner Geo.	Godfrey Richard
Chapple Robert	3 Patch Wm.	Simmons John	Pratt Rd. *par. clk.*
Chown Wm.	Payne Edw.,*Ford*	2 Smart J.	2 Silway Henry
Cox N., *Westcott*	2 Payne Robert		

SALCOMBE-REGIS is a small village, about two miles E.N.E. of Sidmouth, and 16 miles E. by S. of Exeter, picturesquely seated in the Sid valley, sheltered by boldly swelling hills, which terminate in the lofty red sandstone sea cliffs. Its parish is bounded on two sides by the sea and the river Sid, and contains 525 souls, 1909 acres of land, and several neat mansions, with tasteful grounds, commanding extensive views of the coast and the English Channel. It includes the small hamlet of *Seed* or *Sid*, and a number of scattered farm houses, &c. The manor was given to Exeter Cathedral by King Canute, but was sold by the Dean and Chapter, under the powers of the land tax redemption act of 1801, when three-fourths of it was purchased by the late Geo. Cornish, Esq. The Rev. Geo. Jas. Cornish is now lord of the manor, but a great part of the soil belongs to C. J. Cornish, Esq., J. M. Wolcott, Esq., C. W. Smith, Esq., and several smaller owners. *Salcombe House,* the seat of C. J. Cornish, Esq., is a large and handsome mansion, standing in a pleasant lawn, upon a bold eminence overlooking Sidmouth. Near it is *Sid Cliff,* where John Tyrrell, Esq., has a neat mansion, with tasteful grounds, recently much improved. *Sid Hill* rises 500 feet above the level of the sea. *Knowle House* is the seat and property of J. M. Wolcott, Esq., and has long been held by his family. The *Church* (St. Peter and St. Mary,) is a fine Norman structure, with a tower and three bells, but has undergone many repairs and alterations. There was anciently a chapel in the parish, dedicated to St. Clement and Mary Magdalen. The parish is in the peculiar jurisdiction of the Dean and Chapter of Exeter, who are appropriators of the great tithes, and patrons of the *vicarage,* valued in K.B. at £14. 12s. 8d., and in 1831 at £160, and now enjoyed by the Rev. J. H. Cardew, B.D., of Curry-Mallett, Somersetshire, for whom the Rev. W. B. Doveton, M.A., officiates. The tithes were commuted in 1739, and the glebe is about nine acres. The parish school is supported by subscription, and attended by about 40 day and 80 Sunday scholars.

Campbell Miss Martha
Christie Thos. W.,Esq., *Salcombe Mt*
Clark Mrs Eliza, *Sid Abbey*
Cornish Chas. Jno.,Esq.,*Salcombe Hs*
Cornish Miss Caroline, *Egypt House*
Doveton Rev.Wm.Blake,M.A.curate, *Vicarage*
Dudley John, gent. || Pinn Miss A.
Hewertson Wm., Esq., *Chelson*
Lloyd Capt. Saml., R.N., *Sid House*
Maunder Mr James
Mortimore Geo., Esq., *Lodge*
Pinney Wm. mason & parish clerk
Smith Chas. Webb, gent., *Hill Cotg*
Stapleton Capt. Wm., *Salcombe Cotg*
Tyrrell John, Esq. judge of county court, *Sid Cliff*
Winsley Robt. wheelwright, *Sid*
Wolcott John Marwood, Esq., and Mrs. Eliz., *Knowle House*

Yates Wm. Wingfield, Esq., *Hill Hs* | Pearse Thomas | Thorne John
FARMERS. | Godfrey Hy., *Sid* | Pike James | Trump John
Butter Thomas | Moore Henry | Roberts James |
Clark Wm. | Newberry Thos., | Silway Samuel |
Cox Mrs | *Dunscombe* | |

SIDBURY, an ancient compact village, in the picturesque valley of the river Sid, three miles N.N.E. of Sidmouth, is sheltered on either side by verdant hills, and had formerly a weekly market on Wednesday, pursuant to a grant of the Dean and Chapter of Exeter. Its market has long been obsolete, but it has still two annual *fairs*, on the Tuesday before Holy Thursday, and the Wednesday before September 20th. The latter is chiefly for cattle and cheese. The parish of Sidbury comprises 8220 acres of land, and had 1772 inhabitants in 1841, but has now about 2000. It includes the long village of SIDFORD, half way between Sidbury and Sidmouth, where there is a good bridge, on the Exeter and Lyme Regis road. It rises in bold hills on both sides of the valley, and comprises many scattered farm-houses, and several handsome villas, with tasteful grounds, commanding pleasing views. The gross yearly rental of the parish is £10,500. On the narrow ridge of *Castle-hill* is an entrenchment, 1400 feet long, and about 300 broad. It is supposed to have been formed by the ancient Britons, and afterwards used by the Romans, Saxons, and Danes. The manor of Sidbury was held from an early period by the Dean and Chapter of Exeter, who sold it in 1801, to Wm. Guppy, Esq., and other freeholders, of whom it was purchased by the late Robt. Hunt, Esq. *Court Hall*, the manor house, is the seat and property of Henry Hunt, Esq., and he and his family own *Woodhouse, Wootton, Sidbury House, Plyford*, and other estates in this large parish. The manor of *Stone and Sidford* was anciently held by the De la Stane family, and afterwards by the Pym, Periam, Pole, and Bartlett families. *Mincombe* and *Sand* estates were held at an early period by families of their own names; but the former now belongs to J. M. Wolcott, Esq., and the latter to John Huyshe, Esq. *Cotford House*, the seat and property of W. R. Bayley, Esq., is a large and handsome mansion, built in 1847, at the cost of £8000. It stands near the site of the old house, in an extensive and well wooded lawn, commanding beautiful views of the surrounding hills. W. Hewertson, Esq., owns Knapp estate, on which he has enclosed and cultivated, during the last six years, about 200 acres of land, formerly a steril common. Jas. Cunningham, Esq., the Rev. T. J. Marker, Thos. Glanville, Esq., and several smaller freeholders, have estates in the parish. The *Church* (St. Giles,) is a fine structure, of Norman and perpendicular architecture, which has undergone many repairs and alterations. The Norman tower was rebuilt in the original style in 1843, at the cost of £500. It contains a clock and six musical bells, and is crowned by a short spire. Two antique stone figures, found in the walls of the old tower, are now placed on either side of the western door. The aisles are separated from the nave and chancel by finely carved arches. The windows are in the perpendicular style, but that at the east end has evidently been altered

from the Norman style, as the external ornaments are of that character. The parish is in the peculiar jurisdiction of the Dean and Chapter of Exeter, who are also appropriators of the great tithes, and patrons of the *vicarage*, valued in K.B. at £28, and in 1831 at £576. The Rev. Hy. Fellowes, M.A., is the incumbent, and has six acres of glebe, and a neat residence, built in 1814, at the cost of £1200. The small tithes were commuted in 1843, for £616 per annum. The *Independent Chapel*, erected here by Presbyterians in 1715, was rebuilt in 1820, at the cost of about £600. It will seat 350 hearers, and is now under the ministry of the Rev. Chas. Howell. The *National School* was built in 1830, at the cost of £320, of which £150 was given by the National Society. For distribution in money, clothing, &c., the poor parishioners have £76. 15s. per annum, arising as follows:—£39 from a house and 34A. of land, left by *Henry Beaumont*, in the 35th of Elizabeth; £25 from 18A. of *Poor Land, at Venn Ottery*, purchased in 1665 by the feoffees of the parish; £6 from 1½A. of land, purchased with £60 left by *Anthony Isaack*, in 1631; and £6. 16s. from two acres called *Stephen's Cross Land*, given by an unknown donor. They have also £5 a year out of Sandcombe estate, left by *Anna Atleigh;* and £1 a year out of Harcombe estate, left by *Timothy Staple*, in 1637.

*Those marked * are in SIDFORD, and the rest in SIDBURY village, or where specified.*

Anning Mr. Jas. || Barrett W. *carter*
Bayley Wm. Rutter, Esq., *Cotford Hs*
Beard Wm. B. steward, *Knapp Farm*
Bishop Mrs. || *Broadbridge J. gent
Clode Isaac, lace manufacturer
Cockel Miss Cath., *Ivy Cottage*
Coulbourn G. & Rt. gent., *Covehill H*
Crabb Henry, cooper
Darke Edwin, thatcher
Darke Mary, schoolmistress
Darke Thomas, parish clerk
Down Wm. policeman
*Ebdon Mr Edm.|| Follett Mr Edm.
Elphinstone Capt. Alex. F., R.N.
Farrant Robert, gardener
Fellowes Rev Hy., M.A., *Vicarage*
Fitzgerald Major Chas., *Mount Edgar*
*Godfrey Mr Jas. || Hamlin Mr Hy.
Guppy Capt J. & Misses, *Roncombe*
Hawkins Geo. corn miller, *Cotford*
Hayman Emma, lace maker
Hewertson Wm., Esq., *Knapp Farm*
Howell Rev Chas. (Independent)
Hunt Rev Chas. A., *Buckley*
Hunt H., Esq., & Mrs Mgt., *Court Hl*
Hutchings James, road contractor
Lapatowcal Hy. gent., *Castle Hill*
Luke Edw. gent., *Primley Cottage*
Moore Thomas, poulterer

*Paltridge Emma, schoolmistress
Pinn Wm. chair maker
Pinn Thomas, tanner
Reed Wm. corn miller
Rickards Wm. mason
Searle John, gent., *Buscombe*
Teed Samuel, butcher
Walker Mrs Ellen, *Lyme Park*
Wheler Mr John || Taylor Mrs E.

PUBLIC HOUSES.
*Blue Ball, Richard Cawley
Hare and Hounds, James White
Red Lion, Robt. Gosling, *builder*
Royal Oak, Thomas Cox

BAKERS.
Clode Isaac
Hayman James
*Horn James
BEERHOUSES.
Cox James
Gould J. *mason*
*Thorn Joseph
*Taylor John
BLACKSMITHS.
Baker Elias
Baker John
Clarke John
*Teed James
BOOT&SHOE MRS.
Amor Wm.
Bovett John
Carslake Timy.

Page Samuel
Salmon Richard
Stark John
*Taylor Joel
*Wheaton Wm.
CARPENTERS.
Brown Robert
Gosling Robert
Maeer John
*Reed George
Wheeker Chas.
FARMERS.
Alford Wm.
Bradbeer Ephm.
Broom Amos
Capron George
*Cawley Richard
*Cawley Thomas

Chown John
England Robert, *Goosemoor*
Griffin Thomas
Halse John, *Mincombe*
Hamlin Joseph
Hooke W. *butcher*
Irish Henry
King Jas., *Sand*
Lee Jno., *Harcmb*
Maeer Wm.
Matthews John
Mitchell Henry

Mogridge James
Moore Wm.
Nosworthy John
Oldrey Wm.
Pym W., *Lincmb*
Smith W., *Rolle's*
Snell Jno., *Sand*
Solman W., *Yard*
*Stone Wm.
Sweetland James
Tilke J. *butcher*
Tripe Jno., *Brook*
Warren G. *Woottn*

White George
GROCERS & DPRS.
Hayman Thos.
Hayman Martha
Heyward My. A.
*Symons Ann
SHOPKEEPERS.
Daniels Henry
Darke Sarah
*Gill Wm.
Wheeker Smn.
TAILORS.
*Stoke Joshua

Watts Wm.
Welsman John
WHEELWRIGHTS.
Brown Wm.
*Gill Wm.
POST - OFFICE
at James Hayman's. Letters
desp. 4½ aftn.
CARRIER to Exeter, Hy. Mitchell, Tues. &
Fri.

SIDMOUTH ranks next Torquay and Exmouth among the fashionable watering places on the southern coast of Devonshire, and surpasses them both as a warm winter residence for invalids, especially those afflicted with pulmonary complaints. It is a pretty market town and bathing place, picturesquely seated at the mouth of the small river Sid ;—open on the south to the English Channel, but sheltered on every other side by the towering sea cliffs, and the verdant hills, rising boldly on either side of the deep valley, to the height of nearly 500 feet above the level of the sea. It is distant 16 miles E. by S. of Exeter, 6 miles S. by E. of Ottery St. Mary, and 10 miles E.N.E. of Exmouth. Its parish contains 1539 acres of land, and increased its population from 1252 in 1801, to 3309 souls in 1841, and they have since been augmented to about 4000. It is said to have been a borough, under the government of a port-reeve, in the 13th century, and to have been, at a much later period, an important fishing station, until the loss of its fishermen and boats, in a severe storm, at an unknown date. We do not find any records of the borough, or of the grant of its market; and it was but an inconsiderable place about 50 years ago, when it began to put forth its pretensions to cure the evils attendant upon luxury and disease ; and if we may judge from the rapid increase of residences and accommodations for that purpose, within the last fifteen years, the public seems to have assented to the claim. The *market* is held every Saturday, and the market-place is also well supplied with provision on Tuesday and Thursday. Here are two annual *fairs*, on Easter Monday and the third Monday in September. There are here a few small fishing boats, a fort, and a coastguard station ; and about 400 women and children are employed in making Honiton lace. The manor of Sidmouth was given by Wm. the Conqueror to the abbey of St. Michael, in Normandy. During the succeeding wars with France, it was given to Sion Abbey. After the dissolution of the monasteries, it was successively leased to the Gosnell, Periam, and Mainwaring families. In the reign of James I., Chpr. Mainwaring, Esq., sold it to Sir Edward Prideaux, Bart., whose descendant sold it to Thomas Jenkins, Esq., whose nephew sold it to Edward Hughes Ball Hughes, Esq., the present proprietor, to whom the town is indebted for many of its modern improvements.

In 1839, an act of parliament was obtained, for building the present commodious *Market-house*, and granting the market dues to the lord of the manor. In 1835, the inhabitants, fearful of the incursions of the sea, which are continually wasting neighbouring parts of the coast, commenced the erection of the excellent *sea wall*, which cost about £2500, of which £1200 was given by the lord of the manor. It was completed in 1838, and affords a dry and very agreeable promenade, upwards of 1700 feet in length. The town is well lighted with *gas*, and has recently been supplied with pure soft *water*, from the Cotmaton springs. It has some highly respectable shops, several good inns and hotels, and many well furnished lodging-houses and villas, suitable for the middle and higher classes of visitors. *Petty Sessions* are held at the Market Hall about once a month, by the magistrates of Woodbury Division. In 1820, Sidmouth was recommended as the residence of the late Duke of Kent, then in a very delicate state of health. He came here accompanied by the Duchess and her present Majesty, but died after a short residence, in the 53rd year of his age. That distinguished statesman, the late Rt. Hon. Henry Addington, was created *Viscount Sidmouth*, in 1805, and in 1844 was succeeded by his eldest son, the present Viscount, who resides at Richmond Park, Surrey, and occasionally at Up Ottery, in this neighbourhood.

The beach at Sidmouth is situated in one of those hollows, or curves, of which there are many in the vast bay of Devon and Dorset, extending from Start Point in the former, to the Isle of Portland in the latter county. On the east and west sides of the town rise two immense hills, about 500 feet high, running northward from the peaked cliffs, with a deep valley between them, through which the little river Sid runs to the sea. Along the bottom of this valley lies the town, with a considerable part of its front towards the sea. On the slopes of the valley, extending about a mile inland, are the suburbs, studded with villas, *cottage-ornées*, and every description of marine residence. The bottom of the valley is an alluvial deposit, formed by the denudation of the hills ; and the escarpments on the rugged and precipitate face of the lofty cliffs shew the stratification of the new red sandstone formations, capped in some places with the upper green sand, and in others with small portions of the chalk formation. Many feet of hard limestone rock crown the top of Dunscombe hill, though great quantities have been taken away for building purposes. These rocks are highly fossiliferous ; many beds of shells, both bivalve and univalve, occur among them ; and various *ammonites* and *echinites* are not rare. The *beach* is pebbly and shelving, and the pebbles consist chiefly of rolled flints, and marbles, often of great beauty ; green sand pebbles, wood agates, chalcedony, and other siliceous productions are often found. Some of them contain crystals of carbonate of lime, which possess the double refracting power of Iceland spar. It was proposed to construct a *harbour* at Sidmouth in 1811, and the subject was revived in 1836, when the first stone was laid with much ceremony ; but after expending a large sum of money, the work was discontinued, as impracticable, or not worth the great expense which its

completion would have required. There are usually nine *bathing machines* on the beach; and on the Esplanade is a commodious *Bath House*, fitted up in a superior manner, with hot, cold, tepid, and shower baths. There is a large *Assembly Room* at the London Hotel; well supplied *Subscription Reading Rooms*, &c., in the late Bedford Hotel; and two large circulating libraries in Fore street. Pleasure boats, wheel chairs, carriages, horses, and donkeys, are always ready for the accommodation of visitors, on reasonable terms. *Fortfield* has recently been appropriated as a place of resort for the public and the Sidmouth cricket club; and the town and neighbourhood afford an inexhaustible mine for the study and amusement of the botanist, geologist, and conchologist, as well as to the lover of picturesque scenery. Balls and concerts are frequently held at the Assembly Rooms; and on every Monday afternoon from July to October, visitors are allowed to inspect *Knowle Castle*, the delightful marine villa of T. L. Fish, Esq. This elegant and tasteful residence is a thatched quadrangular building, of one story, containing about 30 rooms, and surrounded by about 11 acres of ground, divided into lawns, gardens, and conservatories, containing rare and choice specimens of botany, as well as many fine specimens of foreign birds and animals. In the house, are several suites of rooms, with tables, on which are spread innumerable articles of bijouterie, vases, minerals, shells, china, &c. *Cotmaton Hall* is the handsome seat of John Carslake, Esq.; and here are several other large and elegant mansions, occupied by wealthy families. The manor of *Radway* belongs to the Jenkins family; and that of *Old Hayes* was held by the late Lord Gwydir. Several beautiful seats in the neighbouring parishes of Salcombe, Sidbury, Bicton, &c., are noticed at other pages.

The *Parish Church* of Sidmouth, dedicated to *St. Nicholas*, was originally in the perpendicular style; but from the alterations and additions of the last and present century, very little of its ancient character remains. It has a tower and six bells, one of which was added in 1844, by T. L. Fish, Esq. A south aisle and gallery were added in 1822, and the church has now room for about 1500 hearers. The Rev. Wm. Jenkins, M.A., is impropriator of the great tithes, and also patron and incumbent of the *vicarage*, valued in K.B. at £18. 15s. 5d., and in 1831 at £484. The tithes were commuted in 1839, and the glebe is about 23 acres. The *New Church*, dedicated to *All Saints*, is a small neat chapel of ease, at the north end of the town, erected in 1839, at the cost of about £2000, raised by subscription. It has a small endowment, and about 800 sittings. The living is a *perpetual curacy*, in the gift of Sir J. Kennaway and others, and incumbency of the Rev. H. Gibbes. Here is an old *Unitarian Chapel*, built about two centuries ago, by Presbyterians. The *Independent Chapel* is a neat building, erected in 1846, at the cost of £1200. Here is also a *Wesleyan Chapel*, built in 1837, at the cost of £600; and the Plymouth Brethren meet in a schoolroom at Fort-field. *Sunday Schools* are attached to all the places of worship; and large *National Schools*, for boys, girls, and infants, are connected with the parish church, and supported partly by sub-

scription and a portion of the parochial charitable funds. *All Saints Church School* was built by subscription, in 1848, and has a house for the mistress. Here is also a *British School*, commenced in 1848. The self-supporting *Dispensary* was established in 1836, for the medical relief of the sick and infirm, who contribute small weekly payments. Religious societies are supported by the congregations of the churches and chapels; and the town also supports a Poor's Friend Society, a Ladies' Benevolent Society, a Penny Club, a Coal Charity, a Blanket Charity, &c.; and has a Masonic Lodge, and several Benefit Societies. The *Gas Works* were established in 1837, and the *Water Works* in 1845, but the latter were enlarged in 1849.

The *Poor's Lands, &c.*, which have been long vested with twelve feoffees, in trust for the poor, and public uses in Sidmouth parish, comprise 22A. 1R. 7P. at Salcombe, let on long leases for £32. 11s.; and 16 acres at Harpford, let for £18 a year. They were partly purchased with £120 left by *Anthony Isaack*, in 1639, and partly received in exchange for some parish land at Dawlish. The rent of the land at Harpford is applied in providing sacramental bread and wine, and in paying the organist's salary. The rent of the land at Salcombe is applied in schooling poor children, repairing the church, and relieving the poor. An old almshouse, given by *John Arthur*, in the 26th of Elizabeth, was exchanged about 1805, for the piece of land on which the parish school and poor-house are built. The *Sexton's House*, given by an unknown donor, was rebuilt about 20 years ago. A tenement, let for three lives, in 1808, for 5s., but now worth £15 per annum, is supposed to have been left to the poor by *Robert Blower*. The master of the parish school has the dividends of £30 old South Sea Annuities, purchased with £40 left by the Rev. — *Burroughs*. The poor have the interest of £60, left by John Conant and John Curtis; and of £50, left by Oliver Cawley, in 1779.

SIDMOUTH DIRECTORY.

POST-OFFICE at Mr. Reuben Barratt's, Fore street. Letters are received and despatched every morning and evening.

Those marked 1 reside in Church street; 2, Chapel street; 3, Fore street; 4, High street; 5, Market place; 6, Marsh lane; 7, New street; 8, Old Fore street; and 9, in Temple street.

Andros Capt. Wm., *Summerland Cotg*
2 Austin Wm. veterinary surgeon
Barratt Wm. lodgings, *Bedford Hs*
Bayley Capt. C. B., R.N., *Sidlands*
Baynes Mrs A. F., *Woolbrook Glen*
Bernard Wm. gent., *Cottington House*
4 Berry Jas. solicitor's clerk
3 Blackmore Mrs Agnes
Blencowe Rev Jas., *Fort House*
Brown Capt. Wm. 9 Fortfield ter
Buckinghamshire Rt. Hon. & Rev. the Earl of, *Richmond Lodge*
Carew Hy., Esq., *Ayshford Cottage*
Carslake Hy. Jph. gent., Spring gdns
Carslake John, Esq., *Cotmaton Hall*
Clapp John, cooper, Temple street
Clarke Mrs. *Sid Abbey*
Coke Wm., Esq., *Green Bank*
4 Coombes Christiana, stay maker
4 Colesworthy Richd. gent
Coplestone Miss Fras. 5 Fortfield ter
Cornish Misses, *Blackmore Hall*
Cornish Chas. Jno., Esq., *Salcombe H*
8 Cowd Wm. town crier
Creighton Mrs., Cobourg terrace
Cullen Wm.Hy.,M.D., surgn., High st
Cunningham Jas., Esq., *Witheby*

Dawson Pudsey, Esq., and Misses, Audley Cottage
Dawson Rd. K., Esq., High bank
Dawson Mrs K. 7 Fort field
Dennis Mrs Emily, 8 Fort field ter
Dolphin Capt. James, High street
2 Dorman Geo. carrier
Drury Mrs. *Asherton*
Elliott Mrs Mary, Emmett's row
1 Ellis R. M. music professor
Elphinstone Capt., *Livonia Cottage*
4 Farrant Chas. Edmd. auctioneer,&c
Fish Thos. L., Esq., *Knowle Cottage*
Fitzgerald Major, Victoria place
4 Foster Robt. Blake, Esq.
Fulford Capt. John, R.N., 6 Fort field
Gibbes Sir Geo. S., *Rose Cottage*
4 Gibbes Rev Heneage, M.D. incumbent of All Saints
Giggs Misses Ann & Sarah, Fortfield
Gilder S. surgeon, May Cottage
Graeme Southerdon, Esq., *Portlands*
Granger Mrs Eliz., Alpha Cottage
4 Grant Peter, policeman
4 Harding Mrs Eliz., & Misses
Harvey Thos., Esq., Cobourg ter
Hayman Paul, accountant, manager of Gas & Water Works, & sec. to Building & Investment Society
Heiffor Thos. machine owner, Beach
Heiffor Wm. lodgings, Clifton ter
4 Heineken Rev Nicholas Samuel
Hetherington Mrs E., Cypress place
Hewett Mrs Frances, Temple street
Hoare Mr John, chief officer of Coast Guard ; h Sid place
Hobson Rev James, *Merino Cottage*
4 Hodge Thos. Stoke, & Benj. Terry, surgeons
9 Holmes John, wheelwright
Hooke Jno., subs. rooms, Esplanade
Hooke Jph. miller, *Merrifield*
Horn Robt. basket mkr., Mill cross
Hutchinson Mrs Ann, Cobourg ter
Hutchinson J. M. gent., *West Knowle*
James Philip H., Esq., *Helens*
Jenkins Miss Jane, High street
4 Jenkins Rev Wm., M.A. vicar
Jewell Mrs Ann, *Retreat Cottage*
Johnson Wm. gent. 2 York terrace
Kennaway Sir Jno., Bart., *Aurora Ctg*
Lester Alfd. solicitor & manor stewrd.
Larkins Wm. gent., *Grove Cottage*
Lousada Emanuel, Esq., *Peak Hs*
Levien John, Esq., *Rose Mount*

Long Mr Fras., *Merrifield Cottage*
Lower Rev Hy. M., B.A. curate
Lucas Rev Jas. (Indpt.) West town
Marriott Miss Eliza, *Temple Cottage*
Marsh Thomas, M.D., Marine place
Mathews Capt. Alfd., R.N., *Lodge*
Newman Mrs T., Marlbrough place
Merchinson Mrs My., *Ivy Cottage*
Mogridge Theodr.,M.D.,Balster'sCtg
Page Capt. Robt., R.N., York terrace
Pike Jas. Brooke Lee, *Grigg's Farm*
Pile Jno., timber & slate mert., Marsh
Potbury Mr Thomas, Bedford place
Price Mr Thomas, Sid place
Radford John Geo. G. solr. & clerk to magistrates, *Sid Mount*
Ridout Miss, *Powis Cottage*
Roberts Thos. bath kpr., York ter
Robberds Rev C. W. (Unitn.) Cobourg terrace
Rookes Mrs Eliz., *Cumberland Cotg*
Sanders Miss Eliz,, *Jubilee Cottage*
8 Sanders Miss Sarah
3 Sawyer Sarah, rope mat maker
5 Sellers John, sen., chimney sweepr.
Shepherd Mrs. lodgings, Marlbro' pl
4 Shortland John, brick & tile maker
Slessor Major Genl. Jno.,*Broadway H*
Slocombe Mrs M. A., Fore street
Smith Chas. Webb, Esq., *Hill's Cottg*
Stapleton Capt. Wm. Pp., *Camden Ctg*
4 Stephens Mrs Sophia
Stocker Geo. Sargent, surgeon, West tn
3 Stone Thos. carver & gilder
Studd Col. Edw., *Arcot House*
Sumtion John, farrier, Victoria pl
Sweet Wm. rope mkr., Mill cross
1 Tancock Robt. coach builder
Tinney Miss Jane, *Bolston*
Turner Mrs Sarah, Old Fore street
Walker Mrs. *Lyme Park House*
6 Westcott Ts. currier & leather cttr
8 Wheaton Miss Julia
Wheaton Hugh, sexton, Church yard
Wheaton Wm. lodgings, Marlbro' pl
White Mrs. 5 Fort field terrace

HOTELS, INNS, & TAVERNS.
8 Anchor, George Power
3 London Hotel, Wm. Cawsey
7 London Tap, Peter Wheaton
Marine Hotel, Danl. Pearcy, Beach
3 New Commercial Inn, Jno. Shepherd
8 Ship, John Plant
Royal York Hotel, Hy. Jph. Hooke, York terrace

FIRE & LIFE OFFICES.

3 County Fire & Provident Life, John Harvey
4 Equity Fire & Law Life, T. Lyde
3 Globe, Wm. Pitwood
3 London Assurance, W. G. Harris
3 Norwich Union, W. S. Hoyte
3 Phœnix, Reuben Barratt
5 Royal Farmers, T. Collier
3 Star, George Sawday
5 Sun, Paul Hayman
1 West of Engld., Lester & Radford

ACADEMIES.
(* are National.)
4 Atkins Sarah
*6 Canniford Ts.
*Coplestone My. Mill Cross
*6 Harding Prscla.
5 Hayman Paul
Knight James S. British School
8 Taylor John Hy.

ATTORNEYS.
1 Lester & Radford (& Exeter)
4 Lyde Thomas

BAKERS.
(* Confectioners.)
3 Jones George
9 Miller John
*3 Russell John
*7 Russell Thos.
*1 Russell Wm.
*8 Sellers John
*4 Skinner Wm.
4 Sprague Robt.
*3 Webber John

BEERHOUSES.
4 Hart Richard
6 Fearnehough W.
Piper John
Pottenger John
9 Newton John
6 Smeath Timy.
6 Smith Henry
9 Turner John
6 Westcott Thos.
6 White Wm.

BLACKSMITHS.
3 Bartlett Jno. S.
Burgoyne Eliza
6 Carnell John
6 Cole Thomas
6 Dean Henry

2 Dean Hy. jun.
4 Hayman Stphn.

BOOKSELLRS., &c.
2 Barratt Reuben
3 Harvey John, (stamp off.)
3 Hoyte Wm. Stevenson

BOOT & SHOEMRS.
8 Barnard Ambrs.
1 Barratt John
3 Beavis Wm.
3 Berry Wm.
3 Bond John
9 Channing Chas.
8 Carslake Jas. C.
1 Ebdon Edw.
1 Goddard Edw.
2 Hunt James
4 Lathorpe Hy.
9 Mc Leod Peter
Mortimore G.
3 Perryman Wm.
8 Stone John
Trickey Robert
2 Troake Wm.
Welsford Wm.

BREWERS & MALTSTERS.
8 Chick Elijah
8 Power George
9 Searle Richard

BRICKLAYERS.
9 Maeer James
6 Smeath Timy.

BUTCHERS.
1 Frost Richard
3 Hook Fredk.
4 Hook James
4 Page John
8 Shapter Samuel

CABINET MAKERS.
Denby Edw.

4 Farrant Chas. E.
1 Saunders Js. B.

CARPENTERS.
(* are Builders.)
Beavis Wm.
*4 Cox Samuel
9 Daniels Robt.
*1 Ebdon John
*9 Gosling Geo.
1 Harding Henry

COAL DEALERS.
6 Beer & Sanders
Denby Sarah
Horn Abraham
6 Pearcy John
3 Pitwood Wm.
3 Potbury John
6 White John
White Wm.

DRUGGISTS.
3 Pullin Edw. B. Medical Hall
5 Talbot Hugh

FANCY REPOSTRS.
Bennington Wm.
8 Evens Louisa

FARMERS.
(* are Dairymen.)
*9 Channon Wm.
Gigg John
4 Hooke Hy. P. J.
*Mitchell Thos.
*9 Pepperell Geo.
*Pepperell John
*1 Tripe John

FLY LETTERS.
3 Arundel Wm.
8 Carslake Jas. C.
4 Gilley George
8 Spencer John

GREENGROCERS.
8 Mc Leod John
3 Stone Richard
5 Woodley My. A.

GROCERS.
3 Avery Eliz.
3 Boon Wm.
1 Cridland John
3 Guppy Samuel, (& porter mert.)
3 Harris W. Gale
4 Holmes Eliz.
8 Prout Wm.
3 Trump John
7 Venman Edwin

HAIR DRESSERS.
Bennington Wm., Esplanade
7 Turner James

HOUSE AGENTS.
Denby Edw.
4 Farrant Chas. E.
3 Harris Wm. G.
5 Hayman Paul
3 Trump John

IRONMONGERS.
1 Ebdon John
3 Farrant Chltte.
4 Hayman Stphn.
3 Potbury John

LACE MAKERS.
4 Blackmore Sus.
4 Chick Samuel
3 Denby Sarah
4 Evans Chltte.
4 Evans Maria
5 Hayman Stphn.
4 Miller Eliza
7 Payton Wm.
4 Radford John

LIBRARIES.
3 Harvey John
3 Hoyte Wm. S.
Subscrptn. Beach

LINEN DRAPERS.
5 Collier Thos.
5 Hall Matthew
4 Hart John
4 Holmes Eliz.
3 Sawday Geo.
4 Stephens John

LIVERY STABLES.
3 Arundel Wm.
Pearcy Daniel
8 Power George
Wheaton Wm.

MILLINERS.
4 Cox Elizabeth
3 Farrant Carln.
5 Hill Mary
3 Pitwood C.
4 Toothill Frances

NURSERYMEN.
Bartlett Joseph
Clark Thomas
Russel My. Fortfield
9 Sampson Geo.

PAINTERS & GLZS.
4 Beavis Abm.

7 Butter Barnbs.
4 Clode James
4 Silleck Saml.
1 Hill Wm. Downham
3 Mitchell Frdk.
PLUMBERS, &c.
4 Blackmore Jno.
4 Hayman Stphn.
SADDLERS.
3 Collacott Thos.
2 Dommett Thos.
7 Tidbury John
SHOPKEEPERS.
4 Hart John
4 Holmes Eliz.
9 Holmes John
9 Newton John
6 Norman James

8 Pidgeon Ann
3 Podbury Wm.
Pottinger John
6 Smith Henry
8 Summerwill L.
4 Underhill M.
6 Westcott Thos.
STONE MASONS.
(* Lapidaries.)
4 Evans Eliz.
*7 Hamilton Alex.
*6 Hamilton J.
*4 Newman Wm.
9 Turner John
STRAW HAT MKS.
9 Bastin M. A.
1 Davey Mary
5 Hayman Hanh.
3 Pitwood C.

Searle Eliz.
Vossey My. A.
TAILORS.
(* Drapers also.)
*3 Avery James
*1 Barratt Wm. B
8 Cowd Wm.
*3 Holwill John
8 Rogers George
9 Newton John
*3 Snell Charles
WATCHMAKERS.
4 Gibbs James
8 Harding Chs. W.
3 Porter Henry
WINE, SPIRITS, &c.
MERCHANTS.
1 Cridland John

3 Harris Wm. G.
3 Trump John
COACHES.
To Exeter every morng. at 8½, & to Extr., Exmth., &c. Mon. Wed. & Sat., at 4 aft.
To Taunton every Tues. Thu. & Sat. 8 morning.
CARRIERS.
Jas. Bole, to Exeter daily.
Geo. Dorman, to Exmth. &c. Mon. & Fri., & Honiton Tu. Thu. & Sat.

VENN-OTTERY, or *Fen Ottery*, a small village and parish on the west side of the Otter valley, three miles S. by W. of Ottery St. Mary, has only 134 souls, and about 1200 acres of land, belonging to Mr. Thos. Yelverton, Mr. J. R. Taylor, the trustees of the late Lord Rolle, and a few smaller owners. The manor was anciently held by the Furneaux family. The *Church* (St. Gregory,) has a tower and three bells, and is an ancient structure, except the chancel, which was rebuilt in 1832. The vicarage is consolidated with that at Harpford, as noticed at page 229, and was endowed with the great tithes by R. Duke, Esq. The glebe is ten acres, and the tithes were commuted in 1840 for £290 per annum.

Brice Wm. farmer
Harding Wm. par. clk., & Hy. *sexton*
Pile Charles, farmer

Salter Thomas, farmer
Taylor John Reed, yeoman
Yelverton Thomas, yeoman

WITHYCOMBE-RAWLEIGH, or *Withecombe Raleigh*, a pleasant scattered village, with several handsome villas, &c., from one to two miles N.E. of Exmouth, has in its parish 1882 acres of land, bounded on the west by the broad estuary of the river Exe. It had 1922 inhabitants in 1841, including 702 residing in that part of the town of Exmouth which lies in this parish, and where many new houses have been erected during the last five years. The parish has now more than 2300 inhabitants, and the soil belongs to various freeholders. The great tithes, and a moiety of the estate called *Hulham*, belongs to *Drake's Charity* to this parish and those of Littleham and East Budleigh. (See page 229.) *Courtlands*, a pleasant seat on the east bank of the estuary, two miles N. by W. of Exmouth, passed from the Roberts to the Baring family, and is now the residence of W. F. Spicer, Esq. The manor of Withycombe-Clavill belongs to Edw. Divett, Esq., and was anciently held by the Clavills by the service of finding the king two arrows stuck in an oaten cake whenever he came to hunt in Dartmoor. The manor of *Broadham* and *Rill* belongs to W. H. Hull, Esq., who has a pleasant seat here, called *Marpool Hall*, in a delightful valley,

half a mile from Exmouth. The hall is a modern structure, and the park is well wooded, and commands extensive views. *Marley Lodge*, the seat of Thos. Cobham, Esq., stands on a commanding eminence, 2½ miles N.E. of Exmouth, encompassed by ornamental shrubberies, sylvan walks, and extensive gardens. Near it is *St. John's Cottage*, late the seat of Chas. Sanders, Esq., standing in the midst of extensive and beautiful pleasure grounds, on an elevated site, commanding a fine view of the sea and coast. It is an elegant cottage *ornée*, and has a beautiful conservatory, and some pretty artificial rocks, and a small waterfall in its tasteful grounds. *Bassett Park*, in a picturesque vale half a mile from Exmouth, is the seat of Chas. Wheaton, Esq. The mansion is a modern structure, in the castellated style, with turrets and battlements, and a tower in the centre. The flower garden is ornamented with a rustic fountain, and near it is a model cottage, approached by serpentine walks, and surrounded by artificial rock work and other ornaments. The lake is crossed by a curious rustic bridge, leading to a plantation on the higher grounds, which command a fine view of Exmouth and the sea. *A-la-Ronde*, the seat of Miss Parminter, stands in a pleasant lawn, and was built from a model of St. Peter's, at Rome. In the centre is an octagon hall, about 25 feet high, around which are the other apartments, each made to close with sliding shutters instead of doors. A gallery, ornamented with curious shell-work, runs round the hall, and on the outside is another gallery, extending round the whole building, and commanding extensive views. Near it is the *Point-in-View*, founded in 1800, by the late Mrs. Parminter, and comprising dwellings for four poor aged maidens, with a small Independent chapel, and a house for the minister. The chapel is in the centre, and the dwellings have small gardens. The minister and the almswomen receive stipends from Miss Parminter, and over the chapel door is inscribed, "Some point in view, we all pursue." The old parish church, commonly called *St. John's in the Wilderness*, was taken down on account of its inconvenient situation about 1748, except the tower and part of the north aisle, still used for sepultural purposes. These venerable remains are in a sequestered spot, more than a mile from Withycombe village, where a *New Church* (St. John the Baptist,) was built by subscription in 1720, on the site of the ancient chapel of ease. This is a brick structure, with a bell turret, and the principal contributor towards its erection was Sir John Colleton, Kt., who also gave the singularly sculptured altar-piece. The benefice is a *perpetual curacy*, annexed to the vicarage of East Budleigh, as noticed at page 220. Here is a *National School*, built in 1841, and the parish receives yearly from *Drake's Charity* (see page 229,) £7 for the incumbent, £2 for the poor, £2. 10s. for apprenticing poor children, and 20s. for repairing a small almshouse. The poor parishioners have £5 a year from three per cent. consols, left by *Fras. Rowe*, in 1844; and the dividends of £500 of the same stock, left by *Wm. Spicer, Esq.*, in 1848. Some of the chapels, &c., in Exmouth are in this parish.

Barnes Hy. grocer & vict. Holly Tree
Bishop Elizabeth, schoolmistress
Burridge Thos. brick & tile maker
Bunker Ann, cook, *A-la-Ronde*

Cobham Thos. Esq. *Marley Lodge*
Doyle John H. gentleman
Gerrard Abel, Esq.
Hoppe Charles, gentleman
Goldsworthy Joseph, sexton
Gifford Charles, Esq. *Cliff Head*
Hull Wm. Hartopp, Esq., and Mrs H. *Marpool Hall*
Lee Rev John Wm. Thos. *curate*
Manning Wm., National schoolmr.
Mercer Rev. James, (*Independent*,) *Point-in-view*
Parminter Miss Mary, *A-la-Ronde*
Phillips Ephraim, corn miller
Secker Rt. gent. || West Arthur, gent.
Setten George, gardener

Spicer Wm. Fras. Esq. *Courtlands*
Wills Thos. gent. Withycombe Ctg.
Wheaton Chas. Esq. *Bassett Park*

BLACKSMITHS.
Beavis George
Maunder John

FARMERS.
(* *at Hulham.*)
Anning John
Ansou Eliza
Bowman John
* Clapp Edmund
Cockram Wm.
Crabb Henry
Crabb Hy. jun.
Crabb Wm., *Ash*

Hallett Wm.
* Hensley John
Manning Henry
* Marchant John
Norton John
* Savery Wm.
Taverner Wm.
Woodman Rd.

SHOEMAKERS.
Brooks Wm.
Carslake John

POST, &c., *see Exmouth*

WOODBURY, a large village, pleasantly situated on an acclivity, 3 miles S.E. of Topsham, and 7 miles S.E. of Exeter, has in its extensive parish 7304A. 2R. 26P. of land, extending eastward from the estuary of the Exe to the lofty hills which overlook the Otter valley. The parish had 1933 inhabitants in 1841, and comprises the chapelry of *Salterton ;* and the smaller hamlets of *Ebford, Exton, Nutwell, Gulliford, Grindle, Woodmanton,* and *Higher Hamlet,* extending more than a mile on all sides of the village, and including many good houses and much picturesque scenery. Many women and children here, are employed in making Honiton point lace. *Petty Sessions* are held at the Globe Inn, every fourth Monday, and Mr. F. G. Coleridge, of Ottery St Mary, is clerk to the magistrates. The trustees of the late Lord Rolle, are lords of the manor of Woodbury, which was part of the royal demesne settled on the Queen of Edward the Confessor, and afterwards passed to the Mandeville, Albemarle, Damarel, Bonville and Ford families. In 1285, it had a grant for a market and fair. It has now only a pleasure fair on the 3rd of May. On the lofty summit of Woodbury Common, overlooking the Exe and Otter valleys, and commanding a view of the sea, are the remains of an ancient *Entrenchment,* sometimes called Woodbury Castle. It is supposed to have been formed by the ancient Britons, and afterwards altered and enlarged by the Romans, Saxons, and Danes. It is now planted with fir trees, but in 1798 and 1803, at the time of the threatened invasion of the French, a camp of considerable force was stationed here, with a park of artillery. NUTWELL COURT, on the east bank of the broad estuary of the Exe, opposite Powderham Castle, is the seat of *Sir T. T. F. E. Drake,* who was created a *baronet* in 1821, and is lord of the manor of Nutwell, which he derived from his uncle, the late Lord Heathfield. The latter obtained the estate from his uncle, *Sir Francis Drake, Bart.*, who died in 1794, and made great alterations in the house and grounds, and converted the chapel into a handsome library. Risden says, Nutwell Court was a castle till Lord Dinham, about the time of Edward IV., converted it into a fair and stately dwelling-house. It was nearly all rebuilt by the late Lord Heathfield, and is now a large

and handsome mansion, in a well wooded park. *Nutwell House*, in Upper Nutwell, is the seat and property of Thomas Porter, Esq. Salterton belongs to the Rolle and Putt families. Grindle or Grindell belongs to the latter, and other parts of the parish belong to the Rev. H. W. Marker, the Vicars Choral of Exeter, the Lee family, and several smaller owners. The *Church*, (St. Swithen,) is a large ancient structure, with a tower and six bells. The organ is a fine toned instrument, and new communion plate was purchased by subscription in 1844. A house and orchard, worth £8 a year, have long been vested for the repairs of the church. A fine of £100, paid by the lessee in 1791, was laid out in new seating the church. The Custos and College of Vicars Choral, in Exeter Cathedral, are owners of the manor of Halstow, appropriators of the tithes, and patrons of the *perpetual curacy*, valued in 1831 at £150, and now enjoyed by the Rev. J. L. Fulford, M.A., for whom a new Parsonage House was built in 1849. The tithes were commuted in 1839, for £1070 per annum. SALTERTON CHURCH, (Holy Trinity,) about a mile S.W. of Woodbury village, is a handsome Doric structure, which was built and endowed in 1833-'4, by the the late Miss Mary Ann Pidsley, of Clist St. Mary, who also founded the neat Parsonage House and School, and the handsome fountain which supplies the hamlet with pure water. The foundress is said to have expended about £13,000 in these useful erections and the endowment. The church has a tower and spire, and is lighted by handsomely painted windows. It has three bells, and the interior is elegantly fitted up. A district of about 700 souls has been attached to it. The perpetual curacy, valued at £80, is in the patronage of Miss E. Pidsley, and incumbency of the Rev. B. W. Stannus, B.A. The Parsonage House and School were erected in 1846-7, and the latter is supported by Mrs. Thornycroft and others, for 80 free scholars. There are National and Infant Schools at Woodbury, and the latter is supported chiefly by Mrs. Pennell. The *Independents* have a small chapel at Woodbury; and at *Gulliford* is an *Unitarian Chapel*, which was built by *Presbyterians*, of this and the adjacent parishes, in 1774, and is now under the ministry of the Rev. E. Squire, of Lympstone. The poor parishioners have the yearly sums of £5. 7s. 2d. from the Mercers' Company, London, and £1. 13s. 4d. from Exeter Corporation, pursuant to the bequests of *John Heydon* in 1579, The sum of £130, given to the poor by various donors, was vested in 1656, in the purchase of an *annuity of* £6 out of a house in Butcher row, Exeter. An annuity of £5 out of Hawkerland estate, was purchased in 1695, with £134, given to the poor by *Benjamin Whetcomb* and other donors. In 1691, *Thomas Weare* left a yearly rent-charge of £4. 10s. for *schooling* poor children of this parish. (See Clist-Honiton.) For the same purpose, *Esaias Broadmead* left £120 in 1728, and it was laid out in the purchase of 13A. of land, now let for about £16 a year. The parish schoolmaster has also the interest of £50, left by *Wm. Hollwell*, M.D., in 1707; and the poor have the dividends of £500, three per cent. consols, left by *Mrs. Mary Hayman*, in 1833.

In the following DIRECTORY OF WOODBURY PARISH, *those marked* 1 *are at* Ebford, 2 Exton, 3 Grindle, 4 Gulliford, 5 Higher Hamlet, 6 Nutwell, 7 Salterton, 8 Woodmanton, *and the rest in Woodbury Village, or where specified.* The POST-OFFICE is at Abraham Green's, Woodbury; and letters are despatched at a quarter to seven evening, *via* Exeter.

Aldridge Capt. John Wm., R.N.
Austin Joseph, vict. White Hart
Bastin Henry, basket maker
Brent Robert, M.D. surgeon, *Sydney Cottage*
1 Butter Miss N. || Pennell Miss
3 Butter James Langdon, brick and tile maker
Cains John, beerhouse
Chapple Mr W. || Clement Mr John
Drake Sir Thos.Trayton Fuller Eliot, Bart., *Nutwell Court*
2 Ebbels John, corn miller
Filmer Rev. Fras. *Oak Hayes House*
Franklin Thomas, corn miller
Fulford Rev John Loveband, M.A., incumbent, Parsonage
Gibbings Thomas, tanner
1 Gibbings Mr Wm.|| Luke Mr G. C.
4 Harris James, gardener
Hayman Wm. *lace mfr.* (and at Bristol, Plymouth, Torquay, &c.)
2 Hayward John, lime burner, &c.
Hole Fras. R. & Mallett W. H. gents.
Kenwood Richard, cooper
Labdon Sir John, *Rose Cottage*
Lee Col. Brice W. *Ebford Barton*
Lee Mrs Hannah, *Ebford Lodge*
Lewis Capt. F. J., R.N., *RoseCottage*
Moore Mrs & Miss, *Mount Ebford*
Phillips Wm. mason
Porter Thos. Esq., *Nutwell House*
Reed Robert, farrier
Rider Wm. gent. *Broadway House*
Saunders Wm. tanner, *Gillbrook Hs.*
Skinner Samuel, thatcher
7 Stannus Rev BeauchampWm., B.A. *incbt. of Salterton*
2 Stogdon Mrs || 7 Ware Mrs Eliz.
4 Woolridge Capt. Wm., R.N.

BAKERS.
Quick James
Perry Thomas
BLACKSMITHS.
Edwards James
7 Furse Wm.
1 Harris Charles
Hitchcock Jph.
Lock John
2 Marshall Chas.
7 Pile Wm.
BOOT &SHOE MKS.
Callaway John
7 Clarke James
7 Havill John
Jerman Wm.
Knowles Henry
Lake Thomas

Marks Israel
Moor John
7 Shepherd Sml.
Sillick John
Tucker James
7 Webber James
BUTCHERS.
7 Harris Fras.
4 Hill Charles
Hyett Wm.
Pile Joseph
7 Saunders John
Saunders Wm.
CARPENTERS.
Moore James
Phillips Robert
Smeath Thomas
Stamp John
FARMERS.
(* *are Owners.*)
* Ashford James, Venmoor
* Ashford Jph., Lower Venmoor
5 Bickley Mrs
1 Bradbeer Wm.
Brice Sarah
3 Butter Jas. L.
2 Clapp Henry
1 Coles Richard
7 Cock Robert
8 Clown Wm.
Diamond John
7 Dagworthy Rd.
6 Franklin Thos.
Gibbings Thos.
Glanville James
7 Hallett John
7 Hallett Thos.
Havill Wm.
7 Harris Fras.
4 Hill Charles
7 Kerslake John
1 Lake Thomas
Lee Lewis
Lindsey Samuel
7 Matthews Thos
4 Neck Eliz.
8 Pepper Robert

7 * Phillips Jph.
Pile John
7 * Pomeroy Jas
8 Raymont Crl.
1 Roe Thomas
Rogers Robert
7 * Saunders Jas.
4 Salter Wm.
5 Simons Wm.
Stevens James
Stevens John
2 Stogdon Robt.
Tapscott Wm.
Thomas Samuel
3 White John
2 * White Rd.
Wilcocks Rd.
SCHOOLS.
Gould Thomas
Leak John
Simons James
Walton John
7 Welland John
SHOPKEEPERS.
Brook John
Green Abraham
Hayman Wm.
Lake Thomas
Livermoor Wm.
7 Mudge My. Ann
Phillips Robert, (and builder)
TAILORS.
Lake Richard
Lake John
Livermoore Wm.
Searle James
Sloman James
WHEELWRIGHTS.
Blake Humphrey
7 Furse Robert
Pabay Wm.
Smeath Thos.

COACH, &c. to Exmouth and Exeter daily
CARRIER to *Exeter*, J. Burton, Tue. &Fri.

CLISTON HUNDRED.

This small Hundred is all in the Southern Division of Devonshire, except Butterleigh parish, which is a detached member of it, in the North Division. It is only about six miles in length and breadth, and extends from 5 to 11 miles N.E. of Exeter. It is a fertile district, watered by the small rivers Culm and Clist, and traversed by the Bristol and Exeter Railway. It had 3871 *inhabitants* in 1841, and comprises 19,552 *acres of land*, celebrated for excellent cider, and divided into the five following parishes :—

Parishes.	Acres.	Pop.	Parishes.	Acres.	Pop.
Butterleigh......	2479 ..	155	Clist St. Lawrence	1060 ..	168
Clist (Broad) ..	10,270 ..	2407	Whimple parish,)	3028	.. (688
Clist Hydon	2725 ..	325	Strete Rawleigh)		.. (128

☞ They are all in the Archdeaconry of Exeter. Butterleigh, Clist Hydon, and Clist St. Lawrence are in Plymtree Deanery, and Broad Clist and Whimple parishes are in Aylesbeare Deanery. Butterleigh is in *Tiverton Union*, and the other four are in *St. Thomas's Union*. (See page 122.)

BUTTERLEIGH is a small village and parish, 3 miles S.S.E. of Tiverton, containing only 155 souls. and 2479 acres of land, rising boldly from a tributary stream of the river Exe. The manor was held for a long period by the Pulleyn and Courtenay families, the latter of whom sold it in 1600 to Sir Simon Leach. It was afterwards dismembered, and now belongs to Wm. Hole, Esq., George Barne, Esq., Mr. John Pitt, and a few smaller freeholders. The *Church* is a plain antique fabric, with a tower and three bells. It was repaired about 1600, by Dr. Peter Muden, a Hollander, who married one of the Courtenays, to whose memory there was a handsome marble monument in the church, but it fell from the wall some time ago, and was broken to pieces. The *rectory*, valued in K.B. at £10. 8s. 8d., and in 1831 at £180, is in the patronage of the Lord Chancellor, and incumbency of the Rev. John Pike Jones, vicar of Alveton, Staffordshire, for whom the Rev. M. Thorne, B.A., officiates. The Parsonage is a neat residence in a picturesque valley, and the glebe is 58A. 2R. 26P. The tithes were commuted in 1837 for £95 per annum. The poor have 28s. a year out of Butterleigh mills, left by *Robert Winn*, in 1800.

Berry John, mason and parish clerk
Bray Wm. & Quick Wm. shoemakers
Clist John, sexton
Ferris Wm. smith and wheelwright
Hodge Wm. corn miller
Manning Geo. butcher& vict.New Inn
Quick Edward, baker
Searle George, beerhouse

Thorne Rev Michl.,B.A.curate,*Rectory*
FARMERS.
Carslake Emanuel, *Coombe*
Matthews Thomas, *Cuttisbeer*
Parkhouse Abraham, *Fillbrook*
Pitt John, (owner,) *Weygate*
Western Richard, *Babbages*

BROAD CLIST, or *Broad Clyst*, is a pleasant village, in the picturesque valley of the small river Clist, 5 miles N.E. of Exeter. It has *fairs* for cattle, &c., on the first Mondays in April and September, and its extensive parish has about 2650 inhabitants, and 10,270 acres of land, extending several miles along the valleys of the rivers Clist and Culm, and comprising many scattered farm-houses, several

handsome seats, and the small villages of *Beer, Budlake, Westwood, Church Hill, and Black Dog;* the latter of which has been built on the Common, since the enclosure in 1832.   Broad Clist, or Cliston, as it was anciently called, is said to have been burnt by the Danes, in 1001.   The manor was held by the Crown at Domesday Survey, but was granted by Henry I. to the Novant family, from whom it passed to the Chudleigh, Arundell, Morice, and other families.   In 1808 it was purchased by *Sir Thomas Dyke Acland. Bart., M.P.,* who owns more than half the parish, and resides at KILLERTON HOUSE, a large and handsome mansion, delightfully seated in an extensive and well wooded deer park, on the banks of the small river Culm, 6 miles N.N.E. of Exeter, near the Bristol and Exeter Railway.   Killerton estate was purchased by Sir Arthur Acland, whose father, Sir John, was created a baronet in 1644.   The house was built by Sir Thos. Acland, who died in 1788, but it has been greatly enlarged and improved by his grandson, the present baronet, who is one of the parliamentary representatives of the Northern Division of Devon, and in 1842, erected a handsome *Chapel* on one side of the park, (dedicated to the Evangelists,) in lieu of the old chapel, founded by his ancestor at Columbjohn.   *Sir John Acland, Kt.,* the charitable benefactor, noticed at page 110, purchased the estate, and built the mansion of *Columbjohn,* in the Culm valley, a little below Killerton, near which he also erected a domestic chapel, and endowed it with £27 per annum.   He died in 1613, and has a handsome monument in the parish church, with effigies of himself and his two wives.   Sir John, the first baronet, was a zealous royalist, and garrisoned his house of Columbjohn for King Charles, but in 1646, it was taken by Sir Thomas Fairfax.   This house, built in the reign of Elizabeth, has been pulled down, since the erection of the more stately mansion of Killerton.   The manor of *Clist Gerald,* or Gerrard, belongs to St. John's Hospital, Exeter.   *Spreydon House* is the property and handsome residence of W. B. Moore, Esq., and *Brockhill House* is the pleasant seat of Major-General Truscott. Lord Poltimore and the Bidgood, Lang, and other families have estates in the parish.   Mr. John Birmingham, after being 60 years in the service of the Acland family, has recently resigned the office of steward to his son.   The *Church* (St. John,) is a large antique fabric, with a lofty tower and six bells.   It has a good organ and several neat monuments.   The *vicarage,* valued in K.B. at £26, and in 1831 at £492, is endowed with one-third of the great tithes, and is in the incumbency of the Rev. P. L. D. Acland, M.A., who has a good residence.   Sir T. D. Acland, Bart., is the patron, and also impropriator of two-thirds of the great tithes, which belonged formerly to Totnes Priory.   His domestic chaplain, the Rev. John Bond, is minister of the chapel noticed above.   The parish has an ALMS-HOUSE, consisting of 12 rooms, with small gardens, for as many poor people, founded by *Henry Burrough,* who endowed it in 1605, with an annuity of £23. 11s., out of the rectorial tithes of Cadbury and Netherexe.   From this annuity the 12 almspeople have divided among them 7s. 6d. weekly, and the vicar 40s. yearly for a sermon preached to the poor.   One of the almspeople is chosen from either

Cadbury or Netherexe, and the others are parishioners of Broad Clist. The *Poor's Lands, &c.*, were purchased in 1737, with about £300 given by various donors, and comprise about 13A., and a house, let for £26 per annum, which is divided among the poor parishioners. Near the above-named almshouse are two small dwellings, built by the parish, and occupied by paupers. For a weekly distribution of bread the poor have £5. 4s. per annum from *Sir John Acland's Charity.* (See page 110.) About 30 years ago, Sir T. D. Acland built two *Schools,* which are supported partly by subscription and partly from the following funds. In 1691, *Thomas Weare* left a yearly rent-charge of £4. 10s. out of Holbrook estate, for schooling poor children. The sum of £50, derived from arrears of this annuity, is vested at interest. A legacy of £100, left by *George Leach,* 1684, was laid out with other sums given for the education of poor children, in the purchase of £326. 17s. 10d. three per cent. consols.

Those marked 1, live at Beer; 2, Black Dog; 3, Budlake; 4, Church Hill; 5, Heath; 6, in Westwood; and the rest in or near Broad Clist village, or where specified. POST *from Exeter daily.*

Acland Sir Thos. Dyke, Bart., M.P. *Killerton House*
Acland Rev Peter Leopald Dyke, M.A. *Vicarage*
Austin Hy. Wm. relivg. officer & regr
Ayshford Giles Reynolds, surgeon
3 Birmingham John, gent. and Wm., steward to Sir T. D. Acland
Boucher Emanuel, gent. *Willow Cottg*
Doble Stephen, revenue officer
Francis Chas. brewer, par. clerk, &c
Gould Ann, ladies' boarding school
Gould and Wish, tanners, *Beer*
Greatwick Geo. & Story Ann, school
Hebron Rev Fras., B.A. curate
Jennings Joseph, saddler, &c
Lake John, plumber and glazier
Lang J., Esq. *Blue Hayes*
Manley Robt. corn miller, *Columbjohn*
Matthews and Martyn, paper manfrs. *Bridge Mills, Huxham*
5 Martin Mr John‖Parsons T. sexton
Merry Wm. Henry, surgeon
2 Miller Rev George, B.A. curate
Modgridge John, veterinary surgeon
Moore Wm. B., Esq. *Spreydon Hs*
Scott Mrs Jenny, *Ford Cottage*
Salter Emma, ladies' boarding school
Stoker John, mason, &c
Tomlinson John, butler, & Aldridge Isaac, under butler, *Killerton*

Truscott Major Genl. *Brock Hill Hs*
Ware Joseph, Esq. *Hayes Villa*

INNS AND TAVERNS.
Crown and Sceptre, John Gibbings
1 New Crab Tree, James Badcock
Plough Inn, Mary Ann Smith
Red Lion, Daniel Harris

BEERHOUSES.
2 Bustard Wm.
Hewett Robert
5 Osbourn Wm.

BAKERS, &c.
Chamberlain Jno.
Hart Francis
Loosemore John
2 Melhuish John
Salter Elizabeth
Sanders Thomas

BOOT & SHOE MRS.
Brewer Charles
Colman Wm.
1 Gouldsworthy J.
6 Hill John
Setten Charles
6 Snow Francis
Tremlett Wm.

BLACKSMITHS.
Brooks George
Hoyle James
Miller George
5 Mitchell Geo.
2 Squire Henry
3 Tremlett James

BUTCHERS.
Chamberlain Jno.
Salter Joseph
Salter Wm.

CARPENTERS.
2 Boutcher Chas.
Chamberlain Jno.
Hawkins John
6 Start Humfry.
Veryard Wm.

FARMERS.
4 Beer Thomas
Bickley J., *South Whimple*
Board Charles
Board Wm.
4 Broomfield —
Boutcher Wm.
Bricknell Isaac
Burton Samuel
Burton Richard
Carnall Rt. & Ths.
Channing Thos., *Wishford*
Corner Moses
Davis Henry
4 Frost Mr
Glanvill Ellenor
Glanvill John
Gould Joseph
Griffin John, *New House*
Griffin Benjamin, *Columbjohn*

Lamacraft John	Ratcliffe Jane	Trickey Martha	2 Southcott Jph.
6 Manley Wm.	Redford Richard	Trump John	Ware Emanuel
Martin John	2 Ridler Wm.	Wish Thomas	WHEELWRIGHTS.
Martin Thomas	Richard Bendct.	SHOPKEEPERS.	2 Harris Samuel
Martin Wm.	Salter John	Eales James	Horn John
Merry John	4 Scanes Henry	Modgridge Richd.	5 Pollard Abm.
Merry Wm.	Skinner Abraham	Phillips Wm.	
Merry Richard	Taylor Robt. *Ash*	Pollard Wm.	*CARRIERS to*
Mowman Jeremh.	*Clist*	Sanders Thomas	*Exeter, Tues. &*
Perkins John	Tout Edward	Ware Wm.	*Friday from the*
1 Pyne Samuel	Trood Mathias	TAILORS.	*Plough.*
1 Pyne Wm.	Trickey Francis	Coles Charles	Lindsay Wm.
Ratcliffe John,	Trickey John	Coles Wm.	Mortimore Chas.
Cooper's			

CLIST HYDON, or *Clyst Hydon*, a small village in the valley, near the source of the river Clist, 4 miles S. by E. of Collumpton, and 10 miles N.E. of Exeter, has in its parish 325 souls, and 2725A. of land, including several scattered farms and neat houses. Mrs. Huyshe is lady of the manor of Clist Hydon, which was long held by the ancient family of Hidon. John Mathew, Esq., is lord of the manor of *Anke* or *Aunck*, and has a handsome seat here called *Ratcliff's House*, encompassed by a woody lawn. He also owns Farrant Hayes; but a great part of the parish belongs to J. Pinsent, E. Wish, Mrs. Drew, J. R. Salter, A. T. Follett, and several other freeholders. The *Church* (St. Andrew,) is a fine antique fabric, with a tower and five bells. It was repaired in 1836, and a gallery was erected in 1848, when a handsome stained glass window was inserted at the expense of John Mathew, Esq. The *rectory*, valued in K.B. at £20. 0s. 7½d., and in 1831 at £494, is in the patronage of Mrs. Harriet Huyshe, and incumbency of the Rev. John Huyshe, M.A., who has a good residence and 89A. of glebe. The tithes were commuted in 1842 for £350 per annum. The rent of a tenement, let for £5, is applied in repairing the church. In 1667, *Robt. Hall, D.D.*, left to this parish two yearly rent-charges out of land at Okehampton, viz., £15 for schooling poor children, and £5 for binding them apprentice. In consequence of there being no demand, accumulations have taken place from time to time of the latter annuity, and there is now belonging to that branch of charity a cottage let for 30s., and £100 three per cent. consols. The poor have the interest of £50, left by the late Mr. Henry Pratt, of Broad Oak.

Burrow John, smith and wheelwright
Eveleigh Abraham, wheelwright
Hart Wm. shoemaker
Hole Elizabeth, shopkeeper
Hole Wm. carpenter
Huyshe Rev John, M.A. *Rectory*
Mathew John, Esq. *Ratcliff's House*
Radford Philip, tailor
Saunders George, M.D. surgeon
Syms Charles, schoolmaster
Symons Henry, beerhouse
Thorne Wm. Coles, shoemaker

FARMERS. (* *are Owners.*)
Baker Thirza || Burrow John
Farrant John, *Farrant Hayes*
Pearse Wm. || Helford Robert
*Pratt Richard, *Broad Oak*
Salter Abraham || Salter Charles
Syms John || Tilke Wm.
*Trump Wm., *Courtenay's*
Warren Thomas || Wheaton Wm.

POST-OFFICE at John Webber's. Letters despatched 3½ afternoon

CLIST ST. LAWRENCE, a small village in the deep and narrow valley of the small river Clist, 9 miles N.E. of Exeter, has in its parish only 168 souls, and 1060 acres of land. The manor and most of the soil belong to *Elize Hele's Charity*, as noticed at page 97. The manor was anciently held by the Valletorts, and afterwards by the Pollards and Heles. The *Church* (St. Lawrence,) is a Norman structure, with a tower and five bells, and was repaired in 1848, when the east window was enriched with stained glass. The interior is neatly fitted up, and has a handsomely carved and gilt screen. The *rectory*, valued in K.B. at £9. 4s. 4½d., and in 1831 at £265, is in the patronage of Exeter Church Charity Trustees, and incumbency of the Rev. C. E. Walkey, B.A., who has a good modern residence, and 47A. 3R. 30P. of glebe. The tithes were commuted in 1842 for £273 per annum. The poor have the dividends of £97. 4s. 5d. four per cent. stock, left by *Wm. Godfrey* in 1817, and the interest of £12, given by *Wm. Lyswell*, and vested with the overseers. A field of 4A. was divided into allotments, for the use of the labouring poor in 1848.

Eveleigh Josiah, parish clerk
Pratt Charles, shoemaker
Squire Edward, carpenter
Squire John, blacksmith
Walkey Rev Charles Elliott, B.A., rector, *Rectory*
Willis Henry, carpenter

FARMERS.
Baker Joseph, *Clapton mill*
Hunt Wm. || Lee Wm.
Manley Wm. || Marks Mark
Partridge Wm. || Ridler John
Ridler Wm., *Woodhouse*
Snell John || Turpin Edward

WHIMPLE, a pleasant village, with several neat houses, on a declivity, 4½ miles W.N.W. of Ottery St. Mary, and 8½ miles N.E. by E. of Exeter, has in its parish 3028A. 3R. 13P. of land, and 816 inhabitants, including 128 in STRETE RALEIGH tithing. The parish also includes the small hamlets of *Slewton, Perreton*, and *Cobdon*, and many scattered farm houses, &c. A *fair* for sheep, &c., is held in the village on the Monday after Michaelmas day. Thomas W. Buller, Esq., is lord of the *manors* of Whimple, Strete Raleigh, and Cobdon, formerly held by the Englefield, Clist, Pudding, Raleigh, Gould, and other families. Abm. Smith, Esq., Geo. Brooke, Esq., Jas. Davy, Esq., Mr. J. S. Wish, the Rev. Jas. S. Townshend, and several smaller owners, have estates in the parish. The *Church* (St. Mary,) is a neat structure in the perpendicular style, and was all rebuilt, except the tower, in 1845, at the cost of about £2000, of which £210 was given by the Diocesan and Church Building Societies, on condition that 207 sittings should be free for ever. The interior is neatly fitted up with carved open seats, and has a monument in memory of the late Rev. Thomas Heberden, who held the benefice 57 years. The *rectory*, valued in K.B. at £30, and in 1831 at £386, is in the patronage of Mrs. Sanders, and incumbency of the Rev. Lloyd Sanders, M.A., who has a neat and commodious residence and 67A. 3R. 14P. of glebe. The tithes were commuted in 1835 for £335 per annum. The *National School* was built in 1848-9, at the cost of £475, of which £126 was given by Government and the National Society. The poor parishioners have the dividends of £180. 2s. 3d. three per cent. consols, purchased with money given by various donors.

Marked 2, are in Cobdon ; 3, Strete Raleigh ; 4, Slewton ; 5, Wood-hayes ; and the others in Whimple, or where specified.

Baber Jno. Monkhouse, Esq., *Fordton*
3 Bennett Jas. saddler, Post-office
4 Brooke Geo. jun. Esq. *Slewton Hs*
3 Buller Capt. Ths. Wentworth, R.N.
3 Buller Mrs and Misses
Cosen John, schoolmaster
Davy Jas. Esq. ‖ Honeywood Col.
Granger Richard, bricklayer
3 Griffin Charles, butcher and vict. Country Hotel, London road
Kenwood John, carpenter
Liscombe John, grocer and baker
Melhuish Richard, thatcher
Munday Benj. parish clerk
4 Pearse John Fortescue, Esq.
Pratt John, baker and shopkeeper
Pratt Wm. sexton
3 Robinson Wm. brick and tile mkr
Rowsel Mr Jas., Newton cottage
Sanders John, tanner, *Fordton*
Sanders Rev Lloyd, M.A. *Rectory*
Sanders Mrs., Rectory House
Smith Abm. Esq. *Rull Whimple*
Vincent Jas. colr. ‖ Venn Mr John

Wish Philip Salter, vict. New Inn
BLACKSMITHS.
Butcher Samuel
Kenwood Robt.
Kenwood Wm.
BOOT & SHOE MKS.
Coleman James
Godfrey Robert
Godfrey Wm.
Humphrey John
Pratt Thomas
FARMERS.
(* *are Owners.*)
2 Baker Wm.
Burrow Richard, Knowle
Carnell Wm.
*Clift Edward
3 Drawer Thos.
Drew John
Glanvill Wm.
Godfrey Wm.
Mulling Richard
Painter Wm.
Patch Thomas
3 Robinson Wm.
Salter Abraham

*5 Sanders Saml.
3 Sanders John, Chas. & Fras.
2 Shapcott Jph.
5 Skinner John
Trickey Wm.
2 Turl John
*Venn Wm. Hex
Warren John, ⎱
  Perreton ⎰
Weeks Frs., *Hitts*
TAILORS.
Dunn Wm.
Godfrey George
WHEELWRIGHTS.
Harris Natl.
Middleton Thos.
POST OFFICE
at J. Bennett's.
Letters despd.
10½ morning
CARRIERS, &c.
pass daily to
Exeter, Honiton, &c. and call
at the Hotel

WEST BUDLEIGH HUNDRED

Is in the Northern Division of Devon and in the Archdeaconry of Exeter. It is all in Cadbury Deanery and in Crediton Union, Petty Sessional Division, and Polling District; except Washford, which is a detached member in Tiverton Union, Deanery and Polling District; and in Collumpton Petty Sessional Division. It lies north and north-east of Crediton, and is only about 8 miles long and four broad. It is watered by the river Creedy and one of its tributaries, and comprises only about 17,366 acres of land, and 3372 inhabitants, as will be seen in the following enumeration of its seven parishes :—

Parishes.	Acres.	Pop.	Parishes.	Acres.	Pop.
Cheriton Fitzpaine	5290	1156	Stockleigh Pomeroy	1240	258
Poughill	1662	361	Upton Helions	1000	146
Shobrooke	3835	787	Washfield	3235	503
Stockleigh English	1104	161			
			Total	17,366	3372

CHERITON FITZPAINE is a pleasant village on an acclivity near one of the tributary streams of the river Creedy, 5 miles N.N.E. of Crediton. Its parish has many scattered farm houses, &c., and comprises 1156 souls, and 5290 acres of land, rising boldly towards

the south and west. The Rev. W. H. Arundel, M.A., is patron and incumbent of the *rectory*, and also lord of the manor, which was anciently held by the Stanton, Fitzpaine, and other families; but the chief part of the soil belongs to Sir H. R. F. Davie, Mrs. Fursdon, (owner of Upcott,) J. C. Luxmore, Esq., and many other freeholders. The rectory, valued in K.B. at £37. 6s. 8d., and in 1831 at £793, has a good residence and 38A. 1R. 21P. of glebe. The tithes were commuted in 1842 for £1000 per annum. The *Church* (St. Mary,) is a large ancient structure, with a tower and five bells, and a painted east window. The parish has an *Independent Chapel* and several charities. The ALMSHOUSE for six poor parishioners was founded by *Andrew Scutt*, who endowed it in 1606 with a house and premises in Exeter, now let for £22 per annum, which is divided among the alms people. The *Poor's Land* consists of a farm of about 45 acres, and was purchased in 1717 for £210. 15s., derived from the gift of *James Courteney*, in the 32nd of Elizabeth. The poor have also the dividends of £200 three per cent. consols, derived from the last named and other donors; and 13s. 6d. per ann. from the *Church Hay* ($\frac{1}{2}$A.) on which eight houses have been built by the lessees. Half of the *Church House* was given to the poor by John Harris in 1648, and is occupied by paupers.

Arundel Rev Wm. Harris, M.A. rector	Oliver John	*Manley John
Body Josiah, surgeon	BOOT & SHOEMRS.	Manley Robert
Greenslade John, wheelwright	Lavis John	*Melhuish John
Hewish Richd. farrier & parish clerk	Melhuish Rd.	MelhuishThos.T.
Langworthy Saml. vict. Ring of Bells	Pike John	*Pitt Thomas
Ley Wm. carpenter	Roberts John	*Pridham Saml.
Manley Robert, corn miller	FARMERS.	Searle Samuel
Oliver John, cattle dealer	(* are Owners.)	Strong John
Prior John, mason	Bradford Richd.	TremlettEdward,
Sharland & Son, tanners,*Waterhouse*	Brown W. *Combe*	Upcott
Skinner Mr Thomas	Chamberlain P.	*Turner John
Stone Henry, smith & wheelwright	Clement Wm.	TAILORS.
Thorne James, baker & shopkeeper	*Francis Philip,	Hewish John
Veysey Frederick L. schoolmaster	Court Place	Hewish Thomas
Wotton James, cooper and overseer	*Frost Jane	Hosegood Luke
Wotton John, cooper and baker	Hatswell Hor.	Whitton Joseph
WottonWm.plumber&vict.HalfMoon	*Heard Richard	
Wotton Wm. baker	Heard John	POST OFFICE at
BLACKSMITHS.	Heard Wm.	John Roberts.
Pope Wm. · Fisher John	*Hewish John	Letters *via* Crediton
BUTCHERS. · Hookings Wm.	*Luxton George	
Squire Thomas		

POUGHILL, a village and parish, 7 miles N. by E. of Crediton, and W.S.W. of Tiverton, has only 361 souls, and 1662A. of land, near one of the sources of the river Creedy. It was anciently held by the Poughill or Poghill family. The Melhuish and Carew families, and the trustees of Mrs. Pyncombe's Charities, own a great part of the parish, and the rest belongs to other freeholders. The *Church* (St. Mary,) has an embattled tower and five bells, and the living is a *rectory*, valued in K.B. at £8. 17s. 8$\frac{1}{2}$d., and in 1831 at £221. The Lord Chancellor is patron, and the Rev. John H. Ward, M.A., of Kew, Surrey, is the incumbent. The Parsonage is a small neat

residence, and the glebe is 22A. 36P. The tithes were commuted, in 1840, for £213 per annum. A new *Parish School* has been erected, at the cost of £130. *Mrs. Gertrude Pyncombe,* who resided at Wels-bere, in this parish, left a large estate, in 1730, to be vested with trustees for charitable uses in this and other parishes, and the aug-mentation of poor livings. The property now held by her trustees yields about £900 per annum. The annual payments made from this charity for the benefit of Poughill parish, are as follow :—£5 for the poor, £5 for the schoolmaster, £5 towards repairing the chancel, and 40s. each to a poor man and two poor women not re-ceiving parochial relief. Mrs. Pyncombe's trustees also provide Bibles and prayer-books for the use of the parish school. The poor have 17s. 8d., and the schoolmaster 17s. 8d. yearly, left by *Robert Gay,* in 1725, out of Lower Yedbury estate. In 1769, the *Rev. Robt. Bradford* left a yearly rent-charge of 20s., to be laid out in buying a blue coat for a poor man of this parish. The poor parishioners have the following yearly doles :—£1. 15s. 8d., left by *Humphrey Brooke,* in 1670 ; £1. 19s. 6d., as the interest of £39. 10s. *Poor's Money ;* and 10s., paid as the rent of a pew in the church, left by *John* or *Catherine Thomas.*

Babbage George, schoolmaster
Brown Jno. baker & vict. Rose&Crown
Collihole Henry, blacksmith
Guscott Wm. shopkeeper
Nicholls Thomas, carpenter
Shalstone Eliz. *letter carrier*
Stockham Rev John Henry, *curate*
Stone John, butcher
Tapp James, wheelwright
Tapp Philip, cooper
White Robert, shoemaker

FARMERS.
Bowden Charlotte ‖ Ellis John
Martin Philip ‖ Moxey John
Melhuish Thomas, *Barton*
Strong Wm. ‖ Thomas Matthew
Thomas Wm. ‖ Thorne Wm.
Trude John ‖ Trude Samuel

SHOBROOKE, a village and parish, in the vale of the small river Creedy, 2½ miles E.N.E. of Crediton, contains many scattered farm-houses, 787 inhabitants, and 3835A. of land. J. H. Hippisley, Esq., owns a great part of the soil, and is lord of the *manors of Shobrooke and Little Fulford,* the latter of which extends into Credi-ton parish. He has a handsome seat here, called *Fulford Park.* The mansion was built by the late R. Hippisley Tuckfield, Esq., who pulled down the old house, built by Sir Wm. Periam, Lord Chief Baron of the Exchequer. The park is well wooded, and stocked with deer. G. S. Fursdon owns part of *West Raddon* estate, and several smaller freeholders have estates in the parish. Part of West Raddon belonged to the Westcote family, and *Thomas Westcote,* the antiquary, was born there in 1567, and was buried at Shobrooke about 1640. His "View of Devonshire" was edited and published in 1845, by the Rev. George Oliver, D.D., and Pitman Jones, Esq.; but it is confined chiefly to the descent of manors and the pedigrees of families. A small *fair* is held at Shobrooke, on July 9th. The *Church* is a fine ancient structure, with a tower and six bells, and the *rectory,* valued in K.B. at £36, is annexed to the Bishopric of Exeter. The glebe is 21 acres, and the tithes were commuted in 1841 for £560 per annum. The Rectory House, built about 60 years ago, is occupied by the curate. In 1715, the Presby-

terians had a meeting-house at Shobrooke, which still exists. The poor have £3. 8s., and the schoolmaster £1. 12s. yearly from the dividends of £200 three per cent. stock, purchased with various benefactions. For teaching poor children the schoolmaster has also a yearly rent-charge of £3, left by *Mary Trenchard*, in 1728, out of land at Shobrooke and Crediton. *Eliz. Tuckfield*, in 1802, left £10 a year to the poor of Shobrooke (see Crediton ;) and they have also the dividends of £142. 17s. 1d. three per cent. stock, purchased with £90, left by *Lydia Hunt*, in 1804.

Brown Mr Wm. || Gibbings Mrs.
Glendinning R., Esq. *Eastwood*
Greenslade Wm. corn miller
Hippisley Jno. Hy., Esq.*Fulford Park*
James Samuel, blacksmith
Knox Rev Robert A., B.A. curate
Manning John, shoemaker
Pascoe John, land steward
Rawl Wm. vict. North Country Inn
Slade Henry, tailor ; and Wm. par. cl
Slade Geo. maltster & vict. Lion
Tucker Elijah, shoemaker & shopr
Woodgate Mr Thomas, *Cider House*

Woodland Uriah, blacksmith

FARMERS.

Arnold Richard || Burrington John
Burton John || Cade Henry
Coles James || Francis Wm.
Godfrey Wm. || Hellier Philip
Helmore Mark || Hole Thomas
Huggins James || Lane Robert
Norris Thomas, *Lower Efford*
Pitts Henry || Rowden John
Tuckett Wm. *West Raddon*

POST from Crediton.

STOCKLEIGH-ENGLISH, a small village and parish, 4½ miles N. by E. of Crediton, has only 161 souls, and 1104 acres of land, on the banks of a rivulet, which falls into the Creedy a little below. J. P. Bellow, Esq., is lord of the manor and owner of most of the soil, and has his seat here. The *Church* (St. Mary,) is a small Gothic structure, with a tower and two bells. The *rectory*, valued in K.B. at £7, and in 1831 at £128, is in the gift of the Lord Chancellor and incumbency of the Rev Thomas Dixon, who has a small thatched residence, and 41 acres of glebe. The tithes were commuted in 1844 for £131 per annum. The poor have a small house, and the interest of £19, given by various donors. *Directory :*—J. P. Bellow, Esq., *Stockleigh Court ;* Rev. Thos. Dixon, *Rectory ;* Abm. Brewer, *blacksmith ;* and Oliver Elworthy, Thomas Hawkins, James Norrish, and Wm. Roberts, *farmers.*

STOCKLEIGH POMEROY, on a bold eminence, four miles N.E. of Crediton, is a village and parish, containing 258 souls, and 1239A 2R. 5P. of land. It was long held by the ancient family of Pomeroy, but is now the property of Sir H. R. F. Davie, Bart. The *Church* (St. Mary,) has an embattled tower and two bells. The *rectory*, valued in K.B. at £15. 6s. 8d., and in 1831 at £260, is in the patronage of the Bishop of Exeter, and incumbency of the Rev. Thomas Young, who has a good residence, with tasteful grounds. The poor have the interest of £112, given by various donors. The glebe is 46A., and the tithes were commuted in 1841 for £180 :—Wm. R. Cockram, *schoolmaster ;* Rd. Harvey, *cattle dealer ;* James Yendell, *butcher ;* Rev. Thomas Young, *Rectory ;* and John Bodley, Wm. Strong, Jas. Tuckett, John Tuckett, and Jno. Webber, *farmers.*

UPTON HELIONS, in the picturesque valley of the small river Creedy, two miles N. by E. of Crediton, is a village and parish, con-

M

taining only 146 inhabitants, and about 1000 acres of fertile land. Mrs. Guerin owns the manor and farm of Helions Barton, anciently held by the Helion family. Sir H. R. F. Davie, Bart., owns *Creedy Widger*, or *Lower Creedy*. Mr. W. C. Dicker owns the estate called *Haske*, or Husk ; and J. C. Luxmore, Esq., owns *Merifield*, or Merryvale. The *Church* (St. Mary,) is an ancient structure, with a tower and one bell, and the living is a *rectory*, valued in K.B. at £10. 6s. 8d., and in 1831 at £275, in the patronage and incumbency of the Rev. W. Wellington, B.A., who has a large and handsome residence, commanding a fine view of Creedy Park, on the opposite side of the river. The house was much enlarged by a late rector,—the Rev. James Carrington, who died in 1794, and has a handsome monument in the church. The poor have the dividends of £132. 8s. 10d., four per cent. stock, purchased with money given by various donors.

Dicker Mr W. C. *Haske Barton*
Godsland Wm. corn miller
Lee Thos., & Tucker Wm. farmers
Ocock Thos. farmer, *Merifield*
Slyman Lieut. Danl., R.N., & Mr Roger
Tremlett John, farmer, and Jno. jun. maltster, *Lower Creedy*
Wellington Rev Wm., B.A., *Rectory*

WASHFIELD, a scattered village, picturesquely situated near one of the sources of the river Exe, two miles N.W. of Tiverton, has in its parish 503 souls, and 3235 acres of land, forming a detached member of West Budleigh Hundred. (See page 262.) Jno. F. Worth, Esq., owns a great part of the soil, and is lord of the manor. He has a pleasant seat here, called *Worth House*, where his family has been settled since the thirteenth century. Messrs. J. and R. Melhuish, Thos. Daniel, W. Talley, and a few small owners have estates here. The *Church* (St. Mary,) is a Gothic structure, with a large tower and five bells. In the chancel are several neat mural monuments. The *rectory*, valued in K.B. at £19. 17s. 6d., and in 1831 at £409, is in the patronage of J. F. Worth, and incumbency of the Rev. John Pitman, B.C.L., of Broadhempston. The glebe is 26A., and the *Rectory House*, occupied by the curate, is a good residence, with tasteful grounds. The tithes were commuted in 1837 for £407 per annum. The *National School*, built in 1836, is attended by about 50 children. A cottage and 8½A. of land, given for the poor by Gregory and Baldwin Harris, in 1651, are let for £14 a year. The poor have also the interest of £5, left by Francis Eveleigh; and two of the most godly poor parishioners have about £5 each yearly from *Blagden's Charity*, as noticed with Tiverton.

Bockett Rev Jph, M.A. rector of Stoodleigh, & curate of Washfield, *Rectory*
Cavill John, wheelwright
Lucas Elizabeth, corn miller
Pearce Wm. gardener
Pook Lucretia, schoolmistress
Tucker Abm. & John, masons
Tucker Simon, parish clerk
Worth John F., Esq., *Worth House*
Worth Miss My. *Beachamp House*

FARMERS.
Ansty Jno.
Baldwin Edwin
Baldwin Robert

Beedell Thomas
Broomfield Rt.
Carter Robert
Chave Wm.
Coles John
Davey Wm.
Elworthy John
Gale Henry
Gale John
Hawkins Edw.
Holway Abel

Melhuish John
Melhuish Robt.
Milford John
Moss James
Musgrove John
Norris Thomas
Poole Thomas
Skinner Wm.
Were Peter
Whitter John

CREDITON HUNDRED

Is in the Northern Division of Devon ; in Crediton Union, County Court District, Polling District, and Petty Sessional Division ; and in the Archdeaconry of Exeter, and Deanery of Cadbury. It is in the centre of the county, extending from two to twelve miles north-west of Exeter, and varying from six to four miles in breadth. It is bounded on the east by the small river Creedy, and traversed by the line of the Taw Valley and Crediton and Exeter Railway, which is still unfinished. It had 12,055 inhabitants in 1841, and comprises 36,924 acres of land, as will be seen in the following enumeration of its six parishes.

Parishes.	Acres.	Pop.	Parishes.	Acres.	Pop.
Colebrooke	4990	878	Morchard (Bishop's)	7088	1880
Crediton	12,039	5947	Newton St. Cyres	4305	1234
Kennerleigh	732	118	Sandford	7770	1998

CREDITON UNION comprises the 29 parishes of Crediton, Cheriton-Bishop, Colebrooke, Hittisleigh, Kennerleigh, Newton St. Cyres, Shobrooke, Sandford, Stockleigh-Pomeroy, Upton-Helions, Brushford, Bow, Clannaborough, Chawleigh, Cheriton-Fitzpaine, Down St. Mary, Eggesford, Lapford, Morchard-Bishop, Nymet-Rowland, Puddington, Poughill, Stockleigh-English, Thelbridge, Wembworthy, Washford-Pyne, Wolfardisworthy, and Zeal-Monachorum. They comprise an area of about 138 square miles, and in 1841, they contained 22,076 inhabitants, and 4673 houses, of which 296 were empty, and 41 building, when the census was taken. Their total average annual expenditure on the poor, during the three years preceding the formation of the Union in 1836, was £12,314. In 1838, their expenditure was £9955, and in 1849, £11,528. The *Union Workhouse* is at Crediton, and was built in 1837, at the cost of about £5000. It has room for 300, but has seldom more than 200 inmates. The Union is divided into two relieving, and nine medical districts. The Rev. W. Wellington is the *chaplain*, and Wm. Comyns Leach and Mrs. Leach are *master* and *matron* of the Workhouse. Mr. Thos. Pring is the *union clerk and superintendent registrar*, W. Wellacott and John Hookway are the *relieving officers*, and Messrs. J. A. Edwards, W. H. Hugo, Wm. Deans, C. Basely, J. Body, J. C. Davy, W. Luxton, and W. R. Warren are the *surgeons*.

COLEBROOKE, a pleasant village, on an acclivity near a tributary stream of the river Yew, four miles W. of Crediton, has in its parish 878 inhabitants, and 4990 acres of land, including the hamlet of *Coleford*, part of *Coplestone*, and many scattered farm houses, &c. A. Coryton, Esq., is lord of the manor, which was anciently held under the Bishop of Exeter. The other principal owners are J. Sillifant, Esq., J. H. Hippisley, Esq., S. Hamlyn, Esq., the Dean and Chapter of Exeter, S. Norrish, Esq., and Mr. R. Madge. *Coombe House*, on the estate called Landsend, or Coombe Lancells, is the pleasant seat of John Sillifant, Esq. *Paschoe* was formerly the seat of the Hamlyn family, and a handsome mansion is about to be erected on the estate by S. Hamlyn, Esq. *Horwell* is the seat and property of Samuel Norrish, Esq. The *Church* (St. Mary,) is a large limestone structure, with a handsome tower, containing five bells. The south transept belongs to S. Norrish, Esq., and the beautiful north aisle to S. Hamlyn, Esq. There were formerly small chapels at Coplestone, Landsend, Hor-

well, Hooke, and Wolmerstone, in this parish.   The Dean and
Chapter of Exeter are appropriators of the great tithes, now leased
to J. Sillifant, Esq.   They are also patrons of the *vicarage*, valued
in K.B. at £20, and in 1831 at £200.   The Rev. Thos. Drosier,
A.B. is the incumbent, and has 14A. of glebe, and a good residence.
The great tithes were commuted in 1845 and '7 for £435. 10s., and
the vicarial tithes for £163 per annum.   The poor parishioners
have the dividends of £120 three per cent. consols, and the interest
of £25, derived from the gift of *Ann Mills*, who also left £100, of
which only £25 remains, towards the support of a lecturer at the
church.   The poor have two annuities of 20s., left by Wm. Hock-
well and John Pidsley.

Arscott Robert, parish clerk
Arscott Thos., & Daw Geo. *shoemkrs*
Arscott Wm. miller, *Ford Mill*
Boundy Ann, shopkeeper
Cann Geo. mlstr. & vict. *Coplestone Inn*
Davey Geo. *wheelgt. ;* and Jas. *smith*
Drosier Rev. Thos., A.B., *Vicarage*
Ebbels John, shopkeeper, *Post-Office*
Ebbels Richard, wheelwright
Glanfield Wm. tailor
Hill Mrs J. *Coplestone*
Hooper James, blacksmith
Kerswell James, schoolmaster
Melhuish Robert, corn miller
Norrish Saml. gent. *Horwell*
Peters Thos. vict. & butcher, *Ship*
Sillifant John., Esq. *Coombe House*
Smale Saml. baker and shopkeeper
Sobey John, carpenter
Southcott My. vict. *New Inn*

Sutton My. Ann, schoolmistress
Tucker John, vict. *Coplestone Cross*
Wreford Jas. carpenter, Coombe
Wreford Thos. D. baker & vict. *Bell*
FARMERS. (** are Owners.*)
Bartlett Richard, *Buttsford*
Burrington George, *Painston*
Cheriton Thos. || Daw Thomas
Dark John and Wm. *Wotton*
*Hill James, *Stidham*
*Lee Francis, *Coleford*
*Lee James || *Madge Johna.
*Madge Robert, *Coplestone*
May John || Partridge Thomas
Norrish Wm. *Colesford*
*Pearce John || Snell Andrew
Stoneman Chpr. || *Wreford James
Willcocks John and Wm.
Wills Geo. G. *Wolmerstone*

CREDITON is an ancient market town, picturesquely seated between two hills, on the western bank of the river Creedy, near its
confluence with the small river Yew, eight miles N.W of Exeter.
It is approached by excellent turnpike roads, and is near the line of
the intended *Taw Valley Railway*, which will here join the *Exeter
and Crediton Railway*, which terminates in the Bristol and Exeter
Railway, near Cowley Bridge, but will not be opened till 1850,
though the rails have been laid more than twelve months.   Owing
to unfortunate disputes, the Taw Valley line may not be finished for
some years.   CREDITON PARISH comprises no less than 12,039 acres
of fertile land, and had 5947 inhabitants in 1841.   It is in eight
divisions or *tythings*, of which the following are the names, with
their population in 1841, viz., *Crediton Borough*, 2245 ; *Canon Fee*,
1411 ; *Town*, 663 ; *Uford*, 286 ; *Uton*, 384 ; *Knowle*, 392 ; *Rudge*,
265 ; and *Woodland*, 301.   These tithing comprise many scattered
farm houses, &c., and several handsome mansions, and extend more
than two miles north, west, and south of the town.   The soil is
generally fertile, and the surface rises in bold hills from the two
rivers.   Crediton gives name to this *Hundred*, to the large *Union*
noticed at page 267, and to a *Polling and County Court District*, as

well as to a *Petty Sessional Division.* The latter comprises this Hundred and that of West Budleigh. Messrs. J. G. and F. E. Smith are clerks to the magistrates, and Mr. G. Tanner is clerk of the County Court, held on the first Monday of every month. Crediton is an *ancient borough,* without either parliamentary or municipal privileges, though it sent two burgesses to the parliament which assembled at Carlisle, in the reign of Edward I. Jas. Wentworth Buller, Esq., is lord of the *manor,* and Mr. W. Rawlings is steward of the Court Leet, at which a *portreeve, bailiff, chief-constable,* and other officers are appointed yearly. The manor and hundred of Crediton belonged to the Bishops of Devonshire from a very early period, and here were the Cathedral and the Palace of the Bishops till 1050, when the See was removed to Exeter, as noticed at page 74. There were twelve *Bishops of Crediton,* the first of whom was *Aidolf,* or Eadulphus, and the last *Leofric,* or Leofricus. All traces of the Cathedral disappeared some centuries ago, and its site, near the church yard, has long been occupied by houses. The manor and hundred continued to belong to the Bishops, and the Palace probably to be their occasional residence, till the reign of Henry VIII., when Bishop Vessey surrendered them to the Crown, after having been *compelled* to convey Crediton Park, to the royal favourite, Sir Thomas Dennis. They were afterwards granted to Lord Darcy, of Chiche, but having been subsequently restored to the See, they were conveyed by Bishop Babington, in 1595, to Wm. Killigrew, groom of the chamber. The parish afterwards passed to various families, and now belongs to many freeholders, the largest of whom are J. W Buller, Esq., Sir H. R. F. Davie, Benj. Cleave, Esq., J. H. Hippisley, Esq., and John Quicke, Esq. The *fee-farm rent* of £146. 8s. 3¼d., formerly payable out of the manor to the Crown, is now vested with Thomas Porter, Esq. *Downes,* in the town tything, is the pleasant seat of J. W. Buller, Esq. *Fulford Park,* partly in this and partly in Shobrooke parish, is noticed at page 267. *Yewe,* in the tything of Uton, was long held of the Bishops by the Barons of Okehampton, by the service of being stewards at their enthronization. It now belongs to the Rev. S. Pidsley. *Tedbourn* and *Posbury,* in the same tything, belongs to J. H. Hippisley, Esq. *Knowle, Higher* and *Lower Dunscombe, Fordton, Trowbridge, Coplestone,* and other estates in this large parish, belong to various owners. Crediton is said to have been the birth place of *St. Boniface,* Archbishop of Mentz, by whose influence with Ethelbald, King of Mercia, the Holy Scriptures are said to have been read in this country in the English language. It is sometimes called *Kirton* by the vulgar, and its great antiquity has passed into a proverb, which says, *" Kirton was a market town; when Exeter was a fuzzy down "*

The town is about a mile in length, and is in two parts, called East and West Town. The latter was formerly much more extensive than at present; upwards of 450 houses being destroyed by a *great fire,* in 1743. A second fire, in May, 1769, consumed many of the new houses that had been built on the sites of old ones, together with the Market house and Shambles; but these were after-

wards rebuilt. Of late years the town has been much improved, chiefly at the expense of the lord of the manor, J. W. Buller, Esq., who, in 1837, erected a neat and commodious covered *Market Place*, on the north side of High street, in lieu of the old one, which stood in the middle of the street. A respectable Inn has also been erected, with a large room for balls, concerts, &c.; and the road, instead of entering the town on one side, now enters by a broad carriage way, from east to west. These and other improvements have been made under the powers of an act of Parliament. *Gas Works* were established in 1843, by a company, with a capital of £2000, in £5 shares. The *market*, held every Saturday, is well supplied with all sorts of provisions; and on the Saturday before the last Wednesday in April, there is a great cattle market. Here are also three annual *fairs* for cattle, &c., held May 11th, Aug. 21st, and Sept. 21st, or on the Tuesdays following, when those dates fall on a Friday or Saturday. The town was one of the principal seats of the *woollen manufacture* from its first introduction into this county, and was long famed for serges, kerseys, &c., as well as for fine yarns; hence the proverb, "As fine as Kirton spinning." The serge market was removed from Crediton to Exeter in the reign of Elizabeth (see page 63,) but the manufacture of serges was carried on here extensively till after the great fire in 1743, when about 1500 pieces are said to have been made in the town and neighbourhood weekly. The woollen trade is now obsolete here, but at Fordton there is a manufactory of coarse linens, dowlas, sail cloth, &c. Crediton was for a short time possessed by the rebels of 1549, and was occasionally occupied by the Royal and Parliamentary forces during the civil wars of the 17th century. (See page 56.) The town is highly salubrious, and has never been visited by plagues or Asiatic cholera.

The Church *(Holy Cross,)* is a spacious and handsome cruciform structure, erected in the 15th century, near the site of the ancient cathedral, which was dedicated to St Gregory. It was enlarged, repaired, and beautified, some years ago, by the Governors of the Church Corporation Trust. It has a massive tower, containing eight bells, and rising from the centre to the height of 100 feet. The large east and west windows are decorated with rich tracery, and over the south porch is an old parochial library. Among the monuments is one of Sir Wm. Periam, Chief Baron of the Exchequer, with his effigy in his judge's robes; and another with an effigy in memory of John Tuckfield, Esq., who died in 1630. The altar-piece represents Moses and Aaron sustaining the Decalogue. At the time of the removal of the See to Exeter, there had been twelve Bishops of Crediton, and the succeeding prelates still remained patrons of the *Chapter* or *College of Crediton*, which consisted of 18 canons, or prebendaries, and 18 vicars, and was valued at the dissolution at £322 per annum. It was dissolved by Edward VI., who vested the tithes of Crediton, and other possessions formerly belonging to it, in twelve trustees, or *Governors*, for the support of the vicar, the assistant minister, and the master of the Grammar School, and for other purposes, as afterwards noticed. These Governors are patrons of the *vicarage*, valued in K.B. at £30, and

in 1831 at £425, and now held by the Rev. Samuel Rowe, M.A. The *Chapel of St. Luke, at Posbury*, in this parish, about two miles S. of the town, was built in 1835, by the late R. Hippisley Tuckfield, Esq., whose successor, J. H. Hippisley, Esq., is patron of the curacy, which is now held by the Vicar. It is a small but neat stone fabric, in the Gothic style, and is conveniently situated as a chapel of ease for the southern parts of this large parish. There are five Dissenting Chapels in the town, belonging to the Unitarians, Independents, Baptists, Wesleyans, and Plymouth Brethren. The Unitarian Chapel was built by Presbyterians, and from 1739 to 1749 it was under the ministry of *Micaiah Towgood*. (See page 89.) The parish has several *endowed schools* and almshouses, and a large amount of *trust property* for public and charitable uses. It has also a *Mechanics' Institution* and several *Friendly Societies*. CREDITON UNION is already noticed at page 267.

CHURCH CORPORATION TRUST AND GRAMMAR SCHOOL.—Edward VI., in the first year of his reign, by his letters patent, incorporated 12 parishioners by the name of the *Governors* of the hereditaments and goods of the Church of Crediton, and vested with them the lands, tithes, &c., which had belonged to the late *College of Crediton* and the chapel of St. Swithen, at Sandford; and directed them to apply the yearly profits thereof for the support of the *vicar and chaplain of Crediton, the vicar of Exminster, and the chaplain of Sandford;* for the support of a *Grammar School*, the reparation of the churches, &c., and for other charitable and public uses. Queen Elizabeth, by letters patent in the second year of her reign, augmented the possessions of this trust. The trust property having greatly increased, it has been several times the subject of litigation in the Court of Chancery, and new schemes have been sanctioned for the extension and general management of the charity, which has again become the subject of another Chancery suit. The *tithes* of about 20,000 acres in the three above-named parishes, belong to the trust, and their annual value in 1823 was £2550, of which £1223 was derived from the tithes of Crediton. There is also belonging to the trust a farm of 110A. at Exminster, let for about £150 per annum. The Vicarage House at Exminster was rebuilt in 1803, and the expense was defrayed by the governors, chiefly from the proceeds of a fall of timber on this farm. There are belonging to the trust in Crediton, six houses, &c., occupied rent-free by the vicar, the chaplain, the master of the Grammar School, the master of Dunn's School, and the clerk and sexton; and a range of small dwellings, occupied by paupers. At Sandford, a house belonging to the trust is appropriated to the residence of the chaplain of that place. The three parsonage houses in Crediton and Sandford were rebuilt in the early part of the present century, at the cost of about £4800. The governors are patrons of the benefices of the three parishes, and also of Kennerleigh rectory. Out of the income derived from the trust property, they pay the following *yearly stipends:*—£400 to the *vicar*, and £200 to the *chaplain* of Crediton; £250 to the vicar of Exminster; £200 to the chaplain of Sandford; about £150 to the master of the Grammar School; £6. 13s. 4d. each to three *exhibitioners* at the University; £2 each to four poor scholars at Crediton School; £27 to the *United English and Blue School;* £8. 8s. to four *almsmen* of Crediton; £22 to the *parish clerk;* and £6. 16s. to the *sexton*. Out of the tithe rents they have to pay about £700 per annum for poor rates, &c., and they occasionally expend large sums in repairing Crediton church, and the parsonage houses of the three above-named parishes. They also contribute towards the support of schools at Exminster and

Sandford. In 1820-1 they expended £303 in erecting a new gallery in Crediton church. The present *Governors* are Sir H. R. F. Davie and J. W. Buller, J. H. Hippisley, P. Francis, D. Tremlett, E. T. Ward, J. Yarde, B. Cleave, sen. and jun., Wm. Pope, E. Norris, and E. Empson, Esqrs.

Sir John Hayward, Knight, in 1635, left extensive property in Kent to Sir Richard Buller and other trustees, in trust that they should sell it and apply the proceeds for the relief of the poor of Rochester and such other parishes as they thought proper. This charity was not established till after the lapse of many years, and much expensive litigation in the Court of Chancery. The trust property was sold about 1800 for £12,621, and in 1805 the trustees obtained the sanction of the court to expend about £2700 in the erection of an *Almshouse and School of Industry* at Crediton. After these were erected, the inhabitants of Rochester instituted several proceedings in Chancery for the recovery of an equal share of the charity funds, and this they accomplished in 1822, when the court determined that the moiety belonging to Crediton consisted of £10,300. 12s. 6d. three per cent. consols, which yield an annual income of £309. 0s. 4d., to which is added about £15, as the rent of a field and several gardens belonging to the Almshouse and School of Industry, which are now mostly occupied by the *United Blue and English Schools,* and by the school in which poor girls are instructed in making gloves. Three or four old men have apartments in the building, and are allowed weekly stipends of 5s. each, with clothing and medical attendance when required. The rest of the income is expended in setting to work and apprenticing poor children. J. W. Buller, Esq., and others, are the *trustees.*

Davie's Almshouse, near the churchyard, consists of four small dwellings, for two married couples and two poor single people. It was founded in 1610, by *John Davie,* who endowed it with a yearly rent-charge of £20, out of Creedy and Longbarn estate, now belonging to Sir H. R. F. Davie. He also charged the same estate with the expense of keeping the almshouse in repair.

Spurway's Almshouse comprises four dwellings for as many poor parishioners, and was founded by *Humphrey Spurway,* in 1555, and endowed by him with a garden of 1R. 3P., at Crediton, and four cottages and 8A. 20P. of land at Witheridge, let for about £11 per annum, which is divided among the almspeople.

The Borough Lands were partly purchased in 1638, with the profits which the burgesses had made out of the tolls of the market, during the 99 years they had held them on lease under the Bishop of Exeter, at the yearly rent of 20s. Other portions of the trust property were purchased with savings of income, &c. The whole comprises about 50A., six cottages, and several gardens, let for £87 per annum, which is distributed at Christmas among all the poor of the parish, together with three-fourths of the rent of two houses and about 16A. of land, called Rookwood, which are let for £55 per annum, and were purchased in 1625, with £200, given by *John Newcombe* and *Walter Young,* one-fourth for the poor of *Inwardleigh,* and the rest for the poor of Crediton.

Various Charities.—In 1771, *Edward Smith* left £1000 to be placed out at interest, and the yearly proceeds distributed at Christmas among the poor parishioners. This sum, with savings of interest, was invested, in 1780, in the purchase of £2008. 7s. 4d. three per cent. consols. In 1787, Wm. Lake left for the same purpose £500, which was laid out in the purchase of £590. 12s. 6d. new four per cent. stock. The yearly sum of £83. 17s. 6d., derived from the two above-named charities, is distributed about Christmas among all the poor parishioners who have not received parochial

relief during the preceding six months. In 1802, ELIZABETH TUCKFIELD bequeathed to the 12 governors of Crediton £3000 three per cent. annuities, upon trust to apply the yearly dividends to various charitable uses in *Exeter, Crediton, Shobrooke, Morchard-Bishop, Thorverton, and Tedburn St. Mary,* as noticed with those parishes. The share belonging to Crediton consists of the annual sums of £20, for distribution among the poor not receiving parochial relief, and £10 towards the support of the *Blue School.* As noticed with Exeter, Sir JOHN ACLAND left an annuity of £2. 12s. for a weekly distribution of 1s. worth of bread at Crediton church. For the same purpose, JOHN WELSH left a yearly rent-charge of £2. 12s., in 1656, out of Welsh's tenement. In 1734, THOMAS COLLITON charged Dickersham field with the weekly payment of 1s. for the poor, and 10s. per annum for the charity schools. *Mrs. Thomasine Colliton,* in 1768, left a yearly rent-charge of £2. 12s. for a distribution of four threepenny loaves every Friday. *Robt. Buckingham* left for the poor 1¼a. of land, now let for £6, which is dispensed in weekly doles of bread, together with the three following annuities, viz., £2. 8s., left by *John Burrington,* in 1643; £2. 12s., left by *Thos. Please,* in 1643; and £3, left by *John Dunscombe,* out of the manor of Coldridge, which is also charged with 6s. 8d. per annum for the vicar. *Thos. Channon,* in 1656, left 1½a. of land in trust to pay 10s. yearly to the poor of Otterton, and to expend the remainder of the rent in clothing the poor of Crediton. This land is now let for £6 per ann. In 1712, ANDREW JEFFERY gave Broad Close in trust that the rent should be distributed yearly among poor decayed *master weavers or their widows.* Part of this close is now an orchard, and the rest is the site of five cottages and a cider-pound house, all belonging to the charity, and now let for £24 per ann. Among the same objects are distributed the rent of a small close, let for £4, and purchased with the gifts of *George and Agnes Ivie* and other donors. In 1718, *Cphr. Saunders* left a yearly rent-charge of 25s. for the poor attending the Dissenting Meeting-house. Twenty poor housekeepers of Crediton have the interest of £100, left by *John Welsford,* in 1821. The poor of *Knowle* have 20s. a year out of an estate in that tithing, now belonging to Mr. Newcombe. The dividends of £1250 three per cent. reduced annuities, purchased with £1000, left by *Grace Mann,* in 1776, are distributed among poor widows and fatherless children.

ENGLISH AND BLUE SCHOOL.—Two *Charity Schools,* one called the English School and the other the Blue School, were united in 1814, and placed under one master, in the building which was erected by the trustees of Sir John Hayward's Charity, as noticed at page 272. Various sums given for the support of the English School by John Cole and other donors, were laid out in the 17th century in the purchase of about 8a. of land, now let for about £30. There is also belonging to the same school, a sum of £200 three per cent. consols, of which £100 was given by John Tuckfield, in 1707. The funds, which belonged exclusively to the Blue School, consist of £1400 four per cent. stock, (purchased with the gifts of *Mrs. Honor Prouse, Wm. Luke,* and other donors;) and the following yearly sums, viz., a rent-charge of £4, left Mary Trenchard, in 1728; 10s. out of a field, left by Thos. Colliton; £4 as the interest of £100 vested in two turnpikes; and an annuity of £10 from Eliz. Tuckfield's Charity. Since the union of the two schools, the charity has received several legacies, among which are £100 three per cent. consols, left by George Bodley, in 1817, and £52. 10s. new four per cents., left by Wm. Elston, in 1821. From the above sources, the charity derives about £116 per annum, to which is added £27, given out of the Church Corporation Trust, and also about £100 per annum, raised by subscription and collections after sermons. The united schools

are attended by about 140 boys and 90 girls; and 55 of them are clothed at the expense of the charity. They are all instructed gratuitously, and provided with books and stationery. The master has a yearly salary of £72, and the mistress £20, and they have the free use of a house adjoining the school.

DUNN'S SCHOOL.—*Samuel Dunn*, in 1794, left to the " Governors of Crediton," £600 in trust to pay the yearly proceeds thereof to a schoolmaster for teaching writing, navigation, mathematics, &c., to at least six boys of the Church of England; preference to be given to those of the names of Dunn and Harris. This legacy was laid out in the purchase of £630 new four per cent. stock, for the dividends of which a schoolmaster teaches 12 boys of Crediton, in the house at Bowdon hill, which was formerly appropriated to the English School.

CREDITON DIRECTORY.

Those marked 1, *are in East Town;* 2, *High street;* 3, *Market street;* 4, *North street; and* 5, *in Parliament street.*

The POST-OFFICE is at Mr. Francis Shute's, High street. Letters despatched at 45 minutes past 12 in the afternoon, and at 10 minutes past 7 in the evening, *via* Exeter; and to Bideford, Barnstaple, &c., every morning.

Backwell Saml. inspr. of weights and measures
1 Badcock John, wine merchant, &c.
2 Baker Rev James, (Independent)
Bent Mrs Emily, Penton cottage
Bishop Wm. earthenware dealer
Blagden Peter, gent. Mill street
4 Boxer Robert, news agent
2 Brown Mr Saml. & 4 Mrs My. Ann
Buller Jas. Wentworth, Esq. *Downes*
1 Burdge Mr Wm. || Berry Mr John
Cade Thos. veterinary surgeon
Carthew John, miller, *Four Mills*
Cleave Benj. sen. and jun. Esqrs. *Newcombes*
Davy and Sons, linen, sacking, &c. manufacturers, *Fordton Mills*
Dawe Mrs Annette, Market street
Day Rev Saml. Phillips, (Indpt.)
2 *Devon and Cornwall Bank;* open Saturday
1 Deans Rev James, M.A. curate
5 Dicker Rt. cabinet mkr. par. clerk, and agt. to Western Provdt. Instn.
Drake John, gent. *Winswood House*
1 Drake Misses Chtte. and Charity
Dutchman Hewson, R.N. High st
2 Francis Mr Wm. and Mr James
Francis Mrs Eliz., Blagden place
Francis Miss, Palace cottage
1 Furse Wm. coal agent
Gorwyn Mr Richard Lambert
2 Gover Jas. brush and bellows mkr
2 Gover John, brush & bellows mkr

Guest John, supervisor, High st
Guppy Jane, beerhouse, High st
2 Hall Mr Saml. || Halse Mr N.W.
1 Haycraft Daniel, fellmonger
1 Hayes Wm. organist
Hippesley J. H. Esq. *Fulford Park*
2 Hoard Wm. Λ. machine maker
Holman Capt. Charles, High st
Hookway Giles, gentleman
Hugo Stephen, gent. High street
2 Kelland Mrs || Kingdon Mrs
4 Langabeer Jas. cheesemonger
Leach Rev George, (Wesleyan)
Leach Wm. Comyns, master of work-
Lee Fras. court bailiff   [house
Lightfoot Mrs and Miss, East town
McCombe Rev Alex. (Unitarian)
2 Madge Wm. supt. of Gas works
2 Madge Mr Thos.||Pearse Mr Wm.
Melhuish Mrs., Fair Park cottage
2 Norrish Abm. tallow chandler
2 Park John, clothes cleaner
Prickman Mr Ts. & Mrs. Blagden pl
2 Renwick Capt. Ts. & Rev. Ts., B.A.
Roberts Mrs Sarah, North street
Rowe Rev Saml., M.A. Vicarage
Rowe Richd. starch manufacturer
Rudall Francis, gent. *Palace*
Rudall Miss Ann, East town
Shute Fras. post master, High st
3 Smith Mrs || Snow Mrs Chtte.
2 Taylor Mr John || Tarrant Mr Wm.
2 Thomas John, china, glass, &c. dlr
5 Tremlett Mrs B. || Temple Mrs

2 Tremlett John, brewer, &c.
2 Tucker James, dyer and scourer
Ward Thomas, coach builder
Wilson Mrs Margaret, East town
Winter Robert, coal and corn dlr
Wreford Abm. accpt. || Yelland Mrs

ATTORNEYS.

2 Cleave Wm. C., High street
Francis John, High street
Langdon Wm., High street
Medland Robert, High street
3 Pring Thos. (union clerk & supt. registrar;) h *Fordton House*
5 Smith John Geo. and Fras. Edw. (clks to magistrates;) h *Oakfield*
2 Tanner Geo. (clk. of County court)

FARMERS. (+ *are Owners.*)

Baker Joseph, *Uton*
Brock Wm., *Westwood*
Brooks Thomas, *Priestcombe*
Brown Richard, *Dunscombe*
Coombe Wm. and John, *Knowle*
+Cornish Wm. || Dodd John
Dark John || David Richard
Ewings John, *Rudge*
Ewings Wm. and Saml., *Bradley*
+Francis Philip, *Moor*
+Francis Wm., *Westout*
+Gorwyn Wm. L., *Bradley*
Gregory Geo. and John, *Park*
Hall John, *Chiddon brook*
+Harris Joseph, *Chapeldown*
Harris John, *Vinnecomb*
James Henry, *Trowbridge*
+Lamacraft Joseph, *Eastacott*
+Lee James, *Warren*
+Lee Francis || Lee James
+Lee James, *Holwell*
Lee James, *Uford*
Lee Thomas || Lee Richard
+Lee Thomas, *Gunston*
+Madge John, *Bewsleigh*
+Madge Thomas, *Landscore*
Matthews Thomas, *Fordton*
May John, *Lower Elston*
Milford John, *Lower Westwood*
Mortimer George, *Uton Barton*
Partridge Silvanus || Pike John
+Pridham Danl. Tremlett, *Rock*
+Rattenbury James, *Ford*
Rowe John, *Westacott*
Searle John, *Lower Easton*
+Skinner Richard, *Hollacombe*
Strong John, *Knowle Barton*
+Tremlett Daniel, *Holcombe*

Ward Elias Tremlett, *Langridge*
Wreford Simon, *Well-parks*
+Yarde John, *Trowbridge House*

FIRE & LIFE OFFICES.

2 Clerical, Medical, & General, Chas. Hainworth
2 County & Provident, S. Backwell
2 Eagle and Law, Wm. Langdon
2 Farmers, W. H. Hugo
2 Imperial, George Newman
2 Norwich Union, Abraham Wreford
5 West of Engd., J. G. & F. F. Smith

INNS & TAVERNS.

Angel, Jas. Collings, High street
5 Commercial Inn, Thos. Odgers
Coplestone Cross Inn, John Tucker
Coplestone Inn, John Cann
Dock Inn, Wm. Davie, High st
2 Duke of York, John Strong
Green Dragon, Wm. Milton, High st
5 Horse and Jockey, John Strong
1 King's Arms, James Stone
4 Lamb Inn, Wm. Bawden
2 London Inn, Eliz. Gover
2 Oat Sheaf, Thomas Brown
Old Swan, Edward Vile, High st
1 Plymouth Inn, Wm. Berry
1 Ring of Bells, Wm. Wollacott
Royal Oak, Thos. Coles, High st
Seven Stars, John Milton, High st
2 Ship Hotel, Jas. Williams, (postg)
Star, Wm. Strong, Mill street
5 Union Inn, Wm. Harvey
1 White Hart, John Rudall
2 White Swan, John Holcombe

ACADEMIES.	BAKERS.
2 Amery Mgt.&E.	1 Badcock John
Amery Mary	2 Bishop Wm.
Berry Mary	2 Burdge John
Bradford James	1 Gale Fredk.
Davy Wm.	2 Glanfield Geo.
2 Edwards Giles	5 Gribble Geo.
2 Jarman Mary	2 Hamlin Giles
3 Jones Thomas	2 Herring Chtte.
LangworthyMiss,	2 Hodge Thos.
Sus. (boardg.)	2 Jennings John
Luxmore Misses	2 Lee John
Manley Rev Jno.,	2 Lee Simon
M.A.,Grm. Sch.	1 Milford Wm.
2 Martin Wm.	5 Squire John
AUCTIONEERS.	2 Strong Thos.
1 Lear Hy. survr.	2 Thomas Wm.
2 Thomas John	2 Watts Samuel
and James	1 Whippell Wm.

BASKET MAKERS.
1 Radford Jas.
1 Saunders Thos.
BLACKSMITHS.
1 Blight Robert
2 Hoard Wm. A.
1 Madge Thos.
2 Madge Wm.
1 Perkins Jonth.
2 Pollard John
2 Risdon John
BOOKSELLERS, &c
2 Luxmore Jno.V.
2 Wreford Sus.
BOOT& SHOE MKS.
2 Backwell Sml.
2 Backwell Jas.
4 Berry Thomas
2 Berry John
1 Berry Wm.
2 Browning John
1 Elston Geo.
1 Elston John
2 Lendon Wm.
2 Marchant Edw.
5 Marchant Jas.
2 Trais John
BREWERS.
5 Finch C. & Son,
(& chandlers)
2 Tremlett John
BRICKMAKERS.
2 Channon Jno.
5 Manning Hy.
BUILDERS.
1 Berry Wm.
2 Channon John
2 Cockram John
2 Hurson John
Shorland James
2 Thomas J. & J.
BUTCHERS.
4 Bond Thos.
2 Hurson Thos.
2 Nichols John

2 Nichols Thos.
5 Shepherd John
1 Tapper Wm.
CARPENTERS.
1 Harris John
5 Dicker Robt.
2 Thomas J. & J.
2 Vowler Wm.
DRUGGISTS.
4 Read Robt. (&
vety. surgeon)
2 Searle Wm.
2 Wreford Ann
COOPERS.
2 HutchingsWm.
2 Kerslake Wm.
CURRIERS.
2 Couldridge Jno.
2 Snell Jno. &W.
GROCERS.
(* Drapers and
+ Spirit Dlrs.)
4 Bully Wm.
2 CouldridgeWm.
1*Glanvill Geo.
2*Harris Robt.
2+Kelland Geo.
2*Mann John
2*Newcombe Jno.
2*Pinson Sarah
2+Searle Wm.
2+Skinner Hy.
2 Stone Robt.
2*Toose & Good
HAIRDRESSERS.
2 Couldridge W.
4 Elston Wm.
HATTERS.
1 Fursman John
4 Pope Wm.

IRONMONGERS.
(* Tinners also.)
2* Berry John
2* Gover Jas.

2* Gover Saml.
2 Heathman Ts.
2 Voysey Jas.
MALTSTERS.
1 Badcock Edw.
Cann John
5 Finch C. & Son
1 Pope Simon
1 James Henry
2 Snow Wm.
MILLINERS.
Backwell Btha.
Good Eliza
2 Pollard Sus.
PLUMBERS,
Glzrs. & Painters.
2 Backwell John
2 Hall John
2 Newman Geo.
ROPE, &c., MKRS.
1 Blatchfield Jno.
1 Dawe Thos.
1 Rice Michl.
SADDLERS.
2 Gibbings Geo.
2 Lee Thos.
2 Tozer & Bailey

SHOPKEEPERS.
2 Andrews Eliz.
1 Berry John
1 Berry Wm.
1 Burrington Jas.
1 Clarke John
2 Endacott Wm.
2 Holmes John
1 Jones Mary
2 Lucas John
1 Milton Richd.
1 Norris Robt.
1 Salter Ann
2 Thomas My. J.
1 Treble Maria
2 Ware John
1 WelsfordRosna.

2 White Thos.
SURGEONS.
3 EdwardsJno.A.
2 Empson Edwin
Hainworth Chas.
Holman Herman
Hugo Wm. Hy.
Yarde Edward
TAILORS.
2 Bondson Jas.
2 Bradford Wm.
2 Glanfield Wm.
4 Lattaney John
2 Mickelborough
John & Co.
2 Norrish John
5 Potter Fredk.
TANNERS.
2 Adams Edw.
1 Francis John
WATCHMAKERS.
2 Bellringer Frs.
2 Lane John
1 Maunder John
2 Webber Geo.
WHEELWRIGHTS.
1 Carthew Jas.
2 Field Daniel
2 LangsfordFras.

COACHES, &c.
pass daily to
Exeter, Barn-
staple, &c.
Omnibuses daily
to Exeter.
Ths. Cole's, from
the Royal Oak
John Rudall's
from the White
Hart
RAILWAY.
The line to Exe-
ter will be open-
ed in 1850

KENNERLEIGH, a small village and parish, in the picturesque valley of the Creedy, 5 miles N. by W. of Crediton, has only 118 souls, and 732 acres of land, nearly all the property of Sir S. H. Northcote, Bart., the lord of the manor, formerly belonging to the Hidon and Dowrich families. The *Church* (St. John,) is a small ancient structure, which was repaired and newly slated in 1847. The *rectory*, valued in 1831 at £110, is in the patronage of the Governors of Crediton Church and Charity Trust, and incumbency of the Rev. A. N. Buckeridge, M.A., who has a good residence erected

about nine years ago. The tithes were commuted in 1836, for £95, and the rectory has been augmented with land at Woolfardisworthy, let for £30 a year, and purchased with Queen Anne's Bounty and benefaction money. *Directory :*—Rev. A. Nugent Buckeridge, M.A., *Rectory ;* Richard Greenslade, shoemaker and beer-seller ; James Lake, tailor ; Thos. Partridge, shopkeeper ; and Wm. Daw, Mary Brown, and John Elworthy, *farmers.*

MORCHARD (BISHOP'S,) a large village, 6 miles N.W. by N. of Crediton, has in its parish 7088 acres, and 1880 inhabitants, including many scattered houses and the small hamlets, &c., of *Oldborough, Knightstone, Lowertown, Middlecott, Woodgate, Frost, Redhill, Leigh, and Woodlane.* It has a large *fair* for sheep and cattle, on the Monday after September 9th. J. H. Hippisley, Esq., is lord of the *manor,* which anciently belonged to the Bishops of Exeter, and afterwards passed to the Carew, Southcote, Boucher, and other families. Lady Churchill, J. C. Churchill, Esq., the Rev. C. Tucker, J. Sillifant, Esq., B. T. Radford, Esq., the Trustees of the late Rev. G. Gregory, and many smaller owners have estates in the parish. The *Church* (St. Mary,) is a fine antique structure, with a painted east window, and a tower containing five bells. The *rectory,* valued in K.B. at £36, and in 1831 at £635, is in the incumbency of the Ven. John Bartholomew, M.A., who has 63A. 3R. 5P. of glebe, and a good residence, built about 60 years ago. J. H. Hippisley, Esq., is the patron, and the tithes were commuted in 1841, for £750 per annum. Here is a small *Chapel* used by Independents and Wesleyans, and another belonging to the Bible Christians. The *Poor's Land* was purchased in 1713, for £250, given by about 20 donors. It consists of a farm of 50A., called Ingoodown, let for about £20 a year, to which is added the interest of £100, which arose from the sale of timber, and the interest of about £220, which arose from the benefactions of donors named Comyns, Quick, Pridham, &c. The poor parishioners have six *yearly rent charges,* viz., 20s. left by John Quicke, in 1660 ; 13s. 4d., left by Alex. Arundell, in 1667 ; 10s., left by John Chilcott, in 1700 ; 10s., left by *Philip Lane,* in 1817 ; and 20s., left by John Quicke, jun., in 1705. *Mrs. Thomasine Tucker,* in 1733, left a yearly rent charge of £10, out of Wolland Down, at Sandford, to be applied as follows : £6 for schooling 16 poor children, and £4 in providing them with blue clothing. She also left 24s. a year out of the same estate to be expended in coats for three poor men. The poor parishioners have £10 yearly from *Mrs. Tuckfield's Charity.* (See Crediton.) In 1809, *Abraham Way* left £100 three per cent. consols, in trust to apply the dividends in providing linen cloth for shirts, to be given to poor men of this parish.

Bartholomew Ven. John, M.A., archdeacon of Barnstaple and canon of Exeter, *Rectory*
Bartholomew Rev C. W. M., B.A., *curate*
Basely Charles, surgeon
Bremridge Rev Jas. Pp., M.A. curate
Cann Stephen, watchmaker
Churchill Lady Henrietta Dorothea, *Barton House*
Drew Hy., Wm., & Rd. wheelwrights
Gibbings Maria, vict. London Inn
Glanfield Bartw. shopr. & blacksmt...
Glanfield John, grocer and draper

Hookway John, relieving officer
Hooper John, vict. Fountain head
Mansfield John, boarding school
Mare Saml. parish clerk & schoolmr
Melhuish John, shoemaker
Mortimer Robert, grocer and draper
Quick Wm. tinner and glazier
Putt John, shopkeeper
Reed John, wheelwright
Russell John, tailor
Skinner John, tallow chandler
Smith Thomas, blacksmith
Strong Robt. vict. Three Horse Shoes
Tucker Rev C. *Hill House*
Tucker John, agrl. machine maker
Webber John, shoemaker

White Robert, watch & clock maker
Wreford Mr Wm. Henry, *Southcott*

FARMERS. (* *are Owners*.)

*Bennett Thomas, *Wood Barton*
*Brown John ‖ Challice Wm.
*Davy Philip ‖ *Densham Roger
Hall Samuel ‖ *Kingdon John
*Leach Edward ‖ *Leach John
*Leach Roger ‖ *Leach Wm.
Maunder John ‖ *Maunder James
Morris George ‖ *Mortimer Wm.
*Pope John, *Oldborough*
Pullman Robert, *Rolston Barton*
*Read George ‖ *Saunders Philip
*Wreford John ‖ Tucker Thomas
Wreford Geo. and John, *Ash*

NEWTON ST. CYRES, a pleasant village, on the south side of the vale of the river Creedy, 4½ miles N.W. of Exeter, and 3½ E.S.E. of Crediton. Its parish contains 1234 souls, and 4305 acres of land, rising in bold undulations from the river, and including the tythings of *Ford, Norton*, and *Smallbrook*, the hamlet of *Winscott*, and many scattered houses. A *cattle fair* is held in the village, on the Monday before Midsummer-day. John Quicke, Esq., is lord of the manor of Newton, and resides at *Newton House*, where his family has been seated since the reign of Elizabeth. This manor was given at an early period to Plympton Priory, by Robert de Pontearal, or Pont-Arch. The estate, called *Hayne*, belongs to Sir S. H. Northcote, Bart., and was formerly the seat of his family, but the mansion was reduced to a farm-house, many years ago. The manor of *Norton* belongs to the Dean and Chapter of Exeter, who have several copyhold tenants here. The *Church* (St. Cyres,) stands on a fine eminence, and has a tower and five bells. It was built in the 12th or 13th century, and has a large burial ground surrounded by fine lime trees, &c. The interior was neatly repewed at the cost of £1000, in 1831, and has several monuments of the Northcote and Quicke families, one of which has effigies of Jacob Northcote, Esq., and his two wives, who died in the 17th century. The *vicarage*, valued in K.B. at £16. 15s. 5d., and in 1831 at £425, is in the patronage of John Quicke, Esq., and incumbency of the Rev. E. H. Quicke, B.A., who has 27A. of glebe and a handsome residence, the outer walls of which have lately been rebuilt, and new windows inserted. The vicarial tithes were commuted in 1844, for £360, and the rectorial for £361 per annum. The latter belong to Sir S. H. Northcote and J. Quicke, Esq. The poor have four *rent charges*, amounting to £3. 5s. per annum, and left by John, Robert, and Thomas Quicke. They have also the interest of £20, which arose from £10 left by John Rock, in 1735. Abraham Franks, in 1795, left £100 secured on the Okehampton turnpike, in trust to pay yearly £1. 18s. to the poor of this parish, and £2. 2s. to Devon and Exeter Hospital. *Dr. Downman*, the poet, was a native of this parish.

Batten Edw. and Cann Wm. butchers
Beer John, and Taylor Wm. tailors
Bonner George, baker
Cudford James, cooper
Elliott Wm. vict. *North Devon Inn*
Holmes Ambrose, wheelwright
Hutchings Thos. shoemaker & shopr
Lang George, vict. New Inn
Luxton Wm. & Pool John, blksmths
Moor Thomas, wheelwright
Quicke John, Esq. *Newton House*
Quicke Rev Edw. H., B.A., *Vicarage*
Rainforth Capt.||Thomas Jno. school
Ware Joseph, vict. Crown & Sceptre

Wyatt Thomas, vict. Old Inn
FARMERS.
Batten John, *Smallbrook*
Batten Wm. *Cold Harbour*
Brown Wm. & Osmond J. *Winscott*
Cade Wm. *Creedy*
Corner Edmund || Elworthy Thomas
Ellis Henry, & Osmond Edw. *Harne*
Ellis Thos. & Pasmore John, *Norton*
Grosvenor John, *Westholme*
Palmer John, *Court Barton*
Pasmore Robert, *Smallbrook*
POST-OFFICE at John Elliott's. Letters, *via* Exeter, daily

SANDFORD, a straggling village, in three detached portions, called *East and West Sandford and New Buildings*, in the vale of the small river Creedy, from 2 to 4 miles north of Crediton; has in its parish 1998 souls, and 7770 acres of fertile land, including many scattered farm-houses, &c. There are two *fairs* at Sandford, on the third Monday in March, and last Monday in July. *Ezekiel Hopkins*, Bishop of Derry and author of several theological works was born here, about 1633. The manor of Combe Lancelles was anciently held by the Lancelles family, but has been possessed more than two centuries by the *Davie family*, one of whom was created a *baronet* in 1641. *Sir H. R. F. Davie, Bart.*, the present owner of this manor and of *Ruxford* and other estates, resides at CREEDY PARK, which is delightfully situated, on the west bank of the river Creedy, about 1½ mile N. of Crediton. The mansion, built by the first baronet, has been frequently altered, and has still a modern appearance. *Dowrich House* belongs with a large estate, to its present occupant, E. I. Clayfield, Esq., and was the seat of the ancient family of Dowrich, from an early period till the death of the last male heir, who was killed by a fall from his horse, in 1717. *West Sandford* was formerly the seat of the Chichester family, but is now the property of John Quicke, Esq. *Park House* is the pleasant seat of John Brown, Esq., and here are about a dozen smaller owners occupying their own land. The *Church* (St. Swithen,) is a neat Gothic structure, with a tower and five bells, and has recently been new seated and enlarged, at the cost of about £1400, exclusive of the handsomely painted east window, which cost 100 guineas, and was inserted by his tenants and friends, as a memorial of the late Sir Humphrey Phineas Davie, Bart., who died in 1846, and built the present large and handsome *National School*, in 1825. The church was built at the beginning of the 14th century, and has a beautiful font of Caen stone, and several memorials of the Dowrich and Davie families. The parish was formerly a chapelry to Crediton, and it derives considerable benefit from Crediton Church Corporation Trust, as noticed at page 271. The Governors of this Trust are impropriators of the tithes, which were commuted in 1843, for £1137 per annum. Three of the twelve Governors are nominated by this parish, and appoint the *chaplain* or incumbent of

the *perpetual curacy*, with the approval of a majority of the parishioners. The Rev. Chas. Gregory is the present incumbent, and the
said Governors allow him a yearly salary of £200, and also repair
the Parsonage House, and contribute towards the support of the
National School. The *Baptists* have a neat chapel here, erected in
1849, in the early English style. The POOR'S LANDS, purchased
in 1702 and 1720, with £205 given by *Thomas Haydon* and other
donors, comprise a farm of 28 acres and several cottages, let for £40,
and a field of nearly 3 acres, let for £10 a year. In 1675, *John
Davie* left six cottages, near the rivulet called St. Swithen's Shoot,
in trust, to divide the rents among poor husbandmen not receiving
parochial aid. They are let for about £10 a year. For a weekly
distribution of 2s. worth of bread, *Emanuel Davie* left a yearly rent
charge of £5. 4s. out of Moor Acre and Beer Meadow, now belonging to Sir H. R. F. Davie, who also pays £5 a year, left by *John
Dowrich*, out of the Barton of Prowse, for clothing poor parishioners.
In 1805, *Daniel Norrish* left £105, to be vested for the benefit of
the poor. In 1677, *Sir John Davie, Bart.*, charged Snow's tenement
with the yearly payment of £10 for schooling 20 poor children, and
£6 for providing them with clothing and bibles. There are also
two yearly rent charges of £3 each for schooling poor children, purchased with the bequests of *Robert Ham* and *Mary Locke*, in 1743
and 1773. These free scholars are taught at the National School.

Bailey John, wheelwright
Baker Rev James, (Baptist)
Bragg Wm. machine maker, wheel-
    wright, and vict. Hare and Hounds
Bragg Wm. jun. corn miller
Brown John, Esq. *Park House*
Brown Samuel, spirit merchant
Brown Silvns. butcher, &Wm.cbt. mkr
Burge Miss Elizabeth
Clayfield Edw. Ireland, Esq. *Dow-
    rich House*
Davie Sir Henry R. Ferguson, Bart.
    Creedy Park
Dawe James, vict. Star
Deans Wm. surgeon
Drew James, blacksmith
Ellis Henry, saddler and vict. Lamb
Ellis John, plumber and glazier
Greenslade Thomas, corn miller
Gregory Rev Charles, incumbent
Hattin James, cabinet maker
Jarratt Thomas, mason
Lake James, vict. Rose and Crown
Luxton Henry, cattle dealer
Morgan Wm. schoolmr. & registrar
Parish James, builder
Reynolds Mr Thos. || Putt W. smith
Wellacott Wm. relieving officer
Wright Jas. & Thomas, blacksmiths
Wright John, wheelwright

FARMERS.   (* are Owners.)
Ansty John, *Combe Lancelles*
Bere Abraham, *North Creedy*
Bickley John || Burrington Daniel
Burrington Wm. || Challice John
Daw Wm. || Field John
Densham Wm. *Bremridge*
Harris Robert and Wm. *Ruxford*
Hattin Daniel || Hattin Wm.
Henwood Daniel || Hookway Jane
Kelland Robert, *Dowrich*
Lake Thomas || Kelland Robert
*Lane Wm. || *Lee Thomas
*Norrish Edward ||*Norrish John
*Norrish John, *Gays*
*Norrish Robert, *Prowse*
*Norrish Wm. *Hele*
Partridge Matthew and Silvanus
Partidge Wm. West Sandford
*Pope John, *Henstill*
*Pope Wm. Sandford Ash
*Tremlett Elias and John
*Tremlett John, *Woolsgrove*
*Wreford Roger || Wreford George
BAKERS.   Snow Rt. & Wm.
Discombe Mary   SHOPKEEPERS.
Snow Peter   Marles Wm.
SHOEMAKERS.   Millman Wm.
Ewings Samuel   Mortimer Wm.
Haydon John   Pickett John

Snow John Strong Wm.	TAILORS. Hattin James Pickett John	Snow Robert Taylor John POST OFFICE at	Jno. Pickett's. Letters, via Exeter, daily

HAYRIDGE HUNDRED

Is of an irregular figure, extending about 16 miles from east to west, and varying from 9 to 6 in breadth. Its soil is various, but generally fertile, and its surface is picturesquely diversified with hill and valley, and wood and water. It includes the market town of Collumpton; and those of Exeter, Tiverton, Honiton, and Ottery St. Mary are within a few miles of its boundaries. It is crossed by the Bristol and Exeter Railway, and the branch to Tiverton; and watered by the rivers Exe and Culm, and several of their tributary streams. It is in the Northern Division of Devon; mostly in Collumpton and Tiverton Polling Districts; and all in Collumpton Petty Sessional Division, and in the Archdeaconry of Exeter; mostly in Plymtree Deanery, and partly in Cadbury Deanery. The following enumeration of its 16 parishes, shews their territorial extent, and their population in 1841.

Parishes.	Acres.	Pop.	Parishes.	Acres.	Pop.
*Bickleigh	1835	.. 362	§Payhembury ..	2698	.. 545
*Blackborough† ..	508	.. 112	§Plymtree	2185	.. 439
*Bradninch......	4212	.. 1714	‡Up Exe *tything*	370	.. 120
§Broadhembury ..	6155	.. 851	§Sheldon	1300	.. 190
*Cadbury	1897	.. 251	*Silverton......	4714	.. 1384
*Cadeleigh	2020	.. 403	§Talaton	2254	.. 462
*Collumpton	8103	.. 3909	*Thorverton	4036	.. 1445
§Feniton........	1822	.. 315			
*Kentisbeare	4000	.. 1184	Total..	48,858	13,783
‡Nether Exe	650	.. 97			

*§ UNIONS.—Those marked * are in *Tiverton and Dulverton Union;* and those marked § in *Honiton Union.* These Unions are also *County Court Districts.*

‡ UP EXE tything is in *St. Thomas's Union* and in Rewe parish, as already noticed at page 201. *Nether Exe* is in St. Thomas's Union.

+ Blackborough is united with Kentisbeare parish for the support of the poor.

BICKLEIGH village, on the east bank of the river Exe, 4 miles S. of Tiverton, and 10 miles N. of Exeter, has in its parish 362 souls, and 1835 acres of land, including *Chederleigh* hamlet. Sir W. P. Carew is lord of the manors, and owner of a great part of the soil; and the rest belongs to Sir T. D. Acland, Dr. Troyte, and a few smaller proprietors. Bickleigh anciently belonged to a family of its own name, and passed from the Courtenays to a younger branch of the Carews. The celebrated *Bampfylde Moore Carew,* commonly called King of the Beggars, was the son of the Rev. Theodore Carew, rector of Bickleigh. He was born here in 1690, and, after his extraordinary and various peregrinations and adventures, spent the two last years of his eventful life in his native village, and was buried in the church in 1758. Here also was buried

Major John Gabriel Stedman, who published the History of Suri-
nam, and died in 1797. The *Church* (St. Mary,) was mostly rebuilt
in 1843, at the cost of about £1400. It has a tower and five bells,
and contains several neat monuments of the Carew family, one of
which has recumbent effigies of a knight and lady. The *rectory*,
valued in K.B. at £18. 4s. 9½d., and in 1831 at £434, is in the patronage of Sir W. P. Carew, and incumbency of the Rev. Robt. B.
Carew, M.A., who has a good residence and 60 acres of glebe. The
tithes were commuted in 1842, for £359 per annum. In 1708, £95
poor's money was laid out in the purchase of 4 acres of land, called
Ware Park, now let for £10. 10s. per annum. There is also £100
three per cent. stock, purchased with money which arose from the
sale of timber felled on the said land. The annual income
(£13. 10s.) is distributed about Christmas, among the most deserving poor; as also is about £15, arising from three-fourths of the
rent of two cottages and 1½ acre of land at Tiverton, left by *John
Lovell*. (See Tiverton.)

Baker John, tailor
Carew Rev Robt. Baker, M.A., rector
Gould Benjamin, wheelwright
Hellier Mary, schoolmistress
Kemp and Carthew, corn millers
Tapscott Fredk. shoemkr. & par. clerk
Upton James, blacksmith

FARMERS.
Berry Wm. || Cook Thomas.
Gill John, *Chederleigh*
Jarman Sus. || Page Charles
Pitt John || Pitt Robert
Pratt Henry || Tremlet Francis
Wippell Wm., *Bickleigh Court*

BLACKBOROUGH, 5 miles E.N.E. of Collumpton, is a small
parish of 126 souls, and 508A. 1R. 22P. of land, adjoining Kentisbeare, and united with that parish for the support of the poor. It
is on the western declivity of the lofty range of hills called *Blackdown*, and was anciently held by the Bolhay family, and afterwards
by the Cobhams and Bonvilles. The Trustees of the late Earl of
Egremont are now lords of the manor, owners of nearly all the soil,
and patrons of the *rectory*, valued in K.B. at £4, and in 1831 at
£140. The Rev. W. C. Thompson, M.A., is the incumbent, and has
74A. 1R. 11P. of glebe, and resides at *Blackborough House*, a neat
mansion, of Tuscan architecture, built by the late Earl of Egremont, who also erected the present *Church*, (All Saints,) in 1838, at
the cost of about £1900. This church is a neat structure, in the
early English style, and its tower is crowned by an octagonal spire,
which is seen at a great distance; the site being about 700 feet
above the level of the sea. The interior is neatly fitted up with 283
sittings, all free except twenty. Before the erection of this church,
the parishioners used that at Kentisbeare, their old church (*Allhallows,*) having gone to decay some centuries ago.

Baker John, beerhouse keeper, &c
Farley George, shoemaker
Fouraker Wm. farmer, *Allhallows*
Middleton Thomas, tailor
Thompson Rev Wm.Cookesley,M.A.,
   rector, *Blackborough House*

Tucker Wm. farmer, *Parsonage*

SCYTHE STONE MAKERS.
Baker John || Baker Wm.
Bond John || Coombe James
Farley Robert, parish clerk

BRADNINCH is a *decayed borough and market town*, upon a
pleasant eminence, on the western side of Culm valley, 3 miles

S.S.W. of Collumpton, 9 miles N.N.E. of Exeter, and about a mile W. of the *Hele Station* on the Bristol and Exeter Railway, near the small river Culm. Its parish, which is co-extensive with the borough, comprises 4212A. 1R. 15P. of land, and had 1714 inhabitants in 1841, but they have now increased to about 2000. The town part is freehold; but the other estates in the parish are chiefly copyhold, under the Duchy of Cornwall. At Domesday Survey, Wm. Chievre, or Capra, held the manor of *Bradninch, Bradenesse,* or *Brameis* in demesne. It was afterwards held as a *honour,* or *barony,* with the Earldom of Cornwall, by Arthur Reginald, natural son of Henry I., and was eventually made, as it still continues, part of the *Duchy of Cornwall.* The BOROUGH claims prescriptive as well as chartered rights, but was not of sufficient importance to be included in the Municipal Reform Act of 1835. In 1208, King John granted the burgesses all such liberties and free customs as the city of Exeter enjoyed. In 1604, James I. incorporated the borough, under the government of a mayor, twelve masters, and a recorder; and in 1685, James II. granted a new charter, under which the *Corporation* consists of a mayor, twelve masters, and an indefinite number of burgesses. The mayor, who is chosen by the masters, burgesses, and freemen, is a justice of the peace for the borough during his year of office and the following year. The recorder is also a borough magistrate; and petty sessions are held every Monday. A court of record was formerly held monthly; but the borough is now in the jurisdiction of the County Court held at Tiverton, though it has still a quarterly court of session. The borough anciently sent members to parliament; but the burgesses complaining that this privilege was burthensome, they were excused, on the payment of five marks. Courts leet and baron are held yearly for the Duchy of Cornwall. R. J. Marker, Esq., is the *recorder;* John Gidley, Esq., *deputy-recorder;* and Mr. Peter Sharland, *town clerk.* The market and fairs, granted by the charters of King John and Henry III., have long been obsolete; but here are two small *fairs* for cattle, &c., on May 6th and October 2nd. The town consists chiefly of one long, irregular street, and has suffered several times by large fires, arising from the thatched roofs of its houses, most of which have lately been judiciously abandoned for slated roofs. In 1665, the guildhall, the prison, the borough charters, and a great number of houses, were destroyed by fire. The town has been much improved during the present century; and a new *Guild Hall,* with a prison under it, was built in 1835. Under a bye law passed by the corporation in 1813, the town has been abundantly supplied with pure *water,* brought in pipes from the neighbouring hills. The woollen manufacture formerly flourished here, and on the Culm are two large paper mills. Part of King Charles's army was quartered here in July and September, 1644; and the parliamentarian forces, under Sir Thomas Fairfax, were here on the 16th of October, 1645. (See page 56.) The unfortunate King was here in person, and slept several nights at the Rectory, now called *Bradninch House,* where the bedstead on which he reposed is still standing. This mansion, formerly the residence of the Sainthill family, is now the seat of Geo.

Pearse, Esq., the lessee of the rectorial tithes and glebe. *Dunmore House*, late the residence of the Hon. L. G. K. Murray, is now the seat of W. H. Besly, Esq. The *Church* (St. Dionysius,) is a fine structure, in the later perpendicular style, and has recently been repaired and beautified, at the cost of about £1100. The tower contains six bells; and the oak screen, which separates the nave and chancel, is richly carved. The north aisle and transept were built in the reign of Henry VII. One of the aisles was the chapel of St. John, founded by the fraternity of St. John, or Guild of Cordwainers, which was endowed with land, &c., worth £19. 10s. 5d. per annum in 1547, when it was dissolved. A curious painting of the Crucifixion, taken from this aisle, is now placed on the west side of the screen. The *perpetual curacy*, valued in 1831 at only £102 per annum, is in the patronage of the Dean and Canons of Windsor, who are also appropriators of the rectory. The Rev. A. R. Webster, M.A., is the incumbent, for whom a new Parsonage has lately been erected, at the cost of about £700. The tithes were commuted in 1838, for £610 per annum, mostly belonging to the lessee of the rectory. The Particular Baptists and the Wesleyans have *chapels* here; and the town has a *National School*, for children of both sexes. In 1616, *Sir John Acland* left an annuity of 52s., for a weekly distribution of 13 penny loaves among the poor of Bradninch, and it is paid by the Corporation of Exeter. An orchard and tenement, left to the poor by *Samuel Whitney*, in 1666, are let for about £18 a year. The *Corporation Charity* comprises four houses, &c., which have been settled for the use of the poor from an early period, and are now let for £7. 12s. per annum. In the 13th of James I., *John Hill* gave five cottages, an orchard, and three acres of land, in trust for the poor of this parish, except 52s. a year for the poor of Collumpton. The parish has also a garden, orchard, and field of 1½A., purchased in 1752 and 1758, with about £120 benefaction money, and now let for about £9 a year. The clear rents of the three last named charities are distributed among all the poor of the parish. They have also 30s. a year, as the interest of £30, left by *Andrew Bowden* and *John Gervis*, and vested with the Corporation.

Baker Rev Charles, (Baptist)
Benham John, watchmaker
Besly Wm. Hy. Esq. *Dunmore Hs*
Bowden Henry Sparks, Esq.
Bowden Henry, surgeon
Bushell Richard, boarding school
Chalice Saml. wheelwgt. & beerhs
Cleeve Fredk. Abm. surgeon & regr
Corass Fredk. tinner and brazier
Coward James, surgeon
Crease Robert, plumber, painter, &c
Dewdney John, paper maker, *Hele*
Drew John, clerk, *Hele Mill*
Dunn John, wheelwright
Jacobs Thos. sergt. at mace & gaoler
Jacobs Wm. horse, &c. letter
King Mrs || Linnington Mrs D.
Martyn Wm. paper maker; h *Combe*
Matthews and Martyn, paper makers, *Kensham and Huxham Mills, &c.*
Matthews Chas. paper maker *(mayor)*
Middleton Mrs Sar. & Miss Eliz.
Pearse Geo. Esq. solr. *Bradninch Hs*
Pearse Miss Jane, *Sainthill*
Sellick Robert, saddler & ironmonger
Sharland Mr Jno., & Peter, town clerk
Sharland Thos.Wm. vetnary. surgeon
Tatham L. F. druggist, &c.
Warren John, National schoolmaster
Warren Peter, accmpt. & dep. regr
Webster Rev Alex. Rhind, M.A. *incbt*
Were Henry B. solicitor
Wooster Thomas, seedsman, &c

INNS AND TAVERNS.
Bradninch Arms, Anthony Nick
Castle Inn, Wm. Govier
King's Arms, Wm. Ireland
Old White Lion, Daniel Wench
Paper Makers' Arms, Saml. Sowden
White Lion, Wm. Clark

BAKERS.
Haydon Richard
Ireland James
Ireland Thomas
Vinnicombe Rd. (&tal.chandler)
Bonner Wm.
Jordan Henry
Pearse Henry
Smith Robert
Wench Edwin G.

BLACKSMITHS.
Hollett John
Lindsey Wm.
Tremlett Richard

BUTCHERS.
Hussey Henry
Hussey John
Manley John
Manley Wm.

BOOT & SHOE MRS.
Berry Thomas

GROCERS & DPRS.
Glover Thomas

Marks Thomas
Mortimer Chas.
Templeman Sml.
Warren Peter

FARMERS.
(* are owners.)
Cumming Chas.
Evens Henry P.
Godfrey Joseph
Ham Joseph
Jarman Richard
Liddon Frederick, Tyronhayes
*Long Danl. Middleton
Matthews Henry
*Murch Clmt.
Palmer Charles
*Palmer Henry

Pitts Humphrey
Salter Robert
Smith Robert
Tremlett Robert
Yeatman Sarah

TAILORS.
Lake Thomas
Lake Thos. jun
Quick Wm.
Squire Robert
Warren Thomas

POST OFFICE
at Hy. Pearse's.
Letters via Collumpton.

CARRIERS to Exeter, Tues. & Fri.
Mortimer Chas.
Vinnicombe R.

BROADHEMBURY, a sequestered village, picturesquely seated among the hills, about 6 miles E.S.E. of Collumpton, and N.W. of Honiton, has in its parish 851 souls and 6155 acres of land, including the scattered hamlets of *Collaton, Luton, Dulford,* and *Kerswell,* extending to within 3 miles of Collumpton. The hills and dales of this parish send two tributary streams to the Culm and the Otter. There is an Agricultural Association at Broadhembury; and a *cattle fair* on December 11th. The manor, anciently held by the noble family of Torrington, and afterwards by Dunkeswell Abbey, was purchased by Edw. Drewe, sergeant at law to Queen Elizabeth. Edw. Simcoe Drewe, Esq., is now lord of the manor and owner of two-thirds of the parish. He has a handsome seat here, called the *Grange,* built about 1610, but modernised and improved some years ago. B. Walrond, Esq., of *Dulford House,* and several smaller owners, have estates in the parish. *Kerswell* or *Carswell* hamlet has about 150 inhabitants, and an Independent Chapel. It had formerly a small *Priory* of Cluniac monks, belonging to Montacute Priory, in Somersetshire. The manor of Carswell-*cum* Dulvet, or Dulford, belongs to Mr. Drewe, who is also lessee of the great tithes, which were commuted in 1835, for £300. 11s., and the small tithes for £216 per annum. The *Church* (St. Andrew,) is an ancient structure, with a tower and five bells. It has a handsome screen, and several monuments of the Drewe family. The Dean and Chapter of Exeter are appropriators of the rectory and patrons of the *vicarage,* valued in K.B. at £16. 17s., and in 1831 at £225. The Rev. W. Heberden, M.A., is the incumbent, and has a good residence and 6A. 3R. 33R. of glebe. The *Free School,* for 20 poor children, is endowed with about 2A. of land, near Fenny Mills, purchased in 1725, with £40 left by the *Rev. John Burrough;* and with £10 a year out of the great tithes of Awliscombe, which see. The poor parishioners have the interest of £65, left by various donors; and about £10 a year as the rent of Butcher's Meadow, left by *Mary Hill,* in 1756.

Marked 2 are at Dulford; 3, Collaton;
4, Luton; 5, Upcott; & 6, at Kerswell.

	FARMERS.	2 Shiles Jane
2 Bydon Richard, surgeon	Acland Wm.	2 Shiles Wm.
4 Coles Henry, farrier	5 Blackmore Fras.	Valentine Thos.
Drewe Edw. Simcoe, Esq. *Grange*	6 Blackmore Rd.	SHOEMAKERS.
3 Granger Wm. carpenter & par. clerk	Blackmore John	Burton John
Hallett John Charles, schoolmaster	4 Blackmore Rt.	Clark Edward
Heberden Rev Wm., M.A. *Vicarage*	Ellis Grace	Granger Joseph
Hockley John, shopkeeper	5 Ellis John	Haymes John
Minifie Robert, blacksmith	Lambert Thos. *St*	TAILORS.
6 Pearcy Mr John, & Potter Mr John	*Andrew's Wood*	Haymes Robert
Stiling Jane, wheelwright	6 Lawrence Ann	Payne Henry
Taylor Catherine, schoolmistress	3 Marks Thomas	
Weeks John, vict. Red Lion	3 Matthews Chas.	POST *from Honi-*
Walrond Bethel, Esq. *Dulford Hs*	Matthews Thos.	*ton*
	4 Mortimer John	

CADBURY, a small village and parish, on the declivities and crown of a bold eminence, 6½ miles N.E. of Crediton, and S.S.W. of Tiverton, contains 251 souls and about 2000 acres of land. It gives name to the Deanery of Cadbury, which comprises 18 parishes. On the crown of a lofty hill is an ancient *Entrenchment*, called Cadbury Castle, commanding extensive views of the surrounding country and the coast. It is of an oval figure, and was the rendezvous of Sir Thos. Fairfax's army, on Dec. 26th, 1645. The centre of it was excavated a few years ago, when many antique ornaments were found, including armlets of fine bronze, rings of jet, coloured beads, a signet ring, &c. Mrs. Fursdon is lady of the manor, and has a pleasant seat here, called *Fursdon House*, with finely wooded grounds; but part of the parish belongs to Messrs. Turner, Kemp, and Townsend, and a few smaller freeholders. The *Church* (St. Michael,) is a substantial fabric, of the 15th century, with a tower and four bells, and contains a Norman font. The *vicarage*, valued in K.B. at £9. 4s. 4d., and in 1831 at £175, is endowed with part of the great tithes, and is in the patronage of the Lord Chancellor, and incumbency of the Rev. N. F. Lightfoot, M.A., who has about six acres of glebe, and a good residence, which was considerably enlarged in 1846, at the cost of nearly £900. Mrs. Fursdon is impropriator of that portion of the great tithes which formerly belonged to St. Nicholas's Priory, Exeter. Her portion of the tithes was commuted in 1842, for £95, and the vicar's for £172. 10s. per annum. This parish is entitled to send a poor person to the almshouse at Broad Clist. The poor parishioners have the dividends of £60. 9s. 1d. new four per cent. stock, purchased with money left by Geo. Turner, John Ambrose, and other donors.

Dart John, tailor, & Amy G. school	Powe James, shoemaker
Edgland Robert, carpenter	FARMERS.
Elsworthy Geo.par.clerk,&Jas.sexton	Back John Henry ‖ Hill John
Fursdon Mrs Har. *Fursdon House*	Manley Richard ‖ Scott Lydia
Lightfoot Rev. Nchls.Fras. *Vicarage*	Sharland Wm. *Chapeltown*
Pooke Richard, vict. Castle Inn	Vicary Thomas, *Turley*
Pooke Thomas, carpenter	POST OFFICE at John Dart's. Letters
Pope Henry, blacksmith	from Tiverton.

CADELEIGH, or CADLEIGH, a pleasant scattered village, 4½ miles S.W. of Tiverton, has in its parish 403 souls and 2020 acres of land, rising in bold undulations, and extending eastward to the river Exe. It includes the hamlets of *Wellton* and *Little Silver.* Mrs. Moore is lady of the manor, but the chief part of the soil belongs to Mrs. Fursdon and many other freeholders. It was successively held by the Chievre, Mohun, Kingston, Courtenay, Leach, and Doble families. The CHURCH (St. Bartholomew,) has an embattled tower and five bells, and contains a costly monument of *Sir Simon Leach* (son of a blacksmith of Crediton,) and his wife, with their recumbent effigies, and two kneeling figures, under a splendid canopy. His son, Simon, was a distinguished royalist in the civil wars, and died in 1660. The *rectory*, valued in K.B. at £13, and in 1831 at £234, is in the gift of Mrs. Moore and incumbency of the Rev. P. F. Brittain, M.A., who has 54A. of glebe, and a good residence, in a picturesque glen. The yearly sum of £10. 13s. is paid out of certain chief rents of the manor of Butterleigh, to the poor of this parish, pursuant to the bequest of *Sir Simon Leach.* A yearly rent charge of £4, left by *James Battin*, in 1665, out of Lower Langley estate, is divided among four poor men not receiving parochial relief. The *Parish Land* (6A.) is let for about £8 a year, which is applied with the church rates.

Badcock Jane, schoolmistress
Brittain Rev Paul Ford, M.A. rector
Clegg Wm. blacksmith
Hosegood Alexander, vict. New Inn
Longmore Rev James, B.D. vicar of Yealmpton
Manley John, grocer & parish clerk
Pearse Thomas, shoemaker

FARMERS.
Dawe Samuel, *Lower Coombe*

Hammond Richard || Jeffrey Robert
Kemp James, *Gotham*
Manley John || Milton Thomas
Melhuish Samuel || Otton Wm.
Partridge Thomas, *High Coombe*
Partridge Wm. || Trude Wm.
Roberts Hugh, sen. and jun.
Stevens Thomas, *Cadleigh Mill*
Widdon Wm. *East Court*

COLLUMPTON or CULLOMPTON, is an ancient market town, consisting chiefly of one long street, pleasantly situated on the west side of the river *Culm*, and the Bristol and Exeter Railway; 11 miles N.E. by N. of Exeter; 6 miles S.E. by E. of Tiverton; 12 miles S.W. of Wellington, and 160 miles S.W. by W. of London. Its parish contains 3909 inhabitants, and 8103 acres of fertile land, rising boldly from the Culm valley, and including the scattered houses and the hamlets of *Langford, Mutterton, Ponsford, Weaver, Colebrooke*, and *East Butterleigh*, extending more than two miles on all sides of the town. The surface is picturesquely broken into hill and dale, and the soil belongs to many *freeholders*, the largest of whom are the Countess of Egremont, and Bethel Walrond, Richard Hall Clarke, Robert Pring Crosse, and Daniel Bishop Sellwood, Esqrs. The town suffered severely in 1839, from a dreadful *fire*, which destroyed about 100 houses and cottages, most of which were covered with that dangerous material, straw *thatch*. Since this calamity the town has been much improved, and the sites of the old houses thus destroyed have been occupied by neat buildings, with slated roofs. It is a polling place for the Northern Division of Devon, and the

head of a large Petty Sessional Division, for which the county magistrates hold petty sessions here monthly, and sometimes twice a month. A *Court House*, with a *lock-up*, was built by subscription in 1849, at the cost of about £400. The *market* held every Saturday, is well supplied with provisions, and on the first Saturday of every month here is a *"great market"* for cattle, &c. Here are also two annual *fairs* on the first Wednesday in May and November. The town formerly enjoyed a large share of the *woollen manufactnre*, but here is now only one large serge and blanket manufactory, belonging to Mr. W. Upcott, of Shortlands. There are in the parish and neighbourhood, several large *paper and corn mills*, and in the town is the *West of England Church Bell Foundry*, established in 1746, and still in high repute. The *manor of Collumpton* was bequeathed by King Alfred to his son Ethelward, and was granted by Richard I. to Richard de Clifford. It afterwards passed to the Earls of Devon, one of whom granted the town a market and fair, in 1278. Elizabeth de Fortibus, Countess of Devon, granted the manor to Buckland Abbey, and after the dissolution, it passed successively to the St. Leger, Risdon, Hellersdon, Colman and Sweet families. The *manor of Langford*, was anciently held by the Langfords, the last of whom gave it to Corpus Christi College, Oxford. The *manor of Bole Aller* belongs to the Dean and Chapter of Exeter; and that of Bradfield to B. Walrond, Esq. That of *Moorhayes* belongs to Mr. J. M. Blackmore; and *Chalvedon* or Chaldon to Mr. E. Baker. *King's-mill*, formerly the residence of Lord Chief Justice Pratt, now belongs to Mr. Rd. Mortimore. *Hillersdon House*, a large and handsome mansion, built in 1849, is the seat of W. C. Grant, Esq. The CHURCH, *(St. Andrew,)* is a large and handsome Gothic structure, mostly erected in the 15th century, and consisting of a nave, three aisles and a chancel, with a lofty tower, containing eight musical bells, and crowned at each corner by tall and elaborately carved pinnacles. The interior is decorated with a richly carved and gilt roof. A gorgeous screen and rood loft divide the nave and chancel; and on the south side is a spacious and handsome aisle, erected in 1526 '8, by John Lane, an eminent woollen cloth manufacturer, and having on the outside a long inscription and emblems of the founder's trade. The windows in this aisle are large, and the roof is ornamented with rich fan-shaped tracery. In the chancel, chaste and judicious renovations and improvements were made some years ago, and the new east window, then introduced, is enriched with brilliant stained glass. The nave and aisles were thoroughly cleansed and newly seated in 1849, at the cost of about £1000, raised by subscription, and a parochial rate of £300. W. C. Grant, Esq., gave £100 towards this necessary restoration. On scraping the walls they were found to be covered with paintings in distemper, some of which are fine specimens of mediæval art, and others of later date. Dugdale says, William the Conqueror gave the *collegiate church* of Collumpton, with its *five prebends* of Colebrooke, Hineland, Waevre, Esse, and Upton, to Battle Abbey, in Sussex; but it was afterwards bestowed on St. Nicholas's Priory, Exeter. There was a *Guild of St. Nicholas* here, which was value at the dissulution at £5. 7s. 2d. per annum.

Queen Elizabeth granted the rectory and the advowson of the vicar-age to Robert Freke and John Walker. The impropriate rectory af-terwards passed in moieties, but the great tithes were purchased by the land owners about 40 years ago. There was anciently a chapel of ease at Langford. The *vicarage*, valued in K.B. at £47. 4s. 2d., has a good residence, 13A. 3R. 1P. of glebe, and a yearly rent-charge of £413, awarded in lieu of tithes in 1842. The Rev. Wm. Sykes, M.A., is patron and incumbent. The *Baptists, Independents, Wes-leyans*, and *Unitarians*, have chapels here ; and the town has a *Men-tal Improvement Society*, established in 1849, and a *Farmers' Club*, supported by a numerous list of subscribers. A large *National School* for about 200 children, was established more than thirty years ago, and the parish has various CHARITABLE FUNDS, as noticed below. Here is also a branch of the *Exeter Savings' Bank*, for which Mr. A. Gribble is receiver.

For distribution in bread and money, the poor parishioners have about £21 yearly, arising as follows :—£2. 12s. left by *Sir John Acland*, in 1616, and paid by the corporation of Exeter; about £10 as the rent of 6A. of land, purchased with £100 left by *John Manning*, in 1617 ; £5. 10s. as the rent of an orchard, left by *Wm. Bone*, in 1620; and an annuity of £2. 12s. left by *John Hill*, as noticed with Bradninch. In 1624, GEORGE SPICER left £300, to be laid out in land, &c., and the yearly proceeds applied in ap-prenticing poor children of this parish, and in presenting them with £5 each at the end of their apprenticeships. There is now belonging to this charity a farm of about 45 acres, let for £80, and about £250 vested at interest. The clear yearly income is applied, according to the donor's will, for the benefit of about 16 boys yearly. In 1632, £150, given to the poor of Collumpton, for providing shirts and shifts, was laid out in the purchase of a fourth part of an estate of 20A., called *White Heathfield*. This charity yields about £5 per annum. In 1657, *Peter Atkins* left a yearly rent-charge of £4, out of land called Padcott and Burridge, for eight poor religious pa-rishioners. For distribution in clothing, the poor have about £50 a year, as the rent of two cottages and nearly 10A. of land, purchased with £150 left by *John and Henry Hill*, in 1631. They have also about £15, as the rent of 14 acres, called *Weaver Wood*, purchased in 1668, with £220 bene-faction money, given by unknown donors. Five small rent-charges, amount-ing to £5. 3s. 2d. per annum, were given in the 5th of William and Mary, by *Margery Arundell*, and are distributed in linen among about 16 poor widows. Six acres of land, called Melhuish Closes, were given by *Thomas Prowse*, who directed the yearly proceeds to be expended in providing linen shirts for the poor. In 1719, *Peter Newte* left 20s. a year to be laid out in religious books, for young men and women of this parish. (See Tiverton.) An *Almshouse*, founded by *John Trott*, in the 14th year of Henry VIII., was in ruins in 1823, and its endowment lost.

COLLUMPTON DIRECTORY.

POST OFFICE at Mr. Thomas Mitchell's, Fore street. Letters are re-ceived and despatched by the Railway Mails four times a day; and Money Orders are granted and paid. There are foot-posts every morning to Brad-ninch, Kentisbeare, Plymtree, &c.

Anning Mrs Harriet and Miss
Arnoll Mr Thos. || Bilbie Misses
Bastin Gideon, dyer, &c
Bennett Giles, rope & sacking mkr
Bennett James, tallow chandler
Blackmore Jno.Moor,gent.*Moorhayes*

N

Blampin Thomas, railway agent
Burrow Betsy, dairy woman
Brooks Robert, chimney sweeper
Casling Henry, basket maker
Chudleigh Thos. timber & slate mert
Cross Wm. veterinary surgeon
Crosse James, Esq. *Knowle House*
Davy Mrs Eliz. || Dennis Mr Wm.
Devon and Cornwall Bank, Fore st ;
    Wm. Toogood, manager
Foot Rev Uriah (Unitarian)
Foster Jph. druggist & spirit mert
Foweraker John, fellmonger
Franklin Mrs My. || Frost Jph. gent
Frost Wm. Hy. druggist, &c.
Fulford Robt. keeper of Court house
Grant Wm. Cs., Esq. *Hillersdon Hs*
Hart Thos. auctioneer, dep. regr. &c
Herbert Rev John, (Independent)
Hine Tristram Collins, gent
Hodges Wm. gentleman
Knight John, timber merchant
Matthews & Martyn, paper makers,
    Langford, (and Bradninch, &c.)
Mills Humphrey Blackmore, paper
    maker, *King's mill*
Mitchell Samuel, ironmonger, &c.
Mitchell Thos. postmaster and inspr.
    of weights and measures
Moor Lieutenant Philip, R.N.
Mortimore Rd. tanner, &c., *King's ml*
Norcross Miss Jane||Orchard Mrs
Pannell Wm. & Son, bell founders
Pidgeon Jno. miller, *Clark's mill*
Rowlinson Rev Wm. (Unitarian)
Fellwood Danl. Bishop, tanner
Shepherd Samuel, coal merchant
Stanford Mrs. My. || Sydenham Miss
Sydenham Rev John Philip, curate
Sykes Rev Wm., M.A., vicar
Taylor Miss Sar. || Trood Mrs
Trood Jas. coal and salt merchant
Underhill Benj. organist, &c.
Upcott Wm. and Sons, (Wm. & Jno.
    S.) serge, blanket, &c. mfrs.
Ward John, station master
Whitter Mr Tristram Walrond
Wills Robt. tallow chandler
FARMERS.
Abbott Thomas, Potshayes
Baker Elias, Peter hills
Baker Thomas Harris, Hackland
Bere George, Knowle
Blackmore Thomas, *Higher Week*
Bond John, Mutterton

Broom Mary, Wheatcroft
Broom Edward, Peverstone
Brown Wm., Cridland
Carnall Robert, *Slough Pool*
Carnull John, Ponsford
Carnull John, jun., Padbrook
Coleman Francis, Head-cellars
Coleman John, Coombe
Coleman Robt. and Jas., Ponsford
Cork Thomas, Westcott
Crosse James, Ponsford
Crosse Edw. Heathfield, Westcott
Crosse Robt. Pring, Bullaller
Curwood Richard, Weaver
East Wm., Hooklands
Foweraker Francis, Knowle
Frost James, Newland
Frost Robert, Ponsland
Godfrey James Palmer, *Colebrooke*
Grant Thomas, *Lower Week*
Griffin Henry, Bullaller
Harris John, Weaver
Hewitt Thomas, *Henland*
Hine John || Farrant Mark
Hitt George and Thomas, Langford
Ion Wm., Andrew's Farm
James Henry, *Halsewood*
Kerslake John, Weaver
King Wm., *Colebrooke*
Manfield John, Batthills
Marks Thomas, *Woost Mill*
Martin James and George, Langford
Mondy John, Langford
Palmer Henry, Fairfield
Pearcy Shadh. & Pratt Thos., *Comers*
Perkins Robert, Moorhayes
Pitt John, *Woodwickswell*
Pitt Robert, *East Butterleigh*
Pring Robert || Pring Thomazin
Pring John and Read Ann, Langford
Rowe Mrs. Elizabeth, Fore street
Rowe Roger, Upton
Salter Jenny, Westcott
Salter Joseph, Whiteheathfield
Sellick Robert, *Mutterton*
Shere Ambrose, Long Moor
Slape Anna, Lower Moorhayes
Staddon Robert, Newtes
Tremlett George, Mutterton
Trott Wm., *East Butterleigh*
Wish Nicholas, *Rull*
FIRE AND LIFE OFFICES.
Atlas, Joseph Davy
Birmingham, James C. Mitchell
Church of England, Thos. Mitchell

Dissenters', Joseph Foster
Globe, James Rawlings
Hand in Hand, R. R. Crosse
Imperial, Wm. Pidgeon
Protector & Phœnix, Joseph Davy
Royal Exchange, Wm. Toogood
Royal Farmers', &c. Thomas Hart
Star, Robert Burrow
Sun, Henry Hill, jun.
West of England, Albert Gribble
INNS AND TAVERNS.
Admiral Hawke, John Luxton
Bell, Silas Frost
Bishop Blaize, Agnes Wescombe
Devonshire Inn, Elisha Berry
Dolphin, Thomas Wolland
George, Mary Wadling
Globe, Robert Welch
Half Moon Inn, Thomas Blampin
King's Head, Sarah Burnard
London Inn, Thomas Isaac
Three Mariners, John Bodley Frost
White Hart Inn, Ann Bowerman

ACADEMIES.
Bath Mary Ann
Davy Margaret & Ann (boardg.)
Gosnay Miss
Hill Henry, jun.
Johnson Fras. F.
Murch Joseph
Reed John
Rowe Elizabeth
Warren John
ATTORNEYS.
Burrow Robert
Crosse Rd.Reeder
Gribble Albert
Leigh Fdk. (coroner and clerk to magistrates)
Rawlings James
BAKERS.
Budd Wm.
Dimond Thomas
Hart Thomas
Luxton Thomas
Luxton Wm.
Marshall Sarah
Pidgeon John
Sturges Thomas (and miller)
Toogood John
BEERHOUSES.
Burton Thomas

Hill Wm.
Salter Hannah
Tuckett John
Walters John
BLACKSMITHS.
Dummett Mary
Kerslake Robert
Westron Richard
BOOKSELLERS,&c
(* Printers.)
*Frost Isaac
Hill Sarah
*Rowe Wm.
Voisey Maria
BOOT&SHOE MRS.
Bale Thomas
Broom Wm.
Incledon Richard
Lowdwill John
Luxton John
Luxton John, jun
Parker James
Poole Wm.
Roberts Richard
Voisey Wm.
Webber Wm.
Williams James
BUILDERS.
Chudleigh Thos.
Jarman Elias
Palmer Robert
Teed Wm.

Webber Thomas
Williams Thomas
Wyatt John
BUTCHERS.
Coleman Wm.
Gibblings George
Goodhind Henry
Middlewick John
Reed John
Veals Wm.
CARPENTERS.
(* Cabinet Mkrs.)
*Benham John
*Gillham John
*Frost John B.
Jarman Elias
Stark John
Webber Thomas
Williams Thos.
CHINA, &c. DLRS.
Rowe Charles
Stark John
Toogood John
COOPERS.
Gard John
Ireland John
CURRIERS.
Luxton Peter
Rowe Joseph
Rowe Charles
GROCERS, &c.
Baker Sarah
Burnard Wm.
Dodge Henry
Dummett Mary
Earland Henry
Gillham John
Harvey Rd.&Sons
Hill Sarah
Monkton Sarah
Palmer Robert
Sanders John
Toogood John
Tooze Wm.
Way Mary
Webber John
HAIR DRESSERS.
Blackmore Henry
Howe John
LINEN &WOOLLEN DRAPERS.
Harvey Alfred
Monkton Sarah
Rowe Mrs

MALTSTERS.
Broom Wm.
King Robert
Welch Robert
MASONS.
(See Builders.)
MILLINERS.
Arnold Susan
Budd Ann
Dennis Eliza
Hucker Mary A.
Murch Jane
Tooze Elizabeth
PLUMBERS AND PAINTERS, &c.
Hole Mary
Matthews Henry
Plumpton Peter
Plumpton Wm.
Summerhayes J.
SADDLERS.
Gillham Edward
Goodhind Richd.
STRAW HAT MKRS.
Murch Jane
Salter Maria
Searle Ann
SURGEONS.
Gabriel Wm.
Justice Chas. (& registrar)
Milsom Geo.P.H.
TAILORS.
Baker John
Drew Wm.
Elliott Richard
Harris Samuel
Hutchins Wm.
Pratt Edward
Tuckett John
TURNERS.
Coombes Thomas
Webber Thomas
WATCHMAKERS.
Benham John
Bidgood George
Hill Wm. jun.
WHEELWRIGHTS.
Bell John
Earland Hy. (& coach builder)
Webber Thomas
CARRIERS.
(See next page.)

RAILWAY.
Trains 7 times a day, Exeter, Bristol, &c

CARRIERS.
Ford & Co. daily, to Exeter, Taunton, &c

Joseph Ellicott, to Exeter, Friday,
and Tiverton, Tuesday.
W. Bazley, to Honiton daily, from
the Station.

FENITON, or *Fenyton,* a small village in the Otter valley, four
miles W.S.W. of Honiton, and N. by E. of Ottery St. Mary, has in
its parish 315 souls and 1822 acres of land, including the small hamlets of *Corscombe* and *Colestock.* The manor was anciently held by
the Malherbe family, who were seated here for thirteen generations,
and had the power of beheading criminals. It now belongs to many
freeholders, the largest of whom are Sir John Patteson, Knt., (who
has a handsome seat here,) Sir J. Kennaway, Bart., J. P. Matthews,
Esq., Mr. W. Porter, and Miss Wright. The *Church* (St. Andrew,)
is a plain structure, with a tower and five bells. The *rectory,* valued
in K.B. at £16. 8s. 6½d., and in 1831 at £372, is in the alternate
patronage of S. C. Flood, G. B. Northcote, and — Woolley, Esqrs.,
and incumbency of the Rev H. E. Head, M.A., who has a good residence and 74A. of glebe. The tithes were commuted in 1839 for
£288 per annum. The poor have 4½A. of land, purchased with benefaction money, in 1717 and 1737, and now let for £8. The church
land (3 roods,) is let for £2.

Carslake Mary, *National School*
Darke Hy. shoemkr. & vict. Feniton Inn
Fry Richard, mason
Head Rev Hy. Erskine, M.A., *Rectory*
Marks Edw. par. clerk & *postmaster*
Murray Jane & My. Ann, *bdg. school*
Patteson Hon. Sir John, Knt., Judge
　of the Queen's Bench, *Feniton Court*
Perry John, shopkeeper

Sanders Wm. blacksmith

FARMERS.

Bath Henry Pyle *(owner)*
Bovett Ptrnla. ‖ Franks Ann
Coombe Sarah (and miller)
Manley Thomas ‖ Horsford J.
Salter Wm. ‖ Tooze Henry
Tooze Wm. ‖ Wheaton Joseph
Wheaton Philip, *Colesworthy*

KENTISBEARE, or *Kentisbeer,* three miles E. by N. of Collumpton, is a considerable village, sheltered on the west by lofty
hills. Its parish contains 1184 souls and about 4000 acres of land,
including *Sainthill* hamlet and many scattered farm houses, &c.
Blackborough parish is united with it for the support of the poor, as
noticed at page 282. It has a fair on Whit Wednesday; an Agricultural and Industrial Association; and an Assembly Room. The
trustees of the late Earl of Egremont are patrons of the rectory and
lords of the manor, formerly held by the Punchardson, Furneaux,
Bonville, and other families. They own a great part of the soil,
and the rest belongs to various freeholders. The *rectory,* valued in
K.B. at £27. 18s. 11½d., and in 1831 at £585, is in the incumbency
of the Rev. R. A. Roberts, M.A., who has 61A. of glebe and a good
residence, built in 1840. The tithes were commuted in 1841, for
£400 per annum. The *Church* (St. Mary,) is a fine ancient structure, with a beautiful screen, and several monumental memorials of
the Eveleigh and other families. The tomb of John Whiting, who
died in 1529, has the figures of himself and wife engraved in brass.
The poor parishioners have about 7A. of land at Ashill in Uffculme,
derived from *various benefactions.* This land is let for about £14 a
year, and there is belonging to the same trust about £140 vested at

interest. The clear income is distributed among the poor, together with a yearly rent-charge of £6 out of Berry Parks, purchased with £100 left by *Robt. Westcombe,* in 1629 ; and an annuity of £3 out of Shepherd's Valley Farm, in Dunkeswell, left by *John Sanders,* in 1719. There is a *Baptist Chapel* at Sainthill, built in 1839, at the cost of £300, and repaired in 1847.

Ackland Samuel, grocer
Ayres Edm. shoemaker & beerhouse
Bennett John, grocer, draper, tallow chandler, and organist
Bishop Henry, shoemaker
Bishop John, wheelwright
Bray Henry and Charles, masons
Broom Ann, shopkeeper
Cauiford Edward, blacksmith
Crossman Rev Humphrey, (Baptist,) *Sainthill*
Dennis Robert, boarding school
Driller John, blacksmith & beerhs
Frost Edmund, confectioner, *Sainthill*
Frost Robert, vict. Golden Lion
Glanville Wm. corn miller
Howe Edward, beer seller
Knight Charles, parish clerk
Leach Wm. gent. *Ford's*
Leach Wm. jun. brewer & maltster
Overend John, vict. Wyndham Arms
Potter Thomas, beer seller
Radford Joseph, schoolmaster
Radford Robert, tailor
Reed Richard, wheelwright

Roberts Rev R. A., *Rectory*
Sanders James, blacksmith
Stone Charles, tailor
Westcott Abel, sexton
  FARMERS. *(* are Owners.)*
*Baker Charles, *Sainthill*
Broom John, *Pirzwell*
*Cleeve Abraham || Cook Henry
*Cook Edward || Elworthy Thomas
Cottrell Adam, *Punchaydown*
Frost James || Frost Henry
Frost Mary || Harris Wm.
Frost Robert, Higher Kingsford
Hewett Wm. || Morrish Edward
*Leach Wm. jun. *Ford's & Lewis's*
Mills John, Lower Kingsford
Northam Wm. || Pratt Thomas
Pearcey Robert || Pearcey Thomas
Rabjohns Wm., *Mortimore's*
Salter Robert || Stark Robert
White Wm., *Orways*
Wood Wm. || Trott Wm.

Post Office at Ann Broom's. Letters desp. 5¼ aftn. *via* Collumpton

NETHER EXE, a small parish, on the east side of the river Exe, 5 miles N. by E. of Exeter, has only 97 souls, and 650 acres of land. Though so small a parish, it gives name to the *Nether Exe Farmers' Club,* which has a long list of members, resident in the surrounding parishes. Francis Hill, Esq., has a seat here, and owns the greater part of the parish, and the rest belongs to the Rev. W. Sweet, Mr. R. Bonner, and a few smaller owners. The *Church,* anciently subject to that of Rewe, is a small ancient structure, with one bell and a handsome font. The perpetual curacy, valued in K.B. at £8. 10s., and in 1831 at £37, is in the patronage of the eight trustees under the will of H. Burroughs, and is now enjoyed by the Rev. John Bond, M.A., of Romansleigh. The poor have 16s. a year, left by Nicholas Warren, and the parish sends a poor person to Burrough's Almshouse, at Broad Clist. The *farmers* are Thomas Bere, Francis Hill, Esq., Thomas Kingdon, John Rewe, and Francis Richards.

PAYHEMBURY, or Peyhembury, is a pleasant village, on a declivity, near a small rivulet, 5½ miles W. of Honiton, and 13 miles N.E. of Exeter. Its parish contains 545 souls, and 2698a. 3r. 25p. of land, rising boldly on the north-west, and including the hamlets of *Cheriton, Tale,* and *Upton,* and many scattered farm-houses, &c.

On a lofty eminence is a large treble entrenchment, called *Hembury Fort*, supposed by some antiquaries to have been the Roman station *Moridunum*, which others suppose to have been at Seaton; but it is not known that any antiquities have been found to support either supposition. Near this entrenchment is a house, which was built by the late *Admiral Samuel Graves*, a distinguished officer, who invented the life-boat. The manor of Payhembury, or *Peahembury*, belonged to the Giffords in the reign of Henry III., and afterwards passed to the Stanton, Crewkerne, Prous, and other families. It now belongs to John Venn, Esq., who also owns part of Upton and Prudholme. Sir John Kennaway, Bart., is owner of the manors of *Coxpit, Morden,* and *Tale,* the latter of which was formerly held by Ford Abbey. *Leyhill* and *Long Rewe* estates belong to E. S. Drewe, Esq., and the old farm-house, on the former, was long a seat of the Willoughby and Trevelyan families. Several smaller freeholders have estates in the parish. The *Church* (St. Mary,) is a handsome Gothic structure, with an embattled tower and six bells. The nave and chancel are separated by an elegant screen and rood loft, and in the chancel is a fine monument in memory of Mrs. Goswell. In the churchyard is one of the largest and oldest yew trees in the county, split with age or lightning, and supposed to have braved the storms of several centuries. The church was appropriated to Ford Abbey, and the great tithes, except a portion belonging to the vicar, are in the impropriation of J. H. C. Wyndham, Esq. The *vicarage,* valued in K.B. at £18. 4s. 2d., and in 1831 at £251, is in the patronage of Mrs. G. Messiter and Mrs. H. J. Tooze, and incumbency of the Rev. Henry Nicholls, M.A., of Rockbeare. The Vicarage House is an ancient ivy-mantled residence, and the glebe is 81A. 2R. 24P. The tithes were commuted in 1839, for £147 per annum to the vicar, and £150 to the impropriator. The poor have a yearly rent-charge of £8, left by *Jane Saunders,* in 1669, out of a house and land. They have also the dividends of £148. 4s. 4d. three per cent. consols, purchased with arrears of this rent-charge, and £26 given by Thomasine Piggott and Richard Venn.

Baker Joseph, tailor
Frost Edmund, miller, *Tuck Mill*
Granger Wm. blacksmith
Haymes Wm. saddler, & Rd. par. clk
Hole Wm. grocer, Post-Office
Loman Wm., & Veyard Jas. shoemrs
Pyle Saml. gent. ‖ Hollings Mrs Eliz.
Salter Jasper, butcher & vict. Six Bells
Salter John, smith & vict. Blue Anchor
Tooze Rev. Hy. Jno., B.A. curate
Trott Robt. vict. Hembury Fort
Venn Mrs Eliz. & Jno. gent. *Upton*
Veysie Wm. C. shopkeeper

FARMERS.
(* are owners.)
Blackmore Wm. *Leyhill*
Bovett James
Cole Ptr. *Coxpitt*
Daniel Han. *Tale*
Daniel Jno. *Tale*
*Glanville John
Hurley Thomas
Pratt Chas. & Wm. *Tale*
*Pratt Rd. *Tale*

Pratt Hy. *Tale*
Pyle Ts. *Cheriton*
Richards Frs. *Tale*
*Trump Wm.
*Venn Jno. *Upton*
*Venn Jno. jun. *do.*
*Venn Wm. *Upton*
*Wright John, *Cheriton*
WHEELWRIGHTS.
Harris Samuel
Harris Wm.
Pearcey Thomas

PLYMTREE is a pleasant village, near a tributary stream of the river Culm, 4 miles S.S.E. of Collumpton. It gives name to a Deanery, and its parish contains 439 souls, and 2185 acres of land, generally fertile, and boldly undulated. The manor was anciently

held of the Honour of Plympton, by the Fitzpaine, Courtenay, and other families, and was dismembered by the heiresses of Thomas Godwyn. The soil now belongs to Wm. Blake, Esq., Charles Harward, Esq., owner of *Hayne House;* Sir J. Kennaway, owner of *Clist-William;* A. Phillpott, Esq., owner of *Fordmore;* J. F. Pierce, Esq., and a few smaller freeholders. The *Church* (Virgin Mary,) is a handsome Gothic structure, with a tower and five bells. An elegant screen, painted and gilt, separates the nave and chancel, and on the west side of the tower is a representation of the Virgin and Child. The *rectory*, valued in K.B. at £21. 18s. 1½d., and in 1831 at £285, is in the patronage of Oriel College, Oxford, and incumbency of the Rev. Joseph Dornford, M.A., who has an old residence and 43A. of glebe. The tithes were commuted in 1847, for £297 per annum. For distribution in money and linen, the poor have the rent of 16A. of land, purchased in 1733, with £225, of which £100 was left by *John Land,* in 1697; £85 was given by various donors, and £40 was raised by the parish. This land is now let for £25. The poor have also £2. 2s. yearly from 1½A. of land left by *Mary* and *Andrew Crosse,* in 1662, and the interest of £20 left by *Dorothy Mundy,* and lent to the overseers.

Dornford Rev Jph., M.A. *Rectory*
Hartwell Mark, baker
Lock John Arthur, Esq. *Hayne Hs.*
Scovern Louisa, schoolmistress
Veysie Mrs & Mary Ann, schoolmrs
Veysie Wm. wheelwright

FARMERS.
Brice John
Cook Wm. sen.& jun., *Lower Weaver*
Crook Wm.
Disney James
Dowell James
Griffin Thomas, *Fordmore*

Hole John
Hussey James
Lawrence Wm.
Parris Benjamin
Salter Jno. *Tyes*
Shiles Henry
Shiles John

BLACKSMITHS.
Quick Edward
Sanders John

SHOEMAKERS.
Davey John
Hockey Wm.
Quick John

TAILORS.
Dearn John
Ireland Henry

POST OFFICE at Eliz. Quick's.
Letters,*via*Collumpton

SHELDON, a small village and parish, picturesquely situated among the hills, about 6 miles E. by N of Collumpton, and N.N.W. of Honiton, has only 190 souls, and 1300 acres of land, belonging to the Bank of Honiton ; Mr. E. Doble, Mr. Henry Ellis, Mr. Geo. Speake, and a few smaller freeholders. The manor was held by Dunkeswell Abbey, and afterwards by the Bourchier and other families. The *Church* (St. James,) is a small antique fabric, with a tower and three bells, and the living is a perpetual curacy, valued in 1831 at £262, in the patronage of W. Miles, Esq., and incumbency of the Rev. Chas. E. Band, M.A., of Combe Rawleigh. There is no Parsonage House, and only half an acre of glebe, but the living is endowed with £140 a year out of the great tithes of Awliscombe parish. The tithes of Sheldon were commuted in 1837, for £145 per annum, and that portion which belonged to Dunkeswell Abbey is now vested in E. S. Drewe, Esq.

Curron James, carpenter
Pring Nancy, schoolmistress
Underwood Richard, blacksmith

FARMERS.
Acland John, *Slades*

Blackmore John & Wm. *Northcott*
Doble Edward || Doble Sarah
Nix George || Payne Wm.
Patten John, *Newhouse*

SILVERTON, a large village, pleasantly situated on the eastern acclivity of Exe valley, 7 miles N. by E. of Exeter, and 5½ miles S.W. of Collumpton, was anciently a market town, and has still two *cattle fairs*, on the first Thursdays in February and July. In 1837 nearly half its houses were destroyed by fire, and some of them have not yet been rebuilt. Its parish contains 1384 inhabitants, and 4714 acres of fertile land, extending eastward to the river Culm, and westward to the Exe; comprising many scattered farm-houses; and divided into four quarters, called Borough, Yalton, Monk-Culm, and North Quarter. Sir Thomas Fairfax was quartered here with his army four days in October, 1645. The manor, which had been part of the ancient demesne of the Crown, was held at an early period by the Beauchamps, whose heiress sold it to Sir John Wadham, in the 14th century. It is now vested in the Earl of Ilchester and the trustees of the late Earl of Egremont, as representatives of the Wadhams. The former has five and the latter seven-twelfths. About a mile west of the village is SILVERTON PARK, where the late *Earl of Egremont,* who died in 1845, built a large and elegant mansion, in the florid and ornamental Grecian order of architecture. A great part of the parish belongs to the Rev. J. Scobell, the Rev. Dr. Troyte, Col. Glover, and many smaller freeholders. *Combe Sachville* was formerly held by the Reigny, Sachville, Browne, and other families; and Monk-Culm, was given by the Earl of Moreton to Montacute Priory. The *Church* (St. Mary,) is a large Gothic structure, with a tower and six bells. The interior has a beautifully painted ceiling, and several neat mural monuments. Adjoining the church-yard was an ancient chapel, of which there are still some traces. The *rectory,* valued in K.B. at £51. 8s. 4d., and in 1831 at £749, is in the patronage of the Earl of Ilchester and the trustees of the late Earl of Egremont, and incumbency of the Rev. Charles Tripp, D.D., who has a good residence and 90A. 16P. of glebe. The tithes were commuted in 1843, for £950 per annum. A Presbyterian Meeting-house was built here in 1715, and the parish has a well endowed school and several charities for the poor.

For a weekly distribution of about 12s. worth of bread, the poor have £2. 12s. per annum from *Sir John Acland's Charity,*—(See Exeter;)— £2. 12s. a year purchased with £50 left by *Gawin Fursdon,* in 1663; 52s. a year left by *Henry Bustard,* in 1697; and about £20 per annum from 4½A. of land, purchased with £250 left by *Thomas Troyte,* in 1750. For distribution in linen cloth they have 30s. a year from two gardens, left by *Wm. Row* and *Wm. Mills,* in 1651 and 1695; and £8 a year as the fourth part of the rent of a house, and 20A. of land at Tiverton, left by *Andrew Arscott,* in 1659. For the relief of poor housekeepers of this parish frequenting the church, *Edward Cotton, D.D.,* left two houses, a cottage, a garden, and an orchard of 2A. 1R. 30P., now let for about £30 a year, which is mostly divided at Christmas, among poor families not receiving parochial relief. Two small houses, occupied rent free by poor families, were given by *Wm. Wreyford,* in 1700. The FREE SCHOOL, which is open gratuitously to all the boys of the parish, was founded by *John Richards,* who, in 1724, left £1200 to be laid out in land for its endowment, which now consists of a farm of 150A. at Cheriton Fitzpaine, let for about £130 a year, and a house and 4A., worth about £10 a year. Attached to the school is a house

or the master, who has usually about 60 free-scholars. Here is a *Girls Free School*, supported by subscription, and an annuity of 50s., left by *Richard Troyte*, out of Netherleigh. The *Church Lands, &c.*, comprise about two acres, and a house, cottage, and other buildings, let for £16 a year, which is carried to the churchwardens' accounts.

Bonner Thomas, wheelwright
Chaplin Hy. wheelwgt. & vict. Lamb
Courtney Elizabeth, schoolmistress
Cutliffe Charles E. surgeon
Hopkins Samuel, *Free Schoolmaster*
Hopkins Wm. vict. New Inn
Kennier Richard, M.D.
MortimerWm.maltr.&vic. ThreeTuns
Norris Jno. gent || Braddick Mr Jas.
Perriman John, builder and mason
Player Chas. vict. Ruffwell Inn
Puddicombe E. D. surgeon
Salter Cphr. and Savery John, gents
Sibthorpe John A., Esq. land agent, *Silverton Park*
Spry Miss || Stevens My. A. schoolr
Talbot James, saddler
Thomas Chas. blacksmith & beerhs
Tripp Rev Charles, D.D. rector of Silverton and Bradon, *Rectory*
Webber Mr Richd. || White Mr Thos.
White John, parish clerk, *Post Office*

FARMERS. (* *are Owners.*)
Aplin John, *Southcombe*
*Bater Robert || Bird John
Cleeve Thomas || Dewdney Thos.

*Gardiner Samuel, *Lower Darwich*
Gould John, *Dunsmore*
Ham Joseph, *Combe Sachville*
*Hewett James || Griffin James
*Hodge John || Madge James
*Mortimore Richard, *Stockwell*
*Player Joseph Wm. || Nix John
*Read Alexander J. T., *Worth*
*Rowe Robert || Squire John
*Thomas Benjamin || Upham Fras.
Webber Wm. || Wolland Edward
Webber Robert, *Ford*

BAKERS.
Hodge John
Miller John
Thomas Joseph
BUTCHERS.
Hopkins John
Hopkins Wm.
Webber Wm.
GROCERS & DPRS.
Berry Samuel
Pratt Sarah
Steventon Hy.
Upham Wm.
Ward John

White My. Ann
SHOEMAKERS.
Burnett John
Kingdon James
Pike Thomas
TAILORS.
Berry Robert
Courtney James
Rowe Rt. chandlr

POST - OFFICE at J. White's. — Letters from Collumpton.

TALATON, or *Tallaton*, a village on a northern declivity, 3½ miles N.W. of Ottery St. Mary, and 11 miles N.E. by E. of Exeter, has in its parish 462 souls, and about 2250 acres of land, rising to a bold eminence, which overlooks the Otter valley, and including 140A. of waste, the hamlets of *Larkbeare, Escot, Talewater*, and *Fairmile*, and several scattered houses. *Sir John Kennaway, Bart.*, is lord of the manor and owner of a great part of the soil, and has a handsome seat here, called *Escot House*, built on the site of the old mansion, which was erected about 1688, and was destroyed by fire, on Dec. 28th, 1808, with all the furniture and most of the pictures and other valuables. The late Sir John Kennaway was created a baronet in 1791, and purchased this estate in 1794, of Sir George Yonge, Bart., who entertained George III., Queen Charlotte, and three of the princesses here on Aug. 14th, 1789. Escot House stands on a well-wooded demesne of 500A., remarkable for the luxuriant growth of its firs and forest trees, which increase rapidly after their roots have spread through the loamy substratum. J. P. Mathew, Esq., owns part of the parish, and resides at *Ridon House ;* and Mr. R. Pratt and a few smaller freeholders have estates here. The *Church* (St. James,) has a tower and five bells, and contains a rich screen, and some memorials of the Eveleigh and other families. The *rectory*, valued in K.B. at £32. 3s. 1½d., and in 1831 at £581,

is in the patronage and incumbency of the Rev. L. P. Welland, who has 62A. 1R. 1P. of glebe, and a rent-charge in lieu of tithes. The *Poor's Land*, 2¼A., let for £3, was purchased in 1657, with £23, benefaction money. The sum of £30, given by *Wm. Eveleigh*, and £30 paid by the parishioners, were laid out, in 1802, in the purchase of two small tenements, worth £8 a year. The poor have also the dividends of £230. 9s. 6d. new five per cent. stock, purchased with £209, left by *Jonah Pynsent, Eliz. Prideaux*, and *Geo. Baker*, and £15 derived from timber felled in the poor's land. Escot DISTRICT CHURCH, for adjacent parts of Talaton, Ottery St. Mary, and Feniton parishes, is about two miles from the respective parish churches, and 5 miles W.S.W. of Honiton. It is a small neat structure, erected a few years ago; and its perpetual curacy, valued at £75, is in the patronage of Sir Jno. Kennaway, and incumbency of the Rev. Fras. Thomas Hill.

Franks Wm. butcher
Godden Wm. schoolmaster
Hill Rev Fras. Thos. *incbt. of Escot*
Hookway Wm. wheelgt. & beerhs
Ireland Jas. & Shepherd Rt. shoemkrs
Kennaway Sir Jno., Bart. *Escot Hs*
MathewJonahPynsent, Esq.*RidonHs*
Pyle Elizabeth, vict. Half Moon
Salter Wm. blacksmith
Stokes Joseph and Wm. tailors
Sweetland Ann, cooper
Welland Rev Lawrence Palk, *rector*
FARMERS. (* are at Escot.)
*Baker Humphrey || Pratt Richard
Grendon Wm. *Larkbeare*
Lovering Wm. || Lovering Ann
North Thomas || Rogers Wm.
Pratt John || *Pratt Wm.
*Pyle Francis || Pyle Wm.
Salter James || Wright Barnabas

THORVERTON, a large village, pleasantly situated on the west side of the Exe valley, about 7 miles N. of Exeter, and E. by N. of Crediton, has in its parish 1445 inhabitants, and 4036 acres of land, including the hamlets of *Raddon, Yellowford*, or *Yoldford;* and many scattered houses. It has two annual *fairs*, one on the last Monday in February, chiefly for *fat sheep*, and the other on the Monday after July 18th, for *lambs*, of which upwards of 40,000 are frequently sold, principally for rearing. The Dean and Chapter of Exeter are lords of the manor of Thorverton, and owners of 1392A., held on leases for 21 years, renewable every seven years on payment of fines. J. H. Hippisley, Esq., is lord of the manor of East Raddon, and owner of 1226A.; Mrs. Fursdon owns 624½A., and the rest of the parish belongs to Lord Clinton and other freeholders. The manor and church of Thorverton were given by Henry II. to St. Martin's Abbey, in Tours; and in the farm-house called *Chapel St. Martin*, may be seen the remains of a Roman Catholic Chapel. The *Church* (St. Thomas a-Becket,) is a large and handsome Gothic structure, with a tower and five bells. It has lately been new-roofed and repaired; and three beautiful stained glass windows have been inserted at the expense of the present Vicar and his family. The Dean and Chapter of Exeter are appropriators of]the great tithes, and patrons of the *Vicarage*, valued in K.B. at £18. 12s. 8½d., and in 1831 at £535, and now in the incumbency of the Rev. J. D. Coleridge, LL.D., who has 27 acres of glebe, and a handsome residence, built in 1840, at the cost of about £1900. The great tithes were commuted in 1843, for £534, and the small tithes for £452 per annum.

Westcote mentions a fine monument of the last of the Wallis family at Thorverton, inlaid with brass, which had been entirely defaced. In the parish is a *Baptist Chapel*, which was built by Presbyterians in 1715, and has a school, built in 1833. The *Parish Land* consists of 24 acres at Faringdon, purchased in 1763, with £580, which had been bequeathed by various donors, for various charitable uses. It is let for about £45 per annum, of which two-fifths are applied in schooling poor children at the *National School* (built 1841,) and providing them with Bibles and clothes; and the remainder is distributed in money, bread, and clothing, among the poor parishioners. Belonging to the same trust are a house and garden adjoining the churchyard, let to the sexton for 50s. a year. To provide petticoats for poor women of this parish, *Mary West* left a yearly rent-charge of 35s. 2d., in 1694, out of a house in Exeter. For distribution in bread among ten poor people, *John West* left 20s. a year out of Yellowford farm, in 1728. For distribution in clothing, the poor of Thorverton have about £5. 10s. yearly from *Grace Bampfylde's Gift*. (See Pinhoe.) They have also £10 a year from *Eliz. Tuckfield's Charity*, as noticed with Crediton; and an annuity of 32s. 6d., left by *James Burned*, in 1790, out of Ridgeman's tenement.

Babbage John, plumber, &c.
Babbage Wm. vict. Dolphin
Bater John, builder
Brock Geo. & Mrs. boarding school
Coleridge Rev Jas.Duke,LL.D.*Vicrge*
Crosse Thomas, surgeon
Gervis Henry, solicitor
Glanfield Grace, Natnl. Schoolmistss
Hillman Wm. Hy. plumber, &c.
Holton John F. vict. Wellington
James Wm. vict. Bell Inn
Mallett John, corn miller
May Wm. apple nurseryman
Milford Ann, Infant Schoolmistress
Phillips John, machine maker
Prowse John, maltster
Reynolds Mrs E. ‖ Tucker Miss
RowThos.Broom, acct.,land agt.&agt. to West of Eng. Fire & Life Office
Sanford Morton, Post Office
Sexton John, auctioneer, &c.
Skinner Thomas, National School
Upcott Philip, druggist ‖ Pugh Mrs
Vicary L. E. T. veterinary surgeon
Yonge Rev Duke, M.A. curate

FARMERS.
Brice Wm.
Cornish John
Cosway Wm.
Hutchings Wm., *Channons*
Jones John, *Yellowford*
Kingdon Saml.
Kingdon Thos.
Kingdon Wm., *Tray Mill*
Locock Henry, *Raddon court*
Pasmore Wm.
Phillips John
Potter Thomas, *Yellowford*
Radmore George, *Easton*
RadmoreGeo. jun *Courthayes*
Radmore John, *Upcott*
Sharland Thos.
Turner Wm.
Vinnicombe Rd.

BAKERS.
Dyer Joseph
Plucknott Thos.
Skinner Wm.
Yelland Henry

BLACKSMITHS.
Commings Saml.

Hosegood John
Prowse Tpn.

BUTCHERS.
Chamberlin Ths.
Prowse Robert
Scott Henry

GROCERS, &c.
Commings Jas.
Heard James
Sexton John
White Richard

SADDLERS.
Churchill Robt.
Lake Jph. irongr

SHOEMAKERS.
Heard John
Tapscott Wm.

TAILORS.
Berridge John
Hooper John
Lake Wm.
Southcott John

WHEELWRIGHTS.
Milford John
Milford Thomas

POST-OFFICE at M. Sanford's

HALBERTON HUNDRED

Is a small district, comprising only the parishes of *Halberton, Sampford-Peverell, Willand,* and part of *Uplowman,* in Tiverton Union, and part of *Burlescombe,* in Wellington Union. It contains only 3021 souls, and about 14,000 acres of land. It is all in the Northern Division of Devon, Archdeaconry of Exeter, Deanery of Tiverton, and Collumpton Petty Sessional Division.

HALBERTON is a large village, 3 miles E. of Tiverton, near the Grand Western Canal, and 1½ mile W. of the junction of the Tiverton branch with the Bristol and Exeter Railway. Its parish contains 1739 inhabitants, and about 7600 acres of land, including the hamlets of *Brethem-Bottom, Seckerleigh, Muxbeare, Ash,* and many scattered houses. Earl Powlett is lord of the *manor* of *Halberton-Dean,* or Lower Town, which he holds on lease under the Dean and Chapter of Bristol. The manor of *Halberton Boys,* formerly held by the Boys and other families, was purchased in 1808, by Richard Hall Clarke, Esq., of *Bridwell House,* a pleasant seat in this parish, 3 miles E. of the village, built in 1779, and encompassed by a fine lawn and luxuriant plantations. Mr. Clarke is also owner of Muxbeare and Sealake estates. The manor of *Morston* belongs to the Countess of Egremont. *Mount Stephen* is the seat of George Wood, Esq., and *Halberton Court* is the residence of Thomas Webber, Esq. The other principal owners of land in this large parish are the Rev. J. Pitman, Capt. Adney, W. Nation, Esq., G. Pearce, Esq., Rev. J. Spurway, and Capt. Cphr. Laroche. The parish is chiefly freehold, and the canal winds through it very circuitously, and is crossed here three times by the high road from Tiverton to Wellington. The *Church* (St. Andrew,) is a handsome structure, of the 14th century, with a tower and five bells. It was re-seated, cleansed, and thoroughly renovated at the cost of about £1400, in 1848. It has a beautiful screen, and a fine old pulpit and font; and had formerly a guild or fraternity of St. John the Baptist, valued at £6, and a chantry, endowed with £5. 4s. 6d. per annum. In 1772, there were in the parish vestiges of three ancient chapels, one in the churchyard, one at Bridwell, and the other at Muxbeare. The Dean and Chapter of Bristol are appropriators of most of the great tithes, and patrons of the *vicarage,* valued in K.B. at £31, and in 1831 at £625, and now in the incumbency of the Rev. C. G. Newcomb, M.A., who has 39A. of glebe, and a large and handsome residence, built in 1848, at the cost of £2000. He has the tithes of apples and hay. The tithes were commuted in 1842, the vicar's for £671, and the appropriate tithes for £358 per annum. Here is an old Wesleyan Chapel, and a Farmers' Club. The poor parishioners have a cottage and 5A. 1R. of land, left by *John Were,* in 1777, and now let for £12 a year. They have also the following yearly doles, viz., 20s., left by *Simon Borrough,* in 1608; 20s., left by *Emlin Comins,* out of Mount Stephen estate; 26s., left by *Sir John Acland,* and paid by the Corporation of Exeter; £20 out of West Pitt Estate, left by *Nicholas Turner;* £8 (and 10s. for the church,) out of the same estate, left in 1647, by *Thos. Were;* 10s., left by *John Maunder,*

out of Chorland estate; and £5 out of land at Collumpton, left by *Peter Newte,* in 1719. The latter is for the support of a school, and the others are distributed in money, clothing, or weekly doles of bread. Nicholas Spicer gave 10s. a year, for the repairs of the church, out of Spicer Meadow.

Adney Miss Ann || Babb Mr. James
Arscott Thomas, wheelgt., smith, and agricultural machine maker
Bale Benjamin, stay maker
Baskerville Nicholas, *boarding school*
Bidgood Thomas, beer seller
Carter Samuel, shoemaker
Chave Lieut. Samuel, R.N.
Chubb John, baker
Clarke Rd. Hall, Esq., *Bridwell Hs.*
Daniel Wm. Hooper, grocer & drpr.
England Mr George
Harwood James, machine maker
Holloway Wm. corn miller
Hosegood Thomas, tailor
James John, shoemaker
James Richard, schoolmaster
Newcomb Rev Chas. Geo., M.A. *vicar*
Passmore Jas. & Pine Wm. tailors
Pearcy Wm. Hellier, tailor
Pocock Henry, Esq. *Rock House*
Pring James, vict. Swan Inn
Radford Jno. & Russell W. butchers
Smith Hy. John, canal manager ; h *Welshford House, Wellington*
Toose Wm. machine maker & smith
Webber Thos. Esq. *Halberton Court*

Wilkins Judith, vict. New Inn
Wood Geo. Esq. *Mount Stephen*

FARMERS.

Adams John || Ansley Elizabeth
Brook John || Burrough Edward
Chave Richard || Chave Samuel
Collins John || Gill Thomas
Cook Henry || Cook Thomas
Cook Henry, jun. *Slough*
Cook John, *Brethem-bottom*
Cook Nathaniel, *Muddiford*
Daw John, *Manley*
Densham James, *Bycott*
Gillard Edward || Gillard D. J.
Haydon Mary || Jackman Mr
Isaacs John || Martin Wm.
Manley Abraham, *Mills*
May Elizabeth || May Henry
Mildon Robert || Merson Thomas
Murch Clement, *Sutton*
Northam Oliver || Parkhouse James
Partridge Thos. || Passmore John
Pitts Thomas || Pyle John
Warren Rt., *Ash* || Scorse John
Were John || Webber Thomas
White Lawrence, *Mount Stephen*

Post from Tiverton daily

SAMPFORD PEVERELL, a well built and pleasant village, near the Grand Western Canal and Bristol and Exeter Railway, 5½ miles E.N.E. of Tiverton, and 9 miles S.W. of Wellington, has in its parish 857 inhabitants, and about 2000 acres of land. It has a great *fair* for cattle, sheep, and horses, on the Monday before the last Wednesday in April, and had formerly a large woollen manufactory. The manor, anciently belonging to the Peverells, and afterwards to the Dinham, Aisthorpe, and Powlett families, was sold with the demesne by the late Earl Powlett, to various freeholders. The parish now belongs to T. Hellings, J. T. B. Notley, Rd. Pedler, D. Harvey, Rt. Pearce and several smaller owners. *Sampford Barton,* was for a long period the seat of the Powletts, and was for some time the residence of the Dowager Queen of Henry VII., who died here. A *Castle* was built here by Oliver Dinham, about 1437, and its remains were cleared away about 1755. The *Church* (St. John,) is an ancient structure, with a tower and five bells, and contains a monument of Lady Powlett, who died in 1602. The *rectory,* valued in K.B. at £23. 8s. 11½d., and in 1831 at £320, is in the patronage of Dr. Lemann, and incumbency of the Rev. A. Boulton, D.D., who has 15A. of glebe, and a good residence, erected in lieu of the old one,

by the Canal Company, at the cost of about £1500. The tithes have been commuted for about £390 per annum. There is a *Wesleyan Chapel* in the village. Eight cottages and three houses, &c., let for about £25 a year, have been vested in trust from an early period, for the relief of the poor parishioners not receiving parochial aid.

Adams Wm. patent axle, lathe, &c. manufacturer
Bennett John, baker
Bidgood John, schoolmr. & agent to Royal Farmers' Insurance Co.
Bidgood Wm. sieve maker
Boulton Rev. Anthony, D.D., *Rectory*
Broom Henry, maltster
Burridge George, coal dealer
Clist James, tailor || Surridge Sus.
Cole John, vict. New Inn
Cowlyn Mr. Rd. Chave & Mrs. Eliz.
Creed Joseph, millwright
Curwood John, slay maker
Darch Rd. & John, shoemakers
Elworth Edward, blacksmith
Harris Richard, grocer and draper
Hellyer Mary, grocer and draper
Hellyer George, grocer and draper
Hodge Wm. corn miller
Lawrence Samuel, boarding school
Maber Wm. vict. Hare and Hounds
Merson Wm. F., physician

Morse & Morton, (Mesdms.) ladies' boarding school
Parr David, basket maker
Pedler Richd. gent., *Sampford Barton*
Penkivile Richard S. surgeon
Saunders Mark, mason
Shackell Richard, butcher
Southwood Thos. & Richard, bakers
Taylor Wm. sen. & jun., tailors
Vickery Jno., Thos. & Js. blcksmths
Vickery John, schoolmaster
Webber Mr Richard
Wood John, vict. Globe Inn

FARMERS.

Baker John || Beedell John
Burrough Richard || Northam Thos.
Payne Wm. || Skinner Richard
Stevens Thos. ||Summers James
Talbot James || Vickery Wm.
Vickery Robert, *Goulsmoor*

Post-Office at W. Taylor's. Letters *via* Tiverton

WILLAND, a small parish and village, in the picturesque valley of the small river Culm, near the Bristol and Exeter Railway and the junction of the Tiverton branch, 2½ miles N. by E. of Collumpton, and 6 miles E. of Tiverton, has only 345 inhabitants, and about 950 acres of land, belonging to C. and E. Salter, the Rev. G. T. Smith, Benjamin Walrond, George Wood, E. Broom, T. B. Rowe, and several other freeholders. The *Church* (St. Mary,) is an ancient structure, with a tower and three bells, and a beautiful screen. The *rectory*, valued in K.B. at £7. 10s. 5d., and in 1831 at £90, is in the patronage of C. and E. Salter and incumbency of the Rev. John Taylor, who is also vicar of Llanarthney. The parsonage is a small cottage, and the glebe is only 1A. 1R. 1P. The tithes were commuted in 1842 for £103. 8s. 9d. per annum. The poor have the following yearly doles :—20s. from an acre of land in Tawney Meadow, given by *Lewis Brooke*, in 1725 ; 10s. out of Black-lands, left by *Robert Hinton*, in 1707 ; 10s. from £10 given by *Thomas Tymewell*, and £1. 17s. 4d. as the interest of £42 left by *Mary Clarke* and another donor. The Wesleyans have a small chapel here.

Adney Rev Richard, *curate*
Brice Wm. vict. White Horse
Dummett Wm. blacksmith
Freeman Edmund, station master
Hawkes Thos. vict. Railway Station
Huggins Mr Geo.|| Binford Miss Ann

James Thos. & Wm. shoemakers
Hutchins Chas. auctioneer & survr.
Mitchell John, tailor
Nash Elizabeth, schoolmistress
Parkhouse Mr Wm.
Pearcy Robert, shoemaker

Quant John, coal dealer
Rice Mary, grocer and draper
Tanner Mrs Ann || Trood Mrs A.
Vickery John, blacksmith
White John, vict. Halfway House

FARMERS.
Brown Simon || Cook Mrs
Hine Sarah || Dummett Wm.
Radford Thomas || Radford Wm.
Salter Jas. Cross, (high constable)
Stephens Thomas || White John

TIVERTON HUNDRED

Comprises only the Borough and Parish of Tiverton, and the four parishes of Calverleigh, Huntsham, Loxbear and most of Uplowman, which contain 10,770 inhabitants, and about 24,00 acres of land, generally fertile, picturesquely undulated, and traversed by the river Exe, and several of its tributary streams. It is in the Northern Division of Devon, in Tiverton Polling and County Court District, in Tiverton Union, and in the Archdeaconry of Exeter and Deanery of Tiverton. The Borough of Tiverton has separate quarter and petty sessions, and the rest of the Hundred is in Collumpton Petty Sessional Division.

TIVERTON UNION comprises the 27 parishes of Bampton, Bradninch, Bickleigh, Butterleigh, Cadbury, Cadeleigh, Calverleigh, Clayhanger, Collumpton, Cruwys Morchard, Halberton, Hockworthy, Huntsham, Kentisbeare with Blackborough, Loxbear, Morebath, Oakford, Sampford-Peverell, Silverton, Stoodleigh, Templeton, Thorverton, Tiverton, Uffculm, Uplowman, Washfield, and Willand. They are all in the jurisdiction of the *County Court*, held at Tiverton; and extend over an area of 171 square miles, and in 1841 contained 32,499 *inhabitants*, and 6836 *houses*, of which 352 were empty, and 77 building when the census was taken. Their total average annual expenditure on the poor, during the three years preceding the formation of the Union was £18,215. In 1838 their expenditure was £14,248, and in 1840, £16,764. 19s. The *Union Workhouse* was built on the site of the old Workhouse at Tiverton Town-end in 1836-7, at a cost of £6000, and is a commodious stone building, with accommodations for 300 paupers. Four guardians are elected for Tiverton, three for Collumpton, two each for Halberton, Silverton, Thorverton and Uffculm, and one for each of the other parishes. This Union, with that of Dulverton in Somersetshire, forms a district of which T. L. T. Rendell, Esq., is *Superintendent Registrar*. He is also *clerk* of Tiverton Union, and the *Relieving Officers* are John Gath, of Tiverton, Edwin Druller, of Brampton, and Henry Doble, of Uffculm. Thirteen *surgeons* are employed by the Union, and Jph. and Mrs. Collard are *master and matron* of the Workhouse. Messrs. F. S. Gervis and John Snell, of Tiverton, are *Registrars of Marriages*; and Messrs. J. J. Owen, J. Edwards, H. Morrish, jun., G. and C. Justice, F. A. Cleeve, W. Jordan, and C. P. Collyns, *are Registrars of Births and Deaths*.

CALVERLEIGH, 2 miles W.N.W. of Tiverton, is a small parish, containing only 81 souls and 501 acres of land, all the property of Joseph Chichester Nagle, of *Calverleigh House*, a large mansion built in 1844-'5, in a small, well-wooded park. The manor was purchased by the late Joseph Nagle, of Viscount Vane, and was anciently held by the Calwodelie family. The *Church* (St. Mary,) is a small fabric, with a tower and three bells, and the *rectory*, valued in K.B. at £12, and in 1831 at £184, is in the patronage of G. W. Owen, Esq., and

incumbency of the Rev. Geo. W. Owen, of Loxbear. The poor have
an annuity of 18s. left by Humphrey Brook, and four of the poor
parishioners have 5s. each yearly from Shorland's Charity. Wm.
Downing, farmer, *Hill Farm ;* Wm. Manley, *church clerk ;* and Jas.
Woolway, *tailor.*

HUNTSHAM, a parish of scattered houses, 5 miles N.N.E. of
Tiverton, has only 157 souls and 2930 acres of land. The Rev. E.
B. Troyte, LL.D., is lord of the manor, owner of a great part of the
soil, and patron and incumbent of the *rectory,* valued in K.B. at
£10. 12s. 11d., and in 1831 at £200. He has a pleasant seat here
called Huntsham House, and 49A. 2R. 14P. of glebe;¼ but the Parsonage is in a decayed condition. The tithes were commuted in
1842 for £187 per annum. The manor was formerly held by the
Stanton, Dunsland, Beare, and Lucas families, the latter of whom
sold it to the Troytes. The *Church* is an ancient ivy mantled structure, with a tower and three bells. It has a fine old screen, and the
seats have all variously carved ends, and bear the date, 1534.

Burton Robert, wheelwright
Kerslake James, shoemaker
Poysay John, blacksmith
Redwood Henry, corn miller
Seymour Rev F. P., curate
Troyte Rev Edward Berkeley, LL.D.
    rector, *Huntsham House*

FARMERS.
Frost Thomas || Heard Mildred
Light Richard || Oxenham Thomas
Shattock Wm. & Edw. || Slape Rt.
Stone Wm., *Huntsham Barton*
Tapscott Wm. || White Wm.

LOXBEAR, or LOXBEER, is a hilly parish of scattered houses, 4
miles N.W. of Tiverton, containing 144 inhabitants, and 1320 acres
of land. Sir T. D. Acland, Bart., is lord of the manor, owner of
nearly all the soil, and patron of the *rectory,* valued in K.B. at
£6. 14s. 9½d., and in 1831 at £135, and now in the incumbency of
the Rev. W. Karslake, of Dolton. The manor was anciently held by
the Trobridge, Richards, and Cudmore families. The *Church* is an
antique structure, with a low tower and three bells. The Rectory
House was burnt down, about six years ago. The poor have the interest of £48, derived from the gift of Thos. Cudmore, in 1637.

Ashford John, tanner, *Chapland*
Ashford Peter Sharland, gent., do.
Marshall John, shoemaker
Maunder Wm. vict. Royal Oak
Owen Rev Geo. W. curate, (and rec-
    tor of Calverleigh)
Pope Richard, blacksmith

Tucker John, church clerk
FARMERS.
Ashford John Hy. || Ayre Thomas
Bidgood Edmund || Crook John
Bowden John || Norrish Richard
Norrish Wm., *Loxbear Barton*

UPLOWMAN, or UPLOMAN, a small scattered village, 4½ miles
E.N.E. of Tiverton, near the Lowman rivulet, has in its parish about
3000 acres of land, and 428 inhabitants, of whom 80 are in *Whitnage* tithing, which is in Halberton Hundred, near the Grand Western Canal. The manor of Uplowman anciently belonged to the
de Lomen or de Lumine family, and afterwards to the Willington,
Beaumont, and Powlett families. The manorial rights now belong
to the Elworthy family, but the soil belongs to various freeholders,
the largest of whom are W. M. Praed, Wm. Nation, and R. H. Clarke,
Esqrs. The Rev. S. Pidsley, B.A., is lord of the *Rectorial Manor,*

(worth £150 per annum,) and patron and incumbent of the *rectory*, valued in K.B. at £21. 0s. 10d. and in 1831 at £601. He has 43A. 3R. 6P. of glebe, and a large residence, which was mostly rebuilt in 1832, and has tasteful grounds. The tithes were commuted in 1842 for £500 per annum. The Church (St. Peter,) is an ancient structure, with a tower and five bells. At the east end of the village was an ancient chapel called *Beauchapel*, but all traces of it disappeared some centuries ago. In 1638, *Bartw. Calwoodleigh* left 40s. a year for the poor parishioners, out of a house and close called Collishaw. They have also the following yearly doles : £2 out of Landrake estate in Tiverton, left in 1684 by *John Chave* ; £3. 13s. out of Splat-ford Meadows, left by *Wm. Chave* in 1719, and £1 out of the poor rates, as the interest of £20 given by *John Chave* in 1723. A *school* for poor children is supported by subscription.

Elworthy Miss Susan, *Coombe*
Parr Humphy. joiner, Wood-end
Redwood Chas., miller, Stag Mill
Redwood John, vict. *Cross ways*
Pidsley Rev Sydenham, B.A., Rectory
Sloman Dorcas, schoolmistress

BLACKSMITHS.
Elworthy James
Holloway & Son

FARMERS.
Badcock John
Brice Thomas, *Whitnage*
Brade John
Chave Edward, *Windhayes*

Clapp Wm.
Frankpitt Rd.
Frankpitt Wm.
Kerslake Wm.
Morse Dennis
Pearse Thomas, sen. and jun., *Whitnage*
Squire Richard
Stooke Edm.

Sweet Ann
Sweet George

SHOEMAKERS.
Barrett John
Dunster Wm.

WHEELWRIGHTS.
Carter Robert
Redwood John
Redwood Robt.

TIVERTON, an ancient *borough and market town*, formerly a principal seat of the woollen manufacture, and now noted for its extensive lace manufactory, and its numerous charities, is pleasantly situated on the sloping banks at the confluence of the river Exe and the Loman rivulet, 13 miles N. by E. of Exeter, 62 miles S.W. of Bristol, and 165 miles W. by S. of London, by road, or 184 by rails. It has a *branch railway*, which extends 5½ miles eastward to the Bristol and Exeter line, and was opened in June, 1848. The *Grand Western Canal* extends north-eastward from this town to Taunton, where it joins the navigation to Bridgewater and the Bristol Channel. This canal is 23 miles in length, and is used chiefly for supplying the neighbouring districts with lime, coal, corn, manure, &c. It has very ingenious machinery in lieu of the ordinary methods of raising barges from one level to another, and is worked on friendly terms with the railway, under the able management of H. J. Smith, Esq. It is the only portion ever completed of that extensive scheme—the Grand Western Canal, for which an act of parliament was obtained in 1796, and which was intended to have proceeded southward to Topsham, and thus to have opened a direct inland navigation from the English to the Bristol Channel. The situation of this ancient town, on the southern declivity between the Exe and the Loman, over which it had two fords, gave it the name of *Twy-ford*, or *Two-ford-town*, which has since been corrupted to *Tiverton*. The PARISH OF TIVERTON is co-extensive with the Borough, and comprises no less than 16,790 acres of fertile land, picturesquely undulated, and forming an irregularly shaped district, extending in

two directions five miles, and in others one to three miles from the town.   Its total *population* amounted in 1801 to 6505, in 1831 to 9766, and in 1841 to 10,770 souls, of whom 7769 were in the *town*, and the others in the four QUARTERS of the parish, viz., 465 in *Clare;* 740 in *Pitt;* 488 in *Prior's;* and 578 in *Tidcombe.* These quarters contain several hamlets, and many scattered farm-houses, neat villas, &c.   In Pitt Quarter, which extends four miles north, are the small villages of *Chettescombe, Bolham,* and *Cove.*   In Tidcombe Quarter, are the hamlets of *Chevithorne, West and East Mere, Craze-Loman,* and *Manley,* extending two miles east and south-east.   In Clare Quarter are *Palmer's* and *Withleigh* villages, and many scattered houses, extending two miles westward.   In Prior Quarter is the hamlet *Ashley,* the seats of Ashley Court, Ashley House, and Collipriest House, and many scattered houses extending two miles south of the town.   The MANOR OF TIVERTON, which had been part of the royal demesne, was given by Henry I. to the Earl of Devon, who is supposed to have built the *Castle* here about the year 1100.   Edward Courtenay, Earl of Devon, who died in 1419, was a distinguished admiral, and made Tiverton Castle his chief place of residence.   After the battle of Tewksbury, in which the Earl of Devon was slain, in the cause of Henry VI., this manor was seized by the Crown, but was restored to the succeeding Earl of Devon in 1485.   Catherine, widow of William Earl of Devon, and daughter of Edward IV., died at Tiverton Castle in 1517, and a handsome monument was erected to her memory; but this and the other monuments of the Courtenay family, with the chapel which contained them, were destroyed in the civil wars.   In 1643, the royalists drove the parliamentarians from Tiverton.   The Earl of Essex and the King were here with the army in 1644   In Oct., 1645, Sir Gilbert Talbot was governor of Tiverton; but General Massey marched thither from Collumpton, and took possession of the town.   Sir Thomas Fairfax joined the latter on the 18th, and on the following day, the church, castle, and outworks were taken by storm, and Sir Gilbert Talbot, several officers, and 200 privates were taken prisoners.   In December, Sir Thomas Fairfax made Tiverton the head-quarters of his army.   In 1549, during the commotion occasioned by the introduction of the Book of Common Prayer, and the enclosure of the monastic lands, a battle was fought at Cranmore, near Collipriest, between the insurgents and the King's army: the former were soon dispersed, and several of them hanged and quartered.   (See pages 55 and 56.)   Edward VI. gave the manor of Tiverton to the Duke of Somerset, and in 1556 it passed to the heirs of the four sisters of Edward, Earl of Devon.   Their several shares were afterwards sold to various purchasers.   The CASTLE was purchased by Roger Gifford, Esq., and in 1605 was sold to John West, Esq.   In 1728, the castle and six-eighths of the manor and hundred of Tiverton, passed with a co-heiress of the Wests to the Carews, and they now belong, with another eighth of the manor, to Sir W. P. Carew, Bart., but a great part of the parish is freehold, belonging to John Heathcoat, Esq., M.P., of *Bolham House;* J. F. Griffiths, Esq., and many smaller proprietors.   The CASTLE, which

stands on the hill north of the town, was dismantled after the civil wars; but the habitable part of it was afterwards formed into a mansion, for the residence of the Wests, and was occupied by the late Lady Carew. It is now occupied by two families, and near it are some remains of the towers and gateways of the ancient fortress. Tiverton is the head of a large UNION, as noticed at page 303.

It is considered one of the healthiest and principal towns of Devon, and was known by the name of *Twyford* as early as 872. Nearly three centuries ago it had become a principal seat of the woollen manufacture; but it afterwards lost much of its trade, in consequence of repeated calamities by *fire*, in one of which, in 1612, no less than 600 houses were destroyed. The property consumed on these various occasions was immense, and utterly impoverished the inhabitants. In 1625, a *flood* destroyed 53 houses; and the town suffered severely from a great *storm* in 1703. The last calamitous visitations by fire were in 1731, when 298 houses were destroyed, and in 1785 and 1788, when 67 were burnt to the ground. The chief cause of these devastating conflagrations appears to have been the prevalence of straw thatched roofs. In 1731, after the great fire of that year, an *Act* was obtained for the substitution of slated and leaded roofs, and for the rebuilding of the town, and determining differences touching the houses destroyed by the late fire, and for the better prevention of such calamities in future. Acts for *paving, lighting,* and otherwise improving the town, were obtained in the 34th of George III., and the fourth of George IV. Under the act of 1731, the streets were widened, and the new houses regularly built. The *town* has now four principal streets, and is about a mile in length and breadth. The central part of it is between the Exe and the Loman, on the slope of the hill, which rises gently to the north from the angle formed by their confluence. Both streams are crossed by stone bridges, and that over the Exe has a considerable endowment for its support, as afterwards noticed. A stream called the *Town Leat*, which rises about five miles above the town, and still supplies the inhabitants with *water*, was given by Isabel, Countess of Devon, about 1262, and was so contrived as to run through the principal streets. Since 1831, the *Gas Works* at Messrs. Heathcoat's factory have been purchased and enlarged by a company of proprietors, and they now supply many of the shops and houses, and about 90 street lamps, at the rate of 7s. 4d. per 1000 cubic feet. Tiverton is now one of the cleanest and best built towns of its size in the West, and its inhabitants have long been characterised for social intercouse: assemblies and concerts are often held, and many friendly societies, clubs, &c., have been formed for mutual benefit. The town has a Lodge of Free Masons, a Lodge of Odd Fellows, and an Agricultural Society. A spacious *Market Place,* with convenient approaches, was built in 1830; and over the entrance from Fore street, were built at the same time large *Subscription Rooms,* for assemblies, reading, billiards, &c. The reading room is well supplied with newspapers and periodicals; and in the same street are commodious rooms, occupied by the recently formed *Literary and Scientific Institution.* There is a small *Theatre* in

Peter street. *Races* are held about the end of August. Sir W. P. Carew, Bart., is master of the *Tiverton Hunt*, which has a full pack of fine hounds. The *markets*, held every Tuesday and Saturday, are well supplied with provisions, and the former is a considerable market for corn, cattle, &c. There are also *great markets* for cattle four times a year, on one of the Tuesdays in February, April, August, and December. Two *fairs* for cattle, horses, wool, &c., are held on the second Tuesday after Trinity Sunday, and on Michaelmas-day. A market and fair were established here before A.D. 1200. The manufacture of serges, druggets, drapeens, and other woollen goods at Tiverton, began to decline about the year 1740, though in 1790 there were in the town and vicinity 1000 looms and 200 wool combers. Here are now only two *blanket, serge*, and *flannel* manufactories; but in 1815, a large woollen mill, which had been built in 1790, was purchased by *Messrs. Heathcoat and Co.*, who, by extensive additions, converted it into an immense *Lace Manufactory*, which now employs about 1500 men, women, and children. In 1809, they obtained a 14 years' patent for a greatly improved lace or *bobbin net machine*, and built a large factory at Loughborough; but owing to the damage done to their machinery by the *Luddites* of the Midland Counties, they removed to Tiverton, and greatly augmented the prosperity of that town. Their machinery here is chiefly set in motion by a water wheel, 25 feet broad, and 25 feet in diameter, and they have lately commenced a large *iron foundry* in their gigantic establishment.

CORPORATION.—In 1615, James I. granted the inhabitants of Tiverton a charter of incorporation, with the privilege of sending two members to parliament; and in the same year, they built the Town-Hall, on the site of St. Thomas's chapel. The privileges granted by this were confirmed by a charter of the 11th of George I., styling the corporation "the mayor and burgesses of the town and parish of Tiverton," and directing that the common council should consist of the mayor, 12 capital burgesses, and 12 assistants; and that the mayor, ex-mayor, and the recorder, should be justices of the peace. Under the Municipal Reform Act of 1835, the borough is included among those which are to have a commission of the peace, a court of quarter sessions, &c., and is divided into three wards, and placed under the government of the borough magistrates, a recorder, a mayor, six aldermen, and 18 councillors. The income of the old corporation in 1833 was only £116, but its expenditure was £160, the difference being paid by the mayor. In 1841, the expenditure of the borough was £628, and its income £695. The number of burgesses entitled to vote for the two parliamentary representatives of the borough in 1837 was 496. It was formerly a "close borough," 23 being the greatest number polled for 30 years previous to 1831. Its present MEMBERS OF PARLIAMENT are *John Heathcoat, Esq.*, the great lace manufacturer; and *Viscount Palmerston*, the present highly distinguished and talented foreign secretary. The former has represented the borough since 1835, and the latter since 1837. The *Town Hall*, or *Guildhall*, built in 1615, was repaired and modernised in 1788, and has lately been enlarged; but the spacious

Mayoralty Room over the adjoining bank is still retained. A spacious and handsome *Borough Gaol* and *House of Correction* was built in 1845-6, on the model plan of the separate system, at the cost of about £4000. The Borough Court of Record has given place to the *County Court,* held here monthly for all the 27 parishes in Tiverton Union. (See page 303.) John Tyrrell, Esq., is *judge* of this court; T. L. T. Rendell, Esq., *clerk ;* and Mr. Richd. Grant Tucker, *high bailiff.*

The BOROUGH MAGISTRATES are Francis Hole, Robt. Baker, Geo. Coles, Wm. Hole, Wm. Kettle, John Barne, Wm. Dickinson, and John Snell, Esqrs. Mr. Wm. Partridge is their *clerk.*

MAYOR—G. H. Voysey, Esq. || RECORDER—John Tyrrell, Esq.
ALDERMEN—Francis Hole, John Heathcoat, J. F. Quicke, Wm. Hornsey Gamlen, Wm. Talley, and J. W. T. Tucker, Esqrs.

COUNCILLORS.

Castle Ward. (No. 3.)	*Lowman Ward (No.* 2.)	*West Exe Ward. (No.* 1.)
Mr. Thomas Foster	Mr. Geo. D. Cobley	Mr. Richard Snow
„ Joseph Sparkes	„ John Hall	„ Robert Wotton
„ T. W. J. Forward	„ James Crease	„ John Gath
„ Samuel Gath	„ Wm. Richardson	„ John Williams
„ Wm. Smale	„ G. H. Voysey	„ George Cosway
John Burne, M.D.	„ J. S. How	„ — Beedell

Town Clerk —Thos. Hellings. || *Clerk of the Peace*—T. L. T. Rendell.
Coroner—Fredk. Mackenzie. || *Gaoler*—John Radford.
Sergeant at Mace—G. Parkhouse. || *Town Sergeant*—J. Smith.
Police Inspector—Edw. Harford. || *Town Crier*—John Fare.
Inspector of Weights and Measures—James Boyce.

Charity Trustees—Francis Hole, Wm. Kettle, John Heathcoat, Thomas Haydon, George Coles, John Radford, Wm. Chappel, Robt. Were, jun., J. S. How, Theodore Parkhouse, T. C. Haydon, and F. S. Gervis, Esqrs. ; to whom Messrs. Hellings and Son are *clerks.*

The PARISH CHURCH *(St. Peter,)* which has about 1300 sittings, is one of the largest and handsomest parish churches in the county, consisting of a spacious nave, chancel, and side aisles, with a south porch and a lofty tower, containing 8 bells. Though the work of different ages, it is tolerably uniform in style. The aisles are separated by clustered columns and pointed arches, and a rich Gothic screen divides the nave and chancel. The interior was cleansed, repaired, and newly-seated a few years ago, and the altar-piece is a fine painting of "The Wise Men offering to Christ," given by the late Rev. Robt. Hole, in 1841. The exterior of the porch and chapel, erected by John Greenway in the reign of Henry VIII., is richly sculptured with tracery, and subjects taken from scripture history. The porch was rebuilt in 1825, when the sculpture was renewed by Mr. Wm. Beck. In the chapel is a painting of "Peter delivered from Prison by the Angel." A library, bequeathed to the parish by the Rev. J. Newte, is in a room over the vestry. The *Rectory* is in four portions, of which the following are the names, with the incumbents, the number of acres in each, the glebe, and the yearly sums for which the tithes were commuted in 1841 :—*Pitt Portion* (5840A.,) Rev. John Spurway, M.A., £850, the glebe 30 acres ; *Tidcombe Portion* (3920A.,) Rev. W. Rayer, M.A., £757, glebe

90 acres; *Clare Portion* (3550A.,) Rev. J. D. Lloyd, M.A., £568; and *Prior's Portion* (3185A.,) Rev. H. P. Measor, B.A., £400. The tithes of 1155A. in other parts of this extensive parish are commuted for £66, which is divided yearly among the four rectors. King's College, Cambridge, has the patronage of Prior's Portion, and the other three are in the alternate patronage of the Earl of Harrowby, Sir W. P. Carew, and the heirs of the late Sir R. Vyvyan and the late Rev. W. Spurway. Four houses with gardens and a close of 4A. have been vested from an early period for the reparation of the church. ST. GEORGE'S CHURCH, at the west end of Fore street, is a plain structure, with a bell turret. It was commenced in 1714, but not finished till 1730, nor consecrated till 1733. It has several neat monuments, one of which is in memory of Henry Blagdon, Esq., who died in 1716, and gave £150 towards the erection. The four rectors and their curates perform duty here alternately, and also at the three following chapels of ease in other parts of the parish. *Cove Chapel*, in Pitt quarter, is an old dilapidated building, but it is in contemplation to rebuild it. *Withleigh Chapel*, in Clare quarter, 3 miles W. of the town, is a neat building, erected in 1846 by subscription; and a school was built near it in 1849. *Chevithorne Chapel*, in Tidcombe quarter, about 2 miles N.E. of the town, is a handsome fabric, erected in 1843, at the cost of about £2000, of which £1500 was given by the Rev. Wm. Rayer, rector of this portion of the parish. There were formerly several ancient chapels in the town, and in other quarters of the parish, but few traces of them are now extant. On the western side of the town is a small *Roman Catholic Chapel*, built in 1838. The *Baptist Chapel*, in Newport street, was built in 1730, on the site of one built about 1687. The *Independent Chapel*, in Peter street, is a large stone building, erected in 1831-2, at the cost of £4683, including the cost of the land, and the school and minister's house. There is another *Independent Chapel*, in Elmore street, built in 1843, at the cost of £750. The *Wesleyan Chapel*, in Peter street, was built in 1814; and in Andrew street is a small *Bible Christian Chapel*, erected in 1843. These chapels have been mostly erected in lieu of old ones. There was a Presbyterian Chapel here as early as 1672, and the ancient chapel of St. Peter was occupied by Independents, in 1687. John Wesley himself opened a chapel here in 1750. *Sunday Schools, Religious Societies*, &c., are liberally supported here by the congregations of the churches and chapels, and the parish has several endowed schools and many valuable charities.

In 1803, *Mary Marshall* left £200 five per cent. Bank Annuities, in trust that one-half of the yearly dividends should be applied in clothing poor children attending the Sunday school; and that the other half should be divided among the two *sextons* and four *rodmen* of the parish church, except what was necessary for keeping her tomb in repair.

To provide a fund for repairing *St. George's Church* and her tomb in the church-yard, MARY PEARD in 1769 gave a farm of 65A. at Awliscombe, and the sum of £1000. The latter, with savings of income, has been invested in the purchase of £1600 three per cent. consols; and the farm is let for about £80 a year.

The Independent Chapel, in Peter street, called *Steps Meeting-house,* has an endowment for the support of the minister, amounting to £56. 18s. per annum, arising from land, house, and stock, left by Thomas and Joan Keene, Thos. Enchmarsh, John Tristram, Eliza Lichigaray, and Mrs. F. Warren. The *Baptist Chapel* has an endowment of 20s. a year for the poor of the congregation, and about £55 a year for the use of the minister, arising from property left by Thos. Glass, M.D., Richd. Hooper, and other donors. The minister's house and garden were given in 1810 by Faith Chorlock, together with two cottages.

BLUNDELL'S GRAMMAR SCHOOL, &c.—*Peter Blundell,* by his will in 1599, directed his executors to lay out £2400 in the purchase of land, and the erection thereon of a school-house and offices for the accommodation of a master, usher, and about 150 scholars ; the latter to be boys not above 18, nor under six years of age, born or for the most part brought up in the parish of Tiverton. For the maintenance of the said *Free Grammar School,* he devised all his lands and tenements in Devonshire to 27 trustees, and directed them to pay yearly salaries of £50 to the master and 20 marks to the usher, on condition that they should teach the scholars without any charge to their parents or friends. He also directed £20 a year to be applied in *apprenticing* four poor boys in husbandry ; and he ordered his executors to bestow £2000 in establishing *six scholarships* for students of divinity from this school at Oxford or Cambridge. Mr. Blundell, the liberal founder of this school, raised himself by his own industry from the rank of a poor clothier to that of a rich merchant, and often said that, though he was no scholar himself, he would be the means of making many. In 1678, *Jno. Ham* gave £200 towards the maintenance of a scholar from this school at Oxford or Cambridge. In 1783, *Benj. Gilberd* left £2000 three per cent. stock to be applied for the benefit of this school at the discretion of the trustees. In 1806, *Richd. Down* transferred £700 three per cent. consols to the mayor and corporation, in trust to pay the dividends towards the support of a scholar from this school at one of the Universities. In 1715, certain lands were left by *John Newte* to Baliol College, Oxford, for the support of a scholar there, to be chosen out of Blundell's school by the four rectors of Tiverton. The property now belonging to the school produces an annual income of about £650, of which more than £210 arises from the dividends of stock. Out of this income, the following yearly salaries are paid, viz. :—£60 to the master, £20 to the usher, and £14 to the treasurer. The *school buildings* are well adapted for a large establishment. The master, who has the care of the upper school, has a house capable of accommodating about 100 boarders, with a garden and meadow. The usher, who instructs the lower school, has a garden and a house capable of containing 40 boarders. This school was formerly in high repute, and had often from 50 to 100 boarders, but no boarders have been admitted since 1847, and there are now only about 60 free scholars. The sum of £2750, derived from Peter Blundell's will, was laid out in estates, vested with Baliol College, Oxford, and Sidney Sussex College, Cambridge, for the maintenance of four *fellows* and four *scholars.* In addition to their emoluments derived from the colleges, the four scholars receive an allowance of £30 each per ann. from the funds of this charity ; as also does another scholar and two exhibitioners under Gilberd's gift. The exhibitioner under Ham's gift receives £23 a year. The trustees expend large sums in repairing the school buildings, &c., and about £26 a year in apprenticing 4 poor boys.

CHILCOTT'S FREE SCHOOL, &c.—*Robt. Comyn,* alias *Chilcott,* by will in 1609, directed his executors to build a school-house at the cost of £400, and vest it with thirteen trustees, to whom he left a yearly rent-charge of £90,

to be applied as follows, viz.:—£20 to the schoolmaster for teaching the poor boys of Tiverton; £2 for repairing the school; £3 to the clerk for keeping the accounts of his charity; £16. 10s. for 15 poor people of Tiverton; £15 for 15 poor artificers; £19. 10s. to provide weekly, 6d. each in bread and money for 15 poor parishioners; £10 towards repairing the church; and £1 towards repairing the highway to Butterleigh mill. This rent-charge, after deducting £12 for land tax, is paid by the Duke of Leeds out of lands in Yorkshire. In 1790, *Benj. Gilberd* left £300 for the augmentation of the schoolmaster's salary, and it was laid out in the purchase of £332. 7s. 11d. three per cent. consols. In 1802, *Richd. Davis* left £50 to be applied in buying books for six of the most deserving scholars. With this sum £75 three per cent. consols were purchased. There is also belonging to the charity £100 of the same stock, purchased with savings of income in 1802. The *school* is in Peter street, where there is a house and garden for the master, who teaches reading and writing to 100 boys on the National system. He has a yearly salary of £20, and is allowed 2s. 6d. per quarter for each of the boys for pens, ink, and paper. All the boys pay 6d. entrance money, and those who learn arithmetic 1s. 6d. per quarter. Two almswomen, in Birchen lane, have 3s. a week from Chilcott's Charity.

The CHARITY SCHOOLS, formerly in the Church yard, now occupy commodious buildings in Frog street, built in 1841. These schools, where 50 boys and 50 girls are educated, and clothed in blue, were established in 1713, and were at first supported by subscriptions and collections at sermons, but they have now an endowment yielding a clear annual income of about £290, arising as follows:—£90 from Great Holwell and Hare Hill farms (115A.,) purchased with £1000, left in 1715 by *Henry Blagdon; £7* from 26A. at Collumpton, and other property, left in 1719 by *Peter Newte;* £30 from 28A. at Ashley, left in 1724 by *John Tristram;* £93 from £210 Old South Sea Annuities, and a farm of 59A. called Middleway, derived from the bequest of *Mary Peard*, in 1777; and £4. 5s. 2d. from £106 10s. 6d. four per cent. stock, purchased with £100, left by *Benj. Gilberd,* in 1792. About 30 children of either sex are admitted in consideration of these benefactions, by the respective trustees, and every annual subscriber of £3 has the nomination of two scholars. They are clothed once a year, and the girls make their own clothes and the caps, shirts, and stockings for the boys. The master has about £54, and the mistress £26 per annum, and they have each a dwelling-house; and fuel, books, stationery, bibles, prayer books, &c., are provided by the trustees.

The NATIONAL SCHOOL, in St. Andrew street, is a large and handsome building in the Swiss style, erected in 1844, at the cost of about £2000, and having dwellings for the master and mistress in the centre, and school rooms on either side, attended by about 140 boys and 80 girls. The BRITISH SCHOOL, in Leat street, adjoining the large factory of Messrs. Heathcoat and Co., is a spacious and handsome structure, in the Elizabethan style, built in 1844 by John Heathcoat, Esq., M.P., and solely supported by him. It has three school rooms for boys, girls, and infants, and the Committee of Council of Education have lately appointed 14 pupil teachers to assist the master and two mistresses. It is attended by 180 boys, 150 girls, and 240 infants. There is another large and handsome BRITISH SCHOOL, in Elmore street, built in 1848 by Ambrose Brewin, Esq., and entirely supported by him, for the education of about 100 boys and 50 girls, under a master, mistress, and six pupil teachers. The *Infant School,* in Bampton street, was also built by A. Brewin, Esq., in 1847, and is supported by him, and attended by 100 children.

Village Schools, &c.:—The rector of Tidcombe pays £3 a year to

schoolmistress at *Cove,* for teaching 12 children to read. This sum arises from one-eighth of the rent of Buckhays farm, left by the *Rev. John Newte,* in 1715. About £4 a year is distributed in bibles and prayer books among the poor parishioners, as one half of the rent of Bible Field, given by the same donor. For instructing ten poor children of *Chevithorne,* and providing them with books, about £5 a year is paid out of Pleshy's and Whitedown farm, (130A.) as one-eighth of the rent of that estate, left by *Peter Newte,* in 1719. Though the land is poor, a much larger share ought to be paid to the four rectors, as trustees of this charity.

The proceeds of the seven following CHARITIES, amounting to about £100 per annum, are distributed by the *Borough Charity Trustees,* appointed under the powers of the Municipal Act, for the management of all the charities vested with the Corporation. The ELMORE LANDS, (16A.) were held of the Crown at a nominal rent, from 1806 till 1837, but they were sold in the latter year, and all that now remains of this once valuable charity are the dividends of £250 navy five per cent. stock. It is said that Elmore was given by *Madam Elson de Rosse,* in 1250, to remain for ever a common for the use of the poor parishioners; and that it formerly comprised 150A. It was afterwards seized by the Crown, and part of it granted on lease for the benefit of the poor, who, in 1837, vainly petitioned for a renewal of the lease. *John Berry,* in 1618, gave a house and 15A. of land, at West Chevithorne, to the Corporation, in trust to pay yearly 50s. each to two labourers, one weaver and a fuller, and to apply the rest of the income to their own use. This estate now yields a clear annual rent of about £35. In 1623, another *John Berry* left to the Corporation £60, to be invested in land, for the relief of the poor. The land purchased was sold to the Canal Company, in 1814, for £250, which was laid out in the purchase of £267 navy five per cents. The sum of £100, given by *Daniel Cudmore* and *Geo. Hartnoll,* in 1637 and 1662, was laid out in the purchase of 4A. of land, now let for about £13. In 1663, *Thomas Leigh* left to the Mayor and burgesses all his eighth part of the market tolls of Tiverton, in trust for the relief of the most indigent poor of the borough. This gift yields about £22 per annum. In 1747, the Corporation laid out £115 poor's money in the purchase of 2A. of land, called *The Shillands,* now let for about £12 per annum. The poor have 1s. worth of bread weekly from *Sir John Acland's Charity.* (See Exeter.)

GREENWAY's CHARITY:—In 1529, *John Greenway* founded an ALMSHOUSE here for five poor men, and endowed it with property then worth only £8. 13s. per annum, but now yielding about £270 a year, including £60 a year, paid in consideration of the old parish Workhouse, and £27. 10s. derived from the seat rents in Greenway's chapel in St. Peter's church. The charity property comprises also a farm at Dipford, let for £52. 10s., and seven houses, and various parcels of land in Tiverton. The almshouses, in Gold street, have been several times repaired and enlarged, and the number of almspeople increased, in proportion to the augmented value of the endowment. The principal management of the charity rests with the town churchwarden, the fourteen trustees never interfering, except in the granting of leases. There are at present on the foundation 25 almsmen, who have a yearly supply of coals. They are paid weekly stipends, varying from 5s. to 2s. 7d. each.

WALDRON's ALMSHOUSES, in Wellbrook street, were built for the reception of eight poor men, by John Waldron, who endowed them, in 1577, with a yearly rent charge of £24, out of the manor of Daccombe. The eight almsmen are appointed by the churchwardens, and each has a weekly

stipend of 1s. They have also divided among them £5 a year from *Enchurch's Gift.*

SLEE'S ALMSHOUSES, in Peter street, were founded in 1610, for six poor widows, or aged maidens, by *George Slee,* who left £500 for their erection and endowment. The endowment is a yearly rent charge of £20, out of the rectory of Coldridge, and from it each almswoman has 1s. per week. The churchwardens are the trustees, and the almswomen have each a further weekly allowance of 1s. from the dividends of £360 navy five per cent. stock, left by *Mary Marshall,* in 1803. The residue of these dividends is divided among the most necessitous poor parishioners, according to the donor's will.

JOHN LANE, in 1679, left 10A. of land, at Buckland, in Somersetshire, (now let for about £30,) and a yearly rent charge of £12. 10s. out of an estate called Slade, at Sheldon. Agreeable to the donor's will, the yearly proceeds are applied as follows:—20s. in bibles for poor boys of Chilcott's school; about £22 in distributions of clothing to six poor people of Tiverton, and two of Collumpton; 3s. per month to each of the said eight poor people; and about £3. 3s. for an annual dinner for them and the trustees. Twenty poor men of Tiverton have 9s. 6d. each yearly, from a rent charge of £9. 10s., left by ROBT. CHATTEY, about 1680, out of a house called Priddice's Tenement. Thirty-two aged poor of the town have divided among them £3. 6s. per annum, arising from six chief rents, purchased with £70 left by WM. HEWITT, in 1689. JOHN ALSTONE, in 1696, left an almshouse and adjoining tenements for six poor shearmen, and £500 to be invested for the use of the general poor of Tiverton. Owing to the mismanagement of former trustees, all that now remains of this charity is part of the almshouse occupied by three poor fullers, and a reserved rent of 7s. 6d. per annum. MARY RICE, in 1697, left the residue of her real and personal property, to be vested in trust, and the yearly proceeds to be distributed in sums of 40s. each among her poor relations of the families of Morrish, Lane, and Tanner, or in default of such, among the honest and pious poor parishioners of Tiverton. The property belonging to this charity now yields an annual income of about £180, arising as follows— £120 from Rix farm, (50A.) at Bolham; £31 from the White Bull Inn; £12. 10s. from the Bampton turnpike, and the rest from the interest of money. The clear income is distributed half-yearly among about 80 poor people, appointed by the trustees, who give a preference to the relations of the foundress. In 1785, MARY MARSHALL left for the poor of Tiverton £100, which was laid out in the purchase of £100 navy five per cent. stock. The dividends are distributed in sums of 2s. or 3s. In 1790, BENJAMIN GILBERD left £1000 to be invested in stock, and the yearly dividends to be distributed at Christmas, among the poor not receiving parochial relief. This charity now consists of £1090 three per cent. consols. In 1808, RICHARD DOWN gave £500 three per cent. consols, in trust that 20s. worth of bread should be distributed fifteen times a year among the poor, after the administration of the Sacrament in St. Peter's church and St. George's chapel.

WALTER TYRRELL, in 1568, left £200 to be invested for the use of the poor, by John Waldron, who, in consideration thereof, granted a yearly rent charge of £10. 13s. out of the manor of Daccombe, to be applie by the churchwardens in weekly sums of 8d. each to six poor people. ROBERT REED, in 1621, left £100 to provide for a weekly distribution of 3s. worth of bread among twelve poor people. The Mayor and burgesses applied this money for the redemption of the Town House, out of which they pay £7. 10s. yearly, in satisfaction of this charity. RICHARD HILL, in 1630,

left to the Mayor and burgesses an annuity of £12. 2s. 8d., for the weekly distribution of 4d. worth of bread each to fourteen poor parishioners. Out of this rent charge £1. 14s. 8d. is deducted for land tax, and the rest is distributed among twelve poor people. It is paid out of three closes, two of which are called Lowman and Alsabrook meadows. EDW. BLAGDON, in 1653, granted four houses and a garden and orchard, in Barrington street, to four trustees, for the equal benefit of two poor men of Tiverton, and two of Washfield parish. These premises were burnt down in 1832, and rebuilt in 1833-4, and now yield a clear yearly profit of about £17. A house and two acres of land, left by JOHN LOVELL, in 1673, are let for £21 a year, and one-fourth of the rent belongs to the poor of Tiverton, and three-fourths to the poor of Bickleigh. PETER ATKINS, in 1657, granted a yearly rent charge of £10 to the poor of Tiverton, out of an estate called Padcott and Burridge. For many years the overseers improperly applied this annuity in aid of the poor rates. The poor parishioners have also £10, and the trustees 10s. yearly, left by GREGORY SHORLAND, in 1658, out of an estate, called Bengewall. Six poor people of Clare Quarter, and four of Prior's Quarter, have 15s., and the trustees 5s. yearly, left by THOMAS MAUNDER, in the 24th of Charles II., out of land at Querk-Hill.

EXE BRIDGE TRUST comprises 32 houses, with gardens, &c., which were let on leases for two or three lives, at rents which amounted, in 1820, to only £18. 5s. 8d., though their real value was then upwards of £300 per annum ; but, as the leases expire, the trustees now let the property at rack rent. Part of this property was vested in trust by *Walter Tyrrell* and Johan, his wife, in 1563, who directed that the yearly proceeds should be applied, as far as necessary, in repairing West Exe Bridge, in Tiverton, and that the surplus, if any, should be distributed among the poor parishioners. Of the houses now in existence, some were rebuilt after the fire in 1785, and the remainder after a similar calamity in 1794. About 30 years ago, upwards of £1500 was expended in repairing and widening the bridge, and, until recently, the poor derived but little benefit from the charity.

MARKET TRUST.—By the gifts of *John West* in 1628, *Wm. Spurway* in 1650, and *Sir John* and *Mr. Jonathan Trelawney* in 1654, several houses and gardens, and seven-eighths of the market tolls of Tiverton, were vested with trustees for the benefit of the poor parishioners. The market-house was built on the site of a house which was burnt down in 1731, and the site of it and several adjoining houses is held by the trustees on a lease for 1000 years, at the annual rent of £30. The market-house and seven-eighths of the tolls produce about £196 yearly, besides which the trustees derive £29 from the rents of eight houses, let on 99 years' leases. The net income, amounting to about £167 per annum, is dispensed in weekly doles of bread to about 120 poor parishioners.

TIVERTON DIRECTORY.

Those marked 1, are at Angel hill ; 2, in Bampton st ; 3, Barrington st ; 4, Bridge st ; 5, Chapel st ; 6, Fore st ; 7, Gold st ; 8, Leat st ; 9, Newport st ; 10, St Peter st ; 11, Wellbrook st ; 12, WEST EXE ; 13, CLARE QUARTER ; 14, PITT ; 15, PRIOR'S ; 16, TIDCOMBE QUARTER ; 17, Palmer's ; 18, Quack hill ; 19, Withleigh ; 20, Chevithorne ; 21, Chettescombe ; 22, Craze-Loman ; 23, at Loman-Green ; and 24, in St Andrew st

The POST-OFFICE is in Fore street, and Miss Emiline Tucker is the postmistress. Letters received and despatched several times a day, and money orders granted and paid from 9 morning till 5½ evening

Aldred Mr Thomas, St Peter's st
1 Anstey Thomas, clerk

6 Aplin Hugh, fellmonger & glover
Baker Robert, Esq. *Collipriest*

o 2

Barne John, Esq., Hammet's square
Barne Mrs My. & Misses, New pl
Bater Mr John, Bampton street
12 Battiscombe Peter, bank clerk
4 Beck George, accountant
9 Beck Thomas Wm. vestry clerk
Beedel Mr John, Bampton street
Berridge Mrs Grace, Andrew st
Besley Mrs Eliz. Ann, Bampton st
Besley Miss Elizabeth, St Peter st
Binney Mrs Anna, Terrace
Blundell Miss Elizabeth, Fore st
7 Boyce Gideon Acland, architect
10 Boyce Jas. supt. of Gas Works, and inspr. of weights & measures
Brewin Ambrose, Esq. *Exeleigh Hs*
Browne Rev John, St Peter street
Buck Rev John Henry, M.A.
Burne John, M.D., St Peter street
2 Carew Misses Ann, Chte.&Dorothea
Carew Thomas, Esq. *Collipriest Hs*
Carpendale Mrs. *Hensley House*
Casey Rev Wm. (Cathlc.) Molton rd
Channon Benj. Jph. station master
Chesney Mrs Sophia, Peter street
11 Chorley John, bird preserver
Clarke Mrs Eliz., St Peter street
2 Clarke Samuel, rope & twine mkr
Cleeve Mr Wm., Twyford place
Clutterbuck Mrs Fanny
Cole George, Esq., St Peter street
Collard Jane, stay maker, Andrew st
Collard Joseph and Eliza, master and matron of *Workhouse*
Cornwall John, Workhouse school
12 Cosway Geo. & Co. woollen mfrs
Cosway Miss Mary, Bampton street
1 Coward Charles Toogood, gent
Crawford John S. railway clerk
Daniel Mr Thos. D., *Collipriest*
Dickens Misses, Gold street
Dickenson Wm., Esq. *Howden Hs*
6 Dunsford Hy. sen. & jun. Esq.
Dunsford Capt Wm. & Walter, gent., *Ashley Court*
Fagan Mrs Elizabeth, St Peter st
Fare John, town crier, Gold street
Follard Mrs Mary, Lowman green
Foster Mrs Mary, St Peter street
7 Fraser John, railway superintendt
16 Gale Mrs Grace and 20 Mr John
Gamlen Wm. Horsey, Esq., *Hayne Hs*
12 Gath John, relieving officer
10 Gibbs Miss Mary Matilda
12 Gillard Robert, clothes broker
Glanvill Mr Samuel, Twyford place
Gloyns Mrs Mary, Peter street
6 Gould Wm. letter carrier
Govett Misses, St Peter street
6 Hanmer Rev Anthy. Jno., B.A., curate
6 Harford Edw. police inspector
5 Harwood James, carrier
2 Hawke Wm. T., bank manager
Hawkins Mrs G., Twyford place
Haydon Thomas, gent. *Castle*
8 Heathcoat John & Co., lace mfrs. and ironfounders (and *London*)
Heathcoat John, Esq., M.P. *Bolham Hs*
Heathfield Mr Thos., *Stoodleigh*
Hellings Thos., Esq. *Great Howden*
2 Hippisley Joseph, furniture broker
Hobbs Mr Nicholas, West Exe
Hodge Mr Wm. Bartlet, Causeway
Hodge Wm. Hy., Esq. *Park villa*
Hodges Mrs Frances, *Castle*
Hole Fras., Esq. *Collipriest Cottage*
Hole Wm., Esq. *Clare House*
Hopgood Mr Jph. *West Exe Villa*
Hughes Rev John Bickley, M.A.
6 Hutchinson Wm. clothier
12 Jackson Edw. Wm. coach builder
James Fras. gent. *Brunswick Cottage*
James Reginald, Esq. and Mrs E. S., *Ashley House*
10 Jamieson James, tea dealer, &c
Kettle Wm., M.D. *Bartlet House*
Langdon Charles B., Esq., Peter st
12 Lardner Misses Maria & Lucy
Lawson Robert, Esq., Fore street
Ley Rev John, *Island House*
4 Lloyd Rev John Daniel, A.M., rector of Clare portion
10 Madgin Rev Henry (Independent)
Mathew Mr Thos., St Andrew st
10 Mayward Captain Joseph, R.N.
2 Measor Rev Henry Paul, B.A. rector of Prior portion
Melhuish Mrs Elizabeth, West Exe
Mills Mr Wm., Barrington street
2 Morrish John, timber merchant
Newton Mrs My. Ann, Twyford pl
16 Noyes Hy. C., Esq. *Canal Cottage*
10 Osbourn Rev John (Wesleyan)
13 Owen Geo. W., Esq. *Bickenwell*
8 Parish Thomas, stone mason, &c
Parkhouse Geo. sergeant-at-mace
10 Parkin John, horse letter
5 Parr Sarah, stay maker
8 Payne Samuel, umbrella maker
Penfold Captain Edward, Gold st

12 Pepperell Wm. tea dealer, &c
20 Perry Samuel, sexton
Phillott John, sweep, Town end
Pike Rev Wm. (Indpt.) Chapel st
Pridd Mrs Jane, *Chettescombe*
Radford John, govr. of the Gaol
Rayer Rev Wm., M.A. rector of Tid-
    combe portion, *Tidcombe House*
7 Reeves Wm, wireworker & tuner
Riddell Mrs L. *Bickenwell*
24 Roberton Col. Peter Taylor
Rossiter John, gent. Newport street
Row Mrs Joan, *Walrond House*
Row Wm. North, Esq. *Cove House*
10 Scott John, dyer, and Mrs Jane
Sellick Mr Jas. || 12 Sharland Miss
Singleton Rev John (Independent)
Slater Har., Workhouse schoolmrs
Smale Wm. gent. *Rus-in-Urbe Villa*
9 Smith John, sergeant-at-mace
2 Snow Richard, brewer & maltster
8 Snow Wm. tallow chandler
Spurway Mr Hy. Hill, St Andrew st
Spurway Rev John, M.A., rector of
    Pitt portion, St Andrew street
Stevenson John, supt. of lace mills
10 Summers Mrs Mary Ann
Talley Thos. Ballamy, Esq. *Prescott Hs*
Talley Wm. gent. & Mrs Fras. Ann
10 Teschemaker Fdk. Thos. Emanuel,
    D.C.L. ; & Jno., Esq., Hammet's sq
Tidbald Mrs Ellen, Twyford place
Toms Rev Wm. curate, *Bradley down*
6 Tucker Miss Emiline, postmistress
6 Tucker Mr John Wm.
13 Tucker John, quarry owner
14 Turner John, millwright
Vickery —, police constable
Voyser Mrs., St Andrew street
Walker Miss Fanny, St Peter st
Wallen Mr John, Frog street
14 Walrond Benj. Esq. *Knightshay*
Warren Mr Wm., Gold street
Waterman Captain Samuel, Leat st
Webb Rev Edward (Bapt.,) Frog st
Webber John, umbrella maker
10 Webber Peter W., traveller
8 Wedden Robert and James, gents
Welland Miss Emily, St Peter st
14 Williams Capt., Court place
Wills Mr Robert, *Chettescombe*
Wood James, accountant, Broad ln
Wood Mrs Mary, St Andrew street
Worth John Fras., Esq. *Worth Hs*
Worth Miss, *Beauchamp*

Wyatt Mr John, Frog street
3 Yates George Kirk, dep. registrar
6 Yeo John, billiard table keeper

ACADEMIES.
*Marked * take Boarders.*
*Beck Sarah & Eliz., Exe square
Blundell's School, Lowman gn.,Rev J.
    B. Hughes,M.A.&Rev J.H.Buck,M.A.
British Schools, John North Single-
    ton, Ellen Davis, and Sophia Pugh,
    Leat street ; George Pugh, Elmore
    st ; & Thirza H. Bater, Bampton st
*Browne Thos. & Mrs., Barrington st
Burton Elizabeth, St Peter street
Capron George, St Peter street
Charity School, Frog st., Jno. Quicke
    and Eliz. Sharland
*Chesney Sophia, St Peter street
Chilcott's School,StPeter st.Rt.Perkins
Follard Wm. (writing,) Lowman grn
*Frost Misses, Kiddel's court
Hancock Harriet, Fore street
Hewett Jane, Barrington street
Hill Louisa, Bampton street
*Mead Francis, Fore street
Mugford Jane, *Tidcombe*
National School, StAndrew st., James
    Middleton and Ann Thayer

ATTORNEYS.
Adney Richard, Fore street
Comins Richd., Exebridge House
Dunsford Francis, St Peter street
Dunsford Henry, Fore street
10 Forwood Thomas Weech Jones
12 Hellings Thomas (and town clk)
How John Shuckburgh, *Lodge*
Loosemore John, Fore street
Owen John Jones, St Peter street
2 Partridge Wm. (& clerk to borough
    magistrates)
24 Patch Frdk. Owen ; h *Broomfield*
2 Rendell Thos. Leigh Teale (clerk of
    peace, and union & county court)
2 Sharland Arthur Cruwys (clerk to
    county magistrates)
2 Strong Charles Blundell
Tripp Wm. Upton, St Andrew st
Toms John Anstey, Gold street
Tucker Richard Grant, Fore street
Wotton James Dennis & Robt., *Gilgal
    House*

BANKS.
6 Dunsford, Barne, & Co. (Tiverton
    Bank,) draw on Sir J. W. Lub-
    bock and Co.

2 National Provincial Bank of England (on London and Westminster Bank,) W. T. Hawke, *manager*

2 *Savings' Bank* (branch of Devon and Exeter,) A.C.Sharland,*actuary*

BRICK & TILE MKRS.&DEALRS.

Beck David, *Elmore*

Goodland Jno. Viney & Co., Railway

Goodland Wm. Chas. & Co., Canal

10 Hartley Richard Walker (& slate)

Quant John and Co., Tiverton road

2 Sparks James, *Town's end*

FARMERS. (* are Owners.)
See also Dairymen.

15*Anstey Wm., *Juryhayes*
17 Baker Wm. ‖ **14** Bere John
15*Beedell Thomas, Southwood
15 Bennett John, Well farm
13 Besley Geo., North Sidborough
13*Besley John, West Sidborough
15 Besley James and James, jun.
13 Besley Wm., Morgan's wood
13 Bidgood Thomas, Way farm
Body Maria, Chevithorne
16 Bowden Eli ‖ **15** Bowring Wm.
13 Browson Roger, Little Bradley
18*Carpenter James; & **19***Richard
19*Carpenter Wm. & **13** Thos. & Mrs
14 Channing John, Landrake
16 Chapple Wm. (and land agent)
13 Chubb Wm. ‖ **15** Clapp John
Cook Nathaniel, *Craze Loman*
16 Cook Robert, *Chevithorne Barton*
16 Cosway Wm. ‖ **15** Cox Robert
13 Dainty Wm. ‖ **15** Davey Sarah
13 Davey Wm. ‖ **16** Densham Geo.
14 Dinham Robert ‖ **13** Elstone Sml
13 Elworthy Wm., *Dapaller*
13 Evett Wm. ‖ Ferris Samuel
14 Ferris Jacob ‖ **13** Ferris Thomas
14 Ferris Wm. ‖ **15** Finch Thomas
14 Forwood John ‖ **16** Frost Edwd.
16 Gale Henry ‖ **20***Gale John
16 Gale Thomas ‖ **14** Garnsey Wm.
16 Glending John ‖ **16** Hancon Rt.
14 Hawkins Wm. & Benj., Marsh
Haydon Frederick, *Higher Pit*
14 Haydon Robt. & Thomas, jun
*Haydon Robt. C., Chettescombe Hs
Haydon Thomas, *Castle Barton*
Hodge John, *Withleigh Mill*
Hole Thomas, *Cold Harbour*
Hooper Emanuel, *East Barton*
15 Jeffery Robert ‖ **15** Jerman Wm.
15 King Wm. ‖ **15** Comins Thos.

14 Knowman John ‖ **15** Lee Thos.
16 Luxton John ‖ **16** Mildon Robt.
13 Mallett Thomas ‖ **15** Manning Jno.
14 Miles Thos. ‖ **16** Middled Thos.
*Munday John, *West Manley*
14 Newton Peter ‖ **15** Nerle Wm.
13 Norris Robert ‖ **13** Norris Wm.
14 Parkin George ‖ **14** Northam Wm.
13*Payne Thomas ‖ **14** Podbury Jno.
21 Poole James ‖ **20** Poole James
15 Ponsford Thomas ‖ **13** Pope Wm.
16 Pretty Sarah ‖ **14** Pyne John
15 Redwood Hugh ‖ **13** Rice Wm.
16*Richards John ‖ **14** RobertsHugh
14 Roberts Michael, and Wm.
15 Sangar Wm. ‖ **14** Sharland Rd.
16 Skinner Geo. ‖ **16** Skinner Thos.
14 Snow John ‖ **14** Snow Isaac
14 Steer James ‖ **15** Stiling John
15 Taylor Isaac, and **15** Thomas
16 Taylor Wm. and Henry, *Horsdon*
15 Thorne George ‖ **16** Tapscott Mr
15 Thorne Robt. ‖ **15** Trude John
16 Trude Thomas ‖ **15** Trude Wm.
15 Veysey Mrs., *White Hall*
16 Veysey Richard ‖ **15** Upton Ann
14*Walters Wm. ‖ **13** Warren Sarah
16*Were Benj. ‖ **14** Were Benj
13 Were Henry ‖ **14** Were Robert
16 Were Wm. ‖ Were Robert, jun
14 Whither John ‖ **16** Williams John
15*Wright Fredk. ‖ **15** Wreford Geo.

FIRE AND LIFE OFFICES.

Albion Life, Rd. Comins, Exe Bridge Hs
6 Atlas, John Wills and F. Boyce
7 Agricultural Cattle, J. A. Toms
7 Clerical, Medical, and General, G.L. Sanders
6 County & Provdt., J. W. Tucker
7 Crown, Thos. Haydon and **14** Robt. Were
6 Freemasons' Life, W. Melhuish
6 Imperial, J. Tucker and Son
10 Law, Thos. W. J. Forwood
6 Legal & Comml., Paul Havill
9 Merts. & Tradsmn.'s, T. W. Beck
6 Mitre Life, Richard Adney
2 Norwich Union, T. L. T. Rendell
2 Phœnix & Pelican, Wm. Partridge
6 Promoter, T. Parkhouse
2 Scotland, Walter Frost
7 Star, G. W. Cockram
6 Sun, Theodore Parkhouse
6 Temperance, &c. Thomas Holmes
6 Union, Francis Boyce

Universal, Thomas Foster
West of England, F. O. Patch
HOTELS, INNS, & TAVERNS.
1 Angel Hotel, Benj. Joseph Cannon
3 Barley Mow, Thomas Cottrell
3 Barrington Bell, James Jesson
9 Black Horse, Charlotte Craze
2 Boar's Head, Sarah and John Body
16 Canal Inn, Elizabeth Davey
24 Country House, Jane Hooper
7 Cross Keys, Jane Easterbrook
12 Dolphin, Wm. Jones
5 Elmore Bell, James Shopland
1 Exe Bridge Inn, Wm. Hopkins
12 Exeter Inn, John Hill
1 Fountain, Mary Blacker
Fox & Hounds, W. Towell, *Bolham*
12 Golden Lion, Wm. Hooper
6 Half Moon, John Chattey
King's Arms, M. Beer, St Andrew st
9 Lamb, Wm. Shaddock
2 Market House, John Tongue
15 New Inn, Ann Upton, Bickleigh Bdg
7 New Inn, Emily Whippie
11 New Inn, Robert Reed
2 New Bampton Inn, George Way
5 Phœnix, John Broom
12 Prince Blucher, George Reed
Prince Regent, Jas. Baker, Lowmangn
Queen's Head, Hy. Warren, Frog st
11 Race Horse, James Sayer
3 Red Lion, Thomas Warren
2 Rising Sun, Robert Borrough
17 Rose and Crown, Chpr. Vickery
9 Royal Oak, George Taylor
4 Seven Stars, John Frost
Ship, Mary Snook, Bampton st
Swan, Thomas Ford, *West Exe*
6 Three Tuns Hotel, Grace Hawkes
4 White Ball Inn, Samuel Besley
7 White Horse Inn, John Goodland
19 Withleigh Inn, John Bennett
8 Worth Arms, Richard Pearse
SURGEONS.
Beedell John, jun., Fore street
Coward James Ayres, Peter street
Gervis Fredk. Sharland, Peter st
Lamotte Alex. Gallye, Newport st
McDonald Donald, Peter street
Mackenzie Fdk., Hammet's square
Quicke John Fraine, Fore street
Reed Walter Hugo, Hammet's sq

ARTISTS.
10 Capron George
Fare G., Beck's sq

AUCTIONEERS.
9 Beck Thos. Wm.
6 Chattey John

6 Foster Thomas
3 Say Richard
2 Wackrill Uriah
BAKERS.
12 Beedell Thos.
12 Besley Thos.
5 Boobier Thos.
12 Bowden Hy. C.
12 Chapple Wm.
7 Clapp John
2 Clark Henry
12 Curwood Ncls.
7 Denham Mary
Gunner James
5 Gunner John
12 Hole Wm.
7 Lock Wm.
2 Paris Joel & Eliz.
4 Pitt James Wm.
6 Risdon Hugh T.
2 Symons Herman
24 Tongue John
7 Voysey George
6 Ward John
2 Wynn Robert
BASKET MAKERS.
Duckham John
1 Mudford Wm.
8 Voysey Thomas
BEERHOUSES.
5 Boobier Philip
12 Burt Philip
5 Candy George
12 Curwood Nchls
16 Dinham Robert
11 Fey Wm.
8 Gould Henry
5 Harvey George
2 Pinkstone Ts. D.
20 Sydenham Jas.
14 Turner Eliz.
18 Webber John
8 Wright Wm.
BERLIN WOOL
DEALERS.
2 Brewer Mary
6 Hancock C. & My
10 Payne Mary
BLACKSMITHS.
9 Dunsford John
12 Gibbins Richd.
14 Gibbens Henry
11 Ganfield Henry
18 Guscott Joshua
2 Harvey John

8 Harvey Wm.
8 Pool Robert
Pullman Samuel
11 Rudd Wm.
3 Stevens John
20 Sydenham Jas.
14 Towell Wm.
15 Upton Thomas
17 Wood John
BOOKSELLERS.
(Printers also.)*
6 * Boyce Francis
6 Marshall Matw.
2 Mead Henry
2 Mitchell Henry
* Parkhouse Thdr.
7 * Sharland Wm.
BOOT & SHOE MRS.
1 Adams Wm.
7 Ascott John
7 Bidgood Wm.
Bowden John,
Frog street
12 Burgess Fras.
12 Burnell Wm.
10 Capron George
7 Carter Edward
6 Carter Joseph
3 Carter Wm.
8 Collins Thomas
2 Cosway Thomas
12 Courtney Jph.
2 Cowlin Abm.
Duckham John
2 East Samuel
2 Frost John
7 Grattan John
1 Hewett Stephen
2 Hill John
11 Hines Wm.
24 Holcombe Ths.
11 Joyce John
Lake John
Lee John
2 Long Speccott
6 Moss John
2 Peter Wm.
20 Phillips Mark
2 Quick James
9 Routley John
3 Richards John
14 Roberts Robert
12 Stoyell James
6 Thomas John
2 Ware Thomas

8 Whitfield John
7 Woodgates Wm.

BRAZIERS AND TINNERS.

6 Craze John
8 Dew James
7 Puddicombe W.
4 Snell Brothers

BRICKLAYERS, &c.

7 Crockford Geo.
5 Long John
Perkins Joseph
3 Parsons Wm.
12 Periam John
Physick Tristram
12 Pleass Samuel
13 Tucker Thos.
14 Tucker Thos.
Watkins Thomas

BUTCHERS.

(* are Pork.)

7 Baker Richard
24 Barrett Peter
6 Beld Thomas
2*Besway Thos.
24 Bird Peter
5 Davey Chas. Geo.
2*Davey James
*Davey Wm.
2 Goodland James
12 Holmes Wm.
11 Loosemore Ts.
12 Newton Wm.
9 Rowcliff Wm.
24*Smith Wm.
Taylor John
3 Venn Jane
12 Wood Samuel

CABINET MAKERS.

10 Hewett James
7 Reed John
1 Sharland Wm.
2 Skinner Henry
12 Tucker John

CHEMISTS AND DRUGGISTS.

6 Beedell John
2 Frost Walter
6 Havill Paul
2 Rossiter George
7 Sanders Geo. Lee
6 Weeks Josias
12 Wellington Wm
12 Wood Samuel

COAL DEALERS.

3 Bell John
Goodland Wm. & Charles
Goodland John
10 Hartley Rd. W.
Quant Jno. & Co.

CONFECTIONERS.

7 Clapp John
1 Hobbs Elizabeth
1 Lee Thomas
6 Risdon Hugh T.
2 Symons Herman
6 Ward John
2 Wackrill Uriah
6 Wilson Enos

COOPERS.

23 Baker James
12 Cox Thomas
2 Morrish John
8 Pidgeon Henry

CORN MILLERS.

12 Coombe Robert
Gath Jno., Elmore
12 Gath Samuel
7 Phillips Robert
17 Sellers Mrs
22 Southey Geo.
12 Wood John

CURRIERS.

2 Burrough Robert
12 Cook Henry
2 Cook John Henry
5 Lake James
2 Pratt John
1 Viney Chtt. & Son

DAIRYMEN.

5 Caudy George
12 Carter John
6 Channing Jas.
9 Combe James
16 Davey Richard
16 Ellis John
16 Fowler Samuel
23 Hellier Wm.
Mead James
15 Morrell James
15 Pook Thomas
Skinner Wm.
20 Webber Richd.

EATING HOUSES.

7 Courtney Wm.
12 Gardener Eliz.
7 Viney Henry
7 Wright John

GARDENERS.

14 Farquharson P.
4 Hepper James
3 Howe John
Pearce Wm.

GLASS, &c. DLRS.

6 Cornish John
6 Holmes Thos.
1 Mudford Mary
8 Richards John

GROCERS, &c.

2 Beck Edward
6 Besley Thomas
2 Brimson Elias
6 Bowerman John
2 Capern Henry
7 Crockford Geo.
6 Cornish John
6 Ellerton Fras.
2 Frost Walter
6 Holmes Thomas
5 Lake James
2 Lane Ann
2 Long Specott
9 Lee Thomas
4 Mallett John
6 Marshall Wm.
2 Martin John
2 Pinkstone Ts. D.
6 Risdon Hugh T.
2 Rossiter George
7 Seward John
4 Snell Brothers
6 Ward John
7 Wills John
12 Wood Samuel

GUANO MERCHTS.

7 Haydon Thos.
7 Sanders Geo. L.

GUNSMITHS.

6 Gill Hy. Sept.
7 Haydon Thos.

HAIR DRESSERS.

12 Capern James
7 Cosway Thomas
2 Mitchell Henry
2 Odam James
7 Oram Joseph
12 Vickery John

HATTERS.

6 Collard Joseph
24 Harris W. H.
7 Howell Robert
6 Marshall Wm.

IRONMONGERS.

6 Craze John
6 Easterbrook W.
6 Gill Henry Sept.
7 Haydon Thos. C.
6 Nott & Co.
4 Snell John

JOINERS & BLDRS.

Baker John
9 Beck Charles
10 Beck Wm.
19 Bennett John
10 Gath Samuel
12 Gillard Wm.
19 Gunn George
7 Morrell John
Paris Joel
Perkins Joseph
11 Reed Robert
7 Seward Richard
3 Seward Robert
10 Williams Edw.
12 Wood & Co.

LIME BURNERS.

Davey & Cosway
Talbot James

L. & W. DRAPERS.

7 Askew George
1 Cosway George
6 Cobley Geo. D.
2 Darch Martha
7 Howell Robert
6 Knight Joseph
6 Lane John
11 Pinkstone Rd.
6 Seward Samuel
6 Trix Hugh
6 Tucker J. & Son
6 Walland Edw.

MALTSTERS.

10 Capern Thos.
12 Curwood Nhls.
3 Hewett John
1 Hill John
2 Snow Richd. (& brewer)
3 Ward Rd. Morgn

MARINE STORE DEALERS.

12 Herring Hy.
Lawton William, Frog street
2 Spinkstone Ann
12 Stenner Wm.

MILLINERS.
2 Beedell My. Ann
2 Catford Mary A.
24 Cornish Ann
2 Cook Elizabeth
Cockram Rosa
9 Force Frances
6 Marshall Sarah
2 Morris Eliz.
7 Perkins Fanny
12 Pepperell Jane
2 Pinkstone C. D.
4 Pitt Emma
8 Russell Ann
2 Searle Louisa
Stevens Sarah
White M. A.
PAINTERS, PLUM-
BERS, & GLAZRS.
7 Crease James
12 Crocker Robert
Hamlin Henry
4 Hewett Henry
1 Nash Wm.
4 Pleass John Wm.
7 Reed James
2 Stephens Jas.
3 Taylor James
POULTERERS.
9 Stoke Charity
12 Veysey Wm.
7 Veysey Ann
SADDLERS.
12 Norrish Saml.
4 Rowden John
6 Skinner H. Ellis
6 Skinner Thos.
4 Snell Brothers
2 Upham Francis
8 Wright Wm.
SHOPKEEPERS.
10 Anstey Wm.
11 Beard Wm.
3 Bell John
15 Blackman John
2 Bishop Eliza
5 Boobier Thos.
Bowden John
12 Brabham M. A.
2 Brock Wm.
3 Buss Hannah
24 Channon Eml.
12 Cocker Mary
3 Colman John
5 Cosway Thomas

5 Cross Ann
8 Darch John
2 Darch Mar
7 Davey Chtte.
13 Davey Robert
12 Ellis John
10 Fisher Hannah
12 Foweraker Wm
12 Gardner Eliza
12 Gillard Robert
20 Hodge John
24 Hooper Jane
24 Hunt Isaac
5 Jess John
5 Long John
12 Marshall John
Marshall John
12 Norrish John
11 Pinkstone Rd.
11 Pinkstone Wm.
20 Pool James
11 Rudd Wm.
24 Rudford Chas.
12 Sayer Wm.
12 Stenner Wm.
2 Taylor Livia
8 Wright Wm.
5 Wonnacott Jas.
STRAW HAT MKRS.
2 Carter Elizabeth
12 Foss Eliza
12 How Jane
2 Land Elizabeth
7 Martin M. A.
1 Mudford Mary
SURVEYORS.
7 Boyce G. A.
16 Chapple Wm.
TAILORS.
(* are Drapers.)
12 Adams Thos.
7 *Askew George
11 Bidgood Wm.
3 Cockram Thos.
1 *Croydon Jas.
3 Ellis Robert
12 Ellis John
Hamlin Wm.
24 Hatswell John
6 Hutchison Wm.
2 Land Thomas
11 Lock John
2 Mead Samuel
11 Melhuish John
6 *Melhuish Wm.

3 Morrell Wm.
2 Morrish Wm.
11 Parkhouse Jno.
Reeves David
6 *Seward Saml.
12 Stoyel James
6 Westaway D. Ts.
TOY DEALERS.
2 Brewer Mary
2 Mitchell Henry
7 Oram Joseph
TURNERS.
6 Amery John
2 Churley Robert
VETY. SURGEONS.
8 Clement John
2 Wotton Wm.
WATCHMKRS., &c.
12 Eames Wm.
6 Foster Thomas
2 Long John
4 Long Wm.
2 Pinkstone Geo.
2 Pinkstone Ts. D.
7 Sharland J. & Co.

6 Tucker J. W. T.
WHEELWRIGHTS.
24 Bell Philip
8 Cross Edward
14 Harley Daniel
1 Hodge Wm.
21 Hurley John
12 Jackson Edw.
11 Rudd Wm.
2 Sydenham Jas.
17 Wood John
18 Wynn John
WHITESMITHS.
6 Cockram John
Doble Mr
6 Dunn James
6 Gill Hy. Sept.
7 Haydon Ths. C.
6 Nott & Co.
4 Snell Brothers
WINE AND SPIRIT
MERCHANTS.
6 Paine Wm.
7 Pratt Thomas
7 Wills John

RAILWAY :— The Station is at *Lowman green.* Passenger Trains four times a day, to Exeter, London, Bristol, &c., &c.; and luggage trains daily.

COACHES, &c.

To *Barnstaple,* from the Angel, the *Mail,* at 4½ morng., and the *Emerald,* at 5½ evening.
To *Barnstaple, Bideford,* and *Ilfracombe, via* South Molton, the *Rival Daily Mail,* from the Three Tuns, 11¼ morning.
To *Exeter,* Parkin and Body's *Omnibus,* from the Boar's Head, Mon. Wed. & Fri. 7½ morning; and W. Snow's, on Tues. at 4 afternoon.
To *Exeter, Honiton,* and *Newton Abbot,* Fletcher's *Omnibus,* from the Seven Stars, every Tues. 4 aftn.

CARRIERS.

To *Bampton,* W. Cottrell, from Royal Oak, Tues. Thur. & Sat. 3½ aftn.
Barnstaple and *South Molton,* from Market House Inn, Sanders & Co. Mon. Wed. & Fri. 5 evening; and Philip Baker, from Boar's Head, Wed. 8 morning.

Bridgewater, Bristol, London,&c. Jno. Bletchly, from Market House Inn, daily, per rails.

Dulverton, from Boar's Head, every Tues. Thur. and Sat. 4 aftn.

Dunster, J. Wake, from Boar's Head, Thurs. 6 morng.

Exeter, by rails, daily, and waggons, &c. as follows :—James Harwood, from Chapel st. Mon. Wed. & Fri. 4 mrng ; Jas. Wake & Wm. Snow, from Boar's Head, Tu.&Wed. 4 aftn.

Silverton, Rawle, from the White Ball, Tues. 4 aftn.

South Molton. (See Barnstaple.)

Thorverton, Wm. James, White Ball, Tues. 5 morng.

Uffculme, John Southey, from Prince Regent, Tues. 7 evening.

Witheridge, J. Southcott, from the Dolphin, **Tues.** 5 evening.

BAMPTON HUNDRED

Is a small district of 6990 souls, and about 30,000 acres of land, picturesquely undulated, and having a bold range of hills on its northern boundary, adjoining Somersetshire. It is bounded on the south by Tiverton Hundred and Borough, and has a variable soil, chiefly a heavy clay, with a gravelly subsoil. It is noted for its fine breed of *sheep,* and for its extensive quarries of *limestone,* great quantities of which are sent for building and agricultural purposes along the Grand Western Canal, which crosses the east end of the Hundred. (See page 305.) It comprises the seven *parishes* of Bampton, Clayhanger, Hockworthy, Holcombe-Rogus, Morebath, Uffculme, and part of Burlescombe, in the Northern Division of Devon, and all in Tiverton Polling District, except Uffculme, which is in Collumpton Polling District. It is all in Collumpton Petty Sessional Division, in the Archdeaconry of Exeter, and Deanery of Tiverton. Burlescombe and Holcombe-Rogus are in *Wellington Union,* which is mostly in Somerset; but the other five parishes are in *Tiverton Union.* (See page 303.)

BAMPTON is a small ancient market town, chiefly built of stone, in the deep narrow valley of the small river Batherm, about a mile above its confluence with the Exe, 6½ miles N. of Tiverton, and 9 miles S.W. of Wivelscombe. Its parish contains 2049 inhabitants, and 7785 acres of land, divided into the *Eastern, Western, Petton,* and *Town Quarters,* and comprising the hamlets of PETTON and SHILLINGFORD ; many scattered farm-houses, &c., and several extensive limestone quarries. The parish extends four miles north of the town, to the bold hills on the borders of Somersetshire, and nearly two-thirds of it are in pasturage. Bampton is supposed to have been the *Beamdune* of the ancient historians, where the Britons were defeated with great slaughter by Cynegilous, King of the West Saxons, in 614, when the former are said to have lost 2046 men. The town is irregularly built, and has a chalybeate spring. Its weekly market on Saturday is of trivial consequence; but it has two *great markets* for sheep and cattle, on the Wednesday before Lady-day, and the last Wednesday in November; and also two fairs on Whit-Monday, and the last Thursday in October. The latter is one of the largest sheep fairs in the West of England, as many as 14,000 being often brought to it. The sheep bred in this neigh-

bourhood are remarkable for their size, and great numbers of them are sold at Bampton fairs. The woollen trade was formerly carried on here, but it began to decline in 1772, and was given up many years ago. *Bampton Farmers' Club* has a long list of members resident in this and surrounding parishes. The honour or barony of Bampton, or Bathermton, was given by Wm. the Conqueror to Walter Douay, and afterwards passed to the Paganell and Cogan families. In 1336, Richard Cogan had a license from the Crown to castellate his mansion here, and to enclose his wood of Uffculme and 300 acres of land for a park. A mound near the town denotes the site of the Castle, but all traces of the building disappeared some centuries ago. John Collins, Esq., who is about to erect a mansion at *Wonham*, is now lord of the manor; and at the court leet, a portreeve, bailiff, &c., are appointed; but the parish is all freehold, and belongs to many other proprietors, the largest of whom are, S. T. Lucas, Esq., C. Rowliffe, Esq., Dr. Troyte, the Trustees of the late Lord Rolle, Thos. Daniel, Esq., H. and R. Badcock, Esqrs., M. B. Bere, Esq., the Nutcombe family, and J. Brown, Esq. Hy. Badcock, Esq., has a pleasant seat here, called *Combehead*. The *Church* (St. Michael,) is a large ancient structure, with a tower and six bells. The interior has a finely ornamented arched ceiling, and a carved oak screen. Among its monuments is one to John Tristram, who died at Duvale in 1722. It had three small endowed chantries, and was appropriated to Buckland Abbey. The *vicarage*, valued in K.B. at £21. 11s. 8d., and in 1831 at £136, is in the patronage of T. L. T. Rendell, Esq., and incumbency of the Rev. T. Rendell, B.A., who has a good residence, and 3A. 2R. 17P. of glebe. Joseph C. Nagle, Esq., is impropriator of the great tithes, which were commuted in 1843. *Petton Chapel*, about four miles N.E. of the town, is a small chapel of ease, which was rebuilt in 1847; but that at Shillingford has been dilapidated many years. In the town is a neat *Baptist Chapel*, in the lancet Gothic style; an *Infant School*, built by subscription in 1836; and a *Free School*, founded in 1821, by Mrs. Eliz. Penton, who endowed it with £2200 five per cent. stock, for the education of 100 children, and the clothing of half of them. For distribution in bread, the poor parishioners have 26s. a year, left by Sir John Acland in 1619, and paid by Exeter Corporation. Out of a farm at Bishop's hill, the poor have £4, and the churchwardens 16s. yearly, left by *Robert Mogridge*, in 1645. The poor have also the following yearly sums, viz.:—36s. left by John Tristram, in 1628, out of Little Pilemore; and £2. 4s. left by Eliz. Lucas, in 1808, out of an estate now belonging to S. T. Lucas, Esq. Bampton Bridge was rebuilt in 1827, at the cost of £654. John de Bampton, a Carmelite friar, who first read lectures in Cambridge on the works of Aristotle, was a native of this parish, and died in 1391.

Badcock Henry, Esq. *Combehead*
Besley George, brick and tile maker
Branscombe Richard, lime merchant
Brook Edmd. druggist & wine mert
Capron John P. whitesmith, &c

Coles Mr John Sweetland
Collins John, Esq. *Wonham*
Crudge Wm. plumber, ironmgr. &c
Davey Mrs Sarah & E., & Miss Marie

Densham Thos. Row, solicitor, and agent to West of England Ins. Co.
Druller Edwin, relieving officer
Edwards John, surgeon, registrar, & agent to Crown Life Office
Ellis Henry, lime merchant
Escott Mrs Eliz. || Gale Geo. turner
Farrant and Williams, tanners, &c
Farrant Samuel George, tanner, &c
Gooding Rt. W. & Ts. Hy. W. gents
Hobbs Elias, watchmaker
Langdon Thomas, surgeon
Lock Mr John || May Rt. overseer
North Mr Rt. || McKie John, tea dlr
Oxenham Thomas, hairdresser
Page George, veterinary surgeon
Parkin Mrs Mgt. || Pomeroy Mr Wm.
Pearse Richard, builder
Periam John T. maltster, lime merchant, and *bank agent*
Phillips Thomas, lime merchant
Radford John, gentleman
Rendell Rev. Edw., B.A., *Vicarage*
Seymour Capt. Fras. Edw. R.N., & Rev Fras. Payne, M.A., *Castle Grove*
Trickey John, lime merchant
Trowey Mrs Eliz. milliner
Walton Rev. Wm. (Baptist)
Williams Charles, tanner, &c

FARMERS.
Ball Mary || Dean George
Bowden Richard, *Court-grove*
Brown John, *Birch-town*
Cape Jph. P. || Chave Wm. *Zeal*
Clark Richard || Elsworthy James
Ellis Henry, *Duvale Barton*
Elsworthy Thomas, *North Hayne*
Gooding John, (and lime merchant)
Heard Grace || Hanson John
Hill Charles, *Westbrook*
Hill Wm. || Hodge Wm.
Hodge Pp. (auctioneer,) *Bowber hill*
Kelland Philip || Leigh Wm. *ditto*
Merson Francis || Oxenham Mary
Oxenham Wm. || Phillips Wm.
Salisbury Edward || Sampson Rd.
Stone Edward || Trapnell Richard
Williams Thomas, *Petton*

INNS AND TAVERNS.
Angell, Wm. Cotterill
Barleycorn, Mary White

Castle Inn, John Berman
Exeter Inn, John Marley
Foxfords, Wm. Bird
Red Lion, Samuel Bray, brewer
Swan Inn, John Trickey
Tiverton Hotel, Wm. Trickey
White Horse Inn, Henry Oaten

ACADEMIES.
(* *Boarding.*)
Davey Eleanor
*Farrant Eliz.
Marley George
*Phillips Jane
Shaddock James

BAKERS.
Burge John
Jutson John
Needs John
Prout Ann

BEERHOUSES.
Pearse John
Searle John

BLACKSMITHS.
Capron Rd. P.
Ching Thomas

BOOT&SHOEMKRS
Escott James
Escott John
Escott Robert
Escott Thomas
Escott Wm.
Oxenham Robt.
Oxenham Roger
Surridge James

BUTCHERS.
Davey John
Gibbings John
Short Wm.
Surridge Wm.

CABINET MKRS.
Crudge Wm.
Standon Robt. L.

CARPENTERS.
Gale Richard
Hawkins Wm.
Stronclave Rd.
Thorn Wm.

COOPERS, &c.
Bowden Richard
Webber Wm.

GROCERS & DPRS.
Crudge John
Darch Wm.
Farrant and Williams
Hellings Thos., (& maltster)
Jutson Wm.

PAINTRS.&GLZRS.
Crudge John
Crudge Wm.
Nott Thomas
Pearse Richard

SADDLERS.
Bryant John
Catford John
Pearse John

SHOPKEEPERS.
Capron Mary
Escott Robert
Radford Jane

TAILORS.
Gibbings John
Gibbings Wm.
Prout Richard
Prout Thomas
Prout Wm.

WHEELWRIGTS.
Phillips John
Searle John
Greenslade Wm.

POST-OFFICE
at J. Catford's.
Letters *via* Tiverton 6 evg.

CARRIERS.
J. Oxenham, to Tiverton and Taunton; and J. Vickery, to Exeter.

BURLESCOMBE, a pleasant village, near the Bristol and Exeter Railway, 8¼ miles E.N.E. of Tiverton, and 5 miles S.W. of Wellington, has in its parish 958 souls, and 3767 acres of land, divided into the *Town tithing*, and *Appledore, Westleigh,* and *Aysh-*

ford tithings and hamlets. The three latter comprise 2600 acres, and are in Halberton Hundred. The parish is hilly, and abounds in limestone. It extends to the borders of Somerset, and is crossed by the Grand Western Canal. In 1841, Appledore had 195, and Westleigh 323 inhabitants. On the farm called *Canonleigh*, was a PRIORY of Augustine canons, founded by Walter Claville, in the reign of Henry II.; but in the reign of Edward I., it was given to an abbess and nuns of the same order, by the Countess of Glouces-ter. At the dissolution, it was valued at £197. 3s. 1d. per annum. The farm now belongs to T. Brown, Esq. The nuns of Canonleigh had a charter for a market in 1286. The manors of Burlescombe, Ayshford, and Westleigh, formerly belonged to the Claville and Ayshford families, and are now held by Edward Ayshford Sanford, Esq.; but a great part of the parish belongs to the heirs of the late Sir Wm. Follett, R. H. Clarke, Esq., Henry Dunsford, Esq., and other freeholders. The *Church* (St. Mary,) is a fine antique struc-ture, with a tower and five bells. The interior has several neat mo-numents of the Ayshford and other families, and has recently been renovated and fitted up with new carved oak seats. Some of the windows have also been enriched with stained glass, and the screen richly emblazoned. E. A. Sanford, Esq., is impropriator of the great tithes, and patron of the vicarage, valued in K.B. at £11. 15s. 10d., and in 1831 at £316. The Rev. Thomas Tanner, M.A., is the incumbent, and has a good residence and 16A. of glebe. His tithes were commuted in 1838 for £330, and the impropriator's for £220 per annum. There is a small ancient chapel of ease at Ayshford, and a Wesleyan chapel at Westleigh. The parish is entitled to send a boy to Uffculme free school.

Marked * are at Ayshford, + at West-leigh, and the others at Burlescombe, or where specified.

Down Thos. & +Wall John, smiths
Fryer Geo. blacksmith, *Appledore*
Harper Edw. & +Venn J. shopkprs
Hewett James, lime burner
Hitchcock Wm. & Simeon, shoemkrs
Hussey James, shopkpr. *Appledore*
*Manley Wm. & +Taylor Wm. tailors
+McLead J. vict. Farmers' Inn
Marder Jas. Wood, gent. *Eastbrook*
Norman John, mason
Norris Wm. gent. *Elm Cottage*
*Pounds Wm. beerhouse
Pounds Richard, vict. Red Bull
Potter John, lime and timber mercht
*Stephens William, gentleman
Radford Henry, shopkpr. *Appledore*
Sully John, corn dealer

Tanner Rev Thomas, M.A. vicar
+Taylor Hy. lime dealer, and beerhs.
Vickery Thomas, smith and farrier
Young Wm. wheelwright

FARMERS.

Barrington Richard, *Canonleigh*
*Cook Nathaniel, *Ayshford Court*
Davey John, *Eastbrook*
Doble Francis || Gilham George
Hewett John || Hewett Wm.
Jackman Wm. || Jefferies Wm.
James Benj. || James Benj. jun.
Land Thomas || Merson Wm.
Morgan John || Stone Robert
+Taylor Henry || Talbot Thomas
Thorne John, *Appledore*
Thorne John, jun. *Houndaller*
Wawman Thomas, *Westleigh*
Webber Wm. *Pugham*
POST from Wellington.

CLAYHANGER, or *Cleyhanger*, a small scattered village, on the borders of Somerset and Devon, 4½ miles E.N.E. of Bampton, and S.W. of Wivelscombe, has in its parish 294 souls, and 2043 acres of land, belonging to Thomas Gould, Esq., Thomas Langdon, M.D.,

and several smaller freeholders. The *Church* (St. Peter,) is an ancient structure, with a tower and three bells. The interior still retains its original carved oak seats, and has some memorials of the Nutcombe family, formerly lords of the manor. The Rev. W. M. Harrison is patron and incumbent of the *rectory*, valued in K.B. at £15. 17s. 3½d., and in 1831 at £302. The Rectory House was rebuilt in 1823, at the cost of about £1000. The glebe is 40A., and the tithes were commuted in 1840 for £244 per annum. The poor have 20s. a year out of Perry-tenement, left by *Mary Sayer*, in 1701. An annuity of £3, left by *Mrs. H. N. Bluett*, in 1747 ; and the dividends of £150 three per cent. stock, given by John Norman and B. N. Bluett, are applied in schooling poor children.

Coxley John, tailor
Cridland Benj. & Lock Wm. shopkrs
Cridland John, smith and beerhouse
Harrison Rev.Wm.Moore,M.A. rector
Haywood Rt. & Vicary Hy. shoemkrs
Post from Wivelscombe

FARMERS.
Corner Wm. || Goddard John
Hill Francis || Hill James
Haywood Thomas || Hill John
Palmer Nathaniel || Palmer Robt.
Thorne George || Wood John

HOCKWORTY, a small scattered village, near the borders of Somerset, 7 miles W.S.W. of Wellington, and 8 miles N.E. of Tiverton, has in its parish 369 souls, and 2526 acres of land, picturesquely indulated, and including the small hamlets of *Staple-Cross* and *Lea;* and abounding in lime and excellent building stone, of which latter troughs, &c., are made. The rectorial tithes and the farm of *Hockford* (112A.) formerly belonged to Canonleigh Abbey, but most of the former have been sold to the land owners, and the latter belongs to Dr. E. B. Troyte, together with other parts of the parish. The other principal freeholders are Chas. and Godfrey Webster, Esqrs., and Mr. Jas. Talbot. The old manor house, called *Court Hall*, is the seat of G. Webster, Esq. The *Church* is an ancient building, except the tower, which was rebuilt in 1848, at the cost of £150, and contains three bells. The *vicarage*, valued in K.B. at £7. 6s. 8d., and in in 1831 at £288, is in the patronage of the Rev. T. H. Britton, M.A., and incumbency of the Rev. Wm. Comyns, of Rackenford. A new Vicarage House has lately been erected in the Elizabethan style, at the cost of about £1200. The glebe comprises 67A. of good land, and the vicarial tithes were commuted in 1842 for £205. 10s. per annum. The poor have 34s. a year out of Thornlands, left by Peter Sharland, in the 26th of James II.

Ash Robt. and Dunn Wm. shoemkrs
Ash Wm. butcher and beerseller
Britton Rev Thomas Hopkins, M.A. curate and patron, *Vicarage*
Frost Mary, shopkeeper
Longman Samuel, stone mason
May Henry, blacksmith
Rose Peter, timber merchant, &c
Webster Godfrey, Esq., *Court Hall*

FARMERS.
Baker Thomas || Bucknell John
Darby Edward || Darby Wm., *Staple*
Fowler James || Gamlin Eliz.
Holway Abel || Kemp John Wallis
Smith Henry || Stevens Wm.
Wright Wm., *Court Hall*
Post-Town, *Wellington*

HOLCOMBE-ROGUS is a village and parish adjoining the Grand Western Canal and the borders of Somerset, 6 miles W.S.W. of Wellington, and 8½ miles N.E. by E. of Tiverton. It comprises

843 souls, and 3024 acres of land, generally fertile and hilly, and abounding in limestone. A market and fair, granted to this parish in 1343, have long been obsolete. At Domesday Survey, the *manor* was held by Rogo or Rogus, under Baldwin the Sheriff. For some centuries, it has been the seat of the Bluett family. P. F. Bluett, Esq., the present lord of the manor and owner of most of the parish, resides at *Holcombe Court*, the ancient manor house, which is in the Gothic style, with a tower. The west wing was taken down in 1845, and the rest of the mansion has lately been repaired. The *Church* (All Saints,) is `a fine ancient structure, with an embattled tower and five bells. In a chapel at the east end are two marble tombs, with recumbent effigies of four members of the Bluett family. The *vicarage*, valued in K.B. at £10. 10s. 2½d., and in 1831 at £240, is in the patronage of P. F. Bluett, Esq., and incumbency of the Rev. Wm. Wills, M.A. They are impropriators of the great tithes, which have been commuted for £220, and the vicarial for about £300 per annum. The glebe is 1½A., and the Parsonage is a good residence. The parish has a small Baptist Chapel, and sends a boy to Uffculme free school.

Baxter John, gent || Bluett Mrs
Bluett Peter Fdk., Esq., *Holcombe Ct*
Cartwright Edw. gent || Hewett Mrs
Clarke John, beerhouse
Dinniscombe Wm. saddler, &c
Elworthy Wm. maltster
Fry George, blacksmith
Greenslade Stephen, butcher
Hellings Charles, maltster
Knowlman John B. land agent
Payne Wm. baker
Pool Hannah, schoolmistress
Scott James, wood turner
Shackell John, butcher
Timewell Mrs Ann
Tooze Samuel, cooper
Trevellian John, wheelwright
Trotter James, surgeon
Wright Samuel, wheelwright & vict. New Inn

Wright Samuel jun. blacksmith

CHAIR MAKERS.
Grant James
Tooze John
Warren Wm.
Woodbury Jas.

GROCERS, &c.
Hill James
Lemon Wm.
Sharland Peter

FARMERS.
Babb James
Barrington Wm.
Bradley James
Cooke John
Hellings Thos., *Kitton*
Hill John
Hodges John

Hooper John
Lock John
TalbotJas. (and lime mert.)
Tooze Wm.
Webber Wm.
White Lawrence

SHOEMAKERS.
Clarke James
Clarke Thomas
Hooper Thomas

TAILORS.
Coleman Thos.
Govier Wm.
Pool Philip
Wyatt James

POST *from Wellington*

MOREBATH, a small village on a bold southern declivity, 2 miles N. of Bampton, has in its parish 466 souls, and 3349A. of land, including the small village of *Exbridge*, which is partly in Somersetshire, near the confluence of the rivers Exe and Barle, where the hills rise in lofty elevations on the borders of the two counties. A *cattle fair* is held here on the Monday after August 24th. Montagu Baker Bere, Esq., is lord of the manor, which was long held by Berlinch Abbey; but part of the parish belongs to John Bere, Esq., Henry Ball, Esq., and several smaller freeholders. The *Church* (St. George,) is an ancient structure, with a tower and five bells, and some remains of a window brought from Berlinch Abbey in the 16th century. It contains a Norman font, and several neat monuments. The *vicarage*, valued in K.B. at £7. 8s. 9d., and in

1831 at £200, is in the patronage of T. L. Clarke, Esq., and incumbency of the Rev. A. B. Hill, who has a good residence at the foot of a high cliff, and 5A. of glebe.   The vicarial tithes were commuted in 1841 for £234.   The *Free School*, and the Almshouse under it for two poor people, were founded in 1688 by *John Brook*, of Ashdown, who endowed them with £10 a year for the master; 12s. a month for the two almspeople; and £4 a year for repairs, &c., out of an estate now belonging to M. B. Bere, Esq.   The poor parishioners have the interest of £45, left by various donors.

Bagg John, carpenter & shopkeeper, *Exbridge*
Bennett Thos. & Winsley Jas. smiths
Bere Rev Richard, LL.D. rector of Skilgate, *Lower Timewell House*
Blake Wm. carpenter & vict. Anchor, *Exbridge*
Burton Jas. shopkeeper, *Exbridge*
Douglas Rev Philip, M.A., *Morebath House*
Harris Wm. schoolmaster, &c
Hill Rev Alfred Bligh, B.A. vicar
Luxton George, stone mason
Popham Rt. & Veen Thos. wheelgts.
Surridge Wm. shoemaker
Tarr Joan, shopkeeper

FARMERS.

Brewer John || Buckingham Wm.
Chave Thomas || Hancock John
Gooding Robert, *Burston*
Gooding John || Henson James
Hill John || May Thomas
Pine John || Pears John
Ponsford Robert || Tribble Wm.
Rawle John, *Ashdown*
Shattock John Gawler, *Whitehall*
Veysey Wm. || Wicks Geo. Henry

UFFCULME, a decayed market town, in the picturesque valley of the small river Culm, 4 miles N.E. by N. of Collumpton, has in its parish 2011 inhabitants,, and 6123 acres of land, including the hamlets of *Craddock*, *Ashill*, *Stenehall*, and *Hayne*, and many scattered houses.   Uffculme had formerly several large woollen and worsted manufactures, and it has still one factory, belonging to Fox Brothers and Co., of Wellington; a large brewery, belonging to Mr. W. Furze; several malting houses, and three corn mills.   Its weekly *market* has long been nearly obsolete, but it has still three annual *fairs*, on the Wednesday after Good Friday, June 29th, and the 2nd Wednesday in Sept.   John Cogan had a grant for a market and two fairs here, in 1266.   The *manors* of Uffculme and Hackpen, formerly held by the Douay, Bourchier, and Stamford families, were sold in parcels, together with the royalties, to various freeholders before 1712.   Benj. B. Walrond, Esq., owns a great part of the parish, and resides at *Bradfield Hall*, a fine antique mansion with pleasant grounds, where his family has been seated since the reign of Henry III.   This mansion has a wooden Gothic roof, and on the outside are numerous coats of arms of the Walronds and their alliances.   It remains nearly in its original form, and is one of the finest specimens of ancient domestic architecture in the county.   Its chapel was taken down many years ago.   The other principal freeholders of the parish are John New, Richd. Hurley, Richd. John Marker, and Rd. Hall Clarke, Esqrs., the Rev. H. K. Cornish, and Messrs. C. Venn, W. A. Wood, Wm. Wyatt, and John Garnsey, some of whom have neat houses here.   The *Prebend of Uffculme*, in Salisbury Cathedral, is endowed with a house and glebe of 133A. 3R. 39P., and the rectorial tithes of the parish, which were commuted for £431 in

.839, when the vicarial tithes were commuted for £589. 19s. 9d.
per annum. The Rev. Fredk. Browning, B.D., of Titchwell, Norfolk, is the present *prebendary*, and has the patronage of the *vicarage*, valued in K.B. at £18. 0s. 2½d., and in 1831 at £350, and now in the incumbency of the Rev. Geo. T. Smith, B.A., who has a good residence, erected by himself, at the cost of more than £2000. The prebendal land and tithes are held on lease by the representatives of the late Robt. Baker, Esq. The parish was in the peculiar jurisdiction of the Dean of Salisbury, but by the late act for abolishing *peculiars*, it has been placed under the ecclesiastical jurisdiction of the Archdeacon of Exeter, except as to probates of wills and administrations, over which the Dean still retains jurisdiction. The *Church* (St. Mary,) is a large and handsome structure, and has recently been [restored, enlarged, and improved, and the tower and spire rebuilt, at the cost of about £3400. A new south aisle was added in 1846. The new tower and spire rise to the height of 120 feet, and the former contains six bells. They were built at the expense of R. J. Marker, Esq., who also gave the great bell and clock. The interior has four pillars and arches of great beauty, of a transition character, between the early English and Decorative styles; and a fine oak screen of the 15th century divides the chancel from the nave and aisles, 67 feet in length. The pulpit and reading desk are handsomely carved, and the organ is a fine toned instrument. Most of the windows are in the perpendicular style, and that at the east end is enriched with coloured glass The *Baptists* and *Independents* have meeting houses here. Uffculme *Free Grammar School* was founded in 1701 by *Nicholas Ayshford*, who gave £400 for its erection and £800 for its endowment. The school was repaired in 1802, at the cost of £300, and the endowment now consists of £1551. 2s. 9d. three per cent. reduced annuities, yielding £46. 10s. 8d. per annum, of which £40 is paid to the schoolmaster for teaching four free boys, two of them to be parishioners of Uffculme, and the other two of Burlescombe and Holcombe Rogus, or one of them. About 5A. of land, called Carter's tenement, was given for the reparation of the church before 1770, and is now let for £12. 12s. per ann. The poor parishioners have the dividends of £171. 14s. three per cent. stock, purchased with £120, left by *Joan Holway* and other donors; and the interest of £1000, left by the late *Mrs. Marker*, for distribution in clothing on New-year Day. They have also a yearly sum from *Wilmot Burrow's Charity*, left in the 9th of James I., and now vested with B. B. Dickenson, R. H. Clarke, and other trustees. *In the following Directory, those marked* 1 *are in Ashill;* 2, *Craddock;* 3, *Smithencott;* 4, *Stenehall, or Stenaller ; and the rest in Uffculme, or where specified.*

Baker James, schoolmaster
Bevan Richd. D. grocer, draper, surveyor, and agt. to the Royal Farmers' Insurance Co., Post-office
Bird Thomas, horse trainer
Blackman Rev Thos. Wm. (Bapt.)
Bowerman Richard, solicitor
Brice Samuel, maltster
Broom Francis, tanner
Burrow Jas. watch and clock maker
Cains George Wm. surgeon
Churley Thomas, butcher
Cook James, draper, *Ashill*
Cottrell Charles, last and clog mkr

Doble Robert and John, maltsters
Fox Brothers and Co. woollen and worsted mfrs. (and at *Wellington*)
Furze Wm. maltster and brewer
Hurley Richd. Esq. *Gaddon House*
Jones Rev Fras., M.A. master of the Grammar School and incumbent of Moreton-Pickney
Marker Rd. John, Esq. *Yondercott Hs*
Morrish Hy. jun. registrar and agt. to the West of England Ins. Co.
New John, Esq. and John, M.D. *Craddock House*
2 Newman Rev Wm. Jas., M.A. curate
Nott James Stuart, surgeon
Radford Henry, chair maker
Skinner Mrs A.||1 Salter Wm. beerhs
Smith Rev Geo. Townsend, B.A. vicar
2 Smith Miss H. and Mrs Pearse
Sparks Saml. manager to Fox Bros.
Stoodley Robert, ironmonger, &c
Sweetland Thomas, gentleman
Trott Philip, butcher
Upcott Wm. woollen manufacturer
Veals Chas. chandler and maltster
Walrond Benj. Bowden, Esq., *Bradfield Hall*
Ware Mary, schoolmistress
Welland Fras. and Wm. coopers
Williams Rev Chas. (Independent)
Williams Wm. hair dresser
Wood Wm. Ayshford, gent. *Leigh Hs*
Woolcott Pp. brick & tile mkr. & bhs
Wyatt Wm. gent. *Landside*

INNS AND TAVERNS.
Commercial, Wm. Burford, smith
George & Commercial, Geo. Tapscott
Half Moon, Ann Bamfield
Lamb, Wm. Wonson
London Inn, Robt. Dunster, shoemkr
Star Inn, Thomas Sparks

BAKERS.
Cook Wm.
Hussey Henry
Parr John
Welland Wm.
BLACKSMITHS.
Burford Wm.
1 Hellier Thos.
Hellier Wm.
2 Minifie Jph.
1 Perry John
4 Sanders Daniel
Woodbury Wm.
CABINET MKRS.
3 Wyatt Edward
Wyatt James
CARPENTERS.
3 Lane Edward

Tucker Philip
Veals John
3 Wyatt Edward
4 Wyatt Wm.
CORN MILLERS.
Millwood Thos.
Southey George
Wood Joel, *Hackpen Mill*
FARMERS.
(* are Owners.)
*Baker Elias
Churley James
*Dickinson Benj.
*Doble Hy.*consb.*
Drake John
4 Drake Wm.
Elston Richard
Evans John
*Furze Wm.
*Garnsey John
4 Grant Mary
*Hewett John
*Hewett Wm. Ts.
Whitmoor
James John
3 Paul Edmund
3 Pearsey Robt.
1*Pook John
Pring John
*Pring Thos.
Rowe Henry
Salter Joseph
Shere Susan
Skinner John D.
Southey Sarah
Sparks Chpr.
Stone John
Talbot John
Tancock John
Taylor Robert
Trott Francis
Trott John
Tucker James
Venn Clement
1 Ware Aaron
Webber J. *Hayne*
1 White Thomas
Wood Wm. *Rull*
4 Wyatt Wm.

PLUMBERS, &c.
Crease Thomas
Graves Richard
SADDLERS.
Thorne John
Thoms Wm.
SHOEMAKERS.
Dunston Henry
1 Graves Richard
Hellier John
Sparks Thomas
Stark Amos
Stark Philip
1 Welsman Jas.
SHOPKEEPERS.
Bevan Rd. D.
Curwood Thos.
1 Hawkins Chas.
Hewett John
Jeans Mary
1 Milton Chas.
2 Minifie Jph.
Skinner Robert
Summerhayes J.
Toogood Michl.
TAILORS.
Hellier George
Hellier Thomas
1 Manley James
1 Mogridge Hy.
Trott Robert
Wyatt John
VETNY. SURGNS.
3 Finnemore Rd.
Jones Thomas
1 Salter Thos. H.
WHEELWRIGHTS.
2 Graves James
Hellier Wm. (& machine mkr.)
1 Hurford Matw.
Holland James
POST-OFFICE
at R. D. Bevan's.
Letters via Collumpton
CARRIER to Tiverton, J. Southey

WITHERIDGE HUNDRED

Is a fertile district of hill and valley, of an irregular figure, averaging about fifteen miles in length and nine in breadth, in the Northern Division of Devon, Archdeaconry of Barnstaple, and Deaneries of South Molton and Chulmleigh, except Templeton parish, which is in the Archdeaconry of Exeter, and Deanery of Tiverton. It extends from 3 to about 18 miles westward from Tiverton, and to the vicinity of South Molton, and to within about four miles of the boundary of Somerset. It is watered by the small rivers Mole, Little Dart, Sturcombe, and Taw, and many tributary streams ; and rises into a bold range of hills on the east and north, but has extensive tracts of rich corn lands and pastures in the valleys. The following enumeration of its 22 parishes shews their territorial extent, and their population in 1841.

Parishes.	Acres.	Pop.	Parishes.	Acres.	Pop.
Bishop's Nympton	9579	1325	Rose-Ash	4988	541
Cheldon	1100	90	*Stoodleigh	} 5000	513
Chulmleigh	8815	1647	*Highley exp.		24
Creaccmbe	1036	58	*Templeton	1900	275
*Cruwys Morchard	5770	670	§Thelbridge	2249	267
King's Nympton	5539	777	§Washford Pyne	1600	197
Mariansleigh	1740	338	Witheridge	9048	1399
Meshaw	1775	305	§Woolfardisworthy	1815	220
*Oakford	5251	641	Worlington East	2363	287
§Puddington	1361	212	Worlington West	2683	218
Rackenford	3940	562			
Romansleigh	2491	239	Total	80,034	10,805

☞ UNIONS.—Those marked thus * are in *Tiverton Union,* § in *Crediton Union,* and the others in *South-Molton Union.*

-* Those marked thus * are in *Collumpton,* and all the others in *South Molton Petty Sessional Division.*

BISHOP'S NYMPTON, a large village, on a pleasant declivity, 3 miles E.S.E. of South Molton, has in its parish 1325 inhabitants, and 9579 acres of land, skirted on the west by the river Mole, and intersected by several small tributary streams. This large parish is hilly and fertile, and comprises many scattered farm houses, and the hamlets of *Ash-Mill,* 1½ mile E. ; *Newton,* 1 mile N. ; and *Bishop's Mill,* or *Bish Mill,* 1½ mile S.E. of the village. A cattle *fair* is held here on the Wednesday before the 25th of October. The *manor* has belonged from an early period to the Bishops of Exeter, and the bishop holds yearly a court leet and baron, of which Fredk. Sanders, Esq., is steward. The soil is held by numerous free and copyholders, the largest of whom are the Rev. W. Karslake, Rev. W. Thorne, Sir R. G. Throgmorton, Rev. P. Johnson, H. Bawden, Esq., Rev. J. Bawden, Rd. Preston, Esq., and Messrs. S. W. Yeo, T. Loveband, S. Passmore, and Alex. Fisher. *Mole Mills,* formerly employed as a woollen factory, are now unoccupied. The *Rev. Thomas Baker,* an eminent mathematician, and author of "The Geometrical Key," was several years vicar here, and died in 1689. *John Loosemore,* who built the fine organ in Exeter Cathedral, was

a native of this parish, and died in 1686.   The *Church* is a fine old
structure, with a lofty and elegant tower, containing six bells.   In
the chancel is a rich altar tomb, without any inscription, to one of
the Pollard family.   An organ has been erected, chiefly at the expense of the vicar.   The Bishop of Exeter is impropriator of the
great tithes, and patron of the *vicarage*, valued in K.B. at
£20. 7s. 3½d., and in 1831 at £315, and now in the incumbency of
the Rev. Joseph Thorne, B.A., who has 2A. 2R. 10P. of glebe, and a
good residence, built in 1846, at the cost of £1300.   The great
tithes were commuted in 1841 for £421, and the small tithes for
£379 per annum.   A large old mansion called the *Parsonage*, now
the residence of Mr. T. Loveband, is supposed to have been an occasional residence of the Bishops, and its barn has evidently been
a chapel, from the appearance of its carved ceiling.   An old manor
house, called *Whitechapel*, was long held by the Basset, Lear, Gibbins, and other families.   Here is a small *Wesleyan Chapel*, built
in 1838, and a *National School*, erected in 1841, on the site of the
old vicarage house.   The poor have the dividends of £480. 12s. 5d.
three per cent. consols, purchased with £263 left by various benefactors.   They have also 1½A. of land, left by John Blackmore,
in 1727.   In the following DIRECTORY those marked 1, *are at Ash
Mill; 2, Bishop's, or Bish Mill; 3, at Newtown; and the rest in
Bishop's Nympton, or where specified.*

Bond Mr. Chas. (*and London*)
Gould Wm. clock maker
Gunn George, schoolmaster
Melton Rd. relieving officer & regr.
Partridge Miss || Webber G. sawyer
Rodd Wm. parish clerk
Spencer Mrs Betsey, *Slough*
Thorne Rev Jph., B.A. *Vicarage*
Toms Wm. gent., and Mrs. *West Rock*
Tripp Timothy, corn miller
Warren Ts. overseer, & Wm. *sexton*

FARMERS. (* *are Owners.*)
*Ayre Wm. *West Welland & Reach*
*Ayre Robt. & Brothers, *Kerscot*
Brownson Roger, *Park*
Baker Wm. || Bond Hannibal
*Balman John || * Balman Wm.
*Chapple Rt. || Cockram John
Collard Wm. & Jno. *S. & N. Hayne*
Cole Thos. || *Colwell Wm.
*Courtney Mrs || *Crang Richard
Davie Honor || Davie Thomas
Dart John || Elworthy Wm.
*Fisher Alex. *Whitechapel*
Furze Edw. || Greenslade John
Heller Jas. *West Knowle Down*
Hill James || Hill John
Hayden John || Hosegood Wm.
*Loveband Thomas, *Parsonage*
Mallet Wm. || Kevill Mr

Martin Henry, *West Avercombe*
*Matthews Wm. || *Packer Wm.
Nott John || Nott John, jun.
*Passmore Saml. || Passmore Wm.
Passmore John and John, jun.
*Pincombe Wm. || *Pincombe John
Rew Thomas || Rowcliffe Philip
*Rowcliffe Geo. || Reed Thomas
Russell Thomas, *West Radleigh*
Russell John, *Grilstone*
Sanders Wm. || Smaldon James
Snell Simon, *Parkhouse*
Stone Clement, *Burlaford*
Thomas Wm. || *Treble John
*Veysey James, *Webbery Moor*
*Warren John, *East Knowle Down*
Webber Richard, *Verraby*

INNS & TAVERNS.
2 Fortescue Arms, Saml. Hulland
Mason's Arms, James Bond
London Inn, Jas Gardener
Red Lion, James Bullied

BAKERS.
Baker Mary
Chanter Hugh
Snell John
Tapp Wm.

BLACKSMITHS.
2 Cole George
2 Cole Richard

Crook Samuel
German Wm. (&
    ironmgr.)
1 Warren Jph.

BOOT & SHOEMRS.
Chanter Alex.
Gloyens George
Rodd James

1 Rodd James
Rodd Thomas
Shapcott George
Shapcott Wm.
Tapp John
  BUTCHERS.
Bond James
Bond Thomas
Catford Henry
2 Hulland Saml.
Milden John
Toms John
Mildon John
  CARPENTERS.
2 Chanter Wm.
Chapple John

Chapple Wm.
Cole George
Cole Thomas
Peagom George
Peagom Thos.
Peagom Wm.
Waldron J.&Sons
Warren Wm.
  COOPERS.
Crispin Wm.
Peagom Geo.
Rendle Thomas
Venn Thomas
GROCERS & DPRS.
BondWm.*saddler*

German John
Gunn George
Shapcott George
  MALTSTERS.
Heyes John
Loveband Thos.
  MASONS.
Baker Edward
Chanter Hugh
Crispin John
Tapp Wm.
  TAILORS.
Upham John
Vernon Wm.
Warren Wm.

  THATCHERS.
Gardener James
Gardener John
Rodd Hugh
  WHEELWRIGHTS.
2 Cole George
2 Cole Richard
German John
WaldronJ.&Sons
POST *from Sth.*
  Molton
C A R R I E R S to
South Molton,&c.
German Geo.
Manley Wm.

CHELDON, a small village and parish, in the valley of the Little Dart river, 3½ miles E. by S. of Chulmleigh, contains 90 inhabitants, and 1099 acres of land, nearly all the property of the Hon. Newton Fellowes, the lord of the manor and patron of the *rectory,* valued in K.B. at £4. 18s. 6½d., and in 1831 at £120. The Rev. R. S. Bryan is the incumbent, and has 36A. 3R. 6P. of glebe, and a good residence. The tithes were commuted in 1841, for £77 per annum. The *Church* (St. Mary,) is a small structure, with a tower and three bells. In the interior are two ornamental iron screens, dated 1737 and 1747. The Church House is occupied by poor people, and its garden is let for 10s., which is distributed with the interest of £50, given by various donors.

Bryan Rev Richard S., *Rectory*
Bryan ——, surgeon
Butt George, wheelwright
Lake Jno. *par. clk.* ‖ Nott J. *shoemkr*

FARMERS.
Bragg John, *Cheldon Barton*
Bragg Wm. *Winswood*
Cawsey George, *East Cheldon*

CHULMLEIGH, a small ancient *market town*, which has recently been much improved, is pleasantly seated on an acclivity on the north side of the Little Dart, about a mile from its confluence with the river Taw, eight miles S. of South Molton, 17 miles S.S.E. of Barnstaple, and 23 miles N.W. of Exeter. Its parish contains 1647 inhabitants, and 8815A. 1R. 4P. of land, genenerally fertile, and rising in bold undulations from the valleys of the Taw and Little Dart, and including the hamlet of *Elston*, and many scattered farm houses. Chulmleigh is described as a borough in ancient records, but it does not appear to have ever sent burgesses to Parliament. In 1803, the town suffered severely from an accidental *fire*, which destoyed 95 houses. It had formerly a share of the wool-combing trade, but it is now solely dependent for its prosperity on its markets and fairs, and the gentry and agriculturists of the neighbourhood. A *Market House*, with a commodious hall for public meetings, &c., was erected in 1848-9, by the lord of the manor, at the cost of about £300. The weekly *market* for corn and cattle is held on Friday, and there are great markets for cattle on the Friday before Lady-day, and in April, June, and September, as well as on the Friday after the 11th of each month. Two large *fairs* are held on

Easter Wednesday and the last Wednesday in July. *Petty Sessions* are held here every fourth Thursday, by the magistrates of South Molton Division.   The *manor* of Chulmleigh passed to the Courtenays, at an early period, as parcel of the Barony of Okehampton.   It afterwards passed to the Russell and Beaufort families, and is now the property of the Rev. Richard Johnson, but a great part of the parish belongs to Earl Fortescue, (owner of *Elston* manor,) Richard Preston, Esq., Mrs. Bury, the Hon. Newton Fellowes, (lord of the manor of *Stone*,) and several smaller owners, mostly freeholders.   The Courtenays are said to have had a castle and a park here, of which all traces disappeared some centuries ago.   *Lee House*, a fine old mansion in the Elizabethan style, in the Taw valley, is the seat of Richd. Preston, Esq.   *Colleton Barton*, built in 1612, was the seat of the late Admiral Bury, and is now the property and occasional seat of John Russell, Esq..   In one of its rooms is a fine piece of carved wainscot.   The *Church* (St. Mary Magdalen,) is a large ancient fabric, with a tower and six bells, and a handsomely carved screen.   It was repaired a few years ago, when four new windows were inserted on the south side.   It was formerly a collegiate church, *five prebendaries* having been established in it at an unknown date, "for the better ministry of God's service within the quire."   The *prebends* have been long consolidated with the rectory, and are called Brookland, Pendalls, Lower Hayne, Higher Hayne, and Deans.   The *rectory*, valued in K.B. at £20. 18s. 1½d., and in 1831 at £440, has 609A. 2R. 33P. of glebe, including the prebendal lands.   The Rev. Geo. Hall, B.C.L., is patron and incumbent, and has a neat thatched residence, with tasteful grounds, near the Little Dart river, built in 1826.   The old Parsonage is occupied by a farmer, and the tithes were commuted in 1840 for £687. 15s. 6d. per annum.   There were anciently small chapels at Cadbury, Lady Well, Colleton, and Stone, in this parish.   The *Independent Chapel* was built by Presbyterians in the reign of Charles II., and connected with it is a School, partly supported by subscription.   Here is also a *Wesleyan Chapel*, erected about thirty years ago, and a small *Bible Christian Chapel*, built in 1836.   *National Schools* for both sexes are supported chiefly by the rector.   The *Poor's Lands, &c.*, which have been vested in trust from an early period, for the repairs of the church and the relief of the poor, comprise a farm of 56A., at Winkleigh, and fifteen tenements in this parish.   They are let for about £60 per annum.   This parish has £10 a year from *Mrs. Pyncombe's Charity* for schooling poor children, and an annuity of 40s. for a poor widow.   (See Poughill.)   The *Rev. Wm. Osborne, D.D.*, left 4A. of land at Ottery St. Mary, in trust to distribute the yearly proceeds among the poor of Chulmleigh, except 20s. for a sermon on Good Friday.   It is now let for £10 a year.   The poor have also the dividends of £185. 16s. 10d. three per cent. consols, purchased with £100 left by *John Shapland*, in 1803.

Armsworth Thos. wine & spirit mert.
Babbage Lnce. regr. & relvg. officer
Bird Mrs Ann ‖ Chanter Miss E.
Bond John, maltster & hop mert.

Brooks Wm. machine maker
Brownscombe Wm. brazier & plmbr.
Crispin Henry, jun., land agent and surveyor, *Lodge*

Croote Thos. stamp distr. & agent to West of England Ins. Company.
Davy Rev Wm. Tanner, M.A. curate
Davy John Croote, surgeon
Hoidge Joseph, (Bible Ctn. min)
Hole Rev G., B.C.L., rector of Chulmleigh & North Tawton, & preby. of Exeter; and Rev Robt.,B.A. curate, *Rectory.*
Langdon Wm. maltster
Marshall Mr John & Mr Robert
Mayer Wm. thatcher
Nott John, bookseller & printer
Preston Richard, Esq., *Lee House*
Pyke John, gent. || Parsons W. *sexton*
Pringle George, schoolmaster
Reed John, miller, *Park Mills*
Roberts Roger, constable
Sharp Rev Thomas, (Independent)
Stiling John, auctioneer
Tamlin Chas. plumber & painter
Tidbald John Adams, surgeon
Tipper George, musician
Tuke John, bdg. school, and Mrs Voysey Geo. & Davey Eliz. school
West Richard, veterinary surgeon
Woolway John, corn miller
Wreford John, currier, and agent to the Star Insurance Company
Wreford Samuel, tanner, *Ford*
Young Rev John, (Independent)

INNS AND TAVERNS.
Barnstaple Inn, Wm. Williams
Black Horse, James Ford
Globe, Jane Williams
King's Arms Inn, John Langdon
Lamb Inn, Ann Snell
Red Lion, Wm. Harding, *(auctionr.)*

BAKERS.
Burgess John
Cockram Charles
Nott Wm. Scott

BLACKSMITHS.
Rowden Richard
Tucker Wm.
Warren John
Westcott Robert

BOOT & SHOEMRS.
Adams Wm.
Dunn Wm. & Jno.
Fewins John
Greensade Roger

Harris James
Harris John
Hunt Wm.
Rice Thomas
Richards John
Rudall Robert

BUTCHERS.
Bond Wm.
Webber Richard
Wreford John

CARPENTERS.
Ford Wm.
Ford Wm. jun.
Howell John

Underhill John
Williams George

DRUGGISTS.
Bird Peter
Bond Luce. V.
Sharp Sarah

FARMERS.
Bond Wm.
Bryant John, *Elston*
Butt James
Cheldon John, *Newnham*
Cobley Ann
Dart Richard
Densham Mrs., *Bunson*
Dowdell Wm.
Dunn Henry
Farley John
Farley Wm.
Ford Wm.
Francis Wm.
Grimshire John
Hosegood John, *Parsonage*
Hunt John
Hunt Wm.
Langdon Jno. S.
Leach Thomas
Litchaly Robert
Luxton John
Miller Mrs & W.
Morgan Wm.
Nott Wm.
Passmore Rd.
Pearse W., *Elston*
Pyke Richard
Raymont Rd.
Routcliffe George, *Colleton Barton*
Saunders Geo.
Saunders Jeffry
Smith Mrs Ann
Staddon John
Tucker George
Tucker Joseph
Vickery Robert
Webber Edmund
Webber George, *Challacombe*

Webber William, *Cadbury*
GROCERS & DRS.
Heale Abel, (and watch mkr.)
Langdon Wm.
Marshall Mary, (& irnmongr.)
Norrington Jph.
Potter Wm.
Woof James

MASONS.
Emery Richard
Heale Enoch
Haywood Geo.

MILLINERS.
Cook Elizabeth
Hill Mary
Payne Francis
Smale Mary

SADDLERS.
Dart John
Partridge John

SHOPKEEPERS.
Born Wm. *cooper*
Joint Wm.
Rice John
Warren John

TAILORS.
Brooks Wm.
Elliott James
Elliott John
Heale Wm.
Tolley Charles
Williams John

WHEELWRIGHTS.
Ford Joshua
Hunt George

POST OFFICE
at L. V. Bonds.
Letters via Sth. Molton

COACHES pass to Exeter & South Molton

CARRIERS.
John Tucker, to Bideford, Tues. & Exeter, Thrs.
Wm. Tucker, to Barnstaple, Fr. & Exeter Mon.

CREACOMBE, a small parish on the hilly banks of the Sturcomb rivulet, 10 miles N.W. by W. of Tiverton, has only 58 souls and 1036A. of land. Richard Comins, Esq., is lord of the manor,

but part of the parish belongs to the Trustees of the late Lord Rolle, the Rev. W. P. Thomas, and a few smaller freeholders. The *Church* (St. Michael,) is a small edifice, with two bells in a wooden frame. The *rectory*, valued in K.B at £4. 18s. 9d., and in 1831 at £166, is in the patronage of the Rev. Wm. Karslake, and incumbency of the Rev. W. H. Karslake, B.A., of Meshaw. The glebe is 96A., and the tithes were commuted in 1842 for £44. 11s. 6d. per annum. The *farmers* are Benj. Elston, *West Batsworthy ;* Jno. Smith, Parsonage ; Thomas Tanner, Creacombe Barton ; and John Voysey, *East Batsworthy.*

CRUWYS-MORCHARD is a hilly but fertile parish of scattered houses, from 4 to 5 miles W. of Tiverton ; containing 670 souls, and 5765 acres of land, including the hamlets of *Cotton, Yedbury,* and *Way.* The manor has been held by the Cruwys family since the reign of King John, if not from a much earlier period. The Rev. G. S. Cruwys, M.A., is now lord of the manor, and patron and incumbent of the *rectory*, valued in K.B. at £21. 11s. 8d., and in 1831 at £501. He resides at his ancient family seat, *Cruwys Morchard House,* which has lately been enlarged and modernized, and has a tasteful and well wooded park, mostly planted in 1834-5. The glebe is 130 acres, and the tithes were commuted in 1839 for £506 per annum. The *Church* (Holy Cross,) is an ancient structure, with a massive tower and six bells. A finely carved oak screen divides the nave and chancel. A new road was cut through the parish, and 300 acres of common enclosed, about 12 years ago. The Rev. John Pitman, the Rev. T. A. Melhuish, and several resident freeholders have estates in the parish. Mr. George Ayre owns and occupies *West Ruckham*, which was for many centuries the residence of the ancient family of Drake. The mansion on this estate has recently been altered and much improved, and is pleasantly situated half a mile north of the church. The *National School*, built by the rector in 1844, at the cost of £200, is attended by about 40 children. The poor have the following yearly sums, viz., £2 as the interest of £40 lent to the overseers and churchwardens ; £1. 15s. 4d. left by *Humphrey Brook*, in 1670, out of Beere farm, and £1. 15s. 9d. left by *Robert Gay*, in 1725, out of Lower Yedbury farm. Of the latter, £1 is paid for schooling four poor boys. A poor woman of this parish has 40s. a year from *Mrs. Pyncombe's charity.* (See Poughill.)

Cruwys RevG.S., M.A. rector, *Cruwys Morchard House*
Greenslade Thomas, wheelwright
Hodge John, shopkeeper, *Tong*
Laurie Rev Rd., B.A. curate, *Rectory*
Nichols John, wheelwright
Pope Henry, blacksmith
Rookes Geo. vict. *Mount Pleasant*
Venn Henry, vict. & smith, Cruwys' Arms, *Pennymoor*
Voysey Wm. corn miller

FARMERS. (* are Owners.)
* Ayre George, *West Ruckham*

Badcock Geo. || Beedell John
* Beedell Thos. || Bellamy Rt.
Bidgood John || Bird Richard
* Bodley John, *Lower Park*
Bray John || Elworthy John
Cornwall Fras. || Cornwall Rd.
Fursden John || Griffin Edward
Hunt Wm. *Higher Yedbury*
Kelland John, *East Ruckham*
Kelland Pp. || * Lake John
* Lake Wm., *Edgeworthy*
* Meechem Joseph, *Moor*
Morrish Richd. (parish clerk)

WITHERIDGE HUNDRED. **337**

Norris Robt. || Pook Wm.
Quick James || Raymont John
Redford James || Redford Wm.
Skinner John || Smale Stephen
* Strong Thos. || Thorne Wm.
* Thorne John, *Lower Yedbury*
Thorne Thos. *Yedbury Mill*

Tidbald Wm. || * Tidbald John
*Waller John || Warren John
*Webber Mildred || Webber John
White John, *Thorne*
*Yoysey Geo., *East Cotton*
Post *from Tiverton.*

KING'S NYMPTON is an old irregularly built village of thatched
houses, on a bold eminence overlooking the Taw valley, 3½ miles N.
by W. of Chulmleigh, and 5½ miles S. S. W. of South Molton. Its
parish contains 777 inhabitants and 5539 acres of land, including
many scattered houses, 91A. of orchards, 540A. of woods, and about
900A. of moor and coarse pasture land, which has been brought into
cultivation during the last ten years. The *manor* was anciently part
of the royal demesne, and was given by Henry III. to Roger le
Zouch. It afterwards passed successively to the Cornwall, Pollard,
Northcote, and Buller families. It was purchased about
12 years ago, by its present owner, James Tanner, Esq., of *King's
Nympton Park*, a handsome and pleasant seat on the east bank of
the small river Mole, near its confluence with the River Taw. The
mansion stands on a commanding eminence, in a large and well-
wooded park, and was built by the late James Buller, Esq., who
died in 1765. The Park was enclosed, and the original mansion
erected in the reign of Henry VII., by Sir Lewis Pollard. The present owner has greatly improved the house and grounds, and built
a new bridge over the Mole. He owns the greater part of the parish,
and has brought much of the moor land into fine cultivation. Mrs.
Byne has a manor here, formerly belonging to the Brown and Melhuish families; and part of the parish belongs to several smaller
owners. The *Church* (St. James,) is a fine ancient structure, with a
tower, crowned by a tall wooden spire, which was covered with lead
in 1833, at the cost of £200. The *rectory*, valued in K.B. at £28.
6s. 8d., and in 1831 at £315, is in the patronage and incumbency of
the Rev. F. A. Savile, who has a thatched residence and 96A. 1R. 18P.
of glebe. The tithes were commuted in 1842 for £462. 19s. 10d.
The Bible Christians have a small chapel here. The *Charity School*,
for 40 boys and 20 girls, was long supported by the late *John Buller*,
Esq., who endowed it with £500, three per cent. consols. The poor
parishioners have the interest of £50 left by *Richard Hele*, in 1759,
and of £25 left by various donors. They have also the dividends of
£152. 7s. 7d. three per cent stock, purchased with £100 left by
Abraham Tossel, in 1773. A poor widow of this parish has 40s. a
year from Mrs. Pyncombe's charity.

Adams John, vict., New Inn
Gumner Ann, shopkeeper
Laddy Wm. schoolr. & Peter, sexton
Moore James, miller, *Wampford*
Passmore Richard, beerhouse
Savile Rev Fredk. A., *Rectory*
Tanner J. Esq., *King'sNymptonPrk.*
Tolley James, tailor

Venn Eliz. vict., Carpenters' Arms
BLACKSMITHS.
Blake Thomas
Knight Wm.
Moore Edward
Simons John
BOOT & SHOEMRS.
Selley John

Selley Richard
Snell James
CARPENTERS.
Ayre Wm.
Hulland Wm.
Knight Wm. *wgt.*

P

COOPERS.	Carter Thomas	Hulland Samuel	* Passmore John
Baker Henry	Ching John	Hunt Richard	Reed John
Crawys James	Darke John	Jarman John	Saunders John
FARMERS.	Dart Francis	* Kemp Jno. Bird	Shapland Cphr.
(* are Owners.)	Dennis Thomas	*Bull Marsh*	Shapland Jph.
Adams Wm.	Downe Elias	KempWm. *Down*	* Skinnar Thos.
* Buckingham A.	Follett George	Lake Jno. *Yeotn*	Webber John
* Buckingham ⎱ Rd., *Callacott* ⎰	Greenslade Ths.	Ley Geo., *Pixey*	Webber Samuel
	Halse John	Ley Wm., *Hele*	POST, &c., from
* Buckingham ⎱ Wm., *Oakwell* ⎰	Hancock James	Luxton Richard	South Molton
	Hancock John	Mildon Henry	& Chulmleigh

MARIANSLEIGH, or *Mary Ansleigh*, a small village on an eminence above the Mole valley, nearly 4 miles S.S.E. of South Molton, has in its parish 338 souls, and 1740 acres of land, including the hamlets of *Alswear* and *Kemp Town*, and many scattered houses. About 540 acres of moor and open pasture land were broken up in 1849. Sir H. R. F. Davie, Bart., is lord of the manor and owner of a great part of the parish, and the rest belongs to Mr. Wm. Toms, Mr. F. A. Cockram, and several smaller proprietors. Mr. Cockram owns Kemp Town, and is about to build several new dwellings there. The *Church* (St. Mary,) is an ancient structure, with a tower and four bells. The living is a discharged *perpetual curacy,* valued in 1831 at £120. The Rev. Geo. James Gould, of Nympton St. George, is the incumbent, and the patronage is in the Charity Trustees of Exeter, as trustees of *John Davye's Almshouses* in that city, founded in the 42nd of Elizabeth. (See page 107.) The founder of these almshouses endowed the perpetual curacy with the great tithes, except the yearly payment thereout of £16, to the above-named almshouses. The glebe is only 2A. 6P., and there is no parsonage house. The tithes were commuted in 1839, for £165. 10s. per annum. In the village is an *Independent Chapel*, built in 1840. The *National School* was erected by the late Sir H. P. Davie, Bart. In 1641, *John Davie, Esq.*, charged the manor with the payment of £6. 10s. yearly to the incumbent for preaching a sermon on Sunday afternoons and catechising the children. The poor have the interest of £20 given by Nicholas Sanger and Henry Adams, in 1707 and 1811. They have also an annuity of 10s. out of the tithes, given by an unknown donor. In the following Directory, those marked 1, are in *Alswear;* and 2, at *Kemp Town*.

1 Babbage Gilbert, butcher, &c.
1 Bird Edward, corn miller
Crewys George, parish clerk
Crewys Wm. assistant overseer
Eastmond John, butcher
Eastmond Elizabeth, schoolmistress
1 Eastmond James, wheelwright
2 Eastmond Humphry, shoemaker
Eastmond Susan, vict. King's Arms
Fewings James, sexton
1 Lockyer Jane, vict. Butcher's Arms
1 Tucker Saml. vict. White Hart
White Mrs Charlotte, *Yeo*

BLACKSMITHS.
2 Adams John
2 Holmes Wm.
1 Moore George
1 Vickery John
CARPENTERS.
2 Adams Wm.
1 Eastmond John
FARMERS.
(* are Owners.)
Adams Wm.
Ayre Thomas
Babbage Wm.

Bennett George, *Moorhouse*
Carter Jas.,*Lower Uppercott*
Chapple James
*Cockram Fras. Jno. *Tidlake*
Davey John
Eastmond John
Harris Robert
1*Kemp John
Lewis John
Matthews Wm.

Mills Wm.	1 Tucker John	Crewys Wm.	1 Tucker Samuel
Pitt Edw. *Furze*	Tucker Wm.	TAILORS.	Webber John
*Toms Wm. *Yeo*	MASONS.	Hill Robert	
Trebble George	Crewys George	1 Lockyer Wm.	

MESHAW is a small village, at the foot of a declivity, nearly 6 miles S.E. by S. of South Molton, and 14 miles N.W. by W. of Tiverton. Its parish encreased its population from 166 in 1831, to 305 in 1841, and comprises 1770A. 3R. 30P. of land, part of which (about 700A.) was an open moor 20 years ago, but is now enclosed and cultivated. It is a hilly district, over which a new road was cut about ten years ago. The manor was held by the Avenells, in the 13th and 14th centuries, and was afterwards in moieties. The greater share now belongs to Richard Preston, Esq., and the rest belongs to John Brown, Wm. Adams, Robert Eastmond, and a few smaller freeholders. The *Church* (St. John Baptist,) was mostly rebuilt in 1838, except the tower, which has four bells. It is a small structure, and contains a handsome monument of James Courtenay, who died in 1683, at Meshaw House, now occupied by a farmer. The living is a discharged *rectory,* valued in K.B. at £7. 4s., and in 1831 at £206, in the patronage of the Rev. W. Karslake, and incumbency of the Rev. W. H. Karslake, B.A., who has a good residence and 83A. 3R. 39P. of glebe. The tithes were commuted in 1838, for £110 per annum. In the village is a National School, and on the Moor is a school and chapel belonging to the Bible Christians, built in 1839.

Boundy John, shopkeeper and clerk
Cockram Humphrey, thatcher
Cockram John, mason
Eastmond Robert, corn miller, &c.
Fewings Simon, tailor, Moor
Hooper John, wheelwright
Karslake Rev. Wm. Heberden, B.A., *Rectory*
Ley Wm. carpenter
Mayne Wm. vict. New Inn, *Moor*
Moore John, blacksmith
Pyke Fanny, schoolmistress
Poole Wm. shopkeeper
Rudd John, schoolmaster and shopr
Saunders Robert, vict. Gidley Arms
BOOT & SHOEMRS.
Garnsey Wm.
Joslin Robt.*Moor*
Saxton Robert
FARMERS.
Boundy George
Brown John
BuckinghamEliz.
Cockram George
Fewings John
Friend Samuel
Kemp John
Stoneman Robert
Ware Thomas
Webber Elizabth. *South Hall*
Webber John, *Meshaw House*

OAKFORD, or *Okeford*, a village on a bold acclivity, between the Exe and one of its tributary streams, 3 miles W. by S. of Bampton, and 8 miles N.N.W. of Tiverton, has in its parish 641 souls, and 5251 acres of land, rising in lofty hills on the north and west. The *manor* was anciently held by the Montacutes, and afterwards by the Pollards. Thomas Daniel, Esq., now owns three-fourths of it, and the rest belongs to the Rev. J. Spurway; but J. Browne, Esq., and a few smaller freeholders, have estates in the parish. The *Church* (St. Peter,) was rebuilt about 12 years ago, and has a tower and eight bells. The organ was given by the late Mrs. Parkin, and a school has been built at her expense. The *rectory,* valued in K.B. at £24, and in 1831 at £384, is in the patronage and incumbency of the Rev. James Parkin, M.A., who has a good residence and 90A. of glebe. The tithes were commuted in 1844, for £437 per annum.

This parish has yearly £5 for schooling poor children, and 40s. each for a poor man and woman, from *Mrs. Pyncombe's Charity*. (See Poughill.) For distribution in bread the poor have £3 a year left by *Richard Hill*, alias Spurway, in 1630, out of three closes.

Arlett Francis, corn miller, *Bridge*
Court Edward, smith & wheelwright
Farmer Daniel, mason and baker
Farmer James, vict. Red Lion
Gunn Wm. schoolmr. & shopkeeper
Langworthy George, vict. Red Deer
Machin James, Esq. *Hamslade*
Melhuish Thomas, blacksmith
Mogford James, beer seller
Parkin Rev James, M.A., *Rectory*
Turner Robert, tailor and draper
Vicary Thomas, carpenter
Winsborrow Wm. boot & shoe maker

Wood Arthur, blacksmith

FARMERS.

Browne Wm. *Stuckeridge*
Browne John, (and *Sandford*)
Bucknell Elias || Channing Robert
Dascombe Gregory || Gibbins Wm.
Haywood Thomas, *Spurway*
Heale Arthur || Hodge Philip
Mildon Michael || Mogford John
Mogford Wm. || Ridler Robert
Snow Robert || Venner Isaac
Vicary George || Vicary Robert
Webber James, *East Loosemoor*

HIGHTLEIGH, or *Highley St. Mary*, is an extra parochial farm and manor, on the hills adjoining Oakford parish, and the borders of Somerset, 4 miles W. by N. of Bampton. It had anciently a chapel, and its land and assessed taxes are collected by the parish officers of Stoodleigh. It belongs to the Trustees of the late Lord Rolle, and is occupied by Mr. Henry Maunder.

PUDDINGTON, or *Podington*, a small village, on an eminence near the source of the river Creedy, 7 miles N. of Crediton, and 8 miles W. by S. of Tiverton, has in its parish 212 souls, and 1361A. of land. The manor belonged at an early period to the Sachvilles, and afterwards to the Walronds. It now belongs, with most of the soil, to C. N. Welman, Esq., of *Puddington Lodge*, a neat thatched residence in the Italian style, on a commanding eminence. The *Church* (St. Thomas-a-Beckett,) has a tower and three bells, and has been mostly rebuilt—the north aisle in 1838, and the nave and chancel in 1848. The *rectory*, valued in K.B. at £6. 8s. 1½d., and in 1831 at £136, is in the patronrge of C N. Welman, Esq., and incumbency of the Rev. David Llewellyn, who has a good residence on a lofty eminence, commanding beautiful prospects, extending to the two coasts of Devon. The glebe is 64A. 3R. 12P., and the tithes were commuted in 1838, for £131. Here is a *National School*, built in 1849, and an *Independent Chapel*, which was built by Presbyterians, about 200 years ago, and has 18A. of land, let for £30, and left by a Mr. Melhuish, towards the support of the minister. The poor parishioners have the interest of £42 given by various donors, and a yearly rent charge of 20s., left by *Humphrey Brook*, in 1670, out of Bere farm.

Foss Wm. carpenter
Greenslade Wm. blacksmith
Llewellyn Rev David, *Rectory*
Vickery Jane, schoolmistress
Welman Charles N., Esq. *Lodge*
White James, shopkeeper and *carrier to Exeter*

FARMERS. (* *are Owners.*)

*Blagdon John || Born Wm.
Crook John ||Manning Robert
Martin Wm. || Waller Edmund
Pugsley John, (butcher,) *Newhouse*
Waller John || Waller Wm.
*Wensley Anthony|| *Wensley James
Wreford John, *Coombe*

RACKENFORD, an ancient village, on the high road, 8 miles W.N.W. of Tiverton, and 18 miles E.S.E. of South Molton, is described as a *borough* in some old records, and had formerly a *market*, granted in 1235, together with an annual *fair*. The latter is still held for the sale of *lambs, &c.*, on the 8th of July, or on the following day, if that date falls on a Sunday. Here is also a small *cattle fair*, which has been held on the Wednesday before the 19th of September, since 1776. RACES are held on or about the last Thursday in July. The parish had 562 inhabitants, on July 1st, 1841, but 59 of them were visitors at the annual feast. It contains 3933A. 2R. 37P. of land, rising in bold hills near the sources of the Little Dart river, and comprising many scattered houses. Chas. Devon, Esq., is lord of the *manor*, for which a court leet and baron is held yearly by Mark Kennaway, Esq., the steward. The former resides at the old manor house, called *Cruwyshaye*, formerly a seat of the Sydenham and Cruwys families. J. G. Pearse and Wm. Hole, Esqrs., and Messrs. Thos. Ayre, M. Thomas, W. Cockram, Robert Tanner, and several smaller freeholders have estates in the parish. There is a *common* of about 30 acres, in which is a never failing spring of pure water. The *Church* (Holy Trinity,) is a small antique fabric, with a tower and five bells, and a finely sculptured font. The *rectory*, valued in K.B. at £19. 17s. 1½d., and in 1831 at 335, is in the patronage of Thomas Comyns, Esq., and incumbency of the Rev. Wm. Comyns, M.A., who has a good residence and 54A. 31P. of glebe. The tithes were commuted in 1842, for £327 per annum. A small Bible Christian chapel was built here in 1848, and a neat *National School* was erected in 1848-'9. The late Rev. John Comyns left the interest of £10 for the poor, who have also the interest of £128, left by the Rev. John Barnes, Thos. Kemp, and other donors; and £2. 14s. a year out of West Bradley and Edgerley farms, left by Humphrey Brooke, in 1670.

Collard John, vict. Bell Inn
Comyns Rev Wm., M.A., rector of Rackenford and vicar of Hockworthy, *Rectory*
Devon Charles, Esq. *Cruwyshaye Hs*
Hill Mrs Mary || Ayre Mr Francis
Turner Robert, vict. Stag's Head
Veysey Robert, cattle dealer
Wood Walter, National schoolmaster
Wood Wm. grocer, auctioneer, &c.
Wood Richard, mason

BLACKSMITHS.
Matthews Thos.
Matthews Wm.
Rawle Michael
BOOT&SHOE MRS.
Phillips Jacob

Wood Thomas

CARPENTERS.
Tuke Wm.
Wreford Matthew

FARMERS.
(* *are Owners.*)
Ayre Richard
*Ayre Thomas
Beedell Wm.
*Cockram Wm.
Comins George
Crewys Wm.
Downey John
Furze James
Gibbins Joseph
*Gunn Thomas
Hawkins John
Kent John
Kent Robert
Maunder Thos.
Moore Richard
Norrish Michael

Reed John
Snell Robert
*TannerRichard, *Middlecott*
Turner Philip
Veysey Richard
Veysey Wm.
Webber John
Webber Joseph
Webber Wm.
TAILORS.
Davey George
Haskings Wm.
Way Robert
WHEELWRIGHTS.
Haskings John
Matthews George

ROMANSLEIGH, or *Rumonsleigh*, commonly called *Rumsleigh*, is a small sequestered village, 4 miles S. by E. of South Molton,

and has in its parish 239 souls, and 2491A. 2R. 34P. of land, generally fertile, and rising to a lofty eminence, called *Beacon Hill*, said
to be one of the highest points in the county. The Abbey of Tavistock, in which St. Rumon, the patron saint of the church, was
buried, had an estate in this parish, and there was anciently a
monk here from the collegiate establishment at Culmleigh, under
the visitorial control of the abbot. Sir T. D. Acland, Bart., is lord
of the manor, but a great part of the parish belongs to the Trustees
of the late Lord Rolle, and several smaller proprietors. The *Church*
(St. Rumon,) is an ancient structure, with a tower containing three
bells, and overshadowed by six beautiful pine trees, formerly forming part of a long avenue to the Rectory House. The chancel was
rebuilt in 1829, and in the interior is a fine Saxon font. The
rectory, valued in K.B. at £10. 14s. 9½d., and in 1831 at £208, is in
the patronage of Sir T. D. Acland, and incumbency of the Rev.
John Bond, M.A., of Stoke Canon. The glebe is extensive, and the
tithes were commuted in 1839, for £200 per annum. The Rectory
House is a neat thatched residence, occupied by the Rev. J. H.
Bond, B.A., who has provided a house for the schoolmistress. The
school room was given by Sir T. D. Acland. The poor parishioners
have 4s. a year left by Thomas Packer, and the interest of £7 left
by five donors.

Adams Wm. vict. Bell Inn
Carter John, blacksmith
Eastmond Wm., carpenter
Hulland My., & Lion John, schools
Parker James, vict. Royal Oak
Polterman John, shoemaker
   FARMERS. (* are Owners.)
*Adams Grace, *Bendbon*
*Adams John, High Thorndon
Ayre John || Drake Mary

Cooke Anthony, *West Rowley*
*Fentiman Alfred, *Hillcott*
Foard Robert, *Lower Thorndown*
Hunt John || Kemp Edward
Manning John, *Little Rowley*
Partridge Samuel, *Horridge*
Veysey Wm., *Odam*
Webber John, *East Rowley*
Webber Wm., *Romansleigh Barton*

ROSE-ASH, formerly called *Ralph Esse*, is a pleasant village, on
an eminence, 6 miles S.E. by E. of South Molton, and has in its
parish 541 souls, and 4987A. 3R. 27P. of land, rising in bold hills
on the east and north, and comprising the hamlet of *Yard*, and
many scattered houses, bearing different names. The manor belonged, in the reign of Henry III., to Ralph de Esse. The three
daughters of Sir Ralph Esse carried it in three moities to the
families of Dennis, Gifford, and Halse. Dennis's share passed in
marriage to the Glynns, and has been sold in parcels, and the other
shares passed to the Downe, Smith, Davy, and other families. J.
T. Davy, Esq., and the Rev. E. Southcombe and his family own a
portion of the manor, and Mr. Davy receives a yearly high and chief
rent from Halse' or Smith's share. The Rev. W. H. Karslake, W.
T. Southcombe, T. Loveband. J. A. Thomas, the Rev. W. P. Thomas,
and several smaller owners have estates in the parish. The ancient
lords of the manor had the power of inflicting capital punishment.
The *Church* (St. Peter,) is an ancient structure, with a tower and
five bells, and the *rectory*, valued in K.B. at £18. 19s. 7d., and in
1831 at £469, is in the patronage and incumbency of the Rev. E.

Southcombe, M.A., who lately rebuilt the Rectory House, and has 105A. 3R. 9P. of glebe. The tithes were commuted in 1841 for £450 per annum. The National School was built in 1848, and the poor and school have the dividends of £189. 4s. three per cent. consols, purchased with £133 left by various donors. *Mr. J. A. Thomas*, of this parish, is a noted cattle breeder, and has carried off many prizes from the shows at Exeter and other places.

Cock Wm. maltster, and vict. Angel, *Ash Mill*

Crispin Mary Ann, shopkeeper

Davy John Tanner, Esq., *Higher-Ash-Town*

Hosegood Wm. shopkeeper

Levin J., National schoolmaster

Pester Wm. wheelgt. and parish clerk

Southcombe Rev Edmond, M.A., *Rectory*

Tapp Geo. & Wm. blacksmiths

FARMERS. (* *are Owners.*)

*Adams John, Wood Hill

Ayre John, *Beckwell*

Ayre Wm. *Rodsworthy*

Blake Joseph || Bond Thomas

Buckingham Miss S., *West Quince*

Buckingham Samuel, *Munson*

Burgess John || Chanter Wm.

*Carter Wm., *Nutcombe*

Clark John || Clark Wm.

Crocombe Wm., *East Ford*

Fewings John || Fewings Robert

Headon James || Hill Edmund

Hepper Robert, *West Catkill*

Kemp John || Locke Philip

*Loosemore James, *North Yard*

*Loosemore Robert, *Overcott*

Luxton Wm., *South Yard*

*Partridge James || Venner Jacob

Reed John, *Frankhill*

Rodd John, West Pearcey

*Southcombe John, Dansdown

*Tanner Wm., *Nethercott*

*Thomas John Ayre, *Ditchet*

Towler Isaac || Tucker Robert

*Veysey Wm. || Veysey James

Warren John || Westacott Wm.

STOODLEIGH, or *Studley*, a straggling village, on an acclivity, 6 miles N.N.W. of Tiverton, and 3½ miles S.S.W. of Bampton, has in its parish 537 souls, and 4336A. of land, extending eastward to the river Exe, and comprising many scattered houses. One of the lofty hills on the west side of the parish, is called *Stoodleigh Beacon*, or Warbrightsleigh Hill, and is said to have had a beacon erected upon it by order of Edward II. The *manor* was anciently held by the Champeaux and Marchant families, and afterwards by the Fitzpayne, Anstill, Kelly, Carew, Brickdale, and Fitzakerley families. Thomas Daniel, Esq., is now lord of the manor, and resides at *Stoodleigh Court*, a neat mansion in a small park, commanding extensive prospects. The Teale, Palmer, and other families have freehold estates in the parish. The *Church* (St. Margaret,) has a tower and five bells; and the *rectory*, valued in K.B. at £20. 0s. 2¼d., and in 1831 at £395, is in the patronage of T. Daniel, Esq., and incumbency of the Rev. Joseph Bockett, M.A., of Washfield. The Rectory House is a neat building with tasteful grounds, and the glebe is 30A. The tithes were commuted in 1841 for £407 per annum. The *Parish School*, adjoining the churchyard, was built in 1847, by T. Daniel, Esq., at the cost of £220. In 1668, *Eliz. Carew* left £400 for the equal benefit of the poor of this parish and Crowcombe, in Somersetshire. This legacy was laid out in the purchase of 33A. of land in the latter parish, now let for about £45 per annum. There is also belonging to this charity £114, which arose from the sale of timber. The poor of Stoodley have half of this charity, and also the interest of £10 left by *Wm. Abraham*, in 1724.

Berry James, blacksmith
Calway John, baker
Cann George James, tailor
Daniel Thos., Esq., *Stoodleigh Court*
Gordon Wm. shopkr. & parish clerk
Heathcoat Wm. shoemaker
Heathfield Thomas, land surveyor
Marley John, butcher & vict. New Inn
Osborne James, wheelwright
Richey Rev James, M.A. curate, and chaplain to the Earl of Charlemont, *Rectory*
Selley John, carpenter
Thorne John, gamekeeper
Venner Abraham, gardener
Venner Margaret, schoolmistress
Woost James, accountant

FARMERS.

Beedell John, *Stoodleigh Barton*
Beedell Robt. (miller) Holridge
Beedell Wm. || Blake Henry
Bere Thomas, *West Whiteknoll*
Bidgood John || Carpenter Thomas
Bowden David || Bowden Wm.
Channing Geo. || Channing Robert
Edwards Richd. || Greenslade John
Greenslade Wm. || Hatswell John
Hewish Andrew, *Warbrightsleigh*
Lock John, *East Stoodleigh*
Loosemore George, *Blatchworthy*
Mugford Geo. || Sayer Jas., *Ford*
Payne Thomas, *Broadmead*
Venner Christopher, *Great Coleford*

TEMPLETON, a parish of scattered houses, from 5 to 6 miles W.N.W. of Tiverton, contains 275 souls, and 1891A. 2R. 24P. of land, picturesquely broken into hill and valley, and traversed by a small rivulet. The manor belonged at an early period to the Knights Templars, and afterwards to the Knights Hospitallers, and is a peculiar jurisdiction. After the dissolution it was granted to George Loosemore, and it afterwards passed to the Periam, Pole, and Chichester families. Joseph Chichester Nagle, Esq., is now lord of the manor, but Lady Constable, the Chichester family, and others have freehold estates in the parish. The *Church* (St. Margaret,) is an ancient structure, with a tower and three bells. It is now in a very dilapidated state, and ought to be speedily repaired. It was dedicated in 1439, and in 1335 the original fabric was called a chapel to Witheridge. The *rectory*, valued in K.B. at £8. 15s., and in 1831 at £178, is in the patronage of Sir J. G. De la Pole, Bart., and incumbency of the Rev. Edward Pole, M.A., who has a pleasant residence and 86A. of glebe. The tithes were commuted in 1842, for £160 per annum. The poor parishioners have 20s. a year out of Bere farm, at Cruwys-Morchard, left by *Humphrey Brooke*, in 1670. Several other small charities are lost.

Cornwell Wm. corn miller
Cottrell Mary, schoolmistress
Knowles John, wheelwright
Matthews John, blacksmith
Partridge Amos, parish clerk
Pole Rev Edward, M.A. *Rectory*
Way John, tailor, grocer, &c.

FARMERS. (* *are Owners.*)

Beedell Joseph || Besley George
Blake Robert || Blake Wm.
Chamberlin Roger, *Cleve*
Collins John, *Ashley*
Jackson George || Rowe Wm.
*Maunder George, *Colstone*
Stevens Wm. || White Henry
*Wreford George, *Middle Town*

THELBRIDGE, a parish of scattered houses, 8½ miles N.N.W. of Crediton, and 6½ miles E. by S. of Chulmleigh, has 267 inhabitants, and 2240 acres of land, bounded on the north by the Little Dart and on the south by Washford rivulet. The manor was successively held by the Charteray, Annelegh, Binley, Stewkly, Shortridge, and Pearse families. It now belongs to John Partridge, Esq., but

the Rev. W. P. Thomas, T. C. Lake, Esq., W. Summers, Esq., Mr. G. Bennett, and several others have freehold estates in the parish. The *Church* (St. David,) is a small ancient fabric, with a tower and five bells. The *rectory*, valued in K.B. at £10. 6s. 5½d., and in 1831 at £220, is in the patronage of Sir Robert Price, Bart., and incumbency of the Rev. W. Y. Draper, B.A., who has a good residence and 148A. 2R. 13P. of glebe. The tithes were commuted in 1844, for £161. 14s. 3d. per annum. For schooling poor children this parish has the interest of £40, left by *Penelope Sydenham.* The poor have three yearly doles, viz., a rent charge of 20s. left by Humphrey Brooke, in 1670, out of Edgerley estate, in Cruwys Morchard; 5s. out of a tenement, left by Richard Greenslade; and 21s., as the interest of £26, given by several donors.

Adams Mr Ths. & Miss, *Provdnce. pl*
Chapple John, parish clerk
Draper Rev Wm. Yorke, B.A. *Rectory*
Greenslade Wm. vict. Rising Sun
Lake Thos. C., Esq., *Champner*
Northcott Mrs Elizabeth, *Bicking House*
Summers Wm., Esq., *Woodhouse*
Weeks Henry, innkeeper, *Cross*

FARMERS. (* *are Owners.*)
*Bennett Geo. *Lower Summerville*
Brydges Jas. Davis || Downey John
Garnsey John || *Northcott George
Leach John P., *Thelbridge Barton*
Leach Robert, *Higher Summerville*
*Partridge Sar. & Mary, *Woodfield*
Raymond Richard || Thorne George
Vickery James, *Buddleswick*

WASHFORD PYNE, a small village, on the banks of a rivulet, 9 miles W. of Tiverton and E. of Chulmleigh, has in its parish 197 souls, and 1600 acres of land, including the small hamlets of *Higher and Lower Black Dog*, and several scattered houses. The manor formerly belonged to the Pyne, Hacche, and other families. The Rev. Comyns Tucker, M.A., is now lord of the manor, owner of a great part of the soil, and patron and incumbent of the *rectory*, valued in K.B. at £6. 0s. 2d½., and in 1831 at £144. The *Church* (St. Peter,) is a small structure, with a tower, containing three bells, and crowned by a short spire. The tithes were commuted in 1842, for £90 per annum. Mr. Thos. Bragg owns *Wenham*, where there was anciently a chapel, and several other freeholders have estates here. The poor parishioners have the interest of £12, given by various donors. In the following Directory, *those marked* 1 *are at Higher, and* 2 *at Lower Black Dog* :—

2 Chapple Robert, shopkeeper
2 Chapple Aaron and John, tailors
2 Chappel John, wheelwright
2 Greenslade James, blacksmith
1 Rattenbury Mary, vict. *Black Dog*
1 Salter Wm. shoemaker
2 Sturges Samuel, mason
1 Symons James, shopr. & smith
Tucker Rev Comyns, M.A. *rector*

.2 Turner John, carpenter
Voysey Wm. miller, Pyneford mill

FARMERS.
Bragg Thomas (owner,) *Wenham*
Bragg Wm. || Bodley Mr
Camm John, *Parsonage*
Elworthy Daniel || Madge John
Selley George || Vinnicombe Wm.

WITHERIDGE, a small, clean, and well-built town, with an open square, or market place, in the centre, gives name to this hundred, and is pleasantly situated on the south-eastern acclivity of the valley of the Little Dart river, 10 miles W. of Tiverton, 9 miles S.E. by S. of South Molton, and 8 miles E. of Chulmleigh. Its

parish contains 1399 inhabitants, and 9048 acres of land, on both sides of the river, picturesquely broken into hill and valley, and including many scattered farm-houses, &c. Witheridge was anciently a *borough*, governed by a portreeve, and had a weekly market, which was disused before 1774. It has still an annual *fair*, on Midsummer day, and *great cattle markets*, on the last Wednesday but one in April, on the Wednesday before Michaelmas-day, and on the first Wednesday in Nov. The *Agricultural Association* of Witheridge and six neighbouring parishes, has a numerous list of members, and holds its meetings and ploughing matches here. The *manor and hundred* of Witheridge were successively held by the Fitzpayne, Poleyne, Marchant, Chichester, and other families. The Hon. Newton Fellowes is now lord of the manor, and owner of a great part of the parish, and the rest belongs to the Rev. W. P. Thomas, and many smaller freeholders. A court leet and baron is held for the manor yearly at the Angel Inn, as also is a court of the Duchy of Lancaster. Mr. W. Croote is steward of the former, and Mr. T. M. Comins of the latter. The small manor of *Bradford Tracey* belongs to the Rev. W. P. Thomas, and was formerly the residence of the Melhuish family, who had previously resided at *Dart Ralph*, an ancient farm-house, belonging to J. H. Tremayne, Esq. *West Yeo*, formerly belonging to the Coplestons, is now the property of Mr. W. B. Adams. *Wm. Chapple*, the antiquary and editor of Risdon, was born at *New House*, or Lower West-Yeo, and in 1781 bequeathed a large prayer-book, to be used at the altar-table of the parish church. This book had once belonged to the royal chapel at Windsor, and was given by the vicar, in 1844, to *Mr. Wm Thorne*, of Dart Ralph, in testimony of his valuable services as churchwarden for more than 20 years. The *Church* (St. John,) is a large and handsome structure, with a tower, which contains five bells, and was heightened 40 feet a few years ago, when the ancient decayed wooden spire was taken down. The east window was enriched with stained glass in 1843, at the expense of the patron. The nave and chancel are neatly fitted up, and the pulpit and font are elaborately carved. The *rectory*, valued in K.B. at £23. 10s. 5d., and in 1831 at £350, is in the patronage of the Rev. W. P. Thomas, and incumbency of the Rev. J. P. Benson, M.A., for whom a new Vicarage House is about to be erected. The glebe is 49A. 2R. 32P. In 1837, the small tithes were commuted for £355 per annum. The patron owns the rectorial manor, formerly belonging to Cannington Priory, but part of the great tithes belong to Mrs. Melhuish. Here is an *Independent* and also a *Bible Christian Chapel*, the former built in 1839, and the latter in 1834. The former cost £650, and in connexion with it is a *School*, built by subscription in 1845, at the cost of £330. A large *National School* was built in 1846, in lieu of the old parish school, at the cost of £400. The old school, with a house and garden for the master, was given in 1804 by *Richard Melhuish*, who endowed it with £700 three per cent. consols, in trust to apply the dividends yearly as follows:—£14 to the master for teaching 40 poor children to read, and the remaining £7 to be laid out in books for the scholars. The vicar and churchwardens

are the trustees. The *Poor's Money* consists of £263. 16s. 7d. three
per cent. stock, and £55 at interest. It arose from a legacy of £100,
left by *Hugh Shortridge, D.D.*, in 1715, and from several small
benefactions. The yearly proceeds (about £10) are distributed at
Christmas, together with £3 from two rent-charges left by *Humphrey
Brooke*, in 1670; and 5s. a year out of Gunhole estate, left by *Richd.
Greenslade.* In the following Directory, those *marked* 1 *are in East*,
2 *South, and* 3 *in West Quarters.*

Babb and Drake, milliners
Benson Rev John Peter, M.A. *vicar*
Bodley Wm. corn miller
Bodley Miss Eliz. || Cobley Misses
Burgess Wm. high constable, &c
Churchill Ann, straw hat maker
Churchill Richard, saddler
Cole Mrs Ann || Collaton Misses
Cole Mr Wm. || Hicks Mr Edwin
Comins Andrew, auctioneer
Comins Mary, grocer and draper
Comins Mrs Mary, *Lawn Cottage*
Comins Richard, Esq. *Stourton Cotg*
Comins Thos. par. clk. & schoolmr
Comins Thomas Melhuish, solicitor,
  clerk to tax commissioners, and
  agent to West of Eng.Insurance Co
Comins Wm. solicitor, clerk to ma-
  gistrates,master ext.in chancery,&c
Coster and Haley, surgeons
Coster Robert Joseph, surgeon
Crook Wm. miller, *Bradford Mill*
Crook Wm. thatcher
Davey Hy. glazier & timber mercht
3 Down Mr Michael, Park Cottage
Ford Wm. cooper
Gardner Mrs Mary, *Rose Mount*
Haley Philip Furneaux, surgeon
O'Neil Rev Wm. (Independent)
2 Partridge Mr James & Miss Eliza
2 Partridge John, gent. Mansion
2 Partridge Mr John, jun. Mill
Phillips George, miller, *Drayford*
Pullen Henry, grocer, draper, drug-
  gist, stamp distributor, and agent
  to Norwich Union Insurance Co
Southcott John, currier
Symons Wm. *Independent schoolmr*
Thorne Wm. organist
Turner John, machine maker
Western Misses, milliners, &c
INNS AND TAVERNS.
Angel Inn, John Brawn
Black Dog Inn, Hugh Foxford
Bell Inn, Richard Churchill
Commercial Inn, Wm. Rippin

Hare and Hounds, Samuel Foxford
BAKERS.
Brawn James
Burgess Henry
BLACKSMITHS.
Dinner John
Gratton George
3 Greenslade Jno.
Moore John
BOOT &SHOE MRS.
8 Anstey Samuel
Blackmore Jas.
Crook Wm.
Manning Wm.
Nichols Joseph
Wey James
BUTCHERS.
Easterbrook Wm.
3 Middleton Jno.
Wreford George
CARPENTERS.
3 Anstey John
Brawn John
Cockram John
Cockram Wm.
Mitchell Richard
3 Moss Wm.
3 Tapp Wm.
Western Thomas
  (and builder)
FARMERS.
(* *are Owners.*)
Adams Alex. *Yeo*
3 Adams John
3*AdamsWm. B.,
  West Yeo
3 Adams Samuel
3*Ansty Wm.
1*Ayre Richard
1*Ayre Sar.*Queen
  Dart*
1 Baker Thomas
2Baker Jno. *Hele*
3 Bater Wm.
1 Blake James
2 Blake Abel

2 Bragg Wm.
2 Brayley Henry
1 Burrows John,
  Wilson's
2 Butt Wm.
2 Clapp James
Cole Abm. *Pelvn*
Cole John
1*Cornell George
2 Crook Thomas
1*Davy George,
  Mabson
*Elworthy Rd.
2 Elworthy Wm.
2 Fewins Wm.
Foxford Hugh
3 Foxford Saml.
3 Foxford Wm.
Furnis George
Heard Thomas,
3 Hill Wm.
3 Kemp Peter
LeachJn.Comins,
  Essebeer
1 Norrish Richd.
2*PartridgeJas H
2 Partridge Jas.
2*Partridge Jno.
Pickard Wm. *Old
  Hele's*
Pillar James
*Rattenbury Ths.
  H. *New House*
3 Rippin James
Rippin Wm.
1 Smale Wm.
1*Thorne Wm.
  Elworthy, *Leat*
3*Thorne Wm.,
  Dart Ralph*
1 Townsend Hy
3 Tucker Saml.
3 Vickery John
1 Westacott Jas.
3 Webber Wm.

| White Thomas
3 White Wm.

MASONS, &c.
Hooper Robert
Parsons John
Selley John
Vaughan James
Western Thos. | TAILORS.
Beck Thomas
Comner Wm.
Foxford Hugh
3 Gardner John
Sowdon John
TuckerJoseph (&
shopkeeper) | WHEELWRIGHTS.
Bodley Edward
Dinner Joseph

POST-OFFICE
at Elizth. Bow-
den's. Letters
despatched *via*
Tiverton, &c | **C O A C H** to
South Molton,
12 noon, and to
Tiverton,2½ aft
CARRIER.
John Southcott,
toExeter Thur.
night, and to
Tiverton Tues.
morning |

WOOLFARDISWORTHY, or *Woolsery*, is a scattered village and parish, 6 miles N. by W. of Crediton ; containing 220 souls, and 1815 acres of hilly fertile land, belonging to several freeholders. The Rev. W. B. Hole, M.A., is lord of the manor, and patron and incumbent of the *rectory*, valued in K.B. at £9. 19s. 4½d., and in 1831 at £280.   The glebe is 95A., and the tithes were commuted in 1840, at £199. 12s. 10d. per annum.   The *Church* is a small neat structure, with a tower and three bells, being entirely rebuilt in 1845, at the cost of about £1000.   The east window is enriched with painted glass, and the pulpit is of stone, finely carved.   The *Rectory House* is a handsome stone building, in the Elizabethan style, erected in 1842-3.   A school, attended by 30 children, is supported chiefly by the rector.

Born Richard, machine maker
Gale Wm. corn miller
Hole RevWm.Brassey,M.A.,*Rectory*
Moore Elizabeth, schoolmistress
Vicary John, shoemaker & par. clerk
      FARMERS. (* *are Owners.*)
Bragg Eliz. || Elson Wm.

*Clapp John, *Lower Bowarthy*
*Eastmond James, *Brendifield*
*Gill James, *Minchen down*
Hall George || Horrell John
Leach Thomas || Norrish Wm.
Rowcliffe John || Searle Thomas
*Tucker Robert || Skinner Thomas

WORLINGTON, (EAST) a small scattered village on the northern acclivity of the valley of the Little Dart, six miles E. of Chulmleigh, has in its parish 287 souls, and 2363A. 1R. 26P. of land, rising boldly towards the north, where there are three farms called East, West, and Middle Barrow, from the *tumuli* or mounds of earth under which ancient Britons are supposed to have been buried. The Hon. Newton Fellowes owns a great part of the parish and is lord of the manor; and the rest belongs to various freeholders. *Denridge Barton* was formerly a seat of the Radfords, who had a deer park here ; and another old house, called *Pidley*, was formerly the seat of the St. Leger family.   About a mile from the Barrows is a square stone, seven feet high, with a cross on each side of it, which has been the subject of much antiquarian conjecture.   The *Church* (St. Mary,) is a small ancient structure, with a tower containing four bells, and crowned by a short spire.   The *rectory*, valued in K.B. at £7. 15s. 10d., and in 1831 at £238, is in the patronage of the Hon. Newton Fellowes, and incumbency of the Rev. Benj. Clay, M.A., who has a neat thatched residence, and 66½A. of glebe.   The tithes were commuted in 1836, for £207. 9s. 10d. per annum.   On Thorndon farm a small Bible Christian Chapel was built, in 1843. An old parish house, which had been built on the waste, was rebuilt

by the parish 45 years ago, and is occupied by paupers. The Church Land (2A.,) is occupied by the rector, on condition of his supplying bread and wine for the sacrament. The poor have the interest of £20, given by *Richard Cooke* and other donors, and the dividends of £200 three per cent. consols, given by *John and Andrew Cobley*, in 1807 and 1814.

Clay Rev Benjamin, M.A. *Rectory*
Marker Mr Thomas, *Grove hill*
    FARMERS. (* are Owners.)
Adams George, Middle Barrow
Cann John || Cornall Richard
Drake Thomas, Three Hammers
Heydon Benjamin, East Barrow
Hosegood Andrew C. *Thorndon*
*Lake Richard, Coombe
Lake Richard Cook || Lee Robert

Lee Robert, *Denridge*
*Melhuish Richard, *Pidley*
Middleton Richard, *Stone Cross*
Middleton Robt. *Higher Blackgrove*
Middleton Rt. jun. *Lower Blackgrove*
Phillips Samuel, *Horridge Mill*
*Price Samuel, *Rull House*
Reed Henry, West Barrow
*Smyth George C., Town Tenement

WORLINGTON, (WEST) a pleasant village, picturesquely seated on an acclivity on the north side of the Little Dart river, 5½ miles E. of Chulmleigh, has in its parish 218 inhabitants, and 2683A. 3R. 26P. of land, nearly all the property of Lewis Wm. Buck, Esq., M.P., the lord of the manor, which was anciently held by the Worlingtons, and afterwards passed successively to the Crawthorne, Marwood, Affeton, and Stuckley families. The old Manor House, now called *Cobley*, has in its neighbourhood many fox covers, from which it is supposed to have obtained its present name. Near the farm house called *Affton Barton* are some remains of the ancient and extensive castellated mansion, which was the seat of the Affeton family in the 13th and 14th centuries. The entrance gateway tower, with a spiral staircase, 49 feet high, is still in good preservation. This was one of the most splendid seats in the county, and had an extensive park, with large fish ponds, woods, a warren, &c. It was built in the form of the letter E, and was last occupied by the *Stuckley* or *Stewkley* family, whose heiress carried the manor in marriage to the Bucks. The *Church* (St. Mary,) is a very ancient structure, with a tower containing six bells, and crowned by a wooden spire. The old Norman font and alms box still remain, and in the chancel is a stately monument in memory of Sir Thomas Stuckley, Kt., who died in 1663, at Affton Barton, and whose brother was chaplain to Oliver Cromwell, but was deprived of his clerical office at the Restoration. The *rectory*, valued in K.B. at £8. 15s. 10d., and in 1831 at £173, is in the patronage of L. W. Buck, Esq., and incumbency of the Rev. W. M. Bruton, B.C.L., who has 84A. of glebe and a good residence, rebuilt in the Italian style in 1847, at the cost of £700. The tithes were commuted in 1841, for £160 per annum. The poor have the interest of £48, left by Richard Cooke and other donors.

Bruton Rev Walter M., B.C.L., *Rectory*
Boundy Saml. parish clerk
Holmes John, blacksmith
Hosegood Wm. miller, *Affton Mill*
Lee George, shoemaker

Lee Wm. vict. Stuckley Arms
Symons Wm. & Willis Wm. tailors
    FARMERS.
Adams John, *West Milltown*
Butt John, *Cole Park*

Coles Richard, *East Milltown*
Hosegood John, *Cobley Barton*
Hosegood Luke, *Cottonhay*
Kemp Peter ‖ Lake John

Tolley Amos ‖ Tolley John
Tolley Edward ‖ Tucker Peter
Troake James, *Affton Barton*

OTTERY ST. MARY HUNDRED.

OTTERY ST. MARY is an ancient and irregularly built *market town*, of about 3500 inhabitants, picturesquely seated on the east side of the river Otter, sheltered on the east and west by boldly swelling hills, and distant 11½ miles E. by N. of Exeter, 15 miles S.E. of Tiverton, 6 miles N. by E. of Sidmouth, and 162 miles W.S.W. of London. Its *Parish* had only 2415 inhabitants in 1801, but in 1831 they had encreased to 3849, and in 1841 to 4194 souls, residing in the *town*, and in the seven *tithings* of *Alphington, Cadhay, Fluxton, Gosford, Rill, Tipton,* and *Wiggaton*, which extend from one to three miles on all sides of the town, and on both sides of the Otter valley, but chiefly on the eastern side, where the hills rise in lofty summits, overlooking the Sid valley on the east, and commanding extensive views of the coast and the English Channel, about six miles to the south. The parish includes also the hamlets *Taleford, Combelake,* and *Metcombe*, and many scattered farm houses, &c. It comprises 9944A. 2R. 4P. of land, and forms a *hundred of itself*, in the Southern Division of Devon, in Honiton Union and Polling and County Court District; in Woodbury Petty Sessional Division; and in the Archdeaconry of Exeter and Deanery of Aylesbeare. The *manor and hundred*, which are co-extensive with the parish, were given by Edward the Confessor to the Dean and Chapter of Rouen, who obtained a charter for a market and a fair here, in 1226. The *weekly market*, formerly held on Tuesday, is now held on Thursday, for butchers' meat and other provisions; and there are *great markets* for cattle, &c., on the first Thursdays in February and December. Here are also three *annual fairs* for cattle, &c., on the Tuesday before Palm Sunday; on the second Tuesday after Whit-Sunday; and on the 15th of August, when it falls on Tuesday, Wednesday, or Thursday, or if not, on the Tuesday after the 15th. The town has an *Agricultural and Industrial Association*, and several good houses, inns, and shops. It had formerly a regular corn market. The woollen manufacture which formerly flourished here is extinct, but there is in the town a large *silk factory*, employing about 400 hands. *Petty Sessions* are held at the London Tavern, on the third Thursday of each alternate month, and Messrs. F. G. Coleridge and Son are clerks to the magistrates for Woodbury Division. F. J. Coleridge, Esq., is *clerk*, and Mr. C. D. Mayne *deputy clerk* to the *Commissioners of Taxes* for East Budleigh and Cliston District, who meet alternately at the Red Lion Inn and London Tavern. Francis Geo. Coleridge, Esq., is inspector of police and steward of the *court leet and baron*, held yearly for the manor of Ottery in October, when an inspector of weights and measures, a water bailiff, ale taster, scavenger, and other officers are appointed.

Sir John Kennaway, Bart., of *Escot House*, is lord of the manor, but a great part of the parish belongs to Sir Thos. Hare, Bart., Sir F. H. Bathurst, the Coleridge family, the Rev. Dr. Cornish, R. J. Marker, and many other freeholders. The ancient mansions called *Holcombe, Knightstone*, and *Bishop's Court*, are now farm houses. *Heath's Court* is the country residence of the Hon. Justice Coleridge ; and *Salston House* is the pleasant seat of the Rt. Rev. Wm. H. Coleridge, formerly Bishop of Barbadoes, &c. *Cadhay*, an imposing Elizabethan mansion, is the property of Sir Thos. Hare, and was the seat of the late *Admiral Lord Graves*, who died in 1802, but it is now occupied by John Collins, Esq. *Gosford House* is the residence of Sir H. A. Farrington, Bart. Sir Walter Raleigh had a residence in the town, but it was destroyed by fire in 1805 ; and *Saml. T. Coleridge*, the eminent poet, was born here in 1772, his father being vicar of the parish. During the early part of the *civil wars*, Ottery was occupied by the King's forces, who retreated on the approach of Sir Thos. Fairfax, in October, 1645. After having been quartered some time round Exeter, General Fairfax made Ottery his head quarters from Nov. 15th to Dec. 6th in the same year.

John Grandison, bishop of Exeter, having obtained the manor of Ottery in exchange, in 1335, founded here in 1337 a *College* of secular priests, and endowed it with the manor and the tithes of the parish. This College consisted of 30 members, comprising warden, minister, precentor, sacristar, four canons, eight vicars choral or priest vicars, three priests, twelve clerks, eight choir boys, and a master of grammar. When suppressed in the 37th of Henry VIII., its yearly revenues were estimated at £303. 2s. 9d. ; but the same property would now yield about £10,000 per annum. The King gave the *great tithes* of the parish to the Dean and Canons of Windsor, to whom they still belong, and by his letters patent he gave the church, the college houses, and the small tithes to "the *Church Corporation*" thereby created under the name of the four Governors and Assistants of the hereditaments and goods of the Church of St. Mary, of Ottery, for the support of the vicar, the chaplain, and the master of the grammar school, as afterwards noticed. The *Church* is one of the largest and handsomest parochial churches in the county, and is now undergoing a thorough reparation. On each side is a square tower, opening into the body, and forming two transepts, as in Exeter Cathedral. The towers are furnished with pinnacles and open battlements, and that on the north side is crowned by a small spire. At the north west corner is a richly ornamented chapel, built by Bishop Grandison ; the roof of which is covered with highly wrought, fan-shaped tracery. The altar screen is of stone, finely carved into niches and tabernacle work, and on the south side of the communion table are three stone seats rising one above another. Most of the windows are narrow and lancet shaped. In the body of the church, between two pillars, arched pyramidally, is the effigy of a man cut in stone, armed cap-a-pie, with a lion couchant at his feet ; and opposite to this is the defaced effigy of a woman. These monuments have been long obscured by seats, and are supposed to have been raised in memory of the father and mother of Bishop Gran-

dison. The *discharged vicarage*, valued in K.B. at £20, and in 1831 at £150, is in the patronage of the Lord Chancellor, and incumbency of the Rev. S. W. Cornish, D.D., who is also head master of the Grammar School. He is assisted by the Rev. R. H. Podmore, M.A., the *chaplain priest*, appointed by the four Governors of the Church Corporation trust, afterwards noticed. The *great tithes* of this large parish were commuted in 1845 for £995. 15s. per annum; and mo-duses, amounting to £250. 12s. 10d. per annum, are paid in lieu of the small tithes. TIPTON ST. JOHN's, in Tipton tithing, is a *district church*, about two miles S. of the town, and was built by subscription in 1837-8. It is in the Early English style, with a bell turret, and its *perpetual curacy*, valued at £80, is in the gift of the Vicar, and incumbency of the Rev. A. A. Hunt, M. A. *St. Michael's Chapel of Ease*, in Fluxton tithing, on West hill, about 1½ mile S. W. of the town, was built by subscription in 1845-6. It is a neat struc-ture, with stained glass windows, and is a perpetual curacy, in the patronage of the Vicar, and incumbency of the Rev. H. B. Lott. *Alphington District Church* (St. James,) in Alphington tithing, about 1½ mile N. E. of the town, was built in 1848-9 by the Hon. Justice Coleridge, and is in the patronage of the Vicar, and incumbency of the Rev. H. J. Coleridge, M.A. *Escot District Church* (St. Philip and St. James,) is in Gosford tithing, about 1½ mile N.N.W. of the town, and was built by its patron Sir J. Kennaway, Bart., in 1837-8 at the cost of about £3000, for a district comprising part of this and part of Talaton parish, as noticed at page 298. It stands near Escot House, the seat of the founder, and is a beautiful structure of Early English architecture, with a turret and bell. Its perpetual curacy, valued at £75, has been endowed by the founder, and is in the in-cumbency of the Rev. F. T. Hill. In the town is an *Independent* and also a *Wesleyan Chapel*, the former of which belonged to Presby-terians in 1715. Here is a *Mutual Improvement Society*, embracing a numerous list of members. The parish has several valuable *Charities* and *Public Schools*, as noticed below.

OTTERY FEOFFEE CHARITY, which yields about £600 per annum, is in two branches called the *Ottery and Somersetshire Trusts*. The former com-prises 220A. of land and 22 houses, &c., in this parish, left by *John Law-rence*, in 1440; and the latter consists of two houses and 73A. of land at Ilton, Ashill, and Abbot's Isle, in Somersetshire, left by *Henry Beaumont*, in 1590. Formerly a large part of the income was improperly applied in aid of the poor rates, but it is now distributed among the poor parishioners, chiefly in sums varying from £1 to £2 to each individual or family. The present *Feoffees* are Thomas Glanville, the Rt. Rev. W. H. Coleridge, the Rev. S. W. Cornish, J. E. Lee, J. Dening, A. E. Salter, and Rd. Dening.

The CHURCH CORPORATION TRUST includes part of property which had belonged to the College of St. Mary Ottery, and which was vested by letters patent in the 37th of Henry VIII., with "four governors" and assistants, for the support of the church and parsonage, and of a vicar, a chaplain-priest, and a schoolmaster. The only property vested with the four governors and seven assistants, which yields an income, consists of the small tithes of the parish and the pews in the chancel, yielding about £100 per annum; but they also hold the houses and premises occupied by the vicar and school-master, and the chaplain. They pay the following yearly stipends,—£20 to

the vicar, £21 to the chaplain-priest, and £10 to the schoolmaster. They are also trustees of *Thomas Axe's Charity*, left in 1691, and now producing about £150 per annum, arising from the rents of two houses in Southwark, and from the dividends of £1426. 5s. 10d. three per cent. stock, purchased with £900 which was paid for three houses taken down in 1790. Out of the income, £8. 8s. each are paid yearly to the vicar, chaplain, schoolmaster, and parish clerk; and £8. 8s. to buy drugs for the poor. Three-twelfths of the rest of the income are given in marriage portions to young people who have lived as servants in the parish, and are qualified according to the donor's will; and the remainder is distributed among the poor parishioners. The *Blandford Property*, which was left by *Thomas Axe*, the above named donor, in trust with his "*right heirs*," has been many years under the management of the Governors of the Church Corporation Trust, and consists of a house, three cottages and land at Blandford, let for £55 per annum, of which 9-12ths belong to the parish clerk; and 3-12ths are to be applied in providing medical and surgical aid for the poor. As noticed with Exeter, three poor persons of Ottery have coats, hats, stockings, and shoes, yearly from *Jeffrey's Charity*. The vicar has £23 a year from land, supposed to have been left by *John Barnard*, in 1721, for preaching a monthly sermon previous to the administration of the sacrament. Pursuant to the will of *Wm. Evans*, (dated 1777,) the trustees of the Independent Meetinghouse, distribute the interest of £100 as follows,—£2 to their minister, and £3 among poor weavers, &c. The poor attending the church regularly have £2 a year as the interest of £50 left by *Dorothea Mundy*, in 1807, secured on the tolls of the Exeter turnpikes. In the same year, *Wm. Woodrow* left £100 in trust to pay half the interest towards the support of the church Sunday School, and to divide the remainder among the poor parishioners. Half of £48. 15s. 8d. bequeathed to the poor in 1816, by *Mary Kestell*, was applied in 1820 in paying the legacy duty on £400, four per cent. stock, left by the *Rev. James How*, in 1817, for the benefit of the *Sunday School*. The Trustees, called the *Church Corporation*, now consist of Wm. Warren, Thomas Davy, John E. Lee, and John Dening, *governors;* and S. Wreford, J. Collins, A. E. Salter, J. Yelverton, Rt. Warren, W. T. Thomas, and T. Burgoin, *assistants*.

The *Grammar School*, commonly called "THE KING'S SCHOOL, as already noticed, forms part of the Church Corporation Trust, the governors of which appoint the master, and allow him £10 a year and the free use of the school premises and a field. He has also 20s. a year as the ground rent of a house adjoining the school. This house will revert to the school in 1867, and is supposed to occupy the site of a tenement given by Edmund Prideaux in 1680. The schoolmaster receives £8. 9s. yearly from Axe's Charity, as already noticed; and about £21 per annum as the rent of 19A. of land at Whimple, bequeathed in the 17th of Charles II. by *Edward Salter*, to be applied towards the support of poor boys from this school at Oxford, or, in default of such, for the education of two free scholars of this parish. All the other boys pay for their instruction, and the master takes boarders, for which he has ample accommodation in his residence called the *College*. The Vicar is the present master, and has two assistants. In the town is a highly respectable commercial boarding school, conducted by Mr. Reed. Here is likewise a large *Parochial School*, and also a *British School*, both partly supported by subscription; and there are small Church Schools, &c., in other parts of the parish.

The Post-Office is at Mr. John Jph. Reed's, Mill street. Letters are despatched 5½ morning, and at a ¼ before 5 evening. Money Orders are granted and paid.

In the following directory, those marked 1 *are at Butt's hill ;* 2, *Broad street ;* 3, *Cornhill ;* 4, *Mill street ;* 5, *Paternoster ;* 6, *Sandhill st ;* 7, *Silver street ;* 8, *Tip hill head ; and* 9, *in Yonder street.*

8 Baker James, whitesmith
3 Baker John, printer & land survr
2 Carnell John, organ builder
Carter Mr Edward, *Lamb's court*
Carter Mr Jas. Elias, *Woodford*
7 Coleridge Fras. Geo. & Son, solicitors & clerks to magistrates, &c.
Coleridge Fras. Geo. solr. *Manor Hs*
1 Coleridge Fras. Jas. solr. and clerk to tax commissioners, *The Cottage*
Coleridge Rev Henry Jas., M.A., *Alphington House*
5 Coleridge Miss Elizabeth
Coleridge Sir John Taylor, kt. judge of the Queen's Bench, *Heath's Ct*
Coleridge Rt. Rev Wm. Hart, D.D., (late Bishop of Barbadoes,) *Salston House*
Collins John, Esq. *Cadhay House*
2 Cook Charles, stationer
Cornish Rev Sidney Wm., D.D., vicar and master of Gram. Sch., *College*
9 Darby John, cooper
Davey Henry, solicitor, Broad st
Deacon Rev Geo. Edw., M.A. curate, *Vicarage*
Dening John, Esq., *Pitt*
5 Evans Mr Samuel
Eveleigh Geo. wheelwright, Jesu st
Farrington Sir Hy. Anthony, Bart. *Gosford House*
Glanvill Mr Thomas, Mill street
5 Godfrey John, cooper
2 Hake Thos. glass, timber, &c. dlr
8 Hearn Matthias, vety. surgeon
Hill Rev Fras. T. incmbt. of *Escot*
Hodge Mrs., Paternoster row
Hunt Rev Augsts. Arthur, M.A. *Tipton*
4 Huxtable Wm. machine maker
4 Jeffery Fras. Robert, solicitor
Keene Mr Francis, Milk street
Lawes Rev Enos, (Indpt.) *Tipton*
Lee John Ellis, Esq., Corn hill
Lott Rev Hy. Buckland, B.A. incmbt. of St Michael's, West hill
3 Mardon My. straw hat maker

7 Mayne Chas. Down, bookseller, stationer, sub. distr. of stamps, &c.
3 Mayne Geo. D. accompt. & news agt
4 Murch Jas. manager, Silk mill
4 Newbery Thos. Cordell, silk mfr. and corn miller
2 Oldridge John, hair dresser
6 Phillips George, fellmonger
Pike Sarah, carrier, Mill street
7 Podmore Rev Rd. Hillman, M.A., chaplain priest
4 Reed John Jph. postmaster
7 Rugg Henry, tinner and brazier
4 Salter Thos. & Philip, curriers, &c.
9 Sanford Mr Saml. & Jno. wheelgt
Smith Lieut. Fdk. A., *Escot Cottage*
4 Smith Wm. corn mill manager
Stagg Robert, gent. *Butt's Cottage*
Sorrell Mr James, Broad street
7 Tapscott George, currier, &c.
4 Taylor George, tanner, &c.
Tozer Geo. wheelwright, *Tipton*
2 Walker Ann, straw hat maker
3 Wreford Saml. gent. & 5 Mrs Grace

ACADEMIES.

4 Bounsell Rev John, (Indpt.)
British School, Wm. & Mrs Sloman
Jobbins Edmund, *Taleford*
King's Grammar School, Rev Sidney Wm. Cornish, D.D and Messrs. — Torquard and Thos. Wyatt
4 Passmore Janet, (*Infant school*)
Parish School, Mr & Mrs Shapland
Reed Wm. (boarding,) Broad st

FARMERS.

(Marked + are Owners.)
Ashford Samuel, Thorn Farm
Broom John, *Holcombe Barton*
Brown Wm., *Fluxton*
+Burgoin Thomas, *Alphington*
Carter James, *Woodford*
Chown Henry, *Ware's*
Clarke Wm., *Ash*
+Collin John, *Cadhay*
Daw John, *Woiggaton*
+Dening John, *Cotley Farm*

+Dening Richard, Waxway
Digby Wm., Mill street
Ellis Edmund, *Straightgate*
Evans Samuel, (& miller,) Westhill
Gayler Elizabeth, *Ash Farm*
+Halse Henry, *Burrow Hill*
Lawrence James, *Slade*
Manley James, *Tipton Mills*
Marks Henry, *Lower Gosford*
Miller James, *Skinner's Ash*
Priddis John, *Bishop's Court*
+Salter Abm. Elliott, *Tipton*
+Salter John, *Combe*, & Wm., *Hayne*
Shorland Thomas, *Alphington*
+Skinner Robert, *Fluxton* and *Rill*
Snell George, *Knightstone*
+Thomas Wm. Taylor, *Fluxton*
+Warren Wm., *Gosford*
Wheaton Joseph, *Great Well*
White Thomas, sen. *Rill*
White Thomas, jun. *Lancercombe*
+Yelverton James, *Metcombe*
+Yelverton James, *Tipton*
Yelverton Thomas, *Fluxton*

FIRE & LIFE OFFICES.
7 Atlas and Western, C. D. Mayne
7 Legal & Coml., North of England,
  & Lic. Victuallers', Geo. D. Mayne
2 Royal Exchange, Sml. Norrington
2 West of England, Henry Davy

INNS AND TAVERNS.
Alphington Inn, James Newton
4 Five Bells, James Harris
Fair Mile Inn, John Baker
Golden Lion, Herman Ham, *Tipton*
Greyhound, George Hartnoll
Lamb and Flag, Jonth. Carter
7 London Tavern, Hy. Canniford

SURGEONS.
Davy Thomas, Mill street
Garland John Slyfield, Cornhill
Hayman Henry, Cornhill
Thompson Chas., Paternoster row
5 Tinney Wm. Sparkes and Son
Wreford Samuel, Cornhill

AUCTIONEERS.
3 Livermore Ts.
  (& surveyor)
4 Pocock Leond.

BAKERS.
7 Burrough John
3 Coles Wm.
4 Gigg John
Littley George
4 Reed Hy. A.

2 Salter Richd.
4 Stone Elias
9 Webb Rowland
  Hill
4 Whicker John
5 Whicker Jno L.
7 Whicker Wm.

BEERHOUSES.
4 Carter Solomon
4 Cunningham Sl.

4 Hallett John
1 Ham Joseph
9 Lathorpe Jph.
Littley John
4 Taylor Wm.

BLACKSMITHS.
8 Coles Wm.
1 Salter James
Sanford Saml.
4 Searle John
4 Toby John

BOOT & SHOE MKS.
4 Berry Wm.
5 Bower Richd.
5 Carnell John
5 Carnell Edw.
4 Carter Solmn.
9 Fisher Richd.
4 Ford Charles
4 Godfrey Wm.
  Henry
4 Green Jas.
2 Hake Thos.
4 Hallett Wm.
4 Hayward Jph.
4 Meldon Wm.
7 Holdridge Hy.
4 Palfrey Abm.
4 Reed John Jph.
9 Shorland Wm.

BRICKMAKERS.
9 Shorland Jas.
Shorland Thos.,
  Alphington

BRICKLAYERS.
2 Digby John
6 Littley John
Pullman John

BUTCHERS.
3 Coles Edwin
4 Digby Wm.
5 Mitchell Jph.
5 Teed Richd.
9 Williams Hy.
3 Williams My.

CABINET MKRS.
4 Pocock Leond.
7 Southcott Geo.

CARPENTERS.
9 Channon Wm.
1 Ham Joseph
3 Livermore Ts.
2 Norrington Sl.
4 Perriman Jno.

DRUGGISTS, &c.
2 Cook Charles
7 Farrant Hy.
3 Parsons John

GROCERS, &c.
5 Bussell Hy.
2 Doudney Jno.P.
Evans Saml. T.
  Market place
2 Hamlin John
4 Perriman Jno.
2 Salter Richd.
7 Shepperd Thos.

IRONMONGERS.
2 Norrington Sl.
4 Warren Saml.
  (& brazier)

L. & W. DRAPERS.
5 Bussell Henry
Evans Saml. T.
7 Shepperd Ths.

MALTSTERS, &c.
9 Newbery Saml.
5 Priddis Wm.

MILLINERS, &c.
Berry Ann M.
4 Passmore Alice
5 Priddis Martha
2 Sanford Jane
3 Stocker My. C.
7 Shepcott Eliza

PAINTERS
AND GLAZIERS.
7 Blackmore Sl.
  Wm.
4 Meldon Jas.
2 Sanford John
3 Searle Wm.

SADDLERS.
3 Coles John
9 Windover Wm.

SHOPKEEPERS.
4 Bole Nicholas
5 Carnell Thos.
9 Channon Wm.
4 Gigg John
Grant Wm.
5 Priddis Ann
6 Stocker Peter
2 Wilson Hanh.

TAILORS.
6 Bending Richd.
4 Bole James
2 Digby Thos.
9 Elliott Henry

7 Evans Samuel
2 Oldridge John
4 Passmore Geo.
5 Passmore Wm.
4 Tobs Wm.

WATCHMKRS., &c.
7 Gillham Wm.

2 Lancey W. J. O.

WINE AND SPIRIT
MERCHANTS.

7 Farrantt Hy.
3 Parsons John
7 Shepperd Thos.

OMNIBUS

To Exeter from the Lamb and Flag,
every Tuesday and Friday, 8 mg

CARRIERS

To *Exeter*, John Baker and Charles
Lee, Tuesday and Friday
To *Honiton*, Sarah Pike, Saturday;
and to Sidmouth Monday
To *Collumpton Station*, John Fisher
To *Hele Station*, Wm. Bower

AXMINSTER HUNDRED.

Though in the Southern Parliamentary Division of Devon, this
hundred forms the north-eastern extremity of the county, bounded
on the east by Dorsetshire and Somersetshire, and on the south by
about six miles of the coast of the English channel, extending eastward from Axmouth to the vicinity of Lyme-Regis. It includes the
towns of Honiton and Axminster, and extends 14 miles northward
to the lofty hills, where the three counties join, and where the rivers
Otter and *Yarty* have their sources; the former running to Honiton, Ottery, &c., and the latter to the river *Axe*, which runs from
Axminster to Axmouth. These small rivers receive here many tributary streams, from the bold hills and deep valley which occupy
three-fourths of this Hundred. It is in *Honiton Polling District*,
in the Archdeaconry of Exeter, and in Axminster and Honiton
Petty Sessional Divisions and County Court Districts, and all in
Honiton Deanery, except Combe-Rawleigh, Luppitt, Yarcombe, and
Up-Ottery, which are in *Dunkeswell Deanery*. The following enumeration of its parishes shews their territorial extent, and their population in 1841.

Parishes.	Acres.	Pop.	Parishes.	Acres.	Pop.
Axminster†	7635	2860	Membury	4089	886
Axmouth	4534	645	Musbury	2179	495
Coombpyne	796	143	Roosdown *Expar.*	190	5
*Coombe-Rawleigh	1747	276	*Stockland*‡	5850	1328
Dalwood‡	1609	513	Uplyme	3149	1057
*Honiton Borough	3046	3895	*Upottery	5830	991
Kilmington	1763	495	§Yarcombe	5400	826
*Luppitt	4730	782	Total	52,547	15,197

* UNIONS.—Those marked thus * are in *Honiton Union*, and thus § in
Chard Union. All the other parishes are in *Axminster Union*. Chard
Union is all in Dorsetshire, except Yarcombe parish.

‡ *Dalwood* and *Stockland* were formerly detached members of Dorsetshire, but were added to Devon by Act of Parliament, in 1842, when *Thorncombe*, a detached member of this hundred, was annexed to Dorsetshire.

† Axminster parish is divided into ten *tithings*. When the census was
taken, July 1st, 1841, there were 187 persons in the *Union Workhouse*, at
Axminster, and 122 in that at Honiton.

AXMINSTER UNION comprises 17 parishes, viz.:—Axminster, Axmouth,
Colyton, Coombpyne, Dalwood, Kilmington, Membury, Musbury, Seaton-

and-Beer, Shute, Stockland, and Uplyme, in *Devonshire;* and Charmouth, Chardstock, Hawkchurch, Lyme-Regis, and Thorncombe, in *Dorsetshire.* It forms a County Court District, and comprises an area of 92 square miles. In 1841, it had 20,585 inhabitants, and 4306 houses, of which 255 were unoccupied, and 29 building, when the census was taken. The total average annual expenditure of the 17 parishes for the support of their poor during the three years preceding the formation of the union was £10,218; during the three years ending 1840, £9058; and during the succeeding three years, £10,029. Their total expenditure for the year ending Lady-day, 1849, was £14,669, including £1297 paid to the county rates, £924 for salaries, and about £90 paid for registration and vaccination fees. The WORKHOUSE, at Axminster, was built in 1836, at the cost of £7000, but it has since been altered and enlarged, at the cost of £2500. It has room for 450 paupers, but has seldom more than 300 inmates. Ten surgeons are employed by the Union, and the other principal officers are Chas. Bond, Esq., *union clerk and superintendent registrar;* Rev. Z. J. Edwards, *chaplain;* Wm. and Mrs. Gomm, *master* and *matron* of the Workhouse; and Robt. P. Pearce and Jph. Edwards, *relieving officers.* Messrs. Thos. Pickering, Thos. Cann, Geo. Fdk. Codrington, and Robt. Bonfield, are the *District Registrars of Births and Deaths.*

AXMINSTER is a small ancient *market town,* upon a pleasant acclivity on the south-eastern side of the river Axe, near the borders of Dorsetshire, 5 miles N.W. of Lyme Regis, 9 miles E. by S. of Honiton, 25 miles E. by N. of Exeter, and 147 W.S.W. of London. Its *parish* contains 2860 inhabitants, and 7637A. 2R. 29P. of land, generally fertile, and divided into ten *tithings,* of which the following are the names and their population in 1841:—*Abbey,* 76; *Beerhall,* 30; *Shapwick,* 26; *Smallridge,* 207; *Axminster Town,* 2139; *Trill,* 39; *Uphay,* 57; *West-Water,* 127; *Weycroft,* 56; and *Wyke,* or *Week,* 103. These tithings extend about three miles along the borders of Dorsetshire, and the banks of the small river *Axe,* which abounds in salmon and other fish, and falls into the sea about six miles south of the town. Axminster had formerly a share of the clothing trade, and, in 1755, the late Mr. Thomas Whitty established here a manufactory of *carpets,* which was discontinued in 1835, after having enjoyed for many years a high celebrity for the beauty and elegance of its productions; its founder having received, in 1759, a premium of £30 from the Society of Arts, for having made the largest and handsomest Turkey carpet that had ever been manufactured in this country, being 26½ feet by 17½. Another carpet made here for the *Grand Sultan,* cost more than £1000. The town is irregularly built, and is now without any manufactures. It has *markets* for provisions, on Tuesday and Friday, and it has three annual *fairs* for cattle, &c., on the Tuesday after April 25, on June 26th, and on the Wednesday after October 10th. *Petty Sessions* are held here and at Colyton alternately once a month, and Chas. Bond, Esq., is clerk to the magistrates. He is also clerk of the COUNTY COURT, held here on the second Monday of every month for the 17 parishes of *Axminster Union,* and those of Catherston, Leweston, and Wootton-Fitzpaine. King Athelstan gave Axminster church to seven priests, who were to pray for the souls of seven knights and many Saxon soldiers, who were slain near the

town in a great battle with the Danes.   In October, 1644, Sir Richard Cholmondely was stationed here with a party of the King's horse, and received his death wound in a battle with the Parliamentarians, fought near the town.   The manor of Axminster was part of the royal demesne until King John gave it to Lord Briwer or Brewer.   Sir Reginald de Mohun, in 1246, gave it to *Newham,* or *Newenham Abbey,* which he and his brother founded in this parish, for monks of the Cistercian order.   A farm house, about a mile from the town, occupies part of the site of this once splendid and richly endowed abbey; but all that now remains of the monastic buildings are a few mouldering walls, and the east window of a chapel,   At the dissolution, the yearly revenue of the abbey was valued at £227. 7s. 8d,, and the site and the manor were granted to the Duke of Norfolk, by whose family they were sold to Lord Petre, in the 17th century.   The manor is now in dispute, but the soil belongs to many proprietors, the largest of whom are W. Gregson, H. Bilke, H. Knight, R. Mallock, J. Davidson, and W. Tucker, Esqrs.; Miss Shiles, and the representatives of the late W. Knight, Esq.   Hillary House, Hill House, Fursbrook House, Sector House, and Leacombe House, are neat and pleasant mansions, and their occupants are stated in the subjoined directory.   Another mansion here, called *Clocombe House,* is now unoccupied.   Smallridge estate was held in the reign of William the Conqueror by Ralph de Pomeroy, and afterwards passed to the Mohun, Raleigh, Mallock, and Campion families, the latter of whom sold it to several tenants.   *Wycroft,* or *Weycroft,* was long held by the Wigot, Gobodisleigh, and Dennis families.   Humphrey, Duke of Gloucester, and others, as trustees of the family of Sir Thomas Brooke, had license in 1426 to castellate Wycroft House, and enclose a park of 800 acres.   It was sold, in 1611, to Thomas Bennett, Esq., sheriff of London, who destroyed the park, and suffered the house to fall to ruins, of which there are still a few remains.   The estate was afterwards sold to various freeholders.   The *Church* (St. Mary,) is a large and venerable structure, displaying several kinds of architecture, with a massive tower rising from the centre.   Leland says, this church, once dignified with the name of "*minster*," was famous for the sepultures of many noble Saxons and Danes, slain at Branesdown and Colecroft.   Some parts of the edifice have the appearance of great antiquity, particularly a Saxon door-way, that has been removed from the south side to the eastern end of the aisle. The east window is large, and enriched with stained glass.   The advowson of the vicarage, the appropriation of the rectory, to which is attached the manor of Prestaller, were given by Edward I. as part of the endowment of the *Prebendaries of Warthill and Grindal,* in York Cathedral, as they still remain.   The *vicarage,* with the curacies of Kilmington and Membury annexed to it, valued in K.B. at £44. 6s. 8d., and in 1831 at £1042, is in the alternate patronage of the two Prebendaries, and is now held by the Rev. Wm. J. Coneybeare, M.A.   The tithes were commuted in 1838, the vicarial for £607. 1s. 3d., and the rectorial for £670. 10s. per annum.   The Very Rev. W. D. Coneybeare, Dean of Llandaff, is lessee of the

latter. The Vicarage House is a modern building. In the cartulary of Newenham Abbey are transcripts of two charters of King John, confirming the Sunday market, and granting that Axminster should be a *free borough*, and have a fair for eight days. The *Rev. John Prince*, author of a biographical work on the Worthies of Devon, was born at the Abbey house. Here is an *Independent Chapel*, built in 1826, in lieu of the old Presbyterian Meeting house, founded in 1698. Here is also a *Wesleyan Chapel*, built in 1796, and a *Roman Catholic Chapel*, erected in 1830.

Axminster Parish Lands, &c., which are vested in trust for the use of the poor, by deeds dated the 19th of James I. and Feb. 10th, 1679, comprise 18A. 2R.; let for £29 per annum, and three tenements, and a house, garden, and orchard, occupied by paupers. Part of this property was purchased with £150, left by *Alex. Every*, in 1588, and the house formerly used as the parish workhouse, was given by *Walter Young*, in 1613. The net income is distributed in bread, at Christmas, and there is belonging to the trust part of a house at Honiton. A yearly rent charge of £5, out of Ham close, left by *John Younge*, in 1612, is distributed in shirts and shifts among poor old men and women. For a similar distribution annually among 20 poor parishioners, *Leonard Periam* left £100, in 1711. Of this legacy £60 was laid out in the purchase of 1½A., called the Brickfield, and now let for £4 a year. The remaining £40 is secured at 4½ per cent. interest, on the tolls of Bridport turnpike. The poor have also the following yearly sums, for distribution in bread, &c., viz., a rent charge of £5, out of 12A. of land, at Week, left by *Anne Palmer*, in 1815; the interest of £100, left by *John Ellard*, in 1815; a rent charge of 20s., left by *Thos. Whitty*, in 1713; and 4s., as interest of £5, left by *Anne Scrivens*. The FREE SCHOOL, for 12 poor boys and girls of Axminster, and two of Kilmington, was built by the parishioners about 1790, and is endowed with 6A. of land, purchased in 1746, with £160 given by *Penelope Saffin*, and other donors; and with 2A. given by the parishioners of Kilmington, on condition that they should send two free scholars.

AXMINSTER DIRECTORY.

The POST-OFFICE is at Mr. Wm. Slyfield's. Letters for all parts are despatched at 20 minutes past 5 evening; and also to Exeter and the west and north, at 45 min. past 7 morning. Posts to Colyton, Seaton, &c., at 8 morning.

Adams Wm. miller, *Weycroft*
Anstice Mr Josiah ‖ Anning Miss
Ash Thos. dyer ‖ Benson Mrs C.
Austin John, schoolmaster
Bond Chas. solr. & clerk to County Ct.,magistrates, &union,Trinity sq
Bradford John, assistant overseer
Bridle Richard, hair dresser
Bussell Edw. miller, *Millbrook*
Coleman George, workhouse school
Coneybeare Rev Wm. Jno., M.A. vicar
Cox John, boarding school
Davidson James, Esq. *Sector House*
Deane Joseph, corn miller
Dommett Emanuel, fellmonger
Edwardes Mr T. B. ‖ Bentley Mrs S.

Edwards Rev Zach. Jas., M.A. rector of Comb-Pyne, & union chaplain
Esworthy Frederick, dyer
Finamore John, veterinary surgeon
French James, deputy registrar
Gomm Wm. and Mrs. master and matron of Union Workhouse
Hussey John B. auctioneer, &c
Kelly Rev P., Catholic priest
Knight Hy. solicitor, *Terrace Lodge*
Knight Mrs Sarah, *Hillary House*
Macalaster Lieut.-Col. *Adrian Cottg*
Mallock Rawlin, solr. *Hill House*
Mitchell Fras. and Geo. W. wine and spirit merchants
Northmore S., Esq. *Fursbrook Hs*

Pearce Robt. Phelps, relvg. officer
Penman Rev Richard, (Indepnt)
Phelps Mrs Ann || Poole MrsM. & R.
Pickering Thomas, land survyr. regr.
   and high bailiff of County Court
Pickering Wm. surveyor
Richards J. H., Esq. *Leacombe Hs*
Shiles Misses Sarah and Elizabeth
Shore Mr G. K. || Sellwood Thos.
Slyfield Wm. post-master
Still Major Nathl. T. *Castle hill*
Swain Joseph, beerseller
Symes Miss Jane || Stocker Mrs
Tompkins Miss A. || Smith Miss
Tucker Wm. court bailiff
Turing Rev J. R. curate
Webber Mrs Cath. boarding school
Webber Thos. Nathl. music profsr
Webster Ann, schoolmistress
        BANKS.
Williams, R. H. and H. (branch of
   Dorsetshire;) Thos. Chapple, *agt*
Wilts and Dorset Banking Co; Mr
   Thos. Baylis Edwardes, *manager*
Savings' Bank, Mr Edward Hallett,
   actuary, Castle hill
   FIRE AND LIFE OFFICES.
Atlas, Wm. Keech
Clerical, Medical, &c. J. Cox
Imperial, Wm. S. Pryer
Legal and Commrl., Samuel Gamis
Norwich Union, Henry Knight
Phœnix & Standard, Wm. Pulman
Sun, Thomas Chapple
West of England, F. Whitty
      FARMERS.
Bradford James, *Weycroft*
Dening John, *Westwater*
Dommett Geo. || Dommett James
Fowler James || Gage John
Harvey Francis, *Unity Farm*
Johnson Joseph, Pain's place
Mullins Wm. *Easthay*
Phillips Samuel, *Great Wood*
Phippen James, *Smallridge*
Pound James || Rowe James
Seward John || Symes Constantine
Swain James, *Newenham Abbey*
Towndrow Thos. || Welch John
White John || Zealley Amos
   INNS AND TAVERNS.
Bell, Thomas Towndrow
Black Dog, Benjamin Westlake
Castle, Robert Hook
George Inn, Jas. Pound, (posting)

Green Dragon, George Harvey
Hotel, Wm. Newbery
Lamb, Samuel Goddard
New Inn, John Ryall, (posting)
Red Lion, John Bunston
Rose and Crown, George Newbery
White Hart, Emanuel Dommett
     BAKERS.
Badcock Henry
Bowdige John
Knight Robt. G.
Phillips Wm.
Welch James
Willmott Wm.
   BLACKSMITHS.
Banfield Chas.
Billing Chas.
Bucknole Edw.
Hoare Elias
Tucker Samnel
   BOOKSELLERS.
Hutchings Thos.
Pulman Wm.
Slyfield Rebecca
Wills Emanuel
  BOOT&SHOEMKRS
Baker George
Bunston John
Henley John
Love Samuel
Phippen James
Raison James
Restarick Saml.
Robins Wm.
  CABINET MKRS.
Smith Francis
Smith Fras. jun
Stone George
Wills James
   COOPERS.
Bridle John
Mills Robert
Newbery Thos.
   CURRIERS.
Rundle Richard
Worthy John
   DRUGGISTS.
Chapple Thos.
Keech Wm.
PryerWm. Symes
   GARDENERS.
Baker Wm. H.
Hill Thomas
  GROCERS, &c.
Chapple Thos.

Tytherleigh John
Willmott Wm.
  IRONMONGERS.
Gardiner Alfred,
  (and founder)
Tytherleigh John
JOINERS& BLDRS.
Newbery Thos.
Parsons Wm.
Smith Francis
Smith Fras. jun
L. & W. DRAPERS
Gamis Samuel
Singleton Chas.
Wills John
  MILLINERS.
Bragg Catharine
Hoare Phillis
Jefford Ann.
Parsons Harriet
PAINTERS & GLZS.
Coombs Caleb
Howe Thomas
  SADDLERS.
Evans Henry
Newbery George
Russell Job
 SHOPKEEPERS.
Blackmore Wm.
Bowdige John
Cross Sarah
Dare Susan
Loveridge Jane
Newbery Sol.
Stephens Sarah
White Thos.
STONE MASONS.
Hoare Matthew
Stedham John
Stedham Wm.
  SURGEONS.
Arnold Chas.
Hayman Chas.
Hayman Philip
Hallett Charles
Symes Jas. Fina
  more

TAILORS.	TINNERS, &c.	Hoare Robert	CARRIERS.
Drower George	Coombs Caleb	Mullins Henry	To Exeter, &c.,
Morgan James,	Morgan John	Parrott Mr	Samuel Ford,
(beerhouse)	WATCHMAKERS.		daily; & Hux-
Newbery Wm.	Jones Eli	COACHES to	ford and Gill,
Pearce Matthew	Pulman Philip	Exeter, Lon-	Tues. and Fri
Pidgeon John	WHEELWRIGHTS.	don, Taunton,	To Taunton,
Rogers David	Batstone Chas.	&c. daily	Crocker and
Squire Edward	Goddard Saml.		Ford, Monday,
Swaffield Isaac	Hoare Thomas		from the Bell

AXMOUTH is a pleasant village, on the coast of the English Channel, at the mouth of the river Axe, 3 miles S. by E. of Colyton, and 6 miles W. by S. of Lyme Regis, and S.S.W. of Axminster. Its parish contains 645 souls, and 4534 acres of land, terminating in the lofty and rugged *sea cliffs*, which are crowned by chalky crags, in some places assuming the appearance of shattered turrets, pin-nacles, &c.; and in others, overtopped by luxuriant plantations. The range of cliffs extending from Axmouth to Lyme Regis, is noted for several remarkable LANDSLIPS. By one of these convulsions, which commenced on Christmas-day, 1839, forty-five acres of arable land was lost to cultivation, at Bindon and Dowsland; two cottages, situated in the lower region of the cliff, were destroyed; and a *great chasm* was formed, more than 300 feet broad, 150 feet deep, and three-quarters of a mile long. Two of the coast-guard, standing on Culverhole beach, on the night when this great landslip occurred, ' observed the sea to be in an extraordinary state of agitation; the beach on which they stood rose and fell; amidst the breakers near the shore, something dark appeared to be rising from the bottom of the sea, amidst the deafening noise of crashing rocks." On Feb. 3rd, 1840, there was another landslip at Whitlands, much smaller than the former. By taking a central position on the undercliff be-tween *Pinhay* and *Whitlands*, and looking inland, the visitor sees the precipitous yet wooded summit of the mainland, and the castel-lated crags of the ivy-clad rocks on the terraces immediately below, and the deep dingle at the bottom; and by turning towards the sea, he beholds the whole range of the great bay of Dorset and Devon, skirted by coast scenery of the finest character. In the early part of the 17th century, large sums were expended by the Erle family in an unsuccessful attempt to construct a new *haven* at Axminster. During the present century, *piers* have been constructed at the mouth of the Axe, where vessels of 100 tons burden can now dis-charge their cargoes in safety. The manor of Axmouth was given by the Earl of Devon, in the reign of Henry II., to Montebourg Abbey, in Normandy; but Henry V. gave it to Sion Abbey. Ed-ward VI. granted it to Walter Erle, Esq. In 1679, it was sold to Sir Walter Yonge, who sold it, in 1691, to Richard Hallett. John H. Hallett, Esq., is now lord of the manor, and owner of a great part of the parish, and of the mansions called *Stedcombe House* and *Haven Cliff*. He is also impropriator of most of the great tithes, and patron of the *vicarage*, valued in K.B. at £22. 19s. 2d., and in 1831 at £263, and now in the incumbency of the Rev. R. S. Hallett,

Q

who has 49A. 2R. 19P. of glebe, and is also rector of ROOSDOWN or *Rousdown*, an *extra parochial estate*, of one house and 190 acres belonging to R. C. Bartlett, Esq., the patron, and lying within the bounds of Axminster parish, adjoining the great landslip of Dowsland and Bindon. This depopulated place was anciently held by the Down family; and its *chapel* (St. Pancras,) has long been desecrated, and is now used as a lumber room to the farm-house. Its rectory is valued at only £35 per annum. *Axmouth Church* is an ancient structure, with a fine Anglo-Norman doorway, and a tower containing three bells. In the interior are several monuments of the Erles and Halletts; and in a recess on the north side, is an antique recumbent effigy of a man, with a dog at his feet. The tithes were commuted in 1846; the vicarial for £175, and the rectorial for £309. In 1726, *Wm. Searle* left a yearly rent-charge of 32s., for schooling poor children of Axmouth.

Ames John, Esq. *Pinhay*
Bartlett Robt. builder & vict. Ship
Beer John, shoemaker
Berry Wm. & Bole Wm. blacksmiths
Clouting Robert, schoolmaster
Coles Mrs E. || Jefford J. par. clerk
Comyns Rev Geo. Thos. curate
Hallett J. H., Esq. and Rev R. S.
Hodgskin Lieut Jas. A., R.N.coastgd
Hoyle Wm. baker and vict. New Inn
Huddleston Mrs Esther M., *Stedcmb*
Love David, shopkeeper

FARMERS.
Bailey James, *Dowsland*
Bartlett Robert || Cawley Richard
Chapple James, *Bindon*
Froom Thos. || Furmidge John
Gage Elizabeth || Gage Simon
Loveridge Wm. || Newbery Thos.
Pile Robert || Pile Samuel
Symes David, *Roosdown*
Welch John & Wm. *Bruckland*
Tucker Thomas, *Whitlands*

COMB PYNE, or *Coompyne*, a small village and parish, 3 miles W. of Lyme Regis, and 4½ miles S. of Axminster, has only 143 inhabitants, and 796 acres of land. H. Knight, Esq., is owner of nearly all the soil, lord of the manor, and patron of the *rectory*, valued in K.B. at £8. 11s. 8d., and in 1831 at £127. The Rev. Z. J. Edwards, M.A., of Axminster, is the present rector, and has about 30 acres of glebe. The parsonage is a small cottage. The tithes were commuted, in 1845, for £120 per annum. The *Church* (St. Mary,) is an interesting little structure, with some very ancient communion plate. The manor was long held by the Coffin and Pyne families, and afterwards by the Bonvilles, Greys, and Petres. *Directory* :—James Loveridge, *blacksmith;* Thos. Snell, *parish clerk;* Fras. Symes, *tailor;* and Robert Bentley, Thos. Marshall, and John Morey, *farmers.*

COMBE RAWLEIGH, or *Comb Ralegh*, a small village, on the bold western acclivity of the Otter valley, 1½ mile N.W. of Honiton, has in its parish 276 souls, and 1747 acres of land, rising to a lofty elevation, overlooking Honiton and the surrounding country. On the highest point, was one of the telegraphs between London and Plymouth. The *manor* was successively held by the Baunton, Matthews, Ralegh, Dennis, and other families. It is now held by the Rev. Wm. Bernard, but part of the soil belongs to Mrs. Woodward and other freeholders. The *Church* (St. Nicholas,) is of the age of the 15th century, and has a tower and three bells. A window

t the west end has been enriched with stained glass, in memory of
he rector's family; and in the churchyard is the tomb of *John Shel-
on, Esq.*, the celebrated professor of anatomy in the Royal Acade-
ny, who died in 1808. The *rectory*, valued in K.B. at £20.0s.10d.,
nd in 1831 at £295, is in the patronage of E. S. Drewe, Esq., and
ncumbency of the Rev. C. E. Band, M.A., who has a good resi-
ence, in a romantic nook, having an extensive prospect in front,
ut sheltered on other sides by woody hills. The glebe is 47A. 1R.
P., and the tithes were commuted, in 1840, for £305 per annum.

Band Rev Chas. Edw.,M.A., *Rectory*
Clapp Richard, wheelwright
Down Wm. schoolmaster
Graves Mrs Mary, *Woodbine Hill*
Pearce Misses, *Hill Cottage*
Perham John, blacksmith

Weeks Mrs. & Roberts Mrs. *Abbots*
FARMERS.
Bright Wm. || Chinnick Thomas
Godfrey James || Godfrey Henry
Godfrey Thomas || Hillard Samuel
Pavey Eli || Trim John

DALWOOD, a village and parish on the hills, 6 miles E. by N.
of Honiton, and 4 miles W.N.W. of Axminster, has 513 souls, and
about 1600 acres of land, formerly a detached portion of Dorsetshire, as noticed at page 356. It has a cattle fair on the Wednesday before August 21st. The soil belongs to Sir E. M. Elton, Bart.,
the Rev. T. F. Dymock, Mr. R. W. Pike, Messrs. White, and several
other freeholders. The *Church* (St. Peter,) is an ancient structure,
with a tower and five bells ; and the living is a perpetual curacy,
consolidated with the vicarage of Stockland. Here is a Baptist
chapel and a Sunday school.

Beer James and Board Wm. smiths
Bowditch John, corn miller
Chapple Wm. & Gould John, coopers
Colverwell Robert, carpenter
Davey John, tailor
DaveyWm.&EdwardsJohn, shoemkrs
Down Simeon, carpenter
Edwards Wm. grocer, &c
Gould Wm. tanner
Mitchell Daniel, shoemaker
Rapsey Mary, vict. Tucker's Arms
Strowbridge Geo. & Joseph, masons

Stroud John, gent. *Dens Villa*
Thomas John, beerseller
Warren Benjamin, glue manufactr
FARMERS.
Banfield Thomas || Bright Robt.
French John || Gould John
Kingsbury Thomas || Lane Robt.
Newbery Wm. || Palmer John
North John, (and shopkeeper)
Pike Robert Wood || Smith John

Post Town, Axminster

HONITON, an *ancient borough and market town*, which has long
been celebrated for the manufacture of beautiful *lace*, is picturesquely situated on rising ground, on the south-eastern side of the
river Otter, 16 miles E.N.E. of Exeter, 9 miles W. by N. of Axminster, 16 miles E.S.E. of Tiverton, 152 W.S.W. of London, and
nearly 10 miles E.S.E. of Collumpton Station on the Bristol and
Exeter Railway. The town is well-built, and consists chiefly of one
broad street, nearly a mile in length, mostly built since the *destruc-
tive fires* of 1747 and 1765, the former of which consumed three-
parts of the town, and the latter destroyed 180 houses. The town
also suffered from fire in 1672 and 1754. It was a great thoroughfare from London to Exeter, before the opening of the abovenamed
railway, and is now well paved and lighted, and has many good
inns and well stocked shops. It has been much improved during

the present century, and the higher parts of it command delightfu
views of the Otter valley, which presents a fine expanse of fertil
corn and pasture lands, and boldly swelling hills, interwoven wit.
that network of luxuriant hedge rows for which Devon is so famous
Its *parish and borough* are co-extensive, and comprise 3046A. 2R. 2
of land, and upwards of 4000 inhabitants;—the population bein
2377 in 1801; 3509, in 1831; and 3895, in 1841. Honiton give
name to a large Union, a Polling and County Court District, and
Petty Sessional Division; the latter of which comprises the 18 pa
rishes of Awliscombe, Branscombe, Buckerell, Comb-Rawleigh, Cot
leigh, Dunkeswell, Farway, Feniton, Gittisham, Honiton, Luppitt
Monkton, North and South Leigh, Offwell, Upottery, Widworthy
and Yarcombe, for which the county magistrates hold petty session
here monthly, at the King's Arms Inn. The Mayor and ex-Mayor are
magistrates for the borough. The *Market House*, for the sale o
corn, cheese, butter, poultry, &c., is in the centre of the town, an
over it is a large *Public Room.* It was built about 25 years ago, by
the late Paving Trust Commissioners, at the cost of more than
£2000. The *market*, held every Saturday, is extensively supplie
with corn, cattle, and all sorts of provisions, especially butter, o
which great quantities are sent to London. Two *great markets*, for
cattle, &c., are held the second Saturday in April, and the Saturday
before the 18th of October; and a large annual *fair* on the Wednes
day after July 19th. The *Gas Works* were constructed in 1835, a
the cost of £2700, raised in £25 shares; and the consumers are
supplied at the rate of 9s. per 1000 cubic feet. The town possessed
the advantage of a market as early as the reign of King John, wh
changed the market day from Sunday to Saturday. It obtained the
grant of a fair from the lord of the manor, in 1257, and is said to
have been the first town in Devon at which *serges* were made. Both
this manufacture, and that of *lace*, are supposed to have been introduced here by the Lollards, who came to England during the religious persecutions in Flanders, in the reign of Elizabeth. (See
page 63.) The serge trade went to decay many years ago; but the
lace manufacture still flourishes here, though not so extensively as
formerly. Much of the rich and beautiful fabric called *Honiton
Point Lace*, and sometimes *bone or thread lace*, is made in the towns
and villages in this and other parts of the county. This lace sells
at from 1s. to upwards of a guinea per yard; and the best kind was
formerly made entirely from the finest Antwerp thread, which once
sold as high as £70 per pound weight. An inferior kind of lace,
made of British thread, in the villages along the coast, is called
Trolley lace. In the early part of the present century, the lace manufacturers of Honiton employed about 2500 women and children in
the town and neighbouring villages; but the introduction of a
cheaper article, about 30 years ago, made of bobbin net, by machinery, gave a great check to this domestic manufacture, which
has lately somewhat revived, in various parts of the county, under
the patronage of her present Majesty, and the late Dowager Queen
Adelaide. Honiton has a *pottery* of brown earthenware, a tannery,
a brewery, an iron foundry, three corn mills, several maltkilns, and

a branch of the National Provincial Bank of England. Its own local BANK, which was many years carried on by *Messrs. Flood and Lott*, has lately failed in *liabilities* amounting to £228,000, with *assets* amounting to about £220,000 ; but of the latter, £33,000 are *doubtful* balances, and £143,000 *bad.* The liabilities will be reduced by £86,000 in the partners' credit balances, so that the loss of the creditors will be less than £80,000, if the doubtful debts are recovered, and the bankruptcy is economically managed. The assizes were held at Honiton in 1590, on account of the plague being at Exeter, and seventeen criminals were executed. On July 25th, 1644, King Charles was at Honiton with his army, on his route westward; and again on Sept. 23rd, on his return. Sir Thomas Fairfax halted here with his army on his march into Devon, Oct. 14th, 1645 ; but, happily, the town was not the scene of any fatal conflict during the civil wars.

The *Manor of Honiton* was possessed by Drago, a Saxon, but was given by William the Conqueror to his half-brother, Robert Earl of Moreton. Henry I. gave it to Richard de Rivers, Earl of Devon. Isabel, Countess of Devon, sold it to Edward I., who gave it to Sir Gilbert de Knovill. It afterwards passed, probably by purchase, to Hugh Courtenay, Earl of Devon. It remained with the Courtenay family till sold by the late Viscount Courtenay, about 1810. Joseph Locke, Esq., M.P., one of the borough representatives, is now lord of the manor, but many other freeholders have estates in the parish, and some of them have neat houses here. The manor was anciently parcel of the barony of Plympton, and its lords had the power of inflicting capital punishment. The estates called *Batteshorne, Littletown, Northcote, Blanicombe, &c.*, belong to various owners. An old *légend* relates that, at an early period, nearly all the women of Honiton were barren, and that to remedy this evil, they were enjoined by the priests to repair to St. Margaret's chapel, and pass one whole day and night in prayer, when by means of a vision, they would become pregnant. The *arms of the borough* seem to allude to this legend, as they represent a pregnant woman kneeling to an idol, with an obstetric hand above them ; and the very name of the town is said to refer to it, as *honi*, in the old Norman-French, signified shame or disgrace.

BOROUGH.—Honiton is an ancient *borough by prescription*, and till 1846 was governed by a *portreeve, bailiff*, and other officers, elected annually on Michaelmas-day, at the court leet of the manor. It first returned two members to parliament in the 28th of Edward the First, and sent two others to a subsequent parliament, after which it neglected this privilege for nearly 400 years, until the 16th of Charles I., when, through the influence of Wm. Pole, Esq., it was restored. The right of election was in all the householders ; but for a time they were disfranchised by a charter of James I., which instituted a mayor and a select number of pocket freemen, consisting of country gentlemen, to whom the right of election was confined. This obnoxious charter was soon abolished, and the borough remained under its portreeve till Nov., 1846, when it received a *Royal Charter of Incorporation*, in accordance with the provisions

of the Municipal Reform Act of 1835. By this charter, the borough
is divided into *two wards*, and placed under the government of a
Town Council, consisting of a *mayor, six aldermen*, and *eighteen
councillors.* The boundaries of the borough previous to the passing
of the *Parliamentary Reform Act* of 1832, were uncertain, but they
were extended by that act so as to comprise the whole parish. Before
the passing of this act, the right of election was in the male householders not receiving alms, but paying scot and lot, and boiling
their own pots, from which they were called *potwallers*, or *pot-
wallopers.* The registered lists of *borough voters* entitled to vote
for the two parliamentary representatives, in 1849, comprised 205
occupiers of houses of the yearly value of £10 or upwards, and 399
potwallers; but many of the former are also on the list of the latter.
The total number on the register in 1837 was 455, of whom 372
were potwallers. The latter, who have enjoyed the elective fran-
chise since 1831, may retain it for life, as long as they remain householders, and are never excluded from the register two years in succession. The borough has not been contested since 1837, and its
present MEMBERS OF PARLIAMENT are Joseph Locke, Esq., and Sir
James Weir Hogg, Bart. The CORPORATION for 1849-'50 is as
follows :—

MAYOR, R. H. Aberdein, Esq. || EX-MAYOR, Captain Basleigh.
ALDERMEN, Capt. Basleigh, Capt. Groube, Edm. Stamp, Wm. Woodward,
J. C. Jerrard, and R. H. Aberdein, Esqrs.
COUNCILLORS, Messrs. John H. Townsend, J. H. Jerrard, B. B. Smark,
Geo. White, Thos. Avery, Wm. Woodgates, Jph. Manley, James Hussey,
and George Catford, for *St. Paul's Ward;* and Messrs. H. V. Mules, John
Murch, J. C. Eames, Samuel Rose, James Smith, Matthew Murch, Wm.
Lee, Thos. Denner, and John McKno, for *St. Michael's Ward.*
TOWN CLERK and *Manor Steward*, Isaac John Cox, Esq.
Clerks to the County Magistrates, Messrs. Townsend and Stamp.
Clerk to the County Court for Honiton District, R. H. Aberdein, Esq. This
court is held monthly at the Golden Lion Inn, for all the parishes in Honi-
ton Union ; and Mr. Joseph Manley is the *high bailiff.*

CHURCHES:—*St. Michael's*, the old parish church, is inconveniently
situated on a bold eminence, half a mile south of the town, near *Littletown*
farm. It was originally a small chapel for mendicant friars, but was enlarged about 1482, chiefly at the expense of the Bishop of Exeter; who also
gave the curious screen which separates the nave and chancel. It has a
tower and five bells, and contains some ancient monuments, and one in
memory of *Dr. Marwood*, physician to Queen Elizabeth, who died in 1617,
aged 105 years. The original parish church is supposed to have stood in
the town, on the site of *Allhallows Chapel*, which was rebuilt after being destroyed by fire in 1765, but was pulled down in 1837, to give place to ST.
PAUL's CHURCH, which was erected near it, and made the parish church,
under the powers of an act of Parliament passed in 1835. This spacious
and elegant structure of Norman architecture, cost about £7600, exclusive
of about £2400 paid for the purchase of old buildings, land, &c., for
fencing the burial ground. It was finished and consecrated in 1838. There
was some great defect in the erection of this noble edifice, as it had to be
new roofed, repaired, and altered, in 1849, at the cost of about £1000. It
was erected and repaired by subscripton, and has 1530 sittings, of which
500 are free. It is 132 feet long and 58 broad, and its tower is a magnifi-

cent specimen of the Norman style, rising to the height of 104 feet, and crowned by elaborately worked pinnacles. The organ is a fine instrument, which cost £400. A beautiful marble monument, by Bacon, has been erected in the north transept, by Sir E. M. Elton, in memory of his great-grandfather, James Marwood, Esq. It is in the form of a Roman altar, surmounted by a vase and the figures of Justice and Benevolence ; with a pelican feeding its young. The altar-piece, presented by Sir Edward, is a fine copy of Raphael's picture of the Transfiguration. The pulpit is of Beer stone, handsomely wrought, and resting on twisted columns. The *rectory*, valued in K.B. at £40. 4s. 2d., and in 1831, at £272, is in the patronage of the Earl of Devon, and incumbency of the Rev. H. V. P. Somerset, M.A., who has 87 acres of glebe, and an ancient residence in a picturesque and secluded situation. The tithes were commuted in 1842, for £632. 9s. 8d. per annum. Service is performed in the old church once a month. The Rev. B. M. Gane, is *curate ;* Mr. John Porter, *clerk ;* and Mr. J. J. Flood, *organist.*

There are four CHAPELS in Honiton, belonging to *Unitarians, Independents, Baptists,* and *Wesleyans.* That belonging to the Unitarians was built in 1776, in lieu of the old Presbyterian Meetinghouse, founded in 1696. The Rev. Wm. Harris, a Presbyterian minister, who died here in 1770, was author of the " Lives of Hugh Peters, James I., Charles II., and Oliver Cromwell." Sunday schools are connected with the church and chapels, and the various congregations subscribe to the support of several institutions for the promotion of religion. The town has a *Literary and Scientific Institution,* which has a valuable library, and a long list of subscribers. It has also a talented *Choral Society* and a *Glee Club ';* and at the Dolphin Hotel and the Golden Lion Inn are commodious *Assembly Rooms,* where balls, concerts, lectures, &c., are often held. *Honiton and Ottery Agricultural Society* has a numerous list of members. Here are two old benefit societies called the " *Friends United* " and the " *New United Brethren,*" and in 1848, a *Tradesmen's Friendly Society* was established at the Dolphin Hotel. The *East Devon Friendly Society,* which has offices here, was amalgamated with the *Western Provident Association,* in November, 1849.

CHARITIES.—For repairing Allhallows Chapel and the school house, &c., which adjoined it, and for such other public and charitable uses as the trustees should think meet, *Sir John Kirkham* and *Elizens Harding,* in the 15th of Henry VIII., left 17 tenements, &c., in Honiton, and a house and 11A. of land at Yarcombe, now worth £150 a year, but let for only £47, on long leases, subject to fines on every renewal of the leases. One of the houses worth £20 a year, is occupied rent free by the master of the Grammar School, and another of the same value was long used as the parish workhouse. The same trustees have the management of the following charities. HENRY BEAUMONT, in 1590, left Rapshays farm, (26A.) at Buckerell, and directed the yearly proceeds to be distributed among the poor of Honiton parish. It is now let for about £40 per annum. ELIZABETH BEAUMONT, widow of the above named donor, gave for the same purpose, in 1595, the *Steevely Land,* (36A. 3R. 29P.,) in Allott's Isle, now let for only £17 a year, under a lease which will expire in 1866. THOS. MARWOOD, in 1617, left for the poor, four small tenements, now let for £6. 8s. 8d. per annum, subject to fines on the renewal of the leases. HAYES TRUST, comprises about 10A. of land in Buckerell parish, purchased in the 16th century with £200, left to the poor by *James Rodge* and three other donors. It is now let for £10 a year. WARWICK LANE TRUST consists of four tenements, purchased in 1658, with £65 poor's money, and now let for only £4. 8s. per annum, in consideration of fines, paid when the 99 years' leases were grant-

ed. The BRIDEWELL HOUSES, purchased with £130 poor's money, in 1675, were formerly one of the county prisons, and now consist of a public-house called the Carpenters' Arms, a large Garden, and several small tenements, worth £30, but let for only £5. 5s. per annum, on a 99 years' lease in 1805, in consideration of a fine of £50. STOCKER'S LAND, (18A. 1R. 3P.,) in the parish of Luppitt, was purchased by the feoffees in 1691, with £270 poor's money, of which £100 was left by *Henry Marwood.* This land is now let for about £36 a year. To the *general fund* arising from the above named charities, are added the dividends of £300, three per cent. consols, purchased with unapplied income; and £12 a year from three *Annuities for the support of the schoolmaster,* viz., £6 and £2, given by JOHN FLEY, in 1614; and one of £4, purchased with £80, given by the parishioners, in 1662. The total annual income arising from all these sources is about £190, of which about £120 is distributed among the poor parishioners, and the remainder is absorbed in repairing the buildings, and in other incidental expenses. The GRAMMAR SCHOOL, sometimes called Allhallows School, has been for many years conducted as a classical boarding school, but for the use of the house and schoolroom and the £12 a year above named, the master is required to teach four free scholars, appointed by the trustees. Here is a large *National School,* built in 1829, and attended by 140 boys and 90 girls; and a *British School,* supported by dissenters. The *Charity School,* which was free to all the poor children of the parish, and was established by subscription in 1813, is consolidated with the National School, together with its endowment of £300, four per cent. stock, left by the *Rev. James How,* in 1816.

ST. MARGARET'S HOSPITAL, on the Exeter road, was anciently a house of *lepers,* and was refounded by John Chard, in 1642, for five poor people, and enlarged in 1808 by the erection of four new houses, so that it is now the residence of nine almspeople, one of whom is called the governor. It is endowed with 18A. 2R. 27P. of land, let for about £60 a year. The governor has 3s., and the other eight inmates have each 1s. per week. Each of them also receives a donation of 10s. or 12s. at Christmas. It was in the ancient chapel of this hospital where the *legend* (see page 365,) says the barrenness of the women of Honiton was miraculously changed to fertility.

The poor parishioners have £6 a year as the rent of half of East Rhodes field, (15¼A.,) purchased with a £100 left by *Richard Minifie,* in 1707. They have also the interest of £50 left by *Eliz. Harris,* in 1782.

HONITON UNION comprises the 28 parishes of Awliscombe, Branscombe, Broadhembury, Buckerell, Combe Rawleigh, Cotleigh, Dunkeswell, Farway, Feniton, Gittisham, Harpford, Honiton, Luppitt, Monkton, Northleigh, Offwell, Ottery St. Mary, Payhembury, Plymtree, Salcombe, Sheldon, Sidbury, Sidmouth, Southleigh, Tallaton, Upottery, Ven-Ottery, and Widworthy, which comprise an area of 131 square miles, and had 23,891 inhabitants in 1841, living in 4591 houses; besides which they had 262 empty houses and 38 building, when the census was taken. Their total average annual expenditure, during the three years preceding the formation of the Union, was £10,244; but for the year ending Lady-day, 1849, it was £12,997. 5s. 10¼d., including salaries, county rates, &c. The *Union Workhouse,* built in 1836, at the cost of £5022, is a stone building, with room for about 230 inmates. Ten surgeons are employed by the Union, and the Rev. H. K. Venn is the *chaplain.* H. V. Mules, Esq., is the *union clerk;* John and Mrs. Coren are *master and matron* of the Workhouse; and Wm. Gayler and Francis George Edwards are the *relieving officers.* Philip Mules, Esq., is *superintendent registrar,* and H. V. Mules, Esq., is his deputy. Mr. John Knight is *registrar of marriages;* and Jph. Manley and Edw. Carter are *registrars of births and deaths,* the former for Honiton District and the latter for Ottery St. Mary and Sidmouth District.

HONITON DIRECTORY.

The Post-Office is in High street, and Mr. Richard Tucker is the *post-master*. Letters are despatched to London and all parts at 7¼ night; to Dorchester, &c., at 20 min. past 5 evening; and to Sidmouth, &c., at 6 morning and 10 min. before 7 night. Money orders are granted and paid.

Aberdein Robt. Henry, solr. coroner, & clerk of county court *(mayor)*
Ashley M. and E. curriers, &c
Austen Thos. James, vety. surgeon
Avery Thos. wine merchant, &c
Basleigh Capt. James *(ex-mayor)*
Botten Thomas, Esq
Brown Miss C. || Conrey Mrs Mary
Coombes John, coach builder
Coren John, master of *Workhouse*
Crydon Mr John || Danby Mrs H.
Davey M. C. gent. *St Leond's Villa*
Drewe E. S. Esq. *The Grange*
Elliott Miss, England House
Elliott J. W. Esq. *Cott House*
FarquharsonS.Esq.D.C.L.*Springfield*
Fisher Mrs H. || Gidley Mrs F.
Flood Mr Christopher Samuel
Flood Joseph, organist, &c
Francis Wm. lessee of gas works
Gane Rev Brisco Morland,B.A.curate
Gauntlett Rev T. H. (Baptist)
Gaylor Wm. relieving officer
Gidley Rev Lewis, M.A. curate of Combe Rawleigh
Godolphin John, brush maker
Groube Captain Thomas, R.N.
Harrison Rd. Patch, tanner & currier
Hartnell Rev M. A. *Gram. School*
Harwood Rev Daniel (Unitarian)
Hellier Radford, deputy registrar
Hill Mrs Chtte. || Hurley Mrs Mary
Hooper Francis, beer seller
Hurd Henry, glover
Hurdle John Pidsley, chandler
Hussey Susan, potter
Kite Wm. surveyor of taxes
Letten Geo. and Reed M. *sextons*
Lott Mr Harry Buckland
Manley Jph. high bailiff of Co. Court
Materface John, whitesmith
Mockridge John, brewer
Murch Ann, haberdasher
Murch Mr Wm. || Marsh Misses
Newberry Mr Jas. || Pearse Misses
Peake —, assistant overseer
Pidgeon Mr. Daniel || Pine Mr Wm.
Pople Miss Cath. *Summerland*
Porter John, parish clerk

Reed Nathl. gent. || Phinn Mrs
Richards Mrs J., Summerland
Rogers John R. doctor of philosophy
Somerset Rev Villiers Henry Planta-genet, *Rectory*
Stamp Edmund, solicitor
Townsend Jno. Honeywood, solicitor; h *Ashfield*
Treby Miss Elizabeth || Tooze Mrs
Tucker Rd. postmaster & stationer
Venn Rev Henry Knott, curate of Monkton & chaplain to the Union
Vimpany Mr Edm. || Wakeford Jph.
Ward Benjamin, coach builder
Ward James, revenue officer
Wethey Edwin, bank manager
White Thomas and Sons, (James and Robert,) ironfounders
Wright Rev Wm. (Independent)

ATTORNEYS.
Aberdein Robt. Hy. (coroner, &c)
Bowerman Richard, (and *Uffculm*)
Cox Isaac John, (town clerk)
Gould Daniel, High street
Guppy Alfred, High street
Lyde Thomas (and *Sidmouth*)
Mules Horace Vibart (union clerk)
Mules Philip (superintendt. regr.)
Smark Benjamin Barker
Smith John Bridgman
Townsend & Stamp (magists.' clerks)

BANKS.
National Provincial Bank of England, High st; E. Wethey, manager
Devon and Exeter Savings' Bank; W. K. Newbery, *agent*

FARMERS.
Abbott Thomas, *Lowman's*
Baker John, *Northcote*
Burroughs Wm. *Livermore*
Corner Richard, *Brand farm*
Cox Susan, *Heathfield*
Davey John, *Cowley*
Denner Thomas, *Rowlhay*
Farrant James, *Roebuck*
Gosling Samuel, *Cheney's*
Hartnoll James, *Stont farm*
Hartnoll John, *Gardener's*
Melhuish Thomas, *Middlehills*

Musgrove Chas. Budd, *Littletown*
Perry Joseph, *Great Hale*
Snell James, *Perry Hale*
Trine Benjamin, *Northcote hill*
Trott Thomas ‖ Plucknett James
Turpin Philip, *Round Ball*
Ware Thomas, *Landside*
Warren George, *Higher Blanicombe*

FIRE AND LIFE OFFICES.
Agricultural & Imperial, A. Guppy
Alliance, Joseph Manley
Church of England, Rev L. Gidley
Clerical & Medical, George Turner
County & Provident, J. Murch
Farmers', Wm. Wheaton
Globe, Mrs R. Davey
Guardian,& Legal & Coml., R.W.Rose
Life Asstn. of Scotland, Jas. Hussey
Medical Invalid, J. P. Hill
Phœnix & Pelican, Basleigh & Avery
Professional & Kent, G. L. Mitchell
Royal Exchange, J. B. Smith
Sun, Matthew Murch
West of Engd., Townsend & Stamp

INNS & TAVERNS.
Anchor Inn, My. Ann Pope
Angel, Elizabeth Lee
Black Lion, Charles Sanders
Carpenter's Arms, Wm. Lee
Chopping Knife, Saml. Walters
Crown & Sceptre, John Croot
Dolphin Hotel, John D. Blake
Exeter Inn, John Broomfield
Fountain, Eleanor Newton
Golden Lion Inn, Mrs Wheaton
Green Dragon, Benjamin Trim
King's Arms, Edward Stroud
London Inn, Daniel Newton
New Inn, Peter Tucker
Red Cow, Robert Parker
Star, Nathaniel Bishop
Swan, Wm. Teed
Three Tuns, John Trickey
Turk's Head, Wm. Stroud
Vine, Amos Broom
White Hart, Wm. Symons
White Horse, Mercy Roderigo
White Lion, Robt. Eveleigh

ACADEMIES.
(* *Boarding*.)
Clark Eliz. *natnl*
Coren Thos. *natl*
* Hartnell Rev.
  M.A. *Grm. Sch*
*Luckham My. A.

*Rowse Joseph
Shepherd Thos.
*Woodgates Wm.
AUCTIONEERS.
Hussey James
Porter John

BAKERS.
Granger Wm.
Humphrey J. M.
Kibby Thos.
Long John
Love James
Melhuish Saml.
Minifie Richard
Wakely Joseph
White Charles
Wills Henry
BASKET MAKERS.
Charles Richard
Sprague John
BLACKSMITHS.
Channon Wm.
Elston Henry
Jennings John
Josland Richard
Manning George
Woodland Thos.
BOOKSELLERS.
And Stationers.
Clark W. B.
Knight Jno. *regr*
Spurway Mary
BOOT & SHOE MKS.
Croot John
Haycraft John
Hooper Richard
Humphrey Henry
Letten Robert
Porter Wm.
Russell Wm.
Stockman John
Swaine Richard
Walters John
Walters Thomas
BUTCHERS.
Burrough Wm.
Crease John
Dare James
Holway John
Hook John
Lee Wm.
Newton Daniel
Rapsey Jas. & Co.
Salter Jasper
Skinner Charles
Symons Wm.
Symons W. jun
Tratt Joseph
CABINET MAKERS.
Frost Richard
Salter Richard

Sydenham John
CHEMISTS & DGTS.
Creak Thos. E.
Needs Wm.
Rogers Wm.
Starke George
Starke John
CONFECTIONERS.
Kibby Thomas
Rippon Edward
Rippon Robert
Saunders John
Wills Henry
COOPERS.
Connett James
Connett Nichls.
Reed John
CORN MILLERS.
Melhuish Saml.
Plucknett James
Skinner John
DYERS.
Darke Peter
Lathorpe Sus.
GARDENERS.
Board Henry
Frost James
Hooper Thomas
Passmore John
GLASS, &c., DLRS.
Eames J. C.
Smith James
GROCERS, &c.
(**Tea Dlrs. only*.)
Avery Thomas
Davy Rebecca
*Ford Edward
*Frazer Matthew
*Frazer Thomas
Fuller Henry
Hellier Robert
*Kerr Thos. Kp.
Lang Joseph
*Mc Kno John
White George
White John
HAIRDRESSERS.
Mitchell Geo. L.
Roach Samuel
Towell John
HOP MERCHANTS.
Basleigh & Avery
Rogers Wm.
White John

IRONMONGERS.
Murch John
Wheaton Wm. (&
slate, &c., mrt.)
JOINERS & BLDRS.
Hooper James
Lee Wm. (& sur-
veyor)
Letten Wm.
Sydenham Jph.
LACE MANFRS.
Blake Mrs
Davy Amy
Godolphin Sarah
Pidgeon Mrs
L. & W. DRAPERS.
Ash James
Gauntlett T. H.
Lathy Amy
Mc Kno John
Newberry Willm.
Kenward
Peake Fredk.
Reed Natl. & Jno.
Rose Saml. & Son
MALTSTERS.
Davey Albion
Thorn John
MASONS, &c.
Fowler Henry
Fowler Robert
Golesworthy Chs.
Golesworthy Hy.
Golesworthy Jph.
Ham Charles
Hooper Fras. (&
beerhouse)
Parker James
Perry James
Reed Moses
Summerhayes J.
MILLINERS.
Austen M. A.
Bamfield Ann

Fowler Ann
Hicks Sarah
Hussey Chtte.
Mitchell Mrs
Porter Leah
Russell Sar. A.
Tucker Eliz.
PAINTERS, PLUM-
BERS & GLAZRS.
Eames Joshua
Channon
Eames Wm.
Hooper Wm.
Patten Joseph
Shute Wm.
Smith James
Smith John M.
Thomas Wm.
SADDLERS.
Catford George
Glanville Fras.
Williams James
SHOPKEEPERS.
Bagwell David
Burrough John
Clark James
Connett Nicholas
Croot Wm.
Dare John
Davey Henry
Gosling Richard
Hellier Robert
Hooper Francis
Munday Thomas
Parker James
Pippin Sarah
Tratt Joseph
Wakely Nathnl.
Willacott Wm.
STRAW HAT MKRS.
Fowler E. & M.
Golesworthy L.
Lowdar Eliz.
Mc Kno Jane

Rattenbury Eliz.
Smith Cath.
Sydenham Eliz.
Tozer Susan
SURGEONS.
Devenish Samuel
Hill Jas. Peter
Holland Ed. Cpr.
Jerrard Jno. Clap-
cott
Jerrard J.H., M.D.
Woodward Wm.
TAILORS.
(* are Drapers.)
*Austen Wm.
Carter Philip
*Clapp John
*Dunning Saml.
*Fry John L.
Hansford Wm.
Hooper Wm.
Parsons Henry
*Rowe Henry
Salter Henry

Stone John
TINNERS, &c.
French James
Stockman Wm.
Willis Thomas
TURNERS.
Russell Wm. R.
Sparke Jno. Day
WATCHMAKERS.
Hurd Thomas
Murch Matthew,
Stamp office
Tovey Henry
WHEELWRIGHTS.
Bromfield James
Bromfield John
Coombes John
Newton James
Ward Benjamin
WINE & SPT. MTS.
Basleigh & Avery
Pidgeon John
White John

COACHES, &c.

To *Exeter*, the Royal Mail and Cornet daily; and Omnibuses, Mon.
Wed. and Fri.
To *London*, Royal Mail and Cornet
daily; and Prince of Wales, from
Sidmouth via Taunton, every other
day

CARRIERS.

To *Axminster*, W. Huxford, Sat.;
Collumpton and *Tiverton*, W. Bas-
leigh, and Shepherd & Co., Sat.
Exeter, Fras. Copp, Thos. Baker,
Wm. Huxford, and Wm. Trace,
Mon. Tue. Wed. and Fri.
London, Ford, Jennings, and Co.,
from the Swan, Mon. Wed. & Fri.
Sidmouth, W. Dorman, Sat.
Taunton, Jas. Kibby, from the Exe-
ter Inn, Tues. and Sat.

KILMINGTON, a village and parish on the western acclivities
of Axe valley, two miles W. by S. of Axminster, has 495 souls, and
1763 acres of land.   It has a cattle *fair* on the first Wednesday in
September.   Wm. Tucker, Esq., owns a great part of the parish,
and has a pleasant seat here, called *Coryton Park*, which was rebuilt by his father in 1756.   The CHURCH (St Giles,) is in the perpendicular style, and has a tower and five bells.   The living is a
curacy, consolidated with the vicarage of Axminster, to which Kilmington is ecclesiastically a parochial chapelry.   The vicarial tithes
were commuted in 1841 for £240, and the rectorial for £100 per

annum. The latter are in the same appropriation as Axminster.
Kilmington sends two children to the charity school at Axminster.
The Baptists have a small chapel here.

Chapple John, vict., Old Inn
Collins Wm. blacksmith
French James, grocer and baker
Newbery Jph. plumber, glazier, &c
Phippen Jas. grocer and draper
Sands Rev. H. B. curate
Snell Wm. farmer, *Old Coryton*
Stembridge Rev. Job, (Baptist)
Thorn Benj. and Geo. farmers
Tucker Wm., Esq., *Coryton Park*

LUPPITT, or *Luppit*, is a village and parish, on a bold range
of hills four miles N. by E. of Honiton. It has 782 souls, and 4730
acres of land, including *Shapcombe* tithing, the small hamlets of
Beacon and *Shaugh*, and a common of more than 500 acres. The
baronial family of Carew were formerly lords of the manor, and were
seated till the 16th century at *Mohun's Ottery*, now a farm house in
this parish. The Rev. Wm. Bernard, of Clatworthy, Somerset, is
now lord of the manors of Luppit and Mohun's Ottery, but a great
part of the parish belongs to C. J. Helyar, Esq., the Revs. H. and
H. W. Helyar, and a few smaller freeholders. The *Church* (St.
Mary,) is in the style which prevailed in the 15th century, and has
a tower and four bells. It contains some ancient monuments of the
Carew family, and was appropriated to Newenham Abbey. The
vicarage, valued in K.B. at £13. 6s. 10½d., and in 1831 at £121, is
in the patronage of the Rev. W. Bernard, and incumbency of the
Rev. John S. C. L. Cabbell, who has held the living since 1796.
The Parsonage House is a small cottage, and the glebe is 5A. 22P.
The tithes were commuted in 1840, the vicarial for £140, and the
rectorial for £150. The latter belong to C. J. Helyar, Esq. There
was anciently a free chapel at Mohun's Ottery; and the Presbyterians had formerly a meeting-house at Shaugh. A house and 2½A. of
land belong to the church for repairs, but were let in 1778 for 99
years, at only 3s. per annum, in consideration of a fine of £96.
Two small *schools* are supported by Mrs. Eliz. P. Simcoe, and the
parish has a *Friendly Society*, with a numerous list of members.

Bastin James, blacksmith
Cabbell Rev John S. C. L. *vicar*
Dimond Joseph, corn miller
Marchant Thomas, tailor
Pearse Chas. gent. *Greenway*
Quick Henry, shoemaker
Rowland Jane, & Stone Mary, *schools*
Sage Chas. vict., Red Lion Inn
Searle Wm. blacksmith
Venn Rev. John Cook, *curate*
Wright John, shopkpr. *Post-Office*
   FARMERS. (* *are Owners*.)
Baker Wm. || Bishop Henry
Bishop James || Bishop John
Bishop Henry || Broom Henry
*Burrough James, *Gullyhays*
*Burrough Edward, *North Week*
*Burrough Jph. || Burrough Richard
Davey Robert || Ewins John
Dimond Thomas, *Shapcombe*
Dommett Thomas, *Mount-Stephen*
Griffin Clement || Godfrey Henry
*Griffin James || *Griffin John
*Griffin Thos. || Griffin Thos. jun
Holway Peter, Stonacre
Hurford James || Moore Thomas
Moore John || Moore Thos. jun
*Pearcey Richard || Roe John
*Pyle John, *Dowlish*
*Rosewell Wm. || Salter Jas.
Russell Thos. || Webber Thos.
Warren John || Warren Thomas
Wyatt John, *Higher Shaugh*

MEMBURY, 4 miles N. by. W. of Axminster, is a scattered village and parish on gentle acclivities, bounded by the Yarty rivulet

and the borders of Dorsetshire. It comprises 886 souls, and 4089 acres of land, including *Furley* and *Longbridge* hamlets, and many scattered farmhouses, &c. It has a cattle fair on August 10th. The Dean and Canons of the Royal Free Chapel of St. George the Martyr, at Windsor Castle, are lords of the *manor*, which they have held since 1474, previous to which it had been given by Robt. de Chandos to Goldcliffe Priory, which became a cell to Bec Abbey in Normandy. They have here a number of copyhold tenants. Lord Sidmouth, Robert Davy, Esq., Mrs. Festing, and Samuel Newbery, Esq., have freehold estates here. The latter has a pleasant seat called *Goodman's,* and is owner of Yarty, an ancient farmhouse, lately the property of the Earl of Lovelace, and anciently the seat of the Yarty and Frye families. Membury has long been annexed ecclesiastically as a parochial chapelry to Axminster, its tithes and curacy being in the same patronage, incumbency, and appropriation. (See page 358.) The Parsonage, occupied by the curate, is a new stone-built cottage; and the tithes were commuted in 1840, the vicarial for £336, and the rectorial for £264. 16s. per annum. The Church (St. John the Baptist,) is an ancient structure, with a tower and five bells. It contains several monuments of the Frye and other families, and its burial ground was consecrated in 1316. The poor parishioners have 1¼A. of land purchased with £40, left by Robert and Francis Frye. They have also a yearly rent-charge of 13s. 4d., given by an unknown donor out of Ridge farm.

Bowdage James, vict. *Bridge Inn*
Burnett Rev Richd. Perry, curate
Davy John, vict. *Red Lion*
Harris Mr S. || Matthews Thos. clk
Newbery Samuel, Esq., *Goodman's*
Staple Robt. maltster, *Rock House*

BLACKSMITHS.
Bazley James
Collins John

CORN MILLERS.
Welch Jered
Wellington Rd.

FARMERS.
Bere W., *Yartyfd*
Bradley Ann

Brown Robert, *Callenger*
Coles Thomas
Denston Wm.
Francis Chas.
Harvey Rt.& Jph.
Harvey Wm.
Jennings John
Marks Sar.

Newton Peter
Newbery Saml. jun. *Yarty*
Parris John
Pearce John,*Waterhouse*
Pearce Wm.
Perham Thos.
Pope Thomas
Roberts Charles, *Godworthy*
Smith John
Smith Charles
Stone John

Walkley Henry
Wyatt Jas. T.
Wyatt Js., *Castle*
SHOPKEEPERS.
Case Mary
Fry John
Matthew Geo.
Symes Samuel
WHEELWRIGHTS.
Denston John
Harris Charles

Post *from Axminster*

MUSBURY, in the vale of the Axe, 3 miles S.W. of Axminster, is a village and parish, containing 495 souls, and 2178A. 1R. 10P. of fertile land, including the hamlet of *Maidenhayne* and several scattered houses. *Ash,* now a farmhouse, was anciently the seat of the De Esse or Ash family, and afterwards of the Drakes. Sir John Drake, who was created a baronet in 1660, rebuilt the old castellated house, which had been destroyed in the civil wars. His nephew, John Churchill, the great *Duke of Marlborough,* was born in the old house in 1650. Ash was occupied by Sir John Pole in 1778, when the stables were burnt down. J. V. Payne, Esq., is lord of the manor of Musbury, which was anciently held by the Courtenays, and afterwards by the Drake and other families. John Gregson,

John Woolcot, and Samuel Parr, Esqrs., Mr. Richd. Wills, Mr. F. Gillett, and several other freeholders, have estates in the parish. The CHURCH (St. Michael,) is an ancient fabric, with a tower and five bells, and contains several handsome monuments of the Drake family, with six kneeling effigies; and one in memory of Judge Grundy, who died of the gaol fever in 1754. The *rectory*, valued in K.B. at £9. 11s. 8d., and in 1831 at £400, is in the patronage of the Trustees of Wm. Payne, Esq., and incumbency of the Rev. Geo. Tucker, B.C.L., who has neither parsonage house nor glebe. The tithes were commuted in 1839 for £435 per annum.

Conway Maria, vict. New Inn
Dowell Thomas, tailor
Gillett C. B. tanner
Griffin Samuel, grocer
Hoare Jph. shoemkr. and parish clk
Lee Wm. beerseller
Rockett Robt. grocer, Post-office
Smith Mrs Juliet, *Mountfield*
Tucker Rev George, B.C.L. rector
Tucker Mr George, Jun.
POST-OFFICE at Rt. Rockett's. Letters desp. 3 aft. *via* Axminster

FARMERS.
Gillett Fras. (owner,) *Knights*
Halse Francis || Harris Thomas
Harris Wm., *Drake's*
Henley John, *Mid Maidenhayne*
Henley Wm., *Little Trill*
Larcombe Matt. || Loveridge Heber
Loveridge Wm., *Bruckland*
Mayne Thomas, *Maidenhayne*
Row John, *Ash Farm*
Slader Samuel, *Hartgrove*
Wills Rd. (owner,) *Newhouse*

ROOSDOWN *(extra parochial)* is noticed at page 362.
STOCKLAND is a large scattered village and parish on the bold range of hills between the Otter and Yarty valleys, about 6 miles N.E. of Honiton, N.W. of Axminster, and S.E. of Chard. It contains 1328 inhabitants, and 5850 acres of land, and with its adjoining parochial chapelry of Dalwood, formed a detached member of Dorsetshire till 1842, when it was added to Devon by act of Parliament. It has a *cattle fair* on the Wednesday after June 11th, and comprises many scattered farmhouses, &c. The Rev. H. W. Marker is lord of the manor; but W. Tucker, Esq., Robert Davy, Esq., Josiah Anstice, Esq., Thomas Culverwell, Esq., the Rev. Wm. Michell, and many smaller owners, have estates in the parish. The CHURCH (St. Michael,) is a fine antique fabric, with a tower and six bells. The *vicarage*, valued in K.B. at £15. 13s. 11½d., and in 1835 at £457, with the curacy of Dalwood annexed to it, is in the patronage of about ten of the principal freeholders and inhabitants. There were originally 56 patrons, under a grant of the 3rd of Edward VI. The Rev. H. R. Surtees is the present *vicar*, and has a good residence and 1¼A. of glebe. The vicarial tithes were commuted in 1844 for £450 per annum. The great tithes belong to the land owners, except those on 261A. 3R. 4P., which belong to about ten persons severally. The *charity lands* of the parish yield about £60 a year, part of which is applied in maintaining a *Free School*.

Beer Jno. shoemkr. and vict. King's Arms
Berry Mr Wm., Yew Cottage
Bowditch John, cooper
Bowyer Charles, saddler, &c.
Brooks J. L. Esq. *Knoll House*
Fry Thos. D. grocer & ironmonger

Kite George, conveyancer
Kite Mr Wm.
Loveridge John, blacksmith.
Lee Edward, gent. *Broadhayes*
Marshall Rev Wm. curate
Mattocks Samuel, schoolmaster
Newbery Wm. shoemaker

Newton Robert, blacksmith
Parsons Thomas, beerseller
Powis Dr., *Welland Cottage*
Surtees Rev Hy. Ratclyffe, vicar
Turner Jas. vict. Rising Sun
Virgint Thomas Apsey, tailor

FARMERS.
(* *are Owners.*)
*Bowditch Jas.
Collins Wm.
Dening Richd.
*Griffin Clement,
    Ford House

Hardy Nathl.
*Herne John
*Herne Samuel
Honniball John
Lane James
Long George
Long Richard

*Moore Wm.
Moore Wm. Jun.
Newbery Eliz.
*Newton Isaac
Newton Robert
Pavey J. C.
Pomeroy Nichls.
Pomeroy Wm.
Pym Wm.
Rockett John
Rockett Wm.
Spiller Robert
Summers Smn.

Summers Wm.
Trivett John
Trott Henry
Trott James
Trott John
Turner Job
Vincent Alfred
Vincent Benj.
Vincent Joseph
Virgint Henry
White James
White John
White Wm.

THORNCOMBE, a village and parish, nearly 6 miles N.E. of Axminster, was formerly a detached part of Devon, but was given to *Dorsetshire* by act of parliament in 1842, in exchange for Stockland and Dalwood, as noticed at page 356. It contains 1425 inhabitants, and 5550 acres of land. It has a *fair* on Easter Tuesday, but its *market* was discontinued about 1770, when the market house was pulled down. John Bragge, Esq., is lord of the manor of Thorncombe, and owner of *Sadborough*, but here are several smaller landowners, and *Ford Abbey* is the seat of — Mills, Esq. This mansion occupies the site of a Cisterian Abbey, which was founded by Richard de Sap, Baron of Okehampton, at Brightley, in 1133, and removed here a few years afterwards. The parish CHURCH (St. Mary,) is an ancient structure, and the living is a *vicarage*, valued in K.B. at £15. 18s. 9d., and in 1831 at £516. J. Bragge, Esq., is patron, and the Rev. John Bragge is the incumbent. Having formerly been a part of Devon, we have deemed it necessary to give this brief notice of Thorncombe, which is now in Whitchurch Canonicorum Hundred, Dorsetshire, and in the Diocese of Salisbury.

UPLYME, a large scattered village, is pleasantly situated at the most eastern extremity of Devon, only about a mile N.W. of the town and sea port of Lyme-Regis, in Dorsetshire. Its parish is a suburb of that town, and comprises 1057 inhabitants, and 3149A. 2R. 5P. of land. The manor was anciently held by Glastonbury Abbey, and afterwards passed to the Drake and Tucker families. The *Hon. Sir John Talbot, K.C.B.*, admiral of the Blue, is now lord of the manor and owner of a great part of the parish. He has a handsome seat here called *Rhode Hill House*. Robert Bourchier Wrey, Esq., of *Ware Cliff House ;* James Davidson, Esq., and the Rev. C. W. Ethelston, M.A., have estates in the parish. The latter is also patron and incumbent of the *rectory*, valued in K.B. at £20. 8s. 11½d.. and in 1331 at £386. The glebe is 35A., and the *Rectory House* is a handsome residence, which was enlarged and much improved in 1838, when the tithes were commuted for £461. 5s. per annum. The CHURCH (St. Peter and St. Paul,) is an ancient structure, with a remarkably low tower. The Methodists and Baptists have chapels here. In this parish was born that skilful geographer *Nathaniel Carpenter,* who published several learned works.

Adams John, schoolmaster
Boon James, woolstapler
Brockway Jas. vict. *Hunters' Lodge*
Ethelston Rev Charles Wicksted, M.A., *Rectory*
Gribble Mrs E. P.
Hallier Gabriel, vict. Black Dog
Marshall Wm. parish clerk
Randel Charles, vict. Talbot Arms
Rhodes Rev E. Duncan, B.D., sinecure rector of Ermington, *Woodhs*
Talbot Admiral Hon. Sir John, K.C.B. *Rhode Hill House*
Wrey Robert Bourchier, Esq., *Ware Cliff House*

BLACKSMITHS.
Dean Richard
Welsman James
CARPENTERS, &c.
Butcher John
Lockyear John
Moore Job
FARMERS.
Clarke Wm.
Davey Benjamin
Davey Wm.
Fowler Job & Son
Gay Samuel
Gay Thornhill
Gratton Wm.

Hansford John
Pattison Wm.
Symes Rbt. *Ware*
Vincent Robert
Webb George
GROCERS, &c.
Fowler Job H.
Matthews Rt. H.
Mountstephen J., (& ironmngr)
SHOEMAKERS.
Cox John
Hoare John
Woolcott Wm.

UPOTTERY, or *Up-Ottery*, is a pleasant village, in the picturesque valley of the river Otter, a few miles from its source, and 5 miles N.E. by N. of Honiton. Its parish contains 991 souls, and 5830A. 3R. 23P. of land, including *Rawridge* tithing, and many scattered farms, and extending to the borders of Somersetshire. Here is a cattle fair on October 17th, and an annual ploughing match. *Viscount Sidmouth* is lord of the manor and owner of a great part of the parish, and resides at the large new *Manor House,* which has been lately erected at a great expense. This mansion is a noble pile in the Elizabethan style, standing on the brow of a gentle slope near the village, and with its clusters of ornamental chimneys, forming a conspicuous object of considerable beauty for some distance. The walls are of pale grey flint, with quoins and dressings of Membury stone. The interior has several elegant apartments, and in the library is a fine collection of books, and a life-size portrait of the first *Lord Sidmouth,* in his robes as Speaker of the House of Commons. (See page 247.) Here are also many other fine pictures, and an admirable bust of the same illustrious statesman, by the celebrated Roubiliac. The stables, which form one side of the village street, are in the same style as the house, and the grounds are tastefully laid out and planted. The manor was given by the Conqueror to Ralph de Pomeroy, and was afterwards given to the church of Rouen, from which it passed to Sir Nicholas Cheyney, in the reign of Henry III. It afterwards passed to the Willoughby, Blount, and Popham families, and was purchased of the latter by *Dr. Addington,* father of the late Viscount Sidmouth. The CHURCH (St. Mary,) is a fine antique structure, with a tower and five bells. The east window is of beautiful stained glass, representing our Saviour, the Virgin Mary, and St. John. The Dean and Chapter of Exeter are patrons of the *vicarage,* valued in K.B. at £15. 5s. 7½d. and in 1831 at £392. The Rev. George Lowe, M.A., is the vicar, and in 1843-'4, erected a new Vicarage House, in the Elizabethan style, at the cost of about £1600. The glebe is about 10 acres, and the tithes were commuted in 1841, the vicarial for £431, and the rectorial for £350. 10s. per annum. The parish is chiefly in pasturage, and forms a pleasing landscape from either side of the valley. The *Independents* and *Baptists* have

chapels here, and the former congregation was Presbyterian in 1715. The *Parish School* was built by subscription on land given by the late Viscount Sidmouth. The poor parishioners have 15A. of land and a barn, left by *Anne Palmer*, in 1714, and now let for £12 a year. The rent is distributed at Easter, together with a yearly rent charge of 40s., left by *Henry Preston*, in 1623, out of Greenhays farm. In 1748, *Robert Newbery* left a yearly rent of 50s. out of Six Acres close, to the Baptist minister.

Viscount Sidmouth and the Hon. Wm.
  Wells Addington, Manor House, (and Richmond Park, Surrey)
Bond John and Wm. wheelwrights
Clapp Josias, shopkeeper
Chapman Rev James
Clarke George, bailiff
Coombe S., Esq. ‖ Bush Misses
Follett Elizabeth, shopkeeper
Hellier Robt. vict. Devonshire Inn
Hoare John, corn miller
Lowe Rev George, M.A. *Vicarage*
Marshall John, blacksmith
Robins John, wheelwright
Shepherd Thomas, tailor
Summerhays John, mason
Summerhays Wm. shoemaker
Turpin John, vict. George Inn

FARMERS.
Anstice Eliz.
Anstice James
Anstice Mary
Anstice Wm.
Blackmore Jas.
Blackmore Rchd.
  Lamb Park
Blackmore Wm.
Brown Wm.
Coles Wm.
Cook Ann
Cuff George
Dimond Wm.
Drake Robert
Drake Thomas
Drake Wm.
Eveleigh Eliz.

Ewins Wm.
Ewins Wm. jun.
Hayman Henry
Newbery Saml.
Pope Wm.
Pym James
Quick John
Quick Thomas
Skinner Joseph
Valentine Wm.
Webber Thos
Webber Richard

Post-Office at Jas. Wright's.
Letters from Honiton

YARCOMBE, or *Yartcombe*, a village and parish, in Chard Union, on the bold western acclivities of the small river Yarty, near the junction of Devon, Dorset, and Somersetshire, 5 miles W. of Chard, and 8 miles N.E. by N. of Honiton, has 826 souls, and 5400 acres of land, rising in lofty hills and comprising many scattered houses. *Sir T. T. F. E. Drake, Bart.*, of Nutwell Court—(see page 254,)—is lord of the manor, owner of a great part of the parish, and impropriator of the great tithes. He resides here occasionally at *Sheaf-hayne House*, a fine old mansion with pleasant grounds. His family has long held the manor of Yarcombe, and he purchased Sheafhayne and the great tithes in 1808. Since then he has greatly improved the estate, and made extensive plantations in the parish. The manor was held by Otterton Priory, and after the dissolution a moiety of it was granted to Robert Earl of Leicester, who sold it to Robt. Drake, Esq., of Ash, who conveyed it to *Sir Francis Drake*, the celebrated circumnavigator, who was possessed of the other moiety by grant from the Crown. The CHURCH (St. John,) is a fine Gothic structure, with an embattled tower and five bells. The interior is neatly fitted up, and has a beautifully carved pulpit. The *vicarage*, valued in K.B. at £28, and in 1831 at £617, is in the patronage of the Lord Chancellor and incumbency of the Rev. Wm. Palmer, D.D., who is also vicar of Ilton, Somersetshire, where he resides. The Parsonage is a small ancient building, and the glebe is 37A. A yearly rent charge of £389. 1s. 1½d. is now paid in lieu of the vicarial tithes. The *Baptists* have a chapel here. In 1630, *Giles Martin* left £250 to the Mercers' Company, London, in trust,

that they should pay £10 yearly to this parish, for the poor. There is now belonging to this charity £211. 2s. 2d. old South Sea Annuities, purchased in 1768, with nine years arrears, so that the poor parishioners have now divided among them at Christmas, £16. 6s. 7d. They have also about £13 a year, as the rent of the *Parish Mead*, (5A.,) purchased in 1692, with £60 poor's money.

Drake Sir T. T. F. E., Bart., *Sheafhayne House,* (& Nutwell Court)
Bower Thos. blacksmith & parish clk
Furzay Wm. tailor
Godwin Silas, vict. Heathfield Arms
Harding Isaac, grocer and draper
Kerly Mr John, *Sheafhayne House*
Mules Rev J. H.,B.A.,curate,*Vicarage*
Palmer Rev Wm., D.D.,vicar ; h *Ilton*
Pulman Rev James, (Baptist)
Virgint John, vict. Drake's Arms
Wadalton Wm. smith & vict. Globe
White Rebecca, vict. Yarcombe Inn
FARMERS.
Billing John
Bowyer John
Chard Betty

Chick John
Hocker John
Knight James
Knight John
Matthews John
Matthews J. jun.
Pring John
Smith John
Spiller James
Spiller Joseph
Spiller Robert
Spiller Robt. jun.
SpillerWm.,Jph., and John
Stickland John

Tolman Wm.
Tucker Wm.
Vincent Henry
Vine Richard
Walden Wm.
Webber Hy. Edw.
Webber Mary
White John
Willie John
Willie Robert

POST-OFFICE at
Yarcombe Inn.
Letters *via* Chard

COLYTON HUNDRED

Is an irregularly formed district, averaging about six miles in breadth, and 8 in length, and bounded on the south by the English Channel, on the west by East Budleigh Hundred, Ottery St. Mary, and the borough of Honiton, and on the north and east by Axminster Hundred. It is in the Southern Division of Devon, in Honiton Polling District, and in Axminster and Honiton Unions, County Court Districts, and Petty Sessional Divisions. It is in the Archdeaconry of Exeter, and all in Honiton Deanery, except Branscombe, which is in Aylesbeare Deanery. The following enumeration of its eleven parishes shews their population in 1841, and their territorial extent.

Parishes.	Acres.	Pop.	Parishes.	Acres.	Pop.
Branscombe	3422	956	Offwell	2206	438
*Colyton	8000	2451	*Seaton and	} 4120	765
Cotleigh	1218	269	*Beer		1231
Farway	2578	376	*Shute	2738	683
Leigh (North)	994	252	Widworthy	1437	257
Leigh (South)	2579	357			
Monkton	2090	141	Total	31,382	8,176

* UNIONS.—Those marked thus * are in *Axminster Union*, and all the other 8 parishes are in *Honiton Union*. (See pages 356 and 368.)
These Unions are County Court Districts.

BRANSCOMBE, a pleasant village, on the coast of the English channel, at the mouth of a rivulet, 5 miles E. by N. of Sidmouth, and S. W. of Colyton, has in its parish 956 souls, and 3422A. 3R. 18P. of land, including *Dean* and *Weston* hamlets, and many scattered houses. The Dean and Chapter of Exeter are lords of the manor,

owners of most of the soil, appropriators of the great tithes, and patrons of the *vicarage*, valued in K.B. at £18. 15s. 10d., and in 1831 at £190, and now enjoyed by the Rev. S. H. Peppin, B.A., who has 10A. of glebe, and an ancient residence, mantled with ivy and vines. The great tithes were commuted in 1843, for £242, and the vicarial for £225 per annum. The *Church* (St. Winifred,) is a cruciform Gothic structure, with a tower and five bells. The Stuckey and Bartlett families were long seated at *Weston Barton*, as lessees of the manor; and *Edge Barton* was anciently the seat of the Branscombes, one of whom was sheriff of the county for five years, in the reign of Edward III. Many women and girls in this neighbourhood are employed in making lace, and here are quarries of excellent freestone. The *Wesleyans* have a small chapel in the village.

Bartlett Joel, builder
Croom John, butcher
Dean Edward, blacksmith
Ferrar Lieut. Wm. Augustus, R.N.
Gill John, carpenter
Peppin Rev Sydenham Hy., B.A. vicar
Prescott Wm. baker and vict. Mason's Arms
Tucker John, lace manufacturer
Williams John, butcher
Williams Wm. tailor
FARMERS.
Bastyan Thos., *Lower Weston*

Basleigh Chas. || Brown John, *Mill*
Burrough Wm., *Higher Weston*
Butter John, *Weston*
Cross James || Croom Thomas
Dawe James || Dean Ellis B.
Ford John || Ford Nicholas
Harding Wm. || Newberry Wm.
Page James || Pyle Thomas
Power Robert, *Elverway*
Richards John || Spiller Abraham
Spiller Robert || Spiller Robert, jun
Studley Henry || Tucker John

COLYTON is a small *market town*, built chiefly of flint, on the western side of the small *river Coly*, about 3 miles north of the English Channel, 5 miles S.W. of Axminster, and 22 miles E. by N. of Exeter. Its parish increased its population from 1641 in 1801, to 2451 souls in 1841; and comprises about 8000 acres of fertile land, including the hamlets of *Purlbridge* and *Colyford*, and many scattered houses. The parish rises boldly on the north to the hills, where the Coly and two of its tributary streams have their sources. It has a paper mill, a tannery, a brewery, a small foundry, and three corn mills, and had formerly a share of the woollen manufacture. The *markets*, held on Thursday and Saturday, are now of trivial consequence. Here are annual cattle fairs on the Thursday after May 1st, and the Thursday after October 14th; and there is another, on the Wednesday after March 11th, at COLYFORD, now called a tithing, though an ancient borough, with a portreeve, who is elected annually, and has the profit of the fair. Colyford was made a borough by the lord of the manor, before the reign of Edward I., and was the birthplace of *Sir Thomas Gates*, governor of Virginia, and discoverer of Bermuda, or Somers Island, in the reign of James I. During the early part of the civil wars, Colyton was held for the King by Lord Percy, who was driven out, in July, 1644, by the Parliamentarians from Lyme Regis. *Petty Sessions* are held at the Dolphin Inn, for the Axminster Division, on the first Tuesday of every month. The town has two good fire engines, and has lately

been provided with several large water tanks. King John granted the town a fair, for eight days, about 1208; and the market is said to have been granted by Peter de Brewose, about 1342. Sir J. G. R. De la Pole, Bart., of Shute House, owns a great part of the parish, and is lord of the *manor* of Colyton, which was held by the Crown at Domesday survey, and was granted by Henry II. to Sir Alan de Dunstanville, whose son give it to Sir Thomas Basset. It was afterwards held in shares, by the Pole, Courtenay, and other families; but the late Sir John De la Pole purchased the other shares in 1787. Sir E. M. Elton, Bart., John Sampson, Esq., Clifford Sherriff, Esq., Admiral Impey, of *Coly Villa;* Mr. Thos. Salter, Mr. H. D. Kingdon, Mrs. Spiller, Mr. Samuel White, and several smaller owners, have estates in the parish. *Colcombe Castle*, part of which is now a farm-house, was a seat of the Earls of Devon, and afterwards of the Pole family, but was dilapidated early in the 17th century. *Yardbury*, another ancient farm-house, was for some generations a seat of the Drakes. *Colyton House* is now unoccupied; but *The Grove* is the pleasant residence of Captain Liddon. The *Church* (St. Andrew,) is a fine ancient structure, in the perpendicular style, 120 feet long, with a tower in the centre, 95 feet high, and containing a musical peal of six bells, and a good clock. In the chancel are several handsome monuments to the Pole and other families. One has effigies of Sir John and Lady Pole, who died in 1628. Under a fine niche, is the effigy of Margaret, daughter of the Earl of Devon, by Katherine, daughter of Edward IV. A fine stone screen, built in 1630, divides the nave and chancel. The aisles were rebuilt in 1765 and 1816. The east window was enriched with painted glass in 1829, and the west window now displays rich perpendicular tracery. The parish registers commence in 1538, and are in good preservation. The Dean and Chapter of Exeter are appropriators of the great tithes, and patrons of the *vicarage*, valued in K.B. at £40. 10s. 10d., and in 1831 at £510, with the perpetual curacies of Monkton and Shute annexed to it. The Rev. Fredk. Barnes, D.D., is the incumbent, but resides at Oxford, where he is canon of Christ Church. The vicarial tithes have been commuted for £372, and the rectorial for £584. 10s. *Thomas Manton*, a learned divine of the 17th century, was vicar here. There was anciently a free chapel at Colcombe; a chapel of St. Edmund, at Colyford; and a chapel at Whitford; the two former endowed by an Earl of Devon, and the latter by a Marquis of Exeter. There are also said to have been small chapels at Gatcombe and Leigh. Here is an *Unitarian Chapel*, which was built by Presbyterians about the middle of the 16th century; an *Independent Chapel*, erected in 1814, and enlarged in 1831; and also a *Wesleyan Chapel*.

Colyton Parish Lands, which have been vested for charitable and public uses with the *feoffees*, or "*Twenty Men of Colyton*," since the time of Henry VIII., comprise 282A. 3R. 13P. of land, and nine houses, let at rents amounting to £221 per annum. This land was part of the forfeited estates of the Marquis of Exeter. The profits of the fairs and markets of Colyton belong to this trust, but are now let for only about £5 a year. All the expenses of bringing water to the town, and of repairing the shambles, &c.,

are paid by the feoffees; and the rest of the clear income is distributed among the poor, except £30 a year paid to the master of the *Free School*, for instructing 20 boys in reading, writing, and arithmetic. The master has also the free use of a house and school-room, built in 1612. The dividends of £200 five per cent. stock, left by the *Rev. James How*, are applied towards the support of a Sunday school. For distributions in bread, the poor parishioners have a yearly rent-charge of £3, out of Rowlandsham, left by *Thomas Holmes*, in 1670; and the dividends of £100 three per cent. stock, left by *Isaac Grigg*, in 1812. In the following DIRECTORY, *those marked * are at Colyford, and the rest in Colyton, or where specified.* The POST-OFFICE is at Mr. E. J. Tett's; and letters are despatched at 3 afternoon. *via* Axminster.

Cooper George, paper maker
Cooper Rev James, (Unitarian)
Cummin Mr Peter || Batstone Mr
Davy Cyrus, surveyor, *Ridgeway*
Dene Rev Arthur, curate, *Vicarage*
Edwards Thomas, brewer & maltster
Evans Brothers, tanners
Hamilton Rev Arthur Hayne, curate of Shute
Hancock Walter, solicitor
Hutchings John, hairdsr. & bookslr
Impey Admiral John, *Coly Villa*
Kingdon Harry Despencer, gent
Liddon Capt. Matthew, R.N., *Grove*
Mayne Mrs R. || Matthews Mrs J.
Murch John, stone mason
Newman John, paper maker
Pady Rev J. (Independent)
Parris Thomas, veterinary surgeon
Pearce Geo. Wm. revenue officer
Powell Capt. Geo. E., R.N., *Cottage*
Quick Mr Wm. || *Ralfe Mr Chas.
Richards James, cooper
Smith John, auctioneer & plumber
Snook Mr John || Northam Mrs
Spiller Mrs Sarah, *Willhayne House*
Stocker Capt. Thos., R.N., *Ridgeway*
Stocker, Saml. tinner and brazier
Stokes Francis, tallow chandler
Tucker Mrs Mary
White Thos. currier and founder
White Wm. whitesmith
FIRE AND LIFE OFFICE AGTS.
Atlas, Henry Seaward
Church of England, E. J. Tett
Globe, Wm. Skinner
Norwich Union, Joseph Spence
Royal Exchange, R. K. Miller
Sun, Henry D. Kingdon
Westminster, John Smith
West of England, Drower and Son
York, W. L. Gill

FARMERS.
Braily John Dennis, *Howberhayne*
Dolling George, *Haniford*
Flood Daniel, *Stowford*
*Halse James || ||Kippy Thomas
Howe Wm. || Hutchings Wm.
Lane Robt. and Thos. *Great House*
Loveridge James, *Colcombe*
Newbery James || Newbery Wm.
Pady Thomas || Pavey Simon
Pearsey Wm. || Smith James
Salter Thomas, *Gatcombe*
Smith Wm. || Snell Wm.
Spiller Wm. || Underdown Jesse
Tillman Wm., *Whitwell*
White John, *Yardbury*
White John, *Bonehayne*
White Samuel, *Road Green*
INNS AND TAVERNS.
Black Bear, John Smith
Dolphin Inn, Arthur Burdon
Stars, James Callender
*Swan, James North
*White Hart, George Griffin

ACADEMIES.
(§ *Boarding*.)
Langley Hy. H.
Miller Richard
Rockett Fanny
§Seaward Eliz.
§Stirling Donald Macnee, (*free*)
§Tett Edw. John
BAKERS.
Mills Samuel
Mitchell James
Marchant John A.
*Newbery Wm.
Salter Eli
Skinner John
BEERHOUSES.
Bull John
Edwardes Fras.

Strawbridge Geo.
Sweetland James
Tillman Charles
Tozer Edward
BLACKSMITHS.
*Lake John
Richards Emnl.
*Richards James
Tillman Charles
BOOT&SHOE MRS.
Drower John
Facey John
Farmer James
French Wm.
Meech Joseph
Mitchell Thomas
Seaward Hy. (& parish clerk)
Snell Jacob

Sweetland James
Woram Wm.
BUTCHERS.
*Boalch Jacob
Hardy Wm.
Hodge Henry
*Pady John
White George
White Robert
CORN MILLERS.
Hawkins George,
(& maltster)
Higgins Robert
Marchant John A.
DRUGGISTS.
Rogers Wm.H.H.
Sellers James

GROCERS & DPRS.
(§ *Drapers only*.)
Brown John
§Drower John
Gill Wm. L.
Kittle Richard
§Smith John
§Spence Joseph
§Tucker Henry
IRONMONGERS.
Brown John
Miller Richd. K.
PRINTRS.&STNRS.
Kittle John
Skinner Wm.
SADDLERS.
Seaward Alfred
Woram Wm.

SHOPKEEPERS.
Bull John
Bussell Mary
Clegg James
Clegg Wm.
*Northcott John
Snell Samuel
Strawbridge John
Strawbridge Ths.
SURGEONS.
Gillett George
Snook Jno. Saml.
TAILORS.
Abrahams James
Abrahams John
Drower Jno.&Son
Farmer Wm.
Woram John

West Matthew
WATCHMAKERS.
Daniel Samuel
*Harner Wm.
WHEELWRIGHTS.
*Richards Simon
Richards S. jun
*Rowland John

CARRIERS.
To Axminster, S.
Pinney, Tue. &
Friday
To Exeter, Wm.
Copp & Philip
Bull,Tue. &Fri
To Honiton, Pp.
Bull, Sat

COTLEIGH is a small village and parish, on a bold acclivity, 3 miles E.N.E. of Honiton, containing 269 souls, and 1218 acres of land. Lord Ashburton owns a great part of the parish, and is lord of the manor, which lately belonged to Lord Clinton, and in early times to the Roche, Le Jew, Yeo, and Roll families. The *Church* is an ancient structure, with a tower and three bells. The *rectory*, valued in K.B. at £9, and in 1831 at £252, is in the patronage and incumbency of the Rev. Wm. Michell, B.A., who is also rector of Barwick, Somerset. The glebe is 26A. 1R. 6P.; and the *Rectory House* is a large and handsome mansion, built about 50 years ago, and having a finely wooded lawn. The tithes were commuted in 1840, for £210. The Langdon, Hamilton, and other families, have freehold estates in the parish. In the 14th of Queen Elizabeth *John Hobbs* left 10A. of land for the reparation of the church.

Michell Rev Wm., B.A., *Rectory*
Reeves J. F., Esq.*Court Hs.*&Tauntn
Searle John, shoemaker
Staple Wm. blacksmith

FARMERS.
Farmer Francis || Broom Aaron
Farmer Joseph || Griffin John
Griffin Thomas || Newton Sarah

FARWAY, or *Fairway*, a village and parish, on a pleasant southern declivity, 3 miles S. of Honiton, and 5 miles E.N.E. of Ottery St. Mary, has 376 souls, and 2578 acres of land, including the small hamlets of *Netherton, Sallicombe*, and *Woodbridge*. The Rev. H. W. Marker is lord of the manor of Farway, formerly held by the Pole, Putt, and other families. Sir E. S. Prideaux, Bart., is lord of the manor of Netherton, and resides at *Netherton Hall,* which was built in the reign of Elizabeth, by *Sir Edmund Prideaux,* an eminent lawyer, who was created a baronet in 1622. It is a neat, substantial mansion, with pleasant grounds. R. H. Tuckfield, Esq., and the Sweet, Guppy, and other families, have freehold estates in the parish. The *Church* (St. Michael,) is a small structure, of neat architecture, with a tower and three bells. The *rectory,* valued in K.B. at £15. 6s. 8d., and in 1831 at £265, is in the patronage of the Rev. H. W. Marker, and incumbency of the Rev. Thos. J. Marker, M.A., of Gittisham. The glebe is 21A.; and the

Rectory House is a good residence, in the Elizabethan style, erected in 1847. The tithes were commuted in 1838, for £295 per annum. The *School* was built by the Rev. Thomas Putt, the late lord of the manor of Farway. In 1795, *Hannah Atkinson* left £250 three per cent. reduced annuities, in trust, to pay the dividends yearly to the schoolmaster, for teaching twelve poor children to read. The poor have the interest of £20, left by *Elizabeth Cox*, in 1784.

Lewis Rev Richd., B.A. curate, *Recty*
Loveridge Joshua, blacksmith
Melhuish Sarah, shopkeeper
Norman Mrs Sarah, *Golacre*
Prideaux Sir Edmund Saunderson, Bart., *Netherton Hall*
FARMERS.
Baker Elijah || Bishop Emanuel

Bishop Thomas, *Netherton Barton*
Bishop Wm., *Withicombe*
Broom Henry || Burrough Samuel
Burrough Wm., *Eastfield*
Newbery John || Newbery Robert
Potter Thomas || Long John
Webber William, *Sallicombe*
Reed Wm. || Wood Amos, *do*

LEIGH, (NORTH) a small village and parish, on the banks of a rivulet 3 miles W.N.W. of Colyton, has 252 souls, and 994 acres of land, including *Triccombe, Bucknall,* and *Puddlebridge.* Mrs. Mary Louisa Proby is lady of the manor, formerly held by the Leigh, Bonville, Petre, How, and other families; but Sir E. S. Prideaux, Sir E. M. Elton, Wm. Tucker, Esq., and a few smaller freeholders, have estates in the parish. The *Church* (St. Giles,) is an ancient structure, with a tower and four bells. It is in a very dilapidated state, but it is hoped that measures will soon be taken for its restoration. It has two beautiful screens, and the seats have carved ends. The *rectory*, valued in K.B. at £10. 9s. 7d., and in 1831 at £240, is in the patronage and incumbency of the Rev. H. P. Daniell, M.A., who has 47a. of glebe, and a handsome modern residence, built of flint and rag, with dressings, mullions, &c., of Beer stone. The tithes were commuted, in 1839, for £174. 10s. per ann. The Parish Lands, given by *Jane Marwood*, and other donors, comprise about 8 acres, let for £12, which is distributed among the industrious poor. The dividends of £175, four per cent. stock, left by the *Rev. James How*, in 1816, are applied, one-half towards the support of the Sunday school, and the other in distributions to the poor.

Daniell Rev. Hy. P., M.A., *Rectory*
Halfyard Mary Ann, beerseller
Langford Eliza, schoolmistress
Norsworthy Wm. baker
Summers Charles, blacksmith

Underdown James, parish clerk
FARMERS.
Baker Elias || Banks Wm.
White John, *Bucknall*
White Samuel, (maltster,) *Suttons*

LEIGH, (SOUTH) a pleasant scattered village and parish, from three to four miles W. by S. of Colyton, has 357 inhabitants and 2579 acres of fertile land, about three miles from the sea coast. The manors of South Leigh and Wiscombe formerly belonged to the Leigh, Courtenay, Bonville, Stow, and other families, and were purchased in 1815 and 1825, by Charles Gordon, Esq., of *Wiscombe Park*, a pleasant seat, about a mile west of the church. Morganhayes belongs to Sir J. G. R. De la Pole; and here are other freehold estates belonging to Sir E. S. Prideaux, Sir E. M. Elton, and a few smaller owners. The *Church* (St. Lawrence,) is an ancient

structure, with a tower and three bells. The north aisle and porch were rebuilt in 1821, and the rest of the fabric, being much dilapidated, is about to be renovated, at the cost of about £500. The *rectory*, valued in K.B. at £11. 8s. 9d., and in 1831 at £215, is in the patronage of Charles Gordon, Esq., and incumbency of the Rev. Wm. James, B.A., who has 35A. 1R. 37P. of glebe, and a good residence, which he has recently improved, at the cost of more than £500. The tithes were commuted in 1841, for £226. In 1816, the *Rev James How* left in trust, with the rector and churchwardens, the dividends of £175 five per cent. stock, one-half for the support of the Sunday school, and the rest for a distribution of bread among the poor, at Christmas. He also left another £175 of the same stock, and directed the dividends to be given in clothing to the poor.

Batstone James, blacksmith
Broom Thomas, carpenter
Drew David, tailor
Gordon Chas. Esq., *Wiscombe Park*
James Rev Wm., B.A., *Rectory*
Whicker John, shoemaker & beerhs

FARMERS.
Collier John, *Moorplash*
Hawkins Wm., *Morgan-hayes*
Newbery Samuel, *Scruel*
Pavey Samuel, *Wiscombe*
Underdown Jesse T., *Horsehayne*

MONKTON, a small village in the picturesque valley of the river Otter, 2½ miles N.E. of Honiton, has in its parish 141 souls and 2090 acres of land, rising in bold hills on the east side of the valley. Richard S. Gard, Esq., is lord of the manor, formerly held by the Marcey, Bonvill, Mohun, Hall, Flood, and other families. Lord Ashburton owns one farm in the parish, and here are a few smaller freeholders. The *Church* (St. Mary Magdalen,) is a small antique structure, with a tower and three bells, and the benefice is a curacy, consolidated with the vicarage of Colyton, both parishes being in the same patronage and appropriation. (See page 380.) The Rev. H. K. Venn, of Honiton, is the *officiating curate*.

Oldridge Thomas, blacksmith
Pavey Emanuel, carpenter
Roe John, vict. Monkton Inn
        FARMERS.
Baker John ‖ Burrough James

Broom John ‖ Griffin Clement
Loosemore James ‖ Tett Job
Snell James ‖ Vincent Robert

OFFWELL, a village and parish on the hills, 2½ miles E.S.E. of Honiton, near the source of a rivulet, has 438 inhabitants and 2206 acres of land. It includes part of *Wilmington* village, which is partly in Widworthy parish. The manor of Offwell, anciently held by a family of its own name, and afterwards by the Orway, Vere, Bray, Collins, and other families, was dismembered many years ago. The parish now belongs to Sir E. M. Elton, Sir E. S. Prideaux, Lord Ashburton, the heirs of the late Bishop of Llandaff, and a few smaller freeholders. West Colwell estate was purchased about 30 years ago, by the late *Rt. Rev. Edward Copleston, D.D.*, who was enthroned *Bishop of Llandaff*, in 1828, and had a seat here, called *Offwell House*. He died in 1849, and was patron of the *rectory*, valued in K.B. at £14. 3s. 6¼d., and in 1831 at £380. The Rev. J. G. Copleston, M.A., is the incumbent, and has 80A. of glebe, and a large and handsome *Rectory House*, in the Elizabethan style, erected in 1845, at the cost of about £1800. The tithes were com-

muted in 1843, for £270 per annum. An ornamental *tower*, on Honiton hill, in this parish, was built by the late Bishop of Llandaff, in 1843, and commands extensive prospects. The *Church* (St. Mary,) has a tower and five bells, and is of the age of the 15th century. The Wesleyans have a chapel at Wilmington, and in Offwell village is a School and a stone pump, built by the late Bishop of Llandaff. In 1752, £60 given to the poor parishioners by Henry and Dorothy Southcott and other donors, was laid out in the purchase of 3½A. of land, called Graystone, now let for £5.

Copleston Rev J. G., M.A., *Rectory*
Aplin Samuel, blacksmith
Cox Mary, shopkeeper, *Wilmington*
Cox Eli, chandler, *Wilmington*
Cox Joshua, beer seller, *Wilmington*
Gosling Jeremiah, shoemaker
Northam Wm. beerhouse
Northam Wm. jun. shoemaker
Northam John, wheelwright

Pippett Wm. cooper, *Wilmington*
FARMERS.
Bishop Sarah || Cottey Abraham
Dunster John, *Wilmington*
Dymond Joseph || Farmer Ashford
Farmer Wm. || Henley John
Hutchins Emanuel || Patch John
Peters Wm. || Pavey Sarah
Summers Wm. || Wright Wm.

SEATON and BEER, the former a pleasant retired village and *sea bathing place*, on the western side of the mouth of the river Axe, and the latter a large *fishing village*, about a mile to the west, on a small cove or creek, which runs to the English Channel through a deep narrow glen; are distant from 2½ to 3½ miles S. of Colyton, and from 19 to 20 miles E. of Exeter. They are in the *parish of Seaton*, which contains 4120 acres of land, and had 1497 inhabitants in 1801, and 1996 in 1841, of whom 765 were in Seaton, and 1231 in Beer tithing. The parish and neighbourhood abounds in that beautiful and durable freestone called *Beer stone*, of which the outer walls of Exeter Cathedral are built. This stone has been extensively used in the erection of churches and mansions in various parts of the county. A part of the high cliff facing the sea, between Beer and Branscombe, called Southdown, was the scene of a great *landslip* in 1790, when upwards of ten acres of land sunk down about 250 feet. *Beer* was formerly notorious for smuggling, and was the birth place of that celebrated smuggler, "*Jack Rattenbury, the Rob Roy of the West*," who, with all his faults, was a brave fellow, as appears from a little work recording the principal events of his life. Great quantities of fish are caught at Beer, and many of the women and girls are employed in making *lace*. The Queen's Wedding Dress was made here, in 1839, and most of the females who made it are now employed by Mr. Tucker, of Branscombe. An act for making a *harbour* in Beer cove was obtained in 1792, and another was obtained for the same purpose in 1820, but nothing has been done by the commissioners of either. *Seaton* has a pleasure *fair* on Whit-Tuesday, and Beer has one on the Monday after Oct. 14th. Seaton is supposed by some of the best informed antiquaries to have been the Roman Station *Moridunum*, which Baxter has placed at Topsham, and Horsley at Eggerton Hill. Half a mile above the village is *Honey Ditches*, an oblong moated camp of three acres. Leland speaks of unsuccessful attempts to build piers at Seaton and Beer, and says a great tempest tore the unfinished pier

at the latter place to pieces, and that in his time there was a "mighty rigg and barre of pebble stones," at the mouth of the Axe. The scenery on the coast from here to Sidmouth, is probably the finest on the southern shores of Devon. The rocks are bold, and by their association with other objects, present some very romantic and picturesque views. Sir W. C. Trevelyan, Bart., is lord of the manor of Seaton, which was formerly held by the Frye, Willoughby, and other families. The Walronds were long seated at *Bovey House*, and were lords of the manor of Beer, which passed with their heiress to the late Lord Rolle, whose trustees now hold it. W. Head, Esq., N. T. Still, Esq., and several smaller owners, have freehold estates in the parish. *Seaton Church* (St. Gregory,) is an ancient structure, with a tower and four bells; and the living is a *vicarage*, valued in K.B. at £17. 0s. 7½d., and in 1831 at £230, and now held by the Rev. C. J. Glascott, B.A., who has 12A. of glebe and a good residence. The trustees of the late Lord Rolle are the patrons, and also impropriators of the great tithes, formerly belonging to Sherborne Abbey. The tithes were commuted in 1839, the vicarial for £260, and the rectorial for £300 per annum. There is an ancient *Chapel of Ease* at Beer, and also an Independent Chapel, which was built in or about 1700, by Presbyterians. At Seaton is a *Wesleyan* and also an *Independent Chapel;* the latter built in 1822. The poor parishioners have the interest of £20, given by Edw. Good and the Rev. Robert Cutcliffe. The late *Lady Rolle* left £3900 three per cent. stock, for the foundation of an *Almshouse* at Beer, for 25 poor infirm fishermen, and 20 poor widows; and £3100 of the same stock for the support of *Free Schools* at Beer, for poor boys and girls. *In the following Directory, those marked † are at Beer, and the others at Seaton, or where specified.* The POST-OFFICES are at Mr. John Ackerman's, *Seaton ;* and at John Tizzard's, *Beer.* Letters are despatched via Colyton.

Akerman John, ironmonger, &c.
Baker Charles George, solicitor
†Burgess Rev Thomas, (Indpt.)
Cann Thomas, surgeon and registrar
Clarke Mrs Eliz., *Halcyon Castle*
Coles Martha, Infant school
Dare Henry, Robt. & Saml. gents
Dimond Richd. ironfounder, &c.
Glascott Rev C. J., B.A. vicar
Gollop Samuel, carpenter
Good Wm. ironmonger, &c.
Hayward John, shoemaker
Head Wm. Esq., *Wessiters*
Head John, coal merchant
Holmes Rev Frederick
Hooper Mrs Sus. || Horsford Mrs G.
Major James, builder
Major Mary, lace manufacturer
Miller George, rope maker
Mills Mrs Eliz., *Beach House*
Ocock Wm. druggist, &c.

Perry James, tinner and brazier
Proby Mrs || Tanner Mrs
Robinson Hy. tailor and beerhouse
Scarbrough John Latoysonere, Esq., *Bovey House*
Shewbrooks Thomas, plumber, &c.
†Sydenham Rev Jno.Wm., B.A. curate
Vaux Mrs || Winton Mr Ebenz.
†Watts John, wheelwright
Woodrow Jonth. wheelwright

INNS AND TAVERNS.
†Anchor, John Holmes
†Dolphin, Lucy Holmes
†George, Mary Abbott
Golden Lion, Joseph Thorne
King's Arms, John Oldridge
†London Inn, James Good
Mariners' Arms, Samuel Cox
†New Inn, James Holmes
Pole's Arms, John Holmyard
†Rose and Crown, Mary Prince

+Ship, Mary Potter

FARMERS.

Aplin Sarah, *Combe Hill*
Broom Wm. || Culverwell Wm.
Hammett Henry, *Gibbs's*
Hammett Mary, *Court Barn*
+Harding John, *Bovey*
Head John || Mattett James
Miller James || Pady John
Thorn John || Turner Wm.

BAKERS.	+Cawley John
+Good Edward	+Mutter Eliz.
Gould George	Robinson Hy.
+Miller Reubin	
+Orley Wm.	BLACKSMITHS.
Skinner Richd.	Oldridge Timy.
BEERHOUSES.	+Rowe John
+Bartlett Sus.	+Stagg Jacob

+Tizzard James

BUTCHERS.

+Aplin Tobias
Loud Henry
+Searle John
Skinner Richd.

DRAPERS.

Hayward Mchl.
White Henry

LODGINGS.

Baddon Davy
Good Joseph
Major Matthew
Newton Wm.
Page Rebecca
Randel Jas. *baths*
Robinson Henry

Sellers Johanna
White Henry
Woodrow James

SHOPKEEPERS.

Akerman John
Bolack Mary
+Clark Mary
+Good John
+Hawkins Louisa
+Orley Robert
Pearce Nathl.
+Skinner Richd.
(& coal mert)
Tizzard John

TAILORS.

Overmass Saml.
Raddon John
Robinson Henry

SHUTE parish contains 683 souls, 2738 acres of land, several scattered houses, and the village of WHITFORD, a mile S. of the church, and 1½ mile N.E. of Colyton. *Sir J. G. R. De la Pole, Bart.*, is lord of the manor, and resides at SHUTE PARK, which is extensive and stocked with deer, and has a larger and handsome mansion, which was mostly rebuilt on a large scale by Sir John Wm. Pole, Bart., about 1790, the ancient house being then fast falling to decay. The plan of the building is a square centre, with two uniform wings, connected by corridors. The manor of Shute was anciently held by a family of its own name, and afterwards by the Pynes, Bonvilles, and Greys. It was purchased of Lord Petre, in 1787, by Sir J. W. Pole. Leland calls Shute Park " a right good manor place of the Marquis of-Dorset," which before had long been the seat of the Bonvilles. Sir Wm. Pole, the learned antiquary, settled it on his eldest son in 1628, during his father's life-time ; and it has ever since been the seat of his family. The *Church* (St. Michael,) is an ancient cruciform structure, with a tower rising from the centre, and containing five bells. It has several handsome monuments of the Poles, one of which has a fine white marble statue of Sir Wm. Pole in full dress, as master of Queen Anne's household. The benefice is a curacy consolidated with the vicarage of Colyton. (See page 380.)

Chown Richd. vict. Beagle Inn
Clegg John, shoemkr. & Wm. smith
Hamilton Rev Arthur Hayne, curate
Pinney Wm. schoolmaster
Pole Sir John George Reeves De la Bart., *Shute Park*
Rapsey John, vict. Hare & Hounds
Smalldon Mary, shopkeeper

White Jas. machine mkr. & founder

FARMERS.

Brown Wm. || Clode Amos
Dening Charles || Dommett Barnd.
Dommett John || Frost John
Gill Jas. || Hill Saml., *Whitford*
Hoskins John || Loud Rt., *Whitford*
Poole George || Smith Robert

WIDWORTHY, a small village on a bold acclivity, 3½ miles E. by S. of Honiton, has in its parish 257 souls, and 1437 acres of land, rising in bold hills, and including part of the village of *Wilmington*, which is partly in Offwell parish. (See page 385.) The

manor of Widworthy was held by a family of its own name, till the reign of Edward I., when their heiress carried it in marriage to the Dinhams. It was purchased of the Chichesters by the Marwoods, who built the houses at Sutton and Cockshayes, now occupied by farmers. *Sir Edward Marwood Elton*, who was created a *baronet* in 1838, is now lord of the manor, and owner of nearly all the parish. He resides at *Widworthy Court*, which he has recently erected in the Doric order of architecture. This large and elegant mansion comprises a quadrangular body four stories high, with a north wing. It stands on a commanding eminence, and the south and east fronts are encompassed by a beautiful terrace, 56 feet broad and 163 feet long. The *Church* (St. Cuthbert,) is an ancient cruciform structure in the lancet Gothic style, with a tower and five bells. It contains several handsome monuments, one of which is of white marble, with figures Justice and Temperance, in memory of Thos. Marwood, Esq., who died 1780. On an ancient altar tomb is the recumbent effigy of a knight in chain armour. The *rectory*, valued in K.B. at £11. 16s. 0½d., and in 1831 at £186, is in the patronage of Sir E. M. Elton, Bart., and incumbency of the Rev. Wm. Marwood Tucker, M.A., of Colchester. The Parsonage is a fine old residence, and the glebe is 30A. The tithes were commuted in 1838 for £206 per annum. The *Parish School* was given by James Marwood in 1759, and was endowed by him and Benedictus Marwood with £6 a year for the master, and £2 a year for repairs, now charged on Widworthy Barton estate. The schoolmaster teaches four free scholars, and has also one-half and the poor the other half of the dividends of £109. 15s. 3d. Navy five per cents., left by the *Rev. Jph. Somaster.* The poor have a yearly rent-charge of 20s., left by Robt. Marwood in 1738, out of Stone Burrows field.

Broomfield John, corn miller
Cox Rev John Pope, B.A. curate, *Rectory*
Davey Benedictus, schoolr. & par. clk
Elton Sir Edward Marwood, Bart. *Widworthy Court*
Mutter James, blacksmith
Raddon Richd. vict. Manor Inn

Raddon Hugo, wheelwright
Thomas Wm., Post-office

FARMERS.

Baker Mary || Dommett David
Broom Thomas, *Suttons*
Davey Henry, *Cockshayes*
Gould Thomas || Raddon James

HEMYOCK HUNDRED

Is a small hilly district, of a very irregular form, comprising part of the Black Down Hills, where the river Culm has its sources, on the borders of Somersetshire. It comprises only seven parishes, viz., *Awliscombe, Buckerell,* and *Dunkeswell,* in Honiton Union; *Clayhidon, Culmstock,* and *Hemyock,* in Wellington Union; and *ChurchStanton,* in Taunton Union. These Unions form County Court Districts, and the two latter are mostly in Somersetshire. The seven parishes comprise 6089 inhabitants, and 28,000 acres of land. They are in the Northern Division of Devon, and all in Collumpton Polling District, except Hemyock, which is in Tiverton Polling

District. They are all in Collumpton Petty Sessional Division, and in the Archdeaconry of Exeter ; and all in the Deanery of Dunkeswell, except Buckerell and Culmstock, the former of which is in Plymtree, and the latter in Tiverton Deanery.

AWLISCOMBE, or *Awlescombe*, a small village, on an acclivity, 2½ miles W. by N. of Honiton, has in its parish 590 souls, and 2569 acres of land, rising in bold hills on the north, and including the hamlets *Weston* and *Wolverston*. It had a grant for a market and fair in 1291, but both have long been obsolete. An estate of about 207a., called the manor of Awliscombe, was given in 1491, by Thos. Calwodeley, to the Corporation of Exeter, for the relief of poor citizens. The rest of the parish belongs to E. S. Drewe, Esq., J. T. B. Notley, Esq., E. W. Greenfield, Esq., the Pring family, and a few smaller freeholders. A handsome *bridge*, over the Otter, connects this and Honiton parish, and was built in 1817. The *Church* (St. Michael,) is a neat Gothic structure, which was mostly rebuilt in 1846, and has a tower and five bells. The *vicarage*, valued in K.B. at £12. 10s. 10d., and in 1831 at £230, is in the patronage of the Duke of Bedford, and incumbency of the Rev. F. T. B. Willesford, B.A., who has a small but neat thatched residence, and 30a. of glebe. The *tithes* have been commuted, the *vicarial* for £220, and the *rectorial* for £176. The latter are vested in trust for the augmentation of the perpetual curacy of Sheldon, and the payment of £10 a year to the schoolmaster of Broadhembury, as noticed with those parishes. The poor of Awliscombe have £10 a year from *Pring's Charity*, for distribution in linen, as noticed with East Budleigh.

Bailey John, carpenter
Clapp Thomas, wheelwright
Elliott Miss || Pring Amy, *shopkpr*
Gard Francis, cooper and turner
Haymes John, vict. Honiton Inn
Hitt Wm. blacksmith
Marker Francis, shoemaker
Marker F. jun., shoemaker, *Weston*
Noble Capt. Jeffery W., R.N.
Shute Charles, shoemaker
Staple Rt. blacksmith, *Weston*
Strongman Arthur, shoemaker
Townsend John Honeywood, solr., *Ashfield* (& Honiton)

Webber Henry, smith, *Post-Office*
Willesford Rev. F. T. Bedford, B.A. *vicar*

FARMERS.

Banfield Wm. || Peacock Edward
Banfield John, *Ivedon*
Granger Wm. *Godford land*
Pring Mrs Ann, *Ivedon*
Pring Francis || Pring John
Pring Fras. & Wm. *Calverhayes*
Rosier Jas. || Rosier Roger & Wm.
Sanders Wm. || Toogood Henry
Tuck Humphrey || Tuck Richard
Wood Benjamin, *Godfordland*

BUCKERELL, a pleasant village and parish, in the Otter valley, 3½ miles W. by S. of Honiton, has 360 inhabitants, and 1559a. 2r. 31p. of land, belonging to W. Porter, W. M. Smythe, G. B. Northcote, and D. Davey, Esqrs., and a few smaller freeholders, the manor, anciently held by the Pomeroys, being dismembered many years ago. *Deer Park*, the pleasant seat of W. M. Smythe, Esq., is on the north side of the river Otter, and was long the seat of a branch of the ancient family of Fry. *Hembury Fort*, the seat of Wm. Porter, Esq., is at the north end of the parish, on a commanding eminence, near the ancient entrenchment of that name, as no-

ticed at page 294. The *Church* (St. Mary,) is a plain cruciform structure, with a tower and three bells. It has a fine coloured glass window, and a richly carved screen. Among its monuments is one in memory of the late *Admiral Graves*, who died at Hembury Fort, in 1787. The vicarage, valued in K.B. at £10. 0s. 2½d., and in 1831 at £120, is in the patronage of the Dean and Chapter of Exeter, who are also appropriators of the rectorial glebe (58A.,) and the great tithes, now leased to G. B. Northcote, Esq. The Rev. E. E. Coleridge, B.A., is the incumbent, and has 3A. 1R. 8P. of glebe, and a good residence, which he has recently much improved. Here is a *National School*, built in 1830, and supported by the landowners.

Band Edward, Esq.
Coleridge Rev. Edwin Ellis, B.A. *Vicarage*
Coles George, wheelwright
Daniels Nathaniel, shoemaker
Goldsworthy Richard, blacksmith
Gould Hy. *smith,* and Jas. *tailor*
Long Thomas, shoemaker
Porter Wm., Esq,, *Hembury Fort*
Smythe Wm. Mead, Esq. *Deer Park*
Symons Sarah, schoolmistress
FARMERS.
Bishop Thomas || Dally John
Horsford Sarah || Pyle George
Salter Daniel || Smith John
Tucker John, *Cothayes*
Turpin Natl. || Wilmington John

CHURCH-STANTON, or *Church-Staunton*, a scattered village, on an eminence near the Black Down Hills, and the borders of Somersetshire, and the sources of the river Culm, 10 miles N. by E. of Honiton, and 8 miles S. of Taunton, has in its parish 1086 inhabitants, and 4980 acres of freehold land. The village is in four portions called *Churchinford*, *Stapley*, *Red Lane*, and *Burnworthy*. There are two annual *cattle fairs* at Churchinford, on the 25th and 26th of January, and the last Friday in April; and at Stapley is a large *silk mill*. Messrs. Bush are lords of the manor, but the greater part of the soil belongs to Wm. Beadon, Jun., Esq., Capt. White, the Earl of Devon, Mr. Richd. Blackmore, Mr. Henry Smith, and several smaller freeholders. *Roystone House* is the pleasant seat of Capt. John White. The manor anciently belonged to the Tudenham family, and afterwards to the Damarell, Bonville, Clifton, Clarke, Popham, and Southwood families. *John Salkeld*, called by King James I. the learned Salkeld, was ejected from the rectory here in 1647, at the age of 72 years. He was author of two treatises on Angels and Paradise, and of several controversial works. The *Church* (St. Paul,) is a fine Gothic structure, with a tower and five bells. The nave is separated from the south aisle by pillars and pointed arches, and in its windows are some remains of ancient stained glass. The pulpit is of ancient carved oak. The east window is of stained glass, representing St. Peter and St. Paul, and on the south side of the chancel is another beautiful stained glass window, in memory of the Rev. R. P. Clarke, the late rector. These windows have been recently inserted by the Rev. Henry Edwards, Jun., B.A., the present *rector*, who has a good residence finely embowered in trees, and about 115A. of glebe, partly allotted under the *enclosure act* of 39th Geo. III., under which the tithes were commuted. He is also patron of the *rectory*, valued in K.B. at

£26. 5s. 5d., and in 1831 at £430. In the parish are two chapels, belonging to the Baptists and Wesleyans. The *Church Land,* about 2A., is let for £2, At Churchinford are the remains of an ancient chapel, now part of a farm building. The poor parishioners have the following small yearly doles :—£4 from 7A. of land, purchased with £56, given by several donors, in 1695 ; £3. 10s. from land left by *Mary Parsons,* in 1693 ; the interest of £10, left by *John Channon ;* an annuity of 10s., left by *Joan Combe ;* and 5s. from the rent of a pew in the parish church. The parish is in Taunton Union.

Beadon Wm., Esq. *Wyke*
Boalch Wm. vict., King's Arms
Board Robert, blacksmith
Doble Jas. & Martha, beersellers
Edwards Rev Hy. jun., B.A., *Rectory*
Ewins John, grocer and draper
Harris Hy. beerseller, *Post-Office*
Lawton Saml. silk throwster, *Stapley Mill*
Lawton Mark, grocer and baker
Moore Abraham, butcher
Moore John, vict., York Inn
Oake James, saddler
Peters Jacob, shopkeeper
Pike Wm. wheelwright
Poole Richard and John, tailors
Rich James, surgeon

Row John, shoemaker
Stark Wm. grocer and baker
White Capt. John, *Roystone House*
FARMERS. (* are Owners.)
*Baker John Wyatt, *Edneys*
*Blackmore Richard, *Cleavehayes*
*Blackmore Thomas, Buttles
Dommett Robt. || Dommett Wm.
Gage Samuel || Hine John
Hartnell James, *Trickey Warren*
Joyce John || Lentill Robert
Phippen Chas. || Raisen Wm.
Rich Charles, *Red Lane*
*Smith Henry || Vincent Mary

POST-OFFICE at Henry Harris's. Letters *via* Honiton.

CLAYHIDON, or *Clayhedon*, is a village and parish on the south side of Black Down Hills, near the sources of the Culm and the borders of Somersetshire, 4½ miles S.S.W. of Wellington, and 15 miles E.N.E. of Tiverton. It contains 849 inhabitants, and 5089 acres of land, rising in bold hills from the small river Culm to the lofty range of *Black Down Hills*, on the borders of Devon and Somerset, where the *Wellington Monument* rears its towering head. This handsome stone pillar was erected by subscription, in commemoration of the Duke of Wellington and the Victory of Waterloo. A pleasure fair is held near it on Waterloo day. Mrs. Gifford, of Wellington, is lady of the manor of Clayhidon, which was anciently held by the Hidon and Dinham families, and afterwards by the Pophams and Sanxeys, the latter of whom sold it to the Giffords. The Blackmore, Farrant, and other families have freehold estates in the parish. The Blackmores have, from time immemorial, kept a pack of hare-hounds here, and it is now kept by Mr. Thomas Blackmore. The *Church* (St. Andrew,) is an ancient Gothic structure, with a tower and five bells. It has recently been new-roofed and re-seated and beautified. The pulpit was restored by the late rector, whose daughter enriched the east window with painted glass. The *rectory*, valued in K.B. at £38. 5s., and in 1831 at £621, is in the patronage of George Burnand, Esq., and incumbency of the Rev. Henry Tippetts Tucker, M.A., who is also rector of Angersleigh, where he resides. The glebe is 111A. 3R. 28P., and the Parsonage is a good old residence, with pleasant grounds, on a bold eminence.

The tithes were commuted in 1839 for £600 per annum. Here is a Baptist Chapel and a National School. The *Poor's Land* comprises about 8A. at Church Stanton, and is let for £7. 10s. a year. Part of it was given by *Mary Parsons* in 1693, and the rest by unknown donors. In 1749, *Mary Waldron* left £110, to be applied in schooling poor children of this parish and Hemyock. This legacy was laid out in the purchase of 6A. of land at Biscombe, to which 5A. of common was allotted at the enclosure. The whole is now worth about £8 a year.

Blackmore Wm. land surveyor
Boult Mary, vict. Half Moon
Buttle Wm. beerseller
Gough Robert, blacksmith
Matthews Fras. vict. Hunters' Lodge
PulmanRevW.W.,M.A. curate,*Rectry*
Redwood Thos. vict. White Horse
Smith Wm. blacksmith
Thomas Elizabeth, schoolmistress

FARMERS.
Blackmore James || Blackmore John
Blackmore Thomas, *Permers*
Blackmore Wm. *Applehayes*
Cridland James || Hellier Jonah
Farrant Wm. *Dunsgreen*
Manley Robert || Marks Thomas
North John || Smith Robert
Snell James || Stradling Samuel
Post from Wellington.

CULMSTOCK, a large village, in the picturesque valley of the river Culm, 7 miles N.E. of Collumpton, and 6 miles S.S.W. of Wellington, has in its parish 1446 souls, and 4530 acres of land, rising boldly from the valley, and including the hamlets of *Upcott Nicholshayne*, *Prescot*, and *Northend*. It had formerly a weekly market on Friday, and a share of the woollen manufacture. It has still two annual *cattle fairs*, on May 21st and the Wednesday before Michaelmas-day. An old *beacon*, on a lofty hill, is still in good condition, and was occasionally used during the late wars. The manor has long been vested in the Dean and Chapter of Exeter, who are also appropriators of the rectory, and patrons of the *Vicarage*, valued in K.B. at £16, and in 1831 at £329, and now in the incumbency of the Rev. J. W. Karslake, who has a good residence and 3A. of glebe. The tithes were commuted in 1841, the rectorial for £320, and the vicarial for £355. The *Church* (All Saints,) is an ancient structure, with a tower, containing five bells, and having a yew tree growing out of one of its sides. In the parish are three *Chapels*, belonging to the *Quakers*, *Baptists*, and *Wesleyans*. The parish has a *National School*, and is mostly leasehold under the Dean and Chapter; but R. H. Clarke, Esq., and a few smaller owners, have estates here. *Culmstock Agricultural Association* was established three years ago. The poor parishioners have 3A. of land purchased in 1795, with £150 given by Henry Rainsbury and other donors; and the interest of £15, given by unknown donors.

Ayshforth A. M. & Coombe Thos. gent
Davey John, butcher
Haddon John, vict. New Inn
Jewell Thos. vict. Three Tuns
Karslake Rev J. Wollaston, vicar
Lane John, blacksmith
Pook John H. cutler
Southey Francis, maltster
Tapscott John, vict., Ilminster Inn

Tapscott Richard, gentleman
Thomas James, beerseller
Wheaton F. W. D. surgeon

FARMERS.
Anning Wm.
Bale John
Blake Wm.
Broom John
Channon John

Collier James
Collier John
Farrant Henry
Fry John
Gear Robert
Knowlman John

Norman John	SHOPKEEPERS.	Sheers Wm.	TAILORS.
Talbot John	Bale George	Southey Robert	Bragg Aaron
Taylor John	Jacobs Robert	Stradling Eliz.	Fry John
White Thomas			

DUNKESWELL, which gives name to a deanery, is a small village, in a narrow picturesque valley, near the source of a rivulet, 6 miles N.N.W. of Honiton. Its parish is boldly diversified with hill and dale, and comprises 536 souls, and about 4000 acres of land, including an open turf moor of 100 acres, and many scattered houses. Mrs. E. P. Simcoe owns a great part of the soil, and is lady of the manor. She has a pleasant seat at the south end of the parish, called *Wolford Lodge*, 4 miles N.N.W. of Honiton. This mansion was the seat of the late General Simcoe, and near it there was anciently a church, called *Wolfer Church*, which was granted by King John to DUNKESWELL ABBEY, which was founded at the north end of the parish, by Wm. Lord Brewer, in 1201, for Cistercian monks, who were endowed with the manor and other lands, valued at the dissolution at £294. 18s. 6d. per annum. There are still some slight vestiges of the abbey, and on its site a handsome *District Church* has lately been erected by Mrs. Simcoe, in the Early English style, with several stained glass windows and a bell turret. She has endowed it with £50 per annum, and is patroness of the *perpetual curacy*, of which the Rev. T. Müller is the first incumbent. He is also incumbent of Dunkeswell perpetual curacy, valued at only £45, and in the patronage of Mrs. Mary Graves, the impropriator of the rectory and great tithes. The *Parish Church* (St. Nicholas,) is in the centre of the parish, about two miles south of the new Abbey Church. It was rebuilt in 1817, and is a small cruciform structure, with a tower and three bells. The *Wesleyans* have a neat chapel here, and the parish has a modern *School House*, in the Elizabethan style. *Peter Holway* left for the poor parishioners £100, which was laid out, in 1651, in the purchase of a house and 10A. of land; the latter of which is let for £10, and the former was the parish workhouse. The poor have two yearly rent-charges, viz., 20s., left by *Charles Ford*, in the 25th of Elizabeth; and 5s., left by *Nicholas Lacke*, in 1670. At an early date, *Nicholas Marke* left a yearly rent-charge of £5 out of Ashcombe estate, to be applied in apprenticing poor children. For schooling poor children this parish has about £4 yearly from *Mary Waldron's Charity*. (See Clayhidon.)

Cox Thomas, blacksmith
Kerby Thomas & Gosling Ann, *school*
Moon Wm. swine dealer
Müller Rev Theodore, incumbent
Parsons James, wheelwright
Salway Edw. tailor and parish clerk
Simcoe Mrs Elizabeth Posthuma, *Wolford Lodge*
Spark Samuel, maltster, *Abbey Mills*
Stuart Henry, blacksmith
Squire Ann, schoolmistress
Willie Edward, beerseller

FARMERS.
Barton Thomas || Bright David
Burrough Robert || Chinnick Wm.
Clement Francis || Clement John
Critchett Hy. || Derham Thos. *Abbey*
Farrant Samuel || Marks Samuel
Paul John || Rosier Roger
Pearcey Robert, *Abbey Wood*
Saunders Henry || Smith Robert
Spark Peter || Spark Samuel
Tucker Wm. || White Henry
White Henry, *Wolford*
Wood John, *Hutshays*

R 3

HEMYOCK, or *Hemiock,* is a considerable village, which gives name to this hundred, and is pleasantly situated on the south side of the river Culm in the picturesque valley, near *Culmbridge,* 5 miles S. of Wellington, and 9 miles N.E. of Collumpton. Its parish is in Wellington Union, and comprises the hamlet and chapelry of CULM-DAVY, on the opposite acclivities of the valley, adjoining the lofty Black Down Hills and the borders of Somersetshire. It also includes *Millhays, Westown,* and many scattered houses and contains 1222 inhabitants, and 5437A. 2R. 15P. of land, belonging to many freeholders. Mrs. E. P. Simcoe is the largest proprietor, and also lady of the *manor of Hemyock,* which was part of the demesne of the crown at Domesday Survey, but was soon afterwards possessed by the ancient family of Hidon, who had a *Castle* here, which was used as a garrison and prison by the Parliamentarians in the seventeenth century. There are still some remains of four of the towers and a gateway of this castle, which passed with the manor, from the Hidons to the Dinhams, and was purchased by the late General Simcoe. The manor of *Culm Davy* is vested in the devisee under the will of the late Henry Pook, Esq., and was formerly held by the Widworthy, Wogan, Corbett, Bowerman, and other families. *Hemyock Church* (St. Mary,) is a large and handsome structure, with a tower and five bells. It was rebuilt in 1846-'7, at a great expense, by subscription and rates, aided by grants from the Incorporated and the Exeter Diocesan Societies. It has 1592 sittings, but the old fabric had only about 1340. The latter had a chantry, founded by Peter Uvedale, and endowed with £1 per annum. The *rectory,* valued in K.B. at £32. 0s. 7½d., and in 1831 at £844, with the curacy of Culm-Davy annexed to it, is in the patronage of Edward Wm. Leyborne Popham, Esq., of Littlecote, Wiltshire, and in the incumbency of the Rev. Francis Warre, LL.B., of Cheddon-Fitzpaine, Somersetshire. The Rectory House is a good thatched residence, embowered in trees, and the glebe comprises about 100A. here, and 20A. at *Culm-Davy,* where there is an ancient *Chapel,* with ninety sittings and a bell turret. In Hemyock are two recently erected chapels, belonging to *Baptists* and *Wesleyans.* The tithes were commuted, in 1842-'3, for £700 per annum. The poor parishioners have 10A. of land, called Hurcombe, purchased in 165 with £100, left by *Peter Holway* and other donors. They have also two yearly rent-charges, viz., 20s., left by *Charles Ford,* in the 25th of Elizabeth out of Strood and Kean's meadows; and 5s., left by *Nicholas Lacke,* out of land at Dunkeswell. *Nicholas Marke,* at an early period, charged Ashcomb estate with the yearly payment of £5 for apprenticing poor children. This parish has a share of Waldron's *Charity* for schooling poor children, as noticed with Clayhidon.

Babb Mark, wheelwgt. & vict. Star
Baker C. cooper, &c
Bennett Wm. gent. *Pounds*
Bowerman James, gent., and James, jun., assistnt. overseer, *Culmbridge*
Cross Rev Robert (Baptist)
Embrow Robert, carpenter
FisherRev Chas.Forrest, curate,*Recty*
Fry Robert, parish clerk, *Post-office*
Hine Jas. and Walker Wm. tailors
Hine John, shoemaker
Hine John, jun. shopkeeper
Masey James and Thomas, butchers
Parsey John, blacksmith
Spurway Wm. Hy.,Esq.*Culm-Davy Hs*

Waldron Philip, gentleman
Walker John, shopkeeper & tailor
Wood Francis, butcher
Wood Henry, gent. *Rosemount Hs*
Wood Thos. R. mason & vict. New Inn
    FARMERS. (* *are Owners.*)
Bennett Frederick, *Newton*
*Bowerman Jas. sen. *Culmbridge*
*Braddick —, *Ashdown*
*Farrant Edward, *New-house*
*Farrant John, *Tedborrow*
*Farrant Robert, *Westown*
*Hine Thos. (maltster,) *Culmbridg*
Lane Frederick, *Lower Westown*
Lock John ‖ Lutley Edward, jun.

Lutley Edward, sen. *Westown*
Lutley Thos. (miller,) *Whitehall*
Manley Henry (maltster,) *Millhays*
Marks Wm. *Great Simonsbro'*

*Townsend Jas. & Jno. *Whitehall*
*Troake James, *Lemonshill*
Tuck James, *Hemyock Castle*
POST *from Wellington.*

EXMINSTER HUNDRED

is of an irregular oval figure, extending about ten miles southward
from the boundary of the County of the City of Exeter, and averging about seven miles in breadth. It is bounded on the east by
the broad estuary of the river Exe, and on the south by the estuary
of the Teign and the English Channel. It is a fertile and pic-
uresque district, rising boldly to the west, and comprising the pleasant bathing places of *Teignmouth* and *Dawlish;* the small market
own of *Chudleigh;* and several handsome *seats.* Its eastern side,
near the Exe, is traversed by the South Devon Railway. It is in
the *Southern Division of Devon;* in the Archdeaconry of Exeter;
and all in *Kenn Deanery,* except Ashton and Doddiscombsleigh,
which are in *Dunsford Deanery.* The following enumeration of its
17 parishes shews their territorial extent, and their population
in 1841.

Parishes.	Acres.	Pop.	Parishes.	Acres.	Pop.
Ashcombe	2200	297	Kenton }	5400	1377
Ashton	1709	319	Starcross *chap.* }		936
Bishopsteignton	4705	992	Mamhead	1220	246
*Chudleigh	6037	2415	Powderham	1452	318
*Dawlish	5017	3132	Shillingford St. George	892	72
Doddiscombsleigh	2391	378	*Teignmouth (East)	670	1576
Dunchideock	950	208	*Teignmouth (West)	403	2883
Exminster	4670	1177	*Trusham	749	213
Ide	1408	795			
Kenn	5316	1078	Total	45,189	18,412

* Those marked thus * are in *Newton-Abbot Union,* and the others are in *St. Thomas's
Union.* (See page 122.) These Unions are also County Court Districts. All the above
parishes are in *Wonford Petty Sessional Division,* except Chudleigh, Ashton, Trusham,
Doddiscombsleigh, Dawlish, Bishopsteignton, and E. and W. Teignmouth, which are
in *Teignbridge Petty Sessional Division.* All the 17 parishes are in *Exeter Polling District,* except Bishopsteignton, Chudleigh, and East and West Teignmouth, which are
in *Newton-Abbot Polling District.*

ASHCOMBE, a scattered village and parish, near the source of a rivulet,
three miles E. of Chudleigh, has only 297 souls and about 2200 acres of
land, including about 500A. of waste and plantations. Sir Rt. L. Newman,
Bart., is lord of the manor and owner of most of the soil. The *Church* was
repaired and partly rebuilt in 1825, at the cost of about £1000. It is a
neat cruciform structure, with a tower and three bells, and a handsome east
window of stained glass. The *rectory,* valued in K.B. at £18, and in 1831
at £247, is in the patronage of the Lord Chancellor, and incumbency of the
Rev. W. H. Palk, M.A., who has 31A. of glebe, and a good thatched residence, with tasteful grounds. The tithes were commuted in 1842, for £242
per annum. In 1802, Robert Moalle left £3 a year for schooling poor
children. The *National School,* for this parish and Mamhead, has a house
for the teachers, and was built by the lord of the manor.

Coysh Edw. par. clk. & Wm. smith
Oliver Thos. & Sar. *National School*
PalkRevWilmotH.,M.A.rector ofAsh-
combe&vicar of Chudleigh, *Rectory*
Putney John, carpenter

FARMERS.
Bussell Wm. *(miller,)* Broomham
Cornish Wm. || Cornelius James
French Thomas || Reed Francis
Towell Samuel, *Court Farm*

ASHTON, a scattered village and parish on an acclivity, rising from a small rivulet, four miles N. by W. of Chudleigh, has 319 souls and 1709A. 3R. 5P. of land, mostly belonging to Viscount Exmouth, the lord of the manor. The Chudleighs were lords of the manor, and were seated here from 1320 till about 1750, and the remains of their mansion may be seen in a farm house. *Sir Geo. Chudleigh* was created a baronet in 1620, but the title became extinct on the death of Sir James, who was killed at Ostend, in 1745. Their house, which had been garrisoned for the King, was taken by the Parliamentarians, Dec. 29th, 1645. The *Church* (St. John,) is an ancient fabric, with a tower and six bells. The *rectory*, valued in K.B. at £11. 10s. 2½d., and in 1831 at £230, is in the patronage and incumbency of the Rev. Geo. Ware, M.A., who has about 60A. of glebe and a large residence, with pleasant grounds. The tithes were commuted in 1839 for £259. 10s. per annum. Two small *Almshouses*, built in 1654, by Sir Geo. Chudleigh and other contributors, are endowed with £5 a year, left in 1675, by *John Stooke*, who also left 20s. a year for the poor parishioners. The *National School* was built in 1836.

Cobley Mary, National School
Cox Thomas, blacksmith
Fragel Jas. smith & vict. New Inn
Harvey Rev Samuel, B.A. *curate*
Pugsley James, wheelwright, &c
Short Jas. par. clerk, & Wm. sexton
Taylor John, vict. Fisherman's Inn
Tuckett Charles, carpenter
Ware Rev George, M.A., Rectory, &
Winsham Vicarage, *Somerset*

FARMERS.
Berry Mary || Bradridge Wm.
Cox John, *Castle Park*
Gay Charles || Lake Abraham
Pook John || Sorcombe Samuel
Seward John || Seward Wm.
Short James || Short Samuel
Stamp Richard || Stooke Edmund
Williams Wm., *George Teign*

BISHOP'S TEIGNTON, a long straggling village and parish, on the north side of the estuary of the river Teign, two miles W. of Teignmouth, and four miles E.N.E. of Newton-Abbot, has 992 inhabitants and 4705A. 3R. 20P. of land, including the hamlets of *Luton* and *Coombe;* many scattered farm houses, and several neat villas, commanding delightful views of of the Teign and its opposite banks, down to the sea coast. The Rev. John Comyns, M.A., who has been patron and incumbent of the *vicarage* since 1801, and also impropriator of the great tithes, owns a great part of the parish, and is lord of the manors of Bishop's Teignton and Radway. He has a handsome residence, 1½ mile W. of the church, called *Wood House.* These manors were held till 1549 by the Bishops of Exeter, who had a Palace at *Radway*, where there are still some remains of the chapel. Lord Clifford is lord of the manor of Luton; and that of *Lindridge* is held by the Rev. Jas. A. Templer, in trust for his son. The mansion at Lindridge was formerly extensive, and was the seat of *Sir Peter Lear*, who was created a baronet in 1683, but the title became extinct on the death of Sir John, in 1736. Miss Pidsley owns *Wear*, and several smaller owners have estates in the parish. The *Church* (St. John,) is an ancient fabric, with a tower containing six bells, and crowned by a shingled spire. It has several neat monuments. The *vicarage*, valued in K.B. at £25. 8s. 10d., and in 1831 at £371, has the curacy of West Teignmouth annexed to it. The glebe is 7A., and the tithes were commuted in 1842, the rectorial for £499, and the

vicarial for £217. The Wesleyans have a meeting room here, and the *Bible Christians* occupy a chapel, formerly belonging to Baptists. The National School is attended by about 100 children, a number of whom are taught free and partly clothed from the rent of a house and 18A. 1R. 27P. of land, at Bovey Tracey, purchased with £557, of which £400 was left by *Cphr. Coleman*, who built a school in 1719. The poor have the rent of Broad Meadow, (2A.,) which was purchased with £100 left by Sir Thomas Lear, in 1705.

Beer George, manager of Gas works
Boone John, painter and joiner
Boone Mr Thomas, *Myrtle cottage*
Boone Miss, schoolmistress
Brock Mr Simon, *Lower Coombe*
Comyns Rev John, M.A. *vic. Wood Hs*
Coombe Wm. miller & baker, *Luton*
Featherbridge Henry, vict. New Inn
Fowler John, carpenter
Goss James, surgeon
Halladay Mrs Spha. || Hamlyn Mrs
Harlston Mrs, *The Lodge*
Harris Joseph, baker
Hill Rev George, *Kithoe House*
Honeywill Wm. butcher
Lamacraft Robert, joiner & builder
Mann Samuel, parish clerk
Martin Wm. sexton
Medland Wm. stoker, *Gas Works*
Noel Edw. Hy. gent. *Cross Cottage*
Norsworthy Robert, *National School*
O'Toole Mrs and Miss
Perkins Hy. Augsts. gent. *Teign Cottg*
Pile Sarah, vict. Commercial Inn
Prinsep Thos. Esq. *Vicarage House*
Rhodes Captain John Henry, R.N.
Stephens Hy. Wm. gent. *Cockhays*
Toby Lieut.Hy. Collett, R.N. *Clanage*
West Capt.Geo., R.N. *Huntley Cottage*

Wills Mr Samuel, *Rixtall*
BLACKSMITHS.
Major John
Major Henry
Scagall Richard
Vincent Simon (& wheelwright)
BOOT & SHOEMRS.
Boarder James
Boone Wm.
Gidley Herbert
Taylor Wm.
Trewman George
FARMERS.
(* are Owners.)
Bennett Wm.
Brock James and Martha, *Coombe*
*Cornish James, *Wolsgrove*
*Cornish Geo. Hy. *Higher Venn*
*Cornish Richd. *Rixtall*
Furze Samuel
Harvey Johanna
Holman Richard
*Paddon Wm.Elliott, *Coombe*

Parnell George
Reed Wm. *Radwy.*
Rossiter W. *Wear*
*Shilston Thos. *Luton*
Turner Turpin
*Underhill John
*Vooght James, *Luton*
Vooght John
Vooght Joseph
Vooght Wm.
*Whidbourne Geo
SHOPKEEPERS.
Berry Joseph
Hill Samuel
Jackman Richard
TAILORS.
Hellier Wm.
Jackman Alex.
Jackman Albert
POST OFFICE
at Jph. Berry's.
Letters from Teignmouth
CARRIER.
Beal John, to Exeter, Friday.

CHUDLEIGH is a small *market town* pleasantly situated on the eastern side of the vale of the river Teign, 9 miles S. by W. of Exeter, and 6 miles N. of Newton Abbot. Its parish rises in bold hills and limstone rocks on the east, and contains 6037A. 1R. 34P. of land, including the hamlets of *Waddon* and *Harcombe*, and several handsome houses. It increased its population from 1383 souls in 1801, to 2415 in 1841. The town was nearly all destroyed by a terrible *fire* which broke out May 22nd, 1807, and destroyed 166 houses. The damage was estimated at £60,000, but £21,000 was promptly subscribed for the relief of the poorer inhabitants. In 1808, an act of Parliament was obtained, for the better and more easy rebuilding the town, and it was not long before that desirable object was accomplished. The town has now a neat modern appearance, the sites of the old thatched dwellings being occupied by slated and substantial dwellings. It has a *market* on Saturday for provisions, &c., and three annual fairs for cattle, &c., on Easter Tuesday, Whit-

Monday, and October 2nd. It had formerly a share of the woollen manufacture, and it has now four corn mills and a large tannery. Its commerce has been greatly facilitated by a *canal*, which extends four miles southward to the estuary of the Teign, at King's Teignton, and was finished in 1843 at the expense of Lord Clifford. The manor belonged from an early period to the Bishops of Exeter, till it was sold by Bishop Veysey, in 1550, to Thos. Brydges. The Bishops had a *Palace* about a quarter of a mile south of the town, where there are still a few slight traces of it. Hugh Lord Clifford purchased the manor in 1695, and it now belongs, with a great part of the soil, to the present Lord Clifford of UGBROOK PARK, a delightful seat in the fertile valley about a mile south of the town. The mansion is a large quadrangular building, with two fronts and four towers, and is furnished with battlements and covered with cement. It stands on an acclivity, and contains many elegantly furnished apartments, and a valuable collection of fine old paintings by some of the best masters. The park is about five miles round, and is stocked with about 500 head of deer. The grounds embrace every variety of scenery ; having hill and dale, wood and water, and rock and chasm. Oaks and elms of the largest growth are interspersed with chesnuts, and an endless variety of ornamental trees and shrubs. On an eminence in one part of the grounds are the remains of a Danish encampment, surrounded with a single trench. In one of the wings of the house is the family Roman Catholic Chapel, decorated with many fine paintings. CHUDLEIGH ROCK, nearly a mile S.E. of the town, is an imposing mass of limestone rock, which rises almost perpendicularly on one side, presenting a bold front several hundred feet in height. On another side a deep woody glen divides it from a similar eminence. Through this hollow an impetuous stream descends, and forms a pretty cataract. The sides of of the rock are partly covered with trees and shrubs, and broken into romantic cliffs and hollows. Midway down is a large cave, which extends some distance into the earth. The view from the summit of the rock is most enchanting, and numerous pleasure parties, from the neighbouring towns, visit it and Ugbrook Park, during the summer season. Anthony Clifford, Esq., obtained Ugbrook in marriage with the heiress of Sir Peter Courtenay, in the reign of Elizabeth. *Sir Thomas Clifford*, a favourite of Charles II., was made Lord Treasurer, and was one of the distinguished statesmen who composed the ministry, called from their initials the *Cabal*. In 1672, he was created *Baron Clifford, of Chudleigh*. The Rt. Hon. Hugh Charles Clifford succeeded as the 7th Lord Clifford in 1831, and was born in 1790. WHITEWAY HOUSE is the pleasant seat of M. E. N. Parker, Esq., and was built by the first Lord Boringdon. Thos. Yarde, Esq., of *Culver House*, and several smaller freeholders have estales here.

Chudleigh Church (St. Martin,) is a large and handsome structure which was renovated and beautified in 1848-9, at the cost of about £2000. It has a tower containing six bells, a clock, and chimes. The east window has been enriched with stained glass by J. Williams, Esq., and the interior has now a handsome appearance. The *vicarage*, valued in K.B. at £21, and in 1831 at £571, is in the patronage of Trustees for the inhabitants, and in the incumbency of the Rev. Wilmot H. Palk, M.A., of Ashcombe Rectory. The Vicarage House is a neat building, occupied by the curate. The tithes

were commuted in 1841, the vicarial for £550, and the rectorial for £250 per annum. Lord Clifford is impropriator of the latter. Here are two *chapels* belonging to Independents and Wesleyans ; and meeting-rooms occupied by Baptists and Plymouth Brethren. That belonging to the Independents was built in 1710, and rebuilt in 1830. The parish has a *Literary Society*, a Grammar School, and various charities.

The FREE GRAMMAR SCHOOL was built on an acre of land, enclosed from the town park, by *John Pynsent*, who endowed it in 1668, with a yearly rent-charge of £30, out of an estate at Combe. For this annuity, the master is required to teach freely the church catechism, and Latin and Greek to all the sons of inhabitants sent to him. He has the free use of a good house which has been much improved by him and his predecessor. He employs two assistant-masters, and has a large number of boarders, the school being in high repute, and the town and neighbourhood highly salubrious. M. E. N. Parker, Esq., John Williams, Esq., Thomas Yarde, Esq., and others, are the trustees.

The PARISH LANDS, with the profits of the *markets and fairs*, were granted in 1597 to feoffees for charitable and public uses, by *Thos. Bridges*, in consideration of £150 and his own benevolent intentions. The tolls of the market and fairs are usually let for about £30 a year, and there are belonging to the trust ten dwellings with gardens, &c., let for only about £10 per annum, in consideration of fines paid on granting the leases. The Church House, occupied by the sexton and a schoolmaster, and an Almshouse, occupied by paupers, belong to the same trust. The two old market houses were destroyed by the great fire, in 1807. The market place was afterwards removed to its present situation. The rents of the " parish lands" are carried to the churchwarden's accounts, out of which £5. 7s. 6d. is paid yearly to the master of Eastchurch's school, and the rest is applied in repairing the town water-courses. A plot of about two acres, belonging to the trust, is left open as a play ground for the parishioners, and for the holding of the cattle fairs, but the vicar is permitted to have the pasturage. Various BENEFACTIONS to the poor of Chudleigh are lost, but the following still remain :—In consideration of £25, given by *Stephen Bloye*, in 1673, the overseers apply yearly 15s. in relieving the sick poor, and 15s. in relieving poor travellers. The poor parishioners have the following *annuities*, viz.—52s. left by *Sir John Acland*, and paid by the Corporation of Exeter ; 30s. left by *Thos. Clarke*, out of two closes at Trusham ; 40s. out of a house, left by *John Soper*, in 1622 ; and £4 from £100 four per cent. stock, purchased with £100, left by *Wm. Stidston*, in 1818. The yearly sum of £4. 12s. 6d., out of a house left by a *Mr. Eastchurch*, in 1692, is paid for schooling ten poor children.

CHUDLEIGH DIRECTORY.

The POST-OFFICE is at Mr. John Petherick's. Letters are received and desp. at 7 morning, and 5½ evening. Money orders are granted and paid.

Adams Jonas, sexton, Fore street
Allen Rev John, (Independent)
Andrew Admiral J. W., Exeter street
Ball Mary, lace maker
Berry John, tanner, Exeter street
Blatchford James, rope & mat maker
Brandreth Col. Thomas A., R.A.
Breay Miss Mary || Cox Mrs
Brown Bernard M. surgeon
Brown Hy. & Martin My. *Nat. School*
Burrington Gilbert, Esq., *Elm Grove*
Buttress Wm. plumber, ironmgr. &c.
Clack Edw. Robert, Esq., *Culver st*
Clark Wm. Esq., *Kerswell*
Cleave Joseph, druggist & hairdresr
Clifford Lord, *Ugbrook Park*
Collins Rev Charles Matthew, M.A.,
     head master, *Grammar School*
Cox Miss & Roberton Miss, *Heightley*
Cottle John, cooper, &c.
Crossman Fdk. Hugh, watchmaker
Day Francis, surgeon
Dunn Capt. Sir David, K.C.H,, R.N.
Flood George, schoolmaster

Flood Mr John || Mogridge Mrs
Hayes George, organist
Hoare Mary, *Infant School*
Jones Mary, glass, china, &c. dealer
Kendall Charles, solicitor
Knight Hy. land agent, *Ugbrook*
Lane Thomas, Esq., *Oaklands*
Langley Charles, solicitor and clerk
     to Magistrates, Fore street
Lethbridge Colonel, *The Elms*
Lomax Rev Charles, (Catholic)
Luscombe John, painter & glazier
Lyne Rev Chas., M.A. *prebendary*
Mills Major Wm. Flicks, *FilleighHs*
Mugg Henry Holman, gent.
Oldham Jph., jun., Esq., *Oakfields*
Orchard Mrs E. || Roleston Mrs
Parker Montague Edm. N., Esq.,
     Whiteway House
Prowse Eliz. reading rooms, &c.
Richards Richd. lime, &c. merchant
Rogers John, veterinary surgeon
Rowse Wm. gent. *Heathfield*
Saunders Miss || Seppings Mrs

Saunders Thomas J. H., auctioneer, estate agent, regr., &c. Clifford st
Scott Capt., R.N. ‖ Yarde Mrs
Scott Wm. Bower, solicitor
Shamler Wm. schoolmaster
Tapper John, cooper, &c.
Tavernor Geo. coal and lime mercht
Terry Edward, music professor
Thomas Rev Chas. A. Neville, M.A., curate, *Vicarage*
Weeks Thomas, parish clerk
Williams John, Esq., *Elm Grove*
Williams Thomas, basket maker, &c.
Wright Hy. T., Esq., *Cobourg House*
Yarde Thos., Esq., *Culver House*

FARMERS.
Archer Samuel, *Filleigh*
Cleave James, *Newhouse*
Cleave Joseph, *Chudleigh Wood*
Cleave Walter, *Roughton*
Cox Wm., *Combeshead*
Cox Rebecca ‖ Hall Robert
Goodridge Richard, *Oxencombe*
Langdon Paul ‖ Lambert John
Wolland George, *Ramscombe*
Wright Hy. Wm. (and maltster)
Wright Thomas, *Hams*

FIRE & LIFE OFFICE AGENTS.
Atlas, Samuel Whiteway
Phœnix & Pelican, T. J. H. Saunders
Sun, Charles Langley
Union, James E. Searle
West of England, C. Kendall

INNS AND TAVERNS.
Clifford's Arms, Ann Cartwright
Globe, Elizabeth Snell
King's Arms, George Strowbridge
Lion, Thomas Martin
Plymouth Inn, Wm. Edwards
Ship, Walter Wotton
White Hart, Prudence Salter

BAKERS.
Bailey Wm.
Copplestone Sml.
Matthews Joseph
Mortimore Geo.
Quint Samuel
Searle B. confectr
Whiteway John

BLACKSMITHS.
Davis George
Goard John P.
Paull Wm.

BOOKSELLERS, PRINTERS, &c.
Crook Robt. libry
Searle George
Searle James E.

BOOT&SHOEMKRS
Babbidge John
Edwards James
Henley James
Latham Thomas
Roleston George
Roleston Joseph
Roleston Wm.
Stephens John

BUTCHERS.
Cornish John
Lambel Thomas
Leare Thomas
Trewman Stephn.
Tucker George
Wright Wm.

CORN MILLERS.
Ball John
Honeywill John
Whiteway Saml.
Wotton Wm.

GROCERS, &c.
(* *Drapers also.*)
Barter Luke

Cleave Thos. (& ironmonger)
Curtis Maria
Honeywill Ann
*Humphrey John
Lodge Samuel
*Petherick Eliz.
*Prowse John & George
Quint Sml.beerhs
Searle Ed. drugst
StrowbridgeFras.
Strowbridge Geo.

JOINERS & BLDRS.
Barter Luke
Cleave Thos. cabt
Collins Robert
Moyle John
Martin Wm.

MASONS.
Ball Thos. &Jas.
Babbage Joseph
Jago Elijah
Train Joseph

SADDLERS.
Cleave Wm. sen.
Trewman Wm.

TAILORS.
Adams Wm.
Shamler George
Trewman John

WHEELWRIGHTS.
Cox Robert
Meadway Henry

CARRIER.
John Gill to Exeter, *daily*

DAWLISH, or *Daulish*, is a large and handsome village, and *bathing place*, delightfully situated near a fine bay of the English Channel, between Exmouth and Teignmouth, nearly 3 miles N. of the latter, and 11 miles S. by E. of Exeter. It is crossed by the South Devon Railway, and at the beginning of the present century was only a small fishing village. It lies in a picturesque valley opening to the sea, and a rivulet, which runs through its principal street, is crossed in several places by small bridges of stone or iron. Its *beach* is comprised within a cove, about 1½ mile in extent, formed by the lofty projecting cliffs of Langstone on the east, and the Parson and Clerk rocks on the west. The principal residences are on the beautiful *terraces* on the beach, the strand, and Teignmouth Hill, all commanding extensive prospects; as also do Barton and Planta-

tion terraces.   The sea bathing here, from the slight inclination of
the beach and the firmness of the sands, is of the best description :
and the climate is said to be milder than that of any of the Devonshire watering places, especially in the winter months, when the
village is usually thronged with respectable visitors.   The *Parish
of Dawlish* had only 1424 inhabitants in 1801, but in 1841 they had
increased to 3132.   It contains about 5017 acres of land, rising
boldly from the valley and the beach, and including the small
hamlets of *Cockwood, Middlewood, Westwood, Holcombe, East Town,
Shattern,* and *Lithwell.*   The village has been greatly improved
during the last ten years, and has a holiday fair on Easter Monday,
and *races* and a *regatta* in August.   The soil and buildings belong
to many freeholders ; the manor and estate, which had been held
for a long period by the Dean and Chapter of Exeter, being sold, in
the early part of the present century, to various purchasers, under
the powers of the act for the redemption of the land tax.   The
Public Baths on the beach are of recent erection, and have a handsome front of Doric architecture.   They have two saloons, and the
baths are supplied with water from the sea, and may be used either
cold, or heated by a steam apparatus.   The *Public Rooms* comprise
ball, billiard, and refreshment rooms, and on the strand is a well
supplied *Reading and News Room.*   The village has several good
inns, and many large and handsome houses.   The *Railway Station*
is on the Beach ; and the *Coast Guard Station* on the Cliff.   *Gas
Works* were established in 1847, at the cost of about £2000, raised
in £5 shares.   *Petty Sessions* are held here every alternate Saturday.   Large quantities of mackerel, herring, and other *fish* are taken
on the coast, and the neighbourhood is celebrated for *orchards* and
excellent *cider.*   The *Parish Church* (St. Gregory,) is at the upper
end of the village, three quarters of a mile from the beach, and was
all rebuilt, except the tower, in 1824-'5, at the cost of about £6000.
It is a large and handsome structure in the early English style, and
will seat more than 1500 hearers.   The tower has six bells, and the
church consists of a nave, aisles, transept, and chancel.   It has an
excellent organ, and its large east window, with its well wrought
tracery and mosaic stained glass, has an imposing appearance.
There are two *monuments* by Flaxman, one in memory of Lady
Pennyman, (ob. 1801,) representing four females kneeling round an
urn ; and the other in memory of the wife of Wm. Hunter, Esq.,
representing Grief weeping over an urn.   The *vicarage,* valued in
K.B. at £25. 5s., and in 1831 at £260, is in the patronage of the
Dean and Chapter of Exeter, and incumbency of the Rev. E. A.
Fursdon, M.A.   The tithes were commuted in 1839, the vicarial for
£440, and the rectorial for £360.   Mrs. Burrell is lessee of the latter
under the Dean and Chapter.   A handsome *Chapel of Ease* was
built in the lower part of the village, in 1849-'50, at the cost of about
£2500, raised by subscription.   Chas. Hoare, Esq., contributed
£1800 towards the building, and £1000 for its endowment.   The
first stone was laid May 15th, 1849, and the chapel will be opened
early in 1850.   It has a tower crowned by a small spire, and will
have several hundred free sittings.   Here are four *Chapels* belong-

ing to Roman Catholics, Independents, Wesleyans, and Plymouth Brethren. Two *Schools*, on Dr. Bell's plan, are supported partly by subscription and an annuity of 36s., left by the Rev. H. Harvey, in 1728. The inhabitants and visitors subscribe to several charitable institutions for the relief of the poor. [For Lidwell, see Teignmouth.]

DAWLISH DIRECTORY.

The POST-OFFICE is at Piermont place, and Mr. John Lowe is the post master. Box closes for Exeter, London, &c., at 7½ night; for the N. and W. of England at 1¼ aftn. ; and for Plymouth, &c., at 9½ night.

Those marked 1 are at Albert place; 2 Barton ter.; 3 Brook st.; 4 Brunswick place; 5 Marine parade; 6 Manor row; 7 Mill row; 8 Old Town street; 9 Park st. or place; 10 Piermont place; 11 Plantation terrace; 12 Queen street; 13 Strand; and 14 Teignmouth hill.

11 Aitchison Misses Eliz. and My.
Barrett Mr. P., Beach House
5 Beard My. || 13 Dodge Mrs Mary
2 Bayley Misses || 14 Bennett Eliz.
Berry Mr Fras., Teignmouth hill
Blatchley Chas. gent. Marine par
Blencowe Misses, Plantation terrace
14 Bloomfield Miss Elizabeth
Bond Jas. Rt., asst. overseer, & sec. to Gas Co., Albert place
Brook Mr George, Hope cottage
4 Burrington Alfred, organist, &c
Burrington Gilbert, gent., Strand
2 Byles Mather, solicitor and clerk to magistrates
Campbell Miss, Luscombe cottage
Cann Wm. More, surgeon
14 Chapman Capt. Benj. and Miss
13 Church Mr Fdk. and Miss Emily
Cole Geo. Esq. Laurel cottage
Cole Miss Eliz., Dawlish water
3 Collett Rev Thos. (Independen)
9 Cornelius Robert, gardener
11 Coryton Miss Jane, Cliff Cottage
Cousins Wm. gent. Langdon House
8 Craufurd Miss Louisa
Deacon Mr. Wm. 17 Strand
9 Dean Robert, basket maker
Dick Capt. Thos. R.N. Brook House
Duncan Dr Fletcher, Strand House
Eales Rd. Esq., clerk of the peace
Eales Rev Wm., M.A. Cross row
9 Ferris Richard, maltster, &c
5 Forster Capt. Charles, R.N.
Foy Mrs Lucy, Strand
Fursdon Rev. Edw. A., M.A., *Vicrg.*
Gamlyn Mrs Eliz., Marine parade
Garrett Mrs E. 2 Barton terrace
4 Gater Thos. glass and china dlr.

Gibbons Misses, Brunswick place
Grant Mrs Charlotte, Brook cottage
Grove Miss Sophia, Lawn terrace
Hoare Chas. Esq. Luscombe House
11 Hodson Mrs Mgt. & Kennett Mrs
Hole Jph. artist, Park street
James Mr Chas. Wm., Strand
Jones Rev Theophilus, M.A. *curate*
9 Knighton Capt. Chas., R.N.
9 Knighton John Fortescue, surgeon
Lake Wm. gardener, Pea lawn
Lipzeatt Percy, gent. *Priory*
Lisle Lord Geo., *Hill House*
Livet Mrs Frs. 7 Barton terrace
Long Miss Rose Ann, *Manor House*
10 Lowe John, postmaster
13 Luckes Elizabeth, lace maker
9 Macnamara James D., gent
5 Margary P. J. civil engineer
McLeese Wm. chair letter, &c
Matthews Jph. builder, *Sea View*
Meyrick Lieut. Genl., Cross row
Montgomery Charles William, Esq. *Cleveland House*
Morgan Mr James, Marine parade
Morgan Peter, *Railway Station*
4 Osmond Mary, stay maker
Palk Rev Wilmot H., *Ashcombe*
Parr Codrington, Esq., *Stonelands*
Payne Mr W., Dawlish water
1 Pearson Sydney, solicitor
Pennell Mr H. B., Teignmouth hill
Penson Mr John || 13 Potts Mgt
Perring Mr Wm. || Perring Mrs Sar
Phillips Misses, Brunswick place
Pinson Mr John, Old Town street
Potts George, Esq. *Elm Grove*
Potts Mrs Elizabeth, Strand
14 Powell Mrs E. & Roebuck Mrs

13 Sclater Miss, shell, &c. dealer
Sclater Thos. madrapore mfr.
13 Short Wm. wine and spirit mert.
2 Smith Chas. Douglas, gent
2 Smith Rev John, (Catholic)
10 Smith Mrs S. || 13 Spear James
Spencer George, sexton
Spyring Mrs M. E, 3 Strand
Stafford Mrs I., *Knowl Cottage*
Stokes Letitia, bath keeper
Strickland Augtn. gent. *Oak hill*
Strickland Miss, *Rice Cottage*
Strickland Martin, gent. Beach
Sugg James, propr. of Public Rooms
4 Till Mrs Sar. || 13 Truman Thos.
Tripe Wm. fishmonger
Truscott Genl., *West Cliff*
Tucker Rev M.; Mrs My. and Miss
14 Vaughan Lady Mallet
Vicary Mrs Eliz., Myrtle cottage
13 Vinning Wm. Skinner, music pfr.
Voysey John, Basket mkr. Chapel st
Walsh Rev T., *New Bridge House*
Walters Mr. Thomas, *Beach Cottage*
Westcott Mr Leond. Augs., Strand
Wight Admiral John *Mindb. Cottg.*
Wilcocks Mr Rd., Old Town street
Wilkins Mr Wm. Barton terrace
4 Williams Wm. saddler, &c
Wood Wm. coast guard officer

FARMERS. (* *are Owners.*)
Adams Nichls. || Batstone Charles
Blackmore Saml. || * Brock James
Branscombe Wm., *Hounds pool*
* Brock Richard || * Brock Wm.
* Carpenter John, *Gatehouse*
Colling Edward, *Holcombe*
Dunsford Robert, *Cockwood*
* Ferris Nich. & Wm. || Cross John
Hole James || Hill John
Humphrey John || Lake John
Lamacraft Robert, Strand
Paul Moses || Medlane George
* Pennell R. B., *Holcombe*
Pitts Mrs || Reed John
Seward Wm. || Sobey John
Williams Jph. || Willis Josias
Willis Wm. || Wood Wm

FIRE AND LIFE OFFICE AGENTS.
County & Provident, L. A. Westcott
Clerical, Medl. & Genl., S. Pearson
Etonian, H. W. Haydon
Legal and Coml., Jas. R. Bond
Palladium, Wm. Short
West of England, D. Litton

INNS AND TAVERNS.
(* *are Family Hotels, &c.*)
2 Brunswick Arms, John Raven
Country House, Robt. Annear
4 Horse and Groom, John Dodge
3 King's Arms, John Lake
Lobster, Thos. Ware, Teign. road
* 13 London Inn, James Melhuish
9 Mariner's Compass, Mary Litton
New York, Wm. Hatcher, Beach
8 Red Lion, Fanny Hill
* Royal Western Hotel, Thos. Smith,
Swan, John Stokes, Old Town street
14 Teignmth. Arms, My. Chichester
* 13 York Hotel, Henry Anning

ACADEMIES.
5 Barrett P.
Bailey Miss, *Natl.*
12 Bond Misses
3 Collett Thomas
Harris Ann
13 Hill Wm.
Panter Fras., *Ntl.*
13 Short Wm.
Stone Mary Ann
12 Young Miss

BAKERS.
6 Pratt Wm.
13 Reed Eliz.
6 Reed Thomas
12 Sparkes Wm.
9 Stocks Henry
3 Tapper James

BEER, &C. DLRS.
8 Poulton Rd.
Sugg James
Tuck Wm.

BLACKSMITHS.
5 Jewell Samuel
Jewell Charles
4 Paddon Chas.
9 Splatt Chtte.
9 Warren Mchl.

BOOKSELLRS., &C.
13 Rond Eliz.
13 Crowther Ann
13 Westcott L.A.

BOOT & SHOE MKS.
14 Batten James
12 Boarder Rd.
6 Brown Wm.
4 Cornelius Wm.
3 Cotton Albert
13 Dunn Thomas
1 Edmonds John

3 Harris Benj.
Hart John
8 Hawkins Edw.
9 Hawkins Wm.
Horrick John
Knighton Wm.
7 Moore Jacob
Moore John
Moore J. jun.
1 Pressell Samuel
13 Pridham W.
9 Smith Thomas
14 Underhill Ts.
8 Voysey George
Weatherdon Ths.
Welmet Robert

BREWERS.
9 Ferris Richard
9 Poulton R. L.

BRICKLAYERS, &C.
Annear Rd.
9 Cole Wm.
Matthews Joseph
9 Paddon George
7 Penny Rd.
6 Elmore Wm.
Spencer George
12 Spencer John
6 Spencer J.
Matthews Joseph
4 Paddon George
7 Tapper Wm.

BUTCHERS.
13 Lamacraft Rt.
Manley Henry,
    King street
13 Smith Nichls.
9 Stone Henry
8 Stone James

CABINET MKRS.
13 Avent John
12 Avent Thos.
9 Burt Wm.
Knight John
Tapper Wm.
CHEMISTS & DGTS.
13 Haydon H. W.
13 Litton Daniel
COAL MERTS.
9 Ferris Richard
13 Tripe Wm.
8 Williams Jph.
CONFECTIONERS.
13 Reed Eliz.
13 Stokes Monh.
COOPERS.
Blacking John
4 Hoare Robert
Tripe Richard
CORN MILLERS.
13 Bussell Henry
Coombe James
Tapper James
Tarr Wm.
FLY &c. OWNERS.
13 Anning Henry
8 Discombe W.
Hayward John
Knight John
Martin Wm.
9 McLeese Wm.
7 Veale Henry

GROCERS.
13 Brooking Rd.
1 Dicker George
13 Hanniford Sl.
12 Jeffreys H. (& chandler, &c)
7 Matthews and Moore
12 Saunders Ths.
Westlake Robert
HAIR DRESSERS.
3 Easterbrook J.
13 Lamacraft S.
IRONMONGERS.
7 Hill James
7 Paddon James
13 Tripe Wm.
JOINERS & BLDRS.
7 Beard John
4 Beard Nicholas
4 Bragg George
Bragg John
12 Bulley John
Burnie John D.
8 Cox James
12 Davis Wm.
13 Ferris Edw.
2 Hexter Wm.
1 Widdicombe J.
L. & W. DRAPERS.
13 Brown James
13 Burt Rebecca

8 Edwards L. & S.
10 Pearse James and Son
13 Twose Rt. B.
MILLINERS.
7 Batstone M. E.
7 Beard Eliz.
9 Bond Ann
1 Curtis Slna.
4 Latham Mary
4 Paddon M. A.
4 Osborne Mary
13 Strowbridge A.
13 Twose Jane
7 Warren Emma
PAINTERS & GLZS.
3 Bickham Geo.
12 Parker Wm.
Tuck Henry
7 Walters Thos.
SHOPKEEPERS.
6 Bragg Caroline
8 Crispin Eliz.
3 Easterbrook J.
9 Oliver Eady
6 Pedrick Wm.
8 Radford John
6 Vanstone Sarah
1 Widdicomb, J.
STRAW HAT MKRS
13 Avant Chtte.
7 Batstone Mary

7 Warren Emma
TAILORS.
7 Batstone James
12 Curtis John
8 Curtis Samuel
Curtis Thomas
12 Lake Cphr.
3 Loram Thomas
1 Toogood Richd.
13 Truman Thos.
7 Wellington Wm.
TINNERS & BZRS.
7 Hill James
6 Lamble Thos.
13 Tripe Wm.
WATCHMAKERS.
4 Bolt Wm.
13 Strowbridge H.
WHEELWRIGHTS.
9 Cole Wm.
8 Cull Moses
Hayward John
Jewell Charles
7 Reed Hugh
RAILWAY.
Trains six times a day to Exeter, Plymouth, &c
CARRIERS to *Exeter daily.*
6 Ellis Elizabeth
6 Lake John

DODDISCOMBSLEIGH, a scattered village and parish, on bold acclivities near the source of a rivulet, 6 miles S.W. of Exeter, contains 378 souls, and 2391A. 3R. 3P. of land, including the hamlets of *Lowleigh* and *Leigh-Cross.* The manor was anciently held by the Doddiscombes, and was divided among their co-heiresses in the reign of Edward III. The parish now belongs to the Palk, Rodd, Buckingham, Pitman, Archer, and other families. The *Town* or *Manor House*, built in 1604, is the pleasant seat of E. G. Rodd, Esq. The *Church* (St. Michael,) is a fine old structure, with much stained glass in its windows, and an embattled tower, containing three bells. The *rectory*, valued in K.B. at £16. 6s. 5½d., and in 1831 at £312, is in the patronage and incumbency of the Rev. James Buckingham, B.C.L., who has 112A. of glebe, and a handsome residence, which was much improved in 1845, and has a finely wooded lawn of nine acres. There was anciently a small chapel at Sheldon. A cottage was converted into a *School* by the rector, in 1842. A Clothing Club was established here in in 1843, and a Lending Library in 1846. The poor have an annuity of 40s., left by Florence Barrow, and 20s. a year left by John Babb. *Manganese* was formerly got in this parish, but the mine was closed some years ago.

Buckingham Rev Jas., B.C.L., *Recty*
Bulley George, blacksmith

Clarke Wm. shopkeeper
Cole Wm. tailor

Diggins Wm. vict. New Inn
Diggins Thomas, wheelwright
Drew Richard, mason
Harrod Wm. fishing tackle manufctr
Luscombe George, shoemaker
Rodd Edw. G. gent. *Town House*
Woolway Mary, schoolmistress
FARMERS.
Archer Samuel, (owner,) *Dent Hs*

Archer Thomas, *Shippen Barton*
Archer Wm. (owner,) Sheldon
Belworthy John || Bond Joseph
Cleave Jonn || Coldridge Eliz.
Crocker John || Esworthy John
Jarvis Wm. || May Mary and Wm.
Rundle Wm. (and parish clerk)
Williams John || Sorcombe George

DUNCHIDEOCK, a small scattered village and parish, in a picturesque valley, 4 miles S.W. of Exeter, has only 208 souls, and 950 acres of land. Sir L. V. Palk is lord of the manor, but the greater part of the soil belongs to James Pitman, Esq., of *Dunchideock House*, a large mansion, with pleasant grounds, on a bold acclivity. The *Church* (Holy Trinity,) was partly rebuilt in 1669, and has a tower and three bells. It contains a handsome monument in memory of *General Stringer Lawrence*, who died in 1775. He has also a monument in Westminster Abbey, erected by the East India Company, in gratitude for his services in India, and the peace which he concluded at Carnatic. The *rectory*, valued in K.B. at £14. 17s. 1d., and in 1831 at £327, with that of Shillingford St. George annexed to it, is in the patronage of Sir L. V. Palk, and incumbency of the Rev. Henry Palk, B.C.L., who resides at Shillingford, there being neither Parsonage nor glebe here. The tithes were commuted in 1842, for £142. 10s. per annum. The poor have the interest of £45, left by various donors, and vested with Sir L. V. Palk. Here is a small *School*, supported chiefly by the rector.

Coplestone Wm. farmer
Endicott Wm. wheelwright
Halse George, tailor and par. clerk
Lawton John, blacksmith
Long Isabella, schoolmistress

Pitman James, Esq., *Dunchidk. Hs*
Rice John, shoemaker
Stook James, farmer
Strong Wm. and Sons, farmers

EXMINSTER is a large straggling village, pleasantly situated, 4 miles S.E. by S. of Exeter, on the western side of the vale of the river Exe, opposite Topsham, and near the South Devon Railway, and the Exeter Canal, which here falls into the estuary at *Turf lock*. The parish contains 1177 inhabitants, and 4670 acres of land, including a fine tract of rich marshes, the hamlets of *Lower Shillingford and Matford;* and several scattered farm-houses and neat mansions, from one to three miles west of the village, where a cattle *fair* is held on the 29th of May. The Earl of Devon is lord of the manor of Exminster, and his ancestors are said to have anciently had a magnificent mansion here, in which Archbishop Courtenay and his brother Sir Peter are said to have been born. After being held by several other families, this manor was repurchased by the Courtenays about 1752. Sir L. V. Palk is lord of the manor of Shillingford, and owner of the estates called Little Bowhay, Breynton, and Lower and North Shillingford, or *Shillingford Abbots*. The latter has a pleasant seat, occupied by Lieut. Temple. *Kenbury House*, a neat mansion, with pleasant grounds, is the seat of A. Stowey, Esq.; and *Peamore House*, a fine old mansion, encompassed by woody hills, is the secluded seat of Samuel T. Kekewich, Esq. They have large estates here, and part of the parish belongs to a few smaller owners. Messrs. Geo. Turner and John Wippell are noted *cattle and sheep breeders;* and the parish has a *Farmers' Club*, of which R. W. Blencowe, Esq., is president. The *Church* (St. Martin,) is a large structure, with a fine tower, containing a clock, chimes, and six bells. The chancel end has lately been rebuilt. The organ and loft were erected in 1839, and the new marble

font and stone altar-piece in 1843. The Governors of Crediton Church Corporation Trust are impropriators of the tithes and patrons of the *vicarage*, valued in K.B. at £12, and in 1831 at £253. The Rev. J. P. Hugo, M.A., is the incumbent, and has 15 acres of glebe, and a pleasant residence, commanding a fine view of Topsham, and the estuary of the Exe. All the tithes were commuted in 1839, for £850 per annum, out of which the impropriators pay a yearly stipend of £350 to the vicar, and £15 per annum in aid of the *National School*. The Church House has been long vested for the use of the poor. The *Poor's Land* (3½A.,) and two houses, with gardens, &c., were given to the poor by unknown donors; and they have also 20s. a year left by *Margaret Taverner*, in 1629, out of Church Stile tenement. DEVON COUNTY PAUPER LUNATIC ASYLUM is an extensive and handsome building in this parish, pleasantly situated about 3½ miles south of Exeter. The first stone was laid June 27th, 1842, and the building was finished in 1845, at the cost of about £60,000, including the sum paid for the 24A. of land, now tastefully laid out in gardens, lawns, yards, &c. The house has accommodations for 400 patients; and the wards, galleries, and apartments are spacious, airy, and well ventilated. The centre building comprises the dispensary, and the residences of the superintendent, matron, &c. Around these, are encircled and connected with corridors, the sick and day rooms of the patients, and other necessary apartments for the attendants. From this circle radiate six wards, comprising the bedrooms of the inmates. On the ground floor is a neat chapel; and the open spaces between the wards are appropriated as airing grounds for the patients. This large house of refuge for those afflicted with the worst of maladies, is under the control of the county magistrates, and T. E. Drake, Esq., of Exeter, is the *secretary*. The officers are enumerated in the following *Directory of Exminster Parish.*

Baker Wm. Henry, butcher
Blake John, blacksmith
Brewer Robert, tailor
Bucknell John Chas., M.D. supt. of Devon Lunatic Asylum
Callaway Wm. shopr. & shoemaker
Cowper Saml. surgeon, *Shillingford*
Esworth Fredk. *National School*
Folkard Chas. gent. *Matford Cottage*
Gale George, carpenter
Gale Wm. par. clerk, & Thos. sexton
Helmore John, wheelwright
Hugo Rev John Philip, M.A. *Vicarage*
Hussey Thomas, auctioneer and land agent, *Waybrook*
Kekewich Samuel Trehawk, Esq., *Peamore House*
Kneels Alexander, cooper
Lardner Philip, Esq., *Church Stile*
Lewis Rev Geo.T. chaplain to Devon Lunatic Asylum
Manley Robert, baker
Parker John, beer seller
Parsy Wm., M.D., Asylum
Roberts Wm. wheelwright

Shobrook ——, blacksmith
Stowey Augs., Esq. *Kenbury House*
Tapp Mary, beer seller
Tapp Wm. shoemaker
Temple Lieut. Hy., R.N., *Shillingford Abbots*
Ware Mary, vict. Stowey Arms
FARMERS. (* are Owners.)
Baker Wm. Hy. || Baker John & Jas.
Burrington Geo. || Burrington Wm.
Elliott Frederick H., *Crablake*
Gale Wm. || Laskey Wm.
Gibbings Richd., *Higher Breynton*
*Hussey Thomas, *Waybrook*
Rowe Mary, *Turner's*
Snell Charles || Vooght Charlotte
*Trood Edward, *Matford House*
*Turner George, (cattle breeder,) *Barton*, near Exeter
Vooght Ann, *Marsh Row*
* Wippell John, (cattle breeder,) *Lower Breynton*
Wilcocks Wm., *Pengilly's*
POST-OFFICE at Wm. Gale's. Letters depatched 6 evg. *via* Exeter

IDE, a neat and pleasant village, in a picturesque valley, 2 miles S.S.W. of Exeter, has in its parish 795 souls, and 1408A. 3R. 17P. of fertile land,

mostly the property of the Dean and Chapter of Exeter, who are lords of the manor, appropriators of the rectory, and patrons of the *perpetual curacy,* which was valued in 1831 at £180 per annum, and is now held by the Rev. J. H. Erle, LL.B., who has a neat thatched residence, and 2A. of glebe. The great tithes were commuted in 1840 for £180, and the small tithes for £170 per annum. The *Church* (St. Ida,) was rebuilt in 1834, at the cost of about £1300, and has 550 sittings, of which 300 are free. It is a neat cemented structure, with a tower and four bells. Those beautiful and romantic grounds called *Fordlands,* which are often visited by pleasure parties from Exeter, are in this parish, and are already described at page 94. They are the property of J. W. Abbott, Esq. Here is a school, partly supported by subscription; and the poor parishioners have two yearly rent-charges, viz., 20s. out of a field at Lower Whiddon, left by *Peter Balle,* in 1648; and £2. 12s., left by *Wm. Smith,* out of three houses at Exeter.

Abbott J.W. Esq. *Fordlands* & Exeter	BUTCHERS.	Tuckett John
Blencowe Mrs. *Earl's Court*	Copplestone Geo.	Turner James
Bugg Sarah, beer seller	Scanes John	JOINERS, &c.
Copplestone John, farrier	COOPERS.	Harvey Robert
Densham Wm. vict. New Inn	Addiscott John	Scanes Samuel &
Erle Rev J. Henry, LL.B. incumbent	Knott Wm.	Jno. (whlgts.)
Honeywill Thomas, schoolmaster	FARMERS.	Shobrook Wm.
Howard Wm. horsebreaker	Carige Thomas	MASONS.
Simpson Wm. surgeon	CopplestoneCphr	Lang George
Slocombe George, corn miller	Copplestone Jas.	Williams Wm.
Terrell John Hull, Esq. solr. *Priory*	Dicker George	Yeo Richard
Tozer Samuel, vict. Huntsman's Inn	DrakeJohn,*Fordlands*	SHOPKEEPERS.
Walkey John Elliott Collyns,solicitor,		Harvey E.
Pole House (and Exeter)	Follett Henry	Hill Elizabeth
BAKERS.	Leak Wm.	Paris Thomas
Nicholls Wm.	BOOT & SHOEMRS.	Milton Matthew	
Richards Joseph	Day Wm.	Milton Thomas	POST OFFICE
BLACKSMITHS.	Lee Wm.	MortimoreRichd.	at Crnls. Chapman's. Letters
Casely John	Reed Richard	Nicholls Thomas	desp. to Exeter
Shobrook John	Rugg James	Scott James	6 evening
Shobrook Wm.	Tucker Samuel	Tucker Joseph	
	Vaughan Wm.		

KENN, or *Kenne,* is a long village, including *Kennford,* pleasantly situated in a picturesque valley on the banks of a rivulet, four miles S. by E. of Exeter. It gives name to a *deanery,* and its parish contains 1078 inhabitants and 5316A. of land, rising in a bold range of hills on the south west side of the valley, where are the handsome seats of *Haldon, Woodlands,* and *Trehill,* commanding fine views over the vale of the Exe. Kennford had a grant of a market and fair in 1299, but both have been obsolete some centuries. The manor of Kenn, formerly held by the Courtenay, Oxenham, Acland, and other families, was purchased about 30 years ago, by Sir L. V. Palk, Bart., of HALDON HOUSE, a large and handsome stuccoed mansion, in a finely wooded park, on a commanding eminence, upon the summit of which are a number of barrows or *tumuli,* in which urns and Roman coins have been found. This mansion was built in 1735, by Sir Geo. Chudleigh, Bart., and was purchased in 1769, by the late *Sir Robert Palk,* who was created a *baronet* in 1782, and greatly improved the house and grounds. The house contains an extensive library and a fine collection of paintings, and commands delightful views. The ornamental grounds are extensive, and the plantations which crown the summits of the hills cover many acres. In the centre of Pen hill rises a castellated building of three stories, called the *Belvidere,* or *Lawrence Castle,* erected by the late Sir Robert Palk, in

memory of his friend *General Lawrence*, whose statue, as large as life, on a
pedestal of black marble, ornaments the entrance. This gallant general
was buried at Dunchideock, as noticed at page 405. The view from the
mountainous ridge of *Haldon Hill*, is grand and extensive, comprising the
whole course of the Exe from Exeter to the sea, and the hills and woodlands
as far as Honiton and the borders of Somersetshire. On the higher ground
of Haldon is *Exeter Race Course*, now but little used. *Woodlands*, a large
and handsome mansion, with sylvan grounds, is the seat of Wm. Ley, Esq.;
and *Trehill*, another handsome mansion, with woody grounds, commanding
delightful views, is the seat of J. H. Ley, Esq., who has a large estate in the
parish, purchased by his family in 1745, and formerly belonging to the
Waltham, Savery, and other families. *Perridge*, a detached member of this
parish, is noticed at page 196. F. B. Short, Esq., owns *Bickham*, and a few
smaller freeholders have estates in the parish. The *Church* (St. Andrew,)
is a large ancient structure, with a tower and six bells, and has several neat
monuments. The *rectory*, valued in K.B. at £46. 13s. 4d., and in 1831 at
£778, is in the patronage of J. H. Ley, Esq., and incumbency of the Rev.
Henry Ley, B.A., who has a good residence and 197A. 2R. 23P. of glebe.
The tithes were commuted in 1842, for £763. 10s. per annum. Here was
anciently a chantry chapel, dedicated to St. John; and *Carswell* farm was
formerly held by one of the prebendaries of the chapel at Exeter Castle.
(See page 73.) The *National School*, at Kennford, with a house for the
teacher, was built in 1849. The poor parishioners have 48s. a year from
Hensley's Charity. (See Exeter.) By grant from James I., the poor parishioners hold the Anchor Inn, at Kennford, and an orchard of three roods,
let for about £30 a year, which is applied with the poor rates. In the following *Directory*, those marked * are at *Kennford*, and the others at *Kenn*,
or where specified.

Anstey John Page, parish clerk
Badcock John, relieving officer
*Bassett George, plumber & glazier
*Day James, vict. Anchor Inn
*Day James Barham, farrier
Dormer Charles, Esq. *Perridge*
Down Richard, vict. Palk's Arms
*Irwin Wm. cooper
Ley John Henry, Esq. *Trehill*
Ley Rev Henry, B.A. *Rectory*
Ley Wm. Esq. *Woodlands*
Mayne Wm. builder
*Murch John, vict. Seven Stars
Payne H. & Spurway L. schoolmrs
Palk Sir Lawrence Vaughan, Bart.
   Haldon House
*Page John, carpenter
*Parr Mr Thomas || Vooght Mrs
Pitts Richard, miller, *Fell Mills*
Short Fras. Baring, Esq. *Bickham Hs*
*Towill Wm. baker || Stokes Rd. sex
  BEERHOUSES.
*Liddon Wm.

BLACKSMITHS.
*Eddy John
Job Sarah
*Mallett Henry
*Warren Hy. wlgt
*Wilcocks John
BOOT & SHOE MKS.
Wills John
Wills Wm.
BUTCHERS.
*Lear Benjamin
*Smith Nicholas
Smith Richard
FARMERS.
Anstey John
Badcock Wm.
Brook George
Cornish James
Cornish Mary Ann
Dewdney Wm.
*Hutchings Wm.
Lear John
Smith Richard

Lovesy Wm. C.
Page Wm.
Palk Geo. *Haldon*
Pitts Frederick
*Pitts Thomas
Rowe Jno. *Carswl.*
Snow John
Tapper George
Walters Nancy
GARDENERS.
Powell Wm.
Tolman Thomas
SHOPKEEPERS.
*Brenton Wm.
Cousins Mary
Job Sarah
TAILORS.
Down Wm.
*Holman Daniel
*Reed Joseph

POST *from Exeter*

KENTON is a pleasant village, in the picturesque valley of the small
river Kenn, opposite the woody grounds of Powderham Castle, and about a
mile W. of the estuary of the Exe, and 7 miles S.S.E. of Exeter. Its parish
extends westward to the lofty range of the Haldon Hills, and comprises

5400 acres of land, including the hamlets of *South Town, Cofford, Fenbridge, Staplake, Lyston, Cheverstone, Wilsworthy, West Town,* and *East Town;* and the large village of STARCROSS, which, with an adjacent part of Dawlish parish, has lately been formed, ecclesiastically, a district parish, as afterwards noticed. The population of the parish in 1841 comprised 2313 souls, of whom 936 were in Starcross. Kenton had formerly a market and fair, granted by Henry III., but they have long been obsolete. The Earl of Devon owns a great part of the parish and is lord of the *manor*, which was a demesne of the Crown till the reign of Henry III. *Oxton House,* a large and handsome mansion with extensive pleasure grounds, on the hill, about 1½ mile W. of Kenton, is the seat of J. Beaumont Swete, Esq., who has a large estate here, and another mansion called *Staplake House.* There are several other neat mansions in the parish, and Sir R. L. Newman, Bart., and several smaller proprietors have estates here. A *court leet and baron* for the Earl of Devon's manors in this neighbourhood, is held at Starcross; and S. T. Kekewick, Esq., is the receiver; and Mr. John Drew, jun., the land agent. *Kenton Church* (All Saints,) is a large and handsome building of red stone, with a lofty tower, containing six bells. It is supposed to have been built in the reign of Edward III., and was repaired about six years ago, when six new windows were inserted. The exterior was formerly adorned with many statues, some of which still remain. A gorgeous screen separates the nave and chancel. Round the entrance gates are sculptured figures of the twelve apostles, and on the panels below the rich open work, are painted figures of saints with numerous labels. The Dean and Chapter of Salisbury are appropriators of the rectory, and patrons of the *vicarage,* valued in K.B. at £34. 13s. 4d., and in 1831 at £265, and now in the incumbency of the Rev. A. L. Dames, M.A., who has a good residence with tasteful grounds. The tithes were commuted in 1842, the rectorial for £460, and the vicarial for £380 per annum. The *Church House,* given by Edward VI., is let for about £8, which is carried to the churchwardens' accounts. At West Town is an old dwelling, which was formerly an ancient chapel dedicated to St. Ann. Here is a *National School,* established in 1838. The poor parishioners have the dividends of £127.8s.2d. three per cent. stock, purchased with various benefactions. They have also the dividends of £100 navy five per cents., left by Jonathan Fyrer, in 1819. The *Wesleyans* have a chapel at Kenton, built about 20 years ago.

STARCROSS, a large and well built village, pleasantly situated on the west side of the broad estuary of the Exe, opposite Exmouth, is distant 8 miles S.S.E. of Exeter, and has a *station* on the South Devon Railway, which runs close to the estuary. It is in Kenton parish, and had 936 inhabitants in 1841, but it has now more than 1200. A few years ago, it was celebrated only for its *cockles* and *oysters,* but it has lately been much improved, and is assuming a genteel appearance, and aspiring to the title of a watering place. Many persons resort to it in the summer season, who cannot bear the stronger sea air of the coast. It had its name from a cross, which formerly stood near the landing place, on the bank of the estuary. The Courtenay Arms is a large respectable inn, and has a spacious room, in which balls and assemblies are held at the time of the Regatta. The principal lodging houses face the estuary, and command pleasing views of the opposite shore. There is a pleasure fair in the village on Whit-Wednesday. *Exeleigh House,* a large and handsome stone mansion, built in 1847-'8, is the seat of *Sir J. L. Duntze, Bart.,* whose grandfather, Sir John Duntze, of Rockbeare, was created a baronet in 1774, and was a wealthy merchant of Exeter. *Starcross Church* (St. Paul,) is a small neat structure, which was built in 1826-'7, as a chapel of ease, but it has recently been

constituted a *District Church,* for Starcross and the adjacent parts of Dawlish parish, comprising *Cockwood, Eastdon, Cofton, &c.* The church has about 700 sittings, of which 350 are free. It has two bells and a fine toned organ. The living is a *perpetual curacy,* valued at £120 per annum, in the alternate patronage of the Deans and Chapters of Exeter and Salisbury, and incumbency of the Rev. Wm. Powley, M.A., who is also incumbent of *Cofton Chapel,* a neat ancient building in Dawlish parish, which, after being in a ruinous state more than 70 years, was repaired in 1839, by the Earl of Devon, the patron of the curacy. It is within the *District Parish of Starcross,* which has a National School, with a dwelling for the teachers, built in 1839.

KENTON.
*(Marked * are in South Town.)*

Anstey J. parish clerk
*Burdon John, surgeon
Cole Thomas, draper
Collings Wm. ‖ Potter Joseph
*Courtenay Mrs and Misses
Dames Rev Arthur Longworth, M.A. vicar, *Vicarage*
HazellChas.brewer &vict.DevonArms
Jones Hy. & Wood My. *Natl. School*
Pitt Edward, saddler & ironmonger
Pycroft George, surgeon
Russell Mrs Ellen, *Court Hall*
Salter Savory Cyrus, druggist
Sercombe George, basket maker
Shapter John, vict. Dolphin Inn
Swete John Beaumont, Esq. *Oxton*
Taylor John, gardener, &c.
Towell John, carpenter
Towell Wm. organist
*Voysey John, watchmaker, &c.
White Wm. cabinet mkr. & plumber
*Wilcocks Wm. vict. Castle Inn
*Wood Joseph, wheelwright

BAKERS.
Anning Thomas
Pearse John
*Wilcocks Abm.
BLACKSMITHS.
Cowell John
*Cruse John
Saunders George
BOOT & SHOE MRS.
*Bradford George
*Edgecombe W.
Fryer John
Gulley Wm.
Paddon George
BUTCHERS.
Anning Charles
Searle John
Southwood John

FARMERS.
Anning James
Anning Mrs
Anning Henry
Beer Wm.
*Bidgood Nichls.
*Brackney Thos.
Haydon Wm.
Hartwell Wm.
Ireland George
Mortimore John
Paul Philip
Rossiter John
Smith Geo. jun.
Splatt Richard
Townsend John, *Cofford*
*West Wm.

GROCERS, &c.
Davies Daniel
French W., miller
Jeffrey Rose
Teague Benj.
TAILORS.
Heale Robert

Reallick Thos.
Snell Samuel
POST-OFFICE at Hugh Ford's.
Lettersdesp.6¼ evg. *via* Exeter

STARCROSS. (DIST. PARISH.)
*(Marked * are in Dawlish Parish.)*

Adams Joseph, schoolmaster
Anderson John, gent. *Warren House*
Anning Wm. mercht. & ship owner
Ash Hy. B. coal mert. & ship owner
Ash Wm. merchant & ship owner
Bendall Geo. Hy. supt. Rail. Station
Bell Mrs Sarah ‖ Collier Mr G. R.
Bishop Wm. R. solicitor, (&*Exeter*)
*Brock R. lime burner, Cockwood
Causey Thos. Anthony, gent. *Warren*
Corneck Lieut. Hy. A., R.N., *Gn. Cot.*
Creasy Wm. cooper
Dickens John, Esq. *Langston Cliff*
Distin Misses ‖ Dondiele Mr B.
Duntze Sir John Lewis, Bart., *Exleigh House*
*Eales Rd., Esq. *Eastdon House*
Fletcher John, church clerk
Fox Jemima, oyster & cockle dealer
Geare John, solr. *Southbrook House*
Glendening Jno.& Harris Thos. gents
*Hind Mr Wm. Hy., *Eastdon*
Hoare Wm. & Woolcott My. school
Howell Frederick, master mariner
Howell Wm. chemist & druggist
Kingdon Mr Robt. ‖Knowles Mrs A.
Lott Mrs Caroline, *Franklin Cottage*
Parker Mrs H. ‖ Peek J. milliner
Pentecost Richd. painter & glazier
Powley Mr John, organist
Powley Rev Wm., M.A., incumbent, *Beach House*
Ralph John, gent. ‖ Rendell Mrs
Shell James, mason and slater

*Snow Jane, *Cockwood School*
St. Leger Rev Rd. Arthur, curate
Southwood James, bookseller & libn
Steer Bartholomew J. S. gent.
Swete Hy. B., Esq. *Staplake House*
Toby Mrs Ann ‖ Upham Mr John
Towell Jane, beer seller
Weeks Susannah, lodgings
White James, bricklayer
Wood Joseph, blacksmith

INNS & TAVERNS.
Courtenay Arms, James Southwood
Eagle, Wm. Wood
Jolly Sailor, James Tapp
*Mount Pleasant, John Tolley
Railway Hotel, Emanuel Saunders
Ship, Wm. Uglar
*Ship, Charles Coombe, *Cockwood*

BAKERS.
Anning John
Davey George
Woolcott John
Winsbrough Jas.

BOOT& SHOE MRS.
Cornelius Daniel,
(ferryman)
Gloyn Wm.
Mills Wm.

Voysey Wm.
Westcott John
Woolcott John

BUTCHERS.
Anning Charles
Southwood John

DRAPERS.
Martin Isabella
Morrish James

GROCERS, &c.
Anning John
Davey George
England Wm.
Mitchell Ann
Stocks Ann

GARDENERS.
Dally John
Discombe John

JOINERS& BLDRS.
Ash Charles
*Baker Wm.
Brock —
Fletcher John

Fox Wm.

TAILORS.
Bridgman Wm.
England Wm.
Smale Robert

POST OFFICE
atWm.Howell's.
Letters desp. 2
aft. & 6 evg. *via*
Exeter

RAILWAY.
Trains 6 times a
day to Exeter,
Plymouth, &c.
Ferry to Exmouth

CARRIER.
Jph. Bartin, to
Exeter daily,
except Sun. &
Thursday

MAMHEAD is a small parish of scattered houses, chiefly on the western acclivities of a bold eminence, 3 miles W. of Starcross, and 4 miles E. by N. of Chudleigh. It has 246 inhabitants, and 1220 acres of land, mostly the property and manor of *Sir R. L. Newman, Bart.*, whose father was created a baronet in 1836. He resides at *Mamhead Park*, which has a large and handsome mansion in the Elizabethan style, erected about 20 years ago on the site of the old house, which was mostly built by Sir Peter Balle, an eminent loyalist who died in 1680, aged 82. It was afterwards the seat of the two last Earls of Lisburne. The house stands on a rising knoll at the junction of three narrow valleys, opening towards the coast, and backed with a high woody ridge of Haldon. The great variety of ground appertaining to this sweetly sequestered mansion, with the extensive umbrageous woods, devious paths, and charming prospects of sea and land, unite in rendering it beautifully picturesque and interesting. On the lofty woody summit of Mamhead Point, stands a noble *obelisk* of Portland stone, built by Thos. Balle, Esq., about 1742. The *Church* stands in the park, and is a neat structure with a tower and five bells. The *rectory*, valued in K.B. at £10. 17s. 6d., and in 1831 at £206, is in the patronage of Sir R. L. Newman, Bart., and incumbency of the Hon. and Rev. H. H. Courtenay, M.A., who has a good residence and 20A. of glebe. The tithes were commuted in 1842 for £145 per annum. The poor parishioners have £8. 1s. 7d. yearly from the Mercer's Company, London, left by *Giles Martin*, in 1613.

Courtenay Hon. and Rev. Hy. Hugh,
M.A. *Rectory*
Newman Sir Robert Lydston, Bart.
Mamhead Park
Babbage James, parish clerk
Hall Geo. wheelwright & blacksmith

FARMERS. *(* are Owners.)*
Adams Wm., *Newhouse*
*Ellis John Atwell, *Pitts*
*Ellis Richard, *Gulliford*
Howard Peter, *Larkbear*
Wills Richard, *Whistley*

POWDERHAM is a picturesque parish of scattered houses on the western side of the broad estuary of the Exe, opposite Lympstone, 6 miles

S.S.E. of Exeter, and 2 miles N. of Starcross Railway Station. It contains 318 inhabitants, and 1452A. 1R. 26P. of land, belonging to the Earl of Devon, of POWDERHAM CASTLE, which stands in an extensive and well-wooded deer park, which rises in bold swelling hills between and near the confluence of the Exe and the Kenn, the latter of which is a small stream falling into the estuary at the southern point of the parish. Camden states that Powderham Castle was built by Isabella de Redvers, Countess of Devon, who died in 1293, but it has been clearly ascertained that it never belonged to her, but to the Bohuns, Earls of Hereford and Essex, under whom it was held by the Powderham family. Towards the middle of the 14th century, it passed to Margaret Bohun, wife of *Hugh Courtenay, Earl of Devon*, who died in 1377; and it still belongs to the same ancient and noble family, of whom a genealogical sketch is already given in the general survey of the county, where it will be seen they have suffered many vicissitudes of fortune. Powderham was anciently described as a strong castle, with a barbican for the protection of the estuary of the Exe. The Castle was probably built either before the Norman Conquest, to prevent the Danes from coming up the river to Exeter; or else by William de Ou, a noble Norman, to whom the Conqueror gave Powderham. The Castle was garrisoned for the King in the early part of the struggle between Charles I. and the Parliament, and was long an object of contention between the two parties; changing hands twice or thrice during the war. When last in possession of the royalists, it was more strongly fortified than before, having at that time eighteen pieces of ordnance mounted on its walls. Since then, it has undergone many alterations in order to adapt it to the requirements of a modern mansion; but it still retains in some degree a castellated appearance, having battlements on its towers and pediments. Until 1752, it retained a considerable portion of its ancient castle-like form, and had a quadrangular court in front, with embattled walls and a tower gateway at the entrance. Its exterior has now a modern appearance, and the interior has many spacious apartments sumptuously furnished, and decorated with numerous valuable productions of art. Among many fine paintings are "The Tribute Money," by Rubens; "The Five Senses," by Teniers; and full lengths of Charles II. and Queen Henrietta Maria, by Vandyck. The Park is very extensive, and is finely planted with trees and shrubs, and diversified with some bold swells. The present noble proprietor has recently spent several thousand pounds in improving the house and grounds. On the summit of the highest ground is a triangular building with three hexagonal towers, called the *Belvidere*, constructed for the purpose of commanding the rich and diversified prospects of the sea, the river Exe, and the surrounding country. This ornamental building was erected in 1773, and is about 60 feet in height to the top of the towers. The park, gardens, and plantations, belonging to this domain extend through a circumference of nearly ten miles, and the pleasure grounds behind the house are replete with a great variety of flowers and botanical rarities. The CHURCH *(St. Clement,)* is an ancient structure, with a tower and three bells, and has recently been renovated and beautified, chiefly at the expense of the Earl of Devon. In the chancel is a fine tomb in memory of the late Countess. Some of the windows have been enriched with stained glass, and the nave and aisles have been newly fitted up with open seats. The *rectory*, valued in K.B. at £27. 3s. 6½d., and in 1831 at £493, is in the patronage of the Earl of Devon, and incumbency of the Rev. Danl. Nantes, M.A., who has 91A. 3R. 28P. of glebe, and a handsome residence with beautiful grounds, overlooking the estuary. The tithes were commuted in 1839 for £298 per annum. The *National School* is supported

by the Earl and the children's pence; and the poor parishioners have 60s. a year out of Newland estate at Exminster, left by John Fletcher, in 1714.

Rt. Hon. Wm. Courtenay, EARL OF DEVON and VISCOUNT COURTENAY, *Powderham Castle*
Hon. Viscount Courtenay, ditto
Drew John, jun. land agent, ditto
Nantes Rev Danl. M.A. *Rectory*

Addiscott Thomas, shoemaker
Bean Mr Henry, Park Cottage
Cornelius Richard, parish clerk
FARMERS, Henry Baker, Wm. Discombe, John Frost, Thos. Frost, and John Mortimore

SHILLINGFORD ST. GEORGE, 3½ miles S. by W. of Exeter, is a small parish in the Kenn valley, sheltered on the south by the lofty Haldon Hill, and containing only 72 souls, and 890 acres of land, belonging to Sir L. V. Palk, the lord of the manor and patron of the *rectory*, which is consolidated with that of Dunchideock, as noticed at page 405. The incumbent has here a good residence. The *Church* has a tower and one bell, and has recently been repaired and beautified.

Bradford Robert, carpenter
Bright Sarah, schoolmistress
Crispin George, blacksmith

Palk Rev Hy., B.C.L. rector of Bridford, Dunchideock, & Shillingfd.
Lear Richard and Wm. farmers

TEIGNMOUTH is a well-built market town, seaport, and bathing place, delightfully situated on the north side of the mouth of the navigable river Teign, partly upon the triangular point of land which projects half way across the estuary, and has the English Channel on one side, and the river on the other; and partly around the bottom and on the acclivities of the hill which rises gradually from the point to the north-west, one side commanding a fine view of the sea, and the other of the river. It is in the two small parishes of *East* and *West Teignmouth*, and is crossed by the South Devon Railway, which winds in a circuitous route along the coast and the north side of the estuary. It is distant about 14 miles S. of Exeter by rails, and 12 by road; 5 miles E. by N. of Newton Abbot, 8 miles N. by E. of Torquay, and 187 miles W.S.W. of London. It increased its population from 2012 in 1801, to 4459 in 1844, and has now about 5500 inhabitants, exclusive of its suburbs of *Shaldon* and *Ringmore*, on the opposite side of the river, and *Bishop's Teignton*, which joins it on the west. (See pages 197 and 396.) EAST TEIGNMOUTH parish contains 670 acres, and had only 484 inhabitants in 1801, but they had increased to 1576 in 1841. WEST TEIGNMOUTH is divided from it only by a small brook, and contains 403 acres of land, and increased its inhabitants from 1528 in 1801, to 2883 in 1841. The Earl of Devon is lord of the *manor* of East Teignmouth, and Lord Clifford of West Teignmouth, the former of which was long held by the Dean and Chapter of Exeter, and the latter by the Bishops of Exeter. The former granted East Teignmouth a charter for a market and fair, in 1253. West Teignmouth was a celebrated haven at an early period, the river being then navigable for large ships, and having no shifting bar at the entrance. It sent members to the council held at Westminster in the reign of Edward I., and furnished seven ships and 120 mariners for the fleet of Edward III. The town was partly burnt by a French pirate, in 1340, and experienced a similar misfortune in

1690, from several ships that were detached for that purpose from the French fleet, then drawn up in Torbay. To repair the injury sustained by this attack, the inhabitants procured a brief, which enabled them to raise upwards of £11,000 towards rebuilding their houses. In 1774, the inhabitants of Teignmouth and Shaldon presented a petition to Sir Wm. Courtenay, stating that the French had plundered and burnt the place, in the second year of William and Mary, and that they then threatened a second visit; they, therefore, petitioned him to allow them to build a small battery on the beach, at East Teignmouth, where it still exists. At this time, Teignmouth and Shaldon fitted 20 ships, of from 50 to 200 tons each, for the Newfoundland trade. A port-reeve and other officers are appointed for each manor at the courts leet and baron, held annually. Teignmouth belongs to the *Port of Exeter*, (see p. 63 & 71,) and has still a large trade with Newfoundland, and a considerable home *fishery* for whitings, herrings, mackerel, pilchards, soles, turbot, &c., caught in the channel; and for salmon caught in the river. It also exports great quantities of *granite*, brought down the Teign from the Haytor quarries; and of fine *pipe and potter's clay*, dug up in the neighbouring parish of King's Teignton. A commodious *quay* on the river was constructed in 1820, by Geo. Templer, Esq., for the convenience of shipping these heavy articles. A convenient *market place* was erected about the same time; and the market, held every Saturday, is well supplied with all sorts of provisions. Here are three annual *fairs* for cattle, &c., on the third Tuesday in January, the last Tuesday in February, and the last Tuesday in September. *Races* and a *Regatta* are held every summer. In the latter part of last century, Teignmouth began to be known as a *bathing place*, and from that time to the present, new houses, &c., have arisen to supply the accommodations of the continually increasing number of visitors, who throng to this favourite place of resort in summer and autumn. The visitant can here choose a locality embracing scenery adapted to his taste. On the Den, or Beach, he will have the " ocean wide, the broad expanse, with towering cliff and shelving shore;" and on the hills the same, with the addition of the town as a foreground; but should his taste incline inland, the north-western end of the town will afford him a magnificent prospect up the Teign and over the country, as far as the high and bold hills of Haytor, Dartmoor, &c. An *Act of Parliament* was obtained in 1836 for the improvement of the town, and, under it, many improvements have been effected, and others are in progress. A good supply of spring *water* has been brought from Haldon hill to a large reservoir, whence it is passed in iron pipes to all parts of the town. *Gas* was introduced in 1840, from the works a mile west of the town, in Bishop's Teignton parish. The *Bridge* which crosses the Teign to Shaldon is the longest in England, and was built in 1826-7, by a company of proprietors, at the cost of about £20,000. It is 1671 feet long, and is composed chiefly of iron and wood. There are 34 arches, and a draw-bridge over the deepest part of the channel. From the action of the salt water on the iron, the principal arch gave way in 1838, but the whole was repaired in a

durable manner, and the bridge was re-opened in 1840. Foot passengers pay 1d. each, and it was a great thoroughfare for carriages, &c., but its traffic has been considerably reduced since the opening of the *railway*, though the latter goes round by the north shore of the estuary. The small *light-house*, on the Den, was built in 1844-5, at the cost of £300, by the Teignmouth Harbour Commissioners. The custom-house officers have an office on the Den, and the excise office is at the Devon Arms. *Petty Sessions* are held every alternate Monday, at the *Court-House*, and Edw. Croydon & Son are clerks to the magistrates. The town has many well-stocked shops, many rows of handsome houses, and several large and commodious hotels. The *beach* is composed of fine sand, and can be used at any state of the tide. The inclination of the shore is gradual, and the bather can use either deep or shallow water. The climate is mild and salubrious, and there are many instances of longevity among the inhabitants. The delightful promenade along the Den is more than half a mile long, running parallel to the sea, and having seats at convenient distances. It commands an extensive view of the ocean, and the Ness and the cliff on the west, and the Parson-and-Clerk rocks on the east. The walks and rides in the neighbourhood are beautifully diversified and picturesque, and in the suburbs are many handsome seats. *Bitton House*, with its beautiful grounds on the West Cliff, is the seat of W. M. Praed, Esq. *Winterbourn House* is the pleasant residence of the Rev. Dr. Richards. About a mile to the north-west, over Haldon hill, is "*The Hennons*," a large and handsome mansion, in the Elizabethan style, built by Rd. Eaton, Esq., but purchased by its present owner and occupant, Wm. B. King, Esq., in 1838. The lodge and stables are in the same style as the mansion, and the grounds command extensive and beautiful views of sea and land, and are laid out with great taste. In the dining room are some fine paintings by eminent artists, and in the drawing room is a richly carved mantel-piece, which is much admired. A *Building Company* has lately been formed in the town, for the purpose of building houses and detached villas, to accommodate the large influx of company which the opening of the railway has introduced. The *Public Baths*, on the beach, are conveniently fitted up with hot, cold, and shower baths. The *Subscription Rooms*, in the centre of the Crescent, on the Den, facing the sea, form an elegant structure, built in 1826, and containing a handsome ball room, 70 feet long, and tea, card, billiard, and news rooms. The *Theatre*, in Northumberland place, was built in 1847-8, at the cost of about £1000. Here is an *Useful Knowledge Society, National and Sunday Schools*, and various charities and institutions for the relief and the religious instruction of the poor. *Teignmouth and Dawlish Dispensary* was established in 1848. by Fdk. Leman, Esq., and is supported by annual subscriptions and donations. It has usually a long list of out-patients, and has accommodations for a few in-patients. Fdk. Leman, of Teignmouth, and J. F. Knighton, of Dawlish, are the surgeons, and their services are rendered gratuitous to this useful charity.

CHURCHES:—In 1815 *an act of parliament* was passed for rebuilding the churches of East and West Teignmouth, and for authorizing the sale of the *church lands, &c.*, belonging to both parishes. This act recites that the expense of rebuilding East Teignmouth church was estimated at £2200, and West Teignmouth church, at £5400; and that the inhabitants of each parish had agreed to raise the sum of £1000 towards such respective expenses. The cost of obtaining the act of parliament amounted to no less than £1760. 3s. 9d.; of which £744. 8s. 11d. was paid by East Teignmouth, and £1015. 14s. 10d. by West Teignmouth. The church lands, &c., which belonged to East Teignmouth, were sold for £1340, and those belonging to West Teignmouth for about £3900. *East Teignmouth Church* (St. Michael,) was rebuilt in 1822-3, and is a neat cruciform structure, with a tower containing a clock and bell. The interior is well arranged, and has a finely carved altar-piece, over which is a painting of Christ, crowned with thorns. The *perpetual curacy*, valued in K.B. at £11. 18s., and in 1831 at £135, is in the patronage of the Vicar of Dawlish, and incumbency of the Rev. W. P. Richards, D.C.L. There is neither glebe nor parsonage, and the great tithes are in the same appropriation as those of Dawlish, to which East Teignmouth was formerly a parochial chapelry. In 1769, Amy Newberry left a tenement, and directed the rent to be applied in buying plate, &c., for the communion table. Being dilapidated, it was let some years ago at a small reserved rent. *West Teignmouth Church* (St. James,) was rebuilt about the same time, at the cost of more than £4000. It is a large octagonal structure, possessing in its outward character very little attraction. The interior, although of a novel and singular appearance, has some pretensions to architectural taste; the slender pillars supporting a richly vaulted ceiling, from the middle of which rises an octagon dome lantern, produce a good effect. It has about 2000 sittings, and a tower containing a clock and four bells. The living is a *perpetual curacy*, valued at £157, in the patronage of the Vicar of Bishop's Teignton, and incumbency of the Rev. L. Gwyne, M.A. There is neither glebe nor parsonage, and the parish was formerly a chapelry to Bishop's Teignton. About 3½ miles N.W. of the town are the venerable ruins of *Lithwell* or *Lidwell Chapel*, where a villainous priest, popularly called *St. Simon*, is said in a *legendary tale* of the 16th century, to have committed many murders on the surrounding heath, for the sake of hoarding up gold in a secret chest under the altar, at the foot of which was a deep well, in which he is said to have buried his victims. This chapel was in Dawlish parish, and the well may still be seen in the middle of the ruined walls, covered with a large granite slab.

In the town are four chapels belonging to *Roman Catholics, Independents, Wesleyans*, and *Plymouth Brethren*. That belonging to the Wesleyans was built in 1845, at the cost of about £1500, in lieu of their old chapel, which was taken down to make room for the railway. That belonging to the Plymouth Brethren was built by Baptists, about 25 years ago. For schooling poor children, East Teignmouth has the dividends of £110, South Sea Stock, left by *Thomas and John Coleman*. In West Teignmouth was a small almshouse, called the *Maudlin House*, which was anciently a *lepers' hospital*, and afterwards the asylum of poor parishioners, but it fell down many years ago, and its site is now a garden. It was endowed with an adjacent field of 2A., now let for about £10, and with a house at Newton Abbot, let for 21s. per annum. These rents are applied to the relief of the poor parishioners, as also are five annuities of 2s. each. The interest of £15. 10s., left to the poor by *Sir Peter Lear and others*, is paid out of the poor rates. *Sir John Elwill and his Son* left £150 to be invested for the schooling of poor children of East and West Teignmouth. This money was invested in

three per cent. consols, yielding £8. 14s. 7d. per annum, for which 12 poor children are instructed by a schoolmistress. A house and land at Bitton, given to the poor of West Teignmouth, by *Mary Risdon*, in 1718, have been sold for £180, which is vested with the overseers, who distribute the interest among the poor not receiving parochial relief.

TEIGNMOUTH DIRECTORY.

The Post-Office is in Bank street, and Mr. John Wreyford is the postmaster. The box closes for London, Exeter, &c., at 10 minutes past 7 night; for the North and West of England at 55 minutes past 12 night; and for Newton, Torquay, Plymouth, &c., at 35 minutes past 10 morning. Money orders granted and paid.

(For *Shaldon and Ringmore* see page 197, and for *Bishop's Teignton* see page 397.)

In the following Directory, those marked 1 *reside in Bank street;* 2 *Bitton street;* 3 *Brunswick place;* 4 *Carlton place;* 5 *Commercial row;* 6 *Courtenay row;* 7 *Dawlish road;* 8 *Exeter road;* 9 *Fore st.;* 10 *Hollands row;* 11 *Lower Brook st.;* 12 *Market;* 13 *Myrtle hill;* 14 *New Market street;* 15 *Northumberland place;* 16 *Old Market street;* 17 *Parson st.;* 18 *Quay;* 19 *Regent place;* 20 *Station road;* 21 *Strand;* 22 *Somerset place;* 23 *Triangle place;* 24 *Upper Brook street;* 25 *Wellington row;* & 26 *Westcliffe.*

Abbott Hon Mr., *Landscore Villa*
Acland Arthur H. Dyke, Esq
Adams Miss Eliza F., Clifton Cotg.
2 Arscott John, sexton of St James's
Atkinson Mr Wm., Bella vista
Bartlett Jacob Bickford, surgeon, *Brimley Villa*
2 Bartlett John, gent. & 14 Mrs Eliz.
26 Beard Mrs Chltte. || Betts Mr W.
4 Beard Mrs Eliz. & Mr John
15 Beater John, rope maker, and registrar of marriages
Beer George, manager *Gas works*
46 Bell Thomas C., civil engineer
13 Bellecour Mons. & Madmsl.
2 Bickford Rd. assistant overseer
25 Biggs Wm. brush maker
11 Blackstone Capt. James
2 Blandford Mr John || 6 Brine Miss
7 Bloxham John, dairyman
16 Bowler John, letter carrier
25 Bradbeer Jph. & Son, brush mks.
Bradley Rev. Richard Beadon, M.A., curate, Hope cottage
18 Bulley George and Collihole Rd. sail makers
Camden Goodridge, Esq., Den Cres.
10 Campbell James, railway inspr.
16 Carpenter Esther, furrier
Cartwright Herbert, Esq. Brimley H.
7 Champernoune Mrs Margaret
Channon E. vety. surgeon, Sack st
Chetwynd Viscount, *Crescent*
11 Churchill Wm. dyer

16 Clapp Mr. Thomas
16 Cole Mr Geo. & 17 John, colr.
1 Collings Geo. sub-distr. of stamps
Copp John, Esq. Dawlish road
Cornelius Mrs Chtte., Bella-vista
15 Coster Mr John Wm.
7 Cousins Mr. Samuel
Cresswell Rev Rd., M.A., Bitton hill
15 Croydon Mrs || 7 Cousins Mrs
Croydon Edw. & Geo. Hy., clerks to magistrates & inspector of weights and measures, &c.
Cunningham Mr James, Clifton ctg.
Curtis Geo. Savage, Esq. *East Cliff*
Day John, tide waiter, Den
Davis G. boat owner, Queen street
Dyee Mrs Clara, Grove Cottage
22 Elliott Rd. Percy, gent.
12 Endicott Hy. eating house
24 Fisher Wm. Fras. gent.
Fulls Richard, coffee house, New st
16 Frome Mrs Georgiana
22 Gater Thomas, glass & china dlr.
16 Goodenough Wm. cooper and porter merchant
Goodridge John Camden, Esq., Cres
Gossett Col. Wm. M., Cliffden
Griffith Lieutenant Smyth, R.N., chief officer Coast Guard, Den
9 Griffith Mr Wm.
7 Gwyne Rev Lwnce., M.A., incbt. of West Teignmouth
7 Hannaford Mrs Sarah
Hallett Miss Car. *Albert House*

s 3

Hammersley Mrs. *Coombe Villa*
25 Harris Mr Thos. || 15 Hughes J.
Haswell Mrs & Miss, Luny House
15 Hatherly Mrs Mary and Miss
Hicks Mr Thomas, Langton place
15 Hoare John, cooper
Hockings Wm. Subsptn. Rooms
Holdway John, revenue officer
Hood James, railway clerk
Hupton Mrs Car., Esplanade House
Hunt Mr Finch, Northumberland pl
11 Hutchings John, tallow chandler
Hutchings Thos. propr. of baths
Hutton Chas. toll colr. Bridge
21 Jenkins Wm. block & pump mkr.
Kelson Chas. Esq., Hennon House
2 Kidston John, nail maker
King Wm.Brooks,Esq., *The Hennons*
Lake Mrs Eliz., *Clampit House*
16 Larkworthy Geo. glass, &c. dlr.
9 Lee Miss Jane || 8 Lusty Mrs H.
2 Lemon John, marine store dealer
Lomax Rev Chas. (Catholic priest)
7 Mackenzie John Henry, Esq. solr.
9 Mardon Joseph, currier
Maxton Lwnce Malcolm, customs
Medland Wm. stoker, *Gas Works*
2 Meik Captain Francis Thomas
Middlewick Fras. supervisor
16 Miller Mr. William
26 Moir Robert, Esq
26 Mitchell Mrs || 2 Morgan Miss F.
24 Mogridge John, town crier
Mudge Col., Spring Gardens
8 Narrowman Mrs Ann || Payne Mr
Patey Mrs Eliza, Triangle House
9 Pedley Susan, toy dealer, &c
15 Perryman Rd. currier, &c.
Pidsley John, gent. *Clarina Cottage*
7 Pope Samuel, police station
2 Portbury James, tinner, &c
4 Potts Mrs and Miss
Praed Wm.Mackworth,Esq.*BittonHs*
Reed Capt. Francis, Grove House
8 Richards Rev Wm. Page, D.C.L.,
   incumbent of East Teignmouth,
   and rector of Stoke Abbas, *Win-*
   terbourn House
Robinson Rev John Travers, M.A.,
   Crescent
8 Rogers Misses || 2RowMrs&Misses
2 Seaman Mrs Catherine
21 Seedgell Wm. block & pump mkr
16 Sharam Samuel, coach builder
Slater Mrs C. P., Myrtle hill

Slayter Rev Thomas (Independent)
24 Smale Wm. marine store dealer
15 Soper Mrs Sar. || Shymell Mrs J.
Spratt Capt. Thos., R.N., Mulberry st
Squire Mrs Eliz., Bitton hill
6 Stiles Mrs L. and Miss
Stirling Chas. gent. *Buckridge House*
4 Stocker Mr Wm. || 2 Symons Mrs
7 Stone Mr Rd. C. || 6 Stiles Mrs L.
Sweetland John, Esq. *Hermosa Hs*
24 Stuart John Geo. railway supt.
Sullock Rd. Bealy, surgeon (B.& S.)
19 Taylor Mrs My. || 16 Temple Cath
Taylor Misses Mary, Charlotte, and
   Fanny, Westbrook House
Templer Mr Henry, Parson street
18 Thomas and Sons, boat owners
Thornborough Lady & Capt. *Crescent*
Tonkin Lady, Old Market street
Tozer John Chappell, solicitor, &c
Turner James T., gent. Grove Hs
7 Underhill Miss || 2 Vaughan Wm.
Veale Henry, farmer, *Northcott*
2 Walker George, gent. Bitton st
Walker Edw.D., M.D., *LathallanCotg*
Walker Saml.& Arthur, gent.*Barnpark*
7 Wannell Rt. sexton of St. Michael's
15 Warren Matthew, ship owner
Watts Wm. John, Esq. *Orchard Hs*
19 Welsford Mrs Eliz. || 2 Welsford Sml.
Watts Wm. Jno.,Esq.,Tucker's Garden
2 Webber Robert, tax collector
Webber Thomas, gent., Crescent
Whidborne Jno. solr. Spring Garden
7 White Charles, dairyman
Williams Rev Jno. (Wes.) Willow Cotg
9 Windeatt John, eating house
Winstanley Clmnt.,Esq.Brookfield Hs
Woolcombe Miss B., Westcliffe Cotg
10 Wotton John, basket maker
Youle John, gent. Courtenay row

ATTORNEYS.
23 Jordan Wm. Rufus (registrar, &c)
23 Jordan Wm., Risdon Hall
3 Schank John Makellar S. G.
9 Tozer, Whidborne, & Mackenzie
14 Wight M. S. G. (and Dawlish)

BANKS.
1 National Provincial Bank of Engld.
   Edw. Augs. English, manager
1 Watts, Whiteway, & Kelson (draw
   on Williams, Deacon, and Co.)

FIRE AND LIFE OFFICES.
9 Architects', Engineers' & Builders,'
   Joseph Wm. Rowell

3 Atlas, J. M. S. G. Schank
1 Crown, John Wreyford
1 Clerical, Medl. & Genrl., J. H. Heale
1 County & Provident, E. A. English
Globe, Thomas Webber, Crescent
25 Medical & General, Geo. Liddon
25 Medical, Legal, &c. W. C. Lake
22 Mitre Life, Francis Allis
23 Norwich Union, W. R. Jordan
25 Pelican Life, Wm. Snelling
1 Phœnix Fire, J. H. Heale
15 Royal Exchange, John Beater
1 Sun, George Collings
20 Universal Life, L. D. Westcott
9 West of England, Tozer, Whidborne and Mackenzie
25 Western Life, J. B. Marles
HOTELS, INNS, AND TAVERNS.
2 Beehive, Mary Smith
16 Blue Anchor, Edward Enon
24 Commercial Inn, Mary Parker
19 Dawlish Inn, John Davy
15 Devon Arms Inn, Robt. Hawkins
9 Exeter Inn, Robert Wilcox
15 Globe Inn, Thomas Smith
10 Half Moon, Wm. Carter
16 Horse and Groom, Jas. Holcombe
15 Jolly-Sailor, Mary Lee
15 King William, Joseph Wilson
1 London Inn, Henry Veale (postg)
Marine Hotel, Ths.Carroll,Esplanade
Marine Compass, Wm. Curtis, Mulberry street
14 Market House, Jph. Thorne
18 New Quay Hotel, Wm. Burgoyne
25 Queen's Hotel, Hy. Searle (postg)
5 Red Lion, Robert Davey
Ring of Bells, James Godfrey
Royal Hotel, Henry Veale, Den

ACADEMIES.
* are Boarding.
7 Blackwell E.
2 Edgelowe Ths.
*Daimond R.&L.
8 DaimondGeo.&
Sus. National
19*Isaac Mary
8*Miller My. C.
7*Powell Chas.S.
Rudall My. Ann
7*SlaterFloreska
12 StephensWm.
19 Stevens Mary
8*Trist Wm. T.

AUCTIONEERS, &c
15 Cotton Wm.
22 CroydonEd.C.
1 Norsworthy W.
25 Partridge W.
7 Tapp Wm.
BAKERS.
2 Adams Thos.
2 BickfordRichd.
15 Coysh John
9 Darke James
24 England Wm.
11 Gaverick Jno.
16 Jones Joanna
15 Gifford Benj.
19 Martin Chas.

16 Pratt John
10 Rowell Agnes
1 Webber Jas. W.
BLACKSMITHS.
20 Born Wm.
3 Furse John
Harris Wm.
16 Leader Mark
15 Nickles Jas.
21 Paddon Jph.
2 Pyne John
13 Ward Richd.
BOOKSELLERS,&c
9 Allen Jno. Edw.
1 Collings Geo.
19 Croydon Edw.
and Son
20 Westcott Leo-
nard Dodge
BOOT&SHOE MKS.
2 Arscott Robert
24 Babb Thos.
11 Berry John
2 Bulkeley Jas.
20 Bulley John
20 Bulley Robt.
24 CorneliusWm.
1 Creedy Robert
18 Ferris Thos.
9 Field Wm.
16 Fowler Wm.
12 Freeman Jno.
15 Gribble Ann
18 Harris Thos.
19 Hoare Fredk.
Howard George
11 Hutchings Jn.
12 James Thos.
19 Matterface Jn.
12 Murch John
9 Murch Henry
2 Murch Robt.M.
19 Parkin Louisa
9 Partridge Rd.
24 PetherickR.W.
9 Pottinger Jas.
10 Pope John
1 Pridham John
24 Thomas Wm.
16 Truman Edw.
24 WellingtonRd.
19 Wylie George
BREWERS.
24 Cock My. Ann
15 Hawkins Rt.

24 MartinJas.Hy.
7 Parker Edw.H.
BEERHOUSES.
11 Stevens John
2 Young Samuel
BUTCHERS.
12 Coleridge Ts.
12 Cowley Chas.
15 Drake Henry
15 Dunrich Ellis
24 Field Wm.
14 Hallett Chas.
2 Neal Thomas
19 Mann Wm.
1 Palk Edward
9 Pike Thomas
25 Snow Francis
CABINET MKRS.
2 Coleridge Jas.
22 CroydonGlan-
ville H.
1 NorsworthyWm
25 PartridgeWm.
16 Tucker Wm.
COAL MERCHTS.
16 BurnettBnj.L.
11 Drake Nichls.
16 Hutchings Ts.
19 Isaac Thos.S.
24 Martin Jas.Hy
CONFECTIONERS.
22 Banbury Wm.
19GiffordWaltrE
19 Martin Chas.
1 Webber Jas. W.
DRUGGISTS.
22 Allis Francis
9 CarpenterTs.E.
1 CarpenterHy.G.
19CorneliusRd.B
25 Lake Wm. C.
25 Liddon Geo.
FANCY REPOSTRS.
9 Bentley Susan
19 Croydon Lsa.
25 PartridgeWm.
25 Snelling Wm.
20 Westcott L.D.
FISHMONGERS.
12 Gilpin John
12 Woodley Sar.
FRUITERERS.
12 Clark Ann
11 Gribble Thos.
11 Martin John

19 Puddicombe
   Thomas
7 Wannell John
12 Wotton Thos.
GROCERS, &c.
15 Beater Diana
19 Boutcher Rd.
9 Cole Wm.
9 Heath Samuel
19 May Benj. Olivr
1 Musgrave Jas.
16 Thomas Hy.
15 Tooley Richd.
16 Tucker John
25 Wilcox John
HAIR DRESSERS.
15 Elms Wm.
1 McHardy Jas.
9 Stoneman Geo.
HATTERS.
2 Edwards Jas.
25 Marles John B.
1 Pridham John
1 Wreyford John
HORSE, &c. LETRS.
14 Cotton Wm.
11 Jordan James
17 Hooper Wm.
5 Watkins James
3 Winsor John
IRONMONGERS.
14 Furse John
16 Stooke Chas.
9 Tibbs John
JOINERS & BLDRS
17 Coldridge Wm.
11 Cole Wm.
15 Cotton Wm.
17 Hayman Sml.
17 Hooper Wm.
22 Rowell J. & Son
7 Tapp Wm.
15 Taylor James
LACE MAKERS.
15 Payne Sarah
15 Richards Eliz.
LIBRARIES.
1 Collings Geo.
19 Croydon Edw.
L. & W. DRAPERS.
1 England Geo. W.
15 Hockey Geo. S.
1 Procter Mattw.
19 Richards Hy.
25 Wilcox Roger

LODGINGHOUSES.
11 Avery John
19 Brooks John
6 Cole Betty
15 Holditch Eliz.
7 Kemble Bruce
   Hutchings Thos.
19 Manly Sally
16 Moxon Rd.
19 Northcott Geo.
15 Parish Ann
10 Pridham Ann
23 Putney Chtte.
10 Rowell Mary
7 Wannell John
3 Winsor John
11 Wingate My.
6 Wright Wm.
MADREPORE MFS.
1 Sclater A. J. R.
15 Sclater Thos.
1 Windeatt Rd.
MSTR. MARINERS.
   Beasley Elias
16 Burton Saml.
11 Blackstone Js.
11 Burgoyne Rt.
   Carlisle George
17 Carlisle Thos.
11 Drake Nichls.
16 Harwood Rt.
16 Potter Wm.
21 Perryman Ts.
16 Turner Wm.
   Wreyford Edw.
MERCHANTS.
   Bassett F. S. & J.
11 Blackstone Js.
16 Hutchings T.
   W. B.
   Carlile George
22 Croydon Edw.
16 Spear & Enon
21 Warren Matw.
   Warren Wm. *Den.*
MILLINERS, &c.
19 Berry Har.
19 Bulley Rsmnd.
9 Burridge Sus.
9 Butchers Lsa.
16 Carpenter Sar.
19 Churchill M.
16 Fowler Mary
16 Knight James
7 Ham Eliza

19 Latham Fanny
9 May Lucy
19 Neck Charity
22 Rowell Eliz.
16 Truman E.
MUSIC DEALERS.
(* *are Teachers.*)
9 Allen Jno. Edw.
19 Croydon Edw.
*23 Lintern Wm.
*25 Snelling Wm.
PAINTERS AND
   GLAZIERS.
7 Bidwell John
2 Bowden Wm.
22 Croydon E. C.
14 Hexter Edw.
10 Lucas John
16 Stooke Chas.
8 Truman Wm.
POULTERERS.
16 Thomas Hy.
19 Hobbs Henry
16 Jones Ann
SADDLERS.
16 Blake John
6 Haymes Hy.
SHIP BUILDERS
21 Owen A. & Son
21 Mansfield J. B.
SHIPPING AGNTS.
15 Beater Jno. W.
   Owen Arthur
   Warren Matw. &
   harbour mstr)
SHOPKEEPERS.
15 Cole Mary
12 Cowley Chas.
16 Gibbs Sophia
18 Hill Wm.
2 Hindom Mary
19 Hobbs Henry
15 Holmes Maria
16 Jones Joanna
2 Knapman Jane
2 Martyn Eliz.
13 Lethbridge Jph
9 Partridge Rd.
11 Parish Mary
24 Petherick R. W
13 Salter Caleb
10 Staddon Jas.
24 Stephens Ann
11 Stevens John
5 Trickey Jane

16 Valentine Jno.
24 Winsor Sarah
STAY MAKERS.
19 Berry Har.
9 Lambe Chtte.
15 Lang Mary
24 Wellington J.
STONE MASONS &
   BRICKLAYERS.
2 Arscott John
16 Bassett Fdk.
10 Hayman Jno.
14 Hine Wm. S.
   Hook Wm.
2 Knott John
16 Knight John
11 Taylor Wm.
24 Tracey John
STRAW HAT MKS.
9 Butchers Lsa.
15 Burden Mary
16 Carpenter Sar.
19 Ellicombe E.
19 Hoare Priscla.
24 Searle Eliz.
1 Sclater E. S.
1 Warren Sophia
SURGEONS.
19 Bartlett and
   Sullick
   Cartwright W. A.,
   Brimley Hs.
15 Forman Geo.
   Ellery, R.N.
   Ingles Hy. *Den*
25 Lake Wm. Chas
23 Leman Fdk.
TAILORS.
(* *Drapers also.*)
10 *Adams Wm.
23 *Biggs Wm.
2 Blackmore Jno.
   Bryant J., Frog-
   marsh
9 Butchers Edm.
7 Cotmore Robt.
24 Down Richd.
19 *Lethbridge G.
25 *Marles J. B.
7 Mortimore Jno.
25 *Rowell Jno. R.
7 Scown John
16 *Squarey Ths.
15 *Symons Hy.
19 *Symons Ths.

19*Tarr Nicholas
2 Wotton Edw.
1*Wreyford Jno.

TIMBER MERTS.
15 Beater John
15 Cotton Wm.
15 ProwseClmnt.

WATCHMAKERS.
19 Bolt Richard
25 Boyce John
1 Bradford Edm.
9 Chasty Wm.

WINE &SP.MERTS.
16 Burnett and
Critchell
15 Rowell Geo. P.

RAILWAY.
Trains six times
a day to Exetr.
Plymouth, &c

OMNIBUSES,
to Exeter, &c.
during season

CARRIERS.
Ford & Co. to all
parts daily
G. Dalby to Exeter daily
Ann Cole to Bp.'s
Teignton
VESSELS to
London, &c.,
every 9 days

TRUSHAM, a small scattered village and parish, in the Teign valley, two miles N. by W. of Chudleigh, has only 213 souls and 749A. of land. Sir L. V. Palk, Bart, owns nearly all the soil and is lord of the manor, formerly held by the Southcotes. The *Church* is a small antique fabric, with a tower and four bells. The *rectory*, valued in K.B. at £9. 4s. 9½d., and in 1831 at £160, is in the patronage of Sir J. G. R. De la Pole, Bart., and incumbency of the Rev. John Buckland, of Laleham, Middlesex. The glebe is 59A. 2R. 28P., and the tithes were commuted in 1840 for £120 per ann. *John Stooke*, in 1675, gave a yearly rent-charge of £4 out of Stonings lands, to be applied as follows,—52s. in a weekly distribution of 1s. worth of bread among the poor, 20s. for annual distribution in corn, and 8s. for the person who makes the said distributions. The same donor built an *Almshouse*, (consisting of two dwellings and a garden,) and endowed it with a farm of 0A. at Christow, let for £22 per annum, from which 12 poor people receive 2s. each yearly. The same donor also gave about 13A. of land for the benefit of the rector, except the quarterly sums of 5s. for sacramental bread and wine, and 5s. for distribution among the poor communicants. He also left for the rector an annuity of £5. (See Christow.) The *School Land,* comprising about 4¼A., purchased in 1723, with £80 benefaction money, is let for £7 a year, which is applied in schooling poor children.

.she Rev Wm., B.A. curate, *Rectory*
.ausley Samuel, vict. New Inn
.ausley Sarah, schoolmistress
.hamberlain Wm. shoemaker
.heeseman Wm. carpenter
.arris Thomas, thatcher
.otter John, parish clerk

Scott Gilbert, blacksmith
FARMERS.
Cleave James || Cleave Joses
Cleave Robert || Edwards Wm.
Cleave Robert, *Tuckett's*
Stooke Thomas || Wollen George

HAYTOR HUNDRED

includes the towns of *Torquay, Brixton, Paignton,* and *Newton Abbot,* and is mostly of an irregular triangular figure, extending south-east from the vicinity of Ashburton to Dartmouth; northward from the latter to *Tor Bay, Babbicombe Bay,* and Stoke-in-Teignhead; and westward from the latter to Newton and Ashburton; but it has a detached member from four to six miles further to the north-west, comprising the parishes of *Widecombe* and *Buckland,* in the mountainous and rugged district of *Dartmoor,* near the *Haytor Rock* granite quarries, from which it has its name. The navigable river Dart bounds it on the south-west, and the sea on the east; and is crossed by the South Devon Railway, which has a branch to the beautiful watering place of Torquay. Haytor Hundred is in the Southern Parliamentary Division of Devon, and all in *Newton Abbot Polling District,* except Brixham, Churston-Ferrers, and Kingswear, which are in Dartmouth

Polling District; and Berry-Pomeroy, Little Hempston, Marldon, Staverton, and Stoke-Gabriel, which are in Totnes Polling District. It is in the *Archdeaconry of Totnes*, and all in *Ipplepen Deanery*, except Berry-Pomeroy and Little Hempston, which are in Totnes Deanery; and Buckland-in-the-Moor, Widecombe-in-the-Moor, and Marldon, which are in Moreton Deanery. It is all in Teignbridge and Paignton Petty Sessional Divisions; and the following is an enumeration of its 22 parishes, &c., shewing their territorial extent and their population in 1841 :—

Parishes, &c.	Acres.	Pop.	Parishes, &c.	Acres.	Pop.
Abbotskerswell	1600	433	*Kingsweare	107	270
*Berry-Pomeroy	} 4525	505	*Little Hempston	1200	268
*Bridgetown *ham.*		644	*Marldon	2254	470
*Brixham	5595	5684	Mary-Church (St.)	2589	1668
Broadhempston	2047	747	*Paignton	5092	2501
Buckland-in-Moor	1457	114	*Staverton	5356	1069
*Churston Ferrers..	} 2527	511	*Stoke-Gabriel	2595	691
*Galmpton *ham.*		261	Torbrian	1450	264
Cockington	1000	203	Tor-Moham	} 2000	1897
Coffinswell	1100	215	Torquay *chap.* ..		4085
Denbury	1068	470	Widecombe-in-Moor	10614	1106
Ipplepen	} 3070	966	Wolborough	} 970	1417
Woodland	1400	206	Newton Abbot *twp.*		1192
Kingskerswell	1740	845			
			Total	61,256	28,702

* *Unions:*—Those marked thus * are in *Totnes Union*, and all the others are in *Newton Abbot Union*. The return of Newton Abbot included 254 persons in the Union Workhouse. *Upton*, in Tor-Moham, has been made a District Parish. The *Unions* are also *County Court Districts*.

ABBOTSKERSWELL, or *Abbot's Carswell*, is a pleasant village, two miles S. of Newton Abbot, and has in its parish 433 souls and 1600 acres of land, including several scattered houses and the hamlet of *Aller*, where there is a paper mill, on a rivulet 1½ mile from the church. The soil is all freehold, and belongs to Sir W. P. Carew, Bart., the Hon. Mrs. Hare, W. Hole, Esq., Wm. and John Creed, and a few smaller owners. The *Church* (St. Mary,) is an ancient fabric in the perpendicular style, with a tower and three bells. It is about to be thoroughly repaired and beautified. The old pews are to give place to new open benches, and the finely carved oak screen is to be restored and opened. The *vicarage*, valued in K.B. at £11. 1s. 3d., and in 1831 at £278, is in the patronage of the Lord Chancellor, and incumbency of the Rev. G. P. G. Cosserat, M.A., who has a good residence and 70A. of glebe. The tithes were commuted in 1836, the vicarial for £220, and the rectorial for £115. The latter are appropriated to the vicar of Cornworthy. A cottage has been converted into a *Baptist Chapel;* and in the parish is a Quakers' Burial Ground, which was reserved for that purpose by a Mr. Tucket, when he sold Court Barton estate. Here is a small National School.

Bradford Wm. mercht. *Moor Park*
Burridge Wm. smith and beerhouse
Codner Thomas, shoemaker
Cosserat Rev Geo. Peloquin Graham, M.A. *Vicarage*
Creed John, gent. *Whiddon House*
Creed Wm. gentleman
Dalton & Co. paper makers, *Aller*
Dalton Daniel, shopkeeper
Emmett John & Nicholas, carpenters
Garratt Richard & Edward, masons
Henley Wm. Codner, cider merchant
Henley Mr Wm. Creed
Langler Cphr. vict. Two Mile Oak
Leaker Thomas, shoemaker
Lee John, shopkpr. || Luscombe Mr
Rendell John, land agent, *Aller*
Ruby George, baker

Taylor Wm. mason
Vanning Wm. parish clerk
Wood Wm. tailor
    FARMERS.
Amery Joseph || Skinner Robert

Elliott John || Leaker John
Elliott Thos. || Maddicott Thos.
Elliott Wm. || Perrott Allen
Heyward Wm. || Ruby John

BERRY POMEROY is a small scattered village, two miles E. of Totnes, and has in its parish 4525A. 1R. 10P. of fertile land, several neat houses and scattered farms, and also BRIDGETOWN, which forms a handsome suburb of Totnes, with which it is connected by a good bridge over the Dart. In 1841 the parish contained 1149 inhabitants, of whom 505 were in *Berry Pomeroy*, and 644 in *Bridgetown*. The latter is now part of the Parliamentary Borough of Totnes, as noticed at a subsequent page. The Duke of Somerset is lord of the two manors and owner of most of the soil. William the Conqueror gave the manor of *Bury* or *Berry* to *Ralph de Pomerai*, who built BERRY POMEROY CASTLE, which for 500 years was the stately residence of the Pomeroys. The extensive and magnificent ruins of this once formidable castle are situated on a rocky eminence, thickly covered with wood, and rising above a pellucid brook, about two miles N.E. of Totnes. It was dismantled during the civil wars of the 17th century. The approach to it is through a thick wood, extending along the slope of a range of hills that entirely intercept any prospect to the south; and on the opposite side is a steep rocky ridge, covered with oak, so that the ruins are shut into a beautiful valley. The fortress appears, from the ruins, to have been originally quadrangular, having only one entrance, which was on the south, between two hexagon towers, through a double gateway; the first machicolated, and further strengthened by angular bastions. Over this gateway the arms of the Pomeroys are still to be seen. The eastern tower commands a fine prospect of the adjacent country, and the room over the gateway appears to have been the chapel. The ruins in the quadrangle, or court, are much more modern than the rest, as they belonged to a magnificent mansion, commenced by the Seymours, in the 16th century, at the cost of £20,000, but never completed. What was finished is thus described by Prince:—"Before the door of the Great Hall was a noble work, whose length was the full breadth of the court, arched over with curiously carved freestone, supported in the fore part by several stately pillars of the Corinthian order, standing on pedestals, having cornices and friezes finely wrought. The apartments within were very splendid, especially the dining room; and many of the other rooms were well adorned with mouldings and fret-work, some of whose marble clavils were so delicately fine, that they would reflect an object from a great distance. Notwithstanding which, it is now demolished, and all this glory lyeth in the dust; there being nothing standing but a few broken walls, which seem to mourn their own approaching funerals." The great gate, the walls of the south front, the north wing of the quadrangle, some apartments on the west side, and a turret or two, are the principal remains; and they are so finely overhung with branches of trees and shrubs, which grow close to the walls, so beautifully mantled with ivy, and so richly encrusted with moss, that they constitute the most picturesque objects that can be imagined. The last of the Pomeroys who occupied Berry Pomeroy Castle, was deeply concerned in the rebellion of 1549, and is said to have saved his life by making over the manor and castle to Edward Seymour, *Duke of Somerset*, whose successors have since held them, and formerly resided here. The present Duke's principal seats are Bulstrode Park, Bucks, and Farley Park, Somerset. *Berry Pomeroy Church* (Virgin Mary,) is an ancient structure, with a tower, and four bells, and contains an elaborate alabaster monument to the memory of Lord Edward

Seymour, and his son, and son's wife, whose effigies are represented lying on three steps, in very constrained positions. The building is mostly in the perpendicular style, and the nave and chancel are divided by a finely carved screen. The Duke of Somerset is impropriator of the rectory, and patron of the *vicarage*, valued in K.B. at £18. 19s. 7d., and in 1831 at £360, and now in the incumbency of the Rev. Wm. B. Cosens, M.A., who has a good residence, and three acres of glebe. The *Free Church*, at BRIDGETOWN was built in 1835 by the Duke of Somerset, at the cost of £7000, and was intended as a chapel of ease for that part of the parish which forms a suburb of Totnes, but owing to a dispute with the Bishop, it was never consecrated. It is now licensed as a nonconformist place of worship, under the ministry of the Rev. James Shore, M.A. It is in the perpendicular style, with a tower, and about 1200 sittings. In 1700, *Susan Bound* left £420 to be invested in land, and the yearly proceeds to be applied in relieving her late husband's poor relations, or other poor people resident in Bridgetown. This legacy, with £180 arrears of interest, was laid out, in 1720, in the purchase of a farm of 29A. 1R. 1P. at Combe, now let for about £40 per annum. *The DIRECTORY of this parish is included with Totnes.*

BRIXHAM, a flourishing market town, sea-port, and extensive fishing station, is delightfully situated on the southern projecting point of Torbay, and is in two parts, called *Upper and Lower Brixham;* the former of which extends in a long straggling street, more than 1½ mile south of Lower Brixham, or *Brixham Quay*, and most of it, (with the parish church,) is in a picturesque valley, opening to the Quay, and bounded on the east by the lofty sea cliffs, and Berryhead,—the most eastern point of the bay. *Brixham Parish* contains 5595A. 2R. 21P. of land, and increased its population from 3671 in 1801, to 5684 in 1841, but it has now about 7000 inhabitants. It is within the jurisdiction of the port of Dartmouth, and is distant 4 miles N.E. of Dartmouth, 10 miles E. by S. of Totnes, 30 miles S. by E. of Exeter, 202 miles W.S.W. of London, and 9 miles S. by E. of Torquay, on the opposite side of the bay, by road, or 5 by water. The *manor* of Brixham belonged at an early period to the Novants, from whom it passed successively to the Valletort, Pomeroy, Corbet, Bonville, and Grey families. The manor is now divided into a great number of *shares*. One quarter of it is held by the Duke of Cleveland, and the Dowager Countess of Sandwich, as representatives of the Bolton family. The rest belong to the representatives of the late Sir J. Seale, Sir J. B. Y. Buller, W. Gillard, Esq., the Quay Lords, and a number of smaller proprietors. One quarter of the manor, which had belonged to P. Gilbert, Esq., was purchased many years ago by twelve fishermen of the Quay, and, though their shares have since been much subdivided, all the propritors are styled the *Quay Lords.* The principal owners of land in the parish are J. F. Luttrell, Esq., Sir J. B. Y. Buller, G. H. Cutler, Esq., H. P. Pierrepoint, Esq., Wm. Gillard, Esq., and J. Clarke, Esq.; and here are many smaller freeholders. The parish includes the small hamlets of *Woodhuish* and *Boohay;* five small *commons;* many scattered farm-houses, and several handsome seats. *Upton Lodge*, at the north end of Brixham, is the seat of G. H. Cutler, Esq.; and *Nethway House* is occasionally visited by its owner, J. F. Luttrell, Esq., of Dunster Castle. *Leywell House*, the residence of Henry B. Pierrepoint, Esq., had its name from an ebbing and flowing spring, which was destroyed some years ago, when the high road was altered. LUPTON HOUSE, about a mile west of the church, is the pleasant seat of *Sir J. B. Y. Buller, Bart.* It is a large and handsome mansion, with well wooded grounds, and was rebuilt by Charles Hayne, Esq., who was sheriff in 1772. About 1788, Mr.

Hayne sold it to the late *Sir Fras. Buller*, one of the justices of the King's Bench, who was created a baronet in 1789. IRON ORE has been discovered in the parish within the last ten years; and two mines are now working with considerable success, one at Upton, on G. H. Cutler's estate, and the other on *Furzham Common*. The latter is worked by R. W. Wolston, Esq , and is his property; and the former is worked by Mr. Edward Prior. The ore of the Upton mine is nearly equal in richness and colour to the Lancashire ore, yielding from 55 to 60 per cent. of metal. That of the Furzham mine yields about 45 per cent. of very superior metal, and is of a bright yellow colour. Great quantities of the ore are shipped from the Quay to be smelted in Wales, &c. The *lode* lies nearly north and south, and is about 35 feet broad. It is worked by open cutting, and the depth already attained is about 40 feet. The ore crops out within a few feet of the surface, and is surrounded by limestone, &c. Fine *yellow ochre* is got with the iron ore, and is manufactured here into an excellent pigment.

Brixham is said to have the largest *fishery* in England. More than 270 sail of vessels, comprising 20,000 tons of *shipping*, and employing about 1600 seamen, belong to the port, and a large number of them are engaged in the fishing trade. They comprise six brigs of about 170 tons, 140 schooners of from 60 to 180 tons, and 130 fishing smacks of from 30 to 50 tons ; and here are also about 80 open boats, carrying two men each, employed in hook fishing. The average weekly amount received here for fish is about £600, and sometimes as much as 350 tons weight is brought to the Quay in a week, but the average weekly quantity is about 150 tons. The Quay is a most interesting sight in the evening after a large catch, when heaps of fish, comprising turbot, soles, whiting, plaice, mullet, mackerel, gurnet, flounders, herrings, &c., are piled up, and a sort of Dutch auction takes place ; after which, all the prime lots are sent to Exeter, Bath, Bristol, London, and other markets. Many vessels are employed here in the coasting, and the Spanish and Mediterranean trades. The harbour being well protected by the bold high promontory of Berry-head, is a great place of refuge for shipping in stormy weather ; and during westerly winds, great numbers of vessels may be seen riding at anchor here and in other parts of Torbay. The old *pier* was built under the powers of the Haven and Market Improvement Act, passed in 1799. It was finished in 1804 ; but enclosing an haven not sufficiently large for the increased size of the vessels and trade of the port, a plan was formed, about ten years ago, for the construction of a *new pier and breakwater*, sufficient to shelter a great number of large class merchantmen and frigates of war. This important work was commenced in 1843, by the Commissioners of the above-named act, who are also proprietors of the *Market House*, near the beach, and derive an income of about £900 per annum from the harbour and market estate. The *markets*, held every Tuesday and Saturday, are well supplied with provisions ; and here is a pleasure *fair* on Whit-Tuesday. *Gas Works* were constructed about eight years ago, by a company of proprietors, in £5 shares. A large *Steam Corn Mill* has just been erected, about half-a-mile from the Quay, at the cost of about £6000, raised by a numerous company, in £10 shares. The old workhouse has been converted into a *Court House*, parish vestry, &c. ; and *petty sessions* are held here every alternate Monday, for part of Paignton Division. The office of the Custom-house Officers is on the beach ; and there is a *Coast Guard Station* near Queen's Quay, and another on the Man Sands Cliff, two miles from the town. *Torbay*, of which Brixham is the principal port, is a beautiful lake-like expanse of water, having a semicircular coast line of about twelve miles, though only four miles across from its two eastern promontories. *William Prince of Orange,*

afterwards King Wm. III., landed here Nov. 5th, 1688, to effect the ever memorable Revolution, as noticed at page 58. The identical *stone* on which he first set his foot on landing, lay neglected till 1823, when it was placed as the landing stone of the late Duke of Clarence, afterwards Wm. IV., who visited Brixham as Lord High Admiral in that year. This interesting stone was then sawn in two halves, one of which was placed in a neat obelisk in the fish market, with an inscription upon it, recording the memorable event of 1688. This obelisk has since been removed, and re-erected on the pier, near the spot where the Prince of Orange landed. The other half of the stone now forms a tablet at the pier end, inscribed in commemoration of the visit of the Duke of Clarence, July 21st, 1823, at which time, an address from the inhabitants was enclosed with a bit of the above stone, in a box of heart of oak 800 years old, and presented to the Royal Duke. During the late wars, Torbay was the general rendezvous of the Channel Fleet, affording at all times a safe and easy accessible roadstead for all descriptions of vessels; and having here a complete watering wharf, supplied from a large reservoir constructed by Government in 1801. The fortifications on the bold promontory of Berry-head, and the barracks which then existed here, are dismantled, and the Military Hospital is now a private residence. In 1815, the *Bellerophon* (Captain Maitland,) anchored in the roadstead here, after receiving on board the fallen Emperor Napoleon, and remained several days before sailing for St. Helena.

CHURCHES, &c.—The *Parish Church* (Virgin Mary,) at Upper Brixham, is a large and ancient structure, in the perpendicular style, with a lofty embattled tower, containing six bells and a clock. It has a richly carved font, of the 14th century, two galleries, and a large organ. It is in contemplation to enlarge the churchyard, by the addition of 1¼ acre. The *vicarage*, valued in K.B. at £25. 15s., and in 1831 at £494, with the curacy of Churston-Ferrers annexed to it, is in the patronage of the Lord Chancellor, and incumbency of the Rev. Robt. Holdsworth, M.A., who has held the living since 1809. The Vicarage House is a neat residence; and the tithes were commuted in 1840, the vicarial for £463, and the rectorial for £538. 10s. Miss Knollis is impropriator of the latter. The *Church Lands*, &c., have been vested in trust since the reign of Elizabeth, for the repairs, &c., of the church, and comprise about 15A., and ten houses and cottages, worth upwards of £60, but let for only about £10 a year, in consideration of the fines paid when the leases were granted. The *District Church at Lower Brixham* was built by subscription, as a chapel of ease, about 1820. It is a plain cemented building, with galleries, an organ, and a turret, containing a bell and clock. It has been lately constituted a *perpetual curacy*, valued at £107, in the patronage of the Vicar, and incumbency of the Rev. J. R. Hogg, B.A. Here is a *Baptist Chapel*, built in 1801, at the cost of about £1200; a *Wesleyan Chapel*, built in 1816, at the cost of £2000; and an *Independent Chapel*, erected in 1843, at the expense of about £1000. The *Assembly Rooms*, in Bolton street, were built in 1837, and are occasionally occupied as a theatre. The town has several Friendly Societies and other provident institutions; and a *Freemasons' Lodge*, built in 1801, at the cost of £450. Sunday Schools and Religious Institutions are supported by the congregations of the churches and chapels; and near the beach is a large building, erected in 1848, by Messrs. Green and Vittery, and used as an auction mart, a sailors' school, &c. The CHARITIES of Brixham are as follows :—

Richard Kelly, in 1633, left a house and about 45A. of land, charged with the yearly payment of £6. 6s. 8d., for the poor of nine parishes, of which 10s. belongs to the poor of this parish; and also with the annual sum of £15 for the maintenance of a *free school*, at Brixham, for the poor children of Brixham, Churston-Ferrers, and Kingswear. He directed the residue of the clear yearly income to be paid to the curate of St. Saviour's, Dartmouth, for preaching a sermon weekly. The property is now let for about £50 a year. A legacy of £40, left to the poor of Brixham, by *Samuel Shardon*, was expended in erecting

a gallery in the church, but £2 a year, paid out of the pew rents, is distributed among the poor parishioners, together with £2. 19s. 4d., derived from the benefactions of *Richard Kelly, John Peter, John Lockram, Elizabeth Serle, and Arthur Luscombe.* An annuity of 10s., left by *John Croote,* out of Blackhouse tenement, in 1640, is distributed among ten poor people. Several small charities formerly belonging to the parish are lost. In 1801, a Freemasons' Lodge was built on the site of a small ancient *almshouse,* subject to a yearly ground rent of 10s., which is carried to the poor rates.

ROBERT LANG, in 1685, left one-half of his estate to be vested in trust for the relief of the poor parishioners of Brixham. In satisfaction of this bequest £1500 was obtained, pursuant to a decree in Chancery, in 1690. This money was vested in the purchase of a freehold farm of 88A., and a leasehold farm of 60A., in Dartmoor Forest, now let at rents amounting to about £70 per annum. Adjoining the charity estate is 66A. 3R. 6P. of land, which was enclosed from the forest in 1808, by the tenant of the last named farm, under a lease of 99 years, granted by the Duchy of Cornwall, at the yearly rent of 11s. 2d. The trustees of this charity can claim the benefit of this lease, by paying the enclosure expenses incurred by the tenant. The clear income derived from the charity estate is distributed among all the poor of the parish.

The FREE SCHOOL, now conducted on the *national system,* in two large rooms, built by subscription, about 1820, is attended by about 130 boys and 110 girls, part of whom pay 1d. each per week, but it is entirely free to all the poor children of Brixham and Churston-Ferrers, that are sent to it by the trustees of Kelly's and Kellond's Charities, the former of which is already noticed, and from it the master derives £15 per annum. In 1712, *John Kellond* left £2000 for charitable uses in Devonshire. Of this legacy £490 was laid out in the purchase of a farm of about 45 acres, at Ashburton, which was vested in trust for the support of a schoolmaster at Brixham, in consideration of his teaching reading, writing, arithmetic and navigation to all the poor children sent to him by the trustees. This farm is now let for £42 per annum, and the master has also the dividends of about £800 three per cent. stock, derived from the sales of timber, formerly growing on the land.

BRIXHAM DIRECTORY.

The POST-OFFICE is in Fore street, Lower Brixham, and Miss Harriet C. Toyzer is the postmistress. There is a sub-post office at Mrs. B. Martin's, Upper Brixham. Letters despatched morning and evening, and money orders granted and paid.

In the following Directory, those marked 1, *reside on the Beach;* 2, *in Bolton street;* 3, *Fore street;* 4, *High street;* 5, *King street;* 6, *Middle street;* 7, *New road;* 8, *Ranscombe; and* 9, *in Upper Brixham.*

3 Alexander Rev John Bird, (Wes.)
5 Babbs Mrs || 7 Bartlett Mrs
9 Bird Capt. Edwd. J., R.N. *West Kent Cottage*
Bowden Mrs Mary, Bolton street
9 Browse Mr Brtlt. || 9 Browse Mr S.
9 Browse Mr Nicholas, *Hill House*
2 Brooking Hy. custom hs. officer
Buller Sir John Buller Yarde, Bart. M.P. *Lupton House*
3 Bussell Mr Wm. || 9 Clarke John
7 Calley Samuel, timber merchant
9 Chilcote Hy. gent. *Hill House*
2 Churchward Miss Mary
1 Clarke Edward, hatter

Cumby Mrs Sarah, *Leywell Cottage*
Cutler Geo. Hy. Esq. *Upton Lodge*
De Saint Dalmas Mr Hy., *Greenswd*
2 Drew Mrs Eliz. || 4 France Mrs A.
Ellis Mr Wm., Prospect place
9 Fogwell Miss Mary
2 Furze Mrs Eliz. || 7 Furze Mrs H.
Furze Mrs Eliz., *Rock Vale*
9 Gatty Wm. excise officer
9 Gempston Mrs Harriet
Gillard Miss My., *Greenover Cotg*
Gillard Pp. & Wm. gents. *Blaek Hs*
7 Green Mrs Susan || 9 Gorley Mr Sl.
Green Wm. Esq. banker, Burton st
1 Hamlyn Wm. coffee house
3 Hillyer Wm. glass and china dlr

7 Hoblyn Edw. Lee, R.N. chief officer of coast guard
Hogg Rev John Ranton, B.A. incbt. of Lower Brixham
9 Holdsworth Rev Robt., M.A. vicar
7 Hooper Mrs Sus. || 7 Langdon Mrs
Hyne Mrs Jane, *Ranscombe House*
Johnson Wm. mert. Mount Pleasant
9 Key Joseph Edward, purser, &c
3 Lee Thos. glass and china dealer
9 Lakeman Mr Stephen
Luttrell John Fownes, Esq. *Nethway House*, (and Dunster Castle)
9 Martin Miss Grace, organist
9 McLean Agsts. Benj. coast guard
Michelmore Mrs || 2 Millman Mrs
3 Michelmore John, cider mert
6 Mogg Thomas, constable
9 Murch Wm. gent. *Greenover Hs*
9 Phillips Mr Wm. *Greenover*
Pierrepoint Hy. B. Esq. *Leywell Hs*
3 Platell Henry, porter merchant
Pollard Edward, gent. *Cumbers*
5 Pomeroy Thos. jun. artist
Prior Edward, Esq. iron ore owner, *Torbay Villa*
Prior Chas. gent. *Verngate Villa*
3 Reed Mrs Eliz. and Miss Eliz.
9 Savage Rev Wm., M.A. curate, *Vicarage*
7 Sanders Rev Moses, (Baptist)
Shaddock Mrs Sus., Fore street
7 Smith Rev George, (Indpt.)
2 Straw Mr Wm. || 9 Togwell Miss
1 Tosswell Wm. eating house
9 Trounsell Mrs Sarah, *Milton Cotg*
Tully Geo. tide waiter, Over gang
2 Tucker John S. dyer
9 Tucker Wm., M.D., *The Lodge*
9 Underhay John, gent
3 Veysey Mrs Catherine
3 Vittery Edw. Chas. Esq. banker
7 Vittery Miss J. || 7 Warren Mrs
Way Mrs Hannah, Prospect place
White Mrs Eliz., Mount Pleasant
Williams Mr Charles, *Hillhead*
7 Willing Saml. J. millwright and machine maker
3 Wills Robert, tinner, &c
9 Wilson Rev Charles Thomas, M.A. curate, *Upton Lodge*
Winter Saml. basket mkr. Overgang
9 Wright Lieut. Wm., R.N.
Wolston Rd. Wltr. iron ore owner, &c
Wyatt Mr Joseph, Bolton street

BANKS.

Green & Vittery, (draw on Andrews, Taylor, and Lloyd,) Fore st
3 *Savings' Bank*, (Branch of Exeter & Devon,) C. H. Brooking, actuary

FARMERS.

Bell John, Summer lane
Beare Thomas, *Raddicombe*
Child John, *Raddicombe*
9 Cruse John || 9*Edwards Isaac
Dimond Thos. *Great gate*
Drew Chpr. Pike, *Brownston*
Drew Walter, *Woodhuish*
Eales Thomas || Harris Wm.
Harris Thomas || 9 Squires Thos.
Hine Richard, Colyton
Honeywill Thos., *Lupton Barton*
5 Putt Thomas || Newte John
Page Robert, *Northway*
Page Richard, *Boohay*
Page Wm., *Hoodown*
Soper Edward, *Upton*
Soper Robert, Southdown

FIRE & LIFE OFFICE AGENTS.

3 Atlas, Richard Couch
1 Commercial, O. H. Bartlett
3 County & Provident, C. H. Brooking and Wm. Bovey
2 Legal & Commercial, Wm. Collier
3 Sun, Western, and Professional, C. H. Brooking
7 West of England, Saml. Calley

INNS AND TAVERNS.

9 Bell, Wm. Stone Tucker
3 Blue Anchor, John Miller
2 Bolton Hotel, Jemima McLean
1 Buller's Arms, Nicholas Adams
1 Commercial Inn, Hanh. Wotton
1 Crown and Anchor, John Barter
1 Dolphin, Nicholas James
3 Globe, John Smerdon
7 Golden Lion, Edw. Carew
3 *London Inn*, Henry Mills
9 Lord Nelson, James Pearce
4 Manor Inn, Philip Apter
5 Maritime Inn, Benj. Brockenshire
1 New Pier, John Barter
9 Ring of Bells, Thomas Squires
1 Old George, Samuel T. Sanders, and harbour master
1 Rising Sun, Nicholas Burridge
9 Town Arms, John Hodgson
1 Victory, John Woodman
9 Waterman's Arms, John Ashe

ACADEMIES.
(* *Boarding*.)
3*Bovey Wm. (& surveyor)
9*DeStDalmasE.
Jarmond Sar.*Natl*
2 King Wm. *Natl*
9 Martin Barbara
3*Toyzer Har. C.
3*Wakeham Roger Steere

ATTORNEYS.
9 Gillard Philip
2 Underhay John
7 Wolston Rd. W.

AUCTIONEERS.
2 Collier Wm. F.
3 Turner Richard
7 WebberWm. (& clk. to magists)

BAKERS.
(* *Confectioners*.)
4 Apter Philip
9 Bowden Chpr.
3*Burn John
4 Corley John
2 Clarke Eliz.
6 Farley Martha
6 Furneaux Sus.
9 Fogwell George
Hamblin Richard
3Harris MaryAnn
3*Lendon James
9 Mardon John
3 Nicholas Daniel
6 Pepper Simon
1 PetersElizabeth
8 Palk Giles
1 Putt Harriet
1 Pearce Barnbs.
5 Rowe John
9 Rowse Josias
8*Skinner Edw.
5 Swaffin Eliz.

BEERHOUSES.
Collier Sml.*Overg*
6 Edward Richd.
Furneaux Samuel
Harris Hy. *Gt. gt*
5Hawkins Rachel
9 Treby John

BLOCK AND PUMP MAKERS.
5 Furneaux Robt. & Christopher

1 Thomas Wm.

BOOKSELLERS,&c.
1 Goodwin Enoch
3 King Ann

BOOT & SHOE MKS.
3 Adams Robert
9 Barter John
1 Davis John
1 Densham Henry
1 Drew Nicholas
6 Drew Samuel
9 Elliott John
1 Furneaux Sml.
1 Gillard Wm.
9 Graham Thos.
6 Hockaday Edw.
6 Howard Wm.
3 Langler Henry
6 Lee Wm.
2 Lockyear Eml.
5 Matthews Hy.
1 Piller John
3 Sewell John
Tally J. H.
3 Wood Agnes

BREWERS, &c.
7 Fogwell Geo.
3 Lakeman Thos.

BUTCHERS.
9 Adams Ann
6Cummings Sml.
9 Johnson Wm.
6 Hoare John
3 Heaward Pp.
1 Hoppin Wm.
3 Partridge John
9WiddecombeJno

CABINET MAKERS.
3 Bartlett Paul
2 Brunt Wm.
2 Foster Rt. bkr
3 Stephens John

COAL MERCHANTS.
7 Browse Nichls.
7 Calley Samuel
3 Green Chpr.

COOPERS.
1 Clements W. W.
1 Millman Wm.
1 Peters John
1 Shepherd Chas.

CORN MILLERS.
7 Fogwell George
9 Parker Henry
2Pepperall Simon

SteamMillCo., W. Johnson, *agent*

DRUGGISTS.
3 Cayme Wm. G.
1Clements W. W.

FISH MERCHTS.
9 Balkwill Wm.
BemfieldJ.Fish st
ClatworthyW. do
Densham My. do
Loram Chas. do
1 Wintle Wm.

GROCERS, &c.
3 Bartlett Jasper
3 Burn John
1 Clements W. W.
2 Dart Harriet
3 Folland George
Hunt John
3 King Ann
5 Larwill Jermh.
3 Lee Thomas
3 Palk Giles
1 Parrott Sarah
9 Podbury Wm.
3 Pool Wm.
5 Pomeroy Thos.
1 Shears Ann
1 Smith Wm.
6 Turpin Amelia
1 Vittery Selina
3 Vittery Cath.

HAIR DRESSERS.
3 Evans Wm.
1 Heath Richard
1 Johnson Joseph
3 Stone Peter

IRONMONGERS.
1 Calley Wm.
1 Tucker Joseph
1 Tyrer Wm.
3 Wills Robert

JOINERS & BLDRS.
3 Brown John
3 Brown Wm.
Goade Wm. G.
Scardon John
9 Scardon Wm.
Searle John
3 Spark Wm. P.
4 Spark Robert
9 Wills John

LINEN & WOOLLEN DRAPERS.
3 Allder George

1 Bartlett O. H. Stamp office
1 Cooke Benj.
6 Lloyd James
2 Mann Joseph
3 Tapper Richd.

MASONS & BLDRS.
Addy Wm., Gt. gt
8 Doust Wm.
5 Maddick Wm.
Peace Philip
Philp George
7 Wilkinson Wm.
2 Wyatt Thomas
Wyatt James
Wyatt Wm.

MILLINERS.
6 Avery Jane
3 Blaney Bessy
5BedfordM.B.&J.
3 Gilbert Mary
6PetherbridgeElz
3 Silly Chtte.
Sprague Sisters
2 Tucker Frances
6 Yeoman Ellen

PAINTERS AND GLAZIERS.
3 Bagshaw Wm.
1 Burman Eliz.
1 Hoare Fredk.
5 Lamzed Wm.
9 Smale Ebenzr.

ROPE, &c. MKRS.
1 Clarke Brothers
6GreenJph.& Son
Green Wm., Burton street
7 Yeo John

SAIL MAKERS.
BirdJno.,*Overgng*
5 Dewdney Daniel
1 Elliott John
7 Fox Samuel
5 Kendrick W. G.

SHIPSMITHS.
AdamsMy.,Bck.st
9 Bulley John
1 Elliott John
5 Hoare Stephen
9 Matthews Roger
9 Pool Geo. Saml.
1 Tyrer Wm.

SHIP BUILDERS.
5Dewdney & Sons

5 Furneaux Robt.
& Christopher
9 Matthews Saml.
4 Richardson John
8 Upham John
SHIP OWNERS.
2 Alward Andw.
5 Austin Wm.
2 Baddeley Frdk.
2 Blake Wm.
3 Bowden Samuel
3 Brooking C. H.
7 Browning John
6 Browse Henry
7 Browse Nichls.
2 Brown John
9 Brown Thomas
9 Buckingham G.
5 Buckingham G.
jun
7 Burrows Thos.
7 Calley Samuel
7 Carter Wm.
Cole Geo. *Cross*
2 Collier Wm.Fdk.
5 Cornhill John
2 Clements Chas.
5 Clarke James
1 Clarke Wm.
2 Collings Joshua
3 Couch Richard
9 Curtis John
2 Dart Wm.
5 Dewdney Daniel
5 Dewdney D. jun
5 Dewdney Saml.
7 Dugdale W. H.
8 Dugdale Hy. J.
2 Emmett Wm. H.
7 Fogwell Geo. jun
7 Fogwell Samuel
7 Furneaux Chpr.

5 Furneaux Robt.
2 Fox Edward
7 Fox Samuel
2 Gortley Samuel
3 Green Chpr.
Green Joseph
6 Green Jph. jun
Green Wm.
3 Hannaford Jas.
2 Kendrick Saml.
7 Kendrick Wm.
3 Kingston Rd. L.
(vice consul)
7 Nowell John
7 Nowell Wm.
9 Mudge Robert
9 Murch Wm.
2 Martin James
Matthews George
Matthews Daniel
Matthews John
7 Palk George
2 Peter Philip
9 Podbury Wm.
5 Popham Rt. B.
Pring Dnl. *Cross*
Sanders Francis
5 Shears John
1 Shepherd Chas.
3 Shillibeer Sus.
5 Sivell John
6 Smith Nicholas
2 Sprague Wm.
Sprague Nichls.
5 Stephens Danl.
3 Tyrer George
2 Tyrer John
5 Tyrer Moses
7 Tyrer M. jun
3 Tyrer Thomas
2 Varwell Peter
2 Varwell Wm.

2 Veysey Wm.
Vittery Samuel
2 Wakeham Edw.
1 Wheaton John
2 Williams Wm.
SHOPKEEPERS.
9 Ashe Eliz.
3 Carter James
6 Collier Maria
6 Day Eliz.
6 Edwards Rd.
6 Farley Martha
9 Furze Nanny
3 Harris My. A.
9 Jones Giles
6 Maunder Jas.
9 Pepperell Rt.
4 Reynolds Ann
9 Rider Philip
Shears Jno. Gt. gt
4 Smith Sar. & M.
2 Snelling John
3 Swaffin John
9 Upham Eliz.
4 Tully John
2 Wakeham Edw.
3 Way Jane
STRAW HAT MKS.
5 Dennis Jane
5 Gillard Ann
3 Tully Eliz.
3 Wood Agnes
SURGEONS.
3 Bowden Sl. Wm.
9 Brooking Chas.
3 Brooking C. H.
Tucker Wm., M.D.
TAILORS.
5 Brockenshire B.
(and ore agt)
Drew Sl., Peace's
row

6 Drew Robert
1 Hamlyn Thos.
1 Lee Joshua
3 Mitchell Edw.
9 Rawl John
3 Prowse Wm.
2 Smale Samuel
3 Stevens Thos.
Tozer G., Pump st
3 Way John
6 Wheaton John
WATCHMKRS. &c.
3 Couch Richard
1 Gill Thomas
3 Trist Sarah
WHEELWRIGHTS.
Bovey Wm., Gt. gt
9 Nowell Thomas
9 Upham Wm.
7 Willing Sml. J.

OMNIBUS
To Torquay, every
morng. at 7½;
& to Dartmouth
evening.

CARRIERS.
To *Dartmouth*—
Rd. Putt, daily
To *Exeter*—Wm.
Balkwill & Cpr.
Shears, daily
To *Totnes*—Cpr.
& Mary Shears,
daily

VESSELS *to*
Guernsey wkly
Boats to Torquay,
&c. when orderd.

BROADHEMPSTON, a village and parish, 4½ miles N. of Totnes, has 747 souls, and 2047A. 1R. 28P. of land, including the hamlets, &c., of *Ford, Bearton, Wenton, Halswill*, and *Bicaton*. Mr. Edward Palk is lord of the manor, but most of the soil belongs to Rt. Michelmore, J. Harris, W. and J. Blackler, W. Venning, G. Bowden, C. Skinner, T. Luscombe, and a few small owners. The manor anciently belonged to the Cantelupes, and its lords had the power of inflicting capital punishment. The *Church* is a large and antique fabric, with a tower and five bells. The *vicarage*, valued in K.B. at £25. 6s. 8d., and in 1831, at £366, is in the patronage of the Crown, and incumbency of the Rev. J. Pitman, B.C.L., who has a good residence and 37A. 2R. 26P. of glebe. The tithes were commuted in 1841, the vicarial for £266, and the rectorial for £139. 19s. 3d. The latter belong to Gunsley's charity to the poor of Rochester and Maidstone. Here is a small

Independent Chapel, built in 1844, by Mr. Edw. Palk; a *Wesleyan Chapel,* built 20 years ago; and a *School*, supported chiefly by the Vicar.   Three cottages, with small gardens, near the church, said to have been given by a *Mr. Prestwood,* are occupied rent free by poor people. The poor parishioners have the following yearly sums, viz. :— 20s. out of the great tithes of Cornworthy, left by John Peter; about £2. 12s. from the tithes of 30A. called Pitt, and 3A. called Gandrell, left by *Wm. Jesse*, in 1679, and an unknown donor; and 8s. from the gifts of Mr. Webber, Mrs. Lake, and John Evans.

Blackler Jas. gent. || Harris Mrs
Coleman George, mason
Fosland Wm. parish clerk
Halwell Wm. wheelwright
Hill Walter, wheelwright, &c.
Kierman Owen, surgeon
Lovecraft Wm. gentleman
Luscombe Thos. gent. *Hall*
Pitman Rev John, B.C.L., *vicar* (and rector of Washford,) *Vicarage*
Preston Wm. schoolmaster
Skinner Wm. schoolmaster
Taylor Richard, blacksmith
Widger Ellenor, *post office*
Williams Thos. vict., *Church House*
Williams John, cooper

BAKERS.
Pearce Wm. | Stones James

BUTCHERS.
Luscombe Jno.
Luscombe Sml.
Palk George

FARMERS.
(* *are Owners.*)
Barons Rd.
* Blackler John
* Blackler Wm.
French Charles
Harris John
Mann Wm.
Mann W. jun.
* Michelmore Rt.
* PalkEdw.,*Pool*
* Skinner Chas.
Skinner Edw.
Skinner Hy. R.

* Venning Wm.
* Way Wm. D.

SHOEMAKERS.
Jenkins Samuel
Pearce Jenkins
Williams Thos.

SHOPKEEPERS.
Evans Carln.
Hamlyn Hannah
Harris Hy. (and cooper)
Williams Thos.

TAILORS.
Bowden Robt.
Madge Samuel
Waycott John

BUCKLAND-IN-THE-MOOR is a parish of scattered houses, partly in the picteresque valley of the Dart, and adjoining Dartmoor Forest, and the Haytor Granite Rocks, 3¼ miles N.W. of Ashburton. It contains only 116 souls, and 1457A. 3R. 13P. of land, of which 805 acres are wood and plantations. E. R. P. Bastard, Esq., owns most of the soil, and is lord of the manor. He has a handsome seat here called *Buckland Court*, which was enlarged and beautified about 25 years ago, by the widow of the late John Pollexfen Bastard, Esq. The *Church* is a small ancient edifice, with a tower and five bells. It is now undergoing a thorough reparation. The *perpetual curacy* is annexed to the vicarage of Ashburton, and has 13A. 2R. 12P. of glebe, but no parsonage. *Reddicliff Farm* (60A.,) has been held from an early period for the repairs of the church and the payment of small salaries to the clerk and sexton. It is let for about £40 a year, and is supposed to have been given by *Eliz. Cake*, in 1566.

Bastard E. R. P. Esq. *Court*
Hamlyn John, blacksmith
FARMERS.
Head John || Hext Thomas
Mann William, *Beera*

Norrish James, (owner,) *Stone*
Smerdon Edward, *Southbrook*
Smerdon James || Smerdon Thos.
Smerdon Elisha, *Bowdens*
Smerdon Wm., *Reddicliffe*

CHURSTON-FERRERS is a pleasant village, on a gentle eminence on the south side of Torbay, 1½ mile W. of Brixham. Its parish has 2527A. 3R. 8P. of land, and 772 inhabitants, of whom 261 are in *Galmpton* hamlet, near the river Dart, 1 mile W. of the village. The lofty eminence of Warborough Common commands an extensive view of Torbay, and the southeastern coast of Devon. Sir J. B. Y. Buller, Bart., is lord of the manor of Churston-Ferrers, and his eldest son resides at *Churston Court*, the ancient seat of the Yardes, which has lately been modernised, and has tasteful

grounds, approached by a fine avenue of lofty elms. It passed at an early period from the Ferrers to the Yardes, whose heiress married the late Sir Francis Buller. J. F. Luttrell, Esq., owns *Galmpton*, and Col. Carlyon has a seat and estate at *Greenway.* The soil is mostly freehold, and well-adapted for the growth of corn. The *Church* is an ancient structure, with a tower and four bells. The interior has a fine old screen, and in a richly-carved niche over the porch, is a representation of the Crucifixion and the two Marys. The *perpetual curacy* is annexed to the vicarage of Brixham; and the tithes were commuted in 1840, the vicarial for £180, and the rectorial for £212. The latter belong to Miss Knollis. Here is a small dissenting chapel. The poor parishioners have 2½a. of land at Broadhempston, purchased in 1683, with £55 left by Saml. Skerdon and Thomas Edwards. They have also 10s. a year from *Kelly's Charity.* (See Brixham.) *In the following directory those marked* * *are at Galmpton.*

Buller Jno. Yarde, Esq. *Court*
Carlyon Col. *Greenway House*
*Gibbs Wm. ship & boat builder
*Gillham Thos. vict., Horse Shoe
*Matthews Wm. vict. *Dartmouth Inn*
Pengelly Henry, vict., Sun
*Winsor John, carpenter
FARMERS.
Bailey John ‖ Collings Wm.
*Chapman John ‖ *Grant Nicholas
Hannaford John, *Greenway*
Jones Giles ‖ Lewis Wm.
Manning Nicholas, *Greenway*

Randall Samuel, *Barton*
*Tilley Jno. ‖ *Edw. ‖ and Wm.
Turpin Jas. (& steward to Sir J. B. Y. Buller, Bart.)
BLACKSMITHS.
2 Gillham John
2 Gillham Thos.
Heath Samuel
SHOEMAKERS.
Hill Peter
Harris Wm.
Harris John
*Holmes John

*Sanders Edw.
SHOPKEEPERS.
*Cuming Robert
*Dart Mary
Harris Henry
Langdon John
TAILORS.
Harris Jeffry
Tucker John

COCKINGTON, a parish of scattered houses, 2 miles W. of Torquay, has only 203 souls, and about 1000 acres of land, extending to the cliffs of Torbay, where a great part of the sea wall was washed down Oct. 13th, 1849, but is now rebuilt. C. H. Mallock, Esq., owns most of the parish, and is lord of the manors of *Cockington* and *Chelston.* He resides at Cockington Court, a large stone mansion, in a well-wooded lawn; and is also owner of *Livermead House*, a beautiful villa on the sea coast. The *Church* is a small antique fabric, and the living is a perpetual curacy, annexed to that of Tor-Moham. C. H. Mallock, Esq., is patron, and also impropriator of the rectory, and has the power of proving wills here. Seven *Almshouses*, for as many poor people of this parish, were built by *Sir George Cary*, who endowed them, in the 6th of James I., with a yearly rent charge of £30, out of the manors of Cockington and Chelston. Seven new houses were given in exchange for the old ones about 1790, and there is a sum of about £230 three per cent. consols belonging to the charity. The seven almspeople are appointed by the lord of the manors, and each has a weekly stipend of 1s. 6d., and a new frieze gown and smock, or shirt, yearly. The poor parishioners have the interest of £88, left by *George Baker* in 1794, and of £20, left by four donors, and vested with the overseers.

Furse Mrs. *Chelston House*
Kellegrew Henry, dairyman
Lander Richard, parish clerk
Ley George, gentleman

Mallock Chas. Herbert, Esq. *Cockington Court*
Murch Mrs My. *Livermead House*
Sowdon Mr William

COFFINSWELL, a small village and parish, 4 miles S.E. of Newton-Abbot, contains 215 souls, and 1100 acres of land, including the hamlet of *Daccombe.* Sir W. P. Carew, Bart., is lord of the manor; but part of the soil belongs to H. L. Brown, Esq., and a few smaller owners. The *Church*

(St. Bartholomew,) is an ancient structure, with a tower and four bells. It was repaired in 1844, and its *curacy* is annexed to the vicarage of St. Mary Church, in the patronage and appropriation of the Dean and Chapter of Exeter. The tithes were commuted in 1843, for £238 per annum.

	FARMERS. (* *at Daccombe.*)
Eastley John, parish clerk	*Codner Wm. ‖ Devonshire Thos.
Leyman John, carpenter	*Grills John ‖ *Harvey Wm.
Perkins George, carpenter	*Hill Joseph ‖ Rendell John, jun
Ridgeway Richard, shoemaker	

DENBURY, a scattered village, pleasantly situated, in a valley 3 miles S.S.W. of Newton Abbot, has in its parish 470 souls, and 1068 acres of land. It has a cattle fair on the 19th of September, and formerly had a market, granted by Edward I. In ancient records, it is described as a borough. General Taylor owns a great part of the soil, and is lord of the *manor*, which belonged to the Archbishop of York in the Confessor's reign, and to Tavistock Abbey at Domesday survey. After the Reformation, it was held by the Russells, who sold it to the Reynells, one of whose co-heiresses carried it in marriage to Captain Taylor, in the reign of Queen Anne. The Rev. R. H. Froude, Mr. J. Badcock, and a few smaller owners, have estates here; and *Denbury House*, a large Elizabethan mansion, is the seat of Miss Froude. The *Church* (St. Mary,) has a tower and five bells, and has been restored and beautified during the last four years, at the expense of Miss Froude and other subscribers. The *rectory*, valued in K.B. at £12. 7s. 6d., and in 1831 at £201, is in the patronage of the Rev. John Richard Bogue, B.A., and incumbency of the Ven. Robert H. Froude, M.A., who is also rector of Dartington, and Archdeacon of Totnes. The *Rectory House* is a good residence, which was enlarged by its occupant, the patron and curate, in 1847. The glebe is 20 acres, and the tithes were commuted in 1839, for £186. 10s. per annum. Here is a *Baptist Chapel*, built in 1843, at the expense of Mr. T. Elliott, and other contributors. Eight cottages, a house, and blacksmith's shop, and about 3 acres of land, have been vested in trust from an early period, for the repairs of the church and highways, and for charitable uses. They are now let for about £24 per annum, part of which is applied towards the support of the *National School*, built in 1821, on land given by Mr. Bartlett. The interest of £10, left by *John Simming*, is distributed in Bibles to poor children; and the poor have 20s. a year from *John Peter's Charity.* (See Cornworthy.)

	BOOT&SHOE MKS.	Elliott T. jun.,
Bogue Rev John Richard, B.A. curate and patron, *Rectory*	Cowell John	*Buckridge*
Fox Thomas, shopkeeper	Lee John	Ford John
Froude Miss Margt. *Denbury House*	Rowe George	Shapley James
Peeke Matthew, butler	Rowe Michael	Tucker Hy. H.
Sanders Jeremiah, cabinet maker	Rowe Wm.	Wakeham Nichls.
Shapley James, *National School*	CARPENTERS.	(& butcher)
Taylor John, vict. Union	Furneaux Wm.	Wakeham Wm.
Thomas James Wm., Esq., *Shute*	Williams John	TAILORS.
Wakeham Thomas, baker	FARMERS.	Mills Wm.
Wills Wm. vict. Church House	Badcock Josiah	Snelling Samuel
Winsor Henry, parish clerk	Bowden Mattw.	
BLACKSMITHS.	Taylor John	Elliott Thomas,	POST OFFICE
Cole Wm.		*Holwell*	at G. Rowe's

IPPLEPEN, a large village, on a pleasant declivity, 3½ miles S. by W. of Newton Abbot, and 4½ miles N.N.E. of Totnes, gives name to a large *deanery*, and has in its parish 966 inhabitants, and 3070 acres of fertile land, including the hamlets of *Daignton*, *Combe-Fishacre*, *Asstor*, and *Castle-*

ford. It had a grant for a market and fair, in 1317, but both have been obsolete some centuries. The manor was given by William the Conqueror to Ralph de Fulgerüs, and one of his descendants gave it to the Abbey of St. Peter, at Fulgers, which had a cell here. In 1658, the manor was sold in parcels to the landowners, by Sir John Pettus. The Rev. N. Brooking John Shepherd, Esq., and James Neale, Esq., are now the principal proprietors, and here are several smaller owners. The parish has some fine rocky scenery and several subterraneous rivulets, in the small valley called *Stony Coombs.* Having been seized by the Crown from the alien Abbey of St. Peter, the *rectorial glebe and tithes* of *Ipplepen and Woodland*, were given to the College of St. Mary Ottery, and at the dissolution they were given, with the advowson of the vicarage, to the Dean and Canons of Windsor, of whom they are now held on lease by the Rev. N. Brooking, who resides at the *Rectory House*, and is also incumbent of the *vicarage*, valued in K.B. at £26. 2s. 3½d., and in 1831 at £119. The Vicarage House was repaired in 1849, and is occupied by Mr. Snape, and the tithes were commuted in 1838. The *Church* (St. John Baptist,) is a large antique fabric, with a tower and six bells. It stands on an eminence at the head of the village, and contains a finely carved old screen and pulpit. Here is a Wesleyan Chapel, built in 1826, and another small chapel is used jointly by Baptists and Independents. The poor parishioners have 20s. a year left by John Peter, out of the great tithes of Cornworthy, and an annuity of 6s. 8d., left by Richard Kelly, as noticed with Brixham. *In the following Directory those marked * are at Castleford, + at Combe-Fishacre, and § at Daignton.*

Adams Ann, vict. Wellington
Adams Edmund, parish clerk
Adams Thomas, carpenter
Adams Wm. vict. Plough
+Bishop John, auctioneer & surveyor
Bowden Jane, milliner
Bowden John, merchant, Park hill
Brooking Mrs Chtte. *Church Park Cotg*
Brooking Rev Nicholas, *Rectory*
Buller Mr Wm. Templer
Calley Thos. gent. || Drake Misses
Elliott Thomas, corn miller
Fletcher Eliz. G., *National School*
Hellyer James, master mariner
Hugo Walter, Esq., *North End Hs*
Kettle —, corn miller
Lee Joseph, travelling tea dealer
Luscombe Thomas, gent
§Mather Mr Wm.|| Murch Richard
+Shepherd John, Esq., & Rev Edw.
Snape Mr Joseph, *Vicarage*
Wainwright Miss Hannah
Wills Wm. surgeon, (& *Totnes*)
FARMERS.
+Berry Jeffery || +Bishop John
Bovey Thos. || *Bushell John

Easterbrook Thos. || *Elliott John
Emery Jasper || Harris George
Fetherbridge Thomas, *Asstor*
§Fletcher John || §Hunt Richard
§Lambshead Sml.||Luscombe John
*Morgan Amos || +Moyse Nicholas
Neale James, *Ambrook*
Palk Richard || +Palk Edward
Smerdon Hugh || Smerdon Robert
§Sowton John || Willis Charles
Symons Edward, *Bully Barton*
Sowton Richard || Yelland Wm.

BAKERS.
Adams John
Vickery Robert
BLACKSMITHS.
Ager Rd. beerhs
Ager Wm.
Langler Jas. whgt
Maddicott James
BUTCHERS.
Bovey Thomas
Yelland Joseph
MASONS.
Bovey Thomas
Winsor Henry

SHOPKEEPERS.
Emmett John
Smith Richard
Smith Robert
SHOPKEEPERS.
Bovey Ann
Bovey Ellinor
Yelland Joseph
TAILORS.
Cload Wm.
Lee Wm.
POST-OFFICE at
Ann Bovey's

KINGSKERSWELL, or KING'S CARSWELL, is a pleasant scattered village, mostly on an acclivity, near the junction of the Torquay and South Devon Railways, 2¼ miles S.S.E. of Newton Abbot, and 4 miles N.W. by W. of Torquay. Its parish contains 845 souls, and 1740 acres of fertile land,

including the hamlets of *North and South Whilborough,* more than a mile south of the church.   Henry Langford Brown, Esq., owns a great part of soil, and is lord of the manor.   He has a handsome seat here, in the Tudor style, called *Barton Lodge,* built in 1838-'9, and '40, at the cost of about £10,000, from a design by Mr. Gribble, the architect, and having a finely wooded lawn, commanding extensive views.   Sir W. W. Yea, Bart., and a few smaller owners have estates here.   The manor was held by the Crown at Domesday survey.   It afterwards passed to the Droun, Fitz-Count, Courtenay, Smyth, and Langford families.   The latter left it to the Browns in 1710.   The *Church* (St. Mary,) stands in the valley, at the foot of the village, and is an ancient structure, with a tower and five bells.   It was re-pewed about ten years ago, at the expense of Mr. Brown, and the Rev. A. Neck, the latter of whom gave the organ and a beautiful altar-piece. It con-tains some ancient monuments of the Dinhams.   The Dean and Chapter of Exeter are appropriators of the rectorial tithes, and the living is a *perpetual curacy,* valued in 1831 at £105, in the patronage of the Vicar of St. Mary Church, and incumbency of the Rev. Aaron Neck, B.A., who built a new parsonage house, about 11 years ago.   The tithes were commuted in 1841, the rectorial for £210. 1s., and the small tithes for £145.   The Wesleyans have a chapel, and the Baptists a meeting-room here.   The incumbent of the church has about 5a. of land, left by Philippa Creed, in 1726, and the poor have 20s. a year, left by John Peter, in 1570, out of the tithes of Corn-worthy.   Here is a *National School,* chiefly supported by the incumbent, who clothes part of the children.   In an orchard are the foundations of an ancient building, in which some Roman coins were found a few years ago. The *limestone rock* in this parish might be worked with considerable profit, for the supply of Exeter and the neighbourhood.

Adams Mr Elias, & John, parish clk
Barter Mr Jas. || Brooking Wm.
Barter Wm. auctioneer, *Rose Villa*
Brown Hy. Langford, Esq. *Barton L*
Bussell Mr John || Codner Mrs E.
Codner Rd., jun. spirit & cider mert
Crocker Wm. *National School*
Dart Cphr. vict. Manor House
Gale Henry, fishmonger
Grills Edw. gent || Elwin Mrs
Harvey Thos. gent || Preston Mrs
Hicks Elisha, vict. Lord Nelson
Jarvis John. gent. *Rock View*
Mason Major Edw.||Stark Mrs
Metherell Ebenezer, relieving officer
Metherell Miriam draper, &c.; h St
    Mary Church
Neck Rev Aaron, B.A.
Neck Wm. gentleman
Stooks John, timber mert. & builder
Stooks Wm. timber merchant, &c
Sweeting Lieutenant Wm., R.N.
Symonds Rev Geo. Edw., B.A. curate
Turner Mr Joseph
Wale Jno. land agent, *Rock Cottage*
Williams Rd. vict. Seven Stars

BAKERS.
Bellamy Henry
Shepherd James
Way George
BLACKSMITHS.
Neck Samuel
Lock Sml. whgt
BOOT & SHOE MRS.
Chenoweth Wm.
Hart John
Hopping John
Melhuish Saml.
Weeks John
Wollacott Saml.
BUTCHERS.
Crocker John
Mann John
CARPENTERS.
Adams John
Ball Wm.
Williams Richard
FARMERS.
(* *are Owners.*)
Barter Wm.
*Barter John
Barter Thomas
Brown Wm.
*Codner Richard

*Duder George
Duder Humphy.
Pridham Richard
Shapley John
Turner Zach.
*Wale Wm.
Whiteway Saml.
Whiteway Wm.
MASONS.
Shepherd James
Wollacott John
SHOPKEEPERS.
Chenoweth Wm.
Cockeram Jane
Crocker John
Ford Richard
Hart John
Popham Thomas
White Samuel
TAILORS.
Lake Wm.
Rich Thomas
Walling James
POST-OFFICE at
Jane Howe's
RAILWAY
Trains to Exeter ,
Torquay, &c

T 2

KINGSWEAR is a remarkably small parish, on a point of land project-ing into the river Dart, opposite Dartmouth, and contracting the entrance to the harbour. It contains only 270 inhabitants, and 107A. 2R. 10P. of land. J. F. Luttrell, Esq., is chief owner and also lord of the manor, which was anciently a royal demesne, and had a small *castle* or *fort*, the walls of which are still standing, and near them are the ruins of another fort, where tradition says, the chain was fixed to prevent hostile ships from entering the harbour. On the brow of the hill, overlooking the village, are some embankments, which were thrown up during the siege of Dartmouth, in 1646. The *Beacon*, an elegant mansion, built in 1848, on a delightful eminence, overlooking the Dart, is the seat of A. H. Holdsworth, Esq. The *Church* (St. Thomas a Beckett,) was rebuilt at the cost of £1600, in 1847, except the tower, which contains a clock and three bells. It is in the de-corated style, and is neatly fitted up with open benches, &c. The *perpetual curacy*, valued in 1831, at £99, is in the patronage of the Vicar of Brixham, and incumbency of the Rev. John Smart. The *Church Lands*, &c., have been vested in trust from an early period, and comprise four houses, nine gardens, and about half an acre of land, let for only £12 a year, in con-sideration of fines paid on the renewal of leases. There are also belonging to the trust five chief rents, producing 9s. 10d. per annum. The *Poors' Land* comprises about 2½A., and with a stable upon it, is let for about £8. 10s. per annum, which is carried to the poor rates. The poor parish-ioners have 40s. a year from *John Peter's and Richard Kelly's Gifts*, as noticed with Cornworthy and Brixham.

Alford Edward, ship builder	Nelson Chas. gent. ‖ Vosper James
Avis Thomas, chair maker	Newman Mrs Mary
Back John, architect & surveyor	Norcombe Wm. tailor
Cox Jas. vict. Plume of Feathers	Peters Charles, cooper
Farley Philip, blacksmith	Roope Major Genl. Benj. & Miss S.
Holdsworth Arthur Howe, Esq. go-vernor of Dartmouth Castle, *The Beacon*	Short Thomas, mason
	Smart Rev John, incbt. *Raven's Well*
	Veale Harriet, shopkeeper
Hyne Samuel, carpenter	Winsor Henry, shoemaker

LITTLE HEMPSTON, a small scattered village, in a valley opening to the Dart, 2 miles N.E. of Totnes; has in its parish 268 souls, and 1270A. 3R. 17P. of fertile land. The manor, anciently held by the Arundells, be-longs to the Duke of Cleveland and the Countess of Sandwich; but F. Cornish, Esq., and other freeholders have estates here. *Gatcomb*, a seat which was rebuilt by the late C. Cornish, Esq., was the birth place of *Zachary Bogan*, a learned divine, who published treatises on the idioms of Homer and Hesiod. The *Church* (St. John,) is a small antique fabric, and the living is a *rectory*, valued in K.B. at £19s. 15s. 2½d., and in 1831 at £201, in the gift of the Lord Chancellor, and incumbency of the Rev. F. H. Hele, M.A. The glebe is 56A. 2R. 11P., and the tithes were commuted in 1838 for £207 per annum. £138, left to the poor by *Cphr. Blackhall*, and other donors, was laid out in 1727, in the purchase of Dreadon close, (10A.) now let for about £13 a year. The poor parishioners have also a yearly rent charge of £9. 5s. 6d., out of the great tithes of Berry Pomeroy, left by *William Bogan*, in 1723. They have likewise the dividends of £111. 2s. 3d. Old South Sea Annuities, purchased in 1744, with arrears of this rent charge.

Elliott James, jun. land surveyor	Holman John, blacksmith
Evans Margaret, vict. Bolton Arms	Jordon Walter, carpenter
Hele Rev Fitz Henry, M.A., *Rectory*	Lake Richard, shopkeeper

Tibbitt Thos. carpenter & vict. New Bridge Inn
Tucker George, parish clerk
Weston Henry, Esq. *Park Hill*
Williams Hy. B., Esq. *Gatcomb*
FARMERS. (* *are Owners.*)
*Blackler John, *Lilliput*

*Elliott Jas. sen. *Top Hempston*
Lang Rt. and John || Evans Agnes
*Palk Charles, (& cider merchant)
Preston John, (& miller,) *Fishacre*
Rape John & Wm. || Skinner Thos.
*Whiteway Thomas, *Bokeyt*

MARLDON, a small village, 5 miles E.N.E. of Totnes, has in its parish 470 souls, and 2254 acres of land, including the village of *Compton*, a mile N. by W. of the church. Parkfield House is the pleasant seat of Francis Garrett, Esq., who owns a great part of the parish, and, a few years ago, purchased the ancient mansion called *Compton Castle*, now occupied by his gardener. This castellated house was the seat of Sir Maurice de Pole, in the reign of Henry II., and it was afterwards held by the Comptons, Gilberts, and Templers. The manor of *Stanton* belongs to Chas. H. Mallock, Esq ; and Wm. Randell, Esq., and several smaller freeholders have estates here. The *Church* is an ancient structure, with a tower and four bells, and the benefice is a curacy annexed to the vicarage of Paignton. The poor have 1¼A. of land, given by an unknown donor, and 6s. 8d. yearly from Kelly's Gift. (See Brixham.) *In the following Directory those marked thus § are in Compton.*

§Adams Richard, smith & shopkpr
Archer Benjamin, beer seller
Bishop Richard, cider merchant
Bridgman Thos. vict. Royal Oak
§Bussell Fanny, corn miller
Garrett Fras., Esq., *Parkfield House*
Lidstone Robert, shopkeeper
§Matthews Robert, gardener
Neck John, shoemaker
§Neck Samuel, shoemaker
Palk Charles, butcher
Partridge Peter, vict. Church House
Rawl Wm. tailor

Shears Wm. parish clerk
§Smith Wm. wheelwright
§White Thomas, mason
Youldon Nicholas, shoemaker
FARMERS.
§Anthony Richard || Bond John
Bartlett Jacob || Bartlett —
Bowden John || Browse Wm.
§Dimond John || §Otteway Wm.
Northcott Thos. || Pook Charles
Sampson Wm. || Whiteway Robert
Upcott John Kingdon

ST. MARY CHURCH, a handsome village and picturesque parish, with many neat mansions and marine cottages, overlooking Babbicombe Bay, may be considered as a suburb of Torquay, being only from one to two miles north of that "queen of watering places." The parish had 1668 inhabitants in 1841, but it has now more than 2000, about 100 houses having been built here during the last seven years. It comprises 2589A. 2R. 35P. of land, including the hamlets of *Babbicombe, Barton, Combe-Pafford, Edginswell*, and *Collaton-Shiphay*, all situated near the bold and rugged rocky cliffs of the southern recess of Babbicombe Bay, which is divided from Torbay by the bold promontory of Tor Point, or Hope's Nose. The road from Mary Church down to Babbicombe, near the beach, is on *marble rock*, and the lofty cliffs are of the same beautiful lime-stone, which is extensively got, and burnt into lime for agricultural and building purposes. The finer blocks are used as building stone, and in the manufacture of beautiful chimney-pieces, vases, urns, tables, monuments, &c., which are made here in great variety, at the extensive *marble works* of Mr. J. Woodley. Here are two good inns, and on the beach are two bathing machines, about 20 fishing boats, two yachts, and a coast guard station. A little south of Babbicombe is *Kent's Hole*, a large cavern, which has been explored about 600 feet, to the point where water prevents any further ingress. Bones of the

hyæna, bear, elephant, &c., have been found in it. About half a mile to the west is *Anstey's Cove*, a very romantic spot. Between the hills opening towards this cove, and at a short distance from the sea, stands BISHOP-STOWE, the new palace of the Bishop of Exeter. This beautiful mansion is in the Italian style, and was built in 1841-'2, from the design and under the superintendence of Mr. Gribble, architect, of Torquay. It is very irregular in its elevations, being composed of several projecting and receding parts, of various heights, forms, and sizes; one of which, at the southern angle, over-tops all the rest, and forms a square tower, with a pointed finial rising from the centre of its roof. The grounds in front rise in three beautiful terraces, connected by flights of steps, and the lower one having a fountain. The house has many handsome apartments, and reflects the highest credit on the skill of the architect; and the views from it and the grounds are varied and pleasing; so much of the sea only being visible as serves to enhance the beauty of the wood and rock in the foreground. *Cadwell House*, built by the late Sir Thomas Louis, who was created a *baronet* in 1806, is now the seat of his son, Admiral Sir John Louis, Bart. *Shiphay House*, another neat mansion, is the seat of the Rev. Thomas Kitson. Part of *Edginswell* is the property of the Rev. Aaron Neck, who resides at the manor-house. The *manor of Combe-Pafford* belongs to Sir J. V. Palk, and that of St. Mary Church to R. S. S. Cary, Esq. H. L. Brown, Esq., Mr. D. Woodley, and several other proprietors have estates in the parish. The *Church* (St. Mary,) is a large ancient structure, with a tower and four bells, and stands on a bold eminence. The Dean and Chapter of Exeter are appropriators of the great tithes, and patrons of the *vicarage*, valued in K.B. at £31. 11s., and in 1831 at £375, with the curacy of Coffinswell annexed to it. The Rev. W. Maskell, M.A., is the incumbent, and has a good residence, but only an acre of glebe. R. S. S. Cary, Esq., is lessee of the rectory. The vicarial tithes were commuted in 1841 for £205 per annum. In the parish are two *chapels*, belonging to *Baptists* and *Wesleyans*; and also *National Schools* for boys, girls, and infants, established in 1828, in a building given by C. Protheroe, Esq. The poor have the interest of £72, left by *George Baker*, and an annuity of 40s., left by Jacob Bickford in 1723. In the following Directory, those marked 1 are at *Babbicombe*; 2, *Barton*; 3, *Combe-Pafford*; 4, *Edginswell*; and 5, at *Collaton-Shiphay.*

Appleton Henry, surgeon
Bartlett Wm., Esq., *Ilsham*
Bishop of Exeter, *Bishopstowe*
Bradshaw Wm. surgeon
Brunel I. civil engineer, *Watcomb*
Carr Wm. & S., Esq., New Park
1 Castley Capt., R.N., *Grove Cottage*
Charlton Thos., Esq. || Daw Mr Wm
Domville Rev Danl. E., M.A. curate
Dowler Wm. gent. || Drane Ts. gent.
Evans Thos. road surveyor, &c
3 Gedge Mr Jno. || Hooper T. *organt*
Hannaford Thos. cooper & collector
Hatch Charles, draper
Johnstone Rev Wm. curate
Jones Josiah, hair dresser
Keble Rev Thomas, curate
Kitson Rev Thos., M.A. incumbent of Haccombe, *Shiphay House*
1 Lear Mr John, lodgings
Louis Admiral Sir John, Bart. *Cadwell House*
Marshall Storer, *National School*
Maskell Rev Wm., M.A. vicar and bishop's chaplain, *Vicarage*
Middy Hy. music professor
Moore John, saddler
Neck Rev Aaron, B.A. incumbent of Kingskerswell, *Edginswell Barton*
Parsons John, constable
Potts Thos., Esq. || Phillips Misses
Russell George, chimney sweeper
Shairp Lieut. S. coast guard
Shore Hon. Mrs || Strong Lud. gent
1 Stoyle Thomas, fly, &c. letter
Taylor Saml. Henley, highway surveyor, & agent to Union Ins. Co.
Thorne Geo. gent., Cary Castle

Waymouth Saml. parish clerk
Waymouth Sophia, schoolmistress
1 Whitehead Geo. gent. & Mrs Eliz.
Wills Sarah, staymaker
Woodley John, marble chimney piece, urn, vase, &c. mfr. *Marble Works*
Woodley Daniel, marble merchant

INNS & TAVERNS.
1 Cary Arms Inn, Wm. Gasking
Commercial Inn, Eliz. Bradley
New Inn, Susan Horne
3 Palk Arms, Hy. Adams, (brewer)
1 Roughwood Inn, Robert Rowden

BAKERS.
1 Bulling Wm.
Lee John
Partridge Richd.
3 Waymouth Jno.

BEERHOUSES.
Hill Thomas
3 Littlejohn Jph.
3 Prowse George

BLACKSMITHS.
Lamble Wm.
3 Littlejohn Jph.

Matthews Thos.
Sandford John
BOOT & SHOE MRS.
Oliver John
Waymouth Saml.
Waymouth Wm.

BUTCHERS.
Bovey Wm.
Medland John
Nickels Cphr.
Tozer Wm.

CARPENTRS. & BDS
Ash Robert
1 Gasking Wm.
Lear Rt. *cabt. mr*
Taylor Saml. sen
Taylor Sl. & Wm
Taylor Wm. sen.

FARMERS.
Adams Joseph
3 Bowden Wm.
3 Collings Thos.
2 Dreaton John
Hall Wm.
4 King John
5 Mudge Thomas
3 Nickels Mary
2 Nickels George
Petherick John
Short Nicholas
4 Sowden John
*Staddon Wm.
Walling John

GROCERS, &c.
Adams Wm.
Hookway Jane

3 Prowse George
Thomas Thomas
Wilcox Martha
LIME BURNERS.
2 Hoddar John
2 Mudge Matthew
MASONS, &c.
Bowden Thomas
1 Matthews John
1 Matthews Rd.
Thomas John
PAINTERS & GLZS.
Hill Arthur
2 Mc Laren Jas.
TAILORS.
Adams Edward
Drew John
TINNERS.
2 Gange Wm.
2 Mc Laren Jas.
POST-OFFICE
at S. H. Taylor's.
RAILWAY.
Trains, &c. from
Torquay.

PAIGNTON, which gives name to a large petty sessional division, is a neat and improving village and *bathing place*, delightfully situated on the central part of the semi-circular shore of Torbay, about 3½ miles S.W. of Torquay, six miles N.W. of Brixham, and 5½ miles E. by N. of Totnes. Its parish increased its population from 1575 in 1801, to 2501 souls in 1841, and has now upwards of 3000. It comprises 5092 acres of land, and the scattered hamlets, &c, of *Collaton-Kirkham, Goodrington, Blagdon, Preston, Polsham, Yalberton, &c.*, extending more than two miles S., and one mile N., along the shore of the beautiful bay. Paignton has risen into notice as a place of resort for invalids during the last fifteen years, and is capable of being made a first-rate watering place, having a good beach, and a large extent of contiguous ground, which may be converted into a beautiful esplanade and carriage drive. The parish and neighbourhood form one of the most fertile parts of Devon, and abound in extensive orchards, celebrated for excellent *cider*, of which great quantities are shipped here for London and other markets, in small vessels, which bring in coal, &c. The district is also famous for very large and sweet *cabbages*, called " Paignton cabbages," of which great quantities are sent to all parts of the county. A pier was constructed here in 1838, under the powers of an Act of Parliament, which enables vessels of 150 tons to load and unload their cargoes. The pier cost about £5000, raised in £10 shares. Paignton was held from an early period by the Bishops of Exeter, who had a palace here, of which there are still some ivy mantled remains near the church. Bishop Veysey conveyed it, by royal requisition, to the Earl of Pembroke, and it was sold in 1644 to Sir Henry Cary. In 1654, it was purchased by S. Kelland. Esq., but it has for some time been held by the Templers, and a minor of that family is now lord of the manor. Collaton-Kirkham belongs to M. E. N. Parker, Esq.; *Primley* is the property and residence of the Rev. Finney Belfield; and *Steartfield House* is the pleasant seat of the Rev. Robert Gee, M.A. The Tyrrell, Jackson, Hunt, Browse, Allen, and other families

have estates in the parish. Paignton had a grant for a *market* and *fair*, in 1294. The former has long been obsolete, and the latter is now held on Whit-Monday, for the sale of cattle, &c. *Petty Sessions* are held at the Crown and Anchor Inn, on the first Monday of every month, and Mr. G. Hearder, of Torquay, is clerk to the magistrates. *Wm. Adams*, a native of Paignton, and buried here in 1687, was one of the five persons whose extraordinary escape from slavery at Algiers, and wonderful preservation in an open boat, in their passage to the coast of Spain, are related in "Wanley's Wonders of the Little World." The *Church* (St. John,) is a large and handsome structure, with a tower and six bells, and has a nave, aisles, chancel, and transepts. The west entrance, under the tower, is a fine specimen of the enriched Anglo Norman style, with receding columns, and the chevron and other ornaments of the period of Henry I. In the interior are several ancient monuments of the Kirkham family, but some of the effigies, &c., are mutilated. The *vicarage*, rated in K.B. at £52. 1s. 0½d., and in 1831 at £498, with the curacy of Marldon annexed to it, is in the patronage of Sir S. H. Northcote, Bart., and the heirs of the late Rev. J. Templer; and in the incumbency of the Rev. Robert Gee, M.A., of Steartfield, who is also lessee of the *rectory and the manor of Preston*, which were appropriated to the Precentor of Exeter Cathedral, by Bishop Quivil, in the reign of Edward I. There are three *chapels* in the parish, belonging to Independents, Baptists, and Wesleyans. The *National School*, built in 1829, with two rooms for boys and girls, was enlarged in 1846, by the addition of a room for infants, and a house for the teachers. It is attended by about 250 children, and is partly supported by subscription and a portion of the parochial charities. The Parish Lands, &c., comprise about 20a., and seven houses, let for about £52 a year, to which are added the dividends of £500 three per cent. consols, purchased by the trustees with money derived from fines paid by the lessees, except £18 left by *Jane Yabbacombe*. Part of the land was purchased with £150 left by *John* and *Charles Kellond*, in 1692 and '5. The rents and dividends are applied chiefly in schooling and apprenticing poor children. The dividends of £1000 three per cent. consols, left by *Allan Belfield*, in 1800, are paid to the schoolmaster for teaching 20 poor children to read, write, and cast accounts, and for finding them school books, &c. The poor have the following *yearly gifts*:—viz., 20s. left by *John Peter*, out of Cornworthy tithes; 6s. 8d. left by *Rd. Kelly*; £4 left by *Matthew Neck*, in 1709, out of Langridge close; 20s. left by *Thomas Butland*; 20s. left by *Wm. Furneaux*; 20s. out of Furze Park, left by *John Gardner*; and 10s. as the interest of £10, left by *Margaret Squarry*, in 1747. In the following DIRECTORY, those marked 1 are at *Blagdon*; 2, *Polsham*; 3, *Preston*; 4, *Southfield*; 5, *Yellands*; 6, *Collaton*; 7, *Goodrington*; 8, *Yalberton*; and 9, at *Roundham place*.

5 Ackrell Wm. bathing machine onr
Barnes Misses || Berry Mr W.
Beckley John, Esq. *Preston House*
Belfield Rev F. & Jno., Esq. *Primley*
Besley Wm. gent. *Oldway House*
Biggs Henry, hair dresser
2 Blackaller Dr Jacob, *Steart House*
Bleazby Rev Wm. curate
2 Bond Mr Wm. || Browse Nicholas
Briscoe Miss || 2 Boyes Misses
Browse Allen, gent *Bay view*
Browse Hy. Jas. surgeon, *Weston*
Bunker Wm. jun., Palace place

Burton Samuel, farrier
Carrington Edm. gent. *Park hill*
3 Carter Samuel || Clark Mrs. A.
Cary Adw. cooper || Bundock Mrs
4 Cockram Edw. printer, &c
Corras Wm. tinner & ironmonger
6 Croaker Mr Thos. || Crews Wm
Deller Wm. Hy. gardener, &c
2 Devon Mrs || Edmonds Mrs
6 Eastley Mrs || Endacott Mrs
Fitzgerald Mrs || Gillard Miss
Gardener Chas. Edward, saddler
Gardner Mrs L. || 5 Geaves Miss

Gee Rev Robert, M.A. vicar, *Steartfield House*
Gillham Hy. coach builder
Goodridge John Jackson, surgeon
Goodridge Lieut Rd. || & Mrs Allen
Goodridge Mrs & Miss *Weston*
Groundwater Mr Lane Thomas
2 Harry Dr John, *The Retreat*
2 Hartland J. C. C. A. gent
2 Hartland Wm. B. surgeon
Hoare Mrs || Hooper Mrs
Hyne Lieut. Thos. Madge, R.N.
Izon Miss Harriet, Weston
4 Jarvis Thos. gent. || Hunt Mrs
Keast Miss || Knapman Robert
Lash Jph. Hy. || Langler Rd. par. clk
Lear Francis, shipwright
Lear Thomas, gardener
Lee Thos. B. tinner & ironmonger
Lome Mr Chp. || Eliz. glass, &c. dlr
Lyde Lieut. Geo., R.N. and Mrs
4 Mc Ilwaine Capt. Wm., R.N.
3 Martin Jemima, poulterer
5 Matthews Mr Jas. || Mercer Henry
Meatherill & Thomas, wheelwrights
Millman Fras. Wm. wheelwright
Mould Mr John Arnold
Narramore Charles, cooper
Nicks Anthony, rope & bag makers
Nutman Mr Rt. || Pemfraze Miss
7 Peel Mrs || Soady Misses, *Weston*
Prowse Mr John, Palace place
Reynell Capt. Jas. Hy. *Torbay Mnt*
Robinson John, bookseller, printer, Berlin wool dealer, &c
Scarbrough Shepherd, solr. *Parkfd*
Shears Jph. accountant & furrier
4 Studdy Misses S. and E.
Thomas Miss
Tappenden Edw. draper, &c
Tipton Mr John B. *Gerston House*
Tompson Jno. Northey, Esq. *Brookfd*
Tompson Miss, *Brookfield*
Toms Miss || 2 Voyses Miss C.
Tovey Alex. gent. || 7 Tulley Mrs
Tozer Mr John || Tozer Mrs Sus.
Wallis Samuel, shipwright
Weinholt Mr Jno. B. || West Mrs
Williams Rev W. H. (Independent)
Wilson Robt. travelling draper
Winsor Thomas, watchmaker
Winsor Wm. basket maker
Wolridge Chas. gent., Polsham

INNS & TAVERNS.
Crown & Anchor, Hy. Goodridge

Gerston Inn, Thomas Luscombe
Globe Inn, Daniel Millman
3 Half Moon, Wm. Endacott
3 Jolly Sailor, John Cross
London Inn, John Lyndon
3 Manor House, Wm. Bunker
New Pier Inn, Fras. Wm. Millman
6 Parker's Arms, Nicholas Cary
Torbay Inn, Mrs Reynolds
Victoria Inn, Wm. Mudge

ACADEMIES.
(* Boarding.)
4*Cockram Miss
Cooksley Saml.
Evans Eliz.
*D'Almaine Agts.
*Fletcher Alex P.
Foster Fdk. H.
*German Misses
*Gibbons Mary
Jenkins Ann

BAKERS.
Ching Robert
6 Cary Nicholas
Coose Wm.
Daniel James
Dolton Cath.
3 Lego Wm.
Pook Henry
Veall George
Winsor Wm.

BLACKSMITHS.
Meatherell A. B.
Pope James
Pope Richard

BOOT & SHOE MKS.
Coad John
George Henry
Hoyles Thomas
Langdon John
Langler Hanbl.
Langler Richard
Lear Wm.
Medland John
Middleton Wm.
Moxey John
Parnell John
Sparkes Thos.
Tulley John
Webber Edwin
Williams Thos.

BUTCHERS.
Carter John
Hannaford Gbl.
Kingwell John

Miller Andrew
Parnell Thos.

CARPENTERS AND BUILDERS.
3 Anderson Wm.
Coombes John
Perrott Thos.
Towell Wm.
Tozer Jno. R. K.
Wallis John
Webber Wm.

CHAIR MAKERS.
Mogridge Thos.
Nosworthy John

CIDER AND COAL MERCHANTS.
Churchward Ths.
2 Eales John
Hannaford Gbl.
Hunt Richard
Marchant Chas.

DRUGGISTS, &c.
Carnell Hy. D.
Merson Wm.

FARMERS.
(* are Owners.)
1 Berry Thomas
Berry Wm.
*7 Browse Jas.
*3 Butland Rt.
Coombes Henry
Coombes John
8 Distin John
*3 Distin Henry
3 Distin Thos.
3 Goodridge Jffy.
*Hanney Danl.
*Hunt Nichls. P.
8 Jackson Gabl.
*8 Jackson John
1 Mudge John
1 Mudge Wm.
1 Palk Mr
Rendell Saml.
6 Rossiter Saml.

Sibley Wm.
1 Searle Wm.
Shepherd John
Sparkes Jno. &W.
Tozer John
*Tozer Richard
Tozer Thomas
Trible Wm.
6 Widdicombe C.
GROCERS, &c.
Deller Edwin, (&
    plumber, &c)
Distin Grace
3 Finson My.
Foster John
Henley Mary
Hoyles Wm.
Lidstone Thos.
    (& ironmngr.)
Penny John
3 Pillar James
Pook Henry

Rossiter John, (&
    miller & regr.)
Steer Sarah
Tozer John
White Maria
Williams Mary
LODGINGS.
7 Angel Philip
Coombes James
3 Eales Wm.
Foster Mrs
2 Hodge Eliz.
2 Ingram Jas.
9 King Richard
7 Langdon Rd.
Lidstone Thos.
Lome Eliz.
Metherell A. B.
5 Mogridge Miss
Penny John
2 Skinner Sar.
Sparkes Wm.

Tappenden E.
3 Terry Jane
Towell Wm.
Tozer Mrs
9 Wood Mary
MASONS.
Drew Wm.
Dyer Thomas
Evans Richd.
King T. and W.
Thomas Henry
Woodley Walter
Weeks Thomas
MILLINERS.
Codbear Cath.
Crossman Jane
Evans Ann
Narramore Eliz.
Williams Mary
TAILORS.
Burge John
Evans Fredk.

Evans Samuel
Evans Wm.
5 Dunscombe Rd.
Footman Wm.
Parnell Wm.
Skinner A. A.
Webber George
Webber James
Winsor Thomas

POST-OFFICE
at Wm. Mer-
son's. Money
Orders granted
and paid
COACH & CARRI-
ERS pass daily
to TORQUAY,
Dartmouth and
Brixham
RAILWAY TRAINS
from Torquay

STAVERTON is a small village at the south-eastern extremity of its large parish, on the south side of the river Dart, 3 miles N.N.W. of Totnes. Its parish comprises 1069 souls, and 5356A. 2R. 5P. of land, rising boldly from the Dart valley, and including the hamlets of *Woolstone Green, Sparkwell,* and *Strechford,* many scattered farm-houses, and about 700 acres of *orchard grounds,* celebrated for excellent cider. In the northern part of the parish, about two miles S. of Ashburton, are the *Penn Recca Slate Quarries,* which have been worked for centuries, but only on a small scale till the last eight years, during which the present spirited company of proprietors have expended about £30,000, chiefly in tunnelling and open cuttings, which dispense with machinery for lifting, and afford facilities for economical working, possessed by no other quarries in the west of England. About 100 hands are now employed in getting the slate and preparing it for roofing purposes. It is found in immense blocks, and is of a beautiful sage-green colour. Great quantities of this durable slate are now sent to various parts of the kingdom, and many of the farm-houses, &c., in this neighbourhood, have been roofed with it since the time of Charles I. and James I. Ashburton Church was roofed in the former reign with slates from these quarries, and they remained till about ten years ago. At Pridhamsleigh is a large and curious *Limestone Cavern.* The Dean and Chapter of Exeter are lords of the *manor* of Staverton, and owners of six-tenths of the parish. Mr. John Maye is lord of the small *manor of Barkington;* and Lord Cranstoun is owner of *Pridhamsleigh.* There are also a few smaller owners, and the Dean and Chapter lands are held on leases renewable every 21 years. The *Church* (St. George,) is a large venerable structure, with a tower and six bells. It is mostly in the decorated style, and the living is a *vicarage,* valued in K.B. at £32. 14s. 9½d. and in 1831 at £394. The Rev. Wm. Martin is the incumbent, and has a neat residence and 3A. 31P. of glebe. The Dean and Chapter are patrons, and also appropriators of the great tithes, now leased to Mrs. Kitson. The tithes were commuted in 1842, the vicarial for £385, and the rectorial for £460 per annum. A handsome *New Church* is now building at *Landscove,* near *Woolston Green,* in the centre of the parish, at the cost of about £3000,

subscribed by Miss Champernoune and several smaller contributors. It will be endowed by the Dean and Chapter, and near it is a *Wesleyan Chapel*, built in 1841. The poor parishioners have 15A. of land, and £100 Navy five per cents., derived from £200, left by *Edward Bovey* in 1709. They have also 13A. of land, purchased with £200, left by *Edward Gould*, together with 20s. a year out of Bottom Park. For schooling and relieving the poor, the Rev. Thos. Baker left £200, which was invested in 1802 in £349. 15s. 4d. three per cent. consols. Of the income, £8 is applied in schooling poor children, together with the dividends of £66. 13s. 4d. of the same stock, left by *Thos. Bradridge* in 1815. The poor have also an annuity of 32s., left by *Wm. Gould*. In the following Directory, those marked 1 are at *Coombe;* 2, *Baddaford;* 3, *Partington;* 4, *Strechford;* 5, *Woolstone Green;* and 6 *at Weston.*

Beer Robert, vict. Ring of Bells
Bowden Mr Henry, *Landscove*
Martin Rev Peter, Vicarage
Penn Recca Slate Company ; Mr C.
   Robins, manager, *Landscove*
Rossiter Jno. R. corn miller, *Bridge*
Skinner Henry, vict. Church House
Towell John, vict. Union
   BLACKSMITHS.
Boon John
Dennis John
Parsons James
   CARPENTERS.
Hill Richard
Hill Matthew
Pomeroy Henry
Skinner Henry
   FARMERS.
(* *are Owners.*)
6 Barter Edw.

Bowden Chas.
2 Bowden John
Bowden Wm.
Bradridge Hy.
Brooking Fras.
Cockram Wm.
Edwards Thos.
2 Elliott Jeffry S.
Foster Mary
Hext James
*Hill Matthew
2 Hoare John

Lemon George
Mann Edward
Matthews Wm.
*3 Maye John
1 Maye Jeffery
3 Maye Philip
Maye Robert
4 Michelmore Pp.
Michelmore Ths.
6 Norrish Wm.
PalkNichs., *Wash*
*Perry Jno. & Rd.
Phillips Wm. & J.
*Rendall Wm.
1 Savery John
1 Sawdye Wm. H.
Searle Ann
Searle Thos.
Searle Wm.
*Searle Richd.

5 Sowerby Jno. Rt.
Stranger Hy. Wm.
2 Wakeham John
   and Son
5 Weymouth Jph.
4 Whiteway Wm.
Whiteway Jno., P.,
   & Thos., *Hole*
Whiteway John
Winsor Geo.
Winsor Thos.
   SHOEMAKERS.
Beer Robert
5 Palk Richard
   SHOPKEEPERS.
Beer Robert
5 Palk Richd.
Skinner Henry
5 Tinkham Peter
Towell John

STOKE-GABRIEL, 3½ miles S E. of Totnes, is a neat village picturesquely scattered on the east bank of the estuary of the Dart, where a small creek projects about a mile eastward, and by being dammed up is made to turn the wheel of a tidal corn mill. Its parish contains 691 inhabitants, and 2595A. of land, fertile and well-wooded, and rising boldly from the Dart and the creek. It has several handsome mansions, and the small hamlets, &c., of *Ash, Watton,* and *Portbridge.* Henry Studdy, Esq., of *Watton Court,* a handsome modern Elizebethan mansion, is lord of the manor of Watton or Wadeton. *Sandridge,* a large and beautiful mansion, built by the late Lord Ashburton, is the property of Lord Cranstoun, but is now unoccupied. Sir R. L. Newman, Capt. Rhodes, Mrs. Douglas, and several residents, have estates here, mostly freehold. The Dart and its creek abound in salmon. The *Church* (St. Gabriel,) is a fine antique fabric, with a tower and five bells. It is mostly in the later decorated style, but has undergone many repairs, and the south entrance is in the Tudor style. It has several neat monuments, and in the church-yard is a remarkably large yew tree. The *vicarage,* valued in K.B. at £16. 11s. 10½d., and in 1831 at £170, is in the alternate patronage of Sir S. H. Northcote, the Rev. F. Belfield, and the Executors of the late Rev. J. Templer ; and in the incumbency of the Rev. Robt. Bowden, who has neither glebe nor parsonage. The rectorial glebe (46A. 1R. 34P.) and the great tithes belong to

the Dean and Chapter of Exeter, and are held on lease by the Rev. F. Belfield. The tithes were commuted in 1839, the vicarial for £198, and the
rectorial for £297. Here is a National School and a Baptist Chapel. The
poor parishioners have 6A. of land, purchased in 1679 with £62, left by J.
Fell and other donors. They have also two annuities, viz., 20s. out of the
great tithes, left by an unknown donor, and 6s. 8d. left by Richard Kelly,
in 1633. *Capt. John Davies*, a celebrated navigator, who discovered *Davies Straits*, was born at Sandridge, in the reign of Elizabeth.

Adams Richard, fisherman
Allamon Misses || Lambshead Mrs
Bowden Rev Robt. vicar, *Castle Hs*
Colson Mr Wm || Wyatt John, smith
Davies Jno. & Jones Jno. shoemkrs
Hales Edward, cider merchant
Hulme Rd. Parrott, Esq. *Maisonette*
Lander John, builder and vict. Al-
bert Inn
Lander Richard, carpenter
Martin John, woolcomber
Martin John, tailor
Matthews Charles, shopkeeper
Narracott Robt. and John, masons
Narracott Roger, mason & parish clk
Parnell Wm. butcher
Rowe Wm. vict. Church House
Studdy Henry, Esq. *Watton Court*
Tapley Mary Ann, shopkeeper
FARMERS. *(† are Owners.)*
†Adams Richard, *Rydens*
†Blight Wm., *Watton*
†Churchward John, *Stoke Hill*
†Churchward Matthew, *Egglesford*
†Collings Wm. C., *Portbridge*
Duder John || Elliott Susan
†Foss Wm., *Sandridge Barton*
Hannaford Philip || Peeke John
†Jackson John Churchward, *Ash*
Searle John || Searle Henry
Widdicombe Thos. (& corn miller,)
Byter Mills

TORBRIAN, a small village in a woody valley, 4 miles N. by E. of Totnes, and S.S.W. of Newton Abbot, has in its parish 264 souls, and 1450A.
of land, anciently belonging to the baronial family of Brian. It now belongs to several freeholders, the largest of whom is the Rev. C. Wolston,
the patron and incumbent of the *rectory*, valued in K.B. at £20.14s. 7d., and
in 1831 at £330. The *Church* (Holy Trinity,) is an ancient structure,
with a tower and four bells, and a fine old screen. The poor parishioners
have 20s. a year, left by John Peter in 1570, out of the great tithes of Cornworthy.

Boss Daniel, cooper
Harvey Wm. carpenter
Hine Rev V., B.A. *Rectory*
Pawley Richd. vict. Church House
Rowland Wm. parish clerk
Wolston Rev Cphr., B.A. rector, *Tor
Newton House*
FARMERS.
Elliott Jeffry || Leafbridge Mr
Quint John || Sowden Wm.
Tripe Thomas || Tapper Jno. miller

TORQUAY AND TOR MOHAM PARISH.

TORQUAY, the Queen of Watering Places, and the Montpellier of England, as it is frequently called, is a handsome *market town*, *seaport*, and
bathing place, delightfully situated on the strand and the picturesque acclivities of the shore of the northern recess of *Torbay*, in the parish of Tor-
Moham, 22 miles S. of Exeter, 7 miles S.E. of Newton Abbot, 8 miles S. of
Teignmouth, 12 miles N. by E. of Dartmouth, and 207 miles W.S.W. of
London. Its terraces and suburban villas extend more than a mile westward, to the old village of TOR, or *Tor-Moham*; and such has been the
rapid increase of buildings and population during the last twenty years,
that they may now be considered as one town, which has been connected
with the South Devon Railway, by a branch *Railway*, extending about four
miles from Kingskerswell to Tor, and opened Dec. 18th, 1848. The *Parish
of Tor-Moham, or Tor-Mohun*, comprises about 2000 acres of land, occu-

pying most of that bold promontory which projects eastward into the English Channel, about three miles in length, and two in breadth, to *Hope's-
Nose*, the point which divides Torbay and Babbicombe Bay. Its population amounted in 1801 only to 838, and in 1831 to 3582; but in 1841 it
had increased to 5982 souls, of whom 4085 were in Torquay Chapelry.
The parish has now about 9000 inhabitants; and UPTON, the central portion of it, between Tor and Torquay, has recently been made, ecclesiastically, a District Parish, comprising most of the higher parts of the town. The
manor of Tor Moham belonged to Wm. de Briwere, or Brewer, in the reign of
Henry II., and his younger daughter carried it in marriage to the Mohuns,
who had a seat here in the 13th century, but afterwards sold the manor to
the Ridgways. About 1768, it was purchased of the Earl of Donegal by
Sir Robert Palk, grandfather of its present owner, Sir L. V. Palk, Bart. In
1196, Wm. Briwere founded TOR ABBEY, in the south western part of the
parish, for Premonstratension canons, and endowed it with considerable
revenues, which were afterwards augmented by his son. On its suppression, in 1539, its yearly income was valued at £396. 11s., and it had then
fifteen monks, besides the abbot. It was granted, with the adjacent estate,
in 1543, to John St. Leger, Esq., who conveyed it to Sir Hugh Pollard. It
afterwards passed to the Seymours, Ridgways, and Stawells, the latter of
whom sold it in 1662, to Sir George Cary, Kt., an ancestor of its present
owners, Mrs. Cary, and Robert Shedden Sulyard Cary and Robert Shedden,
Esqrs., who reside at the Abbey House, which has picturesque and well-
wooded grounds, adjoining the coast, and commanding a view of the noble
bay, and the rocky tors, or hills, in the neighbourhood. The house is
mostly modern, though some parts of the old Abbey are still preserved. It
consists of a centre and two wings; one of which is connected with a castellated gateway, having octagonal towers and battlements. Beyond this
gateway is a large barn, which formerly belonged to the Abbey, and is decorated with loop-holes and numerous buttresses, and profusely mantled
with ivy. The Roman Catholic Chapel attached to the house is ornamented
with a superb altar, and fine paintings of the Crucified Saviour and the
Virgin Mary. There are several interesting ruins in different parts of the
grounds, and among them is a large Norman arch, with a small one on either
side, richly adorned with sculpture, and clad with ivy. The Cary and Palk
families own most of the parish; and the rest belongs to many smaller
owners, some of whom have neat houses here.

Torquay, which was merely a small fishing hamlet at the close of last
century, is now a large and handsome town, comprising, with its western
suburbs of Tor and Upton, about 9000 inhabitants. It is situated at the
foot and on the sides and summits of that bold amphitheatre of hills which
rise from its strand and harbour in the northern recess of Torbay, about
two miles from Hope's Nose,—the extreme eastern point of the promontory.
The houses are built of a sort of transition limestone, or marble, of which
the cliffs are composed, varying in colour, and containing numerous remains
of shells and madrepores, which beneath the lapidary's hands are suscep-
tible of as fine a polish as the best Italian marble. Such has been the increasing influx of visitors to Torquay, during the last ten years, that its
number of dwellings has been doubled in that period, and many wealthy
families have now handsome mansions here, in which they reside continually, or during autumn and winter. Few places possess a more inviting appearance, especially as a winter residence, being open to the sea breezes of
the south, and sheltered by lofty hills from the piercing winds of the north,
east, and west. The lower part of the town, built round three sides of the
harbour, with the quay and piers in front, is occupied chiefly by the shops

and houses of the tradesmen. The next tier, which is approached by a winding road at each end, and by steps in other places, comprises handsome *terraces*, as also do the upper tiers, and the detached hills on either side; where the ranges of neat houses and elegant villas, towering one above another, on the rocky platforms, gracefully exhibit their marble fronts amid the luxuriant foliage of various trees and shrubs, which bedeck their pretty gardens, the carriage roads, and the intervening slopes. The sides and summits of the beautiful valleys on either side are dotted over with cottages, pavilions, and detached villas, to the extent of about two miles; and the once secluded cove of *Meadfoot*, more than half a mile east of the Quay, has recently been adorned with several handsome terraces, and with a row of fifteen large and elegant mansions, called *Hesketh Crescent*, and erected by those spirited architects and builders, Messrs. J. T. and W. Harvey. The views from the various terraces are magnificent, taking in the whole of Torbay, where numerous fleets can ride in safety; and where is always to be seen the trim yacht and pleasure boat, the dusky sail of the Brixham trawler, or coasting merchantman; and frequently one of Britain's bulwarks—a man-of-war. The beautiful scenery and marine villas along the shores of Torbay on the south, and Babbicombe Bay on the north, are already noticed at preceding pages, in the descriptions of the neighbouring parishes of St. Mary-Church, Cockington, Paignton, and Brixham. Babbicombe, Anstey's Cove, the Bishop of Exeter's new Palace of *Bishopstowe*, and the large cavern called *Kent's Hole*, are noticed at pages 437-'8; and the landing of *William Prince of Orange*, at page 426. Here are hot, cold, shower, and vapour baths, for the invalid and the convalescent; and an illimitable ocean bath of spotless purity, for the recreation of the healthy bather and the experienced swimmer. On the beach and sands are found a variety of beautiful pebbles. The opening of a new road, and the cutting away the base of Waldon hill, in 1842, brought the beautiful beach along the sands of Livermead within ten minutes' walk of Torquay. Here are all the usual requisites of a favourite watering place, including *assembly rooms, reading rooms, libraries, literary institutions, a museum*, &c.; and a *regatta* takes place yearly, in July or August. The *climate* of Torquay is so mild, that citrons are produced in the open air, and myrtles grow in gardens to a great size and age, as also do many tender exotics. The first houses at Torquay are said to have been erected about the end of the last century, for the accommodation of families of officers and invalids belonging to the Channel fleet, which was frequently at anchor in Torbay during the last French war. After this, its reputation for the restoration of invalids spread rapidly, and from that time to the present it has continued to increase in buildings and population faster than any other watering-place in Devon. The *Quay and Piers*, which enclose a basin 500 by 300 feet, were formed under an act of parliament obtained in 1803, but the western pier was not completed till many years afterwards. A small Market Place was built near the strand, in 1823; but in 1849, the Torquay Market Company obtained an act of parliament for the erection of a spacious *Market Place, Slaughter Houses, &c.*; and these and other improvements are now in progress. The markets, held every Tuesday and Friday, are well supplied with all kinds of provisions. *Gas Works* were constructed in 1835, by a company of proprietors, in £5 shares. The government of the town is vested with a body of commissioners, who are elected annually, under a local act of parliament. It is well supplied with water, brought in iron pipes from springs in the neighbourhood, and is within the limits of the port of Dartmouth. Its commerce consists chiefly in the importation of coal, timber, and other articles for home consumption; but it has a small trade with

Newfoundland, and a number of coasting vessels trading to London, &c.; as well as steam packets, which ply regularly to Guernsey, Jersey, Plymouth, Portsmouth, and Southampton. The *Town Hall* is a plain building, in Lower Union street, where *petty sessions* are held every Monday, by the magistrates of Paignton Division, to whom Mr. G. E. Hearder is *clerk*. Another public building in the same street is called *Union Hall*, and is used for lectures, theatrical exhibitions, &c. At the Royal Hotel is a large *Assembly Room*, very chastely fitted up for balls, concerts, &c.; and at Hearder's Family Hotel is a spacious Subscription Reading and News Room. The large centre mansion on the Higher Terrace has been opened as a *Club House*, by many of the nobility and gentry of the town and neighbourhood; but its ground floor is occupied by the *Natural History Society*, which has a valuable library and museum, and was established in 1844. Here is also a *Literary and Scientific Institution*, an *Horticultural Society*, a *Mechanics' Institute*, a *Temperance Hall*, and a *Book Society*. On the Torwood road, adjoining the town, are the *Public Gardens*, comprising about four acres of land, lately appropriated by the lord of the manor to the use of the public, and tastefully planted and laid out with gravel walks, forming a pleasant sheltered promenade.

CHURCHES AND CHAPELS.—The *Parish Church* at Tor-Moham, more than a mile west of the Quay, is an ancient structure, which was re-pewed and thoroughly repaired in 1849. It has an embattled tower, two galleries, and a good organ; and contains some handsome monuments, one of which supports the effigy of one of the Ridgway family, father of the first Earl of Londonderry, who resided at Torwood manor house, now pulled down. The living is a *perpetual curacy*, valued at £360 per annum, with that of Cockington annexed to it. C. H. Mallock, Esq, is the patron, and the Rev. J. H. Harris, D.D., is the incumbent. The living has been augmented by Queen Anne's Bounty and Parliamentary grant; and the great tithes were purchased some years ago, by the two principal land owners. On the summit of a hill is the shell of St. Michael's chapel; and there was another small chapel at Torwood, built by Reginald de Mohun, in 1251. *Upton District Parish Church* (St. Mary Magdalen,) is near the high road between Tor and Torquay, and is a handsome Gothic structure, which has been recently erected by subscription, and was consecrated April 12th, 1849, but the intended tower and spire are not yet built. It is neatly fitted up with open seats, and has room for about 1000 hearers. The late P. Dawson, Esq., gave £2000, on condition that a large portion of the sittings should be free; and the site was given by Sir L. V. Palk. It has been endowed, and constituted a parish church, by the Ecclesiastical Commissioners, and its perpetual curacy, valued at £130, is in the alternate patronage of the Crown and the Bishop of Exeter, and is now enjoyed by the Rev. R. R. Wolfe, M.A. *St. John's Chapel of Ease*, at Montpellier place, in the centre of Torquay, was built in 1822, by Sir L. V. Palk, Bart., and was enlarged at the east end about sixteen years ago. It is a neat structure, partly in the Doric order, and has a small cupola and bell. It has about 500 sittings, and its east window has been enriched with stained glass. Its perpetual curacy, valued at £207 per annum, is in the patronage of the incumbent of Tor-Moham, and is now enjoyed by the Rev. W. G. P. Smith, M.A. *Trinity Chapel*, at Park hill, Torquay, is a neat cemented structure, of mixed architecture, which was erected by subscription, in 1837-'8, at the cost of about £5500, and will seat nearly 900 hearers. The Rev. Richard Fayle, M.A., is the incumbent and patron. There is a *Roman Catholic Chapel* at Tor Abbey, as noticed at page 445. Here are three *Independent Chapels*, situated in Lower Union street, Braddon's place, and Abbey road. The latter was built in 1847, at the cost of £2200, and is a handsome building in the Italian style. There is a *Baptist Chapel* in Temperance street; an *Unitarian Chapel*, in Lower Union street; a *Wesleyan Chapel*, in Warren place, built in 1807; and an "All Christians" meeting-house, in South street, Tor. There are large *National Schools* at Pimlico and East street, built in

1826 and 1841; and another at Meadfoot, erected in 1842. The latter belongs to Trinity Chapel; and there are also schools attached to St. John's and some of the other places of worship. The various congregations are liberal contributors to various institutions for the relief and the religious instruction of the poor.

The *Torbay Dispensary and Infirmary* was established in 1844, but the handsome building which it now occupies was not erected till 1850. Here are *Clothing Clubs*, a *Lying-in-Charity*, a Shipwrecked Fishermen and Mariners' Benevolent Society; several Friendly Societies, and a Lodge of Freemasons. The latter is at the Union Hall. The *poor parishioners* have the interest of £62, left by Thomas Kingsley and other donors; and the dividends of £468. 8s. 6d. Navy five per cent. stock, purchased with £500 left by *George Baker*, in 1800.

TORQUAY AND TOR DIRECTORY.

The POST OFFICE is at Meadfoot row, Torquay. Mr. Benj. Ambrose Hill is the *postmaster*. Letters delivered daily, at 7 morng. and 2 aftern.; and *Money Orders* granted and paid. There is a sub post office at Mr. Thos. Abbott's, 1 South street, Tor; and a *receiving box* at Mr. Hall's, 21 Lower Union street.

AlbanMrsAnn,Pmbtn.Villa
Alleyne Mrs Rose, Cottage
Anstey Misses, *The Brake*
AtkinsonGeo.Esq.*Nth.Court*
Augustus Mrs.,Geneva ctgs
BaldwinC.B.Esq. *RockView*
BastowW.bellhngr. South st
Benthall Jno.gent.*Furzewell*
Bettington Mrs.,Montplr.pl
Bezzi Mrs Charlotte, *Villino*
Bligh Miss T. *Overton*
Bovill Edw.Esq. Glenthorne
Bower Mrs., South Town
Bourchier Mrs., Hazlewood
Brittain Miss, Bellmont
Bully Mr John, Geneva ctgs
CarrCapt.Jas.R.N.Hgar.mt
Carpenter Mrs A. Percy Ldg
Cary Robt.SheddenSulyard,
　Esq.&MrsCary, *Tor Abbey*
Cather Mr John, South cotg
Charles Emanuel,bill poster
　and town crier, George st
Cholwich Mrs., Upton cotg
ClarkJas.organ bdr.Union st
Coghlan Rev Thomas Lloyd,
　M.A. curate
Cole Mrs P., Geneva cotgs
Cole Mrs Sar., Upr Union st
Cornish Mrs E., Chapel hill
Connor Mrs M., Abbey road
Croome Mrs., Duncan Hs
Crabb Jas. dyer, Madeira pl
Dashwood Cs.Esq StMchl's
DashwoodJno.Esq.Ringrove
Dashwood Lady, *Braganza*
Diamond Abm. mariner, Tor
Diamond Ed Esq. Aldum.Lg
Douglas Capt. R. P., Sthtwn
Dove Mrs., Mount Hermon
Duckworth Mrs.,Southtown
Dunbar Mrs., Cliff House
Dunsford Mrs., Union st
Edwards Miss,22 Orchard pl
Edwards & Ash, coach bldrs.
　45 Lower Union street
Elliott Misses, Mornay Ldg
Elliott Wm. gent.Tudor Ldg
Fanshaw Misses, St Mary's
Fayle Rev Rd.M.A. incbt.of
　Trinity chapel, Park hill

Fetherbridge Saml. worsted
　manufacturer, Tor
Field Miss, Upr Union st
Ford & Co.carriers,102 Lower
　Union st.,O.Channing,*agt*
Fordyce Misses, Normount
Garratt Fras.gent.*Ellacombe*
Gillard Miss M., Woodville
GodfreyW.ship onr.Orch.ter
Gooch Mrs., Woodend
Goodenough Miss, Bay Mt
Gore Rev Fras. L., Torwood
GrantWm.currier,10 LUn.st
Grenfeld Miss S., Victoria pl
Grey RevHarry,*E Braddons*
GryllsMiss,MountBraddons
Hack Jas. Esq., Woodside
Hall B A. postmr. Meadfoot
Hall Major T., Fernhill
Hall Rev T. G., *Wenlock*
Hare Hon Mrs., *Rockend*
Harris Rev J. H., D.D.inct.
　of Tor *Kanescombe Lodge*
HarrisGeo.H.Esq.Rooklnds
Harris Mrs., Verney House
Harris Wm. Esq. Tor hill
Harrison Mr Wm., UpUn.st
Harvey Jcb.gent.6 Park cres
HarveyJno.ship onr. Vic.par
Hastie Mrs Eliz., Vale View
HearderG.E. clerk to magis-
　trates, Family Hotel
Hedger Pp. railway supt.
Higgins MissEliz.,Elmvilla
Hill RevGeo.curate,Vict.ctg
HindRevWm.,Vaughan par
Hodges Mrs C., Waldon ter
Homeyard Mrs., Glen view
Honeywood Lady, Torwood
Horsey Rt. turner, Lr Un.st
HurryRevNicholas,(Indpt.)
　Warley cottage
Jackson RevW.H.,StNichls
Jermyn Mrs.,*The Hermitage*
Johnson Capt. Hy., Parkhill
Jones Mrs., Weston cottage
Jones Major Fielding,Islgtn
Josland John, bath propr.
　Beacon terrace
KempsterJno.billiardsVc.pr
KingWm.A.gnt.Provdc.ctg

Kirby Capt.Walter,Rock ctg
Kitson Chs. solr.Collaton ctg
Kitson Rev Wm. and Wm.
　solicitor, Vaughan parade
LakemanMiss,Richmnd.Hs
Lamble Rd. pawnbkr. Geo.st
Langley Fdk.gnt.Broadlnds
LangleyW.mert.Chesnutctg
Leach Flk.Ed.gnt.*Dunstone*
Lee Captain, Balsdon Lodge
Leigh RvPtr. M.A.,Woodlds
Ley Miss Ann, Hill garden
LuscombeMrN.,Madrporepl
Madge John, carrier, Geo. st
Maitland Mrs., Orchard ter
Majendie Mrs Susan, *Cintra*
Mallett Mrs Eliz., Oakfield
Marker Rev Henry Wm.,
　Beaumont House
Martin Mrs., Waldon hill
Matthews Jn.shipnr.Wal.tr
Medland J. carrier, Geo. st
Merrivale Mr E.,Madeira pl
Meyrick Col. Hy., *The Cove*
MicklethwaiteW., ColliuaV
Miller Mr Jno., Waldon ter
Montgomery RevJ.R.(Unit)
　Orchard terrace
Mudge Mtw.limebnr.Ntn.rd
Mudge Nchls.gnt.MyrtleGv
Murray Mrs.,KingstonVilla
NankivellBnj.gnt.Abbeyctg
Nepean Miss Har., *Landon*
NeckWm.hay dlr.Brunsk-st
Nicholson Jno.gent.Oak Ctg
Oak John, mast, block, and
　pump maker, Quay
Orange Rev John, (Indept.)
　Penton Villa
Ord Alex. gent. *Hardwicke*
Ovington Capt. F. P., *Knoll*
Paget Misses, The Elms
Palmer Robt. railway clerk
Peace Mr Geo. 3 Church st
Phillipps H. C. M. Esq.
　Wellswood
Phillips Captain, *Warberry*
Phillpotts Capt., *Watcombe*
Pilkington Mrs., Oversfield
Piper Rd. Rt. custom hs. offr
Pitcairn Rev Dd.,AlbynLdg

Pollard Wm. gent. 8thlnd.Hs
Pollard Wm.bathprpr.Vic.pr
Pouget Major, *The Elms*
Power Rev M.J. (Cth.)*Abbey*
Pullen Mrs Amelia, *Beulah*
Rendell Miss I.,Orchard ter
Rider Mrs Ann, George st
Robinson Miss, Fir bank
Roberts Mrs., *Bay view*
Rossiter Mrs Mary,Orchd.ter
Rowe Mrs G. 11 Waldon ter
Salter Mrs Har. *Bloomfield*
Saunders Col., *Plymswood*
Saville Mrs., *The Grove*
Seppings Jno Esq *Greenfield*
Shedden Rt. Esq. TorAbbey
Shapley Mr T.N., Brunsk.pl
Shapley John, assist. over-
  seer, Orchard terrace
Short Sml. mangr*Gas Works*
Sinclair Lord, *Pilmuir*
Slade Rt. harbour master &
  sail maker; & Saml. ship-
  owner, 12 Victoria parade
Slater Rev Wm.P. (Weslyn)
Smith Rev W.G.Parks,M.A.
  incbt.St John's,Belvdr.Hs
Smithweek Rev George, *Tor*
South Mrs., Abbey Villa
Spragge Fras. Hoare, Esq.
  Octon House
Spragge Mr Wm.,SouthTwn
Stabb John, mert. Cary par
Staddon Ts.gent.UpUnion st
Steele Thos. Esq. Edgley Hs
Stephens Miss, Up Union st
Strachan Rev L., Melville st
Streeten Rv Edm.C.,StAnn's
Swete J. B. Esq. Park pl
Thomas Mrs A. *Belmont Hs*
Tramlin Mr W., Waldon ter
Trant Wm.H. Esq.*Woodfield*
Turner Ths.fishmert.Vic.par
Vincent Misses,2 Beacon ter
Vivian Edw.Esq. Endsleigh
Wadlington Wm. colr. Quay
Walker Edw.Esq. *Engadina*
Ward Capt.,R.N. *Sidney Ldg*
Ward Wm. Esq. CintraVilla
Wardlow R.Esq.MarineVla
Warrington Mrs.,Berner's hl
White Andrew, gent. Lau-
  reston Hall
Williams Cs. Esq Meadfoot
Williams Js.Esq. BannerCrs
Williams Jno.Esq. ElmBnk
Williams Mrs Sus.,George st
Wills Mr John, Up Union st
Wilson Mrs., *Fairfield*
Wollen Rev Jas.,Portland pl
Wolfe Rev Rd.Robins, M.A.
  incmbt. of Upton, *Ashill*
Wotton Miss, Waterloo Cotg
Wyatt My.shell&c.dlr.Trwd

ACADEMIES&SCHOOLS
(* *take Boarders.*)
*Bibbins Misses,Palestn.vil
*Cairn Helen, Lr Union st
*Colliver Rev G., Verney hs
Free Girls'Schools,St John's
  place & Lr Union street

Hartland Chs.Jas.,Genv.cot
Hatch Ella, South street
Holman —, Temperance st
Infant, Sarah Markham,Tor
*Jenkins M.A.&E.,OakInds
Moyse Chs.W., Braddons pl
National, Hy.Dart, & Misses
  Baker & Cornish, Pimlico;
  John&Mary Harris,Mead-
  foot ; &AnnJ.Freegard,Tor
*Nicholson Emma MaryB.&
  Ellen, Oak cottages
*Paige Philip, Montvidere
*Rotton Jane, Ellersleigh
Smith Johanna, South st
Street Benj., Waldon ter
Teage Ths.Gordon,Market st
*Walker Lieut.John,Cliff hs.
Willey Sarah, Lr Union st
Youldon Edm., Up Union st
  AGENTS, (HOUSE, &c.)
Burt Wm. Charles, 8 Strand
Harvey Jacob, 6 Park cres
Harvey John, Victoria par
Matthews John R., Vic. par
Rahy John, Victoria parade
Slade Bobert J.(harbour mas-
  ter,) 12 Victoria parade
Stark John C. 12 Strand
  ALE & PORTER MERTS.
Berry Wm., Park lane
Carroll Fisher, & Co. Strand
Farrant Wm., Lr Union st
Hodgson Thos., Orchard ter
Prowse Mary Ann, Palk st
  ARCHITECTS & SURVS.
Cockings Samuel, Oaklands
Gribble Ed.Wynne,8 Park pl
Harvey J.T.&Wm.,Park crs
Luscombe Rd., Warren pl
  ARTISTS.
Crane Thos., Beanland pl
Hodges Jph. L., Waldon ter
Walker R., Waldon hill
Wills James, Upr Union st
  ATTORNEYS.
Bartlett Jacob, Waldon ter
Carter Frdk. Roger, Fleet st
Eastley Yarde, Victoria par
Kitson Wm.&Cs. 2Vaugn pr
  AUCTIONEERS, &c.
Burt Wm. Chas. 9 Strand
Lemon Richd. C., George st
Luscombe Wm., Lr Union st
Peckins W.N., Lr Union st
Raby Joseph C.,Victoria par
Stark John E., 12 Strand
  BAKERS.
(* *are Confectioners.*)
Austin Paul, Lr Union st
*Baker Aaron.3 Torwood row
*Bowden Henry, 1 Strand
Butland Rt.,Laburnum row
*Chave Wm., Victoria par
Collard Thos., Hr Union st
*Coombe Jph., Lr Union st
*Coombe Jph., Braddon's pl
Coplestone Herbert,Pimlico
Cove Wm., Swan street
*Coysh Wm. 13 Lr Union st
*Gale Robert, Lr Union st
Griffiths Ann, Victoria par

Ellis Wm., East street
Harris John, Waldon ter
Hooper John, 3 East street
Lane John, Pimlico
Lang Wm., Hr Union st
*Lethbridge Fdk., Abbey pl
Munford John, 4 Tor place
*Pater A. J., Torwood row
Rattenbury H., Lr Union st
Rossiter James, Hr Union st
Sawyer Saml., Warren hill
Sessions John, South street
Smale Mary, Lr Union st
Stocks Fredk., Hr Union st.
Stocks Thomas, Church st
Street Joseph, 1 Park lane
Tarr John, Market street
Webber Jas., Brunswick pl
Wills John H., George st
Windeatt John, Lr Union st
  BANKS.
Vivian, Kitson, and Co. 2
  Vaughan parade,draw on
  Barnard, Dimsdale, & Co.
Savings' Bank, (branch of
  Devon&Exeter,)13Strand,
  Jno. Cowell Stark, *actuary*
  BASKET MAKERS.
Fowler Saml., Lr Union st
Somerwill Robert, Park st
  BERLIN WOOL,&c. DRS.
Collins & Brown,Bradns.row
Croydon Edw., Victoria par
Jago Jane & Ann, Market st
Wyatt Wm., Torwood row
  BLACKSMITHS.
Dyer Wm., Hr Union st
Gibbings Pp., Hr Union st
Hall John, Hr Union st
Heath Robert, Hr Union st
Lamble Wm., Lr Union st
Short Thos. & Son, South st
Snooks Henry, Church lane
  BOOKSLRS.& STATNRS.
(* *Printers, & † Libraries.*)
Ardley Daniel,Braddon's rw
*†Cockrem Edw., 10 Strand
*†Croydon Edw., Vic. par
†Elliott Wm., Vaughan par
Hall Wm. H., Lr Union st
Jago Jane & Ann, Market st
Narracott John Laskey,
  (binder,) 5 Tor place
Poulton Wm., Lawrence pl
Richards Grace, Lr Union st
*Stark Wm.H S., Bradns.rw
*†Wreford Rt.T.8Bradns.rw
  BOOT & SHOEMAKERS.
Abbott Thomas. South st
Ash John, South street
Bailey Wm , Lr Union st
Bartlett Charles, Abbey pl
Bearne Andw., Lr Union st
Bennett Joseph, George st
Bowyer John Saml., Strand
Branscombe W., Bradns. rw
Bridgman Saml.,Torwood rw
Chenoweth J., Hr Union st
Dart Charles, 8 Torwood rw
Elliott Wm., Upr Union st
Goodall Fras., Meadfootr
Jones Thos., Hr Union st

Lander Wm., Victoria par
Lawrence Geo., Hr Union st
Legge Philip, Waldon ter
Marks Wm., Hr Union st
May George, Lr Union st
Morgan John, 4 East st
Mugford M.A., Braddon's rw
Nunn George, Pimlico
Searle Thos. Lr Union st
Tarr John, Palk street
Thomas Edw. Lr Union st
Thomas Rt. E., Hr. Un st
Way James, East street
Way Richard, Church lane
Wheeler John, Market st
Woolcombe Gabl. Church st
Woolcombe Geo. Lr Union st

BREWERS & MALSTRS.
Bridgman Sl. 9 Warren pl
Smerdon Rd., Lr Union st

BRICK &TILE MAKERS.
Carder Wm., Hr Union st
Chilcott J. W., Lr Un. st

BUILDERS.
Bailey Wm., Orchard ter
Coysh Wm., Waldon hill
Dashpler Geo., Lr Union st
Harvey J. T. & W., Park st
Harvey John, Melville pl
Jenkins Geo , Madrepore pl
Luscombe Wm., Lr Union st
Pearce John, Tor
Peeke Edwin, Rose hill
Pope James, Abbey road
Reed Jph., Braddon's pl
Richards Thos., Lr Un. st
Rossiter John, Waldon ter
Taylor John, Orchard ter
Towell Dd. Clairville
Watson John, George st
Yeo Geo. 7 Geneva cotgs

BUTCHERS.
Addems Wm., Lr Union st
Churchward M., Lr Un. st
Draw Geo., Lr Union st
Hannaford W., Braddon's rw
Henley Edw., Lr Union st
Hook Rt., Braddon's row
Luscombe Thos., Lr Un. st
Marley John, (& provision dlr.,) Lower Union st
Rossiter Fredk., Market st
Scott Rd., South street
Shapley T. J., Market st
Skelton Wm., Tor hill
Stokes Richard, South st
Tulley Geo., Brunswick pl
Tulley John, Hr Union st
Tulley J. W., Hr Union st
Weeks James, Fleet st

CABINET MAKERS, &c.
Allen Giles, 17 Waldon ter
Bailey John, Lr Union st
Burt Wm. Chas., Strand
Balson John, Victoria cotg
Carpenter Hy., Lr Un. st
Crockwell Hy., Lr Un. st
Hammick Wm., Lr Un. st
Lemon Rd. C., Braddon's rw
Matthews John R. (&under-taker,) Victoria parade
Matthews Wm. M., Sth. st

Oliver Thos., Lr Union st
Sawyer Wm., Lr Union st
Strodrinsky Stanisland,'(po-lisher,) South street
Wotton James, Lr Union st

CARPENTERS & JNRS.
(See also Builders.)
Lander Rd., Victoria par
Perrett F. G. N., Pimlico
Rice George, Hr Union st
Richards John, Lr Union st
Rossiter Edw., Upr Un. st
Scott Charles, Warren hill
Warren John, Berner's hill

CARVERS & GILDERS.
Beavis George, Lr Union st
Sewell Wm., Hr Union st
Trist Anthy., Temperance st

CHEMISTS &DRUGSTS.
Glynn Wm., Madeira place
Hearder Wm., Victoria par
Lodge Thos., 28 Hr Un. st
Narracott Hy., 6 Strand
Rendall John M., Cary par
Titcher Rt. A., Torwood rw
Webber & Alderton, Strand
Weeks Caleb, (regr. of mar-riages, &c.) 83 Lr Un. st
West James, Braddon's rw
Wyatt Rd. T., Lawrence pl

CHIMNEY SWEEPERS.
Frost John, Swan street
Jenkins J., Temperance st
Wells John, Hr Union st

CHINA, GLASS, &c.,DLS.
Buck Edw. 89 Lr Union st
Carder Antony Wm. (brown ware mfr.) Hr Union st
Coniam Wm., Warren pl
Gater Thos. 1 Fleet street
Jeboult H P., Lr Union st

CLOTHES DEALERS.
Bannister Hy., Lr Union st
Branscombe Hy., Lr Un. st
Goss Thos., Lr Union st
Redwood Henry, East st
Smith Bnt., Madrepore pl

COAL MERCHANTS.
Cocking Sml., Lr Union st
Cornish Robt., Newton rd
Ford &Co. (corn,) Lr Un. st
Godfrey Francis, Nth.Quay
Godfrey Wm., Victoria par
Raby Chas. & Saml., North Quay & Victoria parade
Rowe Ann, Lr Union st
Whiteway Wm., North Qy

COOPERS&LATH RNDS.
Bowden John, Lr Union st
Fowler Sml., Lr Union st
Mudge Richard, Market st
Quint John, South street
Sims John, George street

EATING HOUSES.
Down Wm., Market st
Mallet Hy., Lr Union st
Matthews J., Upr Union st
Perryman Ann, Lr Un. st
Scowns Thomas, Warren pl
Wotton Mary, Brunswick pl

FARMERS.
Anthony Rd., Lr Union st

Austin Thos., Hr Union st
Dreaton Geo., South town
Gale Wm., Newton road
Hingston John, East street
Lane Peter, Hr Union st
Mudge Thos., Lr Union st
Narracott Wm., South town
Preston Thos. 1 Cary par
Staddon Wm., George st
Stand Wm., Shiphay

FIRE & LIFE OFFICE AGENTS.
Alliance, Henry Drake
Architects' Engns' & Build-ers', Wm. Harvey, Prk. cs
Argus, J. C. Stark
Atlas, G. E. Hearder
Birmingham, R. T. Wreford
Britannia, J. Matthews
City of London, Thos. Lodge
County & Prvt., W. Wish
Colonial (Life,) Vivian, Kit-son and Co
Crown, Wm. Elliott
Etonian, W. H. Stark
Farmers', Hy. Crockwell
General, Wm. H. Hall
Globe, Rt. Stark, Cary par
Guardian, Thomas Atkins
Imperial, J. C. Raby
Liverpool, Geo. Richardson
London Assnc., Jno. Harvey
London Union, C. Weeks
Minerva, Rt. T. Wreford
Mercantile, J. O. Williams
Mitre, Wm. Glyn
Norwich Union & Mutual, Webber & Alderton
Palladium, F. R. Carter
Reliance, Hy. Narracott
RoyalExchange,E.Cockrem
Star, Joseph Morgan
Sun, G. Grey, Victoria par
Temperance, Joshua Toms
Tradesmen's, S. H. Slade
West of England, Wm. J. B. Beasley
Western, James West
Yorkshire, W. N. Peckins

FLY, HORSE, &c. LTRS.
Abbott John, Tor square
Cawdle Thos., East street
Collard Isaac, Lr Union st
Dear Wm. Lr Union st
Grist Alfred, Market st
Lightfoot Charles, Mews
Pope Samuel, East street
Shapter Jph., Lr Union st
Southwood Jas., Lr Union st

FRUITERERS, &c.
Anthony Jph., Torwood rw
Dart Cphr., Lr Union st
Davey Ann, Lr Union st
Fisher Henry, Torwood
Gillison Thos., Meadfoot rw
Huxham Wm., Lr Union st
Moose Rd., Abbey place
Pepperell John, Lr Union st
Tennell Jacob, Hr Union st
Treeby John, Higher ter
Woodley Wm. H., Market st

TORQUAY AND TOR DIRECTORY.   451

FURNITUREBROKERS.
Bant Wm., Lr Union st
Sawyer Wm., Lr Union st

GROCERS & TEA DLRS.
Abbott Eliz. 32 South st
Adams Geo., Torwood row
Adds Thos. 3 Madrepore pl
Amphlett Jas., Lr Union st
Angel Thos. 14 Melville st
Barnes Wm., Hr Union st
Blackmore Rt., Fleet st
Bread & Co., Hr Union st
Carroll Fisher & Co. Strand
Charlton Geo., Market st
Goss Thos., Lr Union street
Harvey Andrew, Lr Un. st
Hatwell & Harvey, South st
Hayward Thos., Lr Un. st
Henley Wm. C., Lr Un. st
Job Sus., Hr Union street
Lombardin Fras., Hr Un. st
Lawrence Jno., Braddon'spl
Medland Thos., Waldon pl
Narracott Brothers, Strand
Pugsley Jas , 2 Tor place
Rowse John, Lr Union st
Ruby Sarah, Lr Union st
Slade John J., Abbey place
Tancock Wm., Hr Union st
Trist Chtte., Lr Union st
Way Chas., Victoria par
Wyatt John Hy., Fleet st

HABERDASHERS.
Godfrey Ann, Strand
Harvey Rebc. & Sus., Vic.p

HAIR DRESSERS, &c.
Ardley Danl., Braddon's rw
Burridge Saml., Market st
Ellis James P., Strand
Elliott W.B., Temperance st
Jones Josiah, Fleet st
Rowe Solon, Hr Union st
Searle Thos. 4 Lr Union st

HATTERS.
Browse Arthur, Lr Union st
Spark J. B., Abbey pl

HOTELS, INNS, & TVNS.
*Marked * are Posting Houses.*
Apsley House, Jph. Marchetti, Park hill
Castle Inn, Wm H. Hall, Lower Union street
Commercial Inn, My. Rowe, Market street
Exeter Inn, Jno. Mogridge, Lower Union street
Globe, J. Hex, Hr. Union st
Golden Lion, Edw. Towell, Lower Union street
Half-Moon, Wm. Dear, Lr Union street
* Hearder's Hotel, Sarah C. Hearder, Victoria par
King Wm., Wm. Seymour, Madrepore place
* London Hotel, T. Woolfinden, Fleet street
Marine Inn, Samuel Bridgman, Palk street
Market Inn, Jas. Dinness, Lower Union street

Maritime Inn, Jas. French, Victoria parade
Rising Sun, J. Scott, Sth. st
* Royal Hotel, Thos. Webb, Strand
Star, Hy. Coram, Hr Un. st
Steam Packet, Joseph Edwards, Victoria parade
Torbay Inn, Rd. Smerdon, Tor square.
White Hart, Lr Union st
White Swan, H. G. Carpenter, Swan street

BEERHOUSES.
Ash Cphr., South street
Baker John, Brunswick pl
Bartlett Chas., Pimlico
Berry Wm. 2 Park ln
Bridgman Jno., Tempnce. st
Bridgman J. jun. Lr Un. st
Chaffe John, Madeira place
Down Wm., Torwood row
Eales Geo., Meadfoot row
Endacott Geo., Melville st
Grills Rd., Meadfoot row
Harvey Wm., South street
Hill Samuel, Temperance st
Kabbel Geo., Hr Union st
Heath Ellen, Church lane
Heath Rd., Braddon's row
Luscombe Thomas, Tor
Medland Thos., Waldon ter
Mudge Jane, Braddon's rw
Satchwell Geo., Madrepr.pl
Sanders Thos., Madeira pl
Scott George, Church ln
Seward Wm., George street
Stentiford Robert, Pimlico
Terry Thos., Melville st
Tuckerman Car., Hr Un st
Voysey Rd., Hr. Union st
White Saml., Lr Union st
Wills John, Lr Union st

IRONMNGRS. BRZS. &c.
Dyer Wm., Hr Union st
Hambling Edw., Market st
Morgan Jas. C., Victoria pr
Pyle Thos., Up Union st
Stark John C. 13 Strand
Williams J. O., Lr Union st

JEWELLERS, &c.
Braham James, 8 Strand
Cullen Saml., Laburnum rw
Jacobs Alex. 14 Strand
Thornton Thos, Hr Un. st

LACE MFRS.
Brimicombe Sus., Waldon t
Chapman Eliz., Lr Union st
Hayman Wm., Fleet st
Searle Maria, Lr Union st
Weeks Ann Eliz , Fleet st

LINEN AND WOOLLEN DRAPERS.
Andrews Eliz. and William, Brunswick place.
Billings Robt , Fleet street
Brown James, Lr Union st
Brunt Eliz., Lr Union st
Burt M. & J., Lr Union st
Cash & Butt, 13 Strand
Chilcott Jph. W., Lr Unionst
Dashper Hy. 5 Strand

Mann W. D., Victoria par
Mather Jas. 22 Lr Union st
Oliver Richard, 1 Tor place
Piller Chas. C. 53 Hr Un. st
Phillips & Belcher, 2 Lawrence place

LODGING HOUSES.
Audley Mrs, Waterloo cotg
Audley Jane, Torwood Mt
Badcock Wm. 6 Park st
Baker Wm., Orchard ter
Baily Wm., Beach wood
Ball Eliz., Merino House
Barrett Mrs., Lower ter
Blackmore John, Park st
Bond Wm., Orchard place
Bowden Sus. 4 Beacon ter
Brand Thos., Beacon ter
Burridge J., Montpelr. pl
Coysh Edw., Woodstock ctg
Chown Wm. Hy., Peamore
Crockwell My., Abbey pl
Earl Jane, Torwood Mt
Edwards Rebea., Orchard tr
Elliott Wm., Vaughan par
Ford Eliz., Victoria place
Field Jane, Cary parade
Gidley Wm., Orchard ter
Godfrey Esther, Park street
Godfrey Eliz., Victoria par
Hall Eliz., Marine House
Hammick My., Hr Un. st
Hatch Mrs, South street
Hamlyn Eliz , Park place
Harvey Isabella, Higher ter
Harvey John, Vaughan par
Hudley Mrs. Duncan Hs
Huxham Ellen, Park cres
Huxham Rd., Geneva cotgs
Jeffreys Geo., Vaughan par
Kilby Chas., (& supt. of police,) Vaughan parade
Lakeman M.&R., Rchmnd v
Lawrence John, Park st
Lougg Thos., Orchard ter
Kempster John, Vaughan p
Matthews Wm, 3 South st
Maybourn Wm., Abbey rd
Mayo Wm. 2 Woodville
Mills James, 5 Park place
Mortimore Wm., Torwood
Moreshead Sarah, Victoria p
Mudge Ellen, Vaughan par
Nethaway Thos. 5 Beacon tr
Nicholls Philip, Geneva ctg
Parnell Eliz., Victoria ctg
Pentecost Wm. J., Park st
Power M. A., Orchard pl
Putt Wm., Geneva cottages
Rendell Mary Ann & Sus., 3 Lower terrace
Rossiter Miss, Victoria par
Skinner Mrs. Geneva cotgs
Skinner My., Orchard pl
Smale My. Ann, Orchard ter
Smale Mrs., Geneva cottgs
Tapley John, Cary parade
Tapper Mrs., Berner's hill
Toose Susan, 4 Park place
Treby Mrs., Geneva cotgs
Treaton George, South town
Weeks Mrs., Lower terrace

Vivian Mrs., Silver hill
Wills John, Retreat
WhitewayThs.,Beanland pl
Williams Sus., Beacon ter
Wilcocks John, Claremont
Wish Wm. 3 Park street
Winsborough Jas.T., Cary p
Wood John, Vaughan par
Wyatt Mary, Rose cottage

MADREPORE MFRS.
Bradford Jas , Victoria par
Jacobs Alex. 14 Strand
Nichols Wm., Temperne. st
Pratt & Putt, Lr Union st
Sharland Hy., Madrepore pl
Thornton Thos., Hr Un. st
Widger Wm , Lr Union st

MARINE STORE DLS.
Anson Saml., Church st
Dart James, Fleet street
Lang Robert, Church st
Smith Barnet, Swan st

**MILLINERS and DRESS
MAKERS.**
Abbott Agnes, Madrepore pl
Brook Grace, Melville pl
Cumming A., Lr Market st
Drew B. & M. A., Lr Un. st
Gilby L. & J., Park st
Hamlyn M., Hr Union st
Harvey E.&M., Braddon's p
Harvey R. & S. Victoria pr
Lake Sarah, Waldon ter
Leat Sophia, Hr Union st
Luscombe B.&S. Bradn's. p
Peperell Eliz., Lr Union st
Phillips Mary, Lawrence pl
Steer Susan, Lr Union st
Stelling M. A., Hr Union st
Symmons & Lear, Market st
Westcott T., Waldon ter
White M. & E., Waldon ter
Winsborough J.&M., Cary p
Withers Mary, East street
Woolcombe Eliz., Lr Un. st

MUSIC SELLERS.
Cockrem Edw., Strand
Melhuish W. Lr Union st
Poulton Wm., Lawrence pl
Reynolds Wm., Torwood rw
Smith George, Torwood row

PAINTERS&GLAZIERS.
Barns Wm., Hr Union st
Beavis George, Lr Union st
Blackmore Jas.,Orchard ter
Densham George,Higher ter
Gould Nicholas, Pimlico
Hayward John, South st
Pentecost W. J. 1 Park st
Perry John, Lr Union st
Pook Richard, Fleet street
Rendell Fras. H. Strand
Richardson G., Waldon ter
Rowland John, Lr Union st
Ryder Thomas, South st
Selley Edw., Lr Union st
Walker Chas., Hr Union st
Watson Wm., Hr Union st
Way Chas. Victoria parade

PAPER HANGERS.
(See Painters & Cabt. mkrs.)
Cooksley Wm., Lr Union st

Tuckett John, Orchard ter

PHYSICIANS.
Battersby R. T. Glen cotg
Black Glass, Torwood
Lucas Carr Ellison,Ashfield
House
Mackintosh C. H., 3 Hr ter
Maddon Wm. H., Gorton h
Nankivell Chas., Layton h
Parkin Hy., Cary bldgs.
Shute Theodore Henry, St
John's villa
Sutherland Alex. Robert,
Silverhill
Tetley James, Belmonte
Toogood Jonthn., Park cres

PLASTERERS, &c.
Angel Wm , Geneva cotgs
Clark Jph , Orchard ter
Goss Henry, Brunswick pl
Goss Thos , Lr Union st
Matthews Frdk., Hr Un. st
Skinner James, George st

PLUMBERS, &c.
Barns Wm., Hr Union st
Beer Chas., Lr Union st
Lee Hy., Meadfoot row
Parr Thos. 2 Lower terrace
Rowland John, (&sheet iron
works,) Lr Union street
Williams John O., Lr Un. st

POULTERERS.
*(Marked * are Game Dlrs.)*
Anthony Jph., Torwood row
Blackmore John, Park st
BridgemanDnl.,LrUnion st
Davey Ann, Lr Union st
*Fragall Geo., Torwood row
*Huxham E., Lr Union st
*Woodley Wm. Hy., Mkt st

PROFESSORS, &c.
(Music and † Dancing.)*
*Boyne Thos. Wm., Tor
†Brodie Ann, Lr Union st
*Churchill James, Tor hill
Connor John, Orchard pl
*Dewe Frederick, Torwood
†Hodgson M.&L., Orchd.ter
Le Clair Nicholas *(French,)*
Gothic cottages
Pengelly Wm. (mathemtcs.)
12 Orchard terrace
*Reynolds Wm., Abbey pl

ROPE & TWINE MKRS.
Bowden Mark, Waldon ter
Luscombe Jno.,Braddon's pl

SADDLERS, &c.
Hellings John, Lr Union st
Mortimore Wm., Market st
Soper John, Lr Union st
Symmons Wm., Market st

SEEDSMEN, &c.
MorganJn.&Jph.LrUnion st
Tozer Charles, Church st
Whately Thomas, South st

SHIP & BOAT BLDRS.
Morgan Simon, Meadfoot rw
Shaw Wm., Beacon yard

SHOPKEEPERS.
Bunker Emily, Lr Union st
Chaffe John, Madeira pl
Coombe Jane, Braddon's pl

Hammett Susanna, Pimlico
Heath Rd., Braddon's place
Lock John, George street
MetherellCath. Madeira pl
Mortimer John, East st
Mudge Jas., Braddon's row
Northam John, Church ln
Patterson James, Park st
Rowland Wm., Church ln
Quint John, 22 South st
Tucker Mark, Pimlico
VoyseyRd. HigherUnion st
Welsford Jas., Tempnce. st

STAY & CORSET MKRS.
Burton M., Braddon's row
Elliott E., Meadfoot row
Paynter Thos., Lr Union st
Soper John, Lower Union st

STONE & MBL.MASONS.
Brimicombe Wm.,Waldon tr
Evans George, Orchard ter
Clark Joseph, Orchard ter
Jacobs Alexander, Strand
Sharland Hy.,Madrepore pl
Wager Wm., Lr Union st

STRAW HAT MAKERS.
BrimicombeE. 14 Waldon ter
Crute Eliza, George street
Cook Elizabeth, South st
Drew Eliza, Lr Union st
Lake S. 3 Waldon terrace
Leat Sophia, Hr Union st
Legge S., Waldon terrace
Luscombe P., Warren pl
MugfordM A.,Braddon's rw
Pook Jane, Fleet street
Stilling M. A., Hr Union st

SURGEONS.
Hunter Thos., Woodbourn
JolleyWm.R.&Son,Abbeypl
Paul Augs., Adwell cottage
Pollard Wm., Lower ter
Tanner John, Waldon ter
Stewart Zach.Rt., Park cres
Toogood John B., Higher ter

SURGEON DENTISTS.
Moseley L. 10 Strand
Rodway H. B. 3 Park cres.

TAILORS.
*(Marked * Drapers also.)*
Angel Alfred, Hr Union st
Barns John, East street
Burge John, Lr Union st
*Burridge Saml.,Mkt st
Campbell Geo., Lr Union st
*Cotton Saml., Torwood row
*Cove Richd.,Braddon's row
Howe John, South street
Lear Benj., Lr Union st
Moore Robt. 13 Church st
*Mugford Richd.L. 13 Brad-
don's row
Merrider Geo. Lr Union st
*Pawley Saml. HrUnion st
Pinkham Edw. Lr Union st
Pook John, Church street
Rich John, East street
Rossiter John, Lr Union st
Sandford Wm., Tor place
SatchwillGeo.,Madrepore pl
Toms Josiah, Lr Union st
*Wakeham Hy., Market st

Webber Rd., Lr Union st
*Weeks Thomas, Fleet st
Zelley Wm. H., Victoria pl
TALLOW CHANDLERS.
Bond Edm., George street
HenleyWm.C., Lr Union st
TIMBER, &c. MERTS.
Baker Jno., Temperance st
Bridgman John, Lr Union st
Crossman John, Lr Union st
Hall W. H., Lr Union st
Webber Jph., Lr Union st
TOY DEALERS.
Jenkins Martha, Fleet st
Rendell Fras. H., Strand
Ruby Mary, Lr Union st
UMBRELLA MAKERS.
Dart James, Lower Union st
Shields B., Victoria parade
VETERNY. SURGEONS.
Cawdle John, 2 East street
Pitts Wm., Orchard ter
SparrowGeo.Jas. 2 Albion pl
WATCH & CLOCK MKRS.
Bradford James, Vic. par
Braham James, 8 Strand
Burton Hy., Braddon's row
Cawdle Wm., Lr Union st
Trist James, Braddon's pl
Turner Geo., Lr Union st
Wheeler Jas., Hr Union st

WHEELWRIGHTS.
Gibbings Pp., Hr Union st
Hatch Ella, South street
Lethbridge Wm., Church ln
WINE&SPIRIT MERTS.
BeasleyTs.&Co.Victoria par
Michelmore Pp., LrUnion st
Northway Saml., Abbey pl
Prowse Mary Ann, Palk st

RAILWAY
Trains to Exeter, London,
Plymouth, &c. five or six
times a day
OMNIBUSES, &c.,
To Dartmouth, Brixham,
&c., daily, and to the
Railway Station, to meet
the trains, from theHotels

CARRIERS.
Ford & Co. from Lower Union
st. by rails and waggons,
to all parts
ToAshburton, S.Edgecombe,
from the Maritime Inn
and Steam Packet Inn,
every Mon. & Fri. 4 aft
ToDartmouth, Brixham, &c.
W. Farrar, from the Mari-
time Inn, Mon. Wed. and
Fri 4 aft

To *Exeter*, Medland and
Madge, George st., Mon.
Wed. and Fri., and Ford
and Co. daily
To *Newton Abbot*, Jno. Win-
ser, from the Maritime
Inn, every Sat. 4 aft
To*Teignmouth*,Elliott'sVan,
from theMaritimeInn,4aft
To *Totnes*, Ford & Co. daily ;
Perryman from Lower
Union st.Sat; Stoyle from
the Castle Inn, Mon.Wed.
and Fri ; and Worth from
the Commercial Inn,Mon.
and Friday

WATERCONVNCE.
Steam Packets to Guernsey
and Jersey, every Mon ;
to Plymouth, Wed. and
Sat; and to Portsmouth
and Southampton, Thurs

Sailing Vessels to London
every nine days

AGENT, R. J. Slade, 12 Victoria parade

WIDECOMBE-IN-THE-MOOR, sometimes spelt *Widdecombe*, or *Wi-thecombe-in-the-Moors*, is a scattered village, picturesquely seated in a valley on the eastern side of *Dartmoor Forest*, 6 miles N.W. by N. of Ashburton. Its parish is a detached member of Haytor Hundred, and contains 1106 inhabitants, and 10,614 acres of land, including the hamlets, &c., of *Cator, Ponsworthy, Poundsgate, Linchaford, Fernhill, Dunstone, Blackslade, Lower-Tor, &c.*, and about 4700 acres of open *commons*, called *Newbridge, Blackdown, Natsworthy, Jourdan, &c.* The parish rises in bold hills from the river Dart and several of its tributary streams, and great improvements have been made of late years in the Forest farms. The late Lord Ashburton purchased a long term in the manors of Widecombe and *Speechwick*, and built a neat house in the latter, in a romantic situation, where he made extensive plantations. These manors are now held by the Rev. — Fry, together with that of Blagdon-Pipard; but that of Blackslade belongs to Mr. W. Norrish. Lord Cranstoun, Sir W. P. Carew, Mr. Bastard, and many smaller freeholders have estates in the parish. The *Church* (St. Pancras,) is a large ancient structure with a lofty tower and six bells. On Sunday afternoon, Oct. 21st, 1638, it was much damaged by lightning, which killed four and injured 62 of the congregation then assembled in divine worship. The tower was shattered extensively, and one of the large pinnacles fell through the roof of the nave, and a large beam dropped between the pulpit and reading desk, without injuring the vicar and clerk. A circumstantial account of this awful visitation may be seen in some lengthy verses, written by an eye-witness, and preserved in the church. The fabric is mostly in the early perpendicular style, and has a nave, aisles, transepts, and chancel; and the tower has octangular turrets at the four corners, crowned by crocketted pinnacles. The *vicarage*, valued in K.B. at £25. 13s. 9d., and in 1831 at £332, is in the patronage of the Dean and Chapter of Exeter, and incumbency of the Rev. Jas. H. Mason, M.A., who has 86A. 1R. 6P. of glebe, and a good residence. The patrons are also appropriators of the great tithes, which

were commuted in 1845 for £168. 6s., and the small tithes for £280 per annum. The *Wesleyans* have small chapels at Widecombe and Ponsworthy, and the *Independents* have one at Watergate. A house, two cottages, and 1½A. of land, have been vested from an early period for the use of the *church* and *poor*, and the latter have 13s. a year, left by Lewis Wills and Sampson Jerman. Two small *schools* are supported by subscription, and the dividends of £142 five per cent. stock, left by a Miss White, about 1797.

Baker John, vict., Old Inn
Bennett George, blacksmith
Hamlyn Pancras, blacksmith
Harvey ——, shopkeeper
Kitson Wm. solr. *Speechwick*
Langdon John, schoolmr., Dunstone
Lee James, beerseller
Mason Rev Jas. H., M.A. vicar of Widecombe & Treneglos, & chaplain of Tor Royal Chapel, *Vicarage*
Townsend Daniel, tailor
Wreyford Rosamond, vict. *Tavistock*

Hamlyn John
Hannaford John
Hannaford Roger
Hannaford Rd.
Hannaford Saml.
Hannaford Ts.
Hern Robert
Hern Jno. & Sl.
Hern Wm.
*Hext Daniel
Hext John
Hext James
*Hext Robert
Kerslake Wm.
*Langdon Geo.
Lemon George
Lemon Joseph
Lindon Elijah
Mann Samuel
May Thomas
*Norrish Willm. *Blackslade*
Nosworthy Jas.
Nosworthy Robt.
Smerdon James

*Smerdon John
Smerdon Robert
*Smerdon N. & E.
*Smerdon Wm.
*Sperwell Thos.
Standcombe Jno.
*Stockman John
*Townsend John
Tremaine John
Warren Jas. *Tor*
White John
*White Wm. H.
Wilcocks Thos.

MILLERS.
Chaffe Jno. jun.
Easterbrook Geo.
Kevill Abraham
Tarr John

BOOT & SHOE MKS.
Andrews Wm.
Coaker Wm.
Hannaford Sml.
Warren Charles

CARPENTERS.
Caunter George
Caunter Wm.
Cleave John

FARMERS.
(* are Owners.)
*Caunter Henry
Chaffe Edward

Chaffe John
Dadd —, *Pitton*
Easterbrook Jno.
Easterbrook Nhs.
Ford John
Ford Thomas
*French Richd. & Elias
French Thomas
French Wm.
Hamlyn Elias
Hamlyn Jas. *Ash*
Hamlyn James

MASONS.
Warren John
Warren Edward
Warren Samuel

POST-OFFICE at Diana Lemon's.

WOODLAND, a small village and parish, nearly three miles E.S.E. of Ashburton, has only 206 inhabitants, and about 1400 acres of land, belonging to various freeholders. The manor is dismembered, and was held for a long period with that of Ipplepen. The Dean and Canons of Windsor are appropriators of the great tithes of both parishes. Woodland *Church* is a small antique structure, with a tower and three bells, and the living is a perpetual curacy, valued at only £56, in the patronage of the inhabitants, and incumbency of the Rev. John White. Three houses and about 11A. of land have been vested in trust for the use of the parishioners from an early period, and are now let for about £12 a year, of which £10 is paid to the officiating minister, and the rest is carried to the churchwardens' accounts. The poor have the following *yearly doles*, viz., 20s. from £20 left by *Wm. Dyer*, in 1696; 40s. out of the poor rates, as interest of £40 left by *Emma Culling*; and 40s. left by *Wm. Culling*, in 1722. The latter is paid out of six fields, and applied in aid of the *Parish School*.

Butcher Wm. carpenter
Smerdon Richard, parish clerk
White Rev John, incbt. *Maryfield*
FARMERS.
Beavis Richard, *Pulfords*

Ford Samuel || Ford John
Hamlyn James || Hamlyn Wm.
Holman Henry || Pearse Wm.
Ruby Henry || Skinner Jeffry
Sherwill John || White Matthew

WOLBOROUGH, or *Woolborough Parish*, comprises only about 970 acres of land, and had 2609 inhabitants in 1841, of whom 1192 were re-

turned as being in *Newton Abbot,* but the whole parish is in the town and suburbs of that improving place, as noticed below.

NEWTON-ABBOT, in Wolborough parish, is an ancient market town, picturesquely seated on the north side of the small river *Lemon,* near its confluence with the navigable river *Teign,* and near the *South Devon Railway,* 15 miles S. by W. of Exeter, 7 miles W. by S. of Teignmouth, 29 miles E.N.E. of Plymouth, and 187 miles W.S.W. of London. It has now about 3000 inhabitants, exclusive of its suburb of NEWTON BUSHEL, which has more than 1000 inhabitants, and forms the northern part of the town, on the opposite side of the Lemon rivulet, in *Highweek parish,* and in Teignbridge Hundred, as afterwards noticed. The town has been much improved during the last ten years, and is situated in one of the most fertile and picturesque parts of Devon. A *canal,* about 2½ miles long, made by the father of the late Geo. Templer, Esq., connects the navigable part of the Teign, about a mile from the town, with a railway which was made at a later period, and extends about 7 miles north-west to the *Haytor granite works,* whence immense quantities of granite are sent down the river, to be shipped at Teignmouth for London and other places, where it is in great request for the erection of public buildings, especially bridges, quays, &c. Newton was the first town in which *William, Prince of Orange,* made a declaration, after landing at Brixham. (See pages 58 and 426.) A stone pedestal, with an inscription, commemorating this event, stands in the middle of Wolborough street. The Prince of Orange, before his advance to Exeter, sojourned a short time at *Ford House,* the manor house of Wolborough, now occupied by Hy. Cartwright, M.D. The *manor of Wolborough,* which includes Newton Abbot, was given to Tor Abbey by its founder, William Lord Briwere, or Brewer. Some time after the dissolution, in the reign of James I., it was purchased by *Sir Richard Reynell,* whose heiress carried it in marriage to Sir Wm. Waller, the parliamentary general. The heiress of the latter married Sir Wm. Courtenay, an ancestor of the Earl of Devon, the present lord of the manor, and owner of most of the soil. Sir Richard Reynell was an eminent lawyer, and built Ford House, where he entertained Charles I. and his suite for several days, in 1625, when he and his brother Thomas received the honour of knighthood. The house remains in its original form, and is a large cemented mansion, with an extensive and well wooded lawn. *Abbot Ley House,* built in 1847-'8, is the pleasant seat of James King, Esq. The Rev. Richard Lane is lord of the manor of *Teignweek,* including *Newton Bushel,* in Highweek parish, which was held in the 13th and 14th centuries, by the Bushell, or Bussell family, whose heiress carried it in marriage to the Yardes, in the reign of Richard II. In 1751, it was sold by Gilbert Yarde, Esq., to Thomas Veale, Esq., from whom it passed to his nephew, Thomas Lane, Esq., father of its present owner. The lord of this manor had a grant for a market at Newton Bushel, in 1246, and one for two fairs at Bradley, in 1308; but they were discontinued in the reign of Philip and Mary, when the Yarde family purchased the rights of the markets and fairs of the adjoining town of Newton Abbot. *Bradley House,* the ancient manor house, is now the property of the Rev. F. S. Wall, B.C.L., lord of the manor of Highweek. The Duke of Somerset, and several smaller proprietors, have estates in the two parishes. NEWTON ABBOT is said to have possessed an ancient charter, and was formerly a *borough,* governed by a portreeve and other officers, still appointed at the courts leet and baron. The office of the portreeve is little more than honorary; but on the night of his inauguration, he gives a good supper to the electors, who light him home to his residence at the close of the entertainment. The town gives name to a large Poor Law Union and County Court and Polling

District, and has a *Town Hall*, (built in 1848, at the cost of about £1000,) where *petty sessions* are held on the last Tuesday of every month, by the magistrates of Teignbridge Division, to whom Mr. Wm. Flamank is clerk. The *County Court* is held monthly, in the same building, for all the 39 parishes of Newton Abbot Union. Mr. P. Pearce is the *clerk*, and Mr. E. Burch the *high bailiff*. The *market*, held every Wednesday, is numerously attended by the farmers, &c., of the surrounding district, and well supplied with all sorts of provisions. Here is a *great market* for cattle, &c., on the last Wednesday in February; and three annual *fairs*, held on June 24th, and the Wednesdays after September 11th and November 6th. The old market-house and shambles stood in the middle of Wolborough street, but they were removed in 1826, after the completion of the present convenient *market place*, built on an open space at the end of Market street. The town has many good houses and shops, especially in the new streets laid out during the last ten years. The *Globe Hotel*, erected a few years ago, by the Earl of Devon, at the cost of about £6000, is constructed of granite, and has a handsome portico, and a spacious and elegant *Ball Room*, for the accommodation of assemblies, concerts, &c. The *Gas Works* were constructed in 1839, at the cost of about £3000, raised in £6 shares. *Woolborough Parish Church* (St. James,) stands on an eminence more than half a mile south of the town, and is a large cemented structure, with a tower and four bells. The chancel has three stained glass windows, and contains a handsome monument, with recumbent effigies of Sir Richard Reynell and his lady, who died in 1633 and 1652. The living is a *donative*, valued at £235, with the curacy of Newton Abbot annexed to it, in the patronage of the Earl of Devon, and incumbency of the Rev. Wm. C. Clack. There is no Parsonage, and only 3 roods of glebe. The tithes were commuted in 1845, for £260 per annum. *Newton Abbot Chapel of Ease* (St. Leonard,) was built by subscription, in 1836, when the old one was pulled down, except the tower, which contains a clock and six bells, and is left standing in the middle of Wolborough street. *Highweek Parish Church* (All Saints,) is in the small village of Highweek, on an eminence about a mile north of the town. It is an ancient structure, with an embattled tower and six bells. It is in the perpendicular style of the time of Henry VI., and in its windows are some remnants of ancient stained glass. The benefice is a *perpetual curacy*, consolidated with the vicarage of King's Teignton, in the patronage of the Bishop, and incumbency of the Rev. H. Woolcombe, jun., for whom the Rev. W. Sadler, B.A., officiates. Here is 13A. 2R. 8P. of glebe, but no parsonage. The tithes of Highweek parish were commuted in 1840, the vicarial for £245, and the rectorial for £183. 10s. The Trustees of the late J. Kenrick are impropriators of the latter. *Newton Bushel Chapel of Ease* (Virgin Mary,) for that part of the parish of Highweek, is an old Gothic fabric, which was repaired and enlarged in 1826, and has a tower and one bell. It stands in Bridge street, and was built by Richard Yarde, Esq., in the 21st of Henry VIII. The interior has now a neat appearance, and contains a good painting of "The Nativity of our Saviour," presented by James Templer, Esq. Here is a small *Baptist Chapel*, rebuilt in 1820; an *Independent Chapel*, rebuilt in 1836, at the cost of £800; a *Wesleyan Chapel*, in Courtenay street, built in 1848, at the cost of £550, and a smaller one in Mill lane, erected many years ago. The Independent Chapel has an endowment of £38 per annum, as afterwards noticed. The town has a *Literary Society*, with a good library; a Mechanics' Institution, established in 1836; a well supplied *News Room;* and an *Agricultural and Labourers' Friend Society*. It has a Savings' Bank, several Provident and Friendly Societies, National and British Schools, and various *Charities, belonging to the two parishes*.

WOLBOROUGH.—The *Parish Lands, &c.*, have been vested in trust from an early period, for the relief of the poor, and the adorning and repairing of Wolborough church and the chapel of Newton Abbot, and for other public and charitable uses in the parish. They comprise 15A. 3R. 2P., and about 24 houses and cottages, let in 1820 at rents amounting to only about £109, but now worth more than £350 per annum. Large fines were paid on the granting of the leases for 99 years, terminable on three lives. The trustees also derive 18s. a year from four small rent-charges. Out of the income about £9 per annum is distributed in linen cloth among the poor, and the rest is chiefly applied in the service of the church and chapel. New trustees of these and other charity estates of this parish were appointed by the Court of Chancery, after much litigation, in 1821. In 1640, LADY LUCY REYNELL founded an ALMSHOUSE in this parish for the reception of *four poor widows of clergymen* of Devonshire or the city of Exeter, to be appointed by the trustees and the owner of her capital messuage of Ford House, the latter of whom to have the casting vote. For the payment of yearly stipends of £5 to each of the four widows, and for other charitable purposes, the foundress gave a house and 29A. of land at Paington, now let for about £63, and a house and several acres of land at Wolborough, worth about £10 per annum. About 1790, the old almshouses were taken down, and two houses were built in their stead, for the residence of *two* clergymen's widows, who each receive £10 per annum. The rest of the clear income is applied to charitable uses, pursuant to a decree of the Court of Chancery. In 1606, ROBERT HAYMAN gave four small almshouses for the residence of poor parishioners, and for their reparation and the relief of the poor he gave an adjoining tenement, garden, and orchard, now let for only 10s. per annum. The poor have the dividends of £100 four per cent. stock, left by *John Sloman* in 1789. A yearly rent-charge of £12 was left in 1777, by *Aaron Tozer*, to be applied as follows, viz., £4 towards the support of a young man preparing for the Independent ministry, and £8 towards the support of the minister of the *Independent Chapel*, in Wolborough street. In 1788, HANNAH MARIA BEARNE gave £1450 vested on mortgage, and £1000 three per cent. consols, in trust that the interest and dividends should be applied in supporting a FREE SCHOOL for the education of poor children of *Highweek and Wolborough*, except £30 a year to be paid to the minister of the above-named chapel, on condition that he should deliver a weekly lecture on Thursday evenings. The mortgages have been redeemed, and the property now belonging to this charity consists of £4471. 12s. 4d. three per cent. consols, yielding £134 per annum, of which about £90 is paid to the schoolmaster and mistress for teaching about 80 boys and 70 girls. A school-house was built by the trustees some years ago, and many of the children belong to the established church, as did the foundress, though five of the seven trustees appointed by her were dissenters. It is now conducted as a *British School*, and here is also a large *National School*.

HIGHWEEK.—The *Parish Lands, &c.*, vested in trust for charitable uses from an early period, comprise about 8 acres and five houses, let for £34. 9s. per annum, and a house and garden occupied by paupers. There is also belonging to the trust a sum of £200 three per cent. reduced annuities, purchased with money which arose from fines and the sale of timber. There is also on the estate a small Almshouse, occupied by poor people. Most of the clear income is distributed in money and clothing among the poor, and £5 is paid yearly in aid of the National School. *Gilbert's Almshouse* was founded as an hospital for *lepers*, by John Gilbert, who endowed it, in 1538, with an adjacent close of one acre, and with a yearly rent-charge of £4, paid by the Corporation of Exeter. The almshouse has five tenements for as many inmates. The acre of land is held by the feoffees of the parish land in consideration of their repairing the almshouse and paying 12s. a year to the inmates. The poor parishioners have the following yearly sums, viz. : 20s. left by *John Peter* out of the tithes of Cornworthy; 2s. left by one *Bickford*, out of Wannell's house; and £2 from a house and garden left in 1632, by *Robert Hayman*, for distributions of shirts and shifts.

NEWTON ABBOT UNION comprises the 39 *parishes* of Abbotskerswell, Ashburton, Beckington, Bishop's Teignton, Bovey-Tracey, Buckland-in-the-Moor, Broadhempston, Cockington, Coombinteignhead, Dawlish, King's Teignton, Hennock, Lustleigh, Moreton-Hampstead, Manaton, North Bovey, Coffinswell, Chudleigh, Denbury, East and West Ogwell, East and West Teignmouth, Haccomb, Highweek, Ilsington, Ipplepen, Ideford, Kingskerswell, St. Nicholas, St. Mary-Church, Stokeinteignhead, Teigngrace, Trusham, Tor-Brian, Tor-Moham, Widecombe-in-the-Moor, Woodland, and Wolborough. These parishes extend over an area of 184 square miles, and had 44,358 *inhabitants* in 1841, living in 8528 *houses*, besides which there were 670 empty houses and 90 building when the census was taken. Their total average annual expenditure on the poor during the three years preceding the formation of the union was £16,756. In 1838 it was £12,938, and in 1840, £15,997. The *Workhouse*, which has room for about 400 inmates, is pleasantly situated on the eastern side of the town, and is one of the best in England, both in external appearance and internal arrangement. The building and furnishing cost about £13,000. The various wards, yards, &c., occupy nearly two acres, and attached to it are about two acres of garden ground. There are 56 elected *guardians*, and the Rev. C. Wolston is chairman. Mr. John Alsop is the *union clerk and superintendent registrar ;* the Rev. W. F. Good, *chaplain ;* and James and Mrs. Blythe, *master*

and matron of the Workhouse. Messrs. Matthew White, Ebenezer Metherell, and John Foaden are the *'relieving officers.* The Union is divided into 13 medical and six registration districts. Mr. Andrew Bearne is *registrar of Births and Deaths* for Newton-Abbot District, and Mr. J. S. Bearne is his deputy. The Board meets every Wednesday at eleven o'clock.

NEWTON ABBOT AND BUSHEL DIRECTORY,

(Including Wolborough and Highweek Parishes.)

The Post-Office is at Market terrace. Mr. Fdk. J. Stokes is the *post master.* Letters despatched morning and night, and delivered at 7½ morning and 2 afternoon. Money orders granted and paid.

☞ *Those marked* 1 *reside in Bridge street,* 2 *Courtenay st.,* 3 *East st.,* 4 *Highweek st.,* 5 *Market place,* 6 *Market terrace,* 7 *in Wolborough st., and* 8 *in Highweek.*

2 Abberley Humphrey, architect, &c.
3 Alsop John, union clerk, superintendent regr., & distr. of stamps.
Babbs Mr Samuel, Exeter road
4 Baker Mr. Nichls. ‖ 3 Baker Wm.
2 Baker Wm. Thos. police supt.
8 Bartlett Mrs Sarah, Church hill
Basting Walter, railway clerk
4 Bearne Hy. sexton, & Andw., regr.
4 Bearne Robt., gas colr. & church clk
7 Bibbings Chas., town crier
4 Bickford Mrs Sus., & 8 Mr Nichls.
3 Blythe James, Workhouse school
3 Bunce Rev John, (Baptist)
4 Burch Edw. high bailiff of County Court
4 Burgoyn John, traveller
Cartwright Hy. Esq., M.D. *Ford Hs*
3 Chapple Rt. tobacco pipe maker
3 Chater Rev John, (Independent)
2 Chudleigh Mrs and Miss
3 Clarke Herbert, Esq. supt of South Devon Railway
7 Clarke Jno. gun mkr., & 3 Mr Wm.
3 Coward Isaac Toogood, Esq
2 Creed Mr Abm. ‖ Crossman Miss
3 Cross Rev Wm. (Baptist)
2 Davis Rev Jno. Wm., M.A., curate
3 Daw Wm. upholsterer
Doke Wm. gent., Exeter road
7 Dottin Pp., brush & patten mkr.
7 Exell Rev ——, (Wesleyan)
3 Farley Lieut. Wm., R.N., & Mrs M.
Ford Mrs Eliz, *Culver place*
Froude Mrs Phillis, *Denbury House*
Gaedy Chas. Wm. railway supt.
7 Gange Wm., tinner and brazier
7 Gaye Miss ‖ 3 Gerrard Mr James
Gidley Gustavus, railway clerk
7 Golding Samuel Fawcett, gent.
8 Good Rev Wm. Fulford, chap. of Union, Ess hill

1 Gray Edw., corn & seed mert.
Hare Reginald, gent. *New Bradley Hs*
4 Heath Ellis, dyer, &c
7 Heath Mr Sl. ‖ 8 Holmes Mrs My.
Hole Wm. Esq. *Park*
7 Holman Mrs Mary Ann
4 Hopkins Mr Rd. ‖ 7 Hugo Mrs
Holmes Mrs Mary, Exeter road
Hutchings Mr Arthur, Railway st
1 Hysum Geo. Edw., carver & gilder
7 Jacobs Thos. paper manufacturer
Kenrick Rev Jarvis, M.A.
King Jas., Esq. *Abbot Ley House*
3 Leach Mr Wm. Pinney
7 Leslie Mr Thos. ‖ 4 Martin John
Leslie Lieut. Walter, R.N. *East Park*
7 Lethbridge Lieut. John, R.N.
Linscott Thos., engineer at gas works
3 Mapleton Mrs L. ‖ 3 Mardon Mrs
Martley Wm., Railway station
3 Merson Edw., gardener, &c
3 Mills Mr John ‖ 7 Mortimore Miss
2 Mills Thos. L. lace manufacturer
7 Neyle Richard, fish hook maker
7 Neyle John, tool maker
Patey Andrew, clerk, Railway st
6 Pearce Parmenas, solr. & clerk to County Court
Pearce Mrs My., Courtenay st
4 Pinsent John, coal mert. & inspr. of weights and measures
1 Polybank John, millwright
7 Pridham John, sexton
6 Rendell Robt. tax collector
3 Richards Misses, M. K. & B.
8 Sadler Rev Wm., B.A., curate
1 Shapley Samuel R. corn & cheese mert., &c.
6 Stokes Fdk. John, postmaster, &c.
8 Storey Mr. Wm., *White hill*
7 Sweeting Misses ‖ 7 Symes Miss
Symes Mrs Eliz., Exeter road

Templer Rev John, M.A., rector of
  Teigngrace, Knowle Hill
Turner Miss || Tores Miss
4 Vicary Mr Moses || 3 Way Thos.
8 Wall Rev Fdk. S., B.C.L., *Bradley*
7 Westcott Miss Jane || 3 Willis Mrs
4 White Mathw., relieving officer
Whidburne Misses, Wolbro' st
3 Wotton Wm. coal merchant
3 Wotton Wm. basket maker
Williams Mr Thos. C. *Culver place*

BANKS.
7 Devon & Cornwall Banking Co.,
  (draw on Barclay, Bevan & Co.)
  E.C. Kent, *manager*
1 Watts & Co., (draw on Deacon &
  Williams)
7 *Savings' Bank*, (branch of Exeter)
  Rev W. F. Good, secretary

FIRE & LIFE OFFICE AGENTS.
3 Agricultural Cattle, J. H.Whiteway
7 Clerical & Medl., W. J. Gaskell
1 County & Provdt., Foss & Harris
7 Crown Life, E. C. Kent
7 Globe, W. F. D'Arcy
7 Kent Mutual, W. J. Gaskell
7 National Merctl., Rd. Bastow
7 Legal & Coml., Rd. Bastow
1 Norwich Union, James Budd
6 Phœnix Fire, P. Pearce
6 Royal Exchange, Rt. Rendell
2 Royal Farmers', J. H. Whiteway
7 Sun, Wm. Flamank
7 Standard of England, S. Hicks
2 Western Life, Hy. Hatchwell
4 West of England, Rt. France

HOTELS, INNS, & TAVERNS.
*(Marked * are posting.)*
7 Bear, Thomas Cowell
5 Bradley Inn, James Barnes
* 2 Commercial Inn, John Magor
4 Commercial, Eliz. Varnham
7 Compasses, John Blacker
3 Dartmouth Inn, John Mills
* 2 Globe Hotel, John Beazley
1 Golden Lion, Sarah Pattison
7 Half-Moon, Samuel Langler
3 Jolly Sailors, Thomas Payne
3 Newfoundland Inn, Chas. Broom
8 Passage House, Thomas Edwards
2 Railway Inn, Thomas Russell
3 Rising Sun, Samuel Field
4 Seven Stars, John Salter
7 Ship, John Mills
South Devon Inn, Charles Cope

7 Turk's Head, Thomas Coombe
3 Union Inn, Edward Beazley
3 White Hart, John Stranger
ACADEMIES.
*(*take Boarders.)*
2 * Bartlett B.
7 Bidder David, *British School.*
7 Burnell My. A.
3 * Chater Mrs J.
2 Crocker Josiah
8 Evans Eliz.
3 Collins Mary
Heath Elizabeth, *Workhouse Sch.*
Gelding Hanh. *do*
3 * Gribble J. W. and R.
Head Mrs. *British*
7 * Ley Eliz.
7 * Lightfoot Jno. Nicholson, B.A.
3 Protheroe Ths., *National Schl.*
3 Robinson E., *do*
ATTORNEYS.
7 D'Arcy Wm. F.
7 Flamank Wm., (and clerk to magistrates)
4 Francis Robt.
6 Lane John R.
6 Pearce&Pidsley
3 Whiteway J. H.
AUCTIONEERS, &c
7 Crews John B.
1 Hearder Wm.
6 Rendell Robt.
BAKERS.
(Confectioners.)*
3 Bovey John
7 * Crews J. B.
7 Edwards John
3 Elliott Jacob
3 Giles John
7 Godfrey Rd.
3 Hunt Mary A.
4 Pascoe Rd.
4 Quick Robert
3 Richards Hy.
7 Roleston Wm.
5 Stockman J.&G.
* 1 Way John
4 Way Wm.
* 3 Winter John

7 Turk's Head, Thomas Coombe
BEERHOUSES.
4 Pascoe Wm.
3 Wills John
3 Winser Ann
BLACKSMITHS.
7 Lamble John
1 Pyle Emanuel
4 Stone Robert
1 White John
BOOKSELLERS.
1 Jacobs Henry
2 Vinning Wm. S.
BOOT&SHOE MKS.
7 Avery John
4 Godfrey Wm.
7 Gribble Wm.
7 Hannaford G.
1 Hearder Joel
1 Jenkins Josias
3 Margery Thos.
3 May Thomas
1 Moxey Thos.
3 Phillips Elzr.
3 Phillips Robt.
3 Shapter Pp.
3 Stantford Thos.
3 Truscott James
4 Underhay John
3 Stranger John
3 Vavasour John
3 Weatherdon G.
7 Weatherdon W.
7 White Wm.
2 Wills John
BREWERS, &c.
7 Creed Wm.
4 Pinsent J. & Co.
7 Symons Mttw.
BUILDERS.
2 Chudleigh J.A.
3 Milward Hy.
3 Winser John
BUTCHERS.
7 Drake Ann
7 Lane Wm.
7 Lavis Robert
7 Luscombe Pp.
3 Matthews Sml.
3 Marshall Geo.
4 Murrin Wm.
7 Stevens Geo.
3 Stranger John

4 Wills Thomas
CABINET MKRS.
3 Buckland F.
5 Cruse Wm.
2 Hatchwell Hy.
3 Hatchwell Rt.
7 Hill Sampson
COACH BLDRS.
Edwards George,
 Railway street
2 Ruby Thomas
3 Milward John
COOPERS.
3 Broom Chas.
4 Randle Jacob
2 Wotton Samuel
CORN MILLERS.
Allen John
Clark Wm.
8 Stockman J.&G.
CURRIERS.
4 Hannaford C.
3 Goodenough N.
1 Wills Elias
DRUGGISTS.
2 Drew Codner
1 Godfrey Fdk.
7 Gaskell W. J.
7 Radley W. C.
EARTHENWARE,
 &c., DLRS.
1 Badcock Wm.
2 Bearne Andw.
1 Cull Samuel
7 Gange Wm.
EATING HOUSES.
3 Bully Peter
5 Davis John
2 Fulford Sml.
5 Rowell Michl.
FARMERS.
(* are Owners.)
8 Bearne Andw.
8 Bickley John
8 * Drew Richd.
8 Edwards James
8 * Elliott Jph.
3 Hurd John
8 Luscombe T.
Madge Wm.
8 Murrin Mary
Nichols John
Norsworthy Jph.
8 Pitts John
8 Prowse Wm.

8 Rowell Jph.
8 * Rowell Wm.
8 * Segar John
8 Shapter Wm.
8 * Shilston Wm.
Taverner John
8 White Elias
 GLOVERS.
4 Branscombe Sl
4 Drew Wm.
 GROCERS, &c.
1 Badcock Wm.
2 Banfill C. T.
7 Bastow Rd.
1 Bearne Andw.
7 Bovey Edw.
1 Budd James
7 Crews J. B.
2 Crocker Josiah
7 Ferris Sarah
1 Foss & Harris
3 Ford Elias
7 Roberts John
2 Ruby Thos.
7 Snow Philip
HAIR DRESSERS.
7 Dottin Henry
3 Elms John
4 Giles Thomas
6 Rowe Solon
3 Stevens Geo.
 HATTERS.
1 Hill James
7 Roberts Wm.
 IRONMONGERS.
1 Amery Edward
7 Davis John B.
1 Hatch Thos.
2 May Thomas
3 Milward John
1 Stitson Thos.
 JOINERS.
4 Bearne John
8 Blackler Thos.
7 Bully John
Bully Samuel
5 Cull Saml. jun
8 Dicker Samuel
2 Stevens John
L. & W. DRAPERS.
4 Bale Wm.
2 Drew Wm.
7 Hicks Samuel
3 More Michael
7 Parrott Wm.

2 Pulsford Thos.
3 Stevens Geo.
1 Sweet Lewis
6 Walker Samuel
MILLINERS, &c.
3 Chudleigh Car.
7 Cook Harriet
7 Cowell Sarah
3 Mugford Eliz.
7 Pridham My.
7 Pitts Jane
7 Rendell Mtha.
6 Walk Eliz.
MUSIC TEACHERS.
4 Chapple Wm.
2 Vinning W. S.
PLASTERERS, &c.
3 Chudleigh Ths.
7 Doble Daniel
7 Hannaford Sl.
3 Mills Hugh
3 Wotton Robert
PLUMBERS, GLZS.
AND PAINTERS.
7 Doble Daniel
7 Hannaford Sl.
3 Head John
4 Pascoe John
3 Parker Wm.
2 Winser Edw.
 PRINTERS.
1 Hearder Wm.
2 Sluman Edw.
 SADDLERS.
4 Rowell Wm.
1 Shilston John
1 Stitson Joseph
3 Sweet Richd.
 SHOPKEEPERS.
3 Biddings Geo.
4 Cane James
4 Clarke Sarah
4 Drew Wm.
3 Mills Hugh
3 Perham John
3 Truscott James
3 Winser Ann
7 Winser Eliz.
STONE MASONS.
7 Bully S. & J.
7 Crossman Hy.
2 Mills Hugh
1 Pollard Thos.
STRAW HAT MKS.
3 Crook Jane

3 Godfrey Eliz.
3 Heward Theop.
3 Mugford Eliz.
 SURGEONS.
8 Bond W. Y.
7 Gaye Charles
7 Gillard F. J.
7 Leslie Andrew
7 Radley Wm. C.
 TAILORS.
(* Drapers also.)
7 Burge Thos.
1 Lamble Wm.
7 * Lavis George
1 * Lavis Wm.
3 Rendell Wm.
3 * Stevens Rd.
7 White Wm.
 TANNERS.
4 Branscombe S.
4 Vicary John
TIMBER MERTS.
1 Bearne Andw.
1 Cull & Son
5 Cruse Wm.
3 Milward John
VETY. SURGEONS.
6 Channon Thos.
Herne John
 WATCHMAKERS.
1 Hyne Chas.
7 Smerdon John
1 Snelling James
7 Thomas James
 WHEELWRIGHTS.
4 Davis George
7 Major Wm.
3 Milward John
WINE AND SPIRIT
 MERCHANTS.
2 Beazley John
7 Creed Wm.
3 Passmore Cpr.
4 Pinsent J.& Co.
4 Vickers Benj.
RAILWAY.
Trains to Exeter,
 Plymouth, &c.,
 six times a day.
John Beazley,
 Globe Hotel,
 agt. for parcel,
 &c., delivery.
Omnibus to meet
 every train.

CARRIERS.
Ford & Co, South st.&*T.J.Brook-ing*,Thomas st. dly. by rails, &c *to all parts.* To *Ashburton & Plymouth*, Elz.

Baker, from White Hart

To *Brixham and Dartmouth*, W. Balkwell, from JollySailor dly.

To *Exeter and Torquay*, Jno. Winser, from Golden Lion, Wed. & Sat. To *Moreton*,Lee, from the White Hart, Wed.

To *Okehampton*, Dart, from the WhiteHart,Fri.

To *Totnes*, Quint, from the Half-Moon, Wed. & Friday.

TEIGNBRIDGE HUNDRED

Averages about ten miles in length and seven in breadth, and includes the towns of Ashburton and Newton Bushel, on its southern border, and Moreton Hampstead, near its northern boundary. Its western side forms part of the eastern hills of *Dartmoor Forest*, including the *Haytor Granite Rock Quarries*, which have a railway and canal to the Teign; but the rest of the hundred is a fertile district of hills and valleys, watered by the East and West Teign, which receive here several tributaries, and unite near Teigngrace, below which the stream becomes navigable. The whole hundred is in the Southern Parliamentary Division of Devon, and it is all in Newton Abbot Polling District, except Moreton Hampstead, which is in Exeter Polling District. It is all in the Archdeaconry of Totnes, and in the Deanery of Moreton. The following enumeration of its 13 *parishes* shews their population in 1841 and their territorial extent. They are all in *Newton Abbot Union and County Court District.*

Parishes, &c.	Acres.	Pop.	Parishes, &c.	Acres.	Pop.
Ashburton Borough	6936	3841	Kingsteignton	3983	1498
Bickington	1375	374	Lustleigh	2939	311
Bovey (North)	5654	660	Manaton	6393	429
Bovey-Tracey	7262	1823	Moreton-Hampstead	7656	2037
*Hennock	3469	828	Teigngrace	1330	180
*Highweek	2422	1303			
Ideford	1472	331	Total	58,454	14,708
Ilsington	7563	1093			

* Highweek parish includes *Newton Bushel*, and Hennock includes *Knighton* hamlet. Moreton-Hampstead, Manaton, North Bovey, and Lustleigh, are in Crockernwell *Petty Sessional Division*, and all the others in *Teignbridge Division.*

ASHBURTON is an ancient *parliamentary borough* and neat *market town*, principally in three good streets, with many neat houses and well stocked shops, and two good inns and posting houses. Before the opening of the railways, it was a great thoroughfare for coaches, vans, &c., between Plymouth and London. It is distant 19 miles S.S.W. of Exeter, 24 miles N.E. by E. of Plymouth, 20 miles E. by S. of Tavistock, 7 miles N.N.W. of Totnes, 193 miles W.S.W. of London, and about 7 miles W. by S. of the South Devon Railway Station at Newton Abbot, to which a branch line is projected from Ashburton, but not yet commenced. The town is picturesquely seated in a fertile valley, opening to the south, and watered by the *Yeo* rivulet, which runs through and partly under the town, and falls into the river Dart about a mile below. The *parish* of Ashburton is co-extensive with the *borough,*

and comprises 6936A. 3R. 9P. of land, beautifully diversified with hills and valleys, and generally fertile, though skirted on the west by the lofty hills and barren summits of Dartmoor Forest. It had 3080 inhabitants in 1801, and 4165 in 1831, but in 1841 they had decreased to 3841, owing to the decline of the *serge and blanket manufacture*, formerly extensively carried on in the town and neighbourhood, where a few factories are still engaged in it. Formerly, about £100,000 worth of serges were made here yearly. In the adjacent parts of Dartmoor are several *tin and copper mines*, under the management of Messrs. Robert Palk, Henry Caunter, and others. Dartmoor abounds in extensive beds of *peat;* and an unsuccessful attempt was lately made here to manufacture the peat into a dense and cheap coal, which would be very useful in smelting the ores of the district, especially the rich ironstone of Brixham, &c. (See p. 425.) In the process of manufacturing *peat charcoal*, large portions of peatine, oil, naptha, acetic acid, tar, gas, &c., are obtained. The *manor* of Ashburton was anciently called *Asperton*, and was vested with the Bishops of Exeter till the reign of James I., when it was alienated to the Crown, Some years afterwards it was in moieties, vested with Sir Robt. Parkhurst and the Earl of Feversham. Lord Clinton and James Matheson, Esq., own a great part of the parish, and are joint lords of the *Borough Lordship;* but the former is sole lord of Ashburton manor; and James Woodley, Esq., is lord of the small manor of Halwell. Lord Clinton's farms, &c., are chiefly held on leases for lives; but there are many small freeholds in the parish. Ashburton was made one of the *stannary towns* in 1328, and a stannary court is sometimes held here, for settling mining disputes, &c. It is an ancient *borough by prescription*, and first sent two members to parliament in the 26th of Edward I., and again in the 8th of Henry IV., after which it ceased to do so till 1640. From the latter year it regularly sent two members till 1832, when it was placed by the Reform Act among the boroughs entitled only to send one representative to parliament. The number of *voters* is now about 200, and Lieut.-Col. Thomas Matheson is their present representative in parliament. The right of election was formerly vested in the freeholders and the holders and occupiers of burgage tenements. The *portreeve* is the returning officer, and is elected annually at the court leet and baron, together with a *bailiff* and other officers. In the reign of Edward II., Bishop Stapledon obtained a charter for a market and fair here; and a charter for two other fairs was obtained by John Quicke, Esq., one of the borough members, about 1712. The *market* for corn and provisions is held on Saturday; and here are now *four fairs*, for cattle, &c., held on the first Thursdays in March and June, and on the 10th of August and 11th of November, provided these dates fall on Tuesday or Thursday, and if not, on the Tuesday or Thursday after. The March fair has a large supply of cattle, and the November fair is a great sheep mart. The old market-house, which stood in the middle of North street, has recently been taken down, and a handsome new *Market House* and large *Public Room* were built on the opposite side of the street, in 1849-'50, at the cost of about £3000, in the Italian style. The Public

Room, for assemblies, concerts, public meetings, &c., is over the market; and the latter has ranges of stalls for flesh, fish, &c., and is supplied with excellent spring water. A turret, containing a bell and public clock, rises at the southern angle of the building. *Gas Works* were erected in 1840, at the cost of £1500, raised in £5 shares. The promenade called *Clinton Terrace* was made a few years ago, by Lord Clinton; and there are many pleasant walks in the neighbourhood. *John Dunning, Esq.*, a native of this town, having distinguished himself by great professional abilities, was made Solicitor-General in 1767, and created *Baron Ashburton* in 1782. He was born in 1731, and died in 1783, when he was succeeded by his son, Richard Barré Dunning, who died without issue, in 1823, when the title became extinct; but it was revived in 1835, when that distinguished statesman, *Alexander Baring*, was created Lord Ashburton. The late *Wm. Gifford, Esq.*, was born here in 1755, of poor parents, and having displayed considerable poetical and mathematical talent, he was taken from his apprenticeship as a shoemaker, by some friends, and sent to the Grammar School. He afterwards rose to eminence and wealth, and was editor of the *Quarterly Review.* He published several valuable works and translations, and died in 1826, leaving £2000 stock for the foundation of *two scholarships* at Exeter College, Oxford, for youths from Ashburton Grammar School. Another worthy native of this town was *Dr. John Ireland*, late *Dean of Westminster*, who died in 1842, and left £2000 to the Grammar School, and £1000 three per cent. consols, in trust for the yearly payment of £5 each, to six reduced housekeepers of this parish, attending the church, and of the age of 60 years or upwards. According to his will, the dean's house remains furnished, though it has been unoccupied since his decease. Ashburton was taken by General Fairfax, in his march westward, in 1646. (See page 57.) The general had his head-quarters here on the 10th of January, and on his departure he left a regiment of soldiers in possession of the town. He lodged at the Mermaid Inn, now a house and shop, retaining much of its ancient appearance. The residence of B. Parham, Esq., in West street, has been held by his family and the Dolbeares more than 300 years, and is said to have been a private residence of the abbots of Buckfastleigh. It contains an ancient oratory, with a richly carved oak wainscoting and canopy.

The PARISH CHURCH (*St. Andrew,*) is a spacious cruciform structure, with a tower rising from the centre to the height of 90 feet, and crowned by pinnacles at the corners, and by a semi-octagonal turret on its southern face. It is a fine specimen of the early perpendicular style, but has undergone many alteration and repairs. About 80 years ago, when the nave was re-seated, a rage seems to have prevailed for selling or destroying every valuable vestige of antiquity. The handsome stone pulpit, which was elaborately carved, and the brass eagle, were sold to the neighbouring parish of Bigbury, and the present unsightly pulpit and reading desk were substituted for them. The beautiful screen which separated the nave and chancel, and the antique screens belonging to the stalls in the south transept, were broken up at the same time, and part sold for a small sum, and the remainder used as fire wood. The chancel underwent a complete restora-

tion in 1840, when several ancient earthen vases were discovered in the walls, and a handsome new east window, enriched with stained glass, was inserted. Previous to that year the church was new roofed. Several of the windows are modern insertions, and on taking down part of the ceiling in the south aisle in 1849, various emblamatical paintings were discovered on the old panneled ceiling, which were placed there when the church was built in the 14th century. In this aisle is a mural tablet in memory of the first Lord Ashburton, with an inscription written by Dr. Johnson. The north porch remains, but that on the south side was removed in the early part of last century. The *vicarage*, valued in K.B. at £38. 8s. 11½d., and in 1831 at £639, with the perpetual curacies of Bickington and Buckland-in-the-Moor annexed to it, is in the patronage of the Dean and Chapter of Exeter, who are also appropriators of the great tithes, now leased to Mrs. Kitson. The Rev. Wm. Marsh, M.A., is the incumbent, and has a good residence and 72A. 1R. 18P. of glebe. The tithes were commuted in 1840, the rectorial for £390 and the vicarial for £538. Near the church stood the ancient *Chapel of St. Lawrence*, of which the ancient tower and spire are still standing, but the body was rebuilt about a century ago, and is now the Grammar school, as afterwards noticed. This chapel was built in 1450, when Bishop Lacy granted 40 days' indulgence to all who contributed to its foundation. It was endowed with £6. 13s. 4d. per annum for a chantry priest and schoolmaster. The *Church Lands, &c.*, most of which are supposed to have formed the endowment of this chapel, have been vested since the Reformation for the use of the church. They comprise about 36A. of land and 11 houses, let in 1821 for only £86. 7s. 11d. per annum, in consideration of large fines paid by the lessees. Some years ago, this estate was saddled with a mortgage debt of £1480, the interest of which absorbed most of the income. About £3 per annum out of the rents ought to be distributed among the poor, in consideration of property derived from the gifts of Robt. Hayman, Robt. Page, and Wm. Feymouth, in the reign of Elizabeth.

The *Wesleyans, Baptists*, and *Independents*, have chapels in the town. The Independent Chapel was built in 1737, but was enlarged some years ago, and a school-room has recently been added to it. It will seat about 800 hearers, and has a small endowment. The present Wesleyan Chapel was built in 1835 at the cost of about £1500, and has room for 600 hearers. *Sunday Schools* are attached to the church and chapels. An *Infant School* is supported chiefly by the vicar, and the parish has two endowed schools, and various charities for the poor. Here is also a *Subscription Library*, containing about 2000 volumes.

The GRAMMAR SCHOOL is kept in *St. Lawrence's Chapel*, which was given for its use, and as a place for public meetings and the holding of the manor courts, in the 36th of Elizabeth. The ancient tower and spire remain, but the body was rebuilt about a century ago. In the 2nd of Charles I., £418, derived from the bequest of a *Mr. Wearing*, was laid out in the purchase of 16A. 19P. of land at North Huish and Loddiswell, and 22A. 3R. 7P. at Aveton Gifford, for the support of the schoolmaster. These lands are now let for about £45 per annum. He has also the rent of 13A. 3P. at Staverton, let for £15, and purchased with £200, left by *Edward Gould* in 1735. A yearly rent-charge of £4, left to the schoolmaster by *Lawrence Blundell* in 1637, is paid out of a house, formerly the Mermaid Inn; and he has yearly 20s. from the churchwardens and 30s. from the overseers, the gifts of a Mr. Warren and another donor. Of the £2000, left by *Dr. Ireland*, in 1842, £1000 was laid out in purchasing a house for the master; £500 was lost by the failure of the Totnes Bank, and the master has the interest

of the other £500. In consideration of these emoluments, the master teaches Latin and Greek to all the children of the parish who apply for such instruction. The above-named *Lawrence Blundell* also left two yearly rent-charges of £6 and £4, to be paid towards the support of two boys at this school preparing for either of the Universities, and until they should attain the degree of Master of Arts. The donor charged these annuities, (and 20s. a year for five *poor widows,*) on land belonging to Sir L. V. Palk, Bart. *Dr. Ireland's* gift and *Wm. Gifford's* foundation of two scholarships are already noticed at page 463.

FREE SCHOOL.—In 1754, £500, given by *Lord Middleton,* and £140, by the *Hon. John Harris,* (two representatives of the borough,) were laid out in the purchase of an estate for the support of a schoolmaster or schoolmasters for instructing the children of this parish in reading, writing, and arithmetic. The estate purchased is called *Bourne Farm,* and comprises 81A. 17P., let for about £110 per annum. Out of the rent, about £70 per annum is paid to the master and mistress for teaching about 50 free scholars on Dr. Bell's system. The rest of the clear income is expended in buying books, &c., for the children. The school was rebuilt about 14 years ago, at the cost of £640, and is commonly called *Bourne School.* A yearly rent-charge of £6, left by *Mary Dunning* in 1805, out of three fields at Halsworthy Hills, in Staverton, is paid to the schoolmistress for teaching ten poor girls.

BENEFACTIONS TO THE POOR.—In 1676, *Robt. Phipps* left £80 to be laid out in land, and the yearly rents to be distributed in linen among the aged poor parishioners. This money was laid out in the purchase of 3A. 1R. 20P. of land, now let for £12. An old almshouse, left to the poor by *Thos. Caunter* in the 34th of Elizabeth, fell down in 1801, and the site was let in 1807 for 99 years, at the annual rent of £2. A legacy of £100, left by *Edward Bovey* in 1709, was laid out in the purchase of 2A. 1R. 26P. of land, now let for about £10 a year, which is distributed among the poor not receiving parochial relief. For weekly distributions of bread, the poor have £5. 4s. per annum, left by *Thos. Prideaux* and *Sir John Acland,* in the 7th and 13th of James I. For distribution in clothing, they have two annuities of 20s., left by *Geo. Knowling* and *John Bounde* in 1625 and 1642. An annuity of £8 for schooling poor children, was left by *John Ford* in 1667, out of the profits of the *market for wool and yarn,* which was held here every Tuesday till 1800, when it was discontinued. In 1702, *Wm. Stawell* left a yearly rent-charge of £10, out of the *town mills,* for distribution in linen among the poor. To provide a blue coat for a poor man yearly, *Edward Gould* left an annuity of 20s. out of the Bottom Park. For a weekly distribution of bread among the poor parishioners, *John Bickham* left £370, which was laid out in 1783 in the purchase of Park Field (7A.,) now let for about £20 a year. In 1778, *Richard Harris* left a yearly rent-charge of £11. 7s. 6d. to this parish out of land at Woodland, to be applied as follows:—£10 for the use of 50 poor people; 21s. for the vicar; 2s. 6d. for the clerk; and 4s. for the two sextons. The dividends of £200 navy five per cent. stock, purchased with the gifts of *Eleanor and Sally Adams,* in 1800, are distributed in linen cloth among the poor. Five poor widows have the interest of £28. 16s., left by *Alicia Donkin* in 1812, secured on the Newton and Ashburton turnpike.

ASHBURTON DIRECTORY.

The POST-OFFICE is at Mr. Wm. Barron's, East street. Letters are received and despatched at 7 morning and ten minutes before 6 evening; and

there are penny posts to Buckfastleigh and Brent.   Money Orders are granted and paid.

Those marked 2 are in East street; 3, North street; 4, West street; 5, Market street; 6, Lawrence street; 7, Back lane; 8, Brownshill; 9, Summer hill; 10, Headborough; 11, Goodstone; and 12, in Heavyhead lane.

Abraham Misses, *Welstor;* 7 Mrs
Amery John Sparke, Esq., *Druid Hs*
3 Berry John, serge & blanket mfr
Berry Richard, Esq. *Hall*
2 Bowden Mrs ‖ 2 Cockey Misses
2 Brown Rev Samuel (Wesleyan)
Caunter Henry, artist, &c. West st
Caunter John, Esq. *Leat Park*
4 Caunter Rd. serge & blanket mfr
Chalker Mr James, Lawrence lane
2 Cousins Mr Thos. ‖ 4 Eales Miss
Dore Rev John (Baptist,) East st
Eales Rev Wm. *Waye House*
3 Foaden John, relieving officer
2 Gribble Mrs ‖ 4 Griffin Mrs
2 Hainsworth Miss‖5 Hurst MrWm.
Hannaford Mr Samuel, East street
2 Hebditch Rev Saml. (Baptist)
Hern Mr John, Bowdley cottage
2 Hill Rev John E. curate
3 Isaac John, worsted manfr
2 Kernick John, mining agent
Kingwill Mr Henry, East street
2 Knowles Mr Samuel Posgate
Lyde Mrs Elizabeth, West street
2 Mann Wm. basket maker
4 Marsh Rev Wm., M.A., Vicarage
Michelmore Mr Jeffry, West street
2 Mogridge Mrs Mary Bovey
2 Paige Rev John Brown, M.A. head master of *Grammar School*
2 Palk Robert, mine manager, &c
Parham Benjamin, gent. West st
3 Poppleston Wm. rope, &c. maker
Routley Wm. dyer, East street
4 Sawdye Mr Wm. & Scagell Henry
4 SoperJohn,M.D. ‖ 2 SearleMrThos.
2 Steer John, veterinary surgeon
2 Tippett Rev Charles (Baptist)
Tucker Mr John F. *Gages*
2 Walrond Mrs F. ‖ Winsor Mr Jno.
Woodley —, Esq. East street
Wrey Sir B. P., Bart. *The Chase*
2 Young Col. Geo.D.& MrFitzwilliam
ATTORNEYS.
Abraham and Kitson, East street
Caunter George, East street
Cockey Wm. Aldridge *(dep. coroner,)* East street

Gribble Joseph *(coroner,)* West st
Tucker Robert, East street
AUCTIONEERS.
4 Creagh Henry C. (and surveyor)
Mann Wm., East street
4 Sawdye Edw. (and land surveyor)
FIRE & LIFE OFFICE AGENTS.
Atlas, R. G. Abraham, East street
Guardian, Wm. Barrons
Legal & Commercial, Fdk. Herron
Phœnix and Pelican, Jph. Fitze
Royal Exchange, Thomas Ferris
Royal Farmers', Edward Sawdye
Star, Thomas Lyle
Sun, Wm. R. Whiteway
Western Life, Wm. Mann
West of England, G. Caunter
INNS AND TAVERNS.
3 Culloden Inn, John Smerdon
4 Duke's Head, Wm. Butchers
4 Exeter Inn, James Burnett
3 Globe, Edward Husson
6 Golden Fleece, George Perkins
2 Golden Lion Hotel, Geo. Bate
2 Golden Lion Tap, Aaron Bickham
4 London Inn, Richard Bracewell
3 New Inn, Eliz. Whiteway
6 Old Bottle, Joseph Mugford
2 Red Lion, Wm. Lukey
4 Rose and Crown, Jph. Collins
2 Royal Oak, Philippa White
2 Seven Stars, Thomas Brock
3 Sun, Thomas Johnson
3 Town Arms, Richard Mugford
SURGEONS.
Bean Edward Fowler, East street
Hele Hy. Herbert & John, East st
Lyle Thomas, East street

ACADEMIES.	BAKERS.
*Gram.School,*Rev J. P. Paige, M.A., Thomas White, B.A., & Mr Barnett	(* *Confectioners.*) 2*Baker Chas. 2*Bowden Robt. Ching Susan
*Free School,*Wm. Honeywill	3*Coulman Sus. 3 Frost John
Crews My. *Infant*	3 Hext Thomas
2 Ferris Emma	2*Lamason Isc.
3 Knapman Ths.	3 Mardon Richd.
	12 Matthews Jno.

4*Maunder Wm.
3 Norris James
6 Perkins Geo.
4 Thorne Wm.
3 Williams Chas.
3 Yolland Jph.
BEERHOUSES.
2 Caunter John
3 Dobell Richd.
3 Luscombe Jno.
BLACKSMITHS.
2 Baker Wm.
6 Coysh Edward
4 Horton Amos
2 Mead Samuel
3 Smerdon Danl.
12 Walkham Rd.
BOOKSELLRS. &c.
4 Chapple Jas. M.
(&music prof.)
3 Mann Samuel
2 Stentiford Geo.
BOOT&SHOE MKS.
2 Boone Chas.
4 Clampit Chas.
4 Codd John
2 Easterbrook Js.
4 Elliott John
4 Foot Peter (and
parish clerk)
3 Giles John
2 Giles John, jun
3 HabberfieldChs
3 Harding Thos.
3 Lopas George
4 MichelmoreWm
2 Thompson Ths.
3 Weeks Samuel
4 Weeks Sol.
13 WoodleyT.&J.
BUTCHERS.
12 Edwards Wm.
2 Mann Wm.
2 Matterface J. C.
4 Pearse John
3 Pope John
3 Smerdon Geo.
3 Smerdon John
3 Smerdon Thos.
2 Yolland Chas.
CABINET MKRS.
2 Halls Richard
3 Husson Edw.
3 Maddock John
3 Mogridge Hugh

2 Mogridge Thos.
CARPENTERS.
(* Builders.)
4 Daw Henry
6 Elliott Robert
4*Foaden Thos.
4 Foot John
3*Hext Thomas
Ireland Wm.
2*Luscombe Rd.
3 Piper Wm.
7 Soper Richard
CHEMISTS &DGTS.
2 Beck Nathan
3 Gilbert Mr
4 Herron Fdk.
COOPERS.
3 Chalker James
3 Dobell Henry
4 Garde John
CORN MILLERS.
2 Osmond Robert
and Alexander
Pengilly Edward,
Lemonford
Underhill Wm.,
Furzeley
Willing Richard,
Largecombe
Yolland Stephen,
Town Mills
CURRIERS.
2 Aggett Joseph
5 Batten Wm.
EARTHENWARE
DEALERS.
4 Coneybear W.
2 Ferris Thos.
3 Norris James
4 Norris Wm.
FARMERS.
Bovey John, Esq.
Pear Tree
Coulton Richard
Croker Richard
EasterbrookElias
Edwards Js. *Way*
FordWm.& How-
arth John
10 Gidley Geo.
Hannaford Jno.
Hext John
Hext Rd. *Hele*
Kingwell Wm.
Langler John

11 Mann Wm.
Maunder Henry
Maunder Thos.
Mogridge Richd.
Mogridge Thos.
Northcott Wm.
Oldrey Wm.
10 Rowlands Jno.
Rowlands Wm.
9 Sawdye John
Scobell Bovey
9 Sherwill Wm.
Skinner Edward
Skinner Joseph
8 Skinner Richd.
8 Skinner Thos.
Skinner Wm.
Smerdon Elias
8 Smerdon Thos.
11 Tarr Nichs.
Underhill Richd.
Underhill Wm.
11 Widger Wm.
Wills John
Wills Richard
Yolland John
Yolland Thomas
GROCERS, &c.
3 Adams James
2 Baker Eliz.
2 Brooking Sus.
3 Brown John
2 Bryant Agnes
3 Ching Sus.
2 Down Wm. F.
2 Floyd Tamason
3 Gidley John
2 HannafordSml.
3 Kingwell Jane
6 Knowling Geo.
3 Lopas George
4 Lopas Mary
3 Mogridge Hugh
4 Mann Eliz.
4 MichelmoreWm
3 Norris James
4 Norris Wm.
3 Parrott James
3 PoppletonSaml.
4 Scagell Eliz.
2 Smerdon Rd.
2 TownsendElnr.
2 Weeks Wm.
3 Westway John
3 Westway Sus.

6 White Jhna.
6 Wolson Sus.
HAIR DRESSERS.
4 Saunders John
3 Taprell Wm.
IRONMONGERS.
3 Chalker James
2 Jones David
2 Luscombe Rd.
3 Penny Edward
L. & W. DRAPERS.
4 Evans Lvgtn.
2 Ferris Thomas
3 Geach Jabez
3 Husson John
2 Ireland George
2 Sampson John
MALTSTERS.
2HoneywillJonas
12 Rowell Geo.
5 Whiteway Wm.
Rolestone (and
land agent)
MILLINERS.
6 Bale Mary
3 Beard Ann
4 Chalk Maria
4 Codd Eliz.
3 Eddy Sarah
4 Mugford Eliz.
2 Steer Ruth
NURSERY AND
SEEDSMEN.
2 Knapman Wm.
3 Mugford Rd.
4 MortimoreEdw.
2 Smerdon John
Stark Wm., *Way*
2 Waycott Wm.
PAINTERS, GZRS.,
AND PLUMBERS.
6 EddyHy. & Son
3 Penny Edw.
2 Saunders John
2 Wotton John
2 Yeo Doctor Dnl.
SADDLERS.
3EdgecombeGeo.
2 Fitze John
3 Perrott Jas. W.
3 Stentiford Hy.
3 Tapprell Wtr.
STAMP OFFICE.
4 Dobell Richd.

STONE MASONS.
2 Eales Wm.
4 Foaden Thos.
3 Hext Thomas
3 Ireland John
12 Matthews Jno. and Sons
7 Matthews Thos.

TAILORS.
2 Bowden Robt.
2 Ferris Thos.
4 Foot Henry
3 Husson John
4 Rapsey Thos.
3 Tapprell Wm.

TANNER.
6 Evans Lavingtn.

TIN MINES.
Waye Alston, Rd.
Palk *manager*
Whiddon & Unitd. Ashburton, Jno.
Kernick *agent*

WATCHMAKERS.
4 Coneybear Jas.
2 Harding John
7 Perryman John

WHEELWRIGHTS.
6 Browse Arthur
2 Ford Wm.
3 Knowling My.

3 Luscombe Jno.

WINE & SPT. MRTS.
2 Bate George
3 Husson Edw.
4 Bracewell Rd.

WOOLSTAPLERS.
3 Berry John
3 Brown John
4 Caunter Rd.
3 Wills Wm.

RAILWAY.
Wm Edgecombe's Buss, at 9 morn. to Totnes stn. and to Newton

station, M. W. and Friday

CARRIERS.
Wm Edgecombe's Buss, to *Newton Abbot* and *Torquay*, M.W. and Fri. ; to *Okehampton*, Fri. & to *Totnes* daily, 9 morning
Jno. Hext, to *Exeter*, Mon. & Th.
To *Plymouth*, — Angel, M.&Th.

BICKINGTON, a scattered village on the banks of the Lemon rivulet, and on the Exeter road, 3 miles N.E. of Ashburton, has in its parish 1375 acres and 374 inhabitants. The manor was dismembered many years ago, and the soil belongs to various freeholders. Here is a *serge* manufactory, employing 150 hands. Wrigwell estate has been held by the Bickford family about 600 years. The *Church* (St. James,) is an ancient structure, with a tower and three bells. The living is a perpetual curacy, annexed to the vicarage of Ashburton. The tithes were commuted in 1842, the vicarial for £110, and the rectorial for £115. The Dean and Chapter of Exeter are appropriators of the latter, and Mr. Richard Skinner is the lessee. Here is a small Wesleyan Chapel; and the poor have £2 a year from Plymouth Corporation, as the gift of Benjamin Baron.

Bickford Mrs Eliza, *Adelaide Cottage*
Bickford Mr Fras. J. D. *Prince Cotg*
Butterworth Edw. manager, *Factory*
Caunter Richd. serge & blanket mfr
Christophers Wm. mason, &c
Christophers Henry, wheelwright, & Mary, vict. Jolly Sailors
Cox Thomas, carpenter
Cutch Wm. shoemaker
Kenshole Wm. beer seller
Mann George, shopkeeper
Mould Mr., Lea Cottage
Pearse Jno. shopr. lime brnr. & beerhs
Smerdon John, shoemkr. & par. clerk
Smerdon Thomas, tailor
Steer Charles, shopkeeper & smith

FARMERS. (* are Owners.)
*Bickford John, *Barton*
*Bickford John, jun. *Wrigwell*
French Wm. *Chipley*
Harris John || Mann Thomas
*Nosworthy Stephen || Mann G.
Rowe Andrew, *Yeo* || Soper John
*Tozer Thomas || Tripe Thomas
*Wills John, *Lower Herebeare*

BOVEY (NORTH) is a pleasant village, with a well wooded green, in the picturesque valley of the West Teign, 1½ mile S. of Moreton Hampstead. Its parish contains 660 souls and 5654 acres of land, including the hamlets of *Wormhill* and *Lettaford*, and about 1000 acres of common, on the eastern hills of Dartmoor Forest, where there are two *tin mines*, called Birch Tor and East Birch Tor. There is a *cattle fair* in the village on the Monday after Midsummer-day. The Earl of Devon is lord of the manor, but part of the parish belongs to a number of small freeholders, and a portion of it is in the manor of West Teign, which belongs to the Duchy of Cornwall. The *Church* (St. John,) is a large antique fabric, in the perpendicular style, with a tower and six bells. The *rectory*, valued in K. B. at £22. 10s. 5d., and in 1831 at £303, is in the patronage of the Earl of Devon, and incumbency of the Rev. Fras. J. Courtenay, who has a good residence

and 25A. 2R. 26P. of glebe. The tithes were commuted in 1839, for £328 per annum. The poor have four tenements, occupied by paupers, and the church one, let for 20s. In 1723, *Thos. Parr* left a yearly rent-charge of £3, out of Higher Langdon, for schooling poor children. Here is a small National School.

Broadmead James, shoemaker
Colridge Susan, vict. Ring of Bells
Courtenay Rev Fras. John, *Rectory*
Creswell Mr ‖ Cornish Mrs Mary
Headland Ts.Robts.vict.BirchTorInn
Hill John, blacksmith & shopkeeper
Rainforth Captain W. *Blackaller*
Shears John, thatcher
Tapper Wm. vict. New Inn
Wallen Joseph, parish clerk, &c

CARPENTERS.
Colridge John
Cunnalt Wm.
Ferris John
CORN MILLERS.
Bovey Thomas
Mortimer Wm.

FARMERS.
(* *are Owners.*)
Berry James
Cole John
Cole Mary
Colridge John

Colridge Thos., Wormhill
Cornish John
Cuming Elias
Cuming Wm.
Dodd Wm.
*French Wm.
French Jno.&Jas.
Harvey Wm.
*Heyward Andw.
Heyward Susan
*Heyward Thos.
*Heyward Wm.
*Heyward W.&T.
Hole John
Hooper Henry

Ireland Joseph, *Lettaford*
Nosworthy John
*Nosworthy Wm.
*Pethybridge Ts. *Langdon*
*Sawdye Andrew
*Shears Wm.
*Windeatt John

MASONS.
Mortimer Edw.
Tapper Wm.
Woollacott Wm.

TAILORS.
Ball Wm.
Jewell Wm.

BOVEY TRACEY, or *South Bovey*, is a small ancient town, picturesquely seated in the valley of the West Teign or Bovey river, 6 miles S.E. by S. of Moreton-Hampstead, 5 miles N.N.E. of Newton Abbot, and 4 miles W. by S. of Chudleigh. Its parish had 1823 souls in 1841, but has now more than 2000; and contains 7262A. 2R. 14P. of land, including part of the heath and rocky moorland hills on the eastern side of *Dartmoor Forest*, and crossed by the railway from Haytor Rock Granite Works, in the adjoining parish of Ilsington. The parish includes many scattered houses; the small hamlets of *Little Bovey* and *Lower Brimley*, and upwards of 500A. of low, flat, peaty land, called *Bovey Heathfield*, under which is got the *Bovey Coal*, which is already noticed in the geological survey of the county, at a preceding page, and is supposed to have been formed from the deposit of trees and other vegetable substances, washed down from the surrounding hills in distant ages, when the Heathfield is supposed to have been an arm of the sea. This coal is used by the poor, and also at the extensive *Pottery*, which was established here in 1772, and is now carried on by a Company, who manufacture coarse as well as the finer sorts of earthenware, equal in quality and design to the best Staffordshire wares. They employ about 300 hands. Since the opening of the Stover Canal, which connects Haytor Railway with the navigable part of the Teign, the *leeches* and morasses of the Heathfield have disappeared, and with them have gone the *ignis fatuus* and the ague, which were often to be seen in the *Vale of Bovey*, which is skirted by towering hills and rocks, commanding extensive views, and affording a diversified field for the study of the geologist. The Earl of Devon owns a great part of the parish, and is lord of the *manor and borough of Bovey Tracey*, formerly held by the Tracey family, as parcel of the barony of Barnstaple, and for which a *portreeve* and *bailiff* are elected annually at the lord's court. The former officer is supposed to have been anciently styled mayor. He has the profits of a small piece of land, for defraying the expense of the annual perambulation of the boundaries of the parish, called "*the mayor's riding.*" Part of the parish is in other manors, and much of the soil belongs to various freeholders. *Cole House* is the seat of G. Manning, Esq.; and the *Park*, a large mansion with extensive grounds, is the seat and pro-

perty of Wm. Hole, Esq. *Indio*, an ancient seat of the Southcotts and Stawells, is said to have been a priory or cell of Black friars. In 1259, Henry Tracey obtained a charter for a *market and fair* here, but the former has long been obsolete. The town had formerly four fairs, but it has now only one, held on Easter Monday, for the sale of cattle. It was at Bovey Tracey where Lieut.-General Cromwell, on January 8th, 1646, with the van of Fairfax's army, beat up the quarters of the royalist general Lord Wentworth, about six at night, and took 400 horse, seven colours, and a crown with C. R. upon it. The principal officers of the royalists were engaged at cards when Cromwell entered the town with his troopers, from Crediton, and they only escaped by throwing their stakes out of the window, and flying through the back door, while the "roundheads" were scrambling for the money in the street. *Jewe's Bridge*, about two miles below the town, was built many years ago, by one of the Jewe family, formerly seated here. The *Parish Church* (St. Thomas-a-Becket,) is a large ancient structure, in the perpendicular style, with a tower and six bells. The brass eagle and some of the old oak benches still remain, and the stone pulpit is richly carved, gilt, and coloured. The *vicarage*, valued in K.B. at £26. 2s. 1d., and in 1831 at £450, is in the patronage of the Crown and incumbency of the Hon. and Rev. C. L. Courtenay, M.A., late chaplain to her Majesty. He has a good residence, and 7A. 2R. 14P. of glebe. The great tithes were purchased by the land owners in 1805, and the vicarial tithes were commuted in 1843, for £450 per annum. Here is a *Wesleyan* and also a *Baptist Chapel*. The latter was built in 1823, near the site of the old one. The New Inn and 1A. 20P. of land, worth about £12 a year, have been vested in trust from an early period, for the benefit of the *poor and schoolmaster*. The latter has also about £30 a year as the rent of 5A. of land and a blacksmith's shop and garden. He has also a dwelling and garden, which have been occupied by the parish schoolmaster for many years. He is licensed by the Bishop, and teaches about 20 free scholars. The moiety of the first-named tenement, which belongs to the poor, was purchased with £100 given by *John Stooke*, in 1709, to provide sacramental bread and wine, and small distributions of money for the poor. The parish officers have long held several tenements, which are occupied by paupers; and several houses and about 2A. of land, let for £7. 11s. per annum.

Ball Samuel, corn miller
Bovey Tracey Pottery Co. *earthenware, drain pipe, &c. manufacturers*
Brook Rev Wm. (Baptist)
Cleave James, cooper
Courtenay Hon & Rev Charles Leslie, M.A. *Vicarage*
Croker J. G., M.D. *Cross Cottage*
Divett John, Esq || Burd Mr W.
Harris Mr Geo. || Puddicombe Miss
Haydon John, surgeon
Hole Wm. Esq. *The Park*
Langley Mr James || Lamble Mr
Mann Thomas, saddler
Manning George, Esq. *Cole House*
Robinson Wm. pottery manager
Rolf Capt. Henry, R.N. *Knowle*
Sharland Wm. sub-manager, *Pottery*
Silson John, basket maker
Walton John E. traveller

Wreford John, painter and glazier
INNS AND TAVERNS.
Bell, George Endacott
Dolphin, Richard Joll
Exeter Inn, John Bartlett
King of Prussia, Robert Pascoe
Union Inn, Eleanor Loveys
FARMERS. (* *are Owners.*)
Aggate Edward, *Lower Brimley*
*Adems Wm. *Elsford*
Barstow Wm. *Lower Brimley*
Bowden Joseph, *Little Bovey*
Bunter Mrs || Cox James
*Burd John || Collard Wm.
Daymond Joseph || Daymond Thos
*French John || Edwards Samuel
Goodman Mr. *Culver House*
*Harris John, *Hawkmore*
*Harris Wm. *Plumbley*
Hellier Wm., John, & Joseph, *Forder*

Hellier Thomas ‖ Hellier George
Hellier Wm. ‖ Hamlyn Mr
Jackson Wm. ‖ Hoare Mr
Langmead John ‖ Jewell Mrs
Merchant Oliver ‖ Pook Wm.
Palk John ‖ Palk Nicholas
Petherbridge John ‖ Searle Wm.
Rowell Thomas ‖ Rowell Josiah
*Sanders John ‖ *Savery Richard
Sercombe Mary Ann, *Bradley*
Soper Wm. ‖ Sparke Wm.
*Stooke My. & Grace, *Little Bovey*
Tapper Thomas ‖ Winsor Thomas

BAKERS.
Baker Isaac
Cade James
Keys George
Murch Samuel
Pearse James

BLACKSMITHS.
Cuming Wm.
Daymond John
Hamick John
Lamble John

BUTCHERS.
Edwards James
Lamble Sarah
Osbourne John
Pinsent Wm.
Soper ——

CARPENTERS.
Callaway John
Cuming Michael
Daymond Wm.
Lock Richard
Winsor John

DAIRYMEN.
Collinder Hugh
Gay Jonathan
Jewell James
Tapper Thomas
Wannell Wm.

FARRIERS.
Hill John
Pike Charles

GARDENERS.
Short Wm.

Smith John

MASONS.
Daymond Wm.
Leaman John
Mardon John
Pascoe Robert
Sampson Abm.

MILLINERS.
Callaway Susan
Clampitt Susan
Goodyear Chty.
Manley Jane
Shilson Elizabeth

SCHOOLS.
Chudleigu Wm.
Loveys Susan
Mann Thomas
Winsor John

SHOEMAKERS.
Coish John
Hamlyn Susan
Prowse Thomas
Steer Jonas
Stonelake John

SHOPKEEPERS.
Aggatt Wm.
Beer George
Coish Elizabeth
Ireland George
Main Mary P.

Pitts Henry
Pike Chas. *drugt*
Pinsent Thomas
Short Joseph
Staddon Mary

TAILORS.
Challis Richard
Crocker John
Hawridge John
Reynolds Daniel
Reynolds Wm.
Sellick Emnl.
Sellick Wm.

WHEELWRIGHTS.
Beer George
Beer John

POST OFFICE
atMy.P.Main's.
Post from New-
ton-Abbot

CARRIERS.
Wm. Brown, to
Newton, Wed.
John Winsor, to
Exeter, Tues.&
Fri; to Newton,
Mon.Wd.& Fri;
& to Torquay,
Sat.

HENNOCK, a small village, on an eminence overlooking the Teign valley, 3 miles W.N.W. of Chudleigh, has in its parish 828 inhabitants, and 3469 acres of land, including the hamlet of *Knighton*, or *Chudleigh Knighton*, which has 234 inhabitants, and a small village in the valley, 2 miles S.W. of Chudleigh. The parish also includes *Warmhill*, and many scattered houses, and abounds in tin and iron ore, which is about to be worked by the "*Hennock Iron-Steel and Tin Mining Company*," recently established on the "cost-book principle," with a capital of £9450, in 4500 shares of £2. 2s. each. Messrs. Kennaway and Buckingham, of Exeter, are solicitors to this company. Lead and copper are also found here ; and the mines have had their merits tested to an extent that fully establishes their capabilities for affording a high remunerative profit. Pipe and potters' clay is found at Knighton. The parish is mostly in the same manors as Bovey Tracey ; but the soil is chiefly freehold, belonging to Sir L. V. Palk, Lord Exmouth, the Duke of Somerset, Wm. Harris, John Caunter, C. Winstanly, and A. Chichester, Esqrs., and several smaller owners. The *Church* (St. Mary,) is a large ancient edifice, in the early perpendicular style, with a tower and four bells. Its ancient Norman font, and the stoup in the porch, still remain ; and in its fine windows are some fragments of stained glass. The *vicarage*, valued in K.B. at £16, and in 1831 at £206, is in the patronage of J. Mason, Esq., and incumbency of the Rev. Wm. Woollcombe, of Christow. The parsonage is a good residence, and the glebe is 20 acres. The tithes were commuted in 1838 ; the vicarial for £233, and the rectorial for £168. The latter are held by the Corporation of Exeter, as the endowment of a city lectureship. *Knighton Chapel of Ease* is a neat structure,

of flint and limestone, in the early English style, built by subscription and grants, in 1841-'2, at the cost of £900, and endowed with £1000. The Rev. C. M. Collins, of Chudleigh, is the *curate.* An ancient episcopal chapel, at Knighton, was turned into a barn many years ago. The Wesleyans have a chapel in the parish; and the poor have an acre of land, given by *John Stooke,* in 1692, and the interest of £5, left by *Eliz. Gribble,* in 1726. In the following Directory, those marked 2, are at *Knighton;* and 3, at *Warmhill.*

Chichester Arthur, Esq. *Stocklake*
Cooch James, vict. Anchor, *Knighton*
Drury Rev Benj. Jph. curate, *Vicarage*
Flood Miss, schoolmistress
Hives Charles, Esq. *Pitt House*
Loveys James, vict. Union Inn
Loveys Wm. vict. Palk Arms
Palmer Charles, mason
Stone Wm. miller, *Pool Mill*
Taylor Wm. G., Esq. *Beals*
Warren Miss Chltte. *Hazlewood*

BLACKSMITHS.
Mann Thomas
Smallridge Geo.
BOOT & SHOE MRS.
Land Wm.
2 Williams Geo.

CARPENTERS.
Loveys John
Loveys James
Loveys Samuel
Loveys Wm.
2 Taylor John

FARMERS.
(* are Owners.)
Ball Nicholas
Ball Wm.
Barber Jane
2 Bishop George
Brock John
Cox Joseph
3 Edwards Chas.
2*Davy Fras. J.,
    (& clay mert)
2*Harris Wm.
*Hill Rose P.
Langdon John
Northcott Mark
Norsworthy Wm.
*Perryman Geo.
Pitts James

Short Wm.
3 Soper James
Soper Wm.
Stanbury Wm.
Stone Philip
Toswill James H.
Tucker Thos.
Vooght Wm.
*Wills James
Winsor James

SHOPKEEPERS.
Petherbridge W.
2 Williams Geo.

TAILORS.
2 Cator Henry,
    (and baker)
Hole Thomas

HIGHWEEK parish includes *Newton-Bushel,* and is a suburb of *Newton-Abbot,* as already noticed at pages 455 to 458.

IDEFORD, a small village, in a well wooded valley, on the west side of Little Haldon hill, 2 miles S.E. of Chudleigh, has in its parish 331 souls, and 1471A. 3R. 16P. of land, including 63A. of wood, and 108A. on Haldon Common. Lord Clifford is lord of the manor; but the soil is freehold, and belongs partly to the Templer, Whiteway, Burd, Endacott, Bowden, Hunter, and Watts families. The *Church* (St. Mary,) is a small antique fabric, with a tower and three bells. It is about to be thoroughly repaired, and its screen, roof, and pulpit are finely carved. The *rectory,* valued in K.B. at £17. 13s. 9d., and in 1831 at £270, is in the patronage of T. B. Owen, Esq., and incumbency of the Rev. E. B. St. John, M.A., who has 63A. of glebe, and a handsome residence, repaired and partly rebuilt in 1845. The tithes were commuted in 1839 for £270 per annum. The poor have 18s. a year out of land called Hayes, left by *Humphrey Borrington,* in 1589. The Church House, occupied by paupers, and five dwellings, with gardens, &c., let for only £8. 18s. per annum, (in consideration of fines paid when the leases were granted,) have long been vested in trust for the use of the poor, who have also the interest of £100, left by *Dr. Jenkins,* in 1821.

Bowden John, corn miller
Burd Mr Robert B., *Coombe*
Friend John, tailor
Hall Isaac, machine maker and vict., Royal George
Mayne Thomas, miller, *Coombe*
St John Rev Edward Beauchamp, M.A., *Rectory*
Vooght Wm. butcher

BLACKSMITHS.
Cornish Andw.
Job Henry
CARPENTERS.
Algor Thomas
Cornish Richard
Small Wm.
FARMERS.
Bowden Wm.

Crispin John, *Olchard*
Dymond Thos.
Endacott Stphn.
Furneaux Arthur
Hellens John, *Holdridge's*
Townsend Wm.
Vooght Joseph

Wills George	Sparkes John	SHOPKEEPERS.	POST OFFICE at
SHOEMAKERS.	Trueman John,	Bray Charles	Maria Bray's. *Post*
Bray Charles	(& beerhouse)	Vooght Mary	from Chudleigh

ILSINGTON, a small village, on an eminence on the eastern side of Dartmoor, nearly 6 miles N.N.E. of Ashburton, has in its hilly parish 1093 inhabitants, and 7563 acres of land, including the scattered hamlets of *Haytor-Vale, Higher Brimley, Sigford, Leveton, Harford, Cold-East,* and *Knighton-Beaumont ;* about 600 acres of modern plantations; and 1080 acres of open common, among the rugged hills of Dartmoor, where the *Haytor Granite Rocks* rear their lofty heads, and command from their summits the most diversified and splendid views in the county. *Haytor Granite Works* belong to a company, who employ about 100 quarrymen, and send immense quantities of granite to London and other places, where it is in high repute. A *railway* is extended from the quarries to a canal, which communicates with the navigable part of the Teign, near Newton Abbot. The Duke of Somerset owns a great part of the parish, and is lord of the manor of Haytor. C. H. Monro, Esq., is lord of the manor of *Ankesdon,* now called *Ingsdon,* where he has a handsome seat. *Lord Cranstoun,* of Scotland, owns *Bagtor,* where he occasionally resides in the ancient manor house, formerly the seat of the Beares and Fords. John Ford, a popular dramatic writer, was born at Bagtor, in 1586. The Rev. S. Nosworthy, and several smaller freeholders, have estates in the parish. Near the church are the ruins of the *Court Barton,* or manor house of Ilsington, anciently a seat of the Dinhams and Arundells. The *Church* (St. Michael,) is a plain ancient structure, with a tower and five bells. The *vicarage,* valued in K.B. at £17. 9s. 7d., and in 1831 at £365, is in the incumbency of the Rev. Charles Marsham, M.A., of Caversfield, Bucks. The vicarage is a good residence, and the glebe is 87A. 2R. 6P. The Dean and Canons of Windsor are the patrons, and also appropriators of the rectory, anciently appropriated to the church of Ottery St. Mary, and afterwards to Plympton Priory. The tithes have lately been commuted ; the vicarial for £300, and the great tithes for £340 per annum. Mr. Wills is lessee of the latter. The *Parish Lands, &c.,* have been vested from an early period, in trust for the poor, and now comprise 11A. 3R. 4P., left for £15, and five houses, let for only 10s. a year. Allotments of land awarded to this and Candy's Charity, at the enclosure of the *Heathfield,* about 35 years ago, were sold for £149, which was invested in stock, now yielding £4 per annum. In 1727, *Wm. Candy* left a farm at Hartford (18A. 3R. 25P.,) and directed his trustees to accumulate the rents till they raised £200, to be invested in the purchase of land, and then to apply the yearly profits of the whole in clothing poor parishioners, except 20s. for an annual sermon. Hartford farm is let for £20, and the 23A. 18P. of land purchased with the £200, is let for £20 a year. The trustees have also about £350 three per cent. stock, which arose from the sale of timber, &c. In 1663, *Jane Ford* left 6A. of land, for schooling poor children. In 1804, *Ann Hale* left £360 for the poor; but it was lost by the failure of a bank at Ashburton, except about £50, which was vested in the purchase of £87. 2s. navy five per cents.

Bulley James, shoemaker & vict. Carpenters' Arms	Mortimore George, miller, *Leveton*
	Paige RevWm. M. T. curate, *Vicarage*
Cranstoun Lord, *Bagtor*	Risdon Richard, basket maker
Hayman Wm. miller, *Bagtor*	Rowell John, vict. Sportsman
Haytor Granite Works Company	Southers Samuel, vict. Haytor Rocks
Milton James, vict. New Inn	BLACKSMITHS.
Monro Charles Hele, Esq. *Ingsdon*	Campion Saml.
Mortimore Wm. butcher, *Woodhouse*	Campion Thos.
	Campion Wm.
	Mead John

CARPENTERS.
Ball Wm.
Candlish John
Cuming John
Cuming Wm.
FARMERS.
(* are Owners.)
Aysh Wm.
Berry Joseph
Berry Joshua
Bowden John
Bulley Wm.
Cleave Thomas

Cleave Wm.
Denley Joseph
Harris Mr
Harvey John
Hayward Thos.
Irish Wm. *Bagtor*
Kingwell My. A.
Kingwell Rd.
Kingwell Stephen
Lamshead John
*Lamshead Saml.
*Lamshead Wm.
Laskey Mr

Mann Joseph
Mitchell Jonas
Moale Nicholas
Mortimore Geo.
Mortimore Nichs.
&Josias, *Sigford*
Mortimore Wm.
Northcott John
Peacock John
Prowse Peter
Reeves John
Rowell John
Rowell Francis

Rowell Joseph
Rowell Wm.
Shapley Samuel
Sherwill Richard
Skinner Wm.
Stark Charles
Stranger Thos.
Stranger Richard
*Wills Charles
*Wills George
Widger Samuel
Winsor Wm.

KING'S TEIGNTON, or *Teignton Regis*, is a large and respectable village, 1¼ mile N.E. of Newton Abbot, pleasantly situated on the north bank of the river Teign, where it has a commodious wharf, near two short *canals*, one extending to the railway of the Haytor Granite Works, and the other extending about four miles northward, to the vicinity of Chudleigh. (See page 398.) Its parish contains 1498 souls, and 3982A. 3R. 16P. of land, including the hamlet of *Preston*, and many scattered houses. The parish abounds in fine *potters' and pipe clay*, of which about 50,000 tons are sent in barges down the Teign, to be shipped at Teignmouth for the Staffordshire and other potteries. About 200 hands are employed in the clay works, where the clay lies in beds varying from 20 to 80 feet deep. Lord Clifford is lord of the *manor* of King's Teignton, which was a demesne of the Crown till Henry II. gave it to Peter Burdon, with a moiety of Teignbridge Hundred, which has its name from a bridge here. He is also owner of *Gappah, Ware*, and a great part of the parish; held on leases for three lives. *Preston* belongs to the trustees of the late Rev. J. Kenrick, and here are smaller proprietors, some of whom have neat houses here. The *Church* (St. Michael,) is a large and venerable structure, with a tower and five bells. It is in the perpendicular style of the 15th century, and its number of free sittings was increased in 1825 from 231 to 311. The *vicarage*, valued in K.B. at £28. 13s. 9d., and in 1831 at £421, with that of Highweek annexed to it, is in the patronage of the Bishop of Exeter, and incumbency of the Rev. Henry Woollcombe, jun., who has a good residence and 21½A. of glebe. The tithes were commuted in 1841, the vicarial for £312. 10s., and the rectorial for £253 per annum. The latter are appropriated to the Prebendary of King's Teignton, in Salisbury Cathedral, but are leased to the trustees of the late Rev. J. Kenrick. Here is an *Independent Chapel*, built in 1815, and a large *National School*, erected in 1848, in the Tudor style, at the cost of £460. The *Church and Poor* have five houses and gardens, let for only 23s. a year, in consideration of fines paid by the lessees. The trustees also hold £134. 13s. 4d. three per cent. consols, purchased with fines, and £60 given to the poor by donors named Proctor, Pidsley, and Ley.

Addems Wm. vict. Union Inn
Bolton Mr || Jewell Mrs
Edwards James B. assistant overseer
Hall Isaac, miller, *Sandygate*
Harris George, miller, *Higher Mills*
Margery Thomas, vict. Bell
Pearce Parmns., Esq. *Teignbridge Hs*
Pinsent Thomas, Esq. *Greenhill*

Smale Mr John W. and Mr Charles
Tucker Rt. H. clay mert. *Rydon Hs*
Walker Rowland, Esq.
Watts Mrs || Whitehead Mr
Whiteway, Watts, & Co., clay merts
Whiteway John Hayman, Esq. *Fishwick House*
Whiteway Daniel, Esq. and Mrs

Whiteway Wm. corn miller
Widdicombe Richard, sexton, &c
Woollacott Joseph, vict. King's Arms
Woollcombe Rev Hy. jun. *Vicarage*
    BAKERS.
Stentiford James
Ward Malachi
    BLACKSMITHS.
Ward Joseph
Ward Richard
Ward Malachi (&
  par. clerk)
    BUTCHERS.
Knowles Thos.
Voysey Mr
    CARPENTERS.
Beardon Thos.
Brady Henry
Bulley Wm.

Gillard Richard
Lear Edw. *whgt*
    MASONS.
Small George
Small Samuel
    SCHOOLS.
Churchward Chs.
Holman Wm.
    SHOEMAKERS.
Pridham Thos.
Trueman Chas.
    SHOPKEEPERS.
Banbury Chas.
SmallridgeAndw.
Snow John

    TAILORS.
Murrin Edward
Northam Wm.
Turner James
    FARMERS.
Addems John
Anning Chas. C.
  S. *Bellemarsh*
Bolt George
Bolt James
Cleave Wm.
Cole Wm.
Cuming John
Dicker John
Edwards Robert
Hamlyn Wm.,
  Preston
Kemp Henry
Maddicott John

Parsons Charles
PinsentJno.*Were*
RichardsJno.jun.
  Gappah
Richards John
Rogers James
Shapter Edward
Smallridge Edw.
Smallridge SamL
Smallridge Wm.
Snell Benjamin
Snow Wm.
Stentiford James
Stevens John
Stevens Wm.
Tapper Henry
Tapper Hy. jun.
Wills My. *White-
way*

LUSTLEIGH, or *Listleigh*, a small scattered village, in a romantic dell, opening to the valley of the West Teign or Bovey river, 3½ miles S.S.E. of Moreton Hampstead, has in its parish 311 souls, and 2239 acres of land, half of which is open commons and waste, on the eastern side of Dartmoor. On the common called *Lustleigh Cleve*, is a fine range of rocks and crags; and in the vicinity is a logan stone, and some other Druidical remains. The manor was dismembered many years ago, and the soil belongs to J. Gould, Esq., the Rev. S. Nosworthy, and several resident freeholders. Barne-Court was anciently the seat of the Barnehouse family. The *Church*, (St. John,) is an antique fabric, with a tower and four bells. On an ancient tomb lie the effigies of Lord and Lady Dinham, and upon another is the figure of a crusader, supposed to represent Sir Wm. Prowse. The font is Norman, and the oak screen is finely carved. The church has been repaired and beautified by the late and present incumbents. The living is a *rectory*, valued in K.B. at £16. 7s. 6d., and in 1831 at £170, in the alternate patronage of the Earl of Ilchester and the Hon. P. C. Wyndham, and in the incumbency of the Rev. Fredk. Ensor, B.A., who has 35A. 3R. 17P. of glebe, and a large and handsome residence in the Gothic style. The tithes were commuted in 1839 for £200 per annum. The *National School* was built in 1825, and has £9. 10s. a year from land given by the late Rev. Wm. Davy.

Bowden George, mason
Cator Sarah, shopkeeper
Crediton Wm. tailor
Easton Jno. par. clrk. & Edw. *sexton*
Ensor Rev Frederick, B.A. *Rectory*
Gilley Edward, shoemaker
Jeffery Emanuel, artist
Smallridge Joseph, blacksmith
Steer Joseph, carpenter
Stone John, butcher
  FARMERS. (* *are Owners.*)
*Amery Wm. *Ellimore*

*Amery John, *Barne Court*
*Amery Thomas, *Higher Coombe*
Bond Thomas || Cuming Edward
*Hole Wm. (& miller) || Rowe Daniel
Hurston John || Scott Philip
Martin Simon (and miller,) *Vorn.*
Nosworthy Stephen, *Vornoxworthy*
Tremlet Wm. || Wills Charles
*Wills Thomas, *East Wrey*
*Wills Francis, *South Harton*
Wills John || Wills George

MANATON, or *Manadon*, is a small village, on an eminence, near the rocky hills and the sources of the West Teign, or Bovey river, on the eastern

side of Dartmoor, 3½ miles S.W. of Moreton-Hampstead. Its parish contains 429 souls, and 6393 acres of land, including the hamlets of *Freeland* and *Water*, and more than 2000 acres of commons and wastes, amid some of the wildest scenery of Dartmoor Forest. *Hountor*, a stupendous group of rocks, appears like ruined turrets and broken pinnacles, and as seen from different points of view, assumes an endless variety of fantastic figures. The *Becky* rivulet flows through a woody dell, where its impetuous stream tumbles over a precipitous bed of large rocks, and forms the beautiful cascade called *Becky Falls*. The ancient Britons are supposed to have had a town on the spot now called *Grimpound;* and in the neighbourhood are some interesting druidical remains and a few small tin mines. The Earl of Devon owns a great part of the parish, and has a rabbit warren of 600 acres here. The rest belongs to the French, Nosworthy, Barham, and Bryant families, and other freeholders; and on the south side of the parish are the *Haytor Rock Granite Works*, noticed at page 473. The *Church* (St. Winifred,) is a fine old structure, in the early perpendicular style, with an embattled tower and four bells. It was much injured by lightning on Dec. 13th, 1779. The *rectory*, valued in K.B. at £13. 12s. 8½d., and in 1831 at £235, is in the patronage of the Rev. Wm. Carwithen, D.D., and incumbency of the Rev. W. P. Wood, who has 40A. 1R. 29P. of glebe, and a good residence, with a large rock behind it, assuming the appearance of a battery, surmounted by a flag staff, and commanding beautiful views. The Church House, given by Thos. Southcott, in 1597, was rebuilt in 1818, and its rent is carried to the churchwardens' accounts. On Mr. Nosworthy's estate is an ancient chapel, in the Tudor style, now used as a barn.

Harvey Andrew, carpenter
Harvey John, blacksmith
Hext Mr Thomas, *Cross Park Cotg*
Lewis John, corn miller
Petherbridge Mr John
Pinsent Mary Ann, boarding school
Roberts Thomas, rabbit warrener
Shears John, vict. Half Moon
Shears Wm. mason & shopkeeper
Tarr Wm. shoemaker
Wood Rev Wm. Paul, *Rectory*

FARMERS. (* *are Owners.*)
*French John, *Hountor*
*French Thomas, *Winkson*
*Harper Wm. || Hamlyn John
*Heyward Thos. || *Holman John
*Nosworthy Wm. *Hountor*
*Nosworthy John and *Robert
*Petherbridge Wm. || Smerdon Rd.
Petherbridge Edw. || White Wm.
Westington Wm. || Winsor Wm.

MORETON HAMPSTEAD is a small *market town*, near the eastern confines of Dartmoor Forest, seated on a fertile and highly salubrious eminence, encompassed by lofty hills, and distant 12 miles W.S.W. of Exeter, 12 miles N.N.E. of Newton-Abbot, 12 miles N. of Ashburton, and 185 miles W.S.W. of London. Its parish had 1768 inhabitants in 1801, and 2037 in 1841, and comprises 7656A. of land, including the small hamlets of *Daccombe, Sloncombe,* and *Houghton,* many scattered farm houses, &c., about 400 acres of wood, and several commons. The soil is various, and the surface picturesquely broken into hill and dale, finely diversified with wood, water, and rock. At the north-west angle of the parish, overlooking the Teign valley, is an ancient entrenchment, called *Cranbrook Castle,* occupying about seven acres, and having a vallum of moorstone, with a double fosse on the north, and a single one on the west, but none on the south, and only a partial one on the east side. The views from this hill are extensive and beautiful, and on the opposite side of the river are the Cromlech, Logan stone, and other

druidical remains, noticed at page 190. Lower down the valley, upon a bold eminence, is another British camp, called *Woosten Castle*, said to be the most considerable and best preserved of any in the neighbourhood. Moreton Hampstead is noted for the health and longevity of its inhabitants, as appears from the statistics of its annuitant society. It had formerly a share of the woollen manufacture, which declined many years ago. The Earl of Devon is lord of the *manor of Moreton ;* but there are three smaller manors in the parish, viz., *High Hayne*, belonging to J. N. Stevenson, Esq.; *North Moor*, belonging to G. Bray, Esq.; and *Daccombe*, or *Dockham*, held under the Dean and Chapter of Canterbury, by the trustees of the late Rev. George Gregory. *Wray Barton*, a handsome Tudor mansion, is the seat of John Courtier, Esq., owner of Wray estate, which has passed by heiresses and bequests, to the Chilverstone, Abbot, Wray, Laford, Corslet, and Southmead families. Part of the parish belongs to many small freeholders, but Daccombe is mostly copyhold. In 1335, Hugh de Courtenay obtained a charter for a market and two fairs here. The *Market* is still held on Saturday, and a new *Market House* and *Shambles* were built by the lord of the manor, in 1827. Great Cattle Markets are held on Whitsuneve and the first Saturday in October; and *Fairs* for cattle, &c., on the third Thursday in July and the last Thursday in November. The *Church* (St. Andrew,) is a large ancient fabric, in the transition style, with a lofty tower, containing six bells, a clock and chimes. The interior, if repaired and cleared of its many coats of whitewash, would have a very handsome appearance. The *rectory*, valued in K.B. at £49. 19s. 7d., and in 1831 at £603, is in the patronage of the Earl of Devon, and incumbency of the Rev. W. C. Clack, who has a good residence and 62A. of glebe. The tithes were commuted in 1839 for £792 per annum. Three houses, let for £30 a year, had been long vested for the repairs of the church, but were burnt down in 1845. Here are *chapels* belonging to the Independents, Wesleyans, Baptists, and Unitarians. The old *Presbyterian Chapel*, which has long been held by *Unitarians*, was built in 1692, and enlarged in 1802. It is endowed with 6A. 2R. 25P. of land at Well Parks. There was a Baptist congregation here as early as 1715; and *Micaiah Towgood*, an eminent divine, was pastor of the Presbyterian Chapel here from 1722 to 1736. Here are two small Independent Chapels, erected in 1817 and 1824; and the Wesleyan Chapel was built in the former year. As noticed with Exeter, this parish has £10 a year from *Hele's Charity*, for schooling poor children. The *National School*, held in a building given by the Earl of Devon, was established in 1840. A *Literary Society* was instituted in the town about four years since, and has now a library of 500 volumes. A *Farmers' Club*, established here about seven years ago, has a numerous list of members, who meet at the *White Hart Inn*, which is a large and well conducted establishment. Near the remains of the ancient cross stands a very large and singular *elm tree*, which has had its lower branches trained so as to form a sort of hollow stage, which is said to have been once boarded over and to have afforded room for nearly 20 couple to dance, while the

fiddler sat in the boughs above. *George Bidder*, the celebrated mental calculator, now an eminent and wealthy civil engineer, was born here of humble parents. Sir Thos. Fairfax was here with his army on the 8th of January, 1646, but the town was not the scene of any conflict during the civil wars of the 17th century. A *port-reeve* and *bailiff* are appointed at the court leet and baron, but it has not been held during the last three years. The POST-OFFICE is at Mr. Silvester Treleaven's; and letters are despatched at 45 minutes past five evening, *via* Exeter. In the following *Directory of Moreton Hampstead*, those marked 2 are at *Daccombe*; 3, *Sloncombe*; and 4, at *Woosten*.

Bevan Rev John, (Independent)
Bidder George & John, masons
Billett Isaac, rope and twine maker
Bragg Geo. Esq || Bishop Mr Thos.
Brely Hy. miller, *Fingle Bridge*
Brock Mr John || Cuming Mrs
Cann Geo. saddler and ironmonger
Clack Rev Wm. Courtenay, M.A.
  Rectory
Cleave John, cooper
Courtier John, Esq., *Wray Barton*
Dormer Dominic, corn miller
French Mrs || German Miss
German John, surveyor, *Meacomb*
German Wm. B., auctioneer
Giles Wm., revenue officer
Hill Samuel, veterinary surgeon
Jackson Mr Geo. || Hooper Mrs M. A.
Langdon Mr Elias || Lang Joseph
Marwood Robert, basket maker
Mead Mrs Eliz. || Piller Mrs Mary
Norrish Abm. W. tallow chandler
Passmore Sarah Ann, currier
Robertson Claude, assistant overseer
Rowden John, wood warden
Short Henry, sexton
Smale Mr Wm. & My. & Eliz. library
Smethurst Rev John, (Unitarian)
Snow John, corn miller
Stevens Mr Wm. || Tozer Hy. engvr.
Stevenson J. N. Esq., *High Hayne*
White Thos.& Edw. tanners & felmgs
Wootton James, fellmonger

FIRE & LIFE OFFICE AGENTS.
County and Provident, W. White
Norwich Union, W. N. Bragg
Star, John Potter
Sun, Alfred Puddicombe
West of England, M. W. Harvey
Yorkshire, John R. Hill

INNS AND TAVERNS.
Bell, John Bennett
Dolphin, Henry Searle

Golden Lion, James Lee
Gregory Arms, Thomas Miller
Plymouth Inn, George Ballamy
Punch Bowl, James Endacott
Ring of Bells, Eliz. Lethbridge
Union, John Steer
White Hart Inn, (posting,) Sl. Cann
White Horse, Mary Gray

ACADEMIES.
Bishop Geo. *Natl*
Gordon Margaret
Hill John R.
Potter Thomas
Tremlett Fras.

ATTORNEYS.
Bragg Wm. N.
Harvey Moses
Wolland (regr.)
White Wm.

BAKERS.
Allen Wm.
Ballamy Geo.
Dayment John
Kernick John
Larker Eliz.
Saunders Sus.

BLACKSMITHS.
Dolbear Saml.
Hill John
Lang James
Wolland Wm.

BOOT&SHOE MKS.
Aggett Wm.
Browne John
Dingle Elias
Lewis John
Marwood Geo.
Parker John
Tozer John
Tremlett Rt. (&
  parish clerk)

BUTCHERS.
Dibble Wm.

Gray James
Harvey Denis
Harvey John
Hewitt Wm.
Peters Wm. jun.

CARPENTERS.
Dymond John
Endacott John
Hutchings Glbt.
Shears Saml.
Shears Wm.

CHEMISTS &DGTS.
Treleaven Svtr.
Watson Alfred

FARMERS.
(* are Owners.)
Adams Nichls.
Amery Jasper
Amery Wm.
Bovey Thomas
Battershock Ths.
Brely Henry
Cowling Mary
* Cuming Elias
Elliott George
Ellis Wm.
Endacott Henry
Endacott John
Endacott Robert
Endacott Thos.
England W. & J.
Farrier Thomas
Gay Ann
* German John
Harvey John

Harvey Richard
Hutchings Robt.
* Hutton Eliz.
Kelly John
Kelly Thomas
Kelly Wm.
Kerslake George
Kerslake James
Laskey John
3 Lovis Aaron
* May John
* Neck Mary
* Newcombe Ts.
P., *Cranbrook*
Northcott John
* Nosworthy Jno
* Osborne James
Peters Francis
Peters Wm. sen
Potter Robert
Snow George
* Stevens John
* Stevens J. jun
2 Taverner Jph.

Taverner Robert
* Taverner Wm.
Thomas Alice
Trace Wm.
Waldron Saml.
Warren John
Wills Robert
Wreford Samuel
GROCERS & DPRS.
Cole Mary Ann
Heyward Eliz.
Hutchings Wm.
Neck Simon
Neck Wm.
Treleaven Silvester, jun
HAIR DRESSERS.
German Wm.
Treleaven Svtr.
IRONMONGERS
AND TINMEN.
Rundell Thomas,
(& *plumber*)
Smith James

White John
MALTSTERS.
Cann Samuel
Harvey John

MILLINERS, &c.
Gray Eliz.
Potter S. G. & E.
Saunders Thza.

SHOPKEEPERS.
Aggett Thomas
Cragg Olivia
Hutchings Glbt.
Hutchings Rt.
Marwood George
Pate Sarah
Sercombe Wm.
Tozer Sophia
SURGEONS.
Nosworthy J. L.
Ponsford Jno. &
Hamilton Ed.
Puddicombe Alf.

TAILORS.
Mardon Wm.
Saunders James
Tarr James
Widdicomb Wm.
Wootton Edw.
WATCHMAKERS.
Ribll Wm.
Treleaven Svtr.
WHEELWRIGHTS.
Ballamy George
Ballamy Simon
Cann Wm.

CARRIERS.

To *Exeter*, John
Weeks, Mon.
Wed. & Fri.; &
J. Lee, Tue. &
Fri., to *Newton
Abbot*, Wed.
To *Plymouth*, J.
Wills, alternate
Wednesdays

TEIGNGRACE is a parish of scattered houses, mostly in the Teign valley, from 1 to 3 miles N.N.W. of Newton Abbot. It contains 180 souls, and 1329A. 3R. 10A. of land, chiefly in pasturage, but including 358A. of wood. The *railway* from Haytor Granite Works, and the *Stover Canal*, which unite at *Ventiford* in this parish, are already noticed at pages 455 and 473. The *Duke of Somerset* owns about 1200 acres, and is lord of the manor, which he purchased in 1829, of the Templer family, who were formerly seated at *Stover House*, which was built by James Templer, Esq., in 1776, of Haytor Granite. The Duke occupies the farm, and resides occasionally at the house, which he has recently embellished with a handsome colonnade of Portland stone. It stands on a pleasant eminence in a finely wooded park, in which are about 20 acres of water. The manor was anciently held by the Bruer, Grace, Downe, and Holcomb families, and afterwards by the Courtenays, the latter of whom sold it to James Templer, Esq., about 1765. The *Church* (St. Mary,) was rebuilt in 1787, at the expense of three brothers of the Templer family, and is a small, neat, cruciform structure, with a tower and spire, but the interior has more the appearance of an elegant domestic chapel than that of a parish church. The south transept is curtained off for the use of the Duke of Somerset, and the rector's family occupy the north transept. On the walls are many handsome monumental marbles in memory of various members of the Templer family; and also an elegant cenotaph, in memory of the great Nelson. The *rectory*, valued in K. B. at £5. 9s. 4½d., and in 1831 at £171, is in the patronage of the Duke of Somerset, and incumbency of the Rev. Jno. Templer, M A., of Newton Abbot. The glebe is 65A., but there is no parsonage. The poor parishioners have 12A. of land and two cottages, which have been vested in trust from an early period.

Duke of Somerset, *Stover House*
Bearne Edw. Snelling, agent to *ditto*
Murrin James, smith, & vict., Union
Templer Rev John, M.A. rector
Perryman Phœbe, schoolmistress

FARMERS.
Coysh Isaac || Edwards Thomas
Murrin Mary || Stawell James
Shilston Thomas, (owner,) *Ley*

COLERIDGE HUNDRED

Extends southward from *Totnes*, along the navigable river *Dart* to *Dartmouth*, and thence along the coast of *Start Bay* to *Salcombe Haven*, which extends northward to Kingsbridge, and has several creeks branching from either side. Its greatest length from Totnes to Start and Prawle Points, is 16 miles, and the breadth varies from 7 to 4 miles. It is encompassed on three sides by tidal waters, and is generally a fertile district, rich in picturesque scenery and splendid marine views. It is in the Southern Parliamentary Division of Devon, and in the Polling Districts of Dartmouth, Kingsbridge, and Totnes ; and in the Deaneries of Totnes and Woodleigh, and in the Archdeaconry of Totnes. The following enumeration of its 20 parishes shews their territorial extent, and their population in 1841.

Parishes.	Acres.	Pop.
* Ashprington	2644 ..	588
§ Blackauton	5589 ..	1449
§ Buckland Tout Sts.	1000 ..	56
Charleton	2380 ..	703
Chivelstone........	2696 ..	591
* Cornworthy	2750 ..	554
*Dartmouth Borough		
* Petrox (St.) par.	40 ..	929
* Saviour (St.) par.	40 ..	2345
* Townstal parish	1689 ..	1321
* Dittisham	3098 ..	917
Dodbrooke	343 ..	1229

Parishes.	Acres.	Pop.
* Halwell..........	3666 ..	445
* Harberton	5755 ..	1496
Poole, (South)	1930 ..	555
Portlemouth, (East)	1973 ..	429
Sherford	2326 ..	450
Slapton	3260 ..	726
Stoke Fleming	3332 ..	736
Stokenham	5920 ..	1619
* Totnes *Borough*...	1039 ..	3849
Total ....51,470 ..20,987		

Those marked thus * are in *Totnes Union*, and all the others are in *Kingsbridge Union*. They are all in *Stanborough & Coleridge Petty Sessional Division*, except the two boroughs. § *Buckland Tout Saints* is only a chapelry in Loddiswell parish, which is mostly in Stanborough Hundred, and is there described. There are *hamlets* in some of the other parishes, as afterwards noticed.

ASHPRINGTON, or *Ashpreignton*, is a small neat village, picturesquely seated on a gentle slope, near the confluence of the river Harbourn with the estuary of the Dart, 2½ miles S.E. of Totnes. Its parish contains 588 souls, and 2644 acres of fertile land, including the hamlets of *Washbourn* and *Yeatson*, and part of *Tuckenhay*, where there is a large paper mill, a corn mill, and quarries of hard stone, of which great quantities are exported in vessels of 160 tons, to London, &c., for Macadamizing roads. Richard Durant, Esq., owns a great part of the parish, and is lord of the manor of *Sharpham*, where he has a large and handsome freestone mansion, with extensive and well-wooded grounds, descending to the western bank of the river Dart, amidst some of the most beautiful scenery of the valley. He has lately much improved the village by erecting a new inn, and rebuilding many of the cottages. This manor has been held successively by the Winard, French, Prideaux, Drewe, Giles, Yarde, Cockey, Pownall, and Bastard families. *Painsford*, an ancient mansion, on the banks of the river Harbourn, is the seat and property of Mr. Philip Michelmore, and has been successively held by the Piperell, Halwill, Somaster, Kellond, Courtenay, and other families. It was formerly much larger than at present, and its dilapidated chapel, though disused since the middle of last century, still retains its pulpit, pews, and altar-piece, and has a suit of armour hanging over the communion rails. The left wing of the house has a fine row of arches. The Rev. G. T. Carwithen, Mr. W. D. Adams, C. Pearce, Esq., Mr. T. Mudge, J. Browne, Esq., and several other freeholders have estates in the parish. The *Church* (St. David,) is a handsome structure, in the per-

pendicular style, with a tower and five bells. It has lately been renovated, and new windows, with mullions and tracery of Bath stone, have been inserted, chiefly at the expense of Richard Durant, Esq. The clustered columns of the nave have foliated capitals, and in the chancel is a fine recedos, in seven compartments, of Caen stone. On the walls are several handsome marble tablets, in memory of members of the Somaster, Kellond, Bastard, and other families. The *rectory*, valued in K.B. at £29. 1s. 8d., and in 1831 at £560, is in the patronage of the Rev. T. G. Carwithen, and has been held by the Rev. Jacob Ley, M.A., since 1795. The Rectory House is a neat mansion, and the glebe is 28A. 3R. 17P. The tithes were commuted in 1844, for £537 per annum. The *Parish School* is a neat building, in the Elizabethan style, erected in 1847, by Richard Durant, Esq., at the cost of £600, and chiefly supported by him. The *Church House* is occupied by poor families, and here is an *Almshouse* for six poor persons, given by Sir Edward Giles, Kt., in 1628, but now much dilapidated, and only partially occupied. Marked 2, are at *Painsford;* 3, *Tuckenhay;* 4, *Yeatson;* and 5, at *Washbourn.*

Durant Richard, Esq. *Sharpham Hs*
Farleigh Valentine, shoemaker
Finch James, carpenter
3 Lakeman Jph. coal merchant, (and *Dartmouth*)
Ley Rev Jacob, M.A. *Rectory*
Martin Mr Robt. ‖ Carter Mr
Michelmore Philip, gent. *Painsford*
Mudge Thos. coal, stone, & manure merchant, *Springfield*
Pearce Cyprian, Esq. *New House*
Northcote Major Hugh, *Dunstone Hs*
Rogers Rt., & Phillips Sarah, school
Roper Thomas, millwright
Turner Rd. paper mfr. *Tuckenhay*

PUBLIC HOUSES.
Ashprington Inn, Wm. Cox
Commercial, Hugh Torring
3 Maltsters' Arms, John Dennis
Waterman's Arms, Robt. Ashwick

BLACKSMITHS.
Ashwick Robert
5 Life Thomas
BUTCHERS.
Tucker Wm.
Williams Richd.
CORN MILLERS.
2 Ball Wm.
Ball Wm. jun. *Stps*
Came Jno. T. *Bow*
3 Mumford John
5 Williams Henry
FARMERS.
(* are Owners.)
5 Bowden Wm.
*Edwards John, *Blackdown*
Earle John
Elliott Mrs. *Bow*
Foale Rt. & Henry

Foale Wm. J. H. *Frogmore*
Hewitt Wm.
*Moysey John
5 Manning Wm.
4 Mumford Mtw.
Taylor Robert
4 Wills Joseph
4 Wright John
MASONS.
Butland Matthew
Newland Benj.
SHOPKEEPERS.
3 Jones Wm.
Phillips Robert
5 Tope John

Post to Totnes, 4 aftn. from the Inn

BLACKAUTON, a straggling village of indifferently built houses, on high ground, 5 miles W. of Dartmouth, has in its parish 1449 souls, and 5589 acres of land, including many scattered houses, and the village and chapelry of STREET, on the coast of Start Bay, more than 4 miles S.S.E. of the church, and S.W. of Dartmouth. Here are also small hamlets or assemblages of houses, called *Bow, Dryton, Hutchley, East Down, Borlestone, Millcombe,* and *Woodford.* A large fishing village, called Undercliff, near Street, is said to have been destroyed by the encroachments of the sea, many years ago. H. L. Toll, Esq., is lord of the manor and owner of a great part of the parish, and the rest belongs to W. Dimes, Esq., J. Netherton, Esq., C. Barter, Esq., Mrs. Hayne, and many small freeholders. The barton of *Cotterbury* has an independent royalty, and was purchased in 1806, by L. Newman, Esq., of Dartmouth. *Fuge,* now a farm house, was built in 1725, by the late C. Hayne, Esq. *Oldstone,* the seat of W. Dimes, Esq., is a large mansion, which was for more than two centuries the seat of the Colwich family. The *Parish Church* (St. Michael,) is a large antique structure, with a tower and six bells. It is in the early perpendicular style,

x

but most of the windows are modern insertions, and the chancel walls have recently been rebuilt. In the chancel are three cinque-foiled sedilia, and a handsome double piscina. The nave has a good screen and a fine Norman font. The vicarage, valued in K.B. at £15. 8s. 9d., and in 1831 at £128, is in the patronage of Sir H. P. Seale, Bart., and incumbency of the Rev. E. T. Seale, who has a good residence and small glebe. The tithes, which formerly belonged to Tor Abbey, are now held by the Trustees of the late Abraham Welland, Esq., and were commuted in 1841, for £739. 6s. 6d. per annum, subject to the vicar's stipend. *Street Chapel of Ease,* at the south end of the parish, was built about 14 years ago, by subscription, and a grant of £250. It is a neat structure, in the Gothic style, with an embattled tower. There are National Schools and small Wesleyan Chapels at Blackauton and Street. The vicar has £8. 12s. a year, left by Wm. Wotton, in 1689, out of land at Collumpton. Several rent charges, left by the Rev. Richard Sparkes, in 1699, have been exchanged for £257 three per cent. consols. The yearly dividends are distributed in bread among the poor, except 30s. for a sermon, and 10s. for the parish clerk. Those marked 2, are at *Street*; 3, *at Hutchley*; 4, *at Millcombe*; and 5, *at Cotterbury.*

Abbot Richard, gent. *Stray Park*
Bragg Thomas, surgeon
Dimes Wm. Esq. *Oldstone*
Grills Wm. corn miller and worsted spinner, *Combery*
Hambling Wm. B. gun maker and church bell founder
Holditch Mr ‖ Narracott G. school
Perring Nichs. painter & glazier
Pillage Mr Andrew ‖ Pitts Mr Wm.
Pinhey Mr Richd. sen. Millcombe
Press Richard, saddler
Rich Richard, miller, *Millcombe*
2 Robinson Rev H. V. curate
Seale Rev Edw. Taylor, *Vicarage*
Underhay Geo. miller, *Washwalk*

PUBLIC HOUSES.
Commercial, James Ellis
Dartmouth Inn, Nicholas Wakeman
Forces, Henry B. Oldreive
George Inn, Wm. Hosking
Posts, Eliz. Punchard, *Hembro'*
2 King's Arms, Wm. S. Oldreive

BLACKSMITHS.
Ferris George
2 Ferris Henry
Pinhey John
Pullen Thomas
Tippett Jno.*Bow*

BUTCHERS.
2 Foale Henry
Foale Henry
Foale Philip
2 Hyne Richard
Hyne Richd. jun.

CARPENTERS.
Hingston Richd.
Lands Matthew
Langworthy Rt.
2 Moysey Philip
Stabb John
TaylorWm.(wgt)
Tucker John

FARMERS.
(* *are Owners.*)
Baker Wm. C.

*Came Mattw. & LambertAndw.
Came Richard
Clark Regnd.
Coad Sml. *Ford*
Coles Nichls. E.
*Cutmore Wm.
Eastley Thomas
5 Ellis Wm.
Edwards Wm.
Ferris H.*Woodfd*
3*Grant John
2 Goodyear Wm.
Hannaford John
2 Hayman Benj.
2 Hayman Philip
Hellings Thomas
Jellard Rd. *Fuge*
Luscombe Robt.
Manning David
3 Mumford John
3 Nicholls Jeffery
Oldreive John
*Oldreive Jno.D., *Landcombe*
Pinhey John
4 Pinhey Richd.
Pinhey Wm.
Pitts John
*Putt John
Soper Richard
Stranger Richd.
*Tozer John L.
5 Webber James

MASONS.
Coombe John
Heath Samuel
Wakeham Wm.

SHOEMAKERS.
Bellatt John
Hosking Thos.
2 Jeffrey Nathl.
Life John
Pinhey Philip
Watson Wm.
2 Wills Wm.

SHOPKEEPERS.
Almond John
4 Burgoyne Wm.
2 Ferris Robert
Hingston Richd.
2 Jeffrey Nathl.
Prout John
Stabb John
Tucker Amelia
Tucker Wm.

TAILORS.
Foxworthy Roger
2 Oldreive W. C.
Rawle J. *Woodfd*
Sandford John

POST OFFICE
at W. B. Hambling's. Letters *via* Dartmouth

CHARLETON, a small village in two portions, on the east side of the estuary, 2 miles S.S.E. of Kingsbridge, has in its parish 703 inhabitants,

and 2379A. 3R. 35P. of land, including the hamlets of *Goveton* and *Lidstone,* and part of *Frogmore* village, which is partly in Sherford and South Pool parishes.   Lord Ashburton is lord of the manor of Charleton, and that of Frogmore is claimed by Lady Sandys, but is in dispute.   Part of the parish belongs to other freeholders, among whom are W. J. Clarke, W. R. Ilbert, and F. Wells, Esqrs., and John and Henry Grills.   *Slade,* a new and handsome residence in the northern part of the parish, is the seat of Capt. Fortescue Wells, whose grandfather married the heiress of the Fortescues, of Fallapit, where his eldest son took their name.   The *Church* (St. Mary,) is an ancient structure, with a tower and four bells.   It was thoroughly renovated in 1849-50, at the cost of about £1000, when the nave and aisles were mostly rebuilt, and new windows were inserted with mullions of Caen stone.   The old screen, rood loft, sedilia, and piscina, remain, and all the new parts are in unison with the old.   The *rectory,* valued in K.B. at £31. 8s. 4d., and in 1831 at £525, is in the patronage of Lord Ashburton, and incumbency of the Rev. Thos. Twysden, M.A., who has a pleasant residence, and 30A. 3R. 33P. of glebe.   The tithes were commuted in 1840 for £557 per annum.   An old cottage was given at an early period by Wm. Bowring, for the use of the church and poor.   Marked 2 are in *East Charleton ; 3, West Charleton; 4, Frogmore; and 5, in Goveton.*

Boon Wm. parish clerk
2 Crimp Wm. beer seller
4 Elworthy Mr John‖Matthews Wm.
3 Finch Wm. vict. New Inn
5 Hosking Hy. vict. Commercial
2 Hutchings Rd. grocer and draper
Shortland Lieut. Willoughby, R.N.
  Cutland
Twysden Rev Thos., M.A. *Rectory*
Wells Capt. Fortescue, R.A. *Slade*

BLACKSMITHS.
5 Grills Henry
4 Hind Wm.

SHOEMAKERS.
5 Frost Israel
3 Lakey John

FARMERS.
Coaker Wm.
Cole John
Cole Stephen
Dimond Faby
2 Finch Jacob
3 Finch Wm.
Grills Jno. & Hy.
  Lower Tor
Hingston John
Jordain John
3 Luscombe Hy.

3 Palfrey John
Prettejohn Abm.,
  Lidstone
3 Smith Jno. and
  Nathaniel
Toll John
Widger Wm.
5 Wyatt John
5 Wyatt Josias
Post from New
  Inn to Kings-
  bridge, 3 aft.

CHIVELSTONE, a small village, nearly 6 miles S.S.E. of Kingsbridge, has in its parish 591 souls, and 2696 acres of land, extending southward to the romantic sea cliffs between *Start and Prawle Points,* near Start Bay and the mouth of Kingsbridge or Salcombe haven ; and including the fishing village of *Prawle,* and the hamlets of *Ford and South Allington.* Prawle has about 312 inhabitants, and a coast guard station ; and below the cliffs is a tract of fertile land.   Thos. Newman, Esq., is lord of the manor, but a great part of the parish is freehold, belonging to N. Pitts, Esq., and several smaller owners.   Mr. Pitts has a handsome mansion at South Allington.   The *Church* (St. Sylvester,) is an ancient fabric, with a tower and five bells, but only one usable.   It was repaired about 30 years ago, when new windows were inserted.   The old rood loft remains, and the pulpit is formed out of a solid block of wood.   The living is a perpetual curacy, consolidated with Stokenham vicarage, there being neither parsonage nor glebe here.   The tithes were commuted in 1842, the vicarial for £164. 10s., and the rectorial for £137.   Here is a small Bible Christian Chapel, and at Ford is an *Independent Chapel,* which was built in 1750, and enlarged in 1818, and is now under the ministry of the Rev. Wm. Miles, of Frogmore. *Marked 2 are at Chivelstone ; 3, Ford; 4, Prawle; and 5, at South Allington.*

4 Burney Lieut. coast guard station
4 Cole Wm. vict. Union
4 Creber Thos. & 5 John, carpenters
2 Edwards Thomas, shoemaker
5 Farrow Rev John R., B.A. curate
2 Folland James, beer seller
Maunder N. miller, *Ford Mills*
4 Pearse Lieut. Wm., A.R., R.N.
Pitts Nichs. Esq. *South Allington Hs*
4 Putt Mary, vict. Providence
2 Tucker John, mason
3 Tucker Thomas, beer seller

BLACKSMITHS.
3 Cuming Edw. | 4 Goodwood Jno.
| 5 Harraden Hy.

FARMERS.
5 Blank Mary
5 Cousins Wm.
3 Friend Fras.
4 Foss Rt. & Hy.
Gillard Mr
4 Heath Richd.
4 Hutchings P.
2 Huxham John
4 Pile Robert
3 Prettejohn Bws.
5 Randall Rd.
Snowden John
4 Sture Henry

4 Tucker Richd.
SHOPKEEPERS.
5 Edwards Jas.
4 Edwards N.
3 Goodyear —
TAILORS.
2 Lidstone Wm.
5 Wakeham John
2 Wood Jph.

POST to Kingsbridge 1 aftn. from W. Lidstone's

CORNWORTHY is a small village, in the picturesque and well woody valley, near the confluence of the Harbourn river with the estuary of the Dart, 4 miles S.S.E. of Totnes. Its parish contains 554 inhabitants, and 2575 acres of land, including the small hamlets of *Allaleigh, East Cornworthy, Tideford,* and part of *Tuckenhay,* where there are quays on the river Harbourn, and paper and corn mills in the adjoining parish of Ashprington. William Newman, Esq., is lord of the manor of Cornworthy, or *Corneorde ;* and George Strode, Esq., is lord of the manor of East Cornworthy; but a great part of the parish belongs to Sir J. L. Duntze, the Rev. Jacob Ley, J. F. P. Phillips, M. P. French, Pp. Michelmore, John and Edw. Holditch, and a few smaller freeholders. The surface is rather hilly, and the soil is generally light and fertile, resting on slate and dunstone, and in some places on limestone. The land is mostly in tillage, but has a fair portion of pasturage, and a number of extensive orchards, producing excellent cider. Cornworthy is spoken of as a borough in ancient records, and Allaleigh is said to have formerly had a large village and tannery. *Cornworthy Priory,* for nuns of the order of St. Austin, was founded at an early period by one of the lords of Totnes, and was valued at £63 per annum at the dissolution. The venerable gateway of the priory is still standing near the farm-house of *Court Prior,* and some remains of the chapel may be seen in the barn. This estate was long held by the Harris family, but now belongs to Mr. John Holditch. The *Church* (St. Peter,) is an ancient structure, in the early perpendicular style, with a tower and six bells, but the stone mullions have been replaced by wooden window frames. The rood screen and the old Norman font remain. In the chancel is a monument, with the effigies of Sir Thomas Harris, his wife, and four children, erected about 1610. The *vicarage,* valued in K.B. at £10, and in 1831 at £220, is endowed with the great tithes of Abbotskerswell (see page 422,) and has a good residence and 35a. 38p. of glebe. The Rev. W. K. Sweetland, M.A., is patron and incumbent. The unredeemed tithes of Cornworthy (on 1012a.) were commuted in 1845 for £195 per annum, belonging to Mrs. Tucker, Edw. Holditch, and John Peeke, but subject to a yearly stipend of £10 for the vicar, and the yearly payments of 40s. for the poor of this parish, and £18 for the poor of 18 other parishes, left by *John Peter,* in 1570. The *Church House,* which has long been vested for the use of the poor parishioners, was used as the workhouse, but is now divided into tenements, let, with the garden, for £12 a year. It has lately been much improved, and part of it is now the *parish school.* There is a stable for the use of persons riding to church on Sundays. In 1633, *Elizabeth Harris* left £100 to be invested in land, &c., for the poor of this parish, and for

other good and religious uses. The property, purchased with this legacy, now consists of a house, two cottages, three orchards, and about 21 acres of land, let for £37. 10s. a year, of which £20 is paid for schooling poor children, and the remainder is distributed among the poor at Easter. The vicar and others are trustees. The late vicar, the Rev. Chas. Barter, held the living 70 years, and died in 1846, aged 95. Near the confluence of the two rivers is a large *entrenchment,* partly covered with wood, supposed to have been a Roman encampment, and still retaining a part of the fosse, 30 feet deep. *Marked 2 are at Allaleigh, and 3 at East Conworthy.*

Harris Rev Thos. || Holditch Mrs
Hawke Richard, thatcher
Newland Nichs. vict. Globe Inn
Newland Nichs. jun. tailor
Sweetland Rev Wm. Keats, M.A. vicar
    FARMERS. (* are Owners.)
Came Richard, *Court Prior*
Denbow Wm., *Tideford*
Earl Richard, *Gitcombe*
2*Elliott John, (and land agent)
Elliott John, *South Hills*
Hodge Thomas, Court Barton
3 Hutchings Geo. || Pedrick Jas.
Langworthy John, *Lr. Broadridge*
Langworthy Robt., *Hr. Broadridge*
*Michelmore Philip, *Dinnscombe*

2 Tozer John || Peeke Wm.
Tozer Robert, *Tideford*
Wakeham Arthur, *Dinnscombe*
Waycott George, *Woolcombe*
3*Widdicombe Wm.||*Tucker Agnes
    BLACKSMITHS.
Ferris Robert
Came Thomas
    BUTCHERS.
2 Goodman Sml.
Eastman Wm.
    CARPENTERS.
2 Damerell John
Damerell Wm.
Efford Robert
Fall George

    MASONS.
Grout James
Newland Wm.
    SHOEMAKERS.
Bowden Jas. P.
Pedrick P.
    SHOPKEEPERS.
Ash Wm.
Tucker John
FOOT POST to
    Totnes daily

DARTMOUTH is an ancient *borough, market town,* and *sea-port,* picturesquely seated on the western side of the estuary of the Dart, opposite Kingswear, which projects nearly midway into the river, about a mile from its confluence with the English Channel; thus narrowing the entrance, and protecting the spacious harbour above, where there is room for an immense concourse of shipping in the broad waters of the Dart and its creeks. A steam packet plies daily up the Dart to Totnes, about ten miles above, where the valley is crossed by the South Devon Railway. The town has now about 5000 inhabitants, and is distant five miles S.W. by S. of Brixham, 28 miles E. of Plymouth, 30 miles S. by W. of Exeter, and 202 miles W.S.W. of London. The stranger accustomed to the straight, monotonous fronts of modern streets, will be much struck with the projecting fronts, carved brackets, and antique gables of Dartmouth, where many of the houses are of the Elizabethan and earlier ages. The town is built close along the edge of the large basin formed by the estuary, and up the sides of the steep hill rising directly from it. So abrupt is the acclivity of the hill, that from the level of the houses in the upper street, people may almost look down the chimneys of those in the lower street. The two lines of streets, one above the other, are remarkably narrow, and communicate with each other by steps, or very steep openings, at various distances. The entrance to the harbour is guarded on either side by the fortifications called *Dartmouth* and *Kingswear Castles,* between which a chain was formerly drawn across the water every night, to keep out hostile vessels. Almost the only improvements that have been made in the town during the last twenty years are the *new*

road from Tunstal to the north end of the town ; the large *floating bridge,* which is there impelled across the river upon chains, and was opened in 1831 ; the introduction of *gas ;* and the erection of the new *Market House,* in 1828-'9, at the cost of about £1200. A wider and more direct road from the middle of the town to the floating bridge is much wanted, and it is hoped that this and other improvements will be effected in a few years. An island of about four acres, called the " *New Ground,*" was warped up from the haven in front of the town about a century ago, and is connected with the lower street by a small bridge, which was widened in 1825. The fairs are held on this island, which has a fine avenue of trees, and forms a pleasant promenade for the inhabitants. The *borough* is called *Clifton-Dartmouth-Hardness,* from the three ancient hamlets now forming the town, and it comprises the two *parishes* of St. Petrox and St. Saviour, and most of Townstal parish. These three parishes had 4595 inhabitants in 1841, of whom 929 were in *St. Petrox,* 2345 in *St. Saviour's,* and 1321 in *Townstal,* but 178 of the latter were beyond the limits of the borough. The population of the three parishes was 2398 in 1801, 4597 in 1831, and 4595 in 1841. The two first-named parishes comprise only about 100 acres, but TOWNSTAL extends north-west beyond the borough, and comprises the hamlets of *Norton, Oldmill, Ford,* and *Warfleet,* and 1688A. 3R. 34P. of land, mostly the property of *Sir Henry Paul Seale, Bart.,* lord of the *manors* of Townstal and Norton-Dawney ; who has a large castellated mansion here, called *Mount Boon,* situated on a commanding eminence, west of the town, and formerly a seat of the Boone and Harris families, the latter of whom sold the estate to the Seales about 1700. The late Sir John Henry Seale was created a *baronet* in 1838, and died in 1844. Sir H. P. Seale is also lord of the manor of *South Town,* comprising the parish of St. Petrox, and formerly belonging to the Fitzstephen, Fleming, Mohun, Carew, and Southcote families. The *manor of Dartmouth* passed as a parcel of the barony of Totnes till the reign of Edward I., after which it was conveyed by succeeding monarchs to various families. Queen Elizabeth granted the manor and borough to persons named Downing, Ashton, and Peter, by whom they were conveyed to the *Corporation,* to whom they still belong, together with the tolls and dues of the market, fairs, and harbour, and the tithes of Townstal, and various houses, quays, &c., from which they derive about £900 per annum ; out of which they support the harbour lights, the town water pipes and cisterns, the police, the fire engines, &c. One item of their expenditure in 1848 was 21s., for the boatmen in attendance during her Majesty's passing visit in the Channel.

A charter for a market and fair at Dartmouth was granted to Richard de Gloucester, son of Wm. Fitzstephen, in 1226 ; and another charter was granted in 1301 for a market and fair at Clifton-super-Dartmouth. Here is now a *weekly market* for provisions every Friday, and also *cattle markets* on the Monday before the third Wednesday of every month. The old fairs are disused, but here are two pleasure fairs in March and October, and a *regatta* in August. Leland says King John granted the " *privilege of Mairalte to*

Dertmuth," but this must be a mistake, as a charter, granted by Edward III., in 1342, expressly invests the burgesses with the power of choosing a mayor every year. Under this charter, the *Corporation* consisted of a mayor, recorder, two bailiffs, and twelve common councilmen. Under the Municipal Reform Act of 1835, it now consists of a mayor, recorder, four aldermen, and twelve councillors; and the borough has a commission of the peace, and a court of quarter sessions. The present CORPORATION and OFFICERS are,—Sir H. P. Seale, Bart., *mayor ;* A. B. Harris, Noah Clift, Chas. Hutchings, and Sir H. P. Seale, *aldermen ;* J. Puddicombe, J. Polyblank, J. Webber, J. Coaker, H. Follett, J. Bulley, H. M. Baker, R. Coombe, J. Greaves, R. F. Burrough, Wm. Follett, and T. Fogwill, *councillors ;* Chas. Dacres Bevan, Esq., *recorder ;* Chas. Hutchings, A. B. E. Holdsworth, A. H. Holdsworth, A. B. Harris, Rt. Harris, D. Codner, Col. Carlyon, and the Mayor, Ex-Mayor, and Recorder, *borough magistrates ;* George Bridgeman, *clerk of the peace ;* F. B. Cuming, *town clerk ;* Sol. Pentecost, *treasurer ;* J. M. Puddicombe, *coroner ;* Wm. Hearn and Jas. Phillips, *sergeants-at-mace ;* and Rd. Backwell, *jailor.* The borough sent representatives to one of the Parliaments in the reign of Edward I., and regularly sent two members from the 14th of Edward III. till 1832, when it was classed by the Parliamentary Reform Act, among the boroughs entitled only to send one member each. The right of election was formerly in the freemen, who were about forty in number, but there are now about 340 voters, of whom about twenty are freemen, and the rest occupiers of houses, &c., of the yearly value of £10 or upwards. *Geo. Moffatt, Esq., is their present representative.* The late Col. Sir J. H. Seale represented the borough from 1832 till his death in 1844, and so anxious were the householders for his return, and for reform in Parliament, that 119 voted for him at the election in 1830, though their votes were disallowed, and the two successful candidates were returned by the votes of only 21 freemen.

In 1347, Dartmouth stood third in the list of 84 sea-ports, which furnished Edward III. with 700 ships for the siege of Calais; its quota being 31 ships and 757 seamen. It was nearly destroyed in 1377 by a powerful army from France; but in 1403, when another French army, commanded by M. du Chastel, again burnt and destroyed Plymouth, it was in a condition to send many well-armed vessels to the fleet, which destroyed 40 of the enemy's ships, captured as many more, and returned laden with booty, after landing at Penmark, in Bretagne. To avenge himself for this loss, M. du Chastel, in the following year, made a descent upon Dartmouth, with a considerable force; but they met with such determined resistance, that the commander and 400 men were killed, 200 taken prisoners, and the rest were glad to fly to their ships, and leave the harbour with all speed. At this period, John Hawley, a rich merchant here, had so many ships, that it was said, *" Blow the wind high, or blow it low, It bloweth fair to Hawley's Hoe."* Leland says that in his time the great ruins of Hawley's Hall were to be seen in that part of the town called Hardness. Chaucer, in his *"* Canterbury Tales,*"* written about this time, says, *" A Shipman was ther, woned fer by west ; For ought I wote he was of Dertemouth."* Having a deep and capacious harbour, where 500 sail of large ships can ride in safety, Dartmouth has from very early times been a place of trade and maritime importance. The fleet destined for the Holy Land assembled here in 1190. Wool, wine, and iron constituted its principal commerce in the reign of Edward I. Until the beginning of the present century, a large Newfoundland trade was carried on here, but it has much declined of late years. The coasting trade of the port is still rather extensive. The imports consist of coal, timber, and general merchandise, and the exports of cider, barley, potatoes,

stone, slate, &c. The number of vessels registered here is 463, amounting together to 34,041 tons. The *Port* extends along the coast from Babbicombe to the river Yalm, and includes Totnes, Brixham, Torquay, Salcombe, and Kingsbridge, so that only about a fifth of the registered shipping belongs to Dartmouth. The harbour is much frequented by steamers and homeward-bound Dutch vessels, and those of other northern nations, which remain during the time the continental rivers are frozen. It is also a safe port of refuge for ships during adverse gales in the channel. The Commissioners appointed by Government, a few years ago, to enquire into the eligibility of the different ports in the English Channel for a foreign mail packet station, gave a decided preference to Dartmouth, but Southampton still retains that privilege. The CUSTOM HOUSE is a convenient building, and the following are the officers:—Alex. More, Esq., *collector ;* Mr. Jph. H. Sparke, *comptroller ;* W. H. E. Godfrey and G. N. Puddicombe, *clerks ;* and W. R. Creed, *tide surveyor.* The gross receipt of customs in 1838 was £4100, and in 1839, £4629. Here are bonded warehouses for all goods except tobacco and East India goods.

In the latter part of the 15th century, means were taken for the better protection of the town and harbour, Edward IV. having then covenanted to pay the burgesses £30 a year for ever, out of the customs, on condition of their erecting " a strong and mighty and defensive new tower," adjoining the castle, properly furnished with arms and artillery, and with a chain to be drawn across the river to the tower at Kingswear. (See page 486.) *Dartmouth Castle* has still its governor (A. H. Holdsworth, Esq.,) fort major, and master gunner, and is mounted with six 12 and four 18 pounders. Near it is an older castellated fort, also mounted with cannon, and rising immediately above the water. Dartmouth was garrisoned by Parliament in the early part of the *civil wars* of the 17th century. After the capture of Exeter in 1643, (see page 57,) Prince Maurice marched to Dartmouth, which he expected to find an easy conquest, but the town did not yield till after a month's siege. The royalists, esteeming it an important place, repaired its fortifications, and strongly garrisoned the castles on both sides of the harbour, and the forts called Gallant's Bower, Paradise, and Mount Flaggon, as well as the West-gate, Townstal Church, and the mansion of Mount Boon; but in January, 1646, it was stormed and taken by the army of Sir Thos. Fairfax. In 1675, Charles Fitzcharles, natural son of Charles II., was created *Baron Dartmouth, Viscount Totnes,* and *Earl of Plymouth,* but these titles became extinct on his death in 1680. George Legge was created Baron Dartmouth in 1682, and his son William was created Viscount Lewisham and *Earl of Dartmouth* in 1750. His descendant, the present Earl, resides at Sandwell Park, Staffordshire. *Mr. Newcomen,* one of the early improvers of the steam-engine, was a native of Dartmouth ; and in the 16th century *Sir Humphrey Gilbert* sailed from this port to establish a settlement in Newfoundland ; and *Capt. Davis* in search of the north-west passage to India. The town and neighbourhood have long been celebrated for " *white ale,*" said to have been first brewed here. The ale taster is an officer appointed by the corporation, and formerly he tasted every brewing of the publicans, and proclaimed at their doors with a loud voice and " uplifted leg and arm," whether the ale was good or not ! The last ale taster died at the age of 91, and shortly before his death he met, at a " tasting," four others of the respective ages of 88, 87, 79, and 76. There are *Assembly Rooms, &c.,* at the Castle, London, and Commercial Inns, and another over the British Schools. Here is a *Literary and Scientific Institution,* which has a museum and occasional lectures. The *Mechanics' Institution* was established in 1846, and the *Dartmouth United Shipping Association* in

1812. There are four churches and three chapels in the three parishes, and various charities belonging to the parishes separately and to the borough at large.

CHURCHES, &c.—*Townstal Church* (St. Clement,) on a bold eminence about half a mile north- of the town, is an ancient structure, of early English architecture, with a lofty tower, containing four bells. The interior has several neat mural tablets, and the living is a vicarage, valued in 1831 at £135, with the curacy of St. Saviour's annexed to it, in the patronage of Sir H. P. Seale, and incumbency of the Rev. John Tracey, B.A., who has a good residence, and two yearly stipends, viz., £105 out of the tithes of Sherford, and about £18 out of the tithes of Townstal parish, which were commuted in 1840 for £294. 17s. 6d. per annum. The latter formerly belonged to Tor Abbey, but have been in the impropriation of the corporation of Dartmouth since the Reformation; and they had also the advowson till they sold it a few years ago. *St. Saviour's Church* is an ancient and spacious structure, said to have been consecrated in 1372. It has a plain embattled tower, and the interior has a splendid screen, and several handsome monuments. In the chancel is the tomb of the before-named John Hawley, with effigies of himself and his two wives on brass plates. The altar-piece is a fine large painting of "Christ raising the widow's son," by Brockedon, a native artist, who presented it to the church. The door within the porch is covered with curious iron ornaments, and seems to be coeval with the building. *St. Petrox Parish Church* stands south of the town, immediately behind the castle, and is a very ancient structure, which has undergone many repairs and alterations. It has a low tower, containing five bells, and crowned by a very short spire. It had formerly a chantry, founded in the reign of Edward III., and the ancient manor house of Clifton stood near it. The living is a *perpetual curacy*, which has been augmented with Queen Anne's Bounty, and was valued in 1831 at £120. It is in the patronage of the rector of Stoke Fleming, and incumbency of the Rev. F. M. Walter, B.D. *St. Petrox' Chapel of Ease* stands in the Higher street, and was built by subscription in 1831, at the cost of about £2000. It is a plain Gothic structure, and many of the pews are free. The *Independent Chapel* is a large and handsome building, erected at the cost of £1200, on the site of the old Presbyterian Meeting-house, which belonged to a congregation of nonconformists established by the Rev. John Flavel, who was ejected in 1662 from St. Saviour's, and was author of some popular Calvinistic works. The *Wesleyan Chapel* was erected in 1816, at the cost of £1300; and here is also a *Baptist Chapel*. At South town are large and handsome *National Schools*, erected in 1823, and attended by about 100 children of either sex; and in the New road are *British Schools*, built in 1848, in the Tudor style, at the cost of about £1000, and attended by about 130 boys and girls.

CHARITIES.—Those vested with the corporation are now under the management of trustees appointed under the powers of the Municipal Reform Act. The poor of the borough have £3. 0s. 4d. yearly, in several small rent-charges left by *Alex. Awdyan*, in 1548. For a weekly distribution of 1s. worth of bread they have £2. 12s. yearly from *Sir John Acland's Charity.* (See Exeter.) In 1627, *John Shapleigh* left £100 for the poor, in trust with the corporation, but they have not paid the interest since 1694. They pay £2. 8s. yearly as the interest of £40 left to the poor by *Thos. Paige*, about 1630. John Plumleigh, in 1641, gave the *Town Close* (1A.) as a place for the inhabitants to *dry and bleach their clothes* in, and the herbage for the poor. The herbage is let for about £6 a year. Adjoining this close is half an acre called Ford Meadow, in which the inhabitants have the right of *washing clothes*, for which purpose there are wells and tables. The interest of £50, left by *George Prestwood*, in 1671, is distributed among the poor in bread and meat. The poor of the three parishes have a yearly rent-charge of £10, left by *Thomas Boone*, in 1677, out of an estate at Townstal; and also £6. 6s., as the rent of a house and garden left by *Richard Langdon*, in 1707. The yearly sum of £7. 10s. is distributed in *shifts* among poor women, as the interest of £125 benefaction money, vested with the corporation.

ALMSHOUSES.—In 1599, *Wm. Ley* left £40 for building an almshouse for poor people of this borough. About 1810, the corporation gave, in exchange for this old almshouse, a more modern building, now occupied by eight or ten poor persons. As many poor widows occupy the *Widows' Houses*, built by a Mr. Street, about 1630. Adjoining the latter are some apartments let for as much as is required for keeping the whole building in repair. In 1633, *Richard Kelly* left two yearly rent-charges of 20s. for the inmates of Ley's and Street's almshouses. The small Almshouse, given by *John Lovering*, in 1671, for poor sailors or their widows, was burnt down in 1794, and the site is now let for about £2 per annum.

The FORDER ESTATE CHARITY consists of a farm of 55A. 1R. 12P., at Blackauton, worth £50 a year, but let for only £18, in consideration of fines paid on every renewal of the lease for lives. This estate was purchased with £600 trust money in 1673, and vested with the corporation, in trust that they should apply the clear yearly profits in five equal portions, as follows:—One-fifth towards the maintenance of the minister of St. Petrox' church; one-fifth towards the better maintenance of a Latin schoolmaster, (but there is not one now) one-fifth towards the support of an English schoolmaster; one-

fifth for distribution among the poor of St. Saviour's parish; and the other fifth for the poor of St. Petrox and Townstal parishes.

The PARISH OF ST. SAVIOUR has the following charities, in addition to its share of the foregoing. For schooling poor children, *Wm. Wotton*, in 1689, left a yearly rent-charge of £5 out of South Whimple farm, at Broadclist. For a weekly distribution of 1s. worth of bread the poor have an annuity of 52s., left by *Lawrence Wheeler*, in 1662, out of land in Townstal. They have also two other annuities, viz., 20s. out of the great tithes of Cornworthy, left by *John Peter;* and 12s. paid by the corporation as interest of £10 left by *Joan Rounsevall.* For preaching a weekly sermon on a working day, the curate has about £20 a year from *Kelly's Charity.* (See Brixham.)

ST. PETROX PARISH.—For maintaining the *watercourses*, and for other public uses, *Robt. Code*, in the 1st of Henry 7th, vested with trustees certain property which now consists of eleven houses, with gardens, &c., worth £120 a year, but let for only about £8, in consideration of fines paid on the renewal of the leases. The fines and rents are all expended in the works which supply *South Town* with water. The industrious poor parishioners have the dividends of £100 navy five per cent. stock, given by the *Rev. Jno. Charter*, in 1821.

TOWNSTAL PARISH.—The *Church Lands, &c.*, have been vested in trust from an early period for the repairs of the church, and now comprise eight houses and gardens and a field of 1A. 24P., worth about £100 per annum, but let for only about £5, in consideration of fines paid by the lessees. The poor parishioners have 20s. a year, left by *John Peter*, out of Cornworthy tithes.

DARTMOUTH DIRECTORY.

The POST-OFFICE is at Mrs. Margaret F. Sparke's, New Road, and letters are despatched at 8½ morning, and 10 minutes past 4 afternoon.

Those marked 1 are in Clarence st., 2 Duke st., 3 Foss st., 4 Hanover sqr., 5 Higher st., 6 Market place, 7 New Road, 8 Lower st., 9 Quay, 10 South Town, 11 Silver st., 12 Smith st., and 13 in Above Town.

7 Atkins Mr Geo. F. || 10 Baker Miss
9 Bachellor Geo. inland rev. officer
Backwell Richard, gaoler
Baker Hy. M. brewer and maltster, Warfleet
6 Baker Mr Geo. || 10 Bate Mrs
8 Bartlett Mr Wm. || 10 Beard P. mr.
6 Beard Mrs E. || 10 Beale Isaac
Blatchford Mr Wm.
9 Bovey Wm. P. corn miller
5 Brewer Rev. Edward, (Baptist)
10 Brooking Misses & Mrs Ann
5 Burgoyne Mr. Jno. || Codd Mrs. A.
Clift Chas. G. supt. Gas Works
5 Coaker Jonas, gentleman
10 Codner Saml. Esq || 7 Cole Mrs E.
Codner Mr Thos. B., Above Town
7 Couch Wm. & Cowell Dnl. lodgngs
10 Creed Wm. R. tide surveyor
7 Davy Mr Jno. || 10 Delme Rd.
10 De Courcey Hon Wm. Almericus
9 Denmark Mr Rt. || 4 Drew Mrs
Durham Mr || Eales Misses
Dyer Sir Thomas Swinnerton, Bart. (Commander R. N.) *Newload*
8 Eales & Windeatt, woolcombers
3 Elliott Wilmot H. M., draper
1 Eran Rev. Wm. Sloane Sloane, B.A.
10 Foale Hy. clerk || Francis Mrs
8 Fogwill Wm. H. ale & porter mert. and shipping agent
Follett Mr Wm. || Goodyear James
Ford Lieut. Arthur || Forster Capt.
Furness Jas. master gunner, *Castle*
1 Gibbs Mrs Grace || Giles Mrs
5 Gibson John, coast guard
Godfrey Lieut. John, R.N.
Godfrey W. H. E., clerk
Goodyear Mr James || Guthrey Mrs
Greaves John, Esq. *Bellevue*
8 Gregory Mr John || 6 Harris My.
Hare Hon. Wm. Hy., *One-gun Cotg.*
Harris Mr A. B. || Hayman Edw. clk.
10 Haye Miss || 3 Hingston Mr Geo.
Hedgeland Rev. R., *Elmgrove*
3 Hellyer Wm. glass, china, &c. dlr.
9 Hingston R. Langworthy, notary, &c
9 Hingston and Sons, *consuls* for all nations, agents to Lloyds, and receivers of admiralty droits
Hockin Mr Wm. L., *Quarry Cotgs.*
2 Holditch George, cider merchant
Holdsworth Arthur Howe, Esq. gov.
Holdsworth Mrs Eliz. & Mrs C.
Hutchings Chas. Esq. *Ford Hill*
1 Hutchinson Mrs || Jackson Miss A.
Jago Mr Edw. || 7 Jancey Mrs J.
10 Kensington E. Esq || Janson Capt.
5 Langdon John, basket maker
Lamzed Hy. & John, mr. mariners
Leathy Mr Thos. || Lock Mr John
1 Lidstone Mr Thos. || Love Joseph

Lidstone Ths. jun. architect, *Coombe*
2 Luke Mr Wm. & John, jun
3 Macey Allen, draper, (M & E.)
Martin Mr || Matthews Mr Wm.
Maypowder Mrs || Millman P., R.N.
2 Mills Edward, brush maker
10 More Alex. Esq. colr. of customs
Morey Miss E. || 8 Newman Mrs
2 National and Provincial Bank of England (Branch,) Rt. Harris, agt.
7 Newman Wm. surveyor to Lloyds'
Newman Wm. Esq., South Town
Nicholls Ambrose, master mariner
10 Pearce Capt. Edwin, R.N.
Pearne Wm. || Pinson Mr Thomas
Petherbridge S. || Perrying Rd. dyer
7 Poynton Lieut. C. W., coast guard
Puddicombe G. N. clerk in customs
7 Prideaux Walter, Esq || Reed Wm.
1 Randall Geo. J. tob. pipe maker
1 Rogers Mr Wm. || 10 Roope Misses
Seilly Mr Thos. & Mrs Ford
Seale Sir Hy. Paul, Bart., *Mt. Boon*
10 Smith Mrs || Sawers Mr John
Snelling Mr Roger || Stuart Charles
10 Southcott Misses || Stuart Mr C.
1 Sparke Jph. Hake, comptroller
10 Stapleton Misses || Swaffin Rd.
Steer Mr Rd. || Sutcliffe Mr Henry
1 Stenner Rev Jno. Flavel, (Indpt.)
2 Symons George, saddler
10 Toswill Mr Rt. || 5 Tolmin Wm.
Tracey Rev Jno., B.A., vicar of Townstal & St Saviour's, Vicarage
10 Walter Rev Fredk. Morton, B.D. incumbent of St Petrox
7 Way Mr Thos. || Weeks Mrs
Waymouth Mrs || 1 Wills Mr Joseph
Wilcox Wm. town crier, Market st
Wilson Mr Rt. || Witney Mrs & Miss
8 Windeatt Wm. B. corn factor
1 Wood Mrs || Woolridge Mr

ATTORNEYS.
1 Bridgman Geo. (clerk of peace)
Brooking John, Lower street
Cuming Fras. Brooking, (town clk.)
Hockin Percy, Hanover square
Prideaux Saml. Were, *Hardness Hs.*
Prior Edward, Lower street
Smith John B., Post-office place

AUCTIONEERS.
8 Vincent Charles, (estate agent)
Way Jph. Delve, Market place

FARMERS (*in Townstal.*)
Barnstone John, Slippery hill

Buckbit George, Mount Boon
Colton Pp. || Coombe Rd., *Norton*
Ellis Samuel, Brown's Norton
Hodge Thos. || Hooper James
Luscombe George || Luckraft Pp.
Nowell John || Standcombe Robert
Stranger Thos., Little Dartmouth
Sluman Thomas || Soper Wm.
Trant Richard, *Milton*

FIRE & LIFE OFFICE AGENTS.
County Fire, Henry Foale
Crown Life, John Windeatt
Dartmouth United Shipping Co., Rt. Cranford, *agent*
General, W. H. Fogwill
Legal & General, S. W. Prideaux
Medical Invalid, &c., J. D. Symons
Norwich Union, Robert Cranford
Phœnix & Pelican, Robert Harris
Royal Exchange & West of England, Hingston & Sons
Sun, Charles Vincent

INNS AND TAVERNS.
10 Admiral Nelson, Ann Prowse
9 Castle, Danl. Donovan (posting)
7 Commercial Hotel, Ambrose N. Jarvis, (billiards, &c.)
8 Commercial, Mary Woodcock
8 Custom House, John Michelmore
8 Dartmouth Arms, Wm. Ash
6 Dolphin, John de Moys
1 Floating Bridge, John Griffiths
8 Free Trade Inn, Hy. Goodridge
11 George & Dragon, Robt. Peek
9 Globe, Robert Hurrell
8 King's Arms, Ann Swaffin
3 London Inn, Nichs. Browse (pstg.)
5 Lord Nelson, Henry Blondett
8 Marine Inn, Wm. Honeychurch
6 Newmarket Inn, My. Ann Rogers
8 Oxford Arms, Wm. Stentiford
8 Royal Oak, Edward Bastard
7 Seale's Arms, Joseph P. Ellis
12 Seven Stars, George Bates
Ship in Dock, Wm. Hext, *Coombe*
1 Shipwrights' Arms, (empty)
Sun, Thos. Beer, Pillery lane
5 Town Arms, Wm. Nicholls
12 Waterman's Arms, Rt. Harrad

ACADEMIES.		13 Thomas Wm.
DeDalmasH.P.E.		10 Walter Rev.
5 Harvey Miss		Frederick M.
10 Jarvis Hubert		4 Wills Mary
7 Simkins Sus.L.		3 Wills Misses

British School, J.
Macey & Clara
Simkins
National Sch., G.
W. Jones

BAKERS.
8 Atkins John
8 Brownson Ann
12 Burgoyne Rt.
10 Came Robert
8 Conroy James
6 Cuming Rd.
3 Dunning Rd.
11 Dunning Rt.
1 Elliott Harriet
3 Goodyear Rd.
8 Goodridge Hy.
5 Langdon Hy.
8 Lanyon J. F.
5 Lidstone Thos.
8 Lock Grace
9 Mills Nicholas
5 Manning R. E.
4 Morgan Thos.
8 Pentecost Sol.
3 Prowse Susan
8 Smale James
1 Wallis Wm.
5 Wood Henry

BEERHOUSES.
6 Cuming Rd.
Drummond Wm.
Hamlyn James
5 Jarmond Mech.
1 Lidstone Mrs
5 Lang John
5 Macey Wm.
Morgan Thomas
1 Nunn Richard

BERLIN WOOL, &c.
DEALERS.
12 Graham My.
2 Holditch Lucre-
tia & Mary
3 Richards J. E.

BLACKSMITHS.
(* *Anchorsmiths.*)
5 Blackwell Rd.
2 * Barter John
5 Chorley W.
11 * Coursens Js.
Edwards Rt. jun
1 * Kelly Wm.
1 Light Chas.
5 Woodmason J.

BLOCK & PUMP
MAKERS.
8 Kemp Thomas
4 Loveys S. M.
Pillow John

BOOKSELLERS,&c.
7 Blondett Mary
8 Cowle Daniel
9 Cranford Rt.
3 Jones My. A.&M.
8 Maddick Mgt.

BOOT & SHOE MRS.
8 Brooking Henry
8 Brown Sarah
8 Coves John
1 Dodd Thomas
5 Grant Henry
3 Heath Samuel
8 Hardy Walter
3 Holloway Rd.
8 Kelland Robert
5 Lawrence Wm.
8 Phillips Thos.
8 Pike John
2 Tucker Jsha.
12 Wakeham Ts.
Widdicombe Hy.
8 Wills Lawrence

BUILDERS.
(*See Carpenters*
and Masons.)

BUTCHERS.
1 Foale Gilbert
Butland
Luke John
7 Manning Ann
9 Manning W. H.
5 Oldreive Rd.
2 Prout Richard
8 Sluman J.
2 Thomas W.C.

CABINET MAKERS.
8 Brown John
4 Lovell T. S.
6 Way Jph. D.

CARPENTERS.
5 Earle John
Edwards Wm.
8 Hendry Jno. R.
5 Lavers Wm.
1 Lidstone Joseph
5 Lidstone Thos.
1 Lidstone T. jun.
7 Macey Samuel
Michelmore Rd.

5 Roberts Henry
Searle Thomas
12 Tucker Rd.
5 Veale John
5 Underhay Ncs.

CHEMISTS AND
DRUGGISTS.
9 Evans Wm.
2 Huxham Thos.
8 Newman Thos.
2 Rees Wm. Hy.
2 Windeatt John

COAL MERCHTS.
3 Fogwill Thos.
8 Fogwill Wm.H.
9 Lakeman Jph.
8 Vincent Chas.

COOPERS.
Blackler Mr
6 Conroy John
7 Ellis Joseph
12 Rowe George

CURRIERS.
8 Eales Jno. and
Chalker Chas.
5 Roberts John
5 Symons Saml.

DAIRYMEN.
Adams Wm.
Blank Thomas
Harris Edward
Langmead Rd.
5 Lavers George
Parsons Ephm.
13 Wallace Wm.

FISHMONGERS.
5 Humphreys Hy.
8 Lewis James
8 Lewis John

GARDENERS.
2 Lowday John
Oldreive Nichls.
1 Stevens Wm.
Tozer John

GROCERS.
9 Adams Richard
8 Andrews Ncs.
9 Ash Wm.
3 Cranford My.
8 Faremouth J.T.
9 Fox John P.
8 Love Agnes
8 Newman Thos.
8 Pike Arthur
2 Symons J. D.

2 Steer Rose
2 Windeatt John

HAIR DRESSERS.
9 Ford Jas. P.
8 Matthews J. M.
8 Rogers John

HATTERS.
3 Hannaford Ncs.
8 Matthews J. M.
2 Tucker Josa.

IRONMONGERS.
9 Ashford Wm. &
Son
2 Luke John
5 Veale Thomas

L. & W. DRAPERS.
2 Atkins W. T.
5 Codner W. S.
9 Daly Eliz.
8 Faremouth J.T.
3 Heath Jno. T.
8 Jellard Agnes
3 Macey & Elliott
9 Neck Wm.
8 Newman Sus.
2 Polyblank Jph.

MARINE STORE
DEALERS.
8 Collings James
5 Foale John
5 Humphreys H.
8 Lewis James
5 Symons John

MASONS.
Baker Wm.
7 Grant George
Grant John
Grant Robert
Lang Edward
7 Luby Wm.
5 Masters James
5 Peek Amos
5 Pillar Thomas
Tozer John

MERCHANTS.
Bulley Jno. *Town-*
stal Villa
Clift Noah, *Ford*
Codner Dl. *Bellmt.*
8 Fox Richard
2 Harris Robert
8 Henley Edw.
3 Hingston&Sons
Scilly Ths., *Ford*
13 Taylor Wm.

8 PetherbridgeH.
8 Vincent Chas.
8 Windeatt W. B.
MILLINERS.
8 Burgoyne E.
6 Graham Mary
7 Jarvis J. C.
4 Pearce Ann
4 Short H. L.
7 Simkins Sarah
3 Thompson M.
PAINTERS, PLUM-
BERS & GLAZRS.
8 Beer Richard
8 Croft Wm.
6 De Moys John
8 Faremouth Rd.
8 Jago John
3 Pearce John
5 Reed Wm.
8 Swaffin Robert
Way Wm. H.
PAWNBROKERS.
8 Lidstone Jno.L.
5 Reed Wm. J.
ROPE MAKERS.
7 Hingston&Sons
8 Pound Samuel,
(patent, &c)
SAIL MAKERS.
8 Brooking John
8 Hutchings Geo.
8 Petherbridge H.
8 Tipper Thos.
SEEDSMEN.
9 Adams Rd.
9AshfordW.&Son
SHIP BUILDERS.
1 Alford Andw.
1 Couch Wm.

11 Follett Saml.
and Henry
11 Follett Wm.H.
10 Lidstone Pp.
11 Nichols Henry
SHIP OWNERS.
Bulley John
Codner D. & Co
3 Fogwill Thos.
1 Follett S. & H.
11 FollettWm.H.
3 Goodyear Rd.
2 Harris Robert
3 Hingston&Sons
8 PetherbridgeH.
Scilly Thomas
8 Steward Peter
1 Wills Joseph
Woolridge Colnl.
Norton House
SHOPKEEPERS.
8 Andrews Ncs.
8 Baker Wm.
5 Barter Mlra.
1 Blagdon Sus.
10 Came Robert
Coysh Robert
2 Dalling George
8 Dean George
11 DunningRobt.
1 Elliott Harriet
8 Fox Ann L.
8 Ford Jane
5 Furze Wm.
12 Graham My.
8 Grant J. T.
5 Jarvis M.
Lawson Harriet
5 Macey John

2 Macey Mary
12 Memery Eliz.
2 Oldreive Wm.
7 PunchardAgns.
8 Rawle Betsy
Rennells Frank
8 Rogers Richard
8 Searle Wm.
Searle Thomas
1 Stephens Wm.
3 Trout Mary
8 Trout Wm.
5 Wills Elizabeth
5 Wogan Wm.
STRAW HAT MKS.
5 Emms Mary
1 Goodyear Sarah
Henley Frances
8 Jackman Eliz.
5 Reeves Eliz.
2 Rich Rhoda
7 Simkins C.G.
SURGEONS.
8 Burrough R.F.
7 Elliott Saml. N.
7 Puddicombe J.
9 Puddicombe J.
M. (coroner)
1 Teage Wm.
4 Tracey Harry
TAILORS.
1 Colton John F.
8 Fox R.
5 Harris Wm.
8 Humphreys J.
8 Pound John
8 Pound Samuel
8 Tucker Wm.
8 Veale Charles

TIMBER MERTS.
3 Fogwill Thos.
9 Hingston&Sons
TINNERS, &c.
9 Ashford & Son
8 Beer Richard
2 Luke John
8 Luke Robert
VETNY. SURGNS.
3 Browne Nchls.
Soper John
WATCHMAKERS.
3 Ash Henry
3 Lidstone Geo.
2 MortimoreR.M.
WINE & SPIRIT
MERCHANTS.
3 Baker Hy. M.
9 Donovan Dl.
9 Fox Jno. P.
8 Soper John,
stamp office.

STM. PACKT.
To Totnes daily,
expt.Sun. *Rails*
from Totnes
CARRIERS.
To Brixham and
Torquay, *Omni-
bus* daily from
Castle; and Putt
Mon. & Fri.from
King's Arms
To Kingsbridge,
Ford, Mon.Wed.
and Friday
To Plymouth, I.
Ferris,Market st
Mon. & Thurs.

DITTISHAM, a pleasant scattered village, on the western bank of the estuary of the Dart, 3 miles N.N.W. of Dartmouth, has in its parish 917 inhabitants, and 3089 acres of land, rising boldly from the valley, and in-- cluding *Capton* hamlet. Sir H. P. Seale is lord of the manor of *Bosom Zeal;* but that of Dittisham Wales belongs to the rectory. H. Studdy, W. Roope, G. Holdsworth, and P. Soper, Esqrs., and several smaller owners, have estates here, mostly freehold. Dittisham manor is dismembered, and was held by Baldwin de Bionüs, under the Bishop of Exeter, at Domesday Survey. The *Church* (St. George,) is an ancient structure, in the early perpendicular style, with a tower and six bells. It has recently been reno- vated, and new mullions, &c., inserted. The east window, and those in the north aisle, have been enriched with stained glass. The pulpit is of stone, finely carved, gilt, and coloured; and the ancient screen, hagioscope, se- dilia, &c., remain. The church was consecrated in 1333, and its restora- tion has been accomplished by the present rector, with the assistance of

several liberal gifts. The *rectory*, valued in K.B. at £34. 15s., and in 1831 at £540, is in the patronage of the Earl of Mount Edgecumbe, and incumbency of the Hon. and Rev. Lord H. F. C. Kerr, M.A., who has a handsome residence, and 87A. 2R. 29P. of glebe. The tithes were commuted in 1841, for £475 per annum. There are still some remains of a chapel in the ancient manor house of Bosom Zeal. The Independents have a chapel in the parish. The *National School* was erected in 1843, in the Tudor style, and is supported chiefly by the rector. The *Church Lands*, &c., comprise eight houses and gardens, let for £43 per annum. The poor have 5s. a year, left by a Mr. Youlden.

Kerr Hon and Rev Lord Hy. Francis Charles, M.A., *Rectory*
Browse Mr Wm., Bramble Tor
Hutchings Miss, and Montague Mrs
Peek John, mason, &c
 FARMERS. (* *are Owners.*)
Coles John ‖ Holmes John
Ferris John, (farrier,) *Capton*
Ferris Mary Anne, *Capton*
Manning Wm., *Bosom Zeal*
Mumford Matthew, (and miller)
*Narracott John, *Coombe*
Punchard John, *Holwell*
Roper Wm. ‖ Soper James
*Searle Thomas, *Court Barton*
Stranger Edward, *Downton*
Trant Wm. ‖ Trant Richard

Trist Richard ‖ Underhay George
Wakeham Wm., *Capton*
 PUBLIC-HOUSES.
Golden Lion, Thomas Smith
Passage House, Thomas Blamfrey, mason and ferryman
*Red Lion, Wm. Punchard
Waterman's Arms, Thomas Beer
 BLACKSMITHS.
Gidley Wm.
Peek John
 CARPENTERS.
Elliott Samuel
Fox Thos. *builder*
Smith Edward
 SHOEMAKERS.
Narramore John

Punchard Wm.
 SHOPKEEPERS.
Bartram Thomas, (& maltster)
Hodge Thomas
Husson Eliz.
POST-OFFICE at J. Beer's. Desp. at 3 afternoon

DODBROOKE, at the head of the Salcombe estuary, forms part of the town of KINGSBRIDGE, with which it is described at a subsequent page. It had 1229 inhabitants in 1841, but comprises only 343A. 1R. 39P. of land. It has a *cattle market* on the third Wednesday of every month, and a fair on the Wednesday before Palm Sunday. (*See Kingsbridge.*)

HALWELL, or *Holwell*, a small village, 6 miles S. by W. of Totnes, and 7 miles W. by N. of Dartmouth, has in its parish 445 souls, and 3666A. 2R. 28P. of land, including *Washbourne* hamlet, (38 souls,) and a number of scattered farm-houses. The soil is various, and on the higher grounds are vestiges of two entrenchments. The manor was anciently held by the *Halghwiks*, and afterwards by the Verneys and Hales, but was dismembered many years ago. The parish is now mostly freehold, and belongs to J. Cornish, Esq., S. Savory, Esq., Mrs. Bastard, Hele's Charity, N. Moysey, Esq., and several smaller owners. The *Church* (St. Leonard,) is an ancient structure, in the perpendicular style, with a fine lofty tower and six bells. The living is a *perpetual curacy*, annexed to the vicarage of Harberton, but it has recently been endowed by the present vicar as a separate curacy, in his patronage, and is now held by the Rev. Henry Hare, who has a new handsome residence. The tithes were commuted in 1839, the rectorial for £235, and the vicarial for £132. 10s. The former belong to the Dean and Chapter of Exeter, but are held on lease by R. Hellyar, Esq. Here is a National School, built in 1839; and an Independent Chapel, erected in 1831. Five houses and 5¼A. of land have been long vested for the use of the church and poor, but are let for only about £7 per annum.

Adams Wm. veterinary surgeon
Baker John, carpenter
Cockram Mr John, *Washbourne*

Cutmore Thos. shopr. & vict. Globe
Damerell Wm. tailor
Hallatt John, vict. Old Inn

Hannaford Robt. and Wm. masons
Hare Rev Henry, *Parsonage*
Hingston Anthony, shoemaker
Hingston Wm. vict. London Inn
Hingston Wm. & Geo. blacksmiths
Langworthy Wm. tailor
Luckraft Joseph, shoemaker
Nicholls Wm. shopkeeper

   FARMERS. (* *are Owners.*)
Brown John || Clark Wm.
Cockram Parnell, *Washbourne*
Crossing John || Coombes Henry
*Edwards John || Ellis Wm.
Hewitt Henry, *Crockerton*

Hill Wm. (miller,) *Chiddlesford*
Honeywill Aaron, (miller,) *Ford*
*Irish Robt. (& Robt. sen.) *Polston*
*Laskey Thomas, *Boreston*
Medway George || Oldreive Arthur
*Moysey Nicholas, *Stanborough*
Peeke Matthew || Scobell Joseph
Snelling Wm. || Smarridge Thos.
Tucker Roger || Williams Roger
Whiteway Edmund, *Rilston*
Whiteway Thomas, *Collaton*
Wyatt James, *Bickley*

   Post *from Totnes*

HARBERTON, a small village of 353 inhabitants, on high ground, in a pleasant valley, $2\frac{1}{2}$ miles S.S.W. of Totnes, has in its parish 1496 souls, and 5755 acres of land, including six hamlets, of which the following are the names and population:—*Harbertonford*, 468; *Luscombe*, 55; *East Leigh*, 171; *West Leigh*, 45; *Belsford*, 55; and *Englebourne*, 49. The soil is generally light and fertile, and in the parish is a remarkable *rock* of trap stone, so hard as to resist the mason's chisel, and surrounded by dunstone and slate. The manor, anciently held by the Valletorts, was dismembered many years ago, and now belongs to many freeholders, some of whom have neat and pleasant *seats* as named below. J. Parott, Richard and John Brown, C. Webber, E. W. W. Pendarves, and John Bidlake, Esqrs., and the Rev. W. B. Bennett, are the principal owners. At Harbertonford, on the banks of the small river *Harbourn*, is an old woollen factory, now occupied as a corn mill and *starch* manufactory; and in the same valley is the large *shovel and reaping hook* manufactory, called Hill Mills. The *Church* (St. Andrew,) is one of the finest specimens of the decorated style in the county, and has a lofty tower and six bells. The stone pulpit is richly carved, gilt, and coloured, and has statues of the apostles on its octagonal sides. The screen and parclose are in the same rich style, and the clustered columns have foliated capitals. The font is Anglo-Norman; and in the chancel are three richly canopied stalls, and a fine altar screen. The *vicarage*, valued in K.B. at £49. 2s. 1d., and in 1831 at £752, with the curacy of Halwell annexed to it, is in the patronage of the Dean and Chapter of Exeter, and incumbency of the Rev. George Martin, B.D., chancellor of the diocese, and canon of Exeter. The glebe (74A.,) and parsonage are occupied by a farmer. The tithes were commuted in 1847, the vicarial for £585, and the rectorial for £400 per annum. The latter belong to the patrons, but are leased to W. H. Hellyar, Esq. There are *National Schools* at Harberton and Harbertonford. The latter was built in 1849, in the Tudor style, and Richard Browne, Esq., has given a house for the use of the master. The *Baptists* have a small chapel here. The *Parish Lands, &c.*, which have been vested in trust from an early period, comprise eleven houses and cottages, with gardens, &c., and 18A. of land, called Cockwell, and let for about £48 per annum, subject to fines on the renewal of the leases. The clear rent and tithes are applied in aid of the church rates, except what is necessary for repairing Harberton school-house. A blacksmith's shop, house, orchard, and garden, let for £5, were left for the benefit of the poor, by *Wm. Huxham*, about 1630. Here is an *Almshouse* of ten small rooms, for as many poor people, built pursuant to the will of *Henry Wyse*, about 1680. Two closes of land, at Bridgewater, are charged with the repairs of this almshouse; and the inmates have a yearly rent-charge of

50s., out of an estate called Symon's Borough, at Hemyock. The founder also charged the same estate with an annuity of 40s., for the poor parishioners of Harberton, who have also the following yearly doles: viz., 5s., left in 1608, by *Wm. Wotton;* £4, out of Higher Langaford estate, left in the sixteenth of Charles I., by *Thos. Risdon;* £2, out of Higher and Lower Hele, left by *John and Richard Norris;* £1, out of Nield's Tenement, left by *Henry Shillbeer;* and 13s. 4d., left by *John Sparke,* out of Dorseley estate. In the following Directory, those marked 2 are at *Harbertonford;* 3, *Belsford;* 4, *Luscombe;* 5, *Leigh;* and 6, at *Englebourne.*

Bennett Rev Wm. Bewes, B.A. *Sandwell*
Bidlake John, gent. *Whiteley*
Browne Richard, Esq. *Englebourne*
Browne John, gent. *Beanleigh*
2 Calley Mr John || 5 Friend Miss
Cann Peter, National School master
3 Collard Mr. lime burner
2 Elliott(Rt.)&Knapman(Jno.)shovel & reaping hook mfrs. Hill Mills
2 Nicholls Wm. wheelwright
2 Nind Philip P. surgeon
Parrott Jasper, Esq. *Dundridge*
Pendarves Edw. Wm. W. Esq. M.P. *Tristford*
2 Rickards Rev Robert Francis Bute, M.A. curate, *Rockford House*
2 Sherlock T. B., Natl. School mr
Tucker Richard, butcher
Watson Mr Robert, *East Leigh*
Webber Charles, Esq. *Winsland*
CORN MILLERS.
2 Gentile James, (& starch, &c. mfr)
Helms Henry, *Tor Mill*
Palk James, *Belsford Mill*
Woodley John, *Crowdy Mill*
PUBLIC-HOUSES.
Beehive, Richard Lavers
Blue Posts, Mr Blatchford
Church House, Charles Lears
2 Cottage Inn, Roger Horswill
Globe, Matthew White
2 Maltsters' Arms, Pp. Grills, maltster
2 Post Office Inn, John Payne
2 Rose & Crown, Betty Blackler
  BLACKSMITHS.
5 Crees Edward

2 Payne Thomas
Soper Wm.
Soper Wm. jun
2 Treby Henry
  CARPENTERS.
2 Tippett Richard
2 Tucker Samuel
Varder Stephen
  FARMERS.
(* *are Owners.*)
Bidlake John, jun
3 Blackler Geo.
Bourne Robert
Burnell Eliz.
Burnell John
2 Chaffin Charles
4 Cockram Saml.
4 Easterbrook Ts.
*Farleigh Richd.
5*Foale Wm.
Harris John
Harris Wm. *Roadster Bridge*
Harvey Thomas
4 Hext Thomas
Hoare Samuel
*Hoppin Richard, *Wood Court*
Huxham Jno. *Vcg*
*Huxham Mary
2 Irish John
4 Jackman Wm.
5 Maddock Robt.
Mason Charles G.
Notle John
Oldreive Robert
2 Payne Ths. Jno.
Stranger R. *Pitt*

Symons Pp. *Lwr. Washbourne*
Taylor Robert
2 Tippett Thos. (& surveyor)
Tucker John
*Watson Rd. H.
6 White Samuel
4 Whiteway Hy.
5 Whiteway John
3 Whiteway Wm.
6 Widdicombe Js.
3 Woodley John
  MASONS.
2 Coles Stephen
2 Horswill Roger
  SHOEMAKERS.
2 Evans Richard
Fairweather Robt.
Fairweather Jph.
2 Holmes John
2 Soper Wm.
Worth Walter
  SHOPKEEPERS.
2 Anderson John
2 Bond Susan
5 Crees Edward
2 Narramore H.
Searle Thomas
  TAILORS.
Bartlett Wm.
2 Lavers John

POST & *Carriers* to Totnes.

POOL, (SOUTH) a small village at the head of a navigable creek, five miles S.S.E. of Kingsbridge, has in its parish 555 souls, and 1929A. 3R. 18P. of land, including *North Pool* hamlet and part of *Frogmore* village. (See Sherford.) W. M. Praed, Esq., is lord of the manor of South Pool, and the Earl of Devon owns that of North Pool; but Thos. Cornish, Esq., Mr. Edw. Garland, and a few smaller owners, have estates here, chiefly freehold. The parish was anciently held by the de Pola, Punchardon, and Scobel families. The *Church* (St. Cyriac,) is a fine specimen of the perpendicular style, with a lofty tower and six bells. The interior has transepts, and has a neat and clean appearance. The screen is elaborately carved; and in the chancel is

a handsome altar tomb or Easter sepulchre, with a representation of the Resurrection in front of it. Here are also monuments for members of the Dare, Lake, and Bastard families. The *rectory*, valued in K.B. at £22. 16s. 5¼d., and in 1831 at £486, is in the patronage of W. M. Praed and A. Kelly, Esqrs., the former having two turns and the latter one. The Rev. Henry Taylor, M.A., is the incumbent, and has a large and handsome residence, and 52A. 2R. 23P. of glebe. The tithes were commuted in 1840, for £387 per annum. The poor have 25s. and the rector 15s. yearly, left by Andrew Horsman, in 1687; and the former have an annuity of 21s., left by Leonard Dare.

*Marked * are at Frogmore.*

Arnold Thomas, vict. Union Inn
Cornish Thomas, Esq. *Scobel*
Cuming Richard, blacksmith
Edmunds Matthew, corn miller
Edwards Roger, Esq. *Wilton*
Garland Mr Edward, sen
*GardeJno.coalmert.&vict.BridgeInn
Gasking Samuel, vict. George Inn
Hewitt James, rope and twine maker
Jennings Samuel, schoolmaster
Partridge Joseph, baker
Stidworthy Jno. tailor, & Rd. par.clerk
Taylor Rev Henry, M.A. *Rectory*

CARPENTERS.
Arundell John
Hoople John
FARMERS.
Adams John
Colwich James
Chipman Agnes
Cuming Richard
Garland Edw. jun
Garland Rt.&Jno.
Goodyear Nichls.
Horsman John
Luscombe Nichs.
*Parsons Thos.
Patey Robert

Robins Richard
Wright Elias,
North Pool
MALTSTERS.
Adams John
*SouthwoodNchs
SHOEMAKERS.
*Ching John
Steeds James
Tucker Thomas
SHOPKEEPERS.
Browse James
Parker Sarah
Tucker Mary

PORTLEMOUTH, (EAST) a small village, five miles S. of Kingsbridge, is picturesquely seated on an eminence on the east side of Salcombe haven, near its confluence with the sea. Its parish contains 429 souls, and 1973 acres of land, including *Rickham* and *Holset* hamlets, and bounded on the south by the lofty sea cliffs, extending to *Prawle Point.* An entrenchment on the hill is supposed to have been used in assaulting Salcombe castle, on the opposite side of the estuary. The Duke of Cleveland is lord of the manor of Portlemouth, but that of *West Prawle* belongs to Blundell's School, at Tiverton. Mr. R. Hurrell, Miss Burnell, and a few smaller owners, have estates here. At Rickham is a coast guard station. Portlemouth commands an extensive view of the English Channel, as well as of the estuary and its creeks, as high as Kingsbridge. The *Church* (St. Onolaus,) is an ancient structure, with a tower and three bells, two of which are cracked. It is in the perpendicular style, and has a richly carved wooden screen. The *rectory*, valued in K.B. at £29. 8s. 4d., and in 1831 at £360, is in the joint patronage of the Duke of Cleveland and Lady Sandwich, and in the incumbency of the Rev. T. B. Wells, M.A., who has 30A. of glebe, and a good old residence with tasteful grounds. The tithes were commuted in 1839 for £347 per annum. The Wesleyans have a small chapel here, and the poor have the interest of £20 left by the Rev. Rd. Cleveland, in 1618.

*Marked * at Rickham.*

Adams Mr Wm. || BaileyLieut.,C.G.
Burgoin Geo. shoemkr. & Mr Nichls.
Heath John, vict. New Inn
Lamble John, tailor
Lamble Wm. Yabsley, corn miller
Thornton Mary & Bowden J. *schools*
Wells Rev Thos. Bury, M.A. *Rectory*
Yeoman N. vict. Exeter Inn

BLACKSMITHS.
Edwards B.
Powsland James
CARPENTERS.
Lapthorn Thos.
Vincent Edward
FARMERS.
Blank Mary
*Burgoin John

*Crispin John
Elliott Philip
Gillard Thomas,
Holset
HannafordRichd.
Heath Peter
Lapthorn Eliz.
Moore Andrew
Nicholls John

Oldreive and Son,	Prettejohn Natl.	Thorning Willm.	Cranch John
West Prawle	Roper James	*Goodshelter*	Yeoman N.
Partridge Sarah	*Thornton Saml.	SHOPKEEPERS.	
Pope John	*Thornton S. jun	Bushell Thomas	

SHERFORD, a small ancient village, in a pleasant valley, three miles E. of Kingsbridge, has in its parish 450 souls, and 2326 acres of land, including part of the village of *Frogmore*, which is situated at the head of a navigable creek, three miles E.S.E. of Kingsbridge, and has 232 inhabitants, of whom 90 are in this parish, 77 in Charleton, and 65 in South Pool parish. Here are lime kilns, coal wharfs, and granaries, where vessels of 100 tons load and unload their cargoes. The manor is dismembered, and the parish now belongs to W. Y. Clarke, W. Pollard, and L. Howard, Esqrs., and a few smaller owners. It anciently belonged to St. Nicholas's Priory, Exeter, and afterwards to the Willoughby, Trevelyan, and Templer families. *Kennedon*, an ancient farm house of the early Tudor period, was successively the seat of the Prall, Halls, and Aldam families, the latter of whom sold it to L. Howard, Esq. Its tower was taken down by the Aldams. *Malston*, another farm house of the same age, was the seat of a family of its own name, and afterwards of the Stighulls and Reynells. The *Church* (St. Martin,) is a fine specimen of the decorated style, and has a lofty tower and five bells. There are stoups at the north and south doors, and in the chancel is a fine trefoiled piscina. The benefice is a curacy, annexed to the vicarage of Stokenham. The tithes were commuted in 1842, the vicarial for £171. 5s., and the rectorial for £249. 19s. 8d. per annum. Of the latter, £105 belongs to the Vicar of Townstal, and the rest to several inpropriators. Here is a small Wesleyan Chapel. Poor seamen or their widows, of this parish, have 3A. of land, purchased with £50 left by George Dottin, in 1701.

*Marked * are at Frogmore.*

*Bastard Samuel, dyer
Carter Mrs ‖ Buck — excise officer
Cornish Miss Eliz., Stancombe Cotg
Elliott John, vict. Malt Scoop
Jarvis George, miller, Kennedon
Matthews Wm. miller, Malston
*Miles Rev Wm. (Independent)
*Parker Edward, maltster
Pillage Mr John ‖ *Randall Mrs
StoneJno.Paine, surgn. *Lr Oddicombe*
*Stone Mrs Maria
*Trant John, vict. Globe
Tucker Rev W. H., M.A. *curate*

BLACKSMITHS.
*Harraden Danl.
West Samuel W.
Wills Robert

CARPENTERS.
Lambles Wm.
Weekes John

FARMERS.
(+ are Owners.)
+Adams John
+Cornish Samuel
+Cornish Pp. N.
+Cornish Rd. N.
Couch Henry W.
*Crocker Henry
EarleJno. *Malstn*
Edwards Richard
Honeywill Wm. *Kennedon*
+Hurrell Richard
+Kevill Thomas
*LangworthyJno.
+Paige Wm.
Parnell Thomas
Palfrey Wm.

*+Tucker John
MASONS.
*Chapman H. R.
Chapman Wm.
SHOEMAKERS.
*Chudleigh Geo.
Hambling Robt.
SHOPKEEPERS.
Dure Robert
*Stone Edward
*Warn Wm.

*POST-OFFICE
at E. Stone's.
Letters despd.
2½ aftn.

SLAPTON, a pleasant village on an acclivity, rising from the central part of the coast of Start Bay, 6 miles S.W. by S. of Dartmouth, has in its parish 726 inhabitants, 3260 acres of tithe free land, and many scattered houses, commanding fine views of the bay and the coast. On the beach is the *Sands Hotel*, from which visitors have a fine promenade at low water along the sands to within a mile of Start Point. The hotel is elegantly fitted up for the accommodation of visitors, and about 200 yards from the beach is a long fresh-water *lake* of about 300 acres, called the *Ley* or *Hey*, well stocked with fish and wild fowl, and divided from the sea in some

places only by a ridge called the *Long Sand*. The manor is dismembered, and was formerly held of the See of Exeter, by the service of being steward at the bishop's installation feast. Sir R. L. Newman, Bart., Major Bent, and the Paige, Tucker, Holdsworth, Bastard, Wise, Wakeham, and other families have freehold estates here. *Pole* or *Poole Priory*, in this parish, was long the seat of the Brians, Ameridiths, and Hawkins, and now be-longs to Mr. Paige. The ruins of the old mansion were removed about 1800, except the lofty tower, which stands in the garden. The *Church* (St. Mary,) is an ancient structure, with a tower and five bells. The screen is beautiful, and the clustered columns have foliated capitals. The living is a perpetual curacy, valued at only £96 per annum, arising from a modus of £15, and land here and at Halwell. Wm. Page, Esq., is the patron, and the Rev. T. G. Dickenson, M.A., is the incumbent. In 1373, Sir Guy de Brian founded a *collegiate chapel*, near the church, for a rector, five fellows, and four clerks. It was dissolved in 1545, when its revenues were valued at £63. 6s. 2d., and granted to Thomas Arundell. The college estate now belongs to W. Paige, Esq. In 1690, *John Kellond* left £100, to be invested for the education of 20 poor children of this parish. His son, *Charles Kellond*, gave £50, to be applied in apprenticing a poor child yearly. These legacies were not paid till 1746, when they were recovered, with £205 as arrears of interest. The whole was then laid out in the purchase of 19A. 3R. 21P. of land, let for £28 per annum. The erection of a school is in contemplation.

Ching John S. vict. New Inn
Dickenson Rev Thos. G., M.A. incbt
Head John, machine maker
Ireling Mr ‖ Moore Mr George
Luscombe John, plasterer
Mitchell John, gardener, Post-office
Paige Wm. Esq. *Start*
Paige Nichs. and Robt. gentlemen
Paige Misses ‖ Simms Mrs My.
Pepperell Sarah, schoolmistress
Pepperell Pp. vict. Queen's Arms
Pepperell Robt. vict. Tower Inn
Pitts Wm. butcher
Pollard Thos. vict. Sands Hotel
Tucker Rd. gent. *Start House*

BLACKSMITHS.
Hyne John
Wills Richard
CARPENTERS.
Kellond George
Kellond Robert
Kellond Wm.
Michelmore John

Pepperell Saml.
CORN MILLERS.
Bastard Richard
Came Richard
Treble Thomas
FARMERS.
(* *are Owners.*)
*Bastard Richd.

*Bastard Wm.
Cawse Richard
Friend John
Grills Wm.
*Hoidge Thos.
Huxham H. & S.
Hyne John
Jarvis Mrs
Jeffrey Wm.
Mordaunt Osmd.
Moore James
Oldrey Thomas
Paige Robt. jun
*Putt Robert
Snell —
Tozer John L.
Tucker Crispin
*Tucker Thos.
*Wakeham E. P.
*Wakeham Sus.
Walters Joseph
*Wise E. P.
*Wise Philip

MASONS.
Fogwill Edw.
Fogwill Wm.
Norrish George
Norrish John
Norrish J. jun
Norrish Timy.
Stabb Rt. Hy.
Weeks John
SHOEMAKERS.
Issell Robert
Issell Thomas
Pepperell Roger
SHOPKEEPERS.
Kellond George
Kellond Robert
Pope Grace
Trist Mary
TAILORS.
Trist John
Trist John, jun
POST from Dartmouth

STOKE FLEMING is a pleasant modernised village, on a commanding acclivity, rising from the northern coast of Start Bay, 2¼ miles S.S.W. of Dartmouth. Its parish contains 736 souls, and 3332 acres of land, mostly having a light fertile soil, resting on dunstone and slate. It includes the small hamlets of *Ash, Buckford, Blackpool,* and *Emeridge,* and several neat mansions, but *Stoke House* is now unoccupied. Sir H. P. Seale, Bt., is lord of the manor. Robt. Leach and John and H. N. Netherton have estates here, and Sir R. L. Newman and several smaller freeholders own part

of the parish. The manor was part of the ancient inheritance of the Flemings, from whom it passed to the Mohuns, Carews, and Southcotes, the latter of whom sold it to the Seales about the close of last century. In a garden near the church are some remains of the ancient Anglo-Norman manor house, consisting of three arches of red sandstone; and some of its other remains are seen in the columns and capitals worked up in neighbouring buildings. The *Church* (St. Peter,) is an ancient fabric, in the early English style, with a lofty tower, containing six bells, which were recast in 1777. In the chancel are two fine brasses of the 14th century, and an ancient effigy. The *rectory*, valued in K.B. at £31. 6s. 0½d., and in 1831 at £725, is in the patronage of the Rev. W. Farwell, and incumbency of the Rev. A. Farwell, B.A., who has 71A. of glebe, and in 1834 erected the present large and handsome *Rectory House*, which has a well wooded lawn of seven acres. The *Rev. Richd. Raynolds* was ejected from the rectory in 1646, when upwards of 80 years old, but he survived the restoration, was re-possessed of the living, and died a few years afterwards, aged nearly 100. The National School was established in 1843. The poor parishioners have 2A. of land, purchased with £50, left by *John Paige* in 1689; a small meadow, left by *Peter Creed* in 1694; and the interest of £25, left by persons named Perring and Haswell. An *almshouse*, with six rooms and a garden, was given by an unknown donor for the residence of poor families. Two houses and gardens at Dartmouth have been long vested for the reparation of Stoke church. *Marked 2 are at Buckford; 3, Coombe; 4, Cotton; 5, Blackpool; and 6, at Emeridge.*

Clarke Mr John, *Redlap*
Farwell Rev Arthur, B.A. *Rectory*
Leach Robt. Esq. *Ash* || Martin John
Mainwaring Rev John, *Start Bay Hs*
Martin Thomas, vict. New Inn
Neal Mr J. W., *Rock vale*
Netherton John, Esq. *Bowden*
Netherton Hy. N. Esq. *Rivers Bridge*
Oldreive Sar. vict. George & Dragon
Pitts Jane, butcher
Randall Miss, schoolmistress
Swainson Mr., *Swannaton*
Topping Stephen, gent. *Belvedere*
Webber Thos. gent. || Hunt Mr
Wise Chas. gent. *Blackpool Cottage*
BLACKSMITHS.
Martin Thomas
Mortimore Wm.
CARPENTERS.
Hamlyn James
Hine Thomas
Martin Jas. wgt
6 Pepperell Wm.
CORN MILLERS.
5 Bussell Wm.

5 Ford Arthur
5 May Robert
5 Treby John
FARMERS.
2 Bickley Wm.
Bidlake John
Brownson Wm.
Buckpit John
3 Buckpit Saml.
3 Clarke John
2 Cockram Geo.
Damerell John
Dawe Hy., *Ash*
Dawe W., *Redlap*
Dingle Eliz.
2 Ford Wm.
Heath Sarah
Lindon Thomas
4 Linkhorne Jno.
Martin J. L., *Ash*

Martin Wm.
Oldreive Wm.
4 Webber Mary
MASONS.
Nunn Robert
Peek Wm. T.
6 Wootton Wm.
SHOEMAKERS.
Horswell Henry
Horswell H. jun
Trist Thomas
SHOPKEEPERS.
Abraham Wm.
(and tailor)
Hambling Jas.
Hannaford Jas.
Martin John L.
Trant Wm.
POST from Dartmouth

STOKENHAM, or *Stockingham*, a small pleasant village, 5½ miles E. by S. of Kingsbridge, has in its parish 1619 inhabitants, and 5920 acres of land, including six villages, extending 4 miles along the picturesque shore of Start Bay, of which the following are the names and population :—*Chillington*, 325; *Beeson*, 106; *Beesands*, 104; *Halsands*, 128; *Kellaton*, or *Kellington*, 105; and *Torcross*, 192. Several of them are fishing villages, noted for fine *crabs*, which are in high repute in London. The parish extends southward to *Start Point*, where there is a *lighthouse*. It includes also the hamlets of *Bickerton*, *Dunstone*, *Cornborough*, and may scattered houses. TORCROSS, near *Ley lake* and Slapton Sands Hotel, (see p. 498,)

is a pretty little bathing place, with several lodging-houses for visitors. An annual *regatta* is held here. The parish is generally fertile, and it extends westward in a picturesque vale to Frogmore, where there is a creek from Kingsbridge estuary. *Sir R. L. Newman, Bart.*, of Mamhead, is lord of the manor of Stokenham, and has a neat marine residence, called *Stokely House*, built about 35 years ago. The manor has been held by the Fitz-johns, Fitzherbert, Courtenays, Hastings, and Carys, and was sold by the latter to the Newmans. Miss Burnell is lady of the manor of Kellaton, and A. B. E. Holdsworth, Esq., owns Stokenham Priory estate, and has a pic-turesquely situated mansion near the bay called *Widdecombe*, rebuilt about 1725. *Coleridge*, a handsome new mansion, in the Elizabethan style, is the seat of John Allen, Esq., who owns the estate which gives name to this hundred. The Nicholls, Edmunds, Pitts, Randall, Cole, and other fami-lies have estates in the parish, mostly freehold. The *Church* (St. Barna-bas,) is a large antique structure, with a low tower and six bells. It is mostly in the perpendicular style, but the stone mullions of the windows have been replaced by wood. When repairing the chancel in 1846, a beau-tiful cinquefoiled and crocketted double piscina was discovered. The *vicarage*, valued in K.B. at £48. 7s. 8½d., and in 1831 at £625, with the curacies of Chivelstone and Sherford annexed to it, is in the patronage of the Crown, and incumbency of the Rev. Hy. Taylor, M.A., of South Pool Rectory. The Parsonage is small, but neat, and the glebe is only 2A. 21P. The tithes were commuted in 1843, the vicarial for £360. 5s., and the rec-torial for £309. 14s. 11d. per ann. Of the latter, £171 belongs to A. B. E. Holdsworth, Esq., and the rest belongs to 41 other impropriators, in sums va-rying from £16 to 2d. The rectory was appropriated by the Earl of Salisbury to Bisham Priory, in Bucks. The hundred court was anciently held here, and there are some remains of an old building called the Prison, near the church and the site of the ancient manor house. There was anciently a market and a fair at Stokenham, but they were removed to Dodbrooke after a long dispute between the lords of the two manors. The old Independent Chapel here was built by Presbyterians about 1715, and at Torcross is a small chapel, erected by Admiral Pearson, about 20 years ago, and now oc-cupied by the Home Missionary Society. As noticed with Exeter, this pa-rish has from *Jeffery's Charity* £4 a year for the dissenting minister, and has hats, shoes, and stockings for three poor men. The *Parish School* is conducted on the British system, and occupies, rent-free, a building belong-ing to R. Peek, Esq.

In the following Directory of Stokenham Parish, those marked 2, *are at Chillington;* 3, *Beeson;* 4, *Beesands;* 5, *Halsands;* 6, *Kellaton;* 7, *Tor-cross;* 8, *Bickerton;* 9, *at Dunstone; and* 10, *at Cornborough.*

Allen John, Esq. *Coleridge*
7 Baker Wm. gent ‖ 2 Dare Mr W.
2 Bowden John, tea dealer
2 Brooking Wm. tailor
3 Bucknell Rev — (Independent)
2 Cove Stephen, painter & glazier
4 Croker Susan, beer seller
Diggle Rev Chas. Wadham, curate
Edmunds Mr Philip, *Cornborough*
2 Edwards Mrs S. ‖ 7 Johnson Miss
Gillard Jno. P. surveyor and auc-tioneer, *Matscombe*
Gillard Peter, surveyor, *Cotmore*
7 Hannaford Mrs E. ‖ Maye Eliz

Holdsworth A.B. E., Esq. *Widdecombe*
Lyde Jas. surgeon ‖ 2 Loye Mr P.
Meldrum Arthur, schoolmaster
Mitchell Robert, gardener
Newman Sir R. L., Bart. *Stokely*
7 Newman Miss ‖ Perrott Mr John
Nicholls Roger, miller, *Landcomb*
2 Patey John, parish clerk
7 Pepperell Mrs My. ‖ Pike Mary
5 Perrott Wm. thatcher
7 Pike John, basket maker
2 Pitts Mr Nicholas ‖ Webb Mr Rt.
Shoemack Wm. *Start Point Light Hs*
Tolcher D. schoolmaster

7 Tucker Edward, butcher
7 Westlake John, stone & slate mert
INNS AND TAVERNS.
7 Anchor, Wm. Pepperell
Church House, Joshua Creber
7 Dartmouth Inn, Betsy Crispin
5 London Inn, Samuel Mingo
2 New Inn, Wm. Luscombe
New Inn, Richard Shepherd
2 Union, John Ingram
BAKERS.
2 Clements Jas.
Mitchell John
BLACKSMITHS.
8 Dunn John
Harraden Henry
2 Harraden Wm.
6 Patey Henry
2 Randall John
BOAT BUILDERS.
5 Adams Wm.
7 Pepperell Pp.
8 Pepperell P. sen
CARPENTERS.
6 Burgoin Wm.
2 Farr Geo. bldr
Kelland Henry

Kelland H. jun
Kelland John
2 Pilditch Wm.

FARMERS.
(* are Owners.)
*Adams John
3 Cockram John
10 Cole John
6*Cole Philip
8 Cole Wm.
*Cole Wm. & Son
10 Drew Wm.
3 Earle Samuel
*Gillard J. P.
2*Helmer Fnx.
9 Helmer Nichs.

3 Jarvis John
Letheron George
Lidstone George
3 Lidstone Wm.
9 Lizard Thos.
Loye Philip, jun
Maye Thomas
*Paige John
2 Patey Wm.
Parnell Samuel
*Pearce John
Pepperell John
Pepperell Saml.
10*Perrott B.
*Pitts John
*Pitts Nicholas
3 Prettejohn Geo.
*Prettejohn Ntl.
*PrettejohnThos.
3*Randall Abs.
3 Randall A. & G.
3*Randall Geo.
*Randall George
*Randall John
*Randall Ptr. &
Nichls. millers
Soper Samuel

10 Timewell Jas.
2 Tolcher Geo.
6 Wood Eli
MASONS.
2 Brooking Jas.
2 Edgeland John
Pedrick John
2 Rhymes Peter
SHOEMAKERS.
6 Dure Edw.
Issell John
2 Perrott Thos.
2 Shepherd John
SHOPKEEPERS.
3 Loggin Mary
2 Randall Nichs.
7 Pepperell Pp.
7 Tucker My. A.
WHEELWRIGHTS.
2 Brown Henry
6 Patey James

POST-OFFICE
at J. Issell's.
—Letters via
Kingsbridge

TOTNES, an ancient *borough and market town*, which retains some portions of its once formidable castle, and gives name to an archdeaconry and deanery, to a large union, and to county court and polling districts; is picturesquely seated on the western bank of the navigable river Dart, opposite its suburb of *Bridgetown*, 10 miles N.W. by W. of Dartmouth, 22 miles S. by W. of Exeter, 22 miles E. by N. of Plymouth, 9 miles W.S.W. of Torquay, and 194 miles W.S.W. of London. It has a station on the *South Devon Railway.* The Dart is navigable to it for vessels of 150 tons burthen, and a steam packet plies daily between it and Dartmouth. Its *parish* contains 967A. 1R. 24P. of land, mostly in meadows and pastures; and had 2503 souls in 1801; 2725 in 1811; 3128 in 1821; and 3442 in 1831; but they had increased to 3849 in 1841, including 253 in the union workhouse. BRIDGETOWN, on the opposite side of the river, in Berry Pomeroy parish, and in Haytor Hundred, is a handsome eastern suburb of the town, and forms part of the *borough of Totnes*, swelling its total population to about 4600 souls. (See pages 423-'4.) The borough comprises the whole parish of Totnes and the manor of Bridgetown, the latter of which was added to it by the Parliamentary and Municipal Reform Acts of 1832 and 1835. A handsome stone *bridge* crosses the river and a small *island*, between the two places, and was built by subscription, at the cost of £12,000, in 1828, in lieu of the ancient narrow bridge. Steps descend from it to the island, which has been laid out in walks, and planted with trees and shrubs, by the Duke of Somerset, for the use of the

public. The situation of Totnes is remarkably fine. The main street is about three-quarters of a mile long, and after climbing the steep acclivity rising from the margin of the river, it stretches itself along the brow of the hill, which commands a fine view of the valley and the winding stream, but is sheltered on every side by higher grounds. The piazzas in front of some of the houses in the upper town, and the higher stories projecting over the lower ones, are manifest proofs of its antiquity, " a claim which is strengthened by the keep of its *Castle*, a very large circular building, turreted, and rising from an immense artificial mound." The erection of this castle is ascribed to *Judhael* or *Joel de Totneis*, to whom the manor was given by William the Conqueror. The ruins are now finely mantled with ivy, and the grounds around them are tastefully laid out and planted, and have been thrown open by the Duke of Somerset as a promenade for the inhabitants. There are some neat and substantial mansions in the town and suburbs, and a considerable number of respectable houses have been erected during the last twenty years, on and near the Plymouth road. During the same period, many of the old houses have been rebuilt or modernized. The beauty of the surrounding neighbourhood, and the fine scenery of the Dart and its creeks below the town, will always ensure for Totnes and its vicinity a genteel resident population, and a constant influx of strangers to visit these attractions. The sporting and angling of the neighbourhood are of the best description, and there is a salmon weir on the river a little above the town, but salmon and other fish abound in all parts of the river, especially in its route to Dartmouth, where it widens into a broad estuary, with several creeks. Since 1833, the Commissioners of the River Dart have expended large sums of money in improving the *navigation*, so as to enable vessels of 150 tons to come up to the quays and wharfs near the bridge, where coal, culm, timber, &c., are imported, and corn, cider, and other agricultural produce exported. Totnes is in the Port of Dartmouth, and had formerly a share of the woollen manufacture. Being in the heart of the fruitful district called the South Hams, or garden of Devonshire, which abounds in rich pastures, meadows, corn fields, and orchards, its *weekly market*, held every Saturday, is abundantly supplied with provisions. Here are also *great cattle markets*, on the first Tuesday of every month; and two *annual fairs*, on May 12th and October 28th, when those dates fall on a Tuesday, Wednesday, Thursday, or Friday, and when not, on the Tuesday after. *Races* are held annually in the latter part of August or the beginning of September, and are usually well attended and liberally supported. The Seven Stars and the Seymour Hotel, are large and well conducted establishments, and there are in the town many respectable public-houses and well stocked shops. The present commodious *Market Place* was erected in 1848, at the cost of £2800, and has a handsome front. *Water* is supplied from the springs in the higher parts of the town, and a stream is continually flowing down either side of the main street. *Gas Works* were established at the Grove, by six families for their own use, but were purchased by a company of shareholders in 1835, and extended to most parts of

the town; but a new gas company has recently been formed, with a capital of £1200, raised in £5 shares, and they have just erected a Gas-House near the old one.

In ancient records Totnes is called *Totton, Totonie, Totneis,* &c. The Roman road, called *Iknald* or *Fosseway,* which traversed through this county into Somerset, and from thence to other parts of the kingdom, began here. The town was anciently encompassed by a *wall with four gates,* of which there are still some slight remains. In Domesday Book it is described as having 95 burgesses, besides 15 without the walls, and is said to be subject to the same services as Exeter, and never to be taxed but with that city. The *honour or barony of Totnes,* which had been part of Edward the Confessor's demesne, was given by Wm. the Conqueror to *Judhael* or *Joel,* who assumed the name of *De Totneis,* and is said to have erected the castle, as already noticed; but being banished by Wm. Rufus, this barony was given to Roger de Novant. It was afterwards held by the Cantilupe and Zouch families. On the attainder of Lord Zouch, Henry VII. gave it to Sir Richard Edgecumbe, whose grandson sold it to Lord Edward Seymour, an ancestor of the Duke of Somerset, its present owner. The castle, long the seat of the barony, was in ruins when Leland visited it in the reign of Henry VIII., except the great tower, or keep, of which the outer walls are still standing. Joel de Totneis founded a PRIORY here in the Conqueror's reign, as a cell to the Benedictine Abbey of St. Sergius and St. Bacchus, at Angiers. It was not dissolved till the reign of Henry VIII., when it contained six monks. It stood near the church, and its site is now occupied by the Guildhall and other buildings. Tanner says there were two convents of friars at or near Totnes, but Leland mentions only one, founded by Walter de la Bon, or Boate, at a place called *Warland,* near a chapel dedicated to the Holy Ghost and St. Katherine. Some small remains of this convent are to be seen in a cottage, and its site belongs to W. D. Adams, Esq., of *Bowden House,* a large and handsome mansion in the adjoining parish of Ashprington, formerly a seat of the Trist and Giles families. The estate of *Little Totnes* has been long held by the Wise family. *Follaton House,* an elegant modern mansion, about a mile W. of the town, is the seat of G. S. Cary, Esq.; and *Broomborough,* the seat of J. F. P. Phillips, Esq., is an elegant mansion, recently erected, in the Elizabethan style. Many other proprietors have estates in the parish. The *manor of the borough of Totnes* was conveyed in the 2nd of Elizabeth, by Piers Edgecumbe, or Edgcombe, to the *Corporation,* subject to a reserved rent of £21 per annum, payable to the owner of the Castle. Geoffrey of Monmouth says that the Trojan Brute landed here, and called the place *Tout al 'esse,* (*all at ease,*) now corrupted to Totnes; but Leland says the ancient name was *Dodonesse,* or rocky town Bede says Ambrosius and Uter-Pendragon came to Totnes, after defeating Vortigern in Wales.

Totnes is said to have been governed by a mayor since the reign of King John, who granted the burgesses a *charter* in 1205. These privileges were confirmed and extended by Henry VII., and other monarchs. Under the charter granted by Queen Elizabeth, in 1596, the CORPORATION consisted of a mayor, a recorder, 14 burgher-masters, councillors, and an indefinite number of burgesses, including a select body, called "the twenty-men." The mayor, recorder, and ex-mayor, were justices of the peace for the borough and parish. The borough limits formerly comprised only the tower, but they have been extended by the Reform Acts of 1832 and 1835, so as to comprise the whole parish of Totnes and the manor of Bridgetown. Under the Municipal Act of 1835, the Town Council now consists of a *mayor, four aldermen, and twelve councillors.* A commission of the peace,

including seven *borough magistrates*, has been granted, but the borough has now neither recorder nor quarter sessions. The revenue of the Corporation in 1841, amounted to £605, arising from rents, tolls, &c. They are trustees of various charities, and in 1823, the Attorney-General instituted proceedings against the old Corporation, for the misappropriation of charitable funds. This long-pending Chancery suit is expected to be shortly brought to a termination in favour of the charities. The borough has returned two members to parliament since the 30th of Edward I. Before the passing of the Reform Act of 1832, the right of election was in the Corporation and freemen, and the greatest number of electors polled for 30 years previous to 1831, was 75. The number of voters registered in 1837, was 297, of whom 34 voted as freemen. The present number is about 360, and their representatives are *Lord Seymour* and *Charles Barry Baldwin, Esq.*, who have sat for this borough in four parliaments. The present CORPORATION, BOROUGH MAGISTRATES, and OFFICERS are—Wm. Bowden, Esq., *mayor ;* George Farwell, Esq,, *ex-mayor ;* John Derry, Jasper Parrott, Geo. S. Cary, C. Webber, Rd. Soper, Edw. Luscombe, and S. E. G. Cary, Esqrs., *magistrates ;* W. F. Windeatt, Edw. Luscombe, John Derry, and Thomas Angel, *aldermen ;* G. S. Cary, J. R. Fogwill, Jas. Gill, Michael Bishop, John B. Paige, Wm. Bentall, Wm. Gilbert, James A. Spargo, George Farwell, Wm. Gill, Wm. Bowden, and Charles Edwards, *councillors ;* George Presswell, *town clerk and clerk to justices ;* J. Bishop and J. Cloake, *serjeants at mace ;* and T. H. Taylor, *inspector of weights and measures.* The Guildhall is a small ancient building near the church, and in it are held once a fortnight petty sessions for Stanborough and Coleridge Division, for which Mr. T. Bryett is magistrates' clerk. The *County Court for Totnes District,* embracing all Totnes Union, is held here monthly, and Mr. Charles Edwards is the *clerk;* and Mr. Thos. Welch, *high bailiff.* In 1626, Lord Carew, of Clopton, was created *Earl of Totnes,* but the title became extinct on his death, without male issue, in 1629. Charles, the natural son of Charles II., was created Lord Dartmouth, Viscount Totnes, and Earl of Plymouth, in 1675, but on his death without issue, in 1680, all his titles became extinct, and that of Totnes has never been revived.

The *Church* (St. Mary,) is a handsome structure, in the early perpendicular style, with a lofty tower at the west end, containing eight bells. Its date was unknown until about 1800, when the south-east pinnacle, being struck down by lightning, fell through the roof of a small room over the porch, in which were found two chests full of ancient records, from which it appeared the church was rebuilt in 1259, and again in 1432. In the latter year Bishop Lacy granted 40 days' indulgence to all who contributed to the rebuilding. An elegant stone screen of ornamental tracery divides the nave and chancel; but the altar-piece, instead of corresponding with the rest of the building, is of Grecian design, with a classical semi-dome, supported by Corinthian pillars. The stone pulpit is elaborately ornamented ; but, about 1786, the beautiful symmetry of the interior was destroyed by various tasteless alterations in the windows and other parts of the fabric. The vicarage, valued in K.B. at £12. 8s. 9d., and in 1831 at £200, is in the patronage of the Lord Chancellor and incumbency of the Rev. J. W. Burrough, who has a good residence. The rectorial glebe (74A. 2R. 21P.,) and tithe, formerly belonging to Totnes Priory, are now the property of the Duke of Somerset; but only 693 acres are tithable, and now pay a yearly tithe rent of £280. There was anciently in or near the town a chapel of St. Peter, and at the west end of the old bridge was a chantry chapel, dedicated to St. Edmund and St. Edward the Confessor, founded by Wm. de Cantilupe, and endowed

Y

with lands valued at £7. 13s. 11d. per annum in 1547. At Follaton House is a *Roman Catholic Chapel*, and in the town is an *Independent Chapel*, and a small *Wesleyan Chapel*. The former was built in 1840, at the cost of £1700, and is a handsome structure, in the early English style. It stands on the site of one of the two Presbyterian meeting houses, which existed here as early as 1715, when the celebrated *John Flavel* was minister of one of them. The *Free Church, at Bridgetown*, built by the Duke of Somerset, and endowed with £200 per annum, is already noticed at page 424, and *Berry Pomeroy Church* and *Castle* at page 423. Among the eminent men born at Totnes were, the *Rev. Edward Ley*, the learned author of the Saxon Dictionary; the late celebrated Hebraist, *Dr. Kennicott*, whose father was clerk of the church ; and *Dr. Philip Furneaux*, an eminent dissenting divine, who published Letters on Religious Liberty, addressed to Judge Blackstone, and an Essay on Toleration. The *South Devon Library*, in Fore street, was established in 1810, and the *Mechanics' Institution* in 1844. The latter has a library of more than 1000 volumes. The Duke of Somerset is patron of this useful institution, and supports a *News Room*, at the Mayoralty House, to which he gives cards of free admission. In Fore street are *Assembly and Public Rooms*, where balls, concerts, &c., take place. There are hot, cold, and shower *Baths* in the Plains.

The Corporation of Totnes are *trustees* of various charities for the poor, and in 1719, sold about 50 small lots of property to pay off their debts. Some of this property belonged to, or was charged with annual payments for charitable uses, but the whole was sold as freehold, unincumbered estates, and for the indemnification of the purchasers, and as security for the payment of the various charities in their hands, the Corporation vested with trustees their *mills, fishery, manorial rights, wharfs, tolls, &c.* The mills and fishery are let by the Corporation for about £190 per annum.

CHARITIES :—In satisfaction of what remains of £230, given by various donors, to be lent to decayed merchants, &c., and of £246, given for apprenticing poor children; the Corporation distribute £16 per annum, in quarterly payments, to 13 *poor widows*. They also pay, or ought to pay, the interest of the following sums left for the relief of the poor of the borough, viz., £100 left by *Elizabeth Wise* and *George Prestwood;* £140 left by *Nicholas Brocking*, in 1666 ; £100 left by *Philip Ley*, in 1663 ; £20 left by *John Wauchope*, in 1704 ; £50 left by *Christopher Blackall*, in 1626 ; £20.6s. 8d. left by *Richard Macy*, in 1633 ; and of £130 left by *John Beare*, in 1693, for a weekly distribution of 2s. worth of bread. As already noticed, these and other charitable funds are still the subject of a Chancery suit.

An orchard, left for the poor by *Nicholas Field*, in 1678, and now worth £3 a year, was let by the Corporation, in 1719, for 2000 years, at 4s. per annum, in consideration of a fine of £45. The Corporation distribute £3 yearly in satisfaction of this charity. *Richard Lee*, in 1619, left £100 to be invested in the purchase of land, for the better support of the *vicar*, or resident preacher of Totnes. The land purchased with this legacy was sold by the Corporation, in 1719, but they do not pay anything to the *vicar* in consideration thereof, though they pay him 40s. as interest of £40, left by the *Rev. Samuel Hall*. Nothing is now paid by them in consideration of £50 left by *Christopher Wise*, and a house at the quay, left by *Christopher Maynard*, for the vicar or lecturer. Towards the support of a *lecturer*, £3. 6s. 8d per annum was left by *Richard Norris* and *Richard Macy*, in two rent charges, which have not been paid for many years.

In 1690, THOS. MARTIN left a house and garden, and a two-acre field, at Barnstaple, to the mayor and overseers of Totnes, in trust, to apply the yearly proceeds in weekly distributions of bread among the poor. This property is now let for £23 a year, and there is belonging to the charity the sum of £302, derived from fines paid on the granting of former leases. The poor have 2s. worth of bread weekly from *Sir Jno. Acland's Charity*. (See Exeter.) They have an annuity of £13. 6s. 8d., out of houses in Whitechapel, London, left by *Henry Ball*, in 1608; also, 18s. a year out of a house in Totnes, left by *Henry Shillibeer*; and a yearly rent charge of £10, left by *Richard Langdon*, in 1707, out of Knighton estate, at Ilsington. One half of the latter is for poor sick people, and the other half for poor housekeepers. *Christopher Lee* left an annuity of 40s., out of Lake Garden, for the relief of poor prisoners in *Totnes Prison*, which was built by subscription in 1624. Mr. G. Dawson is treasurer of the fund for the relief of the *widows and orphans of poor clergymen of the Archdeaconry of Totnes*.

ALMSHOUSES :—A house occupied rent-free by several poor families, placed there by the Mayor, was given by the Corporation, in lieu of an ancient almshouse, founded by *Wm. Douse*, in the 20th of Elizabeth. The only endowment for the inmates is 17s. per annum. In 1589, *John Norris* left £250 for the erection and endowment of an almshouse for two poor people. The Corporation expended £100 in building the almshouse,

and granted an annuity of £10 a year for the inmates, in consideration of the remaining £150. This almshouse is near the Quay, and adjoining it are eight other ancient rooms, for as many poor people, placed there by the Mayor. *Magdalen Hospital,* which stood near the town, was a house of lepers, but all that now remains of it are some traces of its chapel. The *Magdalen Lands,* given for its endowment at an early period, were sold by the Corporation, in 1719, subject to 19 small reserved rents, amounting to only £14. 2s. 3d. per annum. For a long period these rents have been applied towards the *repairs of the church,* together with £10. 14s. 1d., arising from several small rents payable out of lands, left by *John Shapleigh,* and other donors. An almshouse for six poor men, was founded by *James Rodd,* in 1654, and endowed with some adjoining buildings, but these premises were converted into the parish Workhouse, many years ago.

The GRAMMAR SCHOOL occupies a room in a building belonging to the Corporation, and is endowed with a farm of 61A. 3R. 14P., at Harberton, given by *Elize Hele,* in 1632, together with other property for schools at Exeter, &c. (See page 97.) This farm is now let for £60 a year, for which the master is required to teach only two free scholars, appointed by the mayor; but he is ordered not to charge more than six guineas each per annum to the day scholars for classical education. He is appointed by the mayor and aldermen.

The CHARITY SCHOOL, in Bay Horse street, is chiefly supported by voluntary contributions. In 1734, *Charles Taylor* bequeathed to it a yearly rent-charge of 40s. out of a house, which now belongs wholly to the charity, and has for a long period been occupied rent free by the schoolmaster and mistress. The charity is also possessed of 12A. of land at Harper's Hill, given by *John Phillips,* in 1714, together with an annuity of 20s. out of a house near the church. The school now affords instruction to about 45 boys and 20 girls, about half of whom are also provided with blue clothing. Here is also a NATIONAL, established in 1813, and a BRITISH SCHOOL, founded in 1846. The former has about 200 and the latter 150 scholars; and there is in the town an *Infant School,* and in Bridgetown a *British School* for girls.

The minister of the *Independent Chapel* has the dividends of £50 four per cent. stock, purchased with £30 left by *Elizabeth Row.* To the Presbyterian minister of the Lower Meeting House, *Barbara Jetsome* left a yearly rent-charge of £4 out of lands at Ashburton; and for the poor of the Presbyterian congregation she left an annuity of £2. 12s., charged on the same lands. Since 1799, the Lower Meeting House has been occupied by Wesleyans, and the annuity of £4 has been allowed to accumulate, and the accumulations have been invested in stock for the benefit of such Presbyterian minister as may hereafter be appointed to the said meeting-house. The annuity of £2. 12s. is disposed of in weekly distributions of bread to the poor people of Totnes, of the Presbyterian or Independent denomination.

TOTNES UNION comprises the parishes of Ashprington, Berry-Pomeroy, Brixham, Buckfastleigh, Churston-Ferrers, Cornworthy, Dartington, St. Petrox, St. Saviour, and Townstal, in Dartmouth Borough; Dean-Prior, Diptford, Dittisham, Halwell, Harberton, Holne, Kingswear, Little Hempston, Marldon, Morley, North Huish, Paignton, Rattery, South-Brent, Staverton, Stoke Gabriel, Totnes, and Ugborough, which embrace an area of 143 square miles, and had 34,126 inhabitants in 1841, living in 6901 houses; besides which there were 440 empty houses, and 39 building, when the census was taken. Their total average annual expenditure on the poor during the three years preceding the formation of the Union, was £13,879. The expenditure of the Union in 1838 was £11,893; and in 1840, £13,183. The *Workhouse* is a large stone building, erected in 1838-'9, at the cost of about £6000, and has room for 380 paupers. W. F. Windeatt, Esq., is the *union clerk and superintendent registrar;* Rev. F. H. Hele, *chaplain;* Mr. Richard and Mrs. Martyn, *master and matron* of the Workhouse; and Thos. Irish and Saml. Randle are the *relieving officers.* The union is divided into 12 *medical and 7 registration districts.* Mr. Richard Harris is registrar of births and deaths for Totnes district.

TOTNES DIRECTORY,

INCLUDING BRIDGETOWN AND BERRY POMEROY.

The POST-OFFICE is at Mr. Wm. Hannaford's, Fore street. Letters are despatched six times a day, and money orders are granted and paid. Letters are delivered at 9 morning and 6 evening; and there are foot posts to Tuckenhay, Stoke Gabriel, Broadhempston, &c.

Those marked 1 *are in Bay Horse street;* 2, *at Berry Pomeroy;* 3, *in Bridgetown;* 4, *Castle street;* 5, *Fore street;* 6, *Grove;* 7, *Plains;* 8, *Plymouth road;* 9, *in Tickelmore street;* 10, *at Peter's quay;* 11, *Leechwell street;* 12, *Ashburton road;* 13, *Queen street;* and 14, *in True street.*

Adamms W. Dacres, Esq. *Bowde Hsn* | 8 Armstrong David, James, & Robert,
Adams Wm. music professor | travelling drapers and tea dealers

12 Andrews Mrs ‖ 8 Angel Mrs Mary
Barry John Milner, M.D. *Lakemead*
Bastard Wm. B. Esq. Bridgetown
7 Bastow Mr Thos. ‖ Blower Mrs
5 Bishop John, town sergeant
8 Boardman Lieut. Thomas, R.N.
5 Bowden Wm. gent. ‖ 3 Blackler Wm.
8 Brian Mr Geo. ‖ Burge J. excise
3 Bundock Mrs ‖ 5 Burnett Mrs
5 Burrough Rev Jas. Walrond, *vicar*
Burrough Misses, Bellevue Cottage
Calley Charles Cphr. Esq. *Priory*
Carew Thomas, Esq. *Rectory*
Cary Geo. Stanley, and Stanley Edw.
    Geo. Esqrs. *Follaton House*
Chivers Mr., Railway Station
3 Churchward Miss ‖ Cole Mrs Sar.
Cleave Mr Fras. *Oke*, Mount Pleasnt
5 Cock Charles, agent to Ford & Co.
7 Cockram Robert, traveller
13 Cole Geo. Heath, sheriff's officer
3 Collier Mrs Harriet ‖ Calley Mrs
5 Compton Hy. music dlr. & profr
Condy Rev Philip, (Indpt.) Grove
3 Cornish Rev Wm. Floyer, (& *Hook*)
2 Cosens Rev Wm. Burrough, M.A.
    vicar of *Berry Pomeroy*
3 Cross Richard, railway clerk
5 Cuming Mrs Eliz. ‖ Daw Mrs
Cuming Saml. architect & surveyor
Davy Capt. Leeshan, R.N. Villas
3 Derry Rd. gent ‖ 8 Distin Mr Rd
3 Diggins John, mailman to Kingsbdg
8 Drew Mr Rd. ‖ 7 Fogwill Mrs
Ellis Robt. tax colr. Farley's hill
Gilbert Mrs Fanny, *Warland Cotg*
Gill James, gent. Northgate
Gortley Mr Geo. ‖ 7 Heales Misses
11 Hakewill Mr Jph. ‖ 8 Hill Mrs
7 Hannaford Mrs ‖ 5 Heath Mrs
7 Hayward Mrs Frs. bath keeper
3 Huxham Mr Thos. ‖ Lampen Misses
3 Irish Thomas, relieving officer
7 Lavercombe Mr ‖ 3 Luckraft Hy.
3 Luscombe Lieut Edw., R.N. *Mt Dart*
3 Luscombe Mrs Jane, & 5, Misses
7 Macvicar Mrs ‖ 3 Mitchell Miss
Marsland Rev Wm. Bourne, B.A.
Martyn Richd. master of *Workhouse*
11 Matthews Samuel, town crier
Michelmore Mrs Eliz. *Highfield Hs*
3 Michelmore Mrs B. & 14 Thos. jun
2 Michelmore Thos. Esq. agent to Duke
    of Somerset, *Berry House*
4 Mitchell Capt. Frdk. Thomas, RN.

3 Mitchell George, tax surveyor
3 Mitchell N. fisherman
5 Mitchell Misses Jane & Betsy
Newton Mr John, Moat hill
5 Old John, dancing master
Oldham Mrs C. B. *Little Priory*
Oldrey Wm. parish clerk & schoolmr
Phare John, inland revenue officer
Phillips John F.P.Esq. *Broomboro' Hs*
5 Phillips Mr Wm. ‖ 14 Pulling Mrs
3 Platt Rev Robert, (Catholic)
8 Prideaux Mrs J. & 5 Mrs W.
Randle Samuel, relieving officer
5 Reeve Elizabeth, toy, &c. dealer
5 Sanders Samuel, coach maker
Seaman Mr Henry, *Guerston*
Scudamore Mr Geo. A., Plymouth rd
10 Shinner Thomas, lime burner
3 Shore Rev Jas. M.A. *Free Church*
8 Smith James, travelling tea dealer
7 Smith Mr J. A. ‖ 5 Sanders Miss
5 Soper Richard & Wm. Esqrs
3 Spry Mrs Ann ‖ 5 Sparkes Mr John
Symons Jno. clerk ‖ 8 Taunton Mrs
Taylor Mrs. *Mount Elwell*
Taylor Charles, gent. Fore street
1 Taylor Thos. Hore, inspr. wgts. &c
8 Toms John, gent ‖ Thornton Mr
3 Tracey Miss ‖ 7 Tucker Mrs A.
7 Tucker John Thos. civil engineer
8 Warren Mrs ‖ 3 Wills Mrs A.
Webb George, surveyor of taxes
7 Webb Mr Wm. ‖ Willson Mr
5 Welch Thos. high bailiff of Cnty.Ct
White J. B. cement & slate merchant
7 Whiteway Wm. ‖ 8 Worth Miss
    ACADEMIES. *(* Boarding.)*
7 Barnes Mr ‖ Richards Mr
British School, Mr Hardinge
1 *Charity School*, James Yabbicom &
    Mary Hannaford
Free Grammar School, Rev W. B.
    Marsland, B.A. & Jph. Hathaway
*7 Heath Emma ‖ 5 Johns John
Infant, Light Hope & Es. Reading
National School, Wm. & Ann Oldrey
*5 Old Martha and Frances
*5 Parnell Mary ‖ 5 Parrott Miss
Workhs. Wm. Tope & My.L. Smalridge
    ATTORNEYS.
5 Bryett Theodore, (clerk to magts.)
5 Cuming Francis Brooking
5 De Cateret John Duniere
5 Edwards Charles, (clerk of County
    Court;) h Villas, Bridgetown

6 Edwards Jeffery John, (proctor)
5 Farwell George, (deputy registrar of archdeaconry;) h *Weston*
Gillard Peter, Bridgetown
5 Michelmore and Presswell
Michelmore Fredk.; h Priory st
5 Presswell George, (town clerk)
Taylor Carew, Fore street
8 Windeatt Wm. Fabyan, (union clk. and superintendent registrar)

AUCTIONEERS.
5 Heath John, (surveyor, &c)
Huxham Frank, *Follaton*
Tippett Robert, Fore street
Melhuish & Croydon, Fore street

BANKS.
5 Devon and Cornwall Banking Co.; Wm. Brown, *manager*
5 National & Provincial Bank of England; Stn. Fras. Shairp, *manager*

FIRE & LIFE OFFICE AGENTS.
Clerical, Medical, & Genl., C. Butland
County & Provident, & National & Mercantile, James Trehane
Economic, Wm. F. Windeatt
General Fire and Life, S. Parnell
Globe Fire and Life, Robert Ellis
Guardian, Henry Hannaford
Legal and General, George Farwell
Liverpool and London, M. Angel
Norwich Union, Wm. Hannaford
Phoenix & British Coml., W. Bentall
Royal Exchange, Evan Evens
Star Fire and Life, John Bearne
Sun Fire and Life, J. A. Spargo
Western Life, Edward Tippett
West of England, John Yabbicom

INNS AND TAVERNS.
3 Anchor Inn, George Gillham
1 Bay Horse, Nicholas Norrish
3 Bell, Samuel Richards
5 Bull, Edward Willis
5 Castle Inn, James Sawyer
7 Dartmouth Inn, Thomas Gillham
5 Devonport Inn, Philip Cole
3 Exeter Inn, John Brown
11 Kingsbridge Inn, Daniel Harvey
5 Lion, Philip Condy, (and brewer)
5 Lord Nelson, Samuel Ellery
3 New Inn, Wm. Holman
10 New London Inn, John Smale
4 North Star, John Chipman
5 Oxford Arms, Mary Holman
5 Plymouth Inn, Wm. Bovey
5 Queen's Arms, Edward Effer

*Railway Hotel,*Jn.Coombe,Ashbtn.rd
7*Seven Stars Hotel*, Halse Ley Harris
3 *Seymour Hotel*, Michael Bishop
Shambles Gate, John Turpin
5 South Devon Inn, John Rd. Adams
5 Town Arms, Richard Adams
3 Victoria Inn, Wm. Farley
5 Victualling House,Edw.Langbridge
Waterman's Arms, Edward Rogers
5 William IV., Samuel Gillham

FARMERS. *(2 in Berry Pomeroy.)*
2 Angel Samuel || 5 Bowden John
2 Dugdale George || 8 Earle Robert
2 Ford Geo. || Endle Thos. *Weston*
Huxham Frank, *Follaton*
2 Holman Wm. || 2 Lizard Mary
Michelmore Thomas, jun. *Holwell*
2 Paige Wm. || 2 Quint Richard
2 Pollard Pascho || 2 Quint R. jun
2 Searle James Dymond, *Longcombe*
2 Searle John || 3 White Wm.
2 Tozer Ann, Benoni, and Charles
2 Turpin Geo. & Thos. *Gt. Court*
2 Venning John Tozer, *Weekboro'*
|| 5 Wotton Richard

BAKERS.
5 Addems Ncs.
5 Allan James
5 Angel Rd. S.
5 Barter Nichs.
3 Barter N. jun
5 Borrett Samuel
5 Bowden Fdk.
5 Crocker Rbn.
5 Earle Robt.
5 Gidley Nichs.
3 Gomerall Wm.
5 Hannaford Ts.
5 Kinsman Thos.
5 Lane John
5 Shore Thomas
Smith Hugh
5 Thomas Wm.
9 Tope John

BASKET MAKERS.
5 Lampen Robt.
Lampen Thomas

BLACKSMITHS.
11 Crawford Hy.
3 Gillham John
5 Harris Richard
9 Heath Henry
9 Heath Samuel
6 Heath Samuel
9 Pearce Wm.
4 Pyle John

BOOKSELLERS, STATIONERS, &c.
5 Bearne John
5 Denner John
5 Hannaford Sl.
5 Hannaford Td.
5 Martyn Richard
5 Taylor John

BOOT&SHOE MKS.
11 Blank Thos.
5 Callender Wm.
3 Coleman James
5 Corney John
5 Ellis Robert
5 Lombardine T.
3 Mitchell Thos.
5 Purnell Saml.
3 Perrott John
5 Port Bartw.
5 Port Samuel
5 Putt Thomas
3 Screach J. S.
5 Sharpham S.P.
5 Shute John
5 Tanner Wm.
5 Weeks Wm.
5 Whiteway Jas.

BRUSH MAKERS.
5 Davis John
3 Hardin Thos.

BUTCHERS.
5 Harris H. L.
5 Holberton Ed.
5 Huxham John
4 Langmead Rt.
5 Tarr Wm. H.
5 Tooley Thos.
2 Turpin Chas.
5 Weymouth F.T.
5 Westaway Eliz.
5 Willis John
1 Winsor Mr
5 Yeoman Sarah

CABINET MKRS.
5 Angel John
5 Bennett Thos.
5 Pulling Wm.(&
plate glass dlr.)
5 Tippett E. Rt.

CHEMISTS &DGTS.
(* Tea Dealers.)
5 * Butland Chas.
5 * Gill Robert
5 Rees Wm.
5 * Spargo J. A.
5 * Trehane Jas.

CIDER MERCHTS.
3 Blackler Wm.
5 Bowden Wm.
3 Endle John
3 Mitchell John
3 Venning Rd.

COAL, &c. MERTS.
7 Bentall Wm.
7 Bowden & Son
7 Bunker & Michelmore
3 Endle John
7 Fogwill J. R.
10 Hannaford Hy.

COOPERS.
5 Gillard Peter
5 Sanders Pp.
3 Tope Henry

CORN DEALERS.
5 Addems Nichs
5 Heath John
7 Manning Wm.

CORN MILLERS.
3 Blackler Edw.
Bowden John
Goodman Hy.
3 Randle Wm.
3 Widdicombe W.

CURRIERS.
5 Andrews Rd.
5 Endle Charles
5 Mitchell Chas.

DAIRYMEN.
Pearce J., Walls
5 Earle Robert
8 Earle Rt. sen
5 Ellis Robert
8 Hill John

DYERS.
Heath Samuel
5 Sloggett Wm.

EATING HOUSES.
5 Fogwill W. N.
8 Gallin Mary

FURNITURE BKRS.
5 Evens Nichs.
8 Pengilly Wm.

GLASS, &c. DLRS.
5 Morgan Robt.
5 Putt Wm.
5 Yabbicom John

GROCERS.
* are Chandlers.
5 Currie Wm.
5 Fitze George
5 Hamlyn Thos.
5 Hannaford Wm. Kay
5 Holmwood G.
5 * Huxham Sl.
5 Laskey Thos.
5 Lloyd Eliz.
5 Prince Richd.
5 * Tucker Edm.
5 * Tucker Wm.
5 Willis Thos.

GUNMAKERS.
5 Hambling Wm.
5 Pulman A. B.

HAIR DRESSERS.
Cload Thomas
5 Elmes John
5 Hammett Hy.
5 Hosking Wm.
5 Saunders Sml.
5 Sharpham Sml.

HATTERS.
5 Niner Pp. K.
5 Simons Chas.

HORSE, FLY, &c., LETTERS.
3 Bishop Michl.
5 Ellis Robert

7 Harris H. L.
5 Heath John

HOSIERS, &c.
5 Craydon E.&E.
5 Stabbs Susan

IRONMONGERS.
5 Angel Thomas
5 Distin Andrew Sparke
5 Distin Thomas
3 Gilbert Wm.(& founder)
5 Sandford Thos. Mattws., (fndr. & stove gt. mfr

JOINERS& BLDRS.
5 Bearne John
Foster Henry
5 Goodridge Mr.
8 Grove Stephen
5 Michelmore W.
Richardson and Reeves
3 Rouswill John
Uren Edw. (and lime burner)
8 Willis Wm.

L. & W. DRAPERS.
5 Bowden Robt.
5 Ferris Jph. & Gill Wm.
5 Hole Wm.
5 Paige Jno. B.
5 Webber Chas. and Wm.

MALTSTERS.
5 Bartram and Whiteway
3 Holman Wm.& Thomas
5 Pack James

MILLINERS.
5 Ackrell Ann
5 Ash Jane
Hannaford A.&M.
5 Huxham Mary
Lavercombe Miss
Mitchell M. A.
5 Pulling M. & J.
7 Sandiford Mrs
5 Snell Jane
5 Westlake Eliz.
5 Whiteway Eliz.

NURSERY AND SEEDSMEN.
5 Allen Wm.
5 Parnell John
1 Penwill James

PAINTRS.&GLZRS.
5 Croydon Edwin
5 Croydon Wm.
5 Harris Richard
8 Hill John
5 Ryder Robert
1 Wilcocks Thos.
5 Woodley Wm.

PATTEN MAKERS.
5 Penny George
5 Winsor Wm.

PLUMBERS, &c.
5 Brimicombe J. (& brass fdr.)
5 Gill James

ROPE MAKERS,&c.
3 Hawkins John
5 Prout Wm.

SADDLERS.
11 Chaster J. W.
5 Cridland Henry
3 Cross Wm.
5 Gardner Allen
5 Kinsman John
5 Melhuish Alx. A
5 Tucker Robert

SHOPKEEPERS.
Ackrell John
5 Allen Thomas
5 Beer George
5 Corney Jane
9 Dare Johanna
5 Diggins George
5 Gardner Allen
5 Gidley Nichls.
5 Gortley James
5 Hamlyn Alice
5 Hannaford My.
Jewell George
5 Lloyd Mrs
5 Langbridge J.
5 Mogford Thos.
5 Parnell John
5 Penny George
5 Scott Isaac C.
11 Scott My.Ann
3 Searle Eliz.
5 Searle Thomas
3 Shears Susan
5 Smith Agnes

5 Tilley Richard
1 Trewolly Eliz.
5 Webber John
5 Weeks Wm.
5 Wills Richard
1 Winsor Richard

STONEMASONS
AND PLASTERERS.
Ackrell John
5 Ash Wm.
3 Blackler Thos.
8 Hill Samuel
Oldrey James
1 Toope Wm.
1 Tozer Sphn.
3 Veasey Wm.
5 Wills James

STRAW HAT MKS.
5 Arscott Jane
5 Collin Car.
3 Field E. & J.
5 Hannaford My.
3 Mitchell Car.
5 Prout Eliz.
6 Saunders Har.
5 Smith Mrs

SURGEONS.
Barry J.M., M.D.
5 Bowden Wm.
7 Derry John
3 Gillard Wm.
7 Haines J.,M.D.
5 Kellock Wm.
5 Tompson, Gillard & Tompson

5 Tompson N. G.

TAILORS.
5 Adams Rd.
5 Angel Edward
7 Baker Edward
11 Bartlett Hy.
8 Bartlett H. jun
8 Cloke John
5 Fogwill W. N.
5 Godfrey Wm.
5 Lane Samuel
3 Penwill John
Perrott Wm.
9 Roberts Geo.
5 Westlake Ths.

TANNERS.
Chaster John W.
3 Searle Thos.

TIMBER MERTS.
7 Bentall Wm.
7 Fogwill J. R.
5 Patey Richard
10 Stoyle Wm.

TINNERS, &c.
10 Crawford Hy.
5 Elliott J. S.
3 Mitchell James
9 Webb John

WATCHMAKRS., &c
5 Bennett Jph.
5 Bradford Jas.
5 Evens Evan
5 Evens Nichs.
5 Preddy Wm.
4 Symons Jas.

WHEELWRIGHTS.
5 Foster Samuel
3 Hawkins John
5 Sanders Sml.
6 Stanning Rd.
3 Turpin James

WINE&SPT. MRTS.
7 Bentall Wm.
5 Bowden & Son
5 Huxham Geo.
5 Pack James

RAILWAY trains six times a day to Plymouth, Exeter, &c. *Omnibus* to meet every train from the Seven Stars and Seymour Hotel

STEAM PACKET to *Dartmouth* twice a day (J. R. Fogwill *agent ;)* and Wm. Foale's *Boat* daily

TRADING VESSELS to London once a week, from Peter's Quay ; Henry Hannaford *agent*

CARRIERS.

The Railway Co., and Ford and Co. to all parts daily ; C. Cock *agent*

To *Ashburton*, Wm. Edgcombe, from Town Arms daily, 4 afternoon

To *Brixham*, John Worth, from Oxford Arms, Wed. & Sat. 10 morn.

To *Buckfastleigh*, James Willcocks, from Tower Arms daily, at 4

To *Kingsbridge*, the mail daily ; and Wm. Foale from Tickelmore st., and Luscombe and Laurie from Oxford Arms, Mon. Wed. & Sat

To *Modbury*, Lavers, Mon. Wed. & Saturday, 4 afternoon

To *Torquay*, from the Exeter Inn, Stoyle, Worth, Veal & Perryman, Mon. Wed. & Fri. 9 mng., & Sat. 4 afternoon

---

STANBOROUGH HUNDRED

Is a long narrow district, extending more than 22 miles southward from the river Dart in Dartmoor Forest, to the English Channel, between Bolt Head and Tail, and the mouths of Salcombe creek and the river Avon ; but averaging only about five miles in breadth. It stretches into the hilly region of Dartmoor on the north west, and is bounded by the river Dart as low as Totnes, where it is crossed by the South Devon Railway. It is traversed southward by the Avon, which receives several smaller streams ; and the haven and creeks from Kingsbridge to the sea form its south-western boundary. It is in the Southern Parliamentary Division of Devon, in Stanborough and Coleridge Petty Sessional Division ; in the Archdeaconry of Totnes, and in the Deaneries of Woodleigh and Totnes. The following enumeration of its 20 parishes shews their territorial extent and their population in 1841.

* Those marked thus * are in *Totnes Union*, and all the others are in *Kingsbridge Union*. These Unions are also *County Court Districts*. The return of Churchstow parish included 211 souls in Kingsbridge Union Workhouse. There are hamlets in several of the parishes.

Parishes.	Acres.	Pop.	Parishes.	Acres.	Pop.
Allington East	3500	722	Kingsbridge	32	1564
Alvington West	4021	998	Loddiswell	3568	1013
* Brent, (South)	10000	1237	Malborough parish	4890	979
* Buckfastleigh	6270	2576	Salcombe chap...		972
Churchstow	1877	542	Milton, (South)	1557	475
* Dartington	3248	603	* Morleigh	1487	202
* Dean Prior	4180	552	* Rattery	2823	485
* Diptford	4144	755	Thurlestone	1763	437
* Holne	2299	394	Woodleigh	2319	269
* Huish, (North)	2662	483			
Huish, (South)	1150	368	Total	61,890	15,633

ALLINGTON, (EAST) a pleasant scattered village, four miles N.E. by
E. of Kingsbridge, has in its parish 729 souls, and 3500 acres of land,
generally having a light fertile soil, and including Combe, Harleston, Yetson, and other scattered farms. *W. B. Fortescue, Esq.*, owns nearly half
the parish, and is lord of the manor, and has a handsome seat here, called
FALLAPIT HOUSE, where his family has been seated for many generations.
The present house is a large and handsome mansion, in the Elizabethan
style, erected about 35 years ago, near the old one, an ivy mantled portion
of which still remains. The house was enlarged in 1849, and is pleasantly
situated in the midst of extensive and tasteful pleasure grounds. *Fallapit*
was anciently the seat of a family of its own name, whose heiress married
Sir Henry Fortescue, Lord Chief Justice of the Common Pleas in Ireland.
She was his second wife, and their descendants in the male line resided
here above 300 years. Sir Edmund Fortescue was created a baronet in
1644, but the title became extinct on the death of his son, in 1683. The
estate then passed to a younger branch, which became extinct in 1734, by
the death of Edmund Fortescue, Esq., whose daughter married Thomas
Bury, Esq., whose heiress carried the estate in marriage to the Rev. Nathl.
Wells, whose eldest son took the name of Fortescue, and was grandfather
of the present proprietor. Sir W. W. Knighton, Capt. Turner, Capt. Owen,
C. Prideaux, Esq., Miss Prowse, Mr. W. Luscombe, and others have freehold estates in the parish. The *Church* (St. Andrew,) is a large ancient
structure, in the early perpendicular style, with a lofty embattled tower,
containing five bells. The nave has octagonal columns on the north, and
clustered columns on the south side. The pulpit is beautifully carved, and
the church has a clean and neat appearance, being renovated in 1848. The
rectory, valued in K.B. at £32. 2s. 1d., and in 1831 at £345, is in the
patronage of W. B. Fortescue, Esq., and incumbency of the Rev. H. R.
Fortescue, B.A., who has 113A. 1R. 37P. of glebe, and a handsome *Rectory House*, built in 1847, in the Elizabethan style. The tithes were commuted in 1839 for £485 per annum. The poor parishioners have 20s. a
year, left by John Peter, in 1570, out of the tithes of Cornworthy.

Cleverly Isaac, corn miller
Delafosse Capt. Edward H., R.N., *Rimpstone*
Fortescue Wm. Blundell, Esq., *Fallapit House*
Fortescue Rev Hy. R., B.A. *Rectory*
Horton Trowbridge, vict. *Union*
Luscombe Wm. gent. *Combe*
Prowse Miss Sarah, *Higher Pool*
Roper Wm. shoemaker

Whiteway Rt. W. vict. *Fortescue Arms*
FARMERS. (* are Owners.)
Andrews John, *Lower Combe*
Codd Robert, *Lower Pool*
Cole Stephen || Foale Thomas
Cutmore Robert, Fallapit
Ellis Jas. & J. H. *Colehanger*
Grills Wm. || Jackman James
Horton Geo. || Horton John
Lakeman Geo. || Morgan Thomas

*Langworthy Robert, *Flear*
*Paige Wm. || Nunn Richard
Parnell John || Pinhay Wm.
Prowse Peter, *Yetson*
Smaridge Wm. Hy. *Higher Pool*
Tooley Henry || Townsend James
Trant Wm. || Widger Richard
Whiteway Rt. W. || Yabsley Rd.

BLACKSMITHS.
Heath Richard
Stear Philip
Trant George
West Susan
CARPENTERS.
Baker Richard
Baker John
Ellis Thomas

Thomas Wm.
MASONS.
Stear Edmund
Stear Thomas
Taylor Henry
SHOPKEEPERS.
Brooking ——
Foxworthy J.
Pitwood John

ALVINGTON, (WEST) or *West Allington*, is a small scattered village, 1½ mile S.W. of Kingsbridge, but its parish extends four miles southward, and includes 998 souls, 4020 acres of land, part of *Malborough* village, and the hamlets of *Woolston, Easton, Sorley,* and *Bawcombe*, on the western side of the estuary and creeks, extending from the English Channel to Kingsbridge. The *manors* and owners are, Woolston and Oldaway, Duke of Cleveland; West Alvington, W. R. Ilbert, Esq.; and Woodhouse, Mr. J. Hingston; but a great part of the parish is freehold, belonging to the Bastard, Luscombe, Walker, and other families. *Combe Royal*, one mile N. of Kingsbridge, is the large and elegant seat of John Luscombe, Esq., whose family purchased it in 1736 of the Gilberts, who had long been seated there. *Gerston*, now occupied by a farmer, is the property, and was, till recently, the seat of the Bastards, of Kitley. *Bowring's-leigh*, a large and ancient Tudor mansion, now a farm-house, was long a seat of the Bowrings, and afterwards of the Ilberts. It still belongs to the latter, and retains some beautiful ceilings, &c., but its chapel was burnt down a few years ago. The fragments of an urn were found in 1818, in a tumulus at Sorley. John de Besill, then lord of the manor of West Alvington, had a grant for a market and fair, in 1270, but they were obsolete some centuries ago. On the front of Addlehole farm-house is a large *vine*, which has produced a ton of grapes in a season. The *Church* (All Saints,) is an ancient structure, with a fine embattled tower, and some memorials of the Bastard and Holditch families. In the chancel is an elaborately carved Easter sepulchre. The *vicarage*, valued in K.B. at £62. 16s. 10½d., and in 1831 at £685, with those of South Huish, Malborough, and South Milton annexed to it, is in the patronage of the Dean and Chapter of Salisbury, and incumbency of the Rev. D. Macdonald, who has a good residence. The tithes of this parish were commuted in 1839,—the vicarial for £330. 2s., and the rectorial for £555. 8s. 3d. W. R. Ilbert, Esq., is lessee of the latter under the patrons. Four cottages have long been vested for the repairs of the church. The poor have the dividends of £250, three per cent. consols, purchased in 1794, with money given by *Cath. Ilbert*, and other donors. *Marked 2, are at Malborough ; 3, at Woolston ; and 4, at Sorley.*

Annis Robert, baker, &c
Fortescue Mrs. *Quay House*
2 Jarvis Mrs Sar. || Wright Andrew
Luscombe John, Esq. *Combe Royal*
Macdonald Rev Douglas, *Vicarage*
Matthews Rd. cider dlr. *Squares Quay*
Murch Ts. vict., Church House
Osborn Wm. vict., Ring of Bells
2 Reynolds Jno. vict. Royal Oak
Weymouth Mr Francis, *Collapit*
Veale Henry, painter, plumber, &c

BLACKSMITHS.
Hine George
2 Hine Roger
2 Huxham Sml.
Morgan Wm.
2 Reynolds John
CARPENTERS.
Sherriff Richard
Tuckerman Jas.
Tuckerman Ts.

BOOT & SHOE MRS.
2 Jarvis Joseph
Trist Joseph
FARMERS.
Adams Wm. J.
Adams Wm.
Adams W. & E.
Balkwill Et. H.
Brooking George,
  Gerston
Clark John

Cole Amy	4 Heath Samuel	3 Pepperell John	Veale Jarvis
Crimp John	4 Hoidge Wm.	Perraton Andrew	Warren Edward
Dingle Mary	Lavers Robert	3 Phillips Adams	Wood Wm.
Edwards John,	3 Lidstone A. R.	Prettejohn John	SHOPKEEPERS.
Addlehole	3 Lidstone John	Stear Thomas	Heath Rd. *tailor*
Goodyear Nichls.	Luscombe Pp.	Tucker Nichls.	2 Jarvis Robert
Bowringsleigh	Luskey Wm.	3 Winter Thos.	Wills Thomas
Grills Geo. *Combe*	Pearce William,	MASONS.	
HannafordAdms.	*Easton*	Payne John	

BRENT, (SOUTH) a large irregularly built village, in the valley of the small river Avon, has a station on the South Devon Railway, five miles N.E. of Ivybridge, 6 miles W. of Totnes, and 7 miles S.S.W. of Ashburton. Its parish contains 1237 souls, and about 10,100 acres of land, of which 6312 acres are cultivated, and the rest open common, &c., in the south-east angle of Dartmoor Forest, where the hills rise boldly from the valleys of the Avon and Erme. The parish includes the small hamlets of *Aish, Charford, Harbournford, Lutton, Wonton, Brent Mill,* and many scattered farm-houses. South Brent was formerly a market town, and has still two annual *fairs,* on the last Tuesdays in April and September, the former called the lamb, and the latter the goose fair, but both are extensive marts for sheep, cattle, and horses, held "*under the glove,*" a glove being suspended on a pole during the fairs. The manor belonged to Buckfastleigh Abbey, and was purchased by Sir Wm. Petre after the dissolution. Mr. John Elliott holds the manor of Lord Petre, but most of the land was sold in parcels many years ago, and now belongs to Sir W. P. Carew, Dr. Butter, and many smaller owners. The *Church* (St. Patrick,) is a large ancient fabric, in the decorated style, with a low tower and six bells. The Rev. Nathl. Cole, M.A., is appropriator of the great tithes, and patron and incumbent of the *vicarage,* valued in K.B. at £29. 15s. 4½d., and in 1831 at £906. The glebe is 31A. 3R. 37P., and the tithes were commuted in 1839, for £975. 10s. per annum. The Vicarage House is a good residence near the church. The Independents and Wesleyans have small chapels here, and on Brent hill are the ruins of an ancient building, supposed to have been a chapel. The *Parish Lands, &c.,* comprise 64A. and five houses, which have been long vested for the relief of the poor, and are let for about £110 per annum. The poor have also 40s. a year, left by John Peter, in 1570. The *Free School* is endowed with about 4A. of land, left by John Wilcocks and Thomas Acland. To buy *bibles* for four poor children, the Rev. Robert Bradford left a yearly rent charge of 20s., in 1800. *Marked 2, are at Charford; 3, Harbournford; 4, Lutton; 5, Aish; and 6, at Stidstone.*

Bowden Wm. gent. *Weir Down*
Cole Rev Nathl., M.A. *Vicarage*
Daykin Thos. surgeon, & Mr. W. P.
DeCarteret Jn.Duniere,gent. *Kerswell*
Elliott John, gent || Lang John
Furneaux Wm. gent. *Charfield Cross*
Gubbins Rev —— (Independent)
Hingston John, gent || Pearce Wm.
Hodgetts Jph. gent || Stranger E.
Hosking Sophia, schoolmistress
Horswell John, woolcomber
Kuper Capt. Augs. L., R.N. *Rock*
6 Langworthy Mrs Mary
Lee John, worsted spinner

Mowatt John, surgeon
Veale Richard, railway station mngr
Webber & Co. slate quarry owners
White Walter, saddler
Woodley Charles, Esq. *Didworthy*

PUBLIC HOUSES.
Anchor, Arthur Langworthy
Globe, Wm. Ward
London Inn, George Luscombe
Pack Horse, Wm. Davis
Royal Oak, Wm. Maunder

BLACKSMITHS.	BUTCHERS.
Scobell Wm.	Codd John
WiddicombeWm.	Hingston Henry

CARPENTERS.
Dodd John
Heath Nicholas
Heath Richard
Veale Jarvis
FARMERS.
(* *are Owners.*)
*Adams Mary
5 Andrews John
5 Bidlake Chpr.
4 Boon Stephen
3 BroadridgeCpn.
3 Broadridge Wm.
Brooking Phln.
Cole James
Cuming Robert
Earle Joseph
2 Ford Mrs
Fortescue Arthur
Furneaux Wm.
6 Goodman Hy.
2 Goodridge Jfy.
*Hamly Thos.
Hannaford Saml.
6 Hard Richard

*Heath Wm.
*Hext Quintin
Hext Thomas
3 Hoare Henry
Hosking John
6 Hosking Richd.
Hosking Wm.
*Jewell John
Jonas Rt. & Hy.
Jordan ——
5*Kingswell Hy.
*Luce John
Luscombe John
Matthews Wm.
Mead Robert
*Nicholls Wm.
Pearce Robert
5*Ryder J. C.
Savery John
Sanders Jeffery
Smerdon Richd.
Smerdon Elijah
Smerdon Thos.
5 Soper John K.
4*Stranger John

4 Stranger Richd.
Wakeham John
3 Wakeham Jsa.
5 Wakeham Ths.
MASONS.
Ford Peter
5 PeathyjohnsRd.
Knott Thomas
Knott Wm.
MILLERS.
Cole Robert
Ellis Reuben
Heath Henry
PLUMBERS, &c.
Cranch John R.
Stidson Wm.
SHOEMAKERS.
Blight Philip
Blight Wm.
Eales John
Farleigh Richd.
Soper John
Veale Henry
SHOPKEEPERS.
Andrews Wm.

Bowyer Robt. (&
   basket maker)
Codd Wm. R.
Joynt Hercules
Wills Thomas
Symons Jno. *schl*
TAILORS.
Cole Solomon
Hurrell Wm.
Joynt Hercules
Toope Wm.
WHEELWRIGHTS.
Clancy John
Cole Wm.
RAILWAY.
Trains 6 times a
   day, to Exeter,
   Plymouth, &c
POST-OFFICE
   at R.Mitchell's.
   Letters *via Ivy-*
   bridge
CARRIER.
Edward Andrews,
   to Plym., Sat

BUCKFASTLEIGH is a large manufacturing village, in two parts, called Higher and Lower Towns, pleasantly seated on the western side of the fertile valley of the river Dart, 2½ miles S.W. by S. of Ashburton. It has about 300 *woolcombers*, several corn mills, and four *blanket and serge mills;* but only two of the latter are at present occupied, and give employment to about 400 hands. Its parish had 1525 inhabitants in 1801, 2445 in 1831, and 2576 in 1841; and comprises 4379A. 3R. 35P. of cultivated land, and 1072¼ acres of open moorland, on the eastern side of Dartmoor Forest, whence two rivulets flow to the Dart, irrigating the meadows in their courses, affording the combers ample means for washing their wool, and uniting their streams near the village, which had formerly a weekly *market* on Tuesdays, granted to the abbot in 1352; and has still two *fairs for cattle and wool*, on the third Thursday in June and the second Thursday in September. The parish rises in bold hills from the village, and has quarries of limestone and a sort of black marble. It comprises the hamlets of *Buckfast, Scorraton*, and *Runnaford Coombe;* several neat mansions, commanding beautiful views; and a number of scattered farm-houses. Great quantities of cider are made here, and in one year, an orchard of one acre produced 4000 gallons. BUCKFAST ABBEY, in the Dart valley, about a mile north of Buckfastleigh, was founded by Ethelwerd, son of Wm. de Pomeroy, in 1137, for monks of the Cistercian order, and was richly endowed by him and subsequent benefactors. Its clear yearly income was valued at the dissolution at no less than £466. 11s. 2¼d. The site of the abbey was granted to Sir Thomas Dennis, and the manor of Buckfast was afterwards held by the Bakers and Doyleys, but was sold in parcels many years ago. The abbey ruins were extensive, but they were mostly taken down about 1806, except a large square tower, and a Norman arch, finely mantled with ivy. The *Abbey House*, built over the abbey vaults, is a modern mansion, in the castellated Tudor style. At the Grange, is the ancient tithe barn, 108 feet long; and some of the neighbouring houses appear to have been

partly built with stones from the abbey ruins.   The Earl of Macclesfield is lord of the manor of Brooke Mainbow, with Buckfastleigh and Button, and owns a great part of the parish.   The rest is chiefly freehold, and belongs to J. J. and Charles Edwards, Esqrs., R. J. King, Esq., and the Savery, Barnes, Gower, Tucker, Furneaux, Michelmore, Hamlyn, Symons, and other families.   About thirty acres are let in allotments to the poor.   The manor of Kilbenland is dismembered, and that of Bosom Zeal extends into this parish.   *Henbury Castle*, on the top of a commanding eminence, north of the village, is a circular entrenchment of about six acres, encompassed by a deep ditch, now covered with coppice wood.   Within the enclosure is a mound, surrounded by a smaller ditch, now almost concealed with trees. This earthwork is supposed to have been thrown up by the Danes.   *Bigaden House*, the large mansion of R. J. King, Esq., has recently been much improved, and contains a fine collection of pictures and some ancient armour. *Coulson Cottage* is the neat residence of Charles Edwards, Esq., who possesses the faldstool which was used at the coronation of her Majesty, and was presented to him by the late Dean of Westminster.   *Brooke House*, occupied by Mrs. Coates, was formerly a residence of the Earl of Macclesfield. The parish *Church* (Holy Trinity,) stands on an eminence, ascended by 144 steps, and is a large antique structure, which, after being long in a shamefully neglected state, has been restored and beautified since June, 1844, at the cost of more than £1400.   The tower contains six bells, and is surmounted by a handsome spire, the upper part of which is new, and replaces what had been gone several centuries.   The interior of the church has now a handsome appearance, and comprises a nave, chancel, transepts, and two side chapels.   A western gallery has been removed, and the old pews replaced by long low seats, to which doors have been added.   There is now a fine open roof, instead of a plastered ceiling; and two beautiful memorial windows have been inserted, one by the vicar and his brother, in memory of their parents, the former vicar and his wife; and the other by Mr. Powning and his family, to the memory of his late father and brother. In the south transept is a mural tablet, in memory of the late Admiral Thomas White, of the Abbey House, who gave the rich furniture of the altar, which was destroyed by fire in 1849, but has been replaced by the liberality of some of the parishioners.   Near the church stands a sepulchral building, over the vault of the Labell family, who were long seated at Brooke House.   The *vicarage*, valued in K.B. at £19. 1s. 0½d., and in 1831 at £182, is in the patronage and incumbency of the Rev. Matthew Lowndes, B.A., who has a large and respectable residence.   The tithes were commuted in 1832, the vicarial for £198, and the rectorial for £232 per annum. Of the latter, £159 belongs to the Earl of Macclesfield, and £73 to the Rector of Ermington and J. J. Edwards, Esq.   Here is a small *Independent Chapel*, built in 1798 ; and a large and handsome *Wesleyan Chapel*, erected in 1835, at the cost of £1000.   Under the latter is a large British School. Here is also a National School.   The *Parish Lands*, &c., given at an early period by two sisters named Damarell, comprise a house and 13 acres, let for about £40 per annum, which is applied in the service of the church, except £2 for the poor.   The *Church House*, formerly the parish workhouse, belongs to the same trust.   The *poor* have the following *yearly sums :*— £2. 10s. out of Hamlin's Tenement, given in 1800, by *Robt. Bradford ;* £2. 12s. left by *Sir John Acland*, and paid by the Corporation of Exeter; 20s. left by *John Peter*, in 1570, out of the tithes of Cornworthy; £1. 12s. left by *Wm. Gould*, out of Wallaford estate ; 20s. out of the poor rates, as interest of £20, left by *Margaret Pomeroy ;* 20s. out of Broom Parks, left by *Andrew Tinckham ;* 24s. 6d., as interest of £24. 10s., lent to the parish officers ; and 20s. out of land at Ashburton, left by *George Knowling.*

Angel Mr Thomas, *Fairies' Hall*
Barnes John, paper manfr. *Kilberley*
Barnes Mrs Sus. ‖ Callard Mr John
Berry John, serge mfr. (& Ashburton)
Butchers John Carns, schoolmaster
Braine Mrs Mary, *Buckfast Abbey*
Chenhall James, watch maker
Clase Rev John, (Independent)
Coates Mrs. *Brooke House*
Edwards Chas., Esq. *Coulson Cottage*
Frogley Henry, druggist
Furneaux Christopher, maltster, &c
Furneaux John, insurance agent, &c
Furneaux Thomas, tailor
Gidley Mr Wm. ‖ Hamlyn Jph.
Gover Mr Stephen, *Black Rock*
Hamlyn Brothers, tanners, wool-
   staplers, & serge manufacturers
Irish John & Rt. gents. *Hawsen Ctg*
King Richd. John, Esq. *Bigaden Hs*
King Mrs Grace, and Miss Ann
Lowndes Rev Mattw., B.A., *Vicarage*
Mitchell John, tinner & ironmonger
Phillips Mrs Ann, *Crappin Park*
Savery Servington, Esq. *Hayford*
Symons John, cider merchant
Symons Thomas, woolstapler
Symons Mrs., Road View House
Trist R., Esq., Milbrook House
Tucker Mr Robert and Mrs
Vaughan Mrs. *Buckfast Cottage*
Warren John, woolstapler & spinner
   FARMERS.   (* *are Owners.*)
Barter Elias, *Scorraton*
*Barter Ann, *Runnaford Combe*
Barter John, *Warnacombe*
Berry Wm. *Abbey Grange*
Bowden Jeffery ‖ Bowden James
*Callard Hy. (miller,) West Mills
Chaffe Roger, *Bigaden*
Chaffe Robert, Broom Parks
Coates John, Brook Farm
Cruse Nicholas, *Buckfast*
Foster John, *Colston*
*Furneaux Samuel, *Button*
*Furneaux Saml. & John, *Hapstead*
Heath Thomas ‖ Hendy Thomas
*Michelmore John, *Northwood*
*Petherbridge Richard, *Scorraton*
Petherbridge Wm. ‖ Hodge Mr
Preston James ‖ Rouse Mr
Preston Richard, *Bowden*
Rowland Jacob, (miller,) *Brook*
Searell Wm. and Thomas, (millers)
*Symons Thomas, *Lovers Combe*

Tooley Sus. ‖ Scott Mr
Waycott Wm. ‖ Wyatt Josias
   INNS AND TAVERNS.
Commercial, Sus. Furneaux
Globe, George Cole
Golden Lion, John Churchward
Half Moon, John Hoarse
King's Arms, John Penny
Prince of Wales, Henry Choake
Royal Oak, Samuel Churchward
Sun, John Churchward
Town Arms, Henry Wilcock
Valiant Soldier, W. Foster
Waterman's Arms, Richd. Gibbins
White Hart, Thomas Petherbridge
   BAKERS.
Chaffe Robert
Gibbins Richd.
Rice Wm.
Voce John
Wing Wm.
   BLACKSMITHS.
Barter Richard
Boys Wm.
Easterbrook Jno.
Petherbridge Jas.
Prowse John
   BUTCHERS.
Churchward Jas.
Holditch Robt.
Tooley John
Trist John
Trist Thomas
   CARPENTERS, &c.
Abbott John
Adams John
Callard Thos.
Murch Adam
Pope Wm.
Prowse John, (&
   cooper)
Wilcocks John
   LIME WORKS.
Coulton Wm.,
   Bully Clay
Furneaux Chas.,
   Baker Pits
   MASONS.
Arscott John
Border John
Churchward Jas.
Furneaux Saml.
Murch Thos.
Putt Thomas
Sincombe Peter

Weeks Jas. & Jno.
Wilcocks Henry
   PLUMBERS, &c.
Codd James
Yeo Doctor Dl.
   SADDLERS.
Easterbrook Jas.
Thomas Agnes
   SCHOOLS.
Bovey John
Butchers Jas. B.
   (and regr.)
   SHOEMAKERS.
Border Thos.
Hannaford John
Lee Edward
Petherick Richd.,
   Buckfast
Tozer James
Tozer Wm.
Winter Wm.
   SHOPKEEPERS.
Arscott Eliz.
Bastow Wm.
Bishop Thos. dpr
Butchers Richd.
Coombe Eliz.
Easterbrook Jno.
Ezekiel Lionel
Petherbridge Wm.
Shapter John
Treleaven Henry
   (and draper)
Warren Andw.
Warren Wm.
Wilcocks Eliz.
Wilcocks John
   SURGEONS.
Evans James
Fisher Thomas

TAILORS.	Bastow Wm.	Hunt John	POST OFFICE
Howell George	Bunclark John	Lock John	At Wm. Foster's
Hayman John	Churchward Jno.	Penny Thomas,	
Hayman Richd.	Codd Philip	Saml., & Geo.	CARRIERS to
Lee James	Cole John	Petherbridge Ts.	*Ashburton* daily,
Warren Wm.	Furneaux John	Shapter John	and J. & T. Wil-
WOOLCOMBERS.	Hamlyn Bros. (&	Warren John	cocks to Totnes
Arscott Wm.	manfrs)	Weeks Andrew	four times a
Bastow Jno. Cole	Howard Wm.	and John	week

CHURCHSTOW, a small village on an eminence, 2 miles N.W. of Kingsbridge, has in its parish 542 souls, and 1877 acres of land, including the small hamlet of *Venn*, and Kingsbridge Union Workhouse, as afterwards noticed. P. S. Lowe, Esq., is lord of the manor, formerly belonging to the Petres, and has a pleasant seat here called *White Hall;* but part of the parish belongs to John Savery, Esq., and a few smaller freeholders. *Ley* or *Leigh* is an ancient house, formerly belonging to the Hayes, Aldhams, aud Bickfords. The *Church* (St. Mary,) has a lofty tower and four bells, and is an ancient structure, in the perpendicular style. It was restored, cleansed, and beautified in 1849, at the cost of about £900. The east window is enriched with stained glass, and the whole interior has now a handsome appearance, the old pews having given place to open benches, and the new windows, &c., being in unison with the general character of the building. The *vicarage,* valued in K.B. at £16. 16s. 11d., and in 1831 at £126, is in the patronage of the Lord Chancellor, and incumbency of the Rev. Rd. Luney, M.A., who has 7A. 3R. 3P. of glebe, and a good residence at Kingsbridge. The great tithes were commuted in 1839 for £328 per annum. They formerly belonged to Buckfast Abbey, and now to *Acland's Charity,* as noticed at page 110. Two houses and several plots of land, vested for the repairs of the church, are let for about £17 per annum. From Acland's Charity, the vicar has £3. 6s. 8d., and the poor £2. 12s. yearly. The poor have also an annuity of 20s., left by John Peter, out of the tithes of Cornworthy.

Hill Wm. carpenter	Farley Jno.,*Venn*	Lethbridge Wm.
Lowe Peter Stanley, Esq., *White Hl*	Foale John, do	Luscombe Rd.,
Lidstone John, blacksmith	Foale Philip	*Elston*
Lidstone Wm. vict. Church House	Foale Robert	Moysey John
Luney Rev Rd., M.A.,vicar, *Kingsbdg*	Harris Edw.,*Ley*	Pepperell Richd.
Savery John, Esq. *East Venn*	*Hodge Rt., *Pool*	*Stear Roger
Stear Wm. veterinary surgeon	Hurrell Peter	
FARMERS.	Huxham Saml.,	SHOEMAKERS.
(* *are Owners.*)	*Lordswood*	Barnes John
Crocker Mr	Crimp Thos.	Helyer Edward
Brown Samuel	DareJno.,*Norton*	Lethbridge John

DARTINGTON parish, from one to three miles N.E. of Totnes, contains 603 souls, and 3248A. 3R. of land, on the south-western side of the fertile and picturesque valley of the Dart, and includes the small hamlets of *Wick, Venton, Brooking, Staple,* and many scattered houses. It was anciently the seat of a barony, which belonged successively to the Falesia, Tours, Martyn, Audley, Vere, Holland, and other families. *Henry Champernowne, Esq.,* owns two-thirds of the parish, and is lord of the manor. His seat, *Dartington House,* has been the residence of his family for many generations, and was an extensive building, consisting of two large quadrangles, one of which is in ruins, and the other was altered and partly rebuilt in the reign of Elizabeth, and has several handsome apartments and pointed windows. The great hall has a finely groined ceiling, embellished with the

arms of Richard II. and the Duke of Exeter. The grounds are extensive,
and descend to the margin of the Dart. The Duke of Somerset, J. D. Moysey, R. and W. Soper, Mrs. Farwell, and a few smaller freeholders, have
estates in the parish. *Venton,* now the property and residence of Mr. Moysey, is a large ancient house, which was formerly more extensive, and was
long the seat of the Ventons or Fentons, from whom it passed to the
Gibbes, and from the latter to the Glanvilles. The *Church* (St. Mary,) is
an ancient structure, with a tower and five bells. It is in the perpendicular style of the time of Richard II., and was renovated and newly fitted
with open benches about 15 years ago. It has a handsome pulpit and
screen, and some antique monuments of the Champernownes. The *rectory,* valued in K.B. at £36. 4s. 4½d., and in 1831 at £924, is in the patronage of Hy. Champernowne, Esq., and incumbency of the Ven. R. H.
Froude, M.A., archdeacon of Totnes, who has 108A. of glebe and a handsome residence, which he has much improved. The tithes were commuted
in 1839 for £700 per ann. Four cottages, erected in 1835 by Mrs. Froude
and Mrs. Spedding, are occupied rent free by poor families. The Parish
Lands, &c., comprise four tenements occupied by the poor, and five houses
and 8A., let for about £30 a year, of which £10 is paid to the church clerk
and singing master. Flotsley meadow (5A.,) let for £16, was given for
the poor by *Chpr. Maynard* in the 17th of Charles II. The poor have
also 28s. a year, left by John Edwards in 1610. A small church or chapel
of ease is about to be erected at *Tigley Cross,* for the accommodation of
that neighbourhood. Totnes Railway station is in this parish.

Anthony Charles, gent. *Longcause*
Branford Mrs Mary, Puddaven
Burdon Saml. farrier, Moors
Camp Stpn. & Clear Peter, smiths
Champernowne Henry, Esq. *Dart-
ington House*
Champernowne Rev Rd. B.A. curate,
Vineyard
Clear John & Emmett John, carptrs
Faremouth Rebecca, schoolmistress
Froude Ven. Robert Hurrell, M.A.
archd. of Totnes and rector of
Dartington & Denbury, *Rectory*
Gower Rev — ‖ Parnell Ann, sch.
Turpin E. mason and builder
FARMERS.
Bearne Thomas, (cider merchant)
Earle Nathl. ‖ Edmonds Nathl.
Faremouth Samuel, Westcombe

Helmes Charles, Belleleigh
Helmes Thos. (and corn miller)
Hoare Samuel ‖ Hannaford John
Lidstone James ‖ Stanning John
Maddick Robt. ‖ Parnell Rhoda
Manning Richd. (miller,) *Venton*
Maye Richard ‖ Marks John
Moysey James Dimond, *Venton*
Soper Rd. & Wm., *Higher Allerton*
Watson Humphrey, *Barton*
Watson Matts., *Shinner's Bridge*
INNS AND TAVERNS.
Champernowne Arms, Wm. White-
way, (shoemaker)
Cot Inn, Thomas Searle
Queen's Arms, George Please
Railway Hotel, Joseph Coombes
Venton Oak, Henry Clear, smith
POST from Totnes

DEAN-PRIOR parish, from 3 to 5 miles S.S.W. of Ashburton, has 552
souls, and about 4000 acres of land, including nearly 1400 acres of open
common, on the eastern side of Dartmoor Forest. Its villages are *Dean
Town* and *Dean Church Town,* on the Exeter and Plymouth road, where
there are several woolcombers, and where the gentlemen and hounds of the
celebrated *Dean Hunt* usually assemble. The manor of Dean Prior was
held by the Prior of Plympton, and now belongs, with that of Skerraton, to
Sir J. B. Y. Buller, but Sir W. P. Carew, and a few smaller owners, have
estates here. *Dean Court,* a large Tudor mansion, formerly a seat of the
Giles and Yarde families, is occupied by a farmer. The *Church* (St. George,)
has lately been rebuilt, except the tower, at the cost of about £1500, by Sir

J. B. Y. Buller, who is impropriator of the rectory, and patron of the *vicarage*, valued in K.B. at £21, and in 1831 at £309. The Rev. R. C. Kitson, who is the incumbent, has a good residence, and 23A. 1R. 17P. of glebe. The tithes were commuted in 1835, the vicarial for £228, and the rectorial for £153. 13s. 10d. The Church House was built by the parishioners in the 5th of Henry VIII., and is let for £4. 10s. *Colly Mead* (1A.,) let for £4, was given by John Edwards in 1610, two-thirds for the poor of this parish, and one-third for those of Dartington. The poor of this parish have also the following yearly sums :—20s., as interest of £20, left by one *Bowerman*, and lent to the overseers; 20s., left in 1800, by *Robt. Bradford*, out of Hamlin's tenement, at Buckfastleigh ; 7s., left by *Thomas Bovey*, and paid by the overseers of Diptford ; and £4. 10s., from £90 navy five per cent. stock, purchased with £90 left by *Wm. Stidston*, in 1818.

Barter John, blacksmith
Beer Ann, vict. Buller's Arms
Blight John, farrier
Cole George, vict. Rose and Crown
Fall Thomas, shoemaker
Gidley George, tailor
Hambling Alice, schoolmistress
Hoare Charles, butcher, &c
Hoare John, carpenter
Hoare Robert, wheelwright
Kitson Rev Charles, *Vicarage*
FARMERS.
Barter John || Brook Joseph E.
Bradridge Henry || and John

Coulton Wm. *Dean Court*
Easterbrook Elias, *Whiteoxen*
Edmunds Silvanus, *Tor-Dean*
Ford John, *Skerraton*
Hambling Henry, *Wellpark*
Meathrell Henry (and *miller*)
Parnell Wm. || Underhill Thomas
Wakeham John, Moorshead

SHOPKEEPERS.
Gidley Eliz.
Parnell Samuel
WOOLCOMBERS.
Abbott John
Abbott Richard

Abbott Wm.
Cole George
Gidley Charles
Parnell Samuel
Smith Wm.

DIPTFORD, a small village, on rising ground, in the vale of the river Avon, 5¼ miles W.S.W. of Totnes, has in its parish 755 souls, and 4144A. 3R. 15P. of land, including many scattered farm-houses, and lying in several manors. The Rev. W. C. Johnson is lord of the manor of Diptford, formerly held by the Boteler, Courtenay, Fitzcourt, Mules, Sture, and Taylor families. The heiress of the latter married the present owner. The manor of Bendley and the barton of *Stert* belong to Mr. Henry Weeks, and were long the property and seat of the Heles. *Diptford Court* is the seat and property of Thos. Butland, Esq.; and J. S. Cornish, Esq., owns *Craberton*. The Rev. H. Hare has an estate and neat mansion here, called *Courtis Knowle*, purchased by the late W. Hare, Esq., who erected the present mansion on the site of the old farm-house. It stands on an eminence, and has extensive pleasure grounds. The Ilbert, Bartlett, Webber, and other families have estates in the parish. One acre belongs to the Queen. The *Church* (St. Mary,) is an ancient structure, on an eminence near the river, and has a tower containing six bells, and crowned by a handsome broach spire. It is in the perpendicular style, but nearly all the windows are modern insertions. The *rectory*, valued in K.B. at £29. 2s. 1d., and in 1831 at £582, is in the patronage and incumbency of the Rev. W. C. Johnson, who has 2A. 3R. of glebe, and a large and handsome residence. The *Parish Lands, &c.*, given for the use of the church by Walter Toker and John Hayes, in the reign of Henry VII., comprise 74A. and two houses, let for about £50 a year. The poor have a small house in the churchyard, given in the reign of Elizabeth, and a yearly rent-charge of 30s., left by R. Nosworthy, in 1727. The *Parish School* is supported by the rector.

Butland Thos. gent. *Diptford Court*
Daykin Mrs. *Bradridge House*

Hare Rev H. *Courtis Knowle*
Johnson Rev Wm. Cowper, *Rectory*

Rake John & Prowse My. A. school
SoperJohn, *clerk*, & Prowse Jno.*sexton*
Weeks Henry, gent. *Stert House*
   FARMERS. (* *are Owners.*)
Andrews Robert, *Bradley*
Bond Wm. || Crocker Elizabeth
Cutmore Robert || Easterbrook Jas.
Evens Richard, *Blogswill*
*Foss Andrew and Peter, *Lr Combe*
Foss Richard || Foss Maria
Foss John, *Trimswell*
Furneaux George || Goss John
Harris Richard, *The Mill*
Hewitt John || Horswill Charles
Hill Wm. miller, Gara
*Jackman James || Jackson Richard
*Jonas John || Keys Joseph
LethbridgeChristopher || Lindon Jno.
Lewis John & Pp. *Binnick knoll*
*Mudge Henry, *Bendley*
Newman Thomas || Penny Mrs
*Petherbridge Robert, *Simpsons*
Pinwell Edward || White Mr
Pyles James, *Murtwell*

Smarridge Henry || Smarridge Jno.
Southwood John || Stranger Richd.
*Steer John || Shillabeer John
Woodley John, *Craberton*
Yabsley John, *New Well*
   INNS AND TAVERNS.
Star, Richard Jonas
Sun, Wm. Horswill
Tailors' Arms, Wm. Tucker
Tradesman's Arms, Samuel Clapp
Victoria, John Jonas

BLACKSMITHS.
Dennis Wm.
Ferris Wm.
Lindon John
CARPENTERS.
Hodge Thomas
Prowse James
Shute Charles
MASONS.
Brown Thos.
Clapp Samuel
Crocker Richard

SHOEMAKERS.
Blake Wm.
Horswill Osmnd.
SHOPKEEPERS.
Horswill Roger
Jonas Thomas
Rape John
TAILORS.
Jonas Thomas
Heath Wm.
Parsons Wm.

HOLNE, a small village, on an eminence, on the south-western side of the Dart valley, 3½ miles W. of Ashburton, has in its parish 394 souls, and about 5000 acres of land, but only about 2300 acres are cultivated, and the rest consists of about 500 acres of wood, and 2200 acres of moorland, in *Holne Chase*, which extends about two miles into Dartmoor Forest, amidst some of the most magnificent scenery in Devon, where the Dart is seen foaming over its rocky bed, between steep and shelving banks, and lofty, woody hills. Sir B. P. Wrey, Bart., is lord of the manor, formerly held by the Audleys and Bourchiers, and has a hunting seat here, called *Holne Chase House*, in a singularly romantic situation. He owns most of the parish, which includes the hamlets of *Michelcoombe* and *Stoke*, and a number of scattered farms; and the Hunting Boxes called *Holne Park* and *Holne Cottage*. George Jarvis, Thos. Hamlyn, George Stranger, and a few others, have small freeholds here. The *Church* was built in the 13th century, and has an embattled tower and five bells. It was renovated and beautified in 1849-50, and has a handsome pulpit and screen. The *vicarage*, valued in K.B. at £8. 5s. 5d., and in 1831 at £195, is in the patronage of the Rev. Saml. Lane, and incumbency of the Rev. John Dolbeare Parham, M.A., for whom the Rev. Saml. Hullah officiates. The Vicarage House is a neat residence, and the glebe is 26¾A. The tithes were commuted in 1837, the vicarial for £192. 11s., and the rectorial for £152. 11s. The latter belong to the patron, in right of his wife. The Church House is let for only 23s. The poor have a small old house, and the dividends of £100 navy five per cents., given by the Rev. John Charter, in 1821. The Rev. Robert Bradford left £40 a year for the poor, half to be given in money, and half in bibles. Here is a National School, established in 1835.

Andrews John, shoemaker
Barnes John, carpenter
Easterbrook Daniel, carpenter and vict. Tavistock Arms
Hullah Rev Thomas, *Vicarage*
Kendall John, Esq. *Holne Cottage*
Lillicraft Ann, schoolmistress
Norris Benjamin, tailor

Pearse Wm. blacksmith
Prowse John, blacksmith and shopr
Scott —, Esq. *Holne Park*
South Plain Wood, Copper and Tin
  Mine, H. Caunter *manager*
Tozer James, shoemaker
Townsend Stephen, carpenter
Wrey Sir Bourchier Palk, Bart.,
  Chase House (& Tavistock Hs)
      FARMERS.
*Marked * are at Stoke, and † at*
    Michelscoombe
Angel Richard, Holne

*Barter John ‖ *Beard James
†Barter George ‖ *Ford Wm.
Channing James, *Park Farm*
Ford John, *Chasegate*
Hamlyn Thomas ‖ Holditch Robt.
Mann Peter ‖ †Pearse Thomas
Petherbridge John, *Stuttaford*
Shapland Christopher, Staddicombe
Shinner Wm. ‖ Toll John
†Stranger George ‖ *Tolchard Jas.
Waycott Thomas
Widdicombe W.

HUISH, (NORTH) is a small scattered village, picturesquely situated on the western acclivities of the Avon valley, 5 miles E. of Ivybridge, and 7 miles W.S.W. of Totnes. Its parish contains 483 souls, and 2662A. 2R. 27P. of land, including *Lupridge*, and part of Newhouse hamlet. The manor, formerly held by the Damarell, Trenchard, and other families, was purchased by Richard King, Esq., in 1786, and now belongs to Thomas King, Esq., of the *Manor House*, which has been modernised and improved. Wm. Bowden Esq., owns Norris, Coombe, and other estates; and *Blackhall* is the handsome residence of Jas. Cornish, Esq., and has a stuccoed front and Doric portico. *Boterford*, now called *Butterford*, is a large mansion, formerly the seat of a family of its own name, and afterwards of the Strodes and Palks, the latter of whom rebuilt the mansion about 1790. It is now unoccupied, and belongs to the representatives of the late T. Kingwell. The *Church* is an ancient structure, with a tower, containing five bells, and crowned by a spire. It is in the decorated style, and was renovated in 1845, when a fine east window was inserted, and a beautiful altar screen erected. The west gallery and small organ were erected in 1848, and all the windows are modern insertions, except that at the west end. The *rectory*, valued in K.B. at £29. 18s. 10½d., is in the patronage and incumbency of the Rev. John Allen, B.A., who has a large and handsome residence, with beautiful grounds. The glebe is 74A. 3R. 35P., and the tithes were commuted in 1849 for £490 per annum. The rector contributed liberally towards the repairs and beautification of the church, and is the chief supporter of the *National School*, erected in 1846, in the Elizabethan style, at the cost of £170. Four acres of land, let for £5. 10s., and the Church-house, let for £7. 10s., have been long vested for the relief of the poor.

Allen Rev John, B.A. *Rectory*
Bowden Wm., Esq. *Coombe*
Cornish Jas., Esq. *Blackhall*
Horswill Samuel, shoemaker
King Thomas, Esq. *Manor House*
Parker John, schoolmaster
Squires George, wheelwright
Tucker James, tailor
      FARMERS.
Andrews Robert E. *Bradley*

Andrews Wm. *Wheeldown*
Bowden Henry, *Norris*
Bowden Thomas, Bickham
Chapple Thomas ‖ Hill Wm.
Cole Roger, miller, *Butterford*
Harris John ‖ Jonas Thomas
Hodges Peter, *Colemore*
Jourdan Wm. ‖ Luscombe John
Wakeham Thos. ‖ Wakeham Richd.
Yabsley George, *Whatcombe*

HUISH, (SOUTH) a parish of scattered houses, from 4 to 5 miles S.W. of Kingsbridge, has 368 souls, and 1150A. 2R. 14P. of land, bounded by the beach of Bigbury Bay, and including the hamlets of *Silverhill, Galmpton,* and *Hope Cove*, the latter of which is a small fishing village, where lodging-houses are about to be erected for the accommodation of sea bathers, by the Earl of Devon, who owns most of the parish, and is lord of the manors. The

Church stands in a deep valley, and is an ancient edifice, with a tower and four bells. The perpetual curacy is annexed to the vicarage of West Alvington, and the tithes were commuted in 1840, the vicarial for £90, and the rectorial for £260 per annum. The latter belong to the Dean and Chapter of Salisbury, but are leased to W. R. Ilbert, Esq. At Galmpton is a small chapel and school, belonging to the Plymouth Brethren. The church has 16s. yearly from the churchwardens of Aveton-Gifford, but the donor is unknown. *Marked* 2 *are at Galmpton, and* 3 *at Hope Cove.*

3 Blank N. vict. Hope and Anchor	Young Rev G. curate
2 Froude Wm. shoemaker	FARMERS. (*are Owners.*)
3 Hambling John, beerseller	Balkwill George ‖ Crimp John H.
2 Hinton Mr Alfred ‖ Lidstone Mrs	Hayne Wm. ‖ Jellard John
2 Jarvis Edward, shoemkr. & shopr	*Jarvis Wm. *Widdimore*
Maddick Thomas, carpenter	2*Lidstone John ‖ Maddick James
2 Mosely John, Plym. Brethren min.	2*Lidstone Richard ‖ Palfrey Wm.
Pearce Mr Thos. *Widdimore*	*Lidstone Wm. ‖ 2 Pedderick Jas.
3 Smith Lieut. *Coast-guard station*	Netherton John, Esq. *Burley*
2 Thornton James, tailor	Snowden Thomas, *Townsend's*

KINGSBRIDGE is a small but busy and improving *market town,* pleasantly situated on rising ground, at the head of the *estuary* which runs up from the English Channel, between Salcombe and East Portlemouth, about six miles below, and has several creeks projecting from either side. It is distant about 20 miles E.S.E. of Plymouth, 34 miles S.S.W. of Exeter, 12 miles from Totnes and Ivybridge Railway Stations, and 205 miles W.S.W. of London. It is in the two PARISHES of KINGSBRIDGE and DODBROOKE, the former of which comprises only 32 acres, and had 1564 souls in 1841; and the latter has 343A. 1R. 39P. of land, and 1229 souls. The town has now upwards of 3000 inhabitants, exclusive of the suburbs in the adjacent parishes of West Alvington and Churchstow, from the latter of which Kingsbridge was separated some centuries ago. Dodbrooke forms the eastern part of the town, and is divided from Kingsbridge only by a small brook, which runs to the estuary under the southern part of the town, where there is a *quay* at which coasting vessels of 150 to 200 tons burden receive and deliver cargoes of coal, corn, timber, and general merchandise. The town is highly salubrious, and has a clean and respectable appearance. It is supplied with *water* brought in pipes from the hills near Combe Royal; and with *gas* from works erected in 1834, at the cost of about £1000, raised in £7 shares. The principal street is of considerable length and breadth, and has several good inns and many well stocked shops. Behind it, on either side, are many neat gardens. The *woollen manufacture* was formerly extensively carried on here, but the last remaining factory was converted into a large *steam corn mill,* in 1845, by a company of shareholders. Here are now two foundries, a manufactory of sheep shears and other agricultural tools, a number of maltsters, and corn, coal, &c. merchants. There were formerly *weekly markets* at both Kingsbridge and Dodbrooke, the former granted about 1256, and the latter about 1461. Dodbrooke market, formerly held every Wednesday, became obsolete about the close of last century, after the establishment of a great cattle market, in 1773, which is still held on the third Wednesday of every month, as well as

a fair on the Wednesday before Palm Sunday. Kingsbridge market for corn, &c., is held every Saturday, and its large annual *fair*, for cattle, &c., is held on the 20th of July, if that date falls on a Tuesday, Wednesday, or Thursday, but if not, it is held the Tuesday after. The market is an extensive corn mart, and is well supplied with provisions, the town being in that fertile part of Devon commonly called the "South Hams." The market-house was built about the close of last century, in lieu of the old one, which stood in the middle of the street. *White Ale*, as noticed at page 488, is extensively used in this neighbourhood, where it is said to have been introduced by a German regimental surgeon, some centuries ago, at Dodbrooke, where it pays a small tithe to the rector. *Barracks* for 600 men were built at Dodbrooke, in 1804, but were taken down after the war, except the hospital and gun room. Kingsbridge has a *Joint Stock Bank.* At the bottom of the town, where the bridge stood, much of the ground has been warped in from the estuary, and below Dodbrooke is the Charleton embankment, which was made in 1805-'6, and encloses about 40 acres. The want of a *Town Hall* has long been felt; and a large and handsome building, called the *Public Rooms*, is now erecting in the Italian style, by a company, at the cost of about £1000, raised in £5 shares. This building will have accommodations for the Petty Sessions, County Court, public meetings, lectures, and the literary institutions of the town; and will have a news room and corn exchange. There is an *Assembly Room* at the King's Arms Hotel, where a large annual ball is held. There are well supplied *News Rooms* at Mr. Parkhouse's and Mr. Smale's. Kingsbridge and Dodbrooke *Literary and Scientific Institution* was established in 1848, and has a library, museum, and frequent lectures and discussions. Here are several Friendly Societies, and a *Farmers' Club.* Kingsbridge is the head of a large *Union*, and *County Court* and *Polling Districts;* and the magistrates of Stanborough and Coleridge Division hold *Petty Sessions* at the Golden Lion, every alternate Tuesday. Mr. Thomas Harris, jun., is their clerk. The *County Court*, for all the parishes in Kingsbridge Union, is held at the same house, monthly; and Mr. T. Harris, jun., is the *assistant clerk*, and Mr. N. Southwood the *high bailiff*. The July fair continues three days, during which a *stuffed glove* is hung out at the market house, as at some other fairs, and like that which is carried in procession at Exeter Lammas fair, and stuck on the top of the Guildhall.

The *manor of Kingsbridge* was held by Buckfast Abbey, as part of Churchstow, and was granted by Philip and Mary to John and Barnard Drake, who sold it to Sir John Peter. In 1793, it was sold by Lord Petre to the Scobells, and it now belongs to John Scobell, Esq. DODBROOKE is more ancient than Kingsbridge, and at Domesday Survey it belonged to the widow of Edward the Confessor, under whom the manor and parish were held, by the *De Dodbrooke* family. The *manor* passed successively to the Fitz Roald, Fitz Alan, Champernowne, Northleigh, Coxe, Southcote, and Hodges families, and is now held by John Froude, Esq.; but W. J. Clark, Esq., J. K. Gillard, Esq., and several smaller owners, have estates in the parish, mostly freehold. *Pindar Lodge*, at the Quay, was the birth-place of *Dr. John Wolcott*, who, under the assumed name of *Peter Pindar*, was the

great satirical poet of the reign of George III., and often made the broad, uncouth dialect of Devonshire, the vehicle of his witty satires. *Langwell House,* a large and ancient mansion, in Dodbrooke parish, is the seat of J. K. Gillard, Esq., and has been modernised and partly rebuilt. A house in Fore street, now Mr. Weymouth's office, is said to have been an occasional residence of the abbots of Buckfast, and still retains some finely carved wainscoting of a monastic character. KINGSBRIDGE CHURCH *(St. Edmund,)* is a large and ancient cruciform structure, with an embattled tower, containing six bells, and crowned by a spire. It is supposed to have been erected about the reign of Edward I., by permission of the rector of Churchstow; but it was rebuilt under a faculty granted by Henry II., in 1414. Its parish contains only 32 acres, nearly all in the town. It is in the same patronage, incumbency, and appropriation as Churchstow, (see page 518,) and the Rev. Richard Luney, M.A., is the present vicar, and also one of the prebendaries of Exeter. He has erected here a handsome Vicarage House; and under his judicous superintendence, the church was repewed and renovated in 1845, at the cost of more than £500. A fine lithographic print of the handsomely restored interior has been published by Mr. Roberts. The Rev. T. L. Hill is the *lecturer,* and has a salary from Duncombe's Trust Estate, as afterwards noticed. The vicar has £20 a year out of the great tithes of Churchstow; £6 a year left by the Rev. Francis Kingston; and also the great tithes of Stanscombe, and certain lands at Sherford, purchased with Queen Anne's Bounty. DODBROOKE CHURCH (St. Thomas-a-Becket,) is an ancient structure, with a tower and four bells, and was repaired a few years ago. The benefice is a *rectory,* valued in K.B. at £8. 11s. 4d., and in 1831 at £183, in the patronage and incumbency of the Rev. S. T. Mosse, M.A., who has 30 acres of glebe, and a large and handsome residence, erected in 1834. The tithes were commuted in 1846, for £104. 18s. 4d. per annum. In Kingsbridge are four chapels, viz., a *Friends' Meeting House,* erected about 1659; a *Baptist Chapel,* erected in 1702, and rebuilt in 1799; an *Independent Chapel,* formerly a Presbyterian Meeting-house, rebuilt in 1847; and a *Wesleyan Chapel,* built in 1814. *Sunday Schools* are attached to the churches and three of the chapels; and in Dodbrooke is a *National School,* established in 1847; and a *British School,* erected in 1842, at the cost of about £720.

KINGSBRIDGE CHARITIES.—The *Town Lands,* &c., which have been vested in trust from an early period, for the reparation of the church and highways, the relief of the poor, and other public uses, comprise 77 acres and 16 houses in this and neighbouring parishes, worth £200, but let for only about £100 per annum, in consideration of the fines paid by the lessees. The income is chiefly expended in repairing the church, streets, and water-works. The FREE GRAMMAR SCHOOL, with a good house for the master, was built by *Thomas Crispin,* who, in 1689, left three yearly rent-charges, viz., £5 a year for repairs; £15 for the head master, in consideration of his teaching at least 15 free scholars in classical learning; and £10 to a master for teaching 25 poor children to read and 12 to write. To provide for these payments, he left a farm of 72 acres at Washbearhays, in Bradninch, now worth about £40 a year. In 1691, WM. DUNCOMBE left all his lands and tenements, and the residue of his personal estate, to be vested, after the death of his wife and sister, for the support of a *lecturer* at Kingsbridge church; for the assistance of one or more boys going from the grammar school to Cambridge or Oxford; for apprenticing poor boys; and for the distribution of religious books. The property belonging to this charity now yields an annual income of about £360, and consists of several houses and about 290 acres of land, mostly in the parishes of Thurlestone, Sherford, and Cornworthy; and of £2330 10s. 8d. Old South Sea Annuities. A new scheme for the appropriation of this charity was sanctioned by the Court of Chancery, in 1819, and another in 1846, at the termination of a long chancery suit relating to this and Crispin's Charity. Under the latter, the lecturer's salary has been advanced from £75 to £120 per annum, and that of the master of the Free Grammar School to £50. The yearly sum of £12 is now paid for teaching poor children to read and write. Twenty free boys are now sent to the Grammar School, and the last new scheme directs that there shall be four *exhibitions* of £50 each per annum, for boys going from this school to either of the Universities, and that four apprentices' fees of £20 each shall be given

with poor boys, on being bound to masters approved by the trustees. Another chancery suit, brought against the trustees of Crispin's and Duncombe's Charities, terminated in favour of the inhabitants, in 1849. The poor of Kingsbridge have 52s. a year from *Sir J. Acland's Charity*, (see Exeter;) and 20s. a year left by *John Peter*, out of the tithes of Cornworthy. The *poor of Dodbrooke* have 20s. a year from the latter, and 26s. a year from the former. *Dodbrooke Parish Lands*, &c., vested in 1640, for the reparation of the church, &c., comprise twelve tenements, worth £72 a year, but let for only £11. 10s. 7d., in consideration of fines paid by the lessees.

KINGSBRIDGE UNION comprises the 26 parishes of Ayeton-Gifford, Buckland-out-saints, Blackauton, Bigbury, Charleton, Churchstow, Chivelstone, Dodbrooke, East Allington, East Portlemouth, Kingston, Kingsbridge, Loddiswell, Modbury, Malborough, Ringmore, South Pool, South Huish, Slapton, South Milton, Stokenham, Stoke-Fleming, Sherford, Thurlestone, West Alvington, and Woodleigh, which extend over an area of 113 square miles, and had 21,537 inhabitants in 1841, living in 4047 houses, besides which there were 260 empty houses, and 22 building, when the census was taken. Of the inhabitants 10,489 were males, and 11,048 females. The total average annual expenditure of the 26 parishes, on the poor, during the three years preceding the formation of the union, was £9069, but in 1838, it was £9118; in 1839, £10,170; and in 1849, £12,087. The *Union Workhouse* stands on the north side of the town, in Churchstow parish, and was built in 1837, at the cost of about £6000. It has room for 350 paupers, and Mr. T. C. and Mrs. Geyle are the *master* and *matron;* Mr. Thomas Harris, sen., is the *union clerk* and *superintendent registrar;* and the Rev. T. L. Hill, M.A., *chaplain.* The union is divided into 13 medical, 2 relieving, and 5 registration districts. W. Jarvis and H. Nicholls are the *relieving officers.* Messrs. F. D. and A. G. Pearce are *registrars of marriages* for the whole union, and the latter is *registrar of births and deaths* for Kingsbridge district.

KINGSBRIDGE AND DODBROOKE DIRECTORY.

The POST-OFFICE is at Mr. Wm. Heywood's, Fore street. Letters are despatched at 25 min. past 9 morning, and at 25 min. past 4 afternoon. Money Orders are granted and paid.

Those marked 1, are in * *Batts lane ; 2, Baptist lane ; 3,* *Bridge street ; 4,* *Church street ; 5, Duke street ; 6, Duncombe street ; 7,* *Ebrington street ; 8,* *Market place ; 9, Mill st.; 10,* *Quay ; 11, at* *South place ; and the others in Fore street, or where specified. Those streets marked thus* * *are in Dodbrooke, and the others in Kingsbridge.*

Adams Mr Thos. & Mrs Elizabeth
Averill Rev John (Independent)
Balkwill Mr John, Quay
9 Ball John C. tax collector
Bartlett Mr Wm. Groves
Bickford Mrs Eliz. || Coad Mrs
Clarke Rev Rt. (Bapt.) || 11 Mrs J.
Cranch Mr Roger D. || 9 Dairs Rd.
Derricott Mrs || Earle Mrs
Elliot Mrs My. || Hannaford John
Evans Mr Robt., Mount pleasant
Geyle Ts. C. master of Workhouse
Gillard John Kingwell, Esq. and Mrs
  My. *Langwell House*
Hambling W. B. gun mkr. *(& Totnes)*
Hawkins Capt. Mills, R.N. *Buttville*
Hawkins Miss || Heath Mr
Heywood Wm. professor of music
Hill Rev Thos. Leonard, *lecturer*
6 Jarvis Jas. Adams, sail maker
Jarvis Wm. relieving officer, &c
6 Kellond Mrs || Light Mr Wm.
Lane Mr Rt. || 10 Lidstone John
1 Lavers Arthur, fellmonger
Loyd Jno., Esq. *Manor House*, D
Luney Rev Rd., M.A. *Vicarage*
Manning Misses || 6 Roope Mrs

4 Martin Ts. wheelgt. & coach bldr
Martin Thomas, *Henacres farm*
Mitchell Rev Jas. & Mycock J. (Wes.)
6 Moore Eliz. nurserywoman, &c
7 Moore Thos. clerk of market
Mosse Rev Samuel Tenison, M.A.
  rector of Dodbrooke
Nicholls Henry, relieving officer
Pearce Wm. Lyfe, gent. || 3 Misses
10 Peek Charles, mariner
Pollyblank Mrs || Prout Mrs
Poulden Miss, Norton lane
Pound Geo. tract, &c. depôt
Prideaux Chas. & Roger Ilbert, Esqs
Prideaux Geo., Esq., South place
Randall Mr. Peter || 6 Roope Mrs
Roope N., Esq. *Green hill*, D
Southwood Nichs. court bailiff
Stear Pp. farmer, *High House*
Taylor Gilbert, basket maker
10 Thomas John, rope & twine mkr
Toms Reuben, cooper, &c
Tucker Rev W. H. *Ivy Cottage*, D
Westlake Fras. Hy. sec. to Mill Co
Wise Misses || Weekes Mr
Young Hy. gent. *Court farm*

Young Rev Geo. curate of South Milton, &c. Victoria place

ACADEMIES. (*take Boarders.*)

British School, Alfred Jones & Louisa D. Stocks, Dodbrooke

*Free Gram. School, Rev J. H. Moor

9*Fitzpatrick Mrs || Fletcher Mr

Gibbs Pp. (*free*) || Tucker John

*Kennedy Miss || Parker J. C.

*Trickey Jane and Elizabeth

National School, Jas. Weekes and Miss D. Fogg, Dodbrooke

Workhouse School, John Hooper

ATTORNEYS.

Haley & Square, Duncombe street

Haley Wm. Colwich, Duncombe st

6 Harris Thos. (union clerk, &c.)

6 Harris Thos. jun. (clerk to magistrates, & ast. clk. of County Ct.)

Hurrell (Rt.) & Lidstone, (Gabriel Beer) Fore street

Square John Henry (Haley & S.)

Weymouth Isaac, Fore street

Weymouth Thos. Wyse, Fore street

AUCTIONEERS.

Parkhouse Wm. (general agent)

Thomas Wm. Hy., Dodbrooke

Trant Fras. Webber, Fore street

BANKS.

Devon & Cornwall Bank; Geo. Fox, manager; & Edw. Polkinghorne, cashier

Kingsbridge Joint Stock Bank (draw on London Union Bank;) Hurrell and Lidstone, managers

FIRE & LIFE OFFICE AGENTS.

Alliance, F. S. Randall

Atlas, John Henry Square

Church of England, Rt. Hurrell

County & Provident, N. Gillard

General Fire & Life, John Worth

Imperial, James Murch

Law Fire, Isaac Weymouth

Legal & Coml., T. H. Burgoyne

Medical & Invalid, W. C. Haley

Merchant's & Tradesman's, H. Nicholls

National Mercantile, H. Eddy

Norwich Union, W. W. Prideaux

Provident Clerks, W. H. Troake

Sun, & Royal Naval & Military, W. H. Balkwill

West of England, H. Strong

Western Annuity, G. B. Lidstone

INNS & TAVERNS.

Anchor, Richard Jarvis

4 Dodbrooke Inn, Owen Sweeny

Exeter Inn, Edwin A. Bignell (and brewer and spirit merchant)

George Inn, Thomas Stear

8 King of Prussia, Wm. Hy. Thomas

King's Arms Hotel, Henry Worth

4 New London Inn, Jno. Luscombe

New Quay Inn, John L. Bond

Plymouth Inn, Cyprian Elliott

9 Seven Stars, Jane Gibson

Tradesman's Arms, Samuel Crimp

White Hart, Mary Osborne

7 White Lion, Wm. Rogers

BAKERS, &c.

Bignell John

Blamy George

Easterbrook Wm.

Foale Thomas

Osborne John

Pawley Ed. & Chs.

Pawley Simon

Prowse Wm. H.

7 Sinkins Geo.

5 White Ann

9 Winter John

BLACKSMITHS.

6 Cox Robert

Ferris Philip

4 Huxtable Wm.

Stear J.

9 Willing Mary

BOOKSELLERS, Printers, &c.

King George A.

Roberts Thomas

BOOT & SHOE MKS.

Adams John

8 Beer Wm.

7 Cousins Edw.

Crouch Edw. D

Davis Andrew

Davis John

Goss Jonathan

5 Hannaford Jno.

Harley Nicholas

Jarvis Edward

Poppleton Andw.

Port John

Port Wm.

Stentiford John

Trist Thomas

Whitell John

Williams Wm.

BRAZIERS AND TINNERS.

Blackler John

Curtis Wm. and Martin

Luscombe Jno. B.

BUILDERS AND CARPENTERS.

Adams James

5 Annis John

Branscombe John

9 Bennett Thos.

Eddy John

Polliblank Jph.

*Weeks Samuel Toup

*Wills Wm.

BUTCHERS.

Crimp Samuel

5 Hannaford Rt.

Hewitt Alice

Hingston Arthur

Langworthy Rt.

7 Lidstone Hy.

*Rogers George

Shillabeer Sus.

Shillabeer Wm.

CABINET MKRS.

Eddy Hy. (and plate glass agt)

Heath John, (& turner)

CHEMISTS & DGTS.

Balkwill W. H.

Bickford J. F.

Stoneman Wm.

Troake Wm. Hy.

Trowt Robert

CIDER DLRS.

4 Dolton Wm.

4 Ford Richard

1 Lavers Anty.

COAL MERCHTS.
10 Bond Wm.
Beer Wm.
Crouch Pp. B.
10 Hingston Jph.
10 Prynn Thos.
CORN, &c. MERTS.
10 Balkwill John
10 Beer Samuel
Beer Wm.
9 Grant Henry
CORN MILLERS.
Cole Stpn., *Washbrook*
9 Flour Mill Co.
*Pepperell Robt.
*Tucker John
CURRIERS.
Cranch John
8 Luscombe Wm.
5 Oxenham Thos
Stear Edwin
DAIRIES.
7 Crimp Mary
*Gay Wm.
Lane Wm.
6 Veale Wm.
FANCY DEPÔTS.
Moore Thos.
Prideaux Eliz. S.
GLASS, &c., DLRS.
Adams Jno. Evans
Worth John
GROCERS.
Bickford John
5 Crimp Wm.
*Crouch Pp. B.
Gillard Nichls.
(& chandler)
9 Hooper Jno. jun
Lakeman John
Murch Jas. and
Andrews Jas.
Pearce Anty. G.
Peek Thos. (tea)
Prowse Richd.
Stoneman Wm.
HAIR DRESSERS.
5 Collings Rd.
Hammett Henry
Hammett Wm.

HATTERS.
5 Garde John
Lamble John
Nicholls Henry
Pound Richd.
HORSE,&c. LETRS.
Foale Robert
5 Oxenham Ths.
IRONMONGERS.
(‡ *are agrl. implement makers and founders.*)
Beer Wm.
Blackler John
Davie Jacob
‡ Lidstone John, jun. (& shear, &c. manfr)
‡ Webber John
L. & W. DRAPERS.
Adams & Co.
Bickford Ulalia
Burgoyne Ts. H.
Lavers Hy. John
Pomeroy Maria
MALTSTERS.
Beer Wm.
9 Grant Henry
9 Hooper Jno. sen
7 Jarvis Jno. A.
7 Toms Reuben
11 Weymouth W.
MASONS, &c.
9 Cox Nicholas
King Thomas
*Kendall John
*Kendall Philip
2 Payme Wm. H.
Stear Thomas
Windeatt John
MERCHANTS.
(*See Coal & Corn.*)
MILLINERS.
Bennett Mrs
Curtis Eliz.
Cox Eliz.
Farnham Miss
Newland S.
MILLWRIGHTS.
4 Hobbs Jph.
Saunders Alex.

PAINTERS & GLZS.
Adams John E.
Bennett John
7 Hammett Ths.
Quarm Wm.
PLUMBERS, &c.
Giles Wm.
*Quarm Wm.
Toms Robert
SADDLERS.
Adams Mary
Brown Henry
Lidstone Wm.
Oxenham Thos.
Prettejohn Hbt.
SEEDSMEN.
Balkwill & Toms
Bickford John
Bond John L.
SHOPKEEPERS.
4 Bignell Geo. E.
4 Brown Thos.
Collings Eliz.
8 Edwards Eliz.
6 Hannaford Jno.
8 Humphries Sar.
1 Huxham Hy.
4 Kendall John
8 Keys Wm.
8 May Wm.
7 Sinkins Geo.
4 Weeks John
7 Whitell John
STRAW HAT MKS.
Bickford Eliz.
4 Brown Mrs
Cox Eliz.
Lane Eliza
SURGEONS.
Cornish Fras. S.
Elliot John
Ford Wm. C.

Pearce Fs. Drake
Toms Wm.
SURG. DENTIST.
6 Fox George
TAILORS.
Ash Thomas
9 Drew Wm.
5 Garde James
7 Humphries Jno.
Lamble John
Lidstone James
4 Martin John
Osborn Robert
4 Popplestone H.
Roberts Wm.
Timewell Wm.
TANNERS.
Beer Wm.
4 Pritchard Jas. and Co.
TILLAGE MERTS.
Bickford John F.
10 Bond John L.
Coaker Wm.
Crouch P. B.
VETY. SURGEONS.
Bickford John F.
1 Stear Wm., *far*
WATCHMAKERS.
Bennett James
Brown Nichls.
Easterbrook Wm.
Osborn Wm.
Small Timothy
Tickell Charles
WINE AND SPIRIT
MERCHANTS.
Bignell Edwin H.
9 Randall Fras.
WOOLSTAPLERS.
Prowse Richd.
Rule Wm.

COACHES from the King's Arms to Plymouth daily

BOATS to Salcombe, daily, according to tide

CARRIERS, Ford and Gillard to *Dartmouth*, Mon., Tu., Thur. and Fri. ; Henry Luscombe and S. Sawyer to *Plymouth*, Mon. and Thur. ; and Luscombe & Lawrie to *Totnes*, M., W., F. and Sat.

LODDISWELL is a considerable village, pleasantly situated on rising ground on the western side of the vale of the Avon, 3 miles N.N.W. of Kingsbridge. Its parish contains 1013 souls, and 3568 acres of land, ex-

clusive of the township of Buckland-Toutsaints, which is afterwards noticed. The *manor* of Loddiswell is in two moieties, belonging to Mrs. E. Wise and Mr. Thos. Harris; that of *Webbiton* belongs to Sir W. P. Carew, and that of *Staunton* to the Rev. C. Osmond; but several smaller owners have estates here. In 1463, Thos. Gyll had license to castellate his house of Hach Arundell, and enclose a park; but it has long been reduced to a farm-house. *Hazlewood*, a large and handsome mansion, with extensive grounds, is the seat of Rd. Peek, Esq., who erected it in 1830, after retiring from business as a merchant in London. *Yellow ochre* is manufactured here, and in the parish is a *copper mine*, which was opened 25 years ago, and was taken by a numerous company of adventurers in 1836, but has lately been closed. *Blackdown hill*, at the north end of the parish, commands extensive views, and has evident traces of an entrenchment. The *Church* (St. Michael,) is an ancient structure, with a tower and five bells. It retains many of its old oak seats, and contains several tablets in memory of the Wise family of *Woolston*, whose heiress married the Rev. C. Osmond. Woolston House is a large mansion, with a well-wooded lawn of 30 acres. The *vicarage*, valued in K.B. at £26. 0s. 2½d., and in 1831 at £286, with the curacy of Buckland-Toutsaints annexed to it, is in the patronage of the Executors of the Rev. C. I. Jones, and incumbency of the Rev. H. Marriott, M.A., who has 111 acres of glebe and a good residence. The tithes were commuted in 1838, the vicarial for £261, and the rectorial for £281. Of the latter, £266 belongs to Mrs. Freke, and £15 to the patrons. Here is a small *Independent Chapel*, and schools are attached to it and the church. A *Reading Room* was established by Mr. Peek, in 1839. The *Parish Lands, &c.*, given by *Sir Matthew Arundell* in 1591, and other donors, for the repairs of the church and other public uses, comprise about 50 acres and three houses, let for about £35 per annum, subject to fines on the renewal of the leases. A house at the east end of the church-yard is occupied rent-free by poor people. In 1728, RICHARD PHILLIPS gave for the relief of poor people of Loddiswell, not receiving parochial aid, a farm of 40A. 2R. 8P., called Luke's Tenement, and now let for about £40 per ann.

Cole John, gardener
Gay John, thatcher
Hill John, woolcomber
Luscombe Jno. and Hy. yellow ochre manufacturers
Manning Mr Charles
Marriott Rev Harvey, M.A. *Vicarage*
Osmond Rev Chas., M.A. *Woolston*
Peek Richd., Esq. *Hazlewood*
Popplestone Jas. vict. Church House
Rundle Thos. vict. Turk's Head
Sandover Elias, wheelwright
Street Edward, schoolmaster
Tollman John, vict. Bridge Inn
Wise Mrs Eliz., *Alleron*

FARMERS. (* are Owners.)
Beer Wm. || Came John
Crocker Thomas || Denbow John
Denbow Wm., *Woolston*
Earle Joseph, *Hach Arundell*
*Friend George || Friend Robert
*Friend Charles || Harvey John

Hurrell Richard || Huxham Wm.
*King James || Pinhay Henry
*Moysey Philip, *Tunley*
*Moysey Nichls. A., *Heathfield*
*Matthews Wm., *Hazlewood*
Pinhay Servington, *Staunton*
Popplestone John || Rundle Peter
*Prettejohn Pp. King, *Hach*
*Prettejohn Nicholas, *Yanston*
Rogers Peter and Richd., *Hazlewood*
*Treby John || Tollman John
Willing Wm. (and maltster)
*Willing Robt. Pp. || Yalland James

BLACKSMITHS.
Kennard John
Rundle John
Weeks W. P.

BUTCHERS.
*Willing Thomas
Yalland James

CARPENTERS.
Hine James

Hine John
Popplestone Jno.
Popplestone Pp.
Popplestone Rt.
Prowse John
Saunders John,
(& painter)

MASONS.
Bowden Wm.

z

Stear Henry	SHOEMAKERS.	Lake Henry	Luscombe Geo.
Taylor John	Harvey John	Lidstone John	
MILLERS.	Hoskin John	TAILORS.	POST-OFFICE
King Thomas	Yalland Thomas	Lake Hy. B.	at James Har-
Saunders Alex.	SHOPKEEPERS.	Lidstone Rd.	vey's. Letters
Willing Richd.	Guest John	Lidstone Wm.	desp. 2 aftn.

BUCKLAND-TOUTSAINTS, or *Buckland All Saints*, is a small parochial chapelry, appended ecclesiastically to Loddiswell parish, though it is
in Coleridge Hundred, and maintains its poor and roads as a distinct township. It is about two miles N.E. of Kingsbridge, and contains only 56
inhabitants, and about 500 acres of fertile land, belonging to Wm. John
Clark, Esq., of *Buckland House*, and Edward Torr, Esq., of *Bearscombe*,
or Woodmaston. The first named mansion is a large and handsome
building, with tasteful grounds, on an eminence commanding fine views.
Mr. Torr, sen., is in his 97th year, and in the enjoyment of all his faculties.
The only tenant farmer is Mr. Josias Whyat, of the *Quarry Farm*. The
manor belonged to the Toutsaint family in the reign of Richard I., and
afterwards passed to the Hills and Southcotes, the latter of whom, after
having been seated here for several generations, sold the manor in 1793 to
the late Wm. Clark, Esq., of Plymouth. The *Chapel* (St. Peter,) was very
ancient, but was mostly rebuilt in 1779, by John Henry Southcote, Esq.
It was appropriated with Loddiswell to Slapton College in the 15th century,
and is now a curacy annexed to Loddiswell vicarage, and in the same impropriation. (See page 529.) The tithes have been commuted for
£51. 10s. 6d. per annum.

MALBOROUGH is a small *village*, on an eminence, partly in West
Alvington parish, about two miles from Salcombe Haven, and four miles
S.S.W. of Kingsbridge. Its parish contains 1951 inhabitants, and 4890
acres of land, bounded on the south by the English channel, between Bolt
Head and Tail, and including the small hamlets of *Coombe, Collaton, Rew,
Bolbury, Batson*, and *Shadycombe;* and the small town, sea-port, fishing
station, and chapelry of SALCOMBE, which is pleasantly and picturesquely
situated on the western side of the estuary, which runs up to Kingsbridge,
and sends out several creeks from either side. Salcombe has now about
1500 inhabitants, though it had only 972 in 1841. It is considered the
warmest place on the south-west coast, as oranges, lemons, and American
aloes bloom in the open air, in the pleasure grounds of Woodville and the
Moult. To the lovers of coast scenery, there are many wild and romantic
spots between Prawle Point on the east, and Bigbury Bay on the west.
Salcombe is a port under Dartmouth, and has a *custom house*, built in 1848 ;
a *coast guard station*; a *market-house*, with a public room over it, erected in
1848, at the cost of £600; a *shipping insurance association*, established in
1831; three ship building yards, many good shops and neat houses, and
several handsome marine villas. It is the out-port of Kingsbridge, to which
passenger boats ply daily. The *haven* has safe anchorage for about 200
ships, and vessels of 200 tons go up to Kingsbridge. It is often used as a
harbour of refuge, and foreign vessels sometimes land their mail bags here.
The number of vessels which entered with cargoes in 1848 was 355, equal
to 16,723 tons, and the number which took cargoes out in the same year
was 211, of the aggregate amount of 7268 tons. The imports are chiefly
coal, culm, groceries, foreign fruit, &c. ; and many of the vessels built here
are employed in bringing fruit, &c., from the Mediterranean, for which trade
they are admirably adapted. The exports are corn, flour, malt, cider, potatoes, slate, &c. Crabs, lobsters, and other fish are caught here. The entrance to the harbour is protected on the west by the bold rocky promontory

of *Bolt Head*, and on the east by that of *Prawle Point*. The sea cliffs rise in rocky grandeur westward from Bolt Head, varying in height from 50 to upwards of 400 feet. Between Bolt Head and Salcombe, in the haven mouth, are two *coves*, where the trees of a *submerged forest* are found under the sands, at the depth of two to three feet, and perfect hazel leaves and nuts have sometimes been dug up. The Earl of Devon, who holds a court of admiralty for an extensive line of coast, is lord of the *manors* of Malborough, Salcombe, Ilton, East Sewer, Bolbury, Batson, Collaton-Prawle, Hope, &c., but part of the parish belongs to W. R. Ilbert, Esq., Miss Hawkins, A. Pinwell, Esq., Miss Burnell, Mr. Bastard, J. Netherton, Esq., Miss Spencer, and several smaller owners. *Ilton* had a castellated mansion, built by Sir John Chiverston, in 1335, and of which there are still some slight vestiges. The Earl of Devon's estates were passed to his family from the founder of this embattled mansion. SALCOMBE CASTLE was a strong fort, built for the defence of the harbour, about a quarter of a mile below the town, upon a rock which is insulated at high water, and sheltered behind by lofty rocky cliffs. There are still large remains of this bulwark, and the walls of the north-west angle are forty feet high, and about six feet thick. At the commencement of the civil wars of the 17th century, this castle was repaired at the cost of £3000, and Sir Edmund Fortescue was appointed governor for the King. After having sustained two other sieges, it was summoned by General Fairfax, on the 23rd of January, 1645, and after a siege of nearly four months, it surrendered on honourable terms to Colonel Weldon, governer of Plymouth; the garrison being allowed to march with their governor to his mansion of Fallapit, where the castle key is still preserved. RINGRONE, a handsome modern marine villa, with gardens extended on terraces into the estuary, is the occasional seat of *Lord Kinsale*, of Ireland, whose other titles are *Baron De Courcy* and *Baron of Ringrone*. About a mile below Salcombe is the *Moult*, the beautiful marine residence of Viscount Courtenay, (the Earl of Devon's eldest son,) picturesquely seated on the headland between the two coves, with charming walks on the slopes of the rocks. The house is in the Elizabethan style, and was commenced in 1764, by the late A. Hawkins, Esq., and sold to S. Strode, Esq., in 1785. *Horsecombe* estate has been held for some centuries by the Fairweather family, and is said to have been given to one of them by the Conqueror. Salcombe has a *fair* for pleasure, toys, &c., on Whit-Tuesday. *Malborough Church* is a large ancient structure, in the perpendicular style, with a tower containing six bells, and crowned by a spire, which may be seen at a great distance. The interior is spacious and handsome, and has an elegant white marble monument, in memory of the late Lord Kinsale. The nave was repaired in 1844, and in some of the windows the stone mullions have been replaced with wood. In the chancel are the remains of a very handsome sedilia, which was partly taken down when the south aisle was extended. As noticed at page 513, the *benefice* is a curacy, annexed to the *vicarage* of West Alvington. The *tithes* were commuted in 1841, the vicarial for £340. 3s., and the rectorial for £581. 16s. per annum. Of the latter £482. 6s. belongs to the Dean and Chapter of Salisbury; £98, under the name of Merrydale, belongs to W. R. Ilbert, Esq.; and £1. 10s. belongs to the Earl of Devon, as the Paul or Pol portion. The old *Chapel at Salcombe*, which was licensed by the bishop in 1401, had been gone to decay some centuries in 1801, when it was rebuilt, chiefly at the expense of John Yates, Esq., of Woodville. It was afterwards augmented with Queen Anne's Bounty, but being too small for the greatly increased population, it has given place to *Salcombe District Church* (Holy Trinity,) a handsome fabric, in the lancet style of the 13th century, erected by subscription and

grants in 1843, at the cost of £2605. It has a tower and bell. The interior is elegantly fitted up, and the east window is enriched with stained glass, given by Viscount Courtenay. The *perpetual curacy* is in the patronage of the vicar of West Alvington, and incumbency of the Rev. Geo. Willcock. There is a small *Baptist Chapel* at Malborough, and a small *Wesleyan Chapel* at Salcombe, the latter built in 1849. The *National School* at Salcombe was erected in 1847, at the cost of £300, and has about 200 scholars. The *Parish Lands, &c.*, comprise more than twenty small tenements, let for only about £30 a year, and mostly given by Alice Bayning and Rd. Dyer, in the 16th and 18th centuries. The income is expended on the church and poor, except £3 to the master of the parish school, which was given by Richard Dyer, in 1730.

MALBOROUGH AND SALCOMBE DIRECTORY.

The Post-Offices are at Edw. Cole's, Salcombe; and Jane Moore's, Malborough. *Those marked 2 are at Malborough, and the rest at Salcombe, or where specified.*

Adams Mr Rd., *South Down*
Andrews John, currier, &c
Ball Mrs Catherine, Baker's Well
Ball Edward, druggist, &c
Cole Edward, carver, turner, &c
Cossins Wm. Hy., custom hs. officer
Courtenay Viscount, *The Moult*
Evans Rev. ——(Baptist minister)
Hawkins Miss Hntta. H., *Alston*
Honey Wm. Ts., regr., Shadycombe
Kinsale Lord, *Ringrone* (& Ireland)
Mason Wilfred, gentleman
Morritt Capt. Geo., R.N., coast guard
Murray Rev. ——, curate
Pinwell Andw., Esq. *Mount Knowle*
Pirie Alexander, gent. *Ringrone*
Prideaux Mrs Sarah, *Cliff House*
Russell E. S. & R. milliners
Turner Rev Geo. Rd., curate, *Snapes*
Weymouth Miss Catherine, *Perrott's*
White Mr John, *Higher Batson*
Willcock Rev Geo. incbt. of Salcombe
FARMERS.
Adams George, Higher Collaton
Adams Nichls., *Rew*, & N. jun. *Ilton*
Adams T., *Clark's*, & W. *My. Knoll*
Adams Richard, Lower Rew
Balkwill Rd., *Yard*, & R. jun, *Ilton*
Fairweather James, *Horsecombe*
Fairweather J. & J., *H. & L. Sewer*
Ford Jno. & Rd., *S. & Furze Down*
Ford Wm., Higher Collaton
Hodder George, Portlemoor
Jarvis Elliott, *Weston Down*
Jarvis Sml., *Ilton*, & Jno., *Collaton*
Jarvis Thos. Adams, *Bolbury*
Jarvis John, jun. *Lodgehill*

Lakeman James, *Batson Hall*
2 Lidstone R. J. || Wm., *Newhs.*
Lindon Richard Snapes
Pepperell Robert, *Beadon*
2 Smith Ts. || Stranger Rt., *Alston*
Thorning Thomas, *Coombe*
Tutley Jph., *Batson* || 2 White Rd.
Weymouth Adams, *Weymouth's*
Weymouth Wm., *Higher Lincombe*
Wood James, *Shadycombe*
INNS & TAVERNS.
Commercial, Ann Ingram
Crown and Anchor, Wm. Rich
King's Arms, Amelia Reeve
2 Old Inn, Jane Moore
Plymouth Inn, Wm. Easton
2 Stag, Joseph Jarvis
Union, Wm. Trenick
Victoria, Mary Dawe

BAKERS.	BLOCK & PUMP MAKERS.
Chapman Henry	
Cove Philip	Cousins Thos.
Frink James	Patey Wm.
Prowse James	CARPENTERS.
Vivian Wm.	Cole Edw. jun
	Hannaford Jph.
BLACKSMITHS.	Patey Wm.
2 Hine Philip	Thorning Thos.
Thorning Hrs.	COAL DEALERS.
Whiddon George	Ball James
Wills Wm.	Chant John
	Narramore Jno.
BUTCHERS.	Pearce Sml. (and
Hannaford Wm.	stationer)
Harvey Thomas	COOPERS.
Hine Henry	Dawe Richard
Manning George	Edwards John

DRAPERS.
Brooking Har.
Hill Thos. R.
Jarvis Wm. P.
Wotton Betsy (& druggist)

MALTSTERS.
Lindon Richard
Strong Henry (& insnce. agent)
White Mr

MASONS.
Chapman Wm.
Steer George

MILLERS.
Ackrill Sarah
Adams Robert
Thorning J.(Exs. cf) *Blanks*

MR. MARINERS.
Adams Wm.
Adams John
Anthony Mr
Ball James
Ball Thomas
Ball Wm.
Cleverley Thomas
Cleverley Stn.
Cove Philip
Cove Wm.
Cowling John
Crispin George
Crispin Thos.
Crocker Henry
Dawe John
Forbes Wm.
Frink James

Frink Wm.
Gifford John
Hannaford John
Hardy Wm.
Harris Frederick
Harris Thomas
Hill John
Hill Frederick
Hingston Wm.
Hornden John & E. (fishg. smks)
Ingram John
Jarvis Peter
Jarvis John
Jarvis Wm.
Jarvis Edward
King Wm.
Lapthorn Rd.
Lapthorne Benj.
Long Samuel
May Wm.
May Thomas
Moore John
Norman T. J.
Osborne John
Osborne Wm.
Partridge John
Peek Charles
Pinwell John
Quick Edward
Quick Wm.
Randle Wm.
Russell James
Shears Wm.
Sladen Thos.
Strong James
Tolcher Joseph

Vincent Wm.
Vivian Philip
Wakeham Richd.
Weeks Samuel
Wills George
Wills Wm.
Yabsley Natl.
Yabsley Joshua
Yeoman Wm.

PAINTERS, &c.
Port George
Steer John
Steer Thomas

SAIL MAKERS.
Jarvis Jonathan
Partridge Thos.
Thorning Wm.

SCHOOLS.
Gillard Mrs
Jarvis Wm.
Lakeman Sarah
2 Pearse Hy. S.
Prowse James
Weymouth Mrs

SHIP BROKERS.
Cook Thos. (& insnce. agent)
Dawe Richard

SHIP BUILDERS.
Bunker Wm.
Evans John
Vivian James

SHOPKEEPERS.
Chapman Henry
Chapman Mary
Edwards Wm.
Evans Honor

Hicks Richard
Jarvis Josiah
Jarvis Joseph
2 Jarvis ——
Pearse Samuel
2 Prowse Edwd.
Sladen Rd. H.
Thorning Wm.
Vivian Sarah
Vivian Wm.

SHOEMAKERS.
Chadder James
Cole John
Cole Joel
Crocker John
Jarvis George
Jarvis John
May George
Port Frederick

TAILORS.
Cole John S.
Cole Samuel
Hext Richard
Jarvis Joseph
Port Charles
Sladen John H.

TINNERS AND IRONMONGERS.
Efford Robert (& plumber)
Jennings Wm.
Rendle Thos.

WINE & SP. MERTS.
Ball E. and Co
Dawe Mary

BOATS
daily to Kingsbdg.

MILTON, (SOUTH) a small village, in a deep fertile valley, 3 miles S.W. of Kingsbridge, has in its parish 475 souls, and 1556A. 3R. 11P. of land, including *Upton* and *Sutton* hamlets. Mrs. Prideaux is lady of the manor, but a great part of the parish belongs to W. R. Ilbert, Esq., of *Horsewell House*, a large and neat mansion, formerly the seat of the Roopes, from whom it passed to the Ilberts. Holwell belongs to Mrs. Gilbert, and the Rev. E. Reed and the Earl of Devon have small estates here. The *Church* is a handsome structure, of perpendicular architecture, with a lofty embattled tower, containing six bells. The benefice is annexed to the vicarage of West Alvington, and the tithes were commuted in 1839, the vicarial for £128. 4s., and the rectorial for £219. 1s. W. R. Ilbert, Esq., is lessee of the latter, under the Dean and Chapter of Salisbury. The *Parish Lands, &c.*, comprise 7 acres, and 4 cottages, let for £15. 6s., applied to the use of the church and poor.

Ilbert Wm. Roope, Esq. *Horsewell Hs*
Lee George, smith & vict. New Inn

CARPENTERS.
Lusmore Philip
Pilditch Jonathan

FARMERS.
Andrews Edward
Bow John, miller

Crimp George	Pollyblank Thos.	SHOEMAKERS.	Winsor Robert
Earle Josh.	Pollyblank Robt.	Murch James	TAILORS.
Lidstone Wm.	Shepherd Philip	Steer John	Luckham James
May Samuel	TimewellStephen	SHOPKEEPERS.	Luckham John
Murch Henry	Toye Wm.	Luckham Wm.	Luckham Wm.
Paige Richard		Wills Agnes	

MORLEY, or *Morleigh*, a small pleasant village, six miles S.S.W. of
Totnes, N.N.E. of Kingsbridge, and E. by N. of Modbury, has in its parish
202 souls, and 1487A. 2R. 24P. of land. It had anciently a market and fair,
granted in 1315. The manor passed in moieties to the Ufflete and Maynard
families, and the parish now belongs to the Rev. H. Hare, J. B. Swete, Esq.,
W. B. Fortescue, Esq., and a few smaller owners. One moiety belonged to
the late Viscount Boringdon, who in 1815 was created *Earl of Morley*, to
which title his son succeeded in 1840. *Petty Sessions* are held monthly, at
the New Inn, for Stanborough and Coleridge Division. The *Church* (All
Saints,) is a small ancient structure, said to have been built in Edward 1st's
reign, by Sir Peter Fizacre, who, in a quarrel, killed the parson of Woodleigh,
to whose parish Morley then belonged. For this crime the Pope enjoined the
knight to build a church at Morleigh. The *rectory*, valued in K.B. at £9. 8s.
1½d., and in 1831 at £157, is in the patronage of Sir H. P. Seale, and incumbency of the Rev. E. T. Seale, of Blackauton. The glebe is 16A., and the
Parsonage is a small neat residence. The tithes were commuted in 1842,
for £150 per annum. Here is an *Independent Chapel*, built in 1844, but it
stands in that part of Morleigh village which is in Halwell parish. The
poor have the interest of £10, given by Mrs. Oldrieve.

Grills Robert, blacksmith	FARMERS.
Hockin Wm. & Damarell Sar. shoprs	Bond Benjamin, *Morley Park*
Joslin Richard, wheelwright	Harvey Richard ‖ Prowse Wm.
Stockdale Rev W. F. curate, *Rectory*	Parnell John, *Place Barton*
Symonds Mr Thos. *Grimstonesley*	Randall Robt. (maltster,) Green
Tucker Wm. vict. New Inn	Symonds John, *Grimstonesley*

RATTERY, or *Rattrey*, a small village on an eminence, four miles W. by
N. of Totnes, has in its parish 485 souls, and 2823A. 3R. 23P. of land.
Marley House, a large and handsome stuccoed mansion, with a fine lawn, is
the residence of the Dowager Lady Carew, who is daughter and heiress of
the late Walter Palk, Esq., and carried the manor of Rattery and other
estates to the late Sir Henry Carew, Bart. Her eldest son, Sir W. P. Carew,
is now lord of the manor, but part of the soil belongs to R. Brown, Esq.,
and a few smaller owners. The *Church* is an ancient structure, with a
tower, containing four bells, and crowned by a small spire. It has been repaired by Lady Carew, and has now a handsome appearance. Some of its
windows have lately been decorated with stained glass. The *vicarage*, valued
in K.B. at £14. 10s., and in 1831 at £240, is in the patronage of Sir W. P.
Carew, and incumbency of the Rev. R. P. Carew, who has a good residence
and 60A. 3R. 5P. of glebe. The tithes have been commuted, the vicarial for
£200, and the rectorial for £189. 9s. The latter belong to Lady Carew.
There are two houses, a garden, and a field, vested for the repairs of the
church; and a small *Almshouse* for six poor people. The poor have £3 a
year, left by Dorothy Savery and Thomas Gould.

Carew Lady, & Hy. Esq. *Marley Hs*	Luscombe Thomas, shoemaker
Carew Rev Robert Palk, *Vicarage*	Palmer Henry, shopkeeper & mason
Chaffe Chpr. & Parnell Wm. smiths	Willsford John, shopkeeper & tailor
Coaker Wm. carpr. & vict. *Church Hs*	FARMERS. (* are *Owners*.)
Hatch Jno. & Jackson Pp. carpenters	Earle Joshua ‖ Grills Wm.

Easterbrook Wm. || Farley John
Easterbrook James, *Marley*
Gidley Mgt. & Jno. || Hatch Wm.
Grant Robert, *Allarcombe*
Hannaford John || and John, jun.
*Luscombe Philip, *Torne*

*Maddock Wm. Felwell
Metherell Edward (and miller)
Skelton Wm. || Symons Chas. & Jph.
Tozer John, *Willing*
Tooley Jeffrey || Tooley Thomas
White Jeffrey, *Luscombe*

THURLESTONE, 4½ miles W.S.W. of Kingsbridge, is a small scattered village, on rising ground, near the beach of Bigbury Bay. Its parish contains 437 souls, and 1763 acres of fertile land, including the hamlets of *Buckland, Avenmouth,* and *Bantham,* the latter of which is a small fishing village, with fine hard sands, and a salmon pool and harbour for barges. The Earl of Devon is lord of the manor, but part of the parish belongs to several smaller freeholders. The river Aven bounds the parish on the north, and the Bay on the west. On the coast is a remarkable *arched rock,* through which boats have sailed. It has for centuries braved the foaming surge : hence the proverb, " Brave every shock, Like Thurlestone Rock." It is of the red conglomerate formation. *Clannacombe,* a large Elizabethan mansion, which has been modernised, is the seat of H. R. Square, Esq. The *Church* is an ancient structure, with a tower and five bells. The pulpit is finely carved, and partly composed of elegant pannels taken from the screen. The *rectory,* valued in K.B. at £25. 10s., and in 1831 at £383, is in the patronage of Sir J. B. Y. Buller, Bart., and incumbency of the Rev. P. A. Ilbert, M.A., who has 36A. of glebe, and a large and handsome residence, erected by himself. The parish school, established in 1844, is supported by the rector. *Marked 2, are at Buckland ; 3, at Bantham ; and 4, at Avenmouth.*

Clampitt Wm. schoolmaster
2 Elliott Geo., butcher, & Mr Wm.
Elliott Nicholas, corn miller
Ilbert Rev Peregrine Arthur, M.A., *Rectory*
Square Henry Roe, Esq. *Clannacombe*
Square Mr Thos. || 2 Mordaunt Osbn.
3 Whiddon John, vict. Sloop Inn

BLACKSMITHS.
2 Ball Wm.
3 Whiddon John

FARMERS.
(* are Owners.)
Cole John

2 Elliott George
Hannaford Jph.
Hannaford Wm.
*Kingwell Thos.
4 Moore Roger
2 Moore Thos.
Robins Wm.
Shath Daniel
3 Sherriff Richd.
2 Sherriff R. jun

*Square H.R. jun
*Square John
Toye Wm. R.
White George
2 Wills Wm.
4*Winsor Wm.
SHOEMAKERS.
Hoskin Stephen
2 Sherriff John
2 Sherriff J. jun

WOODLEIGH, which gives name to a *deanery,* is a small village, in a healthy and elevated situation, on the east side of the Aven valley, 3½ miles N. of Kingsbridge. Its parish contains 269 souls, and 2319 acres of land, including the hamlets of *Priston* and *Hendham.* The manor belonged at an early period to the Damarells, but it now belongs—⅜ths to J. B. Swete, Esq., ⅛th to the heirs of F. Wise, Esq., ¼ to the heirs of Mrs. S. Edmonds, and ¼ to the heirs of Mrs. E. Netherton. The chief owners of the soil are J. B. Swete, J. Netherton, J. Luscombe, and W. B. Fortescue, Esqrs. *Wood Barton,* formerly a seat of the Fortescues, was a large quadrangular mansion, of the 15th century, but only two of its sides now remain. The *Church* (St. Mary,) is a small antique fabric, with a tower and three bells. It has lately been renovated, and a new east window inserted. The interior has several handsome mural tablets, belonging to the Luscombe, Cornish, Edmonds, and other families. The silver flagon given by Lady Amy Fortescue in 1686, weighs 4lbs. 12oz., and is emblazoned with the Fortescue and Courtenay arms. The *rectory,* valued in K.B. at £22. 8s. 4d., and in 1831 at £420, is in the patronage of Exeter College, Oxford, and incum-

bency of the Rev. George Dawson, M.A., who has 85A. 2R. 6P. of glebe, and a large and handsome residence. The poor have a yearly rent-charge of 35s. out of Lowerdale estate.

Baker Robert, carpenter, *Priston*
Blake Thos. smith & vict. New Inn
Dawson Rev George, M.A. *Rectory*
Ford Wm. tailor, and Rebecca, shopr
Gillard Mr Natl.|| Kellond Ann, *school*
    FARMERS.
Adams John Turner, *The Farm*

Bond Edward || Geyle Wm.
Gillard Richard K. *Wood Barton*
King George, (and miller)
Lavers Wm. and John, *Priston*
Luscombe George, *Priston*
Luscombe Henry, *Hendham*
Morgan Rt. *Lrdale* || Rogers Nichs.

ERMINGTON HUNDRED

Extends 14 miles northward from Bigbury Bay, and averages about six miles in breadth. The northern part of it comprises a portion of the hilly region of Dartmoor Forest, whence the river *Erme* flows southward to the ocean at Bigbury Bay, where the *Aven* also empties itself through an estuary which forms the south-east boundary of this Hundred, which is in the Southern Division of Devon, in the Archdeaconry of Totnes; in the Deaneries of Woodleigh and Plympton; in Ermington and Plympton petty sessional division; and mostly in Kingsbridge and Plymouth Polling Districts. The following enumeration of its eleven parishes shews their territorial extent, and their population in 1841:—

Parishes.	Acres.	Pop.	Parishes.	Acres.	Pop.
‡Aveton-Gifford	3952	1057	‡Kingston	2233	529
‡Bigbury	2902	652	‡Modbury	5977	2048
*Cornwood	10,680	1080	*Newton-Ferrers	2991	778
*Ermington	4952	1607	‡Ringmore	1420	362
*Harford	3680	193	§Ugborough	8659	1523
*Holbeton	4623	1120	Total	52,069	10,949

☞ Those marked * are in *Plympton St. Mary's Union*; ‡ in *Kingsbridge Union*; and § in *Totnes Union*.

AVETON-GIFFORD is a neat village, pleasantly situated in the picturesque valley of the river Aven, 3½ miles N.W. of Kingsbridge, and S.E. of Modbury. Its parish contains 1057 souls, and 3952A. 2R. 39P. of fertile land, including the small hamlets of *Ashford, Lixton, Waterhead*, and many scattered houses. The river is crossed by a good bridge, and is navigable for barges, and has a *salmon fishery* belonging to Mr. Bastard and Mr. Lowe. The manor was anciently held by the Giffards or Giffords, and afterwards passed to the Dynham, Prous, Mules, Damarell, and Berry families. It now belongs to E. R. P. Bastard, Esq.; but here is a small manor called *Heathfield*, belonging to P. Hyne, Esq., and the Barton estate belongs to J. M. Woollcombe, Esq. Part of the parish belongs to several smaller owners. A market and two fairs were granted to the lord of the manor in 1289, but they have been obsolete some centuries. The *Church* (St. Andrew,) is a large cruciform structure, in the early English style of the time of Henry III. Its tower contains six bells, and is crowned by a lofty circular turret. It is one of the finest and oldest churches in South Devon, and the interior would have a very handsome appearance if the mouldings, columns, capitals, &c., were cleansed of their many coats of whitewash. The *rectory*, valued in K.B. at £38. 1s. 8d., and in 1831 at £662, is in the patronage and incumbency of the Rev. W. P. Pitman, M.A., who has 97A.

1R. 38P. of glebe, and a large and handsome residence in the Elizabethan style, erected in 1849, and having tasteful grounds. The Baptists, Wesleyans, and Bible Christians, have small chapels here. There are 2A. of land, and several tenements and rent-charges, given by Peter Bateman and others, in the reign of Elizabeth, for the repairs of the church, and now producing £6. 8s. 10d. per annum, exclusive of fines. The poor have 8s. 4d. yearly, left by Mary Magdalen and John Elliott, and the interest of £20, left by John Horswell in 1711, and vested with the churchwardens in 1784. Marked 2 are at *Ashford ;* 3, at *Lixton ;* 4, at *Waterhead ;* 5, at *Efford ;* 6, at *Heathfield ;* and 7, at *Stadbury.*

Edgecombe Mr Rd. || Ellis Wm.
Froude Robt. grocer and insurance agent, Post office
Hyne Philip, Esq. *Grove Park*
Parker John, schoolmaster
Parsons Mrs Eliz. || Stagg Mr
Pitman Rev Wm. Parr, M.A. *Rectory*
Saunders Roger, thatcher
Sinkins George, baker
Tuckerman Mr John
PUBLIC HOUSES.
Church House, Robert Davy
Harraton Inn, Wm. Adams
King's Arms, George Prowse
King's Head, Samuel Waycott
Ring of Bells, Henry Willcocks
BLACKSMITHS.
Damarell Henry
2 Luckraft John
Morgan Peter
BOOT & SHOE MKS.
Phillips Thomas
Stentiford Thos.
Yabsley Wm.
BUTCHERS.
Pearce Wm.
Pitts Charles
CARPENTERS.
3 Sandover Wm.
Torring Rd. (& painter)

Willcocks Saml.
CORN MILLERS.
Ellis John
Pulliblank Jph.
2 Trick Charles
FARMERS.
(+ are Owners.)
6 Cowles Chas.
Daw Walter
Denbow Wm.
Dingle Thomas
Elliott Thos. L.
3 Harris John
2+Hingston Adw.

+Hodder Saml., *Harraton*
Hodder Rd., *Ley*
Kerswell Nichs.
Kerswell Wm.
Langworthy Edw.
Langworthy Fdk.
+Lauzun A. G.
Lidstone Geo.
Luggar Wm.
7 Luscombe Jno.
4 Matthews Edw.
4 Moore Thos.
+Parsons Robt.
Pearse Nathl.
+Pearse John A.
5 Peek Samuel
6 Pepperell Nchs.
Phillips John
Pitts Charles
+Sherwill Thos.
Snowden Geo.
5 Taylor Geo.
6 Toms Wm.
+Torring Grace
Torring James
2 Torring Nathl.
Torring Nchs. (& coal mert.)
2 Trick Charles

7 Wills John
Willcocks Geo.
Yabsley Josias
MALTSTERS.
Cole John
6 Cowles Chas.
Macey Richard
Matthews Edw.
Wakeham Geo.
Willcocks Hy.
MASONS.
Elliott Richard
Macey Walter
Steer James
Steer John
SHOPKEEPERS.
Froude Robert
Laskey Alex.
Parker John
Phillips John, (& ironmonger)
Tolchard John
Toms Joseph
White Sarah
TAILORS.
Chubb Edward
Chubb John
Laskey Alex.
Rolle Wm.

BIGBURY, a small village on the west side of the Aven valley, about 1¾ miles from Bigbury Bay, and 3½ miles S. of Modbury, has in its parish 652 souls, and 2902A. 2R. 29P. of land. It includes many scattered houses, and a hamlet called *St. Ann's Chapel.* The manor was held for nine generations by a family of its own name, and afterwards passed to the Champernownes, Willoughbys, and Pawlets. It now belongs to the Duke of Cleveland and the Countess Dowager of Sandwich, who are also patrons of the rectory, but part of the parish belongs to W. L. Prettejohn and several smaller owners. The *rectory,* valued in K.B. at £28. 7s. 11d., and in 1831 at £688, is in the incumbency of the Rev. Terence Livingston, who has 99A. 2R. 39P. of glebe. The tithes were commuted in 1843 for £500 per annum. The *Church* (St. Lawrence,) is an ancient structure, in the perpendicular style, with a tower containing five bells, and crowned by a spire.

Its pulpit was formerly in Ashburton church, and is finely carved. Here is a small *Baptist Chapel.* The poor parishioners have the interest of £25, left by a Mr. Lee and a Mr. Lome.

Amm James, vict. Hare & Hounds
Cocker Philip, vict. Royal Oak
Fortescue Rev Rt. Hy., M.A. curate
Hallett Jane, shopkeeper
Livingston Rev Terence, rector
Saunders John, vict. King's Arms
Taylor Jas. miller, *Nodden Mill*
Woodmason James, basket maker

BLACKSMITHS.
Foale John, *St.*
    Anne's Chapel
Luckraft Thos.

BOOT&SHOE MKS.
Bardens John
Coaker John
Lane John

CARPENTERS.
Steer Simon
Steer Thomas
Steer Thos. jun

FARMERS.
(+ *are Owners.*)
Adams John,
    Houghton
Andrews Wm.

Crocker Richard
Cuming John
Cuming Richard,
    Cumery
+Gill Nicholas
Gill Wm.
Grant James
Hancock John
Hingston Andw.
Hooppell Robt.,
    Hexdown
Hooppell Benj.
Hooppell Wm.
+Morgan Amos
Parraton Henry
+Pearse Thomas

Pepperell James
Pepperell Wm.
Reeve Wm.
Terry Richard
+Trant John,
    Foxhole
+Wroth Samuel,
    Court
Wroth S., *Tuftld*

TAILORS.
Amm James
Foot Richard

CARRIERS (*Sat.*)
    to Plymouth
Roach Nicholas
Terry John

CORNWOOD, a small village (commonly called *Cross,*) in the Yealm valley, on the southern borders of Dartmoor Forest, 4½ miles N.E. of Earl's Plympton, has in its parish 1080 souls, and 10,680 acres of land, including 700A. of woodland, and 7438A. of common, extending six miles northward, among the hills and dells of Dartmoor, to the sources of the rivers Yealm and Erme. This large parish includes many scattered houses, the small hamlets of *Cross, Lutton, Torr, Waterleet, Houndle,* and *Dunaton,* and part of the large village of *Ivybridge,* which has a post office, a district church, and a railway station, as afterwards noticed. (See Ermington.) There are *cattle fairs* at Cornwood on the first Monday in May, and the last Monday in September. Wm. M. Praed, Esq., is lord of the *manor* of Cornwood, and has a pleasant seat here, called *Delamore,* which formerly belonged to the Coles, who built the present mansion, and afterwards to the Belmaine, Maynard, Treby, and Hayes families. *Slade* is the seat of W. Pode, Esq., and formerly belonged to the Coles, Saverys, and Spurrells. *Fardell,* an old farm-house, was formerly a seat of the Raleighs, and is said to have been the occasional residence of the great Sir Walter Raleigh. (See page 220.) *Sir F. Rogers, Bart.,* is lord of the manor of Blackford, and resides at *Blackford House,* a large substantial mansion, in a delightful situation, commanding fine views. Some of the apartments are large and elegant, and graced with many good paintings, some by Vandyke, Canalitte, Vanloo, and other eminent masters. He is also owner of South Hele and Wisdom estates. John Rogers, who resided at Wisdom Barton, was created a baronet in 1699. The old farm-house, called *Colwich-town,* was the original seat of the Colwich family. The Earl of Morley and a few smaller owners have estates in the parish. The *Church* (St. Michael,) is an ancient structure, with a tower and six bells. It is chiefly in the perpendicular style of the 15th century, except the tower and part of the chancel, which are much older. It has lately been renovated, and has many mural tablets, belonging to the Rogers and other families. Sir Frederick Rogers, who died in 1777, was recorder of Plymouth, and his son, Sir F. L. Rogers, who died in 1797, represented that borough in Parliament. They were descendants from Dr Rogers, who suffered martyrdom in Queen Mary's reign. The *vicarage,* valued in K.B. at £33. 4s. 7d., and in 1831 at £350,

is in the patronage of the Bishop of Exeter, and incumbency of the Rev. H. G. Adams, B.A., who has a good residence and about 60A. of glebe. Sir F. L. Rogers, Bart., is impropriator of the great tithes, which were commuted in 1842 for £280. In 1700, £150, derived from the sale of some old *poor's land*, was laid out in the purchase of a farm of 27A. 3R. 2P., now let for about £40 a year, which is distributed in blankets and clothing among the poor parishioners. There are, belonging to the same trust, two houses, occupied rent-free by poor persons. The *Parish School*, with a house for the teacher, was built about 1818, at the expense of the Rev. *Duke Yonge*, except what was derived from the sale of an old cottage belonging to the poor. In 1811, the same Rev. D. Yonge gave the reversion of a house, garden, orchard, and two meadows at *Lutton* or *Leeton*, in trust to apply one-half of the rent in providing medical aid for the poor parishioners ; £10 a year in schooling poor children; and the residue to be distributed in bibles, prayer books, &c.

Adams Mr John, *Prettypool*
Adams Rev Herbert Geo., B.A. *Vicg*
Bidgood Mr and James Mrs. *Ivybdg*
Doddridge Jas. vict. Tavistock Inn
Northmore Mary Ann, schoolmrs.
Pode Wm., Esq. *Slade*
Praed Wm. Mackworth, Esq. *Delamore*
Rogers Sir Fredk. Lemon, Bart. *Blackford House*
Shepheard Mr Sampson
Sherwill Mrs & Wills Mr., *Ivybridge*
Sandover John, butcher and vict. Butchers' Arms, *Moor Cross*
Tregellis George, tailor
Vivian John, parish clerk

CORN MILLERS.
Barons Wm., *Wisdom Mill*
Bickle John, *Slade Mill*
Jeffery John, Old Park Mill
Leeman Henry, Fardell Mill

FARMERS. (* are Owners.)
Andrews Wm. || Atwill Richard
Carpenter Wm., *Corntown*
Chapple John, *Park* || Colton Nichs.
Colton Charles || Colton Richard
Doddridge Wm. || Honey Richard
Hillson Rt., *Stone* || Horton Alex.

Horton Alexander, jun. *Hele*
Horton Honor || Horton John
Horton John, jun || Horton Thos.
Horton Arthur Trowbridge, *Fardell*
Horton Trowbridge || and T. jun
Horton Wm., *East Start & Uppaton*
Luscombe Philip, *Colwich-town*
Luscombe Joshua N. || and Samuel
Luscombe Thomas || Mudge Hy.
Luscombe Wm. and John, *Rooke*
Nicholls Samuel || Rouse Edward
Northmore John || and John, jun
Phillips Roger || and Roger, jun
*Roberts Robert, *Lutton*
Sampson Edward || Sandover Wm.
Sanders Wm. || Walker Thomas
Sercombe Robert, *Wisdom*
Walker Dinah, *Gazeworthy*

CARPENTERS.
Nelder James
Vivian Wm.

SHOEMAKERS.
Bakerville Els.
Beal Wm.
Chalice Wm.
Elford Robert
Elford Rt. jun

SHOPKEEPERS.
Blackler James
Vivian Chtte.

WHEELWRIGHTS.
Ford John
Mudge Robert

POST from Ivybridge

ERMINGTON, which gives name to this Hundred, is a small village upon a bold eminence on the west side of the river Erme, encompassed by high hills, 10 miles E. of Plymouth, and 2 miles N.W. of Modbury. Its parish contains 1607 souls, and 4952 acres of land, including many scattered farm-houses, &c., and a large portion of the village of *Ivybridge*, noticed below. In 1623, a *meteoric stone*, weighing 23lbs., fell with a great noise from the atmosphere, at Strachleigh, in this parish, and buried itself a yard deep in the ground. A similar stone fell from the heavens in Yorkshire in 1795, and was exhibited in London. Fragments of this stone and of one which had fallen in India, were analysed, and they proved to be of the same peculiar ingredients, containing iron, nickel, &c. Lady Elizabeth

Bulteel is lady of the manor and hundred of Ermington, which was anciently a demesne of the Crown, and afterwards held by the Peverell, Fitzstephen, Bensted, Stoner, Rouse, and other families. The manor of Ivybridge belongs to Sir F. L. Rogers, Bart., and was held by the *De Ponte Hederæ*, or *Ivybridge* family, from whom it passed to the Bonvilles and Crokers. E. R. P. Bastard, Esq., T. Bulteel, Esq., the Rev. S. W. Pearse, W. Pode, Esq., and several smaller owners, have estates in the parish. *Strachleigh*, an old farm-house, was long the seat of a family of its own name. *Fawn Hotel* is a large house delightfully situated in the picturesque valley, near Erme bridge, where there is excellent trout fishing and delightful scenery. Three packs of hounds often hunt in the parish. The *Church* (St. Peter,) is a large ancient fabric, with a lofty embattled tower, containing five bells, and crowned by a crooked spire, which leans considerably on one side. It is chiefly in the early perpendicular style, and portions of its screen and sedilia remain, with the ancient piscina, stoup, &c. It has a mutilated monument in memory of the last male heir of the Strachleigh family, who died in 1583, and whose heiress married Chpr. Chudleigh, Esq. Near the church is a never-failing spring, from which water has lately been conveyed in pipes to the village. The *vicarage*, valued in K.B. at £33. 11s. 3d., and in 1831 at £411, with the curacy of Kingston annexed to it, is in the patronage of the Crown and the Rev. E. D. Rhodes, and incumbency of the Rev. Courtenay Bulteel, of Holbeton. The Rev. E. D. Rhodes is also patron and incumbent of the *sinecure rectory*, which was valued in 1831 at £463 per annum, and has about 40a. of glebe. The tithes of this parish were commuted in 1841, the vicarial for £312. 18s., and the rectorial for £557. 3s, per annum. Of the latter, £259 belongs to Lady Eliz. Bulteel, £270 to the Rev. E. D. Rhodes, £25 to Mrs. Ann Brooking, and £33 to Sir F. L. Rogers. The Vicarage House is a large building, with 2a. of glebe. Here is a small Wesleyan Chapel. The National School was built in 1841, and has a house for the master. The *Parish Lands*, &c., comprise 12a. at Kingston, given by *Alice Hatch*, in the 4th of Henry VIII., and now let for £20 a year; and two houses and two fields, given by Lady Fortescue and other donors, and now let for only 6s. 6d. per annum, in consideration of fines paid when the leases were granted. These fines are vested in £100 navy five per cents. Out of the income, £10 is paid yearly to the schoolmaster, and the rest is distributed among the poor, who have also the interest of £100, left by the *Rev. Wm. Pearse* in 1743.

ERMINGTON.
(See also Ivybridge.)

Chapple Mr Rt. || Gill Mr Nicholas
Coleman Richard, tailor
Edgecombe John, gardener
Elliott Thomas, cooper
Harben Wm. schoolmaster
Pearse Rev Saml. Wm., B.A. curate of Shaugh, &c. *Cadleigh Park*
Sandover Pp. veterinary surgeon
Toms John, gent. *Erme Villa*
Vigers Rev Wm. Edw., B.A. curate, *Vicarage*
Witheridge Philip, wheelwright
FARMERS. (+ *are Owners.*)
Barratt John || Coleman Nicholas
+Dearing John || +Gill John
Gillard John, (and lime burner)

+Hillson John || Hooppell Samuel
+Hooke James, Executors of, *Cliff*
Horton Haley || Hosking Richard
Hosking Henry || +Hosking Thos.
+Jackson Richard || James Philip
+Lethbridge Thomas, *Cadleigh*
Lethbridge Fras. & Chpr., *Hunsdon*
Luscombe George || Meathrell Wm.
Norrington Jas. || Northmore Peggy
+Northmore John, *Cadleigh*
Pedrick Robert || Rowe John
Ryder Wm., *Strachleigh*
+Rogers Ann || Sandover Thomas
+Shepheard Wm. || Shepheard John
+Toms P. M. || Trenemen Richard
+Trenemen John, *Preston*
Ward Anthony |₁ Wyatt John

INNS AND TAVERNS.
Fawn Hotel, John Gillard
Julian Arms, Haley Horton, jun.
Cadleigh Park
New Inn, Stephen Lapthorne
Old' Inn, Henry Witheridge, (and
painter, plumber, builder, &c.)
BLACKSMITHS.
Carlile Richard
Coleman Philip
Conway Wm.
Sandover Jas.
BAKERS.
Arthur Wm.
Lee John

CORN MILLERS.
Brown Wm.
Fice Henry
MASONS.
Stentiford Edw.
Stentiford Oliver
SHOEMAKERS.
Bunker George
Chapple James
Ford Henry

Ford Robert
SHOPKEEPERS.
Coleman Nichs.
Coleman Richd.
Velvin George

POST-OFFICE at
Fawn Inn. Let-
ters from Ivy-
bridge

IVYBRIDGE is a large and respectable village, with many neat houses, picturesquely seated on the banks of the river Erme, where there is an ancient ivy mantled bridge, on the Plymouth and Exeter road, 11 miles E. by N. of the former, and 34 miles S.S.W. of the latter. The South Devon Railway crosses the valley by a bridge and viaduct, a little to the north, and has a *station* here. More than half of the village is in Ermington parish, and the rest is in the three parishes of Cornwood, Harford, and Ugborough. It has a post office, several neat villas, and many good lodging houses; three large and commodious *inns*, two paper mills, a large corn mill, several good shops, an extensive joint-stock tannery and leather manufactory, a district church, and two chapels. About 17 years ago, when the new road was made, a *new bridge* was erected a little below the old one. The bed of the *river* shews, by its jagged rocks, the impetuous nature of the stream, which having but just escaped from the high moorlands, rushes down, after heavy rains, like a wild cataract, through the deep and narrow valley, the woody banks of which rise in some places, above the old bridge, so abruptly, that the foliage of the trees on either side meet, and form a sylvan arch over the river, which runs southward to Bigbury Bay, about seven miles below. The enchanting scenery of the village and neighbourhood attracts numerous visitors in summer and autumn, from Plymouth, Devonport, and other places; and the inns and lodging houses afford excellent accommodation for all ranks. Sir F. L. Rogers, Bart., is lord of the manor of Ivybridge, which extends into Cornwood and Ermington parishes. In that part of the village in the former parish, a Chapel of Ease was built by subscription in 1790, and in 1835 it was consecrated as a *District Church*. It has an embattled tower, and the living is a perpetual curacy, in the patronage of Sir F. L. Rogers, and incumbency of the Rev. J. D. Cork, M.A. An Infant School was established in 1849; and here is a small *Wesleyan Chapel*, built in 1812; and an *Independent Chapel*, erected in 1845. In the following Directory of IVYBRIDGE, *those marked* 2 *are in Harford;* 3, *Cornwood;* 4, *Ugborough; and the rest in Ermington parish.*

Abbott Wm. painter, &c
3 Bidgood Mr || 4 Blight Pp. farmer
Carkeet Wm. manager *Tanning Co*
Chapman Wm. tinner and brazier
Cole Maurice, mngr. *Union Corn Mill*
Cork Rev J. D., M.A. incumbent
Cotton Wm. Esq. *Highland House*
4 Curber John, farmer
Devon & Cornwall Tanning & Leather Co. (manufr. on a new process)
Fincher John, schoolmaster
Garrard Wm. inland revenue officer
Hartley Edmund, surgeon
Hortop Elizabeth, cider seller
3 James Mrs. *Erme House*
Lethbridge Robert, (*private lunatic asylum,*) West Park House
Mackay Wm. schoolmaster
Mathias Captain Thomas, R.N.
Menzies James, gentleman
3 Phillips Roger, gardener, &c
2 Rivers Hy. Bowen & Henry, Esqrs
Seldon Mr John || 3 Wills Mr
Sherwell John Adams, surgeon
3 Sherwell Mrs || 2 Toogood Matthew
Smith Rev P. Parker, curate

Spreat Samuel, saddler
INNS AND TAVERNS.
2 Bridge Inn, Solomon Northmore
Ivybridge Hotel, Richard Hillson
King's Arms Inn, John Seldon, jun
2 *Rivers' London Inn*, Wm. Rivers
4 Grocers' Arms, Wm. Atwill, carrier
BAKERS.
4 Blackmore Ths.
Edgecombe Jas.
Lethbridge Wm.
Methrell Joseph
Turner Henry
BLACKSMITHS.
Bird Mark
Bird Samuel
Lethbridge Chas.
BUTCHERS.
Ford Robert

Huxham Henry
Huxham Thomas
Huxham John
CARPENTERS.
Pearse Richard
Richards Edw.
LODGINGS.
Cameron Ann
Collard John
Collander Mrs
Methrell John

PAPER MAKERS.
2 Allen John
Windsor John
SHOEMAKERS.
Rowe James
Tozer Jno. barber
Traher John
Willis James
SHOPKEEPERS.
Bavin Johanna
Bird John
Bird Wm.
4 Blackmore Ths.
Blight Philip
Moore Edward
Sherwell Rd. & B.
TAILORS.
Lavers John

Sherwell Rd. & B.
Traher Wm.
WHEELWRIGHTS.
Dyer Joseph
Skelley Robert

POST-OFFICE
at John Bird's
RAILWAY.
Trains 6 times a
day, to Exeter,
Plymouth, &c
CARRIERS
To Plymouth.
Wm. Savery, daily,
& Atwill, Blight,
& Stevens, Mon.
Tu. Thu. & Sat.

HARFORD is a small scattered village, in the picturesque valley of the river Erme, 2½ miles N. of Ivybridge. Its parish includes part of Ivybridge, and contains 193 souls, and about 3600 acres of land, of which 1571 acres are cultivated, and the rest open moorland, at the southern extremity of Dartmoor Forest, where the hills rise in bold disorder from the rivers and streamlets. H. B. Rivers, Esq., is lord of the manor; but the Hall and other estates belong to Sir F. L. Rogers, Bart., and several smaller owners have estates in the parish. The *Church* is an ancient structure, with a tower and three bells: and the living is a *rectory*, valued in K.B. at £11. 14s. 4½d., and in 1831 at £210, in the patronage of T. Sanders, Esq., and incumbency of the Rev. W. F. Sanders, B.A., who has a good modern residence, and 50A. of glebe. The tithes were commuted in 1838, for £180 per annum. The Independent Chapel, the London and Bridge Inns, and one of the paper mills, at *Ivybridge*, are in this parish.

Rivers Henry Bowen & Henry, Esqrs
Sanders Rev Wm. Fdk., B.A. *Rectory*
Savage Miss Grove ‖ Crispin John
FARMERS.
Crocker Matthew, *Combeshead*

Hillson George, *Broom hill*
Sanders Henry, *The Hall*
Smith Samuel, The Glebe
Rowse Jas. Hele, *West Combeshead*
Walke Thomas, *Lukesland*

HOLBETON, a large straggling village, on an eminence, west of the Erme estuary, and four miles S.W. by W. of Modbury, has in its parish 1120 souls, and 4623 acres of land. extending to *Bigbury Bay*, and including the hamlets of *Mothecombe, Creacombe,* and *Ford,* and many scattered farm-houses, &c. Lime is burnt here, and barges of 70 tons come up the estuary. *Lady Eliz. Bulteel*, (daughter of Earl Grey, and relict of the late J. C. Bulteel, Esq.,) is lady of the manor, and has a large and elegant mansion here, called *Flete House*, which was long the seat of the ancient family of *Hele*, one of whom was created a *baronet* in 1627. This branch of the family became extinct in 1716, when the estate passed to the Bulteels. The mansion was built in the reign of Elizabeth, but its two principal fronts were altered in the castellated style, about 14 years ago, by the late J. C. Bulteel, Esq., who made other extensive improvements, one of which is a large and splendid picture gallery, well stored with the works of ancient and modern artists. *Membland Hall*, the seat of Robert Robertson, Esq., formerly belonged to the Rev. Sir Pp. Perring, Bart., and was the occasional residence

of his family, one of whom, *Sir John Perring*, was Lord Mayor of London in 1803, and was created a *baronet* in 1808. His uncle purchased the estate of the Bulteels, and rebuilt the house. Rd. Holland, Esq , the Rev. W. J. Pinwill, and several smaller owners, have estates in the parish. The *Church* (All Saints,) is a large and handsome cruciform structure, with a tower, containing six bells, and crowned by a spire. It is mostly in the early perpendicular style, and in the south aisle is a canopied monument, with a recumbent effigy of one of the Heles, and several kneeling figures. The *vicarage,* valued in K.B. at £24. 1s. 8d., and in 1831 at £300, is in the patronage of the Crown, and incumbency of the Rev. Courtenay Bulteel, who has 3A. 1R. 36P. of glebe, and an ancient residence. The tithes were commuted in 1839, —the vicarial for £340. 15s., and the rectorial for £499 per annum. Of the latter, £255 belongs to Lady Bulteel, £96 to H. R. Roe, Esq., £85 to the Rev. J. Froude, and the rest to four smaller impropriators. The rent of an acre of land, and a yearly rent-charge of 18s., are applied in repairing the church. Here are two small *chapels*, belonging to the Independents and Wesleyans; and a school, supported by Lady Bulteel. *Marked 2 are at Mothecombe ; 3, at Creacombe ; 4, at Luson ; and 5, at Battisborough.*

Axworthy Mrs. miller, *Pool Mills*
Bignell Capt. Rd. Roe, *Carswell*
Bulteel Lady Eliz. *Flete House*
Bulteel Rev Courtenay, vicar
Burrow John Charles, Esq. *Efford*
Crimp Wm. butcher
Lapthorne Robert, wheelwright
4 Pike Mr || Sandover Pp. butcher
Rabbich Thomas, vict. George Inn
Robertson Robt.Esq.*Membland Hall*
Shepheard Robert, thatcher
Wyatt Benjamin, vict. Union Inn

BAKERS.
Brooking Edw.
Penwill James
Rabbich Thomas
BEER SELLERS.
Chadder Thomas
Evens John
Giles Wm.
BLACKSMITHS.
Baker John
5 Baker Thomas
3 Brown Wm.
Lake Richard
Lake Wm.
BOOT&SHOE MKS.
Axworthy Henry

Coleman Richard
Ford Wm.
Lane John
CARPENTERS.
3 Ferris Robert
Penwill James
Rogers Andrew
Rogers Thomas
2 Stone Nicholas
Tarring Robert, (& ironmongr)
Tarring Wm.
FARMERS.
(* are Owners.)
3 Adams George
5 Avent James

5 Beer John
*Cutmore John, *Fursdown*
Elliott George
Evens John
4 Ford Henry
Ford Richard
Friend Nichls. D.
Giles Joseph
Giles Robert
*Grills John
3 Irish Elizabeth
Jarvis John
Kerswell Robert
4 Maddock John
May Jonathan
*MillmanJoseph, *Ford*
4 Nicholls Robert
Nicholls Rt. jun. (& maltster)
4 Nicholls Richd.
Roe Henry Wm.
Rowlings John
Sherrell John
Steer Spsn. L.
Tarring Jcb.& M.
Tope James

Wakeham John
Weymouth Ed. & Nics. *Pamfleet*

GROCERS, &c.
Camp Robert
2 Elliott Chpr.
Evens Ann

MASONS.
Chaffe Wm.
Godfrey John
Shephard James
Wyatt Benjamin

TAILORS.
Avery Richard
Avery Wm.
Martin Richard
Penwill Thomas
2 Stone Richard

CARRIERS
To Plymouth.
Ball Thomas
Clark Samuel
May Thomas
Stentiford —

KINGSTON, a small scattered village, 3½ miles S.S.W. of Modbury, has in its parish 529 souls, and 2233 acres of land, extending westward to the Erme estuary, and southward to Bigbury Bay. The manor of Kingston belongs to Rd. Julian, Esq., and that of Scobbescombe to T. Bulteel, Esq. The Wise family own Langston and Wonwell, and the Duke of Somerset and a few smaller owners have estates here. The *Church* is a small ancient structure, and the living is a curacy, annexed to the vicarage of Ermington. Here is a small Wesleyan Chapel.

Crimp Mr Wm. ‖ Matthews Edwin
Martin Joseph, cider dealer
Ponsford John, vict. Britannia
Prout John, miller, *Cling Mill*
Ryder Jno. brhs ‖ Trigg Js. par.clerk
Wise Arthur, Esq., Langston

BLACKSMITHS.
King James
Tollack Wm.

BOOT&SHOE MKS.
Edgecombe Els.
Pearce Wm.

CARPENTERS.
Hackworthy Sml.
Hackworthy Ths.

FARMERS.
(* *are Owners*.)
*Brooking Lewis
Brooking Wm.

Crimp Samuel
Crocker Richard
Dingle Joseph
Lakeman Rd.
Langworthy Edn.
Loy Rd. *Wonwell*
Martin Jph. *Tor*
Pearce Richard
Ryder John
Ryder Henry, *Tor*
*Sparrow John
Stidson James
Stidson Wm.

Triggs Philip
*Walker Wm.
White Jane
Willson Robert
Worth Wm.
Wyatt Francis

MASONS.
Hackworthy Geo.
Lee James
Triggs James

TAILORS.
Hackworthy Wm.
Tippett Wm.

MODBURY is a small ancient *market town*, consisting chiefly of
four streets, diverging to the cardinal points, and pleasantly situated
at the foot and on the sides of three acclivities, in the heart of a fertile district, 12 miles E. by S. of Plymouth, 4½ miles S.E. of Ivybridge Railway Station, seven miles N.W. of Kingsbridge, and 208
miles W.S.W. of London. Its *parish* contains 5977 acres of land,
extending westward to the navigable river Erme, and including
143A. of woodland, 181A. of orchards, 144A. of waste, and 85A. of
common. Its population amounted in 1801 to 1813 souls, and in
1831 to 2116, but in 1841 they had decreased to 2048. It has a
small weekly *market* on Thursday; a *great cattle market* on the
second Monday of every month ; and a large annual *fair*, for cattle,
&c., on the 4th of May, if that date falls on Tuesday, Wednesday, or
Thursday, and if not, on the Tuesday after. *Petty Sessions* are held
at the White Hart Inn, every third Tuesday, by the magistrates of
Ermington and Plympton Division, to whom Mr. Thomas Kelly, of
Yealmpton, is clerk. Modbury is said to be an ancient *borough*,
though neither incorporated nor represented. It sent two members
to Parliament in the 34th of Edw. I., soon after which it petitioned,
like many other places, to be exempt from this expense, on account of
the poverty of its inhabitants. Among the officers appointed at the
court leet of the manor, is a portreeve, who is commonly called the
mayor; and by permission of the lord of the manor, he and the leet
jury and officers have the profits of the fair, which they expend in two
dinners annually. The *woollen manufacture* was formerly carried on
here extensively, but here is now only one small serge factory. The
town consists chiefly of small old houses, but is highly salubrious,
and has numerous springs of pure water and three public conduits,
one of which was built by Adrian Swete, Esq., in 1708. The parish
has many scattered farm-houses and five corn mills; and the small
hamlets of *Caton, Leigh, Brownston, Penquit,* and part of *Ludbrook.*
It is in several *manors*, of which the following are the names and
owners,—*Modbury*, Geo. Henry Legassicke Crispin, Esq.; *Orchardton*, Lady Bulteel ; *Wymston*, W. L. Prettejohn, Esq.; *Shilston*, or
Shilveston, C. Savery, Esq.; *Edmerston*, Archdeacon Froude ; and
Traine, J. B. Swete, Esq. Other manors and estates were sold to
the tenants many years ago ; and W. M. Praed, Hy. Collins-Splatt,
S. T. Hood, J. B. Yonge, and S. Tozer, Esqrs., and several smaller

owners, have freehold estates in the parish. Modbury, the chief manor, anciently belonged to the Valletorts, from whom it passed to to the Okestons. Sir John de Okeston, by command of Edward II., conveyed it to Sir Richd. Champernowne, whose family resided here in great splendour till the end of the 17th century, in a noble mansion called *Modbury House*, which was castellated in 1334, by royal license, but was all taken down in 1705, except a small portion, now a stable and hay-loft. Tradition speaks very highly of the grandeur of this seat, and of the magnificent manner in which the *Champernownes* lived; and particularly of their keeping a very fine band of singers and musicians, in the reign of Elizabeth, when they are said to have sold nineteen manors in this neighbourhood. Several of them were knighted for military services. In 1642, Modbury House was taken by a party of parliamentarians from Plymouth, and Mr. Champernowne, with Sir Edward Fortescue, the sheriff, and others, were taken prisoners. In February, 1643, Sir Nicholas Slanning, having intrenched himself at Modbury, with 2000 men, was defeated by the Devonshire clubmen. In the reign of Stephen, a *Priory* was founded here for Benedictines, as a cell to the Abbey of St. Peter-sur-Dive, in Normandy, but it was dissolved, with other alien monasteries, in the time of Henry VI., when its revenues were valued at £70 per annum, and granted to Eton College, to which the manors *Priory* and *Penquit-and-Upton* still belong, together with the great tithes of the parish. The Champernownes of Dartington are a younger branch of the family which was seated at Modbury. *Oldaport*, or *Old Port*, a farm in the south-west part of the parish, anciently belonged to the De la Ports, and afterwards to the Somaster and Hele families. On this farm, upon a tongue of elevated land, on the east side of the river Erme, where the stream spreads into an estuary, are the foundations of an ancient *fort*, the outer walls of which may still be distinctly traced, four to five feet in thickness, and enclosing about 29 acres. When excavating, some time ago, on the south and north-west sides, the foundations of two round towers were found, and also two openings in the walls, nine feet wide. Near the latter is a well of pure water, in which was found the head of a spear, now in the possession of Mr. Pearse, the occupier of the farm. *Traine, Yarnacombe,* and some other ancient "bartons" in this parish have long been occupied as farm-houses. During the late wars, here were *barracks* for a troop of horse.

Modbury Church (St. George,) is a spacious and handsome structure, with a tower, containing six bells, and crowned by a spire, rising to the height of about 134 feet. It is about to undergo a complete renovation. The spire was rebuilt soon after 1621, but the lower part of the tower and the body of the church are very ancient, but evidently underwent considerable repairs and alterations in the 15th century. Three galleries were erected in 1716. In the south aisle is an alabaster effigy, supposed to represent one of the Champernownes; and on another altar tomb is a mutilated statue, supposed to be the effigy of a knight of the Prideaux family. The *vicarage*, valued in K.B. at £19. 11s. 0½d., and in 1831 at £355, with Brownston curacy annexed to it, is in the patronage of the Masters and Fellows of Eton College, and incumbency of the Rev. N. Oxenham, M.A., who has a good residence and 9A. of glebe. The tithes were commuted in 1840.

the vicarial for £406. 15s., and the rectorial for £788. 8s.   The latter be-
long to the patrons, but are leased to J. H. Rhodes, Esq. *Brownston
Chapel of Ease* is a small Gothic building, which was erected in 1844, by
subscription and grants, and has a small endowment from Eton College.
In the town is a small *Friends' Meeting-house*, built in 1799; a *Baptist
Chapel*, erected in 1805; and a small *Wesleyan Chapel*.   The Independent
Chapel is now a *British School*, opened in 1832.   The *National School* was
built in 1836, at the cost of £269.   *Modbury Literary and Scientific Institution* was founded in 1840, by Mr. Richard King, who was born here, but
in early life settled at New York, in America, where he amassed considerable wealth.   During one of his visits to his native place, he erected a neat
and commodious building for this institute, and also two adjoining dwellings for its endowment.   He vested the buildings in trust for the promotion of literature and useful knowledge, especially among young men.   The
institute has now a library of more than 500 volumes, and has occasional
lectures.   The building is the handsomest in the town, and its front is in
the Doric order.   Its members number about 100, and J. Andrews, Esq., is
the president.   The *Church-house* and garden were let on a lease for three
lives, about 48 years ago, at only 13s. 4d. per annum, in consideration of
a fine.   The income is expended in the repairs of the church, as also is a
yearly rent-charge of £5 out of Waishwell field, left by *Thomas Prideaux,*
in the reign of James I.   A *Charity School* for 12 poor boys was founded
by subscription in 1730, and afterwards endowed with the interest of about
£280, which arose from various benefactions.   It is now connected with
the National School.   In 1684, *John Swete* left a house and a quarter of an
acre of land, for the residence of poor parishioners.   Here is also a small
garden belonging to the poor, and now let for about 25s.   This garden is
supposed to have been charged with the yearly payment of 6s. 8d. for the
poor, by *Thomas Hill*, in 1567.

In the following DIRECTORY OF MODBURY, *those marked* 2 *are in
Brownston st;* 3, *in Church st;* 4, *at Palmcross green;* 5, *in Poundwell
street;* 6, *in Broad street; and* 7, *in Galpin street.*   The POST-OFFICE is
at Mr. Richard Hosking's, Church street, and letters are despatched at
11 morning and 2 and 4 afternoon.

Andrew Mr Thos. || and 3 Miss Eliz.
2 Avent John, gent || 3 Mrs Eliz.
3 Bartlett Misses Susan & Virginia
5 Boon Charles, hairdresser, &c
2 Bowker Mrs || 3 Dawson Rev Isaac
Burford John, horse dealer, *Yutsford*
2 Bussell Rev Joseph (Baptist)
3 Cornish Wm. chemist and druggist
5 Cridland Fras. tanner & woolstapler
Daw George, bookseller, printer, &c
2 Dobell Wm. Hy. librarian, Instn.
Edwards Captain, *Ludbrooke*
6 Flashman John, jun. tal. chandler
4 Grills Mrs Eliz. || 7 Gee Rd. crier
4 Harris John Wm. gentleman
Hood Capt. Silas Thompson, R.N., *Caton Cottage*
Hunt Mrs. *Penquit Lodge*
3 Nicholes Wm. gent || 2 Hicks Mrs
Oxenham Rev Nutcombe, M.A. vicar
3 Parminter Rev Geo. Hy., B.A. curate

Pearse Mrs Jane, *Stollaford*
3 Pearse (Fras.) & Andrews (Edwin,) saddlers
3 Pearse Cyprian, gent. & Mr Geo.
Pearse Wm. gent. *Thornham*
2 Pinhey Mr John || 7 Pollyblank J.
2 Preston Mr John || Watts John, sex.
Prettejohn Walter, gent. *Wimpston*
6 Prideaux Mary, ironmonger, &c
5 Prout Thomas, rope and bag mkr
2 Purrier Rev Hy. T., B.A. curate
2 Putt Rd. serge mfr. & woolcomber
2 Rogers Mr || 3 Terry T. excise offr
2 Sawyer James, gentleman
2 Sharland John, supervisor
6 White Jeffrey, saddler
SCHOOLS.
2 Worth Wm. || Luscombe Eliz.
British, Abraham Foster
National, Geo. Pearse & Jane White

ATTORNEYS.
Andrews John, Brownston street
Avent John, jun. Palmcross green
3 Kellock Thomas Creaser
3 Kelly Thomas; house *Yealmpton*
2 Savery John Thomas

CORN MILLERS.
Brown Richard, *Sheepham*
Chidley John, New Mill
Gale Wm. *Ludbrook*
Treeby John, *Swallow Bridge*
Williams Mrs. *Spriddlescombe*

FARMERS. (* are Owners.)
Adams Wm. *Weeke*
Adams Thomas || Andrews Richard
*Andrews Charles, *Traine*
Blackler Philip, *West Leigh*
Cowles Maria, *Yarnicombe*
*Cowles Wm. *Stubson*
Denbow John, *East Leigh*
Dingle John, *Great Orchardton*
Edwards Benj. || 2 Kerswell John
Hodder John, *Edmerston*
Horton Philip, *Shilveston*
Lakeman John N. *Spriddlescombe*
*Lakeman Nicholas, *Ashridge*
Lakeman Thomas, *Stockinbridge*
Lavers Philip, *Penquit*
Lethbridge Richd., Little Modbury
Luscombe John, *Spriddlescombe*
2 Luscombe Temperance
Luscombe Wm. *Ley*
May Elisha V. || Moysey Richard
Norrish Wm. *Shilveston*
*Pearse Richard, *Oldaport*
*Pearse Thos. (*auctioneer,*) Stollaford
2 Pickford Edward || 7 Purdy James
*Pinhey Robert || Priddle Wm.
*Prettejohn John, *Wimpston*
Rendle Thomas || Rogers John
Stroud John || 2 Taylor John
Symons Thomas, *Shilveston*
7 Tippett John || Wotton Ann
White Wm. & Edmund, *Orchardton*
Willcocks Wm. *Penquit*
*Willing Samuel || Williams Samuel
Wyatt Nicholas, *Tre-Hele*

FIRE & LIFE OFFICE AGENTS.
Atlas, John Avent
Legal and Commercial, Rd. Pearse
Norwich Union, Geo. Shepheard
Star, Philip Luscombe
West of England, J. T. Savery
Yorkshire, George Daw

INNS AND TAVERNS.
6 Bell Inn, Grace Taylor
6 Dartmouth Inn, Rt. Lyndon
2 Devonport Inn, Thomas Lock
3 Exeter Inn (empty)
Kingsbridge Inn, Robert Pinhey
3 London Inn, Wm. Brown
2 Maltman's Arms, John Oldrey
2 New Inn, Reuben Rolle
5 Plymouth Inn, John Boon
6 Tanners' Arms, James Boon
5 Union Inn, Wm. Treeby
3 White Hart, Rd. Garland (posting)

SURGEONS.
Cornish Wm. Neyle, *Brownston*
2 Langworthy Wm. Southmead
7 Langworthy Wm. Froude

BAKERS.
2 Brown Philip
3 Brown Wm.
3 Cuming Rd.
6 Pinhey Jno. B.
7 Rendle Richd.

BLACKSMITHS.
Baxter Richard
6 Bowhay John
5 Fox Francis
6 Fox Richard
7 Lavers John
2 Nichols Richd.

BOOT & SHOE MKS.
3 Cove John
7 Crocker John
2 Curzon Chas.
7 Gee Robert
3 Horswell Robt.
2 Hosegood Rt.
7 Lawry Philip
2 Pearse Thos.
2 Stentiford Edw.

BRAZIERS AND TINNERS.
6 Lear Josias
2 Trist James
7 Winter Wm.
5 Wroth Wm.

BUTCHERS.
3 Coyte Wm.
6 King Henry

COOPERS.
2 Boon John
5 Colliver Edw.
3 Cove Richard
5 Cove Peter

CURRIERS.
7 Andrews Arthur
6 Ashley Martin
   and Son

GROCERS, &c.
3 Andrews Rd.
6 Flashman Jno.
3 Hosking Rd.
7 Lyndon Rt. jun
2 Pearse Wm.
3 Spry Thomas

HATTERS.
5 Phillips Wm.
2 Shepheard Jno.

JOINERS, &c.
5 Davis James
5 Davis John
7 Davis Wm.
2 Elford John
2 Froude Robert
Tiddy David

L. & W. DRAPERS.
6 Callard Saml.
3 Knowsley Jno.
3 Shepheard Geo.

MALTSTERS.
2 Harris Sus.
3 Lakeman Geo.
2 Luscombe Pp.
   (& brewer)
3 Stidworthy Edw.
2 Webber James
   (& spirit mert)

MASONS, &c.
3 Bowhay Wm.
2 Crocker Saml.
Mortimer John
3 Stentiford Jno.

5 Toms Robert
Wyatt Samuel
    MILLINERS.
5 Callard Sus.
7 Cove Ann
2 Crocker Agnes
2 Light Maria
2 Watts Agnes
PAINTERS &GZRS.
3 Flashman Geo.
3 Flashman Wm.
2 Randall James
2 Randall J. jun
SHOPKEEPERS.
2 Crocker Saml.

5 Davis John
3 Flashman Ann
2 Gill Thomas
7 Horswell Jno.
2 Jenkins Arthur
2 Pearse Wm.
2 Perring John
2 Putt Richard
3 Roberts David
2 Shepheard Eliz.
7 Steer Thomas
    TAILORS.
2 Boon Robert
2 Coaker James
3 Coaker Robert

5 Fox John
2 Gee Anthony
WATCHMAKERS.
6 Flashman Jph.
3 Daddon Wm.
WHEELWRIGHTS.
2 Coyte Thomas
7 King John
2 Walke Nicholas

COACHES.
Two pass daily to
Plymouth and
Kingsbridge

CARRIERS.

To *Dartmouth*, J.
Tucker, Sat.
*Kingsbdg.*Sawyer
and Luscombe,
Tues. & Fri.
Plymouth, Fox
Field, Kerswell,
Sawyer & Lus-
combe, daily
Totnes, J. Lavers,
Wed. & Sat.

NEWTON FERRERS is a pleasant scattered village, on rising ground, at the head of a small creek from the estuary of the Yealm, 7 miles S.E. by E. of Plymouth, and 2 miles from the sea-coast. Its parish contains 778 souls, and 2991 acres of land, extending two miles northward along the east side of the estuary, and including the small hamlet of *Torr*, and a number of scattered farms. There are *oyster-beds* in the estuary, belonging to companies in London and Southampton; and a variety of other fish are taken here. The *manor* of Newton anciently belonged to the Ferrers family, whose co-heiress carried it in marriage to Lord St. John. It afterwards passed to the Bonville, Copleston, Hele, and other families. It now belongs in moieties to H. R. Roe and John Holberton, Esqrs., the latter of whom has a pleasant seat, called *Torr House*, where his family has resided many generations. *Gnaton Hall*, the seat of H. R. Roe, Esq., was long the residence of the Heles, and was rebuilt about twenty years ago. It is now a handsome mansion, with extensive and well-wooded grounds. The manor of *Postlinch*, or *Puslinch*, was given by one of the Ferrers to the De Pust-linch family, from whom it passed to the Mohuns, and from the latter to the Uptons. It passed with an heiress of the latter, in 1709, to Jas. Yonge, M.D., of Plymouth, and it now belongs to his great-grandson, the Rev. Jno. Yonge, who resides at *Puslinch House*, a large and handsome mansion, which was built by Dr. Yonge, soon after he came to the estate, at the cost of about £9000. The house has tasteful grounds, and commands a fine view of the vale of the Yealm. *Torr Villa*, the delightful residence of J. B. Yonge, Esq., was built about 25 years ago, and is shut in on the east and west by high tors and woody acclivities. E. R. P. Bastard, Esq., and a few smaller owners, have estates in the parish. The *Church* (Holy Cross,) is an ancient structure, with a tower and five bells, and was repaired and new seated about 60 years ago. Near Puslinch House stood the ancient chapel of *St. Toly* (Olave,) but its remains were removed some years ago. The *rectory*, valued in K.B. at £45. 2s. 1d., and in 1831 at £533, is in the patronage and incumbency of the Rev. John Yonge, B.A., whose ancestor, the above-named Dr. Yonge, purchased the advowson of the Duke of Leeds in 1728. The glebe is 88A. 3R. 6P., and the tithes were commuted in 1839 for £440 per annum. An *Almshouse*, supposed to have been founded by Sir Warwick Hele, in 1625, was rebuilt by the parishioners about thirty-five years ago, but has no endowment. The poor have 10s. a year, left by Walter Carkeete. The *National School* is supported chiefly by the rector.

Marked * are at Torr.
Adams Saml. land surveyor, *Rectory*

Baker Elizabeth, blacksmith
Bone Mr Edward ‖ Depone Mrs

Bunker Robert, corn miller
Dolling Saml. purser || Sholl Miss
Glanville Capt Wm. Fanshaw, R.N.
Hingston John, boat builder
Holberton Lieut Jno., R.N. *Torr Hs*
Kingcome Henry, ferry & fisherman
Loye Peter, vict. *Dolphin Inn*
Parsons John, thatcher
Pemphraze Alex., purser, R.N.
Roe Hy. Richard, Esq. *Gnaton*
*Rowe Richard, cider dealer
Winter Silas, auctioneer
Yonge Rev John, B.A. rector, *Puslinch House*
Yonge John B., Esq. *Torr Villa*

BOOT&SHOE MKS.
Fowler John
Irish John
Loye John

CARPENTERS.
Sanders Wm.
*Knight Thos.
Stevens Wm.

Tope Wm.

COAL DEALERS.
Shillabear Agns.
Winter John

FARMERS.
Chaffe Richard
Cornthwaite Jno.
Doddridge Wm.
Loye Richard
Luscombe Robt.
Martin Charles
Matthews Wm.
Parnell Samuel
PittsWm.*Brownston*
*Shepheard Jno.
*Steer George
Wilcocks Jph. D.
Willing Andrew ·

*Wills Richard
Winter John

MASONS.
*Barnes Thomas
Miller Wm.

SHOPKEEPERS.
Candish James
Leonard Philip
*Rowe James
Stone John

TAILORS.
Leonard Philip
Leonard Wm.

CARRIERS to
*Plymouth, Tu.
Thurs. & Sat*
*Jones Wm.
Winter John

RINGMORE, or *Rinmore*, a small scattered village, near Bigbury Bay, 1½ miles S. of MODBURY, has in its parish 362 souls, and about 1400 acres of land, bounded on the south and east by the sea and the mouth of the river Aven. H. R. Roe, Esq., is lord of the manor, formerly held by the Fitzstephen, Fishacre, and other families. The *Church* is an ancient fabric, with a tower and two bells, and the living is a *rectory*, valued in K.B. at £19. 10s. 7½d., and in 1831 at £309, in the patronage and incumbency of the Rev. G. Butland. The poor parishioners have a house, given by Fras. Kirkham, in 1768.

Butland Rev Gilbert, *Rectory*
Jay Robt. shopr. & vict. *New Inn*
Treble Robert, mason.

BOOT & SHOEMKS.
Elliott John
Hooppell Nichs.

CARPENTERS.
Cocker James
Cocker Jas. jun.

FARMERS.
Crimp John
Crimp Benjamin
Hodder John, *Marwell*
Loye Jno. *Renton*
Martin Wm.

Randle Peter
Randle Robert
Sparrow Benj.
Sparrow John
Triggs James
WhiteJno.&Jane, *Okenbury*

UGBOROUGH is a neat and pleasant village, on the slopes of an eminence, surrounded by higher hills, 2½ miles E. of Ivybridge, and N.N.E. of Modbury, and 1½ mile S.W. of Kingbridge Road Station. Its parish contains 1532 souls, and 8659 acres of land, generally fertile, and extending westward to the river Erme. It includes several handsome mansions, and many respectable farm-houses, and the small hamlets of *Ludbrooke. Cheson, Nilham, Wrangaton, Fileham*, and part of *Ivybridge*. (See page 541.) There is a conduit in the centre of the village, and the church stands on the crown of the hill, which commands delightful views. Large *cattle fairs* are held here on the last Tuesdays in May and November, and here was formerly a monthly fair. The manor of Ugborough (*Ulgeberge*,) belonged to Alured Brito at Domesday Survey. It afterwards passed to the Briwere, Loring, Bonville, Grey, Harris, and Palk families. The heiress of the latter married Sir H. Carew, whose son, Sir Walter Palk Carew, Bart., is now lord of this and other manors in this parish, which comprises 200A. of wood, 150A. of orchards, and 2631A. of open common, rising in bold hills on the north. S. Savery, G. Mitchell, W. Widdicombe, J. Lang, J. P. Sawyer, and J. L. Templer, Esqrs., have estates here, and part of the parish belongs to several smaller owners, mostly freeholders. FOWELLSCOMBE,

the large and handsome seat of Servington Savery, Esq., is a fine mansion, in the Tudor style, delightfully situated about a mile from the village. It was built in 1537, by *Sir Thos. Fowell,* whose family resided here for many generations. Sir Edmund Fowell was created a *baronet* in 1661, and on the death of his grandson, the last baronet, the estate passed to the Champernownes. It was afterwards held by the Herberts and Kings. The mansion has been enlarged in modern times, and contains many large and elegant apartments. Its grounds are extensive, and tastefully laid out, and command charming views. *Ludbrooke* and *Fileham* were the seats of families of their own names, and *Stone* was long held by the Damarells. The *Church* is a large and handsome structure, with a lofty embattled tower, and a richly ornamented stone pulpit. It is in the perpendicular style of the 15th century, and the interior is about to be cleansed of the many coats of whitewash which now disfigure the beautiful capitals and mouldings. The *vicarage,* valued in K.B. at £20, and in 1831 at £260, is in the patronage of the Grocers' Company, London, and incumbency of the Rev. John May, B.A., who has a good residence, and 70A. of glebe. The rectorial tithes were appropriated to Plympton Priory. In 1786, Cphr. Savery, Esq., sold nearly the whole of these tithes to the principal landowners, and the remainder, with the advowson, to the Grocers' Company. By a commutation in 1842, the vicar has £185, and Sir W. P. Carew £202 yearly, in lieu of tithes. The poor parishioners have 50s. a year, out of Rope-ridge-field, left by Sir John Fowell. *Sir John Kempthorn,* an eminent naval commander, who died in 1679, was born at Witchcombe, in this parish. The *Independents* have a small chapel here. *Marked* 2, *are at Bawcombe ;* 3, *Caton ;* 4, *Fileham ;* 5, *Ludbrooke ;* 6, *at Wrangaton ;* 7, *at Cheston ; and* 8, *at Ivybridge.*

Baker Ann, schoolmistress
Crimp George, saddler
Crocker Lieut. Hy., R.N., *Newhouse*
May Rev. John, B.A., *Vicarage*
Middleweek Robt. cattle dealer
Mitchell George, Esq. *Venn*
Sanders Mr John || Soper Mr Henry
Savey Servington, Esq.,*Fowellscombe*
Sawyer Jno. Pearse, Esq., *Fileham*
Templer John Line Esq., *Torr hill*
Toms Mr Richard, Quarry
Velvin Robert, butcher
White Arthur, steward to Sir W. P. Carew
Widdicombe Wm. & Son, (John,) auctioneers & land surveyors and agents, *Hey and Ludbrooke*
Willing Mr Samuel, Peepmill cottage
CORN MILLS.
Lavers John, *Earlscombe*
Parker Edward, *Bittaford Mill*
Parker Alexander, *Owley Mill*
Torr ——, *Turtley Mill*
INNS AND TAVERNS.
Anchor, John Rogers
Aven Inn, (empty,) *Newhouse*
Carew Arms, Henry Langworthy
Church House, Philip James

8 Grocers' Arms, Wm. Atwill
Horse&Groom, S. Truman, *Bittaford*
Ship, John Newman
BAKERS.
8 Blackmore Ts.
Garratt John
BLACKSMITHS.
5 Bowey Richd.
Dodderidge Jph.
Henley Richard
6 Mumford Jno.
Newman John
BOOT&SHOE MKS.
Hurrell Henry
Kent Thomas
Moore Wm.
Scoble Joseph
Stentiford Chas.
CARPENTERS.
Horswill Henry
Jeffrey Wm.
Watts Wm.
FARMERS.
(* are Owners.)
Beable Edward
Beable Wm.
Beable Thos.
8 Blight Philip

Bradridge Thos.
Cole Richard
7 Crocker John
Crossing Thos.
4 Cuming Geo.
8 Curber John
Denbow John
7 Dennis Wm.
Dewdney Thos.
Gill Wm.
Goodman James
Heath J., *Turtley*
Hewitt John
* 2 Hodder Stvn.
* 2 Hodder Wm.
HoskingR., *Stone*
Kingwell Isaac
* Lang Jno. Z. S.
Lang Wm. & J.
Lavers Wm.
Luscombe Geo., *Witchcombe*
Luscombe Saml.
Luscombe Thos.
Luscombe Wm.

Marshall John
Matthews Henry
Middleweek Pp.
Moysey Nichls.
6 Newman Thos.
Newman Wm.
Paige Francis
4 Parsons Wm.
Pearn Joseph
Pulleyblank Jno.
Pulleyblank Fdk.
Sanders Thomas
Sherwill Thos.
Sherwill James
Smerdon Robert
Stolley David
Stroud Wm.

4 Tapson Wm.
Trist John
Trist Wm.
Veale Samuel
Velvin Robert
Wakeham John,
 Monks moor
6 * White John
* Widdicomhe S.
Winter Richard
Wotton Wm., *Tor*
MASONS.
Baker Wm.
Hurrell Richard
Lethbridge Rd.
Lethbridge Rt.
Mabin Wm.

SHOPKEEPERS.
Chapple Eliz.
Ford Robert
Jeffrey Robert
Prettejohn Wm.,
 Newhouse
Stentiford Chas.
Toulcher Wm.
Vollett ——
TAILORS.
Beare Robert
Beare John
Toulcher Wm.
Tucker Thos.
WHEELWRIGHTS.
Beable Edward
Willing G., *Caton*

POST-OFFICE
at Rt. Beare's.
Letters desp.
4 afternoon
RAILWAY.
Trns. from Kings-
bridge Road &
Ivybridge stns.

CARRIERS.
To *Plymouth,*
Veale & Toulcher,
Thurs. & Sat.
To *Totnes,* Wm.
Toulcher, Tu.,
& to *Kingsbdg.*
Monday

PLYMPTON HUNDRED

Extends more than sixteen miles southward from the hilly region of Dartmoor Forest to the English Channel, between Plymouth Sound and Bigbury Bay, but it is only from 6 to 4 miles in breadth. It is bounded on the west by the river Plym, which falls into Plymouth Sound; and on its south-eastern side, it has the estuary of the Yealm. It is crossed by the South Devon Railway, and is in the Southern Parliamentary Division of Devon, in Plymouth Polling and County Court District, in the Archdeaconry of Totnes, and Deanery of Plympton. It comprises only the eight *parishes of Brixton, Plympton-Earl or Plympton-Maurice, Plympton St. Mary, Plymstock, Revelstoke, Shaugh-Prior, Wembury, and Yealmpton,* which comprise about 33,000 acres of land, and 10,722 inhabitants.

PLYMPTON ST. MARY UNION comprises the eight parishes of this Hundred, and those of Cornwood, Compton, Ermington, Egg-Buckland, Harford, Holbeton, Newton-Ferrers, St. Budeaux, Tamerton, Pennycross, and Bickleigh. These 19 parishes comprise an area of 116 *square miles,* and had 19,817 *inhabitants* in 1841, living in 3687 *houses ;* besides which, there were 210 unoccupied houses, and 34 building, when the census was taken in that year. Of the inhabitants, 10,148 were *males,* and 9669 *females.* The total annual average expenditure of the 19 parishes on the poor during the three years preceding the formation of the union, was £8952. In 1838, their expenditure was £7066 ; and in 1840, £8206. The *Union Workhouse,* at Underwood, near Plympton St. Mary, is a large substantial building, with room for more than 200 inmates. Harry Bulteel Harris, Esq., is *chairman,* and J. B. Yonge and Hy. Rivers, Esqrs., are *vice-chairmen* of the Board of Guardians, who meet every Friday. Mr. Nicholas Lockyer, of Plymouth, is *union clerk and superintendent registrar ;* and Mr. Thomas Southwood, of Underwood, is *relieving officer* for the whole union. The *registrars of births and deaths* are Messrs. Wm. Pearse, for Yealmpton District; and Thomas Southwood, for Plympton District. Mr. Fredk. C. Nettleton, of Ridgway, is the *registrar of marriages ;* Christpr. Harris, Esq., *treasurer ;* and Mr. Wm. Hughes, *auditor.* The union is divided into eight *medical districts ;* and Messrs. J. Sherwell, G. Harrison, W. H. Winchester, W. S. Langworthy, J. F. Coad, and D. Jones, are the *surgeons.*

PLYMPTON ST. MARY UNION FARMERS' CLUB has a numerous list of members, including the Earl of Morley, and most of the gentry of the district and neighbourhood. It holds its annual meetings at the George Inn, Ridgway.

PLYMPTON MAURICE, or PLYMPTON EARL, is an ancient disfranchised *borough*, and a small *stannary and market town*, pleasantly situated in a fertile vale, about 5 miles E. by N. of Plymouth, and 2 miles E. of the river Plym. It has in its parish only about 170A. of land, and 933 inhabitants, including 95 in Plympton House Lunatic Asylum. It had a grant for a market and fairs at a very early period. It has now a *market* for provisions, every Saturday ; a *cattle market*, on the first Wednesday of every month ; and four annual *fairs*, on Feb. 25th, April 5th, Aug. 12th, and Oct. 29th. The town consists of four small streets, with a few respectable dwellings in the suburbs. The barony of Plympton was given by Henry I. to Richard de Redvers, or Rivers, whom he created Earl of Devon. His son Baldwin, the second Earl, rebelled against King Stephen, and was banished, but afterwards returned, and died in possession of the earldom, to which his son and his two grandsons, in their turns, succeeded. Richard, the first earl, built *Plympton Castle*, which was long the baronial seat of his family, and of which the large artificial mound on which the keep stood still remains, with some portions of the walls and fosse. Leland calls it " a faire large castelle and dungeon, whereof the waulles yet stonde, but the logginges within be decayed." Camden describes the ruins as the miserable remains of a castle ; yet so lately as 1606, the office of constable of Plympton Castle was reckoned among those of the royal household, with a fee of £4. 11s. 1d. per annum. It is said, that while Baldwin de Redvers was defending Exeter against King Stephen, the garrison at Plympton Castle surrendered it to the King, by whose orders it was dismantled, and nearly levelled with the ground. It was probably never afterwards occupied as a fortress, though some of the habitable part was suffered to remain. At the commencement of the civil wars, Plympton was the head quarters of the small force which the royalists had then in the county ; and it was one of the principal quarters of Prince Maurice's army, whilst besieging Plymouth, from October to December, 1643. The King had a garrison here, which was taken by the Earl of Essex, in July, 1644, with eight pieces of ordnance. The barony of Plympton, except during short intervals, when it was vested in the Crown by attainder, was possessed by the successive Earls of Devon, till the death of Edward Courtenay, the 18th Earl, in 1566, without issue, when this and other large estates were divided among his four aunts, or their representatives. The Earl of Morley is now lord of the manor and barony, of which a considerable portion was purchased by his father of the Prideaux family. Plympton sent two members to parliament from the time of Edward I. till 1832, when it was disfranchised by the Reform Act. Though not included in the Municipal Act of 1835, it is an ancient *borough*, claiming prescriptive rights, and having a governing *charter* of the 4th of Wm. and Mary, styling the *Corporation*, " the mayor, bailiff, and burgesses of the borough of Plympton-Earle," and appointing it to consist of a mayor, nine capital burgesses, or aldermen, and an indefinite number of burgesses, or freemen, with a recorder, town clerk, &c., &c. ; the aldermen to form the common council, and the mayor, recorder, and deputy, and the ex-mayor, to be justices of the peace, with exclusive jurisdiction. A commission of the peace has since been granted to the borough. The *Guildhall* is a neat building, with the date 1696 on its south front, and contains a fine portrait of *Sir Joshua Reynolds*, painted by himself. This eminent artist was born here, and his father was master of the Grammar

School. The following is a list of the present *Corporation, Borough Magistrates, and Public Officers.*

MAYOR—Rev. W. J. Coppard. || RECORDER—D. Boger, Esq.
Borough Justices—Rev. Dr. Williams, W. H. Molesworth, Esq., and Thomas Pode, Esq.
ALDERMEN—Paul O. Treby, H. H. Treby, J. S. Arscott, Thos. Pode, Robt. Aylwin, and D. Boger, Esqrs.; Rev. Dr. Williams & Rev. W. J. Coppard.
TOWN CLERK—Thomas Harris || TREASURER—Thos. Sherwill.
Sergeants at Mace—John Sendey and Thos. Michelmore.
Inspector of Weights and Measures—John Hurrell.

The *Parish Church* (St. Maurice,) is said to have been originally founded as a chantry chapel, by John Brackley, who endowed it with land which was valued at the dissolution, in 1547, at £7. 5s. 8d. per annum. It is a small neat fabric, standing near the castle mound. The benefice is a perpetual curacy, valued in 1831 at £100 per annum. It is in the patronage of the Dean and Canons of Windsor, and incumbency of the Rev. C. K. Williams, D.D. The tithes were commuted in 1845, the vicarial for £56, and the rectorial for £2. The patrons are impropriators of the latter, and the Earl of Morley is the lessee. The *Independents* and *Wesleyans* have small chapels here. The GRAMMAR SCHOOL, a fine building in the perpendicular style, with a good house for the master, was built in 1664, pursuant to the will of *Elize Hele*, who, in 1658, left £1800 for its erection and endowment, and directed that it should be free for the poor children of Plympton, Brixton, and other parishes, under the control of Sir John Maynard and his heirs. The endowment consists of Holland Farm, (140A.,) let for about £170 per annum. Since 1838, the master has only received £80 a year, and the rest of the income is accumulating for the establishment of an English School, so that the poor may derive some benefit from the charity, as intended by the founder. In 1687, *Mary Moulton* left Hiley Field, (1A.) for the poor parishioners; Prior's Park, (1A.,) for the perpetual curate and the poor; and Horsman's Meadow, for the sole benefit of the curate. The poor have also 14s. a year from Rawlin's and Revel's Charities; (see Plymouth;) 30s. a year from 2 roods of land, purchased with £40, left by Sir Wm. Hele and Mary Drake. The dividends of £180 four per cent. stock, left by *Wm. A. Kite*, in 1816, are applied as follows:—£4. 10s. 6d. to the poor of this parish; 10s. 6d. to poor widows of the Archdeaconry of Totnes; and £2. 2s. to the Plymouth Dispensary. *Plympton House*, a handsome mansion, with tasteful grounds, was formerly the seat of the Treby family, but is now a a well-conducted *Lunatic Asylum*, established in 1835, and having accommodation for about 90 patients. It was first opened by Dr. Duck, but was taken by Mr. Richard Langworthy, in 1842, and the reports of the inspecting magistrates are highly complimentary to his skill and management. *Wm. Cotton, Esq.*, of Highland House, Ivy Bridge, has a very extensive and valuable collection of paintings, original drawings, costly engravings, and other works of art, which he has liberally offered for the use of the public, provided a suitable building is erected and supported by subscription for their reception, at Plympton Earl, the birth-place of that great artist, Sir Joshua Reynolds. No money has yet been subscribed towards the foundation of the necessary building; but it is hoped the gentry of the neighbourhood will not suffer this munificent offer to be lost. Only one of the four *fairs*, noticed at page 552, are now held, on the Tuesday after Oct. 28. The weekly *market* is now obsolete; and the cattle market has been changed to the first Monday of every month. Plympton Grange belongs to Mr. P. T. Treby; and the Hunt, Bodger, Molesworth, Mudge,

Scott, and other families, have houses and small estates in the *parish*, which comprises 203A. 3R. 37P., including roads, &c.

Adams Mr R. || Cole Mr Samuel
Anderson Wm. cooper
Arscott John Strode, solicitor
Axworthy Rev Wm. (Independent)
Bodger Deeble, solicitor
Bodger, Bodger, & Bewes, solicitors
Brook George, beerseller
Brown Thomas, tanner
Clements Mr Wm. || Creft Mrs
Crews George, brewer and maltster
Eveleigh Wm. hat manufacturer
Forster Mrs and Miss Harriet
Greenhow ———, civil engineer
Hewlett Mr Wm. S. || Jones Misses
James Mr W. T. || White Edw. tailor
Langworthy Richard, surgeon and proprietor of the *Lunatic Asylum*, Plympton House
Molesworth Walter Hele, Esq.
Mudge Admiral Zachary
Patey Rev Geo. W. P., B.A., master of the *Grammar School*
Pode Stephen Henry, surgeon
Pode Thomas, surgeon
Roberts Richard, tea gardens
Scott Rev George M.
Sherwill Thos. clerk || Rowe Wm.

Smith Major Geo. || Washer H. *exc*
Sunderland Captain, R.N.
Toop Wm. vict. London Inn
Williams Rev. C. K., D.D., incumbt

ACADEMIES.
Grigg Miss
Hook Chrltte.
PateyRevG.W.P.
Stuttiford Mr

BAKERS.
Dyer Benjamin
Julien George
Murch Samuel

BLACKSMITHS.
Lavers James
Maddock Robt.

BOOT&SHOE MKS.
Ballhatchett Rd.
Hurrell John

BUTCHERS.
Crossing Wm.
Elford Thomas
Hillson John
Pearse Joseph

CARPENTERS.
Hellings Wm.
Redpath Richd.

Webber Edward
FARMERS.
Goodman Thos.
Pearse Joseph
Watkins Edward
MASONS.
Daily Thomas
Murch Wm.
SHOPKEEPERS.
Elford Thomas
Julien George
Jerman Samuel
Murch Wm.
White Edward

POST OFFICE
at S. German's.
Letters from Ridgway
RAILWAY.
Trains to Exeter, Plymouth, &c., six times a day

PLYMPTON ST. MARY adjoins Plympton-Earl, and is an extensive parish, on the east side of the vale of the river Plym, from 3 to 5 miles N.E. of Plymouth. It contains 9984A. of land, and 2757 inhabitants. It has no village of its own name, but includes those of RIDGWAY, UNDERWOOD, and COLEBROOK, and the hamlets of *Hemerdon, Sparkwell, Venton,* and part of *Lee Mill Bridge.* It includes the *seats* of Saltram, Newnham Park, Furzdon, Beechwood, Hemerdon House, Goodamore, Chaddlewood, &c., and many scattered farm-houses, some of them about four miles N.N.E. of the church, among the hills on the southern borders of Dartmoor Forest. RIDGWAY is a large and respectable village near the church, and *Plympton Railway Station,* 3½ miles N.E. of Plymouth. It has three inns, at one of which (the George,) *petty sessions* are held every alternate Tuesday, by the magistrates of Ermington and Plympton Division, to whom Mr. T. Kelly, of Yealmpton, is clerk. UNDERWOOD is a considerable village, near Ridgway, and in it is the *Union Workhouse*, as noticed at page 551. This workhouse is a large stone building, in the Elizabethan style, erected in 1841. There is a *cattle fair* at Underwood, on the 5th of July. A *College* was founded at Plympton St. Mary, by one of the Saxon kings, for a dean and four prebendaries, or canons; but it was suppressed by Bishop Warlewast, in 1121, because the chapter "wold not leve their concubines." The bishop founded on the site of the college a *Priory of Black Canons,* which was endowed by the Earl of Devon, Walter de Valletort, and other benefactors, and became one of the most opulent monasteries in the county. Its revenues were valued at the dissolution at £912 per annum. In 1534 it was surrendered by John Howe, the last prior, who, with twenty

monks, subscribed to the king's supremacy. The site, with the demesne, was granted to Arthur Champernowne, and was afterwards sold to the Strodes. The estate was subsequently sold in parcels, and the immediate site of the Priory now belongs to Mr. Heal, corn miller. The Earl of Morley is lord of the manor and barony of Plympton, and resides at SALTRAM, a stately mansion, in an extensive and finely wooded park, on the east side of the river Plym, about 2 miles E.N.E. of Plymouth. In the reign of Charles I., Saltram was the property and residence of Sir James Bagg, Knight. Having been forfeited to the crown, it became the property of Lord Carteret and Mr. Wolstenholme, who sold it in 1712 to *Geo. Parker, Esq.*, great-grandfather of the late Earl of Morley. In 1774, *John Parker, Esq.*, was created *Baron Boringdon;* and his son, in 1815, *Viscount Boringdon and Earl of Morley.* The latter died in 1840, and was succeeded by his eldest son, the *Right Hon. Edmund Parker,* the present Earl, who was born in 1810, and his eldest son in 1843. The noble mansion of Saltram is the largest in the county, and was mostly built by *Lady Catherine Parker,* mother of the first Lord Boringdon, and daughter of Earl Poulett, who was Secretary of State to Queen Anne. The superior beauty of this situation induced the Parkers to continue the enlargement of the mansion and the embellishment of the grounds, and to leave their ancient family seat of *Boringdon,* which is now a farm-house, but its deer park is still preserved as an adjunct to the grounds of Saltram, which possesses many singular attractions; for, exclusive of a great diversity of landscape, and many massy woods, the prospect of Plymouth Sound, the town, citadel, Mount Edgecombe, and the endless variety of effects peculiar to the sea and harbour, are extremely interesting and amusing. The groves and lawns of Saltram, overlooking the waters of the estuary of the Plym, called the Lara, are the scenes of many pic-nic parties during the summer season. The house has been much improved by the late and present Earls, and is surrounded by a beautiful lawn and grounds of about 300 acres. Its western front is 170 feet, and its southern and eastern fronts 130 feet in length. It contains many large and elegant apartments, and an extensive and costly collection of paintings of the most famous ancient and modern artists; as well as many other choice and rare articles of *virtu.* Among the paintings are some of the finest works of Titian, Rubens, Michael Angelo, Vandyke, Paul Veronese, Guido, Domenichino, Vandervelde, Poussin, Salvator, &c. In the great staircase is a magnificent picture of the Assumption, by Sabbatini; and in the library are some fine portraits by Sir Joshua Reynolds. The ceilings of the grand saloon and dining room were painted by Zucchi. Not far from this princely mansion is an extra-parochial piece of land, of 175 acres, called *Chelson Meadow,* which was recovered from the tides in Chelson Bay, by means of an embankment, 2910 feet long, and about 16 in height. This improvement was effected by the late Earl, at the cost of £9000, in the early part of the present century, and he received for it the gold medal of the Society of Arts. Plymouth races are held on this meadow. Among other improvements effected by him, may be named the new approach, which, after passing through a gloomy wood, leads the visitor to a most delightful prospect of the sea, and its promontories, bays, harbours, &c. He also constructed a dry dock in Catwater Bay, for the repairing of large vessels.

A great part of the parish of Plympton St. Mary belongs to Geo. Strode, R. Z. Mudge, E. Tolcher, H. H. Treby, Geo. Woollcombe, G. W. Saltau, and Wm. Bratton, Esqrs., Mrs. Symons, and several smaller freeholders, most of whom have pleasant seats here. The Earl of Morley owns *Cole-*

brook, which came to his family with the heiress of the Mayhews. *Hemerdon House* is the seat of Geo. Woollcombe, Esq. Newnham, the ancient seat of the Newnhams and Strodes, is now a farm-house; but the mansion in *Newnham Park*, built about the beginning of last century, is the handsome residence of Geo. Strode, Esq., several of whose family have at various periods represented the borough of Plympton in Parliament. *Beechwood House*, built in 1797, is the seat of Colonel Mudge; and *Chaddlewood*, anciently belonging to the Snellings and Martyns, is now the seat of Mrs. Symons. *Goodamore* is the pleasant seat of H. H. Treby, Esq., and was purchased by his grandfather, the late Commissioner Ourry. The *Church of Plympton St. Mary* was anciently the conventual church of the Priory. It is a spacious and handsome structure, built at the period when a mixture of the decorated and perpendicular styles prevailed. It consists of a chancel, north and south porches, a fine tower, and a spacious nave, with two side aisles, and also two exterior aisles, which have anciently been chapels. The columns are clustered and composed of granite. The chancel has three ancient sedilia, with a cinquefoiled arch, and a piscina. The east window is very rich in marygold tracery, and below it is a neat Gothic altar screen of stone, in five compartments, recently erected. The rood loft and screen are gone, but the spiral staircase which led to the loft remains. The crypt, under the chancel, is the burial place of the Earl of Morley's family. There is a piscina in each of the exterior aisles, and in that on the north side is a highly enriched monument of 1460, in memory of Richd. Strode, Esq., and another in memory of Sir Wm. Strode and his two wives, with their effigies, dated 1637. In the south chapel is an ancient tomb, with a recumbent effigy in armour, to the memory of one of the Courtenays. The tower contains six heavy bells, and rises to the height of 82 feet, exclusive of the four octagonal turrets, crowned by small crocketted spires, which increase the height to 110 feet. The south porch is finely groined, and has a stoup and three canopied niches in the interior, and one on the exterior. On entering the church, the eye is struck by its extent, there being no galleries to intercept the view of the columns and arches, which present themselves in their full proportions and unusual combination. After the dissolution of the Priory, the Dean and Canons of Windsor became appropriators of the *tithes*, and patrons of the *perpetual curacy*, now valued at £150, in the incumbency of the Rev. W. J. Coppard, M.A. He has a yearly stipend of £54. 12s. out of the tithes, and the benefice has been augmented with £300 from Queen Anne's Bounty, and a parliamentary grant of £1000. The tithes were commuted in 1840 for about £1500 per annum, and are leased to the Earl of Morley. There are small *Wesleyan Chapels* at Ridgway and Lee Mill Bridge. There are large NATIONAL SCHOOLS at *Ridgway* and *Sparkwell*, the former founded in 1844, and the latter built by Col. Mudge, and used as a *chapel of ease* for that part of the parish, which is four miles from the church. The *Maudlin Lands*, comprising about 10 acres, are let for about £30 a year, which is distributed among the poor parishioners. They formerly belonged to a small *lepers' hospital* here, but have been long vested in trust for the poor. An old almshouse was sold in 1810 for £163, which was expended in erecting five rooms adjoining the old parish workhouse. The poor have also £2. 5s. 6d. yearly out of the Crown Rents, under the name of "a pension for the poor men of Plympton Hospital." The Earl of Morley and others are trustees. The rent of a small garden is applied in aid of the church rates.

In the following DIRECTORY OF PLYMPTON ST. MARY PARISH, *those marked* 2 *are at* RIDGWAY; 3, *at* UNDERWOOD; *and* 4 *at* COLEBROOK.

EARL OF MORLEY, *Saltram House*
Adams Mr Wm. || 4 Bickley John
2 Andrew John, auctioneer & survr
Bratton Wm. Esq. *Blackland*
2 Chubb John, coal dealer
Coppard Rev Wm. J., M.A. incbt. and rural dean
3 Croker Mr John || 2 Creft Mrs
3 Croker Elias || 2 Edmonds Misses
Daw John Crossman, master of the Union Workhouse
2 Dixon Noel, timber mert & sawyer
2 Earl John, plumber, &c
Eastlake Geo. Esq. *St Mary's hill*
Evans Wm. Esq. *Mount Priory*
Fox Thomas Weare, Esq. *Fursdon*
Fox Wm. Esq. *Elford Leigh*
Giles Mr and Mrs. *National School*
2 Grills John, gardener
Holman Benj. paper mkr. Lee mill
2 Jenvey Mr & Mrs. National Schools
3 Jones Misses || 3 Kingdon Mrs S.
2 Laskey Edward, lodgings
2 Lister Wm. painter, &c
3 Manning Mr Rd.||McCullock Mrs
Molesworth Walter Hele, Esq. *Goodamore*
Mudge Col. Rd. Z. *Beechwood Hs*
2 Newman Wm. rope and bag mkr
2 Nicholls John, watchmaker
2 Osmond James, surgeon
2 Pye Rev Wm. P. curate
Sibley Colonel, Rose Cottage
2 Smyth Rev John, St Stephen's
2 Southwood Thos. relieving officer
Strode Geo. Esq. *Newnham Park*
Symons Mrs., *Chaddlewood*
Tolcher Edward, Esq. *Harewood Hs*
Toms Jonathan, timber merchant
Treby Henry Hele and Paul Ourry, Esqrs. *Goodamore*
Vaudon Constantine Esq. *Blkmoor*
2 Walker Mr Andrew
2 Willis Richard, carrier
Woollcombe Geo. Esq. *Hemerdon Hs*

FARMERS.
Adams Aaron, *Chaddlewood*
Andrews Edward || Cock Manley
Annis John, *Venton*
Beer John || Beer Wm
Butland James, *Boringdon*
Coaker George || Curber Benj.
Cottle Wm., *Priory* || Cose Wm.
Dennis John, *Hemerdon*
Dewdney Geo. || Dewdney Isaac

Gardner John || 4 Martin Robert
Horton James || Horton Henry
Kingwell Samuel
Kingwell Wm., *Challonsleigh*
Knott Edmond, *Elfordleigh*
Mumford Rd. || Oliver John
Pearse Henry || Pearse Thomas
Pearse John & Jph., *Yealmpstone*
Phillips Sus. || Pode Richard
Pitts Wm. (lime burner,) *Hey*
Rowe Elias || Rowe Thomas
Rowe Jph. & Benj., *Hooksbury*
Sanders John || Symons Wm.
Stephens Wm., *Heath*
Tozer John || 4 Willcocks Rd.
Vosper Thomas, *Merafield*
Willing Richard, *Hardwick*
4 Wyatt Wm. || White George

CORN MILLERS.
Frean and Daw, *Marsh Mills*
Heal Samuel, *Priory Mill*
Moore Anthony, *Loughtor Mill*

INNS & TAVERNS.
4 Colebrook Inn, John Stephens
2 Devonshire Arms, Robert Goss
2 George Inn, Samuel Wollacott
3 Hele Arms, John Smith
Lyneham Inn, Rd. Pitt, *Battsfd*
2 Plymouth Inn, Sarah Bickley
3 Ring of Bells, Samuel Hambly
3 Union Inn, Wm. Pitt

BAKERS.
2 Andrews Jas.
2 Andrews Thos.
2 Brown Thos.
4 Cole Wm.
3 Luke Richd.
4 Webb Wm.

BLACKSMITHS.
4 Clynick Hy.
4 Lamacraft J.
Mumford J.
Sandover Jas.

BUTCHERS.
Dewdney Rd.
4 Kingdon Rd.
2 Worth John

CARPENTERS.
2 Redpath Rd.
3 Stockman Hy.
Yalland Daniel

MASONS.
3 Pethrick Wm.
2 Roberts Saml.
2 Sendy Henry

3 Soper James
4 Truscott Wm.

SADDLERS.
2 Cann Wm.
2 Lane Mr

SHOEMAKERS.
2 Brown Thos.
4 Cloke James
3 Congdon Rd.
3 Doidge My.
2 Luscombe Rd.
2 Willis James

SHOPKEEPERS.
2 Andrews Jas.
3 Brown James
2 Brown Thos.
2 Earl John
4 Harry John
3 Luke Rd.
2 Seccombe Wm.
3 Wellington Eliz.

TAILORS.
2 Bickley Wm.
2 Crispin Wm.

3 Cuming John,	WHEELWRIGHTS.	**POST - OFFICE** at Plympton-Earl
jun	2 Stanbury Hy.	**RAILWAY**, &c. *Trains, Coaches,*
3 Young John	2 Stanbury Hy.	and *Carriers* to Plymouth, Exeter,
	jun	&c. daily

BRIXTON, a pleasant village, 4½ miles E. of Plymouth, has in its parish 822 souls, and 2865 acres of fertile land, bounded on the south-east by the Yealm estuary, and including the small hamlets of Spriddleston, Hareston, Winston, and Coombe. The manor of Brixton, anciently called *Britricheston,* was long held by a family of its own name, but after passing to various other families, it was dismembered many years ago. T. W. Parrott, Esq., is lord of the manor of *Hareston,* which he derived from the Winters. This manor was successively held by the Reynald, Hareston, Silverlock, and Wood families; the latter of whom resided for many generations in the old mansion, which was built in the reign of Henry VII., and was partly destroyed by fire in the early part of last century. The remains of this ancient building are still preserved. Mr. Elliott is lord of the manor of *Spriddleston,* which has been held successively by the Spriddle, Fortescue, Lane, and other families. E. R. P. Bastard and Sir T. T. F.'E. Drake own a great part of the parish, the former having Wollaton, and the latter the Sherford estate. The *Church* has a lofty tower and five bells, and is an ancient structure in the decorated style. It was appropriated to Plympton Priory. The *perpetual curacy,* valued at £107, is in the patronage of the Dean and Canons of Windsor, and incumbency of the Rev. Richard Lane, who has neither parsonage nor glebe. The tithes belong to Henry Collins-Splatt, Esq., and were commuted in 1839, for £640. They were sold by the patrons in 1800. The benefice is endowed with a farm of 37A. 3R. 5P., at Modbury, purchased with £400 left by Elize Hele, in 1658. The parish has three tenements, occupied rent free by poor people; and ten cottages, with gardens, &c., purchased with poor's money, in 1594 and 1596. Belonging to the same charity are £250 three per cent. consols, which arose from fines paid by lessees. The clear yearly income, about £30, is distributed in clothing among the poor, about Christmas. Half an acre of play ground, called the *Parish Park,* was planted with elms by Edward Fortescue, Esq., in 1677. Marked 2, are at *Hareston; and* 3, at *Spriddleston.*

Binnear Mr Thos. || Harvey Mrs
Cane Benjamin, wheelwright
Cawse Wm. tailor, and Mr John
Collins-Splatt Henry, Esq. *Brixton House* and *Exeter*
Hubber James, vict. Foxhound
Jones David, vict. Red Lion
Kendell Philip, miller, *Coffleet*
Kitt Henry, basket maker, *Coombe*
Lane Rev Rd. in umbt. *Coffleet*
Lavers Wm. corn miller
Parrott Thos. Winter, Esq. *Hareston*
Stoyles John, timber dealer
Symons Hy. land survyr. *Whifferton*
Veale Joseph, butcher
Yonge Captain Edmund, R.N.
Yabsley John, thatcher
BOOT&SHOE MKS. | Wright John
Toop Jonathan | Wright Robert

CARPENTERS.
Cawse Thomas
2 Fisher Wm.
Pearse John
FARMERS.
(* *are Owners.*)
3 Avent Richard
3 Beer Wm.
3 Button Thos.
Butland Edward
*Cane Joseph
Chaffe Richard
Cockrem John, *Wollaton*
Cook James
Ford Richard
Hard Jno. *Combe*
Lavers Chpr.
Mullins James

2 Parsons Lewis
Pepperell Wm.
3 Pursley James
Revell Joan
*Rowe Benjamin
*Rowe Henry
*Scoble Richard, *Chittleburn*
Scoble Robert
2 Scoble John
Wright Joseph
MASONS, &c.
Rowse James
Rowse Samuel

SHOPKEEPERS.
Cawse Rebecca
Scoble Walter
Wotton James

PLYMSTOCK is a large straggling village, with some good houses, in a pleasant valley, near *Catwater Harbour* and Plymouth Sound, 3 miles E. by S. of Plymouth. Its parish contains 2966 inhabitants, and 3550 acres of land, including the villages, &c., of *Oreston, Turnchapel, Hooe, Elburton, Pomphlet,* and *Staddiscombe,* mostly lying on the eastern shore of Plymouth Harbour, where the river Plym finds its way to the ocean. Oreston and Turnchapel are the largest villages, and have ship yards on creeks of the Catwater. Lime stone is got extensively in the parish, and ships take in water at *Bovi Sand,* on the shore near the Breakwater, where there are water works, a pier, a preventive station, and a circular watch tower, called *Mount Batten.* The stone for the construction of the Breakwater was taken from the Oreston quarries, and in a cavity of the rock, 60 feet deep, were found bones of the rhinoceros, wolf, deer, &c. The *marble,* dug from these quarries, is beautifully veined, and will bear a high polish. Plymstock was the head quarters of the besieging army, when Plymouth was invested by Colonel Digby, in September, 1643, and it remained one of the principal stations, after Prince Maurice arrived with his army. The royalists had batteries at Oreston and Mount Batten, and a guard at Hooe. Staddiscombe was the birth place of *Dr. Nathaniel Forster,* the editor of Plato, and author of several learned works. The Duke of Bedford is lord of the manor of Plymstock, to whose family it was granted at the dissolution, as part of the possessions of Tavistock Abbey. H. B. Harris, Esq., is lord of the manor of Goosewell, and has a fine ancient seat here, called *Radford,* where his family has been settled more than four centuries. E. R. P. Bastard, Esq., owns the manor of Staddiscombe, and Sir F. L. Rogers owns West Hooe, but a great part of the parish belongs to the Earl of Morley, and several smaller owners. *Plymstock Church* (St. Mary and All Saints,) is a large and well-proportioned structure, mostly in the perpendicular style, with a tower and five bells. The interior has recently been improved at the expense of Colonel Harris, to whose family the chapel in the south aisle belongs. The church was formerly appropriated to Plympton Priory, and the Dean and Canons of Windsor are now appropriators of the tithes, and patrons of the *perpetual curacy,* valued in 1831 at £188, and now in the incumbency of the Rev. E. F. Coke, M.A., who conducts a highly respectable academy, called the *Church Grammar School,* to which a reading room and library are attached. The *Parsonage House* is a commodious mansion in the Elizabethan style, erected a few years ago, by the patrons, on land given by the Duke of Bedford. The tithes were commuted in 1842 for £781. 3s. 6d., and are leased to Colonel Harris. There is a *Chapel of Ease* at Turnchapel, and there was formerly one at Hooe. There are small *Wesleyan Chapels* at Turnchapel, Plymstock, and Oreston, and at the latter place is an Independent Chapel. The *National School* was built in 1827, at the cost of more than £400. The parish has an *Almshouse* for five poor people, founded by *Sir Christopher Harris,* in 1617, and endowed with a yearly rent-charge of £10, out of the manor of Goosewell. The poor of the village of *Elburton* have a house, let for £7, and left by *Philip Anderson,* at an early period. The poor parishioners have the following yearly doles: 20s. from *Lanyon's Charity,* as noticed with Maker; £2 from £50, left by *Hugh Bickford,* and vested with the overseers; and £1. 5s. 6d. from £25. 11s. 5d. Navy five per cents., left by *John Burrows,* in 1818. Out of the dividends of £200 three per cent. consols, left by the *Rev. Vincent Warren,* in 1790, £41 is expended yearly in clothing ten poor boys and ten poor girls; and £12 is paid to a schoolmistress for teaching them. The rest is dispensed in religious books, &c., except 10s. given yearly to ten poor children of Egg Buckland.

In the following Directory of Plymstock Parish, those marked 2, are at Oreston; 3, Turnchapel; 4, Elburton; 5, Pomphlet; 6, Hooe; 7, Staddiscombe; and the rest at Plymstock, or where specified.

6 Beard John, tea gardens
Bulteel Fras. F., solr. *Furzatt*
Coke Rev Edw. Fras., M.A. incbt., and Gram. School, Parsonage
Courtenay Jas., Esq. || Cobbe Mrs E.
3 Cree Mr Robt. || Dixon Mrs Mary
5 Eva John, stone agent
Ferguson Wm. overseer of Water Works, Bovi Sands
3 Ford John, quarry owner
Hare Major Wm. Hy. *Retreat*
Harris Col. Harry Bulteel, *Radford*
Harris Rev Jas. L. *Mount Pleasant*
Harris John Crichton, Esq.
Harris Thos. Hillersdon, Esq.
Harris Cphr., Esq. *Thorn Cottage*
3 Kelly Edward, sail maker
Lane Miss Penelope, *Benhay Cotg.*
2 Lapthorn Wm. boat builder
Lugg Wm. overseer, &c
Macdonald Mr Hy. *Ballicombe*
2 Perry Jane, fishery owner
6 Rogers, A., Esq. || Nutt Mrs
Taylor Mrs Jane || Whyte Miss J.
Turner Lieut. Chas. coast guard
Walker John, coast guard
Walker Wm. harbour master
Wright Geo. stone merchant

INNS & TAVERNS.
3 Boringdon Arms, Jane Smith
Church House, Thos. B. Mann
2 King's Arms, John Taylor
7 Manor House, Mary Gould
5 Morley Arms, Philip Lang
3 New Inn, Jph. Hilton
2 Old Inn, Jane Newman
6 Royal Oak, Thomas Ryder
6 Victoria Inn, Abm. Ryder
4 *Elburton*, Henry Williams

ACADEMIES.
Coke Rev E. F.
6 Jenkins John
Pitts Miss

BAKERS.
6 Brown Richard
2 Brooks Richard
2 Dean John
2 Ellis Nicholas
3 Kelly Robert
Peters Simeon

BEERHOUSES.
4 Avery John

Green Samuel
Hine John, *Mount Batten*
BLACKSMITHS.
Baker John
7 Coleman Geo.
Dodridge James
2 Dodridge John
2 Dodridge Robt.
4 Willing John
CARPENTERS.
Hendy Edward
3 Walke Richard
COAL DEALERS.
3 Hart John F.
2 Passmore Geo.
2 Piller James
FARMERS.
7 Barber Thomas
Clarke Wm. Hy. *Goosewell*
Cook Jno. *Belle V*
4 Crispin Wm.
2 Denness Geo.
Edwards Edward
4 Edwards John, Somerford
Edwards John
4 Gascoigne Ann
6 Hart John
4 Harvey Wm.Ts.
Harvey Richard
Harvey Wm. Parker, *Coombe*
Hendy John
4 Hendy William Watts Harris
Hodge Elias
Hill Simon
2 Kerswell Rd.
2 Lang Joseph
Little Thomas
4 Parsons Rd.
2 Pearse John Q.
Pearse Thomas

2 Pearse Wm.
7 Pearse Wm.
Popplestone Rd.
6 Redpath Robt.
7 Rowe Arthur
Rowe Robert
4 Rubbidge Edw.
Wotton Andw. R. (& butcher)
4 Watts John
4 Watts Prisla.
MASONS.
2 Goldsworthy J.
2 Spencer John
Staddon Thomas
SHOEMAKERS.
3 Dean Abm.
6 Ford James
Lugg Wm.
Underhill Wm.
Welch Thomas
2 Williams Jas.
SHOPKEEPERS.
2 Cooms John
4 Creber Wm.
3 Taylor John
Willing Mary
SURGEONS.
Jones David
Mould Wm. Pp.
Nutt Wm.
TAILORS.
6 Burn Daniel
3 Line Francis
WHEELWRIGHTS.
Lavers John
Mann Thos. B.
Rendle John

POST-OFFICE at Wm. O. West's
COACHES & CARRIERS to Plymth., Kingsbridge, &c. daily

REVELSTOKE parish has its church on the sea coast, near Stoke Point and Bigbury Bay, but most of its inhabitants are in the large fishing village of NOSS MAYO, which lies in a low situation, on the south side of a creek from the mouth of the Yealm, opposite Newton Ferrers, nine miles S.E. of Plymouth. Crabs, lobsters, herrings, and other fish are caught at Noss Mayo, where the villagers suffered severely from *cholera* in 1849, when about

50 of them died, and more than 200 were afflicted with the dreadful malady. Liberal subscriptions were made for the relief of the sufferers, and a medical gentleman was sent down from London to their assistance. The parish had 613 inhabitants in 1841, and contains 1470A. 2R. 19P. of land. The manor of Revelstoke was long the property and seat of the Revels, and was sold about 12 years ago, by Sir J. Perring, to its present owner, Robert Robertson, Esq., of Membland. W. W. Pendarves, Esq., owns the manor of Lambside, and part of the parish belongs to a few smaller owners. The *Church* is an ancient structure, with a small belfry and two bells; and in Noss Mayo, is a small *Chapel of Ease*, erected in 1839. The benefice is a perpetual curacy, consolidated with the vicarage of Yealmpton. Here is 4A. 3R. 37P. of glebe, but no parsonage. The tithes have been commuted, the vicarial for £116, and the rectorial for £140 per annum. The trustees of the late Rev. J. Kenrick are lessees of the latter. The poor have a house and garden, purchased with £20, left by *Sir Wm. Hele*, in 1625, and other benefaction money.

In Noss Mayo, or as specified.

Boden Mrs Sar. || Giles Sampson, R.N.
Carter John, blacksmith
Elliott Sarah, beer seller
Kingcombe Hy. ferryman & cider dlr. *Passage House*
Kingcombe Geo. vict. Globe Inn
Leonard John, tailor
Merrill Wm. vict. Swan Inn
Pope John, carpenter, &c

FARMERS.
Antony Jane, *Rowden*

Brooking Wm., *Revelstoke*
Crocker Henry, *Coombe*
Huxham George, *Netton*
Tuckett Jas. *Higher Coombe*
Wilcock John & Ann, *Worswell*

BAKERS.
Popham Humpy.
Kingcombe Jsh.

BOOT & SHOE MKS.
Bunker Richard
Reeves Fredk.

Sims Wm.

SHOPKEEPERS.
Perrett Phpi.
Walke Andrew
Williams John

SHAUGH PRIOR is a large parish of scattered farm houses, &c., in the valley of the river Plym, and among the hills and dales at the south end of Dartmouth Forest, extending from 7 to 10 miles N.N.E. of Plymouth. Near Shaugh Bridge, on the Plym, the *Dewerstone* rock rears its beetling crags in majestic altitude above the channel of the Cad rivulet; and in the vicinity are other granite tors. This neighbourhood is often visited by anglers and the lovers of picturesque scenery. *Revels* are held here at Easter and Whitsuntide. The parish contains 698 souls and 7170 acres of land. Excellent clay is got here for the china manufacturers. Sir R. Lopes, Bart. is lord of the manor, which formerly belonged to Plympton Priory. The Earl of Morley, the Rev. S. W. Pearse, and other proprietors have estates in this parish. The *Church* is an ancient fabric in the perpendicular style, with a tower and six bells. The *perpetual curacy*, valued at £107, is annexed to that of Sampford-Spiney, in the patronage of the Dean and Canons of Windsor, and incumbency of the Rev. S. W. Pearse, B.A., for whom the Rev. Hy. Colson, of Tavistock, officiates. The patrons are appropriators of the great tithes. The *parish land* (6 A.) and a house, were purchased in 1627 with £23 left by 35 donors. The land is let for £10, and the house was converted into the parish workhouse about 1717, at the cost of £100. As noticed with Walkhampton, *Lady Modyford* left £50 to this parish, and directed the interest to be distributed in bread among the poor.

Brock Wm., blacksmith
Mumford Wm., corn miller
Phillips John and Wm., potters' clay merchants

FARMERS.
Abbott John, *Harscombe*
Andrew Wm., *Henwood*
Andrew Walter, *Colstone*

Atwill Wm. ‖ Brock Wm.	Luscombe Phillip ‖ Maddock Eml.
Baskerweale Wm. ‖ Cole Samuel	Maddock Jas. ‖ Maddock Saml.
Damerell John, *Brixton*	Mallicott John ‖ Mead Robert
Damerell Edward, *Fawnstone*	Marshall Philip, *Colland*
Damerell Thomas ‖ Gray Richard	Mumford Thos ‖ Mumford James
Dennis Wm., *Higher Colland*	Pearse Nichls. ‖ Perkins Edward
Gullett Elizabeth ‖ Lavis John	Selleck George ‖ Stephens Robert
Lillicrap Thomas and Margaret	Tozer Thomas ‖ Worth John

WEMBURY, a scattered village near the sea cliffs between Plymouth Sound and the mouth of the Yealm, 6 miles S. E. by S. of Plymouth, has in its parish 616 souls and 3670 acres of land, including the hamlets of *Knighton* and *Down Thomas*. The manor of Wembury belonged to Plympton Priory till the dissolution, and afterwards passed to various families. In the 16th century it belonged to *Sir John Hele*, sergeant at law, who built here a magnificent mansion, at the cost of £20,000, and enclosed a park, which had a salt water lake, supplied by the tides. After his death this manor was sold for the payment of his debts. It was purchased in 1803, by Thos. Lockyer, Esq., who pulled down the mansion, and built a smaller house for his residence. E. R. P. Bastard, Esq., is now lord of the manor and of the royalty of the river Plym, from Kitley to Plymouth Sound. C. B. Calmady, Esq., is lord of the manor of Langdon, and resides at *Langdon Hall*, a neat Elizabethan mansion, which has been the seat of his family for several generations. T. Lockyer and several smaller owners have estates here, and Sir Edward Thornton, G.C.B., has a handsome seat in the parish. The *Church* (St. Werburg,) stands near the sea cliff, and is a small antique structure, with a tower and three bells. It contains several handsome monuments in memory of the Heles, and an iron helmet supposed to have been worn by Sir Warwick Hele. The perpetual curacy, valued in 1831 at only £83, is in the patronage of the Dean and Canons of Windsor, and incumbency of the Rev Rd. Lane, jun., of Brixton. The *Wesleyans* have a small chapel here, built in 1820. The church and poor have £40 three per cent. consols, given in lieu of two ancient rent charges. The *Almshouses* for ten poor people were founded by *Sir Warwick Hele*, who endowed them in 1625 with £30, arising from six tithe rent charges. *Sir John Hele* left two yearly rent charges to this parish, viz.: £6. 13s. 4d. to the perpetual curate, and £2. 12s. for the poor. They are paid out of land at Clifton in Dorsetshire, belonging to the Marquis of Anglesea. The incumbent has also £20 a year as the interest of £500, left by *Josias Calmady* in 1682, and now secured on an estate called Higher Edgecombe and Ransdown, at Milton Abbott. The same donor also left a yearly rent charge of £2. 12s. for the poor, out of Colebrook estate. *Marked 2 are at Down Thomas, and 3 at Knighton.*

Calmady Charles Biggs, Esq., *Langdon Hall*	FARMERS. (* are Owners.)	* Light Anty. P.
8 Colman John, blacksmith	Atwill Ts. & Sar.	Lobb Thomas
Cook Thomas, corn miller	Barons H., *Langdon Barton*	2 Lyndon Wm.
Gregory Richard, vict., Jubilee		Nelder J. & T.
Lockyer Thomas, Esq	2 Blackler Thos.	2 * Parrott John
Natt John, cider seller	3 Brewer Wm.	Pursley John
Newland R. R., gent. *Bovi Sand*	Cane Daniel	2 Wilson James
2 Taylor John, vict. New Inn	2 Edwards Wm.	
Thornton Sir Edward, G.C.B., *Wembury House*	Hern Henry	SHOPKEEPERS.
	* Hook A. & S.	Avery Wm.
Willson Edw., beerhouse, *Gabber*	Horton Eliz.	3 Wire Chtte.

YEALMPTON, a large and respectable village, with many good houses, is pleasantly seated on a salubrious acclivity, overlooking the river Yealm, 7 miles E. by S. of Plymouth, and 5½ miles W. of Modbury. It is on the high road to Kingsbridge, &c., and about a mile below it the Yealm spreads into a broad estuary. It has a great *cattle market* on the fourth Wednesday of every month, and is noted for the social and friendly intercourse of its inhabitants. *Petty Sessions* are held here every third Monday, by the magistrates of Ermington and Plympton Division, to whom Mr. Thomas Kelly is clerk. The parish contains 1317 souls, and 3432A. 3R. 36P. of land, generally fertile and mostly arable, and including the hamlets of *Dunstone* and *Yealm Bridge*, and many scattered farm houses, &c., and three corn mills. Yealmpton is described as a borough in ancient records, and tradition says the Saxon King Ethelwold had a palace here, where his lieutenant *Lipsius*, is said to have died, and to have been buried in the churchyard, where his gravestone is still to be seen. The *manor* was given by King John to Matthew Fitzherbert, and afterwards passed to the Earls of Huntingdon, one of whom sold it in 1580 to Sir John Hele. The heiress of Edmund Pollexfen brought it to an ancestor of its present owner, E. R. P. Bastard, Esq., of KITLEY, a large and elegant mansion, in the Elizabethan style, erected in 1825 by the late Edmund Pollexfen Bastard, Esq., from designs by Mr. Repton. It has many handsome and elegantly furnished apartments, and stands in the picturesque valley about a mile from the village, upon a finely wooded lawn, embellished with terraces and a sheet of water. " The Pollexfens resided in the old house at Kitley, as early as the reign of Elizabeth, and the Bastards removed to it from Garston. Wm. Bastard, Esq., was created a baronet in 1779, and the creation was gazetted, but he declined the intended honour. The late E. P. Bastard, Esq., was one of the representatives of Devon in Parliament, from 1816 till 1830, and his uncle held the same office from 1784 till his death, in 1816. The manors of *Bowden* and *Dunstone* also belong to Mr. Bastard, and he has large estates in many other parishes. Bowden, an ancient house, near the village, was long the seat of the Coplestons. *Lyneham*, now a farm house, belongs with the estate to Lady Bulteel, and was the seat of the Lynehams and Crockers. Thos. Holberton, Esq., has an estate here, and a neat mansion near the bridge. *Coffleet* is the seat and property of the Rev. Richd. Lane. George Woollcombe, Esq., and several smaller owners, have estates in the parish. The *Church* (St. Bartholomew,) was a very ancient structure, but is now being completely renovated and nearly all rebuilt, chiefly at the cost of Mr. Bastard, in the decorated style which prevailed in the time of Edward II. The chancel was rebuilt in 1849, and the nave is now undergoing a similar restoration. The arches and windows are of Caen stone, and the columns are of the limestone marble got at Kitley, and every alternate block is polished, and a band of the same polished marble is carried round each arch. The expense of its restoration will be about £7000, and when completed it will be one of the handsomest churches in the county. It has several neat monuments of the Pollexfens and Bastards. The *vicarage*, valued in K.B. at £35. 16s. 4½d., and in 1831 at £444, with the perpetual curacy of Revelstoke annexed to it, is in the patronage of the Bishop of Exeter, and incumbency of the Rev. James Longmore, of Cadleigh. Here is a good parsonage, and 22A. of glebe. The tithes were commuted in 1841, the vicarial for £307, and the rectorial for £355. The latter belong to the trustees of the late Rev. J. Kenrick. The Wesleyans and Plymouth Brethren have small chapels here; and a handsome *National School* was built in the village in 1849, of the grey limestone got in the parish. Under a hill near the church is an extensive limestone *cavern*, which was discovered by

the quarrymen about 60 years ago, and in it were found the bones of a large animal. It may be entered from the bank of the river, and has a splendid appearance when lighted up. The poor parishioners have the interest of £100, given by Mrs. Croker and Mrs. Knowling, and vested in the Modbury turnpike.

Anthony Misses || Bulteel Miss
Bastard Edmund Rodney Pollexfen, Esq., *Kitley*
Blackler James, saddler
Brooks & Co. lime burners, Bridge
Coad John Foote, surgeon
Constantine Nathan, organist
Desbrisay Rev Thos. curate, *Vicarage*
Ford Lieut. Wm., R.N. *Yeo*
Harris Capt. Wm., R.N.
Holberton Thos. Esq. *Yealm Bridge*
Lane Rev Rd. vicar of Brixton,*Coffleet*
Mann Thos. & John, wheelwrights
Oldreive Lewis John, land agent
Pearse James, plumber and tinner
Popham James, dairyman
Kelly Thos. solicitor & clerk to magistrates & comssrs. of taxes
Ratcliffe Wm. tallow chandler
Shillabear John, wood ranger
Walters E. milliner
Williams Charles, timber merchant, Saw Mills
Yelland Major || Yonge Miss
CORN MILLERS.
Anthony John, Yealmpton
Barratt Thos.& Southwood Hy.*Bridge*
Lavers Richard, *Weston Mill*
INNS AND TAVERNS.
Yealmpton Inn, Rebecca Glanville
Yealm Bridge Inn, Wm. Arscott
Volunteer, John Burford
FARMERS.
(2, *at Dunstone ;* 3, *at Weston.*)
Anthony John || 2 Adams James

3 Brooks Philip || Crocker Richard
Chaffe Richard, *Wilberton*
Coyte James, *Lyneham*
2 Daw Henry || Elliott George
Ellis Elizabeth || Ford Henry
Horton Philip || Fox Thomas
Jenkins Maria || Lavers Wm.
3 Lavers Richard || Shepheard Wm.
Parnell Thomas, *Bowden*
Shepheard Samuel || Wilton James
Southwood Nichs. || Willcocks John

ACADEMIES.
Brock Samuel
Burt Mrs
Turner Henry
BAKERS.
Hake Sampson
Rudd Agnes
Rudd Edward
BLACKSMITHS.
Barratt Elias
Barratt Wm.
Symons John
Symons Joshua
Symons Wm.
BUTCHERS.
Barratt Thomas
Southwood Nics.
CARPENTERS.
Kingcombe Adw.
Pearse Wm. *regr*
Shillabear Wm.
MASONS.
Gully John
Luke Philip

PAINTERS.
Coad Caleb
Hicks David
SHOPKEEPERS.
Fox Wm.
Lapthorne Robt.
Lavers Jhna.
Turner John
TAILORS.
Brimblecombe J.
Crispin Wm.
Parrott Wm.
Tapley Thomas

POST OFFICE
at Sml.Brock's.
Letters from Plympton.
COACHES to Plymouth and Kngsbdg. daily
CARRIERS to Plymouth and Exeter pass dly

BRAUNTON HUNDRED

Is a picturesque and irregularly formed district, bounded on the west and north by the Bristol Channel, and on the south-west by the estuary of the River Taw, from Barnstaple to the Bay. Its coast presents to the sea a bold and circuitous line of cliffs and rocky promontories, extending from Barnstaple or Bideford Bay to Trentishoe, a distance of 24 miles. It includes Ilfracombe, Combe-Martin, &c.; and its northern and western parishes form a hilly district, extending to the borders of Somersetshire and Exmoor Forest. The Borough of Barnstaple is within its limits, but has a separate jurisdiction. The whole Hundred is in the Northern Parliamentary Division of Devon, and in the Archdeaconry of Barnstaple, and Deaneries of Sherwill and Barnstaple. It is all in Braunton Petty Ses-

sional Division, except East and West Buckland and Filleigh, which are in South Molton Division. The following enumeration of its 21 parishes shews their territorial extent and their population in 1841.

Parishes.	Acres.	Pop.	Parishes.	Acres.	Pop.
Ashford	359	176	Georgeham	4650	923
Barnstaple Borough	1096	7902	Goodleigh	1180	335
Berrynarbor	4958	899	Heanton Punchardon	2300	626
Bittadon	1000	78	Ilfracombe	5513	3679
Bratton Fleming	3940	708	Kentisbury	3400	422
Braunton	9951	2274	Marwood	5596	1012
*Buckland East	1304	167	Morthoe	2500	379
*Buckland West	1700	275	§Pilton	835	1805
Combemartin	3815	1399	Trentishoe	1572	132
Down East	3643	473			
Down West	4060	637	Total	65,652	24,694
*Filleigh	2200	395			

* East and West Buckland and Filleigh are in *South Molton Union;* and all the other 18 parishes are in *Barnstaple Union.* These unions are also *County Court Districts.* § Pilton is mostly in Barnstaple Borough.

LUNDY ISLAND, though situated in the Bristol Channel, about 18 miles west of the mainland, is a detached member of Braunton Hundred. It is about three miles long and one broad, and comprises about 1800 acres. On account of the lofty rocks with which it is encompassed, it is inaccessible, except by a narrow entrance on the eastern side, where a small beach admits a secure approach, and is sheltered by a detached portion of rock called the *Isle of Rats.* There are on the island a farm-house and a few small cottages. It is farmed by *Mr. John Lee,* and belongs chiefly to *J. H. Haven, Esq.* It has long been famous for butter, and the feeding of cattle and sheep; and some parts are in tillage, and produce good crops of oats, turnips, potatoes, &c. Towards the northern extremity, the island rises to the height of 800 feet above the level of the sea, and is terminated by a lofty pyramidal rock, called the Constable. †It was formerly the retreat of *pirates,* particularly one of the name of Wm. de Morisco, who, in the reign of Henry III., fled thither, after an unsuccessful attempt against the life of the King; and having fortified it strongly, contrived to live in safety for some time, till being taken, with 16 of his followers, he suffered the penalty of the law for his crimes. Edward II., when he was hurried by his disaffected nobles from one part of the kingdom to another, had thoughts of retiring to this island for safety; but he was driven by the wind to Glamorganshire, where he was afterwards betrayed by the Welch. The chief antiquities on the island are what is called *Morisco's Castle,* and the ruins of *St. Anne's Chapel.* The castle is near the south-east end, and was strongly fortified with large outworks and a ditch. In the reign of Charles I., Lord Say and Seale held this fortress for the King; and in the time of William and Mary, the French surprised it by a stratagem, and plundered and kept it for some time. About the middle of last century, this island was sold by Government to a nobleman, who entrusted it to the care of *Benson,* a notorious smuggler, and member of parliament, who was at length obliged to make a precipitate flight. It afterwards belonged to Sir J. B. Warren, and has since frequently changed owners. In 1840, it was sold for 9400 guineas. Some years ago, two excellent *lighthouses* were erected upon it; and it has lately been discovered to have a good roadstead, in which a large fleet might ride securely in easterly gales.

ASHFORD, a small village and parish, on the north side of the estuary of the Taw, 2 miles W.N.W. of Barnstaple, has only 174 souls, and about 359 acres of land, successively held by the Beaumont, Bassett, Moore, and Bampfylde families. About 1815, the estate was sold in lots by Sir C. W. Bampfylde, and it now belongs to George Langdon, Esq., and a few smaller owners. The *Church* (St. Peter,) is an ancient fabric, with a tower and three bells. It is in good repair, and has a small organ. The *rectory,* valued in K.B. at £8. 13s. 9d., and in 1831 at £119, is in the patronage of the Lord Chancellor, and incumbency of the Rev. John Kendall Fletcher, D.D., of Callington, Cornwall. The glebe is 8A. 2R. 30P., and the parsonage is a small thatched dwelling. The tithes have been commuted for £85 per annum. The poor have the interest of £8, and here is a small Baptist Chapel.

Blackmore Rev John, M.A. curate
Cutcliffe John, beerseller
Giddy Richard, tailor
Hardy John and Wm. wheelwrights
Hopkins Wm. blacksmith
Joce Geo. carpenter & parish clerk

FARMERS AND OWNERS.
Badcock James || Badcock Wm.
Bynon Wm. || Hodge Wm.
Langdon George, Esq. *Strand*
Morcom Wm. *Marshes*

BARNSTAPLE, the principal *port, market-town,* and *borough* in North Devon, gives name to an *archdeaconry* and *deanery,* to a large *union,* and to a *county court and polling district ;* and is pleasantly seated on the north-east side of the navigable river Taw, where it receives the small river Yeo, and is crossed by a handsome bridge of sixteen arches, below which the stream expands into a broad tidal estuary, abounding in salmon and other fish, and flowing seven miles westward, where it mixes its waters with those of the river Torridge, in Barnstaple or Bideford Bay. It is a very ancient borough and respectable town, and is distant 40 miles N.W. of Exeter, 9 miles N.E. of Bideford, 11 miles W.N.W. of South Molton, and 192 miles W. by S. of London. The *parish of Barnstaple* comprises about 1096 acres of land, in the broad and fertile vale of the river Taw, which is to be traversed by a railway from Exeter, but only a few miles at each end have yet been constructed. The parish had only 3748 inhabitants in 1801, but in 1821 they had increased to 5079, in 1831 to 6840, and in 1841 to 7902. The *Borough* has now about 11,000 inhabitants, having been extended by the Reform Acts of 1832 and 1835, so as to include most of PILTON parish, and part of BISHOP'S TAWTON parish, the former of which has 1805 inhabitants, and 834 acres, on the north side of the town ; and the latter has 1826 souls, and about 4500 acres, extending three miles southward, but including the southern suburbs of *Newport, &c.,* in South Molton Hundred. The population return for Barnstaple parish in 1841, included 107 persons in the Union Workhouse, 17 in the Borough Gaol, and 58 in the North Devon Infirmary. Before the Norman Conquest, Barnstaple was a royal demesne ; and King Athelstan is said to have constituted it a borough, and to have built a *castle* here, of which nothing remains but the artificial mound on which it stood, near the confluence of the two rivers. At Domesday Survey there were 40 burgesses within the borough, and nine without; and the inhabitants were exempted from serving on any expedition, or paying taxes, except at the same time as Exeter and Totnes. Judhael de Totnes, on whom the Conqueror bestowed the manor, founded a *Priory* here for Cluniac monks, which was valued at the dissolution at £123. 6s. 7d. per annum. The lords of the manor and honor of Barnstaple claimed a market and fair from a very early period. Risdon says Henry I. incorporated the borough, and that King John enlarged its privileges. Among the records in the Tower, are some inquisitions taken in the reign of Edward III., in consequence of a dispute between the lord of the manor and the burgesses, the latter of whom claimed various privileges, and the right of choosing a mayor, said to have been granted by King Athelstan, whose charter was lost. In the early part of the present century, Sir John Chi-

chester sold the manor to the Corporation. Edward IV., by his charter of the 17th year of his reign, recites and confirms the charter of King John. The charter of James I. adds a high steward, recorder, &c. The borough has returned two members to Parliament since the 23rd of Edward I., and until 1832 the right of election was in the corporate body and the burgesses, numbering about 600, but by the Reform Act of that year it was extended to the occupiers of houses of the yearly value of £10 or upwards, not only in the old borough, but in the suburbs within the adjoining parishes of Pilton and Bishop's Tawton. Previous to the Municipal Act of 1835, the government of the borough was vested in the mayor, high-steward, recorder, two aldermen, and 22 common councilmen. It is now governed by a mayor, recorder, six aldermen, and eighteen councillors, and is divided into two wards. Its expenditure in 1837 amounted to £1374, being an excess of £669 above its income, which arises chiefly from rents and redeemed land tax, and tolls and dues. The *town common*, which comprised 108A., was enclosed under an act passed in the 26th of George III. An act for paving and improving the town, and regulating the markets and fairs, was obtained in the 53rd of George III., and another for enlarging the market places, &c., in 1821. The borough has had a commission of the peace and a court of quarter sessions granted, under the powers of the Municipal Act. The quarter and petty sessions are held at the GUILDHALL, a spacious and handsome edifice, in the Grecian style, erected in 1826, over the entrance to the *butchers' market*, which was built in 1812, and consists of 34 shops, extending in a double line from High street to Anchor lane, and having over them a commodious *Corn-Exchange*. A new fish market was erected a few years ago. The *Borough Prison and Bridewell* form a neat and substantial building, in the Square, erected in 1828, at the joint expense of the corporation and the parish. It has two rooms for debtors, and two day rooms and fourteen cells for felons, &c. The cost of the Guildhall, new prison, and the market improvements, was about £9000. *Petty Sessions* for Braunton Division are held once a fortnight, at the office of Mr. J. S. Clay, the magistrates' clerk. The *County Court* for all the parishes in Barnstaple Union, except Instow and Westleigh, is held at the Guildhall monthly, and Mr. L. T. Bencraft is the *clerk*, and Mr. H. K. Thorne *high bailiff*. The Recorder is judge of the *Borough Court of Record*, and L. T. Bencraft, registrar. The freemen are exempt from borough tolls and quay dues, and the number of electors is now about 800. The following is a list of the borough members, magistrates, corporation, and officers.

Members of Parliament, the Hon. John Wm. Fortescue and Richard Bremridge, Esq.

Lord High Steward of the Borough, Earl Fortescue.

BOROUGH MAGISTRATES, the Mayor, Ex-Mayor, and John May, John Marshall, Robt. Budd, Jas. Whyte, John R. Griffiths, and Geo. Harris, Esqrs.

Charity Trustees, Rev. Hy. Luxmoore and John May, Rt. Budd, J. Marshall, Wm. Avery, Jas. Marsh, John Dicker, and John Avery, Esqrs.

MAYOR, Jno. M. Fisher, Esq. ‖ RECORDER, Wm. M. Praed, Esq.

ALDERMEN, John S. Clay, Richard Thorne, and John K. Cotton, for the *North Ward;* and Robt. Budd, Wm. F. Latham, and W. Avery, for the *South Ward.*

COUNCILLORS, John W. Tatham, J. H. Toller, Wm. Avery, John Gould, G. K. Cotton, Wm. Carpenter, John Norrington, Rt. Mortimer, and J. M. Fisher, for *North Ward;* and Wm. Arter, sen., John Harris, J. K. Marsh, Thos. Hodge, Geo. Kingson, Wm. Parkin, Wm. Young, and Wm. Dyer, for the *South Ward.*

TOWN CLERK, Lionel Thomas Bencraft, Esq.

CLERK OF THE PEACE, William Gribble, Esq.

Coroner and Clerk to the Borough Magistrates, Alfred Drake, Esq.

Treasurer and Inspector of Weights and Measures, Mr. John Baker.

Inspector of Weights and Measures for County, Mr. Fdk. Jones.

Gaoler, Wm. Trawin. ‖ *Superintendent of Police,* Byron Aldham.

Sergeants-at-Mace, Thos. Britton and John Evans.

Beadles, Wm. Whitefield, (and *crier,*) and Wm. Gabriel.

The *Market and Fairs* of Barnstaple have for a long period been in high repute, and much resorted to. In the reign of Edward III. it claimed two weekly markets, on Wednesday and Friday, and they continued to be held till 1760. The market is now held on Friday only, and is an extensive mart for corn, and all sorts of provisions. Four great cattle markets or fairs are held on the Fridays before March 21st and April 21st, on the last Friday in July, and on the second Friday in December; but the great "*Barnstaple Fair*" commences on the 19th of September, and continues several days, the first for cattle, &c., the second for horses, &c., and succeeding days for sight-seeing, and all kinds of amusements. This fair is one of the largest in the county, both for business and pleasure; and on the second day a stag hunt takes place, starting on the borders of the Exmoor. The money expended at this fair in the purchase of cattle often amounts to £20,000. The cattle fairs and markets are held in Boutport street, but their removal to the Port Marshes, or some other eligible place, is in contemplation. Barnstaple was a *naval port* in the reign of Edward III. Besides equipping three vessels for the fleet which destroyed the Spanish Armada, it sent out several privateers, one of which returned with a prize, taken on the coast of Guinea, "having in her four chests of gold, worth £12,000," and other articles of great value. The staple trade of the town, from a very early period till the latter part of the last century, was the manufacture of *woollen goods,* termed duroys, tammies, serges, shalloons, baizes, flannels, plushes, &c., but this trade is now obsolete in the town, though there are several serge and blanket mills in the neighbourhood. Here are, however, several extensive *wool-staplers,* a large *lace factory,* many extensive *malting* establishments, two *paper* mills, four *tanneries,* two *potteries,* an extensive *ship building yard,* and several *stocking weavers, brush makers, ropers,* &c. Since 1822, when *bonded warehouses* were established here, the port has had an increasing foreign trade, and it has now many highly respectable merchants, who import goods from the Baltic, France, Spain, Portugal, North America, &c. They are also extensively engaged in the coasting trade; importing coals, timber, iron, groceries, spirits, porter, freestone, &c., and exporting grain, wool, bark, leather,

paper, &c. The *Port of Barnstaple* includes Ilfracombe, Combe-martin, Linton, and all that part of the coast of Devon extending north-east from the mouth of the Taw. The *Custom House* is a plain building, and Rd. White, Esq., is the *collector ;* Mr. W. A. Gent, *comptroller ;* and Robt. Westacott, locker. The *Inland Revenue Office* is in Boutport street, and Jas. Johnston, Esq., is the *collector ;* and Mr. Jph. Hancock, *supervisor*. The town has four commodious *quays*, at which vessels of 100 to 200 tons receive and discharge their cargoes ; but about three miles below, in a creek of the estuary, called Fremington Pill, or Penhill, is a sort of dock, where larger vessels anchor and receive and deliver cargoes. The river is navigable for barges and small craft to about three miles above the town. *Queen Anne's Walk*, on the west side of the principal quay, is a piazza or corridor, which formerly served as an exchange for the merchants. It is 67 feet long, and 12 broad, and has a series of stone columns supporting the roof, and a parapet, on which is a fine full-length statue of Queen Anne, in whose reign it was rebuilt. The statue is dated 1708, and was the gift of Robert Rolle, Esq. In consequence of the plague being at Exeter, the spring assizes were held at Barnstaple, in 1590, when 17 prisoners were hanged on the Castle-green. During the *civil wars*, Barnstaple was strongly attached to the interests of the Parliament. It was taken for the King by Prince Maurice, in September, 1643. In July following, the inhabitants rose and took possession of the town, and the Earl of Essex sent Lord Roberts and Sir Pp. Stapleton, with about 500 horse, who repulsed Digby and others sent to the relief of the royalists. The Earl of Essex then garrisoned the town, but it surrendered on honourable terms to General Goring, in September. In October, 1645, the clubmen of Devon declared for the Parliament, and killed several of the royalists at Barnstaple, where Sir A. Apsley was then governor. In March, 1646, Sir Thomas Fairfax blockaded the town, which surrendered to him on the 10th of April, after the fall of Exeter. (See pages 56 and 57.)

The town has been much improved and enlarged during the present century, and now extends about a mile in length, including its suburbs of Pilton and Newport. Many new buildings have been erected on the south and east sides of the town during the last ten years, and it has kept pace with most other towns in its public improvements, its new and fashionable residences, its modern and well stocked shops, its flag-paved streets, and its gas and water works. It has two large inns and posting-houses, many respectable taverns, and coaches and carriages daily to all parts; and a steam packet from Bristol calls at the docks weekly. The *Gas Works* were constructed in 1833, at the cost of £2000, raised in £10 shares. The town has three *Banks*, and a branch of the Exeter Savings' Bank ; a handsome *Theatre*, built in 1834, at the cost of about £1000 ; and a commodious *Assembly Room*, erected in 1800, at the cost of about £1100, raised in £30 shares. It had two weekly *newspapers*, one of which, the *North Devon Journal*, is still published every Friday, by Mr. Wm. Avery. The *Literary Institution*, which occupies a large house in High street, was established in 1845, chiefly from the munificence of W. F. Rock, Esq., of London, who is a native of the town, and subscribes £100 per annum, for the admission of 100 free members. It has a valuable library of about 3000 volumes, an

interesting museum, two reading rooms, and a large lecture room, in which lectures are delivered by gentlemen of the town and neighbourhood, once a fortnight, during the winter months.   J. R. Chanter, Esq., is the honorary secretary.   Here is a highly talented *Musical Society*, and balls and con- certs are frequently held in winter at the Assembly Room.   Here are also a *Farmers' Club*, and an Horticultural Society; and the *Barnstaple and North Devon Agricultural Society* holds its meetings in the town.   A *Lodge of Freemasons* meets at the Assembly Room on the first Wednesday of every month, and in the town are several Friendly Societies, and other pro- vident institutions.   The town has now a clean and handsome appearance, and the surrounding country is fertile and picturesque, affording many delightful walks and drives, commanding pleasing views, terminated on the north by the bold semicircular range of hills, on the borders of Exmoor. There are in the town and suburbs four churches, five chapels, several public schools, and various charitable institutions.

Barnstaple Parish Church (St. Peter and St. Paul,) is a large ancient structure, said to have been rebuilt about 1318, and enlarged and altered at subsequent periods.   It has a low tower on the south side, containing six bells, and crowned by a spire.   It was much damaged by lightning in 1816.   The interior has sittings for about 2000 hearers, and contains many mural monuments.   On each side of the chancel window are figures of Moses and Aaron, and in a room over the porch is a parochial library, founded by John Doddridge, Esq.   The organ is a large and fine toned instrument, which was given by Sir George Amyard, one of the borough members, in 1764.   Leland mentions four ancient chapels here, one of which (St. Nicholas's,) is now a warehouse, called the Quay-hall, and ano- ther, which had two chantries, is now the Grammar School, and was used by the French refugees till the middle of the last century.   The great tithes of Barnstaple were appropriated to Malmsbury Priory, and afterwards passed with the priory estate to the Incledon family.   The *vicarage*, valued in K.B. at £15. 8s. 9d., and in 1831 at £324, is in the patronage of Lord Wharncliffe, and incumbency of Rev. H. Luxmoore, M.A.   The tithes were commuted in 1841,—the vicarial for £245, and the rectorial for £36. The latter belong to the Misses Incledon.   In the parish are two handsome district churches, opened about 1845.   *Holy Trinity Church*, at the Barbi- can, was built and endowed as a perpetual curacy by the Rev. John James Scott, M.A., its present patron and incumbent.   It is in the perpendicular style, and was commenced in 1843, but its elegant tower, which rises to the height of 133 feet, was not completed till 1847.   The west window, and the stained glass of the chancel windows, are fine specimens of modern art, and the general interior arrangements are much admired.   There are about 800 sittings, one third of which are free.   The pulpit is of Caen stone, and was given by Sir P. Acland.   The font was given by Dr. Budd.   The cost of the church was about £4000, and of the tower £1500, and the founder has endowed the benefice with £1000, and erected neat schools, at the cost of £300.   The total cost of the church, burial ground, schools, endowment, &c., was about £10,000.   The other new church, built about the same time, is dedicated to *St. Mary Magdalen*, and stands at the head of Bear street.   It is a handsome building, with a tower, crowned by a spire, rising to the height of 115 ft.   The nave and aisles are neatly fitted up with upwards of 800 free sittings.   The burial ground comprises an acre, and the cost of the church was more than £3000, raised chiefly by grants, and partly by subscription.   The Ecclesiastical Commissioners have endowed the *perpe- tual curacy* with £150 per annum.   It is in the alternate patronage of the

Crown and the Bishop of Exeter, and the Rev. James Pycroft, M.A., is the incumbent. The church was finished in 1846.

PILTON PARISH CHURCH *(St. Margaret,)* stands on an eminence, near the north entrance to the town, and its parish contains 1805 souls, and 834A. 3R. 26P. of land, mostly within the borough of Barnstaple. The *manor of Pilton* belonged to a Benedictine *Priory*, which was founded here as a cell to Malmsbury Abbey, and was valued at £56. 12s. 8d. per annum at the dissolution, when it and the manor were granted to the Chichester family. The manor, after passing to the Sydenham, Northmore, and other families, was dismembered. John Whyte, Esq., owns the site of the priory, and Westaway estate, and has a handsome mansion here, called *Pilton House ;* but a great part of the parish belongs to the Trustees of the late Lord Rolle, J. R. Griffiths, Esq., Capt. May, and several other freeholders. *Upcott,* about 1½ mile north of the town, is the pleasant seat of T. W. Harding, Esq., owner of Pilland estate. *Raleigh House,* formerly occupied as a woollen factory, and afterwards as a lace mill, was anciently the seat of the Raleigh family. *Bradiford* is a small hamlet in this parish. The *Church* is an ancient Gothic structure, with an embattled tower, and six bells. The tower was partly destroyed during the siege of 1646, and was rebuilt in 1696. In the church are many memorials of the Chichester, Incledon, Rogers, Lethbridge, and other families. The living is a *perpetual curacy,* valued at £108, in the patronage of Wm. Hodge, Esq., and incumbency of the Rev. W. C. Hall, M.A., who has a neat modern residence, and about 20A. of glebe. The tithes, formerly belonging to the priory, have been mostly sold to the landowners. The parish has National Schools, and various *Charities,* as afterwards noticed.

Barnstaple has five DISSENTING CHAPELS. The Independents and Presbyterian congregations here were united about the middle of last century. That eminent dissenting divine, *Samuel Badcock,* was minister here from 1770 to 1778, but he afterwards conformed to the church, and was ordained Bishop of Ross. The present *Independent chapel* is a neat building, erected in 1839, at the cost of £1600, and has a stone front, in the perpendicular style. The *Baptist chapel,* in Boutport street, was built in 1833, at the cost of £900, but galleries have since been erected, at the additional cost of £168. The Baptists have a small chapel in Vicarage lane, erected in 1824. The *Wesleyan chapel* was built in 1815, and enlarged in 1839, and is a neat building, with a gallery and organ. Its total cost was about £3000. The *Plymouth Brethren* have a small chapel here. In the following account of the SCHOOLS and CHARITIES of the borough of Barnstaple, it must be observed, that those *vested with the Corporation* are now under the management of the CHARITY TRUSTEES, appointed under the powers of the Municipal Act of 1835, and named at page 567.

The GRAMMAR SCHOOL is kept in an ancient building in the churchyard, which is repaired by the Corporation, who also allow the master the free use of a house belonging to them, though for this privilege and the undermentioned small emoluments, he is only required to teach one free scholar, who receives a classical education in common with about 30 other boys, mostly day scholars. The endowment consists of an annuity of £10, left by *Richard Ferris,* in 1646, and £4 a year, as the interest of £100 left by the *Rev. John Wright,* in 1760, and now secured on the Barnstaple turnpike. At this school were educated *John Jewel,* bishop of Salisbury; and his great polemical opponent, *Thomas Harding,* the Jesuit professor at Louvain ; also *Gay, the poet,* and the learned Dr. *Musgrave.*

The BLUE COAT SCHOOLS, in the North walk, were erected in 1834, for the use of the *Boys' and Girls' Charity Schools,* previously held in separate buildings. They form a handsome stone building, with dwellings for the teachers, and schools for 50 boys and 30 girls, who are clothed at the expense of the charities. The *Boys' School* was established by subscription in 1710, and various donations of money and rent-charges have been made to it from time to time. An estate, called Francis and Bowden, at Ilfracombe, was purchased for it in 1746, at the cost of £1150, but that included £100, be-

longing to Penrose's Almshouse, to which the estate pays £4 a year. This estate consists of a farm of 160A., let for £90 a year. There are also belonging to it eight rent-charges, producing collectively £7. 1s. 4d. per annum ; and £954 three per cent. stock, yielding £28. 10s. per annum. Its total yearly income from these sources is £125. 11s. 4d., which is increased by an annual collection at the church. The *Girls' School* was founded by *Alice Horwood*, in 1652, for the education of 30 poor girls, who are clothed out of the above-named funds. Its endowment consists of a house and 3A. 30P. of land, at Newport, let for £15 a year. The trustees pay yearly salaries of £45 to the master, and £20 to the mistress. There are large NATIONAL SCHOOLS in Castle street, Newport, Salem street, and Pilton ; and *Sunday Schools* are attached to the churches and chapels.

The *North Devon Infirmary*, at the entrance to the town from Newport, is a neat building, of which the centre was erected in 1824, when the first stone was laid by the late Earl Fortescue, the projector and principal contributor. The wings of the building were added afterwards, and the interior is now spacious and admirably adapted for the benevolent purposes to which it is appropriated. It is supported by subscriptions and donations. Earl Fortescue is *patron ;* Drs. Britton and Budd, *physicians ;* Messrs. Curry and Law, *surgeons ;* Mr. Morgan, *house surgeon ;* and Mrs. Harbour, *matron.*

The DISPENSARY, in Boutport street, was established in 1832, and in connexion with it is a branch of the Royal Humane Society. Dr. Bignell is the *physician ;* Messrs. March, Hiern, and Harding, *surgeons ;* and Mr. J. C. Turner, *dispenser and secretary.*

SALEM ALMSHOUSES, in Salem street, for the residence of 24 poor men and women, were built in 1834, at the sole expense of Charles Roberts, Esq., of Bickington. They are neatly built of stone and comprise 12 cottages, forming three sides of a square, with a grass plot and pallisades in front. The founder, the two Misses Roberts, the Rev. J. R. Roberts, the Rev. Robert Hole, H. Gwyn, Esq., J. Sharland, Esq., and other donors gave about £1000 for the endowment, and the money was invested in the funds, and yields about 30s. per annum for each inmate.

PENROSE'S ALMSHOUSE is a large building in Litchdon street, consisting of twenty dwellings, each containing two almspeople, who have each a portion of a large garden. They are appointed from the poor parishioners, a preference being given to natives, and usually to women. The mayor for the time being nominates a person to fill the first vacancy which occurs during his year of office, and the others are supplied alternately by the two acting trustees. Each of the 40 almspeople receives 6s. per lunar month from the funds of the charity. The almshouse was founded in 1624, by *John Penrose*, who left property for its erection and endowment. The latter was afterwards augmented with the following benefactions, viz : £420, left by *Richard Beaple*, in 1641 ; 23A. 1R. 3P. of land in Yelland, left by *Wm. Palmer*, in 1653 ; £55 given by *Richard Harris*, in 1655 ; £100 given in 1763, by *Denys Rolle ;* and £20 left by *Joan Stanbury*, in 1772. The property now belonging to the charity consists of an undivided moiety of 202A. of land, at Hartland, given by the founder ; 23A. in Yelland ; 22A. 2R. 38P. in Georgeham ; two houses and 1A. 3R. 34P. in Barnstaple ; £100 vested in the Barnstaple and South Molton turnpike ; and £155. 2s. 11d. Old South Sea Annuities. From these sources the total annual income is upwards of £200. The yearly sum of £4 is divided among the inmates, as interest of £100 left by *John Phillips*, in 1734.

HORWOOD'S ALMSHOUSE, in Church lane, consists of eight dwellings of two rooms each, occupied by 16 poor people, with a small garden plot allotted to each dwelling. It was built by *Thomas Horwood* and his widow, who vested it in trust with the mayor and capital burgesses, and endowed it in 1674, with 7A. 3P. of land, and a house, barn, &c., at Newport, now let for £57. 18s. per annum, and a stable at Barnstaple, let for two guineas a year. There are also belonging to the charity, £114. 4s. 11d. Old South Sea Annuities. The 16 almspeople have each 5s. per lunar month, and 1s. 4¼d. at Christmas ; besides some small yearly allowances from other charities.

PAIGE'S ALMSHOUSE, in Church lane, has rooms for eight poor persons, and occupies the site of an ancient almshouse. It was built on the foundations of the old one by *Eliz. Paige*, who, in 1656, endowed it with £50, vested with the Corporation. It is also endowed with a yearly rent-charge of 6s. 8d., left by *Wm. Canford*, in 1553, and with a house and 1A. 20P. of land at Newport, left by *Robert Appley*, in 1594, and now let for £14 per annum. The almspeople are appointed by the mayor, and have 3s. a year each from Phillips' and Tippetts' Charities, arising as follows :—*John Phillips*, who was a benefactor to the Charity School and Penrose's Almshouse, in 1734, also left £40 to the inmates of Paige's Almshouse. This £40, with £24 accumulated by unapplied interest was vested in the purchase of a yearly rent charge of 50s., out of land at Maidenford. *Henry G. Tippetts*, in 1795, left a yearly rent-charge of £3. 6s. out of Hole Ground field, to be divided in sums of 6d. each among the 66 inmates of this and the before-named almshouses.

HARRIS'S ALMSHOUSE is a small dwelling adjoining the churchyard, occupied by the sexton, and supposed to have been built with £20 given by Thomas Harris in 1646.

BENEFACTIONS TO THE POOR :—In 1642, *Richard Beaple* left a clear yearly rent-charge of £17. 6s. 8d., out of Hedd estate, to the Corporation, in trust for distribution among the poor of Barnstaple, who have also about £20 a year from 7A. 29P. of land, purchased with £200 left by *Ephraim Skinner*, in 1677 ; and about £10 from 2A. 1R. 21P. left by *Richard Cornish*, in 1709. The annual proceeds of these three charities are dis-

tributed among all the resident poor of the town. In 1681, *Roger Jeffery* left 5s. each per annum for 12 poor housekeepers, to be raised as follows, 30s. from a yearly rent-charge out of land at Bickington, and 30s. to be paid by the Corporation, as interest of £25 vested with them. Two houses in Boutport street, left to the poor by *Robert Appley*, in 1594, are let on lease for only £8, but are worth above £25 a year. A legacy of £100, left to the poor by *Adam Lugg*, in 1622, was laid out in the purchase of 8a. 2r. 6p. of land at Pilton, now let for £20 per annum. The poor have 40s. a year out of a house in Holland street, left by *Richard Ferris*, in 1622 ; 52s. yearly from *Sir John Acland's Charity*, (see Exeter ;) 20s. a year, as interest of £20, left by *Hugh Horsham*, in 1653, and lent to the Corporation ; and 12s. a year, left by *Thomas Webber*, in 1696, out of Yeoland's garden, at Pilton. In 1636, *Katherine Westlake* left £300, to be invested for the relief of poor artificers, and £100 to be invested, and the yearly profits applied towards setting up young men newly come out of their apprenticeship. These sums were laid out in the purchase of £390 Old South Sea Annuities, now standing in the names of four trustees. A yearly rent-charge of £6, left by *George Baron*, in 1681, out of an estate at Brinsworthy, in Fremington, is distributed among poor weavers or their widows. In 1646, *Richard Ferris* left two yearly rent-charges out of Middleton estate, at Parracombe, viz., £10 in aid of the Grammar School, and £20 to be applied in apprenticing poor children. In 1810, *Margaret Newcommen* left two annual sums of £4 each, to two dissenting schoolmistresses of Barnstaple, for teaching poor children to read. (See Bideford.) An annuity of £5, left by Mrs. *Martin*, out of Great Fisherton farm, in Bishop's Tawton, is paid to the *Vicar*, in consideration of his catechizing the children of the parish. He has also the dividends of £624. 6d. Old South Sea Annuities, purchased with £500 left in 1772, by *Joan Stanbury*, for the better support of a minister, who should read *daily morning prayers* at the church. In the reign of Elizabeth, there was in Barnstaple a *Company of Cordwainers*, or *shoemakers*, governed by a master and wardens, but it ceased to exist many years ago. The property belonging to it was conveyed to new trustees in 1787, and consists of three tenements worth about £30, but let only for about £2 per annum, subject to fines paid on the renewal of the leases. The clear income is distributed in small sums among poor shoemakers, or their widows.

PILTON :—The *Parish Lands, &c.*, which have been vested with feoffees from an early period for the relief of the poor parishioners, comprise eleven cottages, occupied as *almshouses*, and about 20 houses and tenements, several gardens, and about 22a. of land, let at low rents, amounting to only £35. 6s. 6d. per annum ; but subject to large fines on the renewal of the 99 years' leases. The charity also derives £46. 10s. a year from the dividends of £1550 Old South Sea Annuities, purchased by the feoffees at various times with money received in fines on the granting of leases. The income is distributed yearly among the poor, chiefly in clothing. Some of the almshouses were rebuilt in 1849, by the Rev. Thomas Bowdler. *St. Margaret's Hospital,* for the reception of lepers, stood in this parish, and its site, and the land and buildings belonging to it, were sold to the feoffees of the parish lands, in 1735, for £70, on condition that they should continue to appoint, as vacancies occurred by death, a *poor brother and sister* of the said hospital from among the poor of Pilton, and divide among them the clear yearly rents of the property belonging to the hospital. This property now comprises 14 houses, with gardens, &c., let for only about £12 a year, in consideration of fines paid when the leases were granted. The rent and fines are divided among the two almspeople, who have no dwelling allotted them under the charity. The poor parishioners have the following *yearly sums;*—26s., left by *Sir John Acland*, in 1616, and paid by the Corporation of Exeter ; 13s., left by *Edward Fairchild*, in 1653, out of Lane estate, in the parish of Charles ; 36s., left by *Robert Incledon*, in 1746, out of the Unicorn Inn ; 55s., as interest of £60, left by *John Rogers and John Exeter*, and vested with the feoffees of the parish lands ; 20s., left by *Thomas Harding*, in 1767, out of Cladovin estate; and 26s. left by *Christopher Lethbridge*, out of Westaway estate ; together with 10s. for repairing his monument and the church roof. The above-named Edw. Fairchild also left 13s. for schooling poor children.

BARNSTAPLE UNION comprises the 39 parishes of Arlington, Ashford, Atherington, Barnstaple, Berrynarbor, Brendon, Bittadon, Bishops-Tawton, Braunton, Bratton-Fleming, Challacombe, Coombmartin, Countisbury, East-Down, Fremington, Goodleigh, Georgeham, Heanton-Punchardon, Highbray, Horwood, Ilfracombe, Instow, Kentisbury, Landkey, Linton, Loxhore, Marwood, Martinhoe, Morthoe, Newton-Tracey, Parracombe, Pilton, Sherwill, Stoke Rivers, Swimbridge, Tawstock, Trentishoe, West-Down, and Westleigh, which contained, altogether, in 1841, a *population* of 37,452 souls, living in 7266 *houses*, besides which they had 603 empty houses, and 41 building, when the census was taken. The *Union Workhouse* is a large stone building, which was erected in 1837, at the cost of £4000, including £900 paid for the land, but it has since been enlarged at the additional cost of £1500. It has room for 320 paupers, and had 220 in January, 1850. The expenditure of the union, in 1849, was £13,974. **J. S. Clay**, Esq., is the union clerk and *superintendent registrar ;* the Rev. George Johnston is the *chaplain ;* and Mr. John, and Mrs. Marsh are *master and matron* of the Workhouse. The *relieving officers* are John Tinson, Wm. Vickery, and John Watts. Mr.

John Barry, of Barnstaple, and Mr. W. C. Aston, of Ilfracombe, are *registrars of marriages;* and Messrs. Edw. Webb, J. Tinson, W. Carpenter, W. C. Aston, J. Watts, and T. Barker, are registrars of births and deaths. The Board of Guardians meet at the Union House every Friday, at 11 morning.

BARNSTAPLE DIRECTORY,

INCLUDING PILTON PARISH, AND PART OF BISHOP'S TAWTON.

POST-OFFICE, 88, High street. Mr. Wm. Petter, *post-master.* Letters despatched to London, Exeter, &c., 23 minutes past 3 afternoon ; to the North at 9½ morning, and to Bideford, Ilfracombe, &c., at 8½ morning. The box closes half an hour before each departure, and *foot posts* are despatched to surrounding villages every morning. The town letter carriers are Thomas Lake, John Bolland, John Parker, and John Hopkins: *Money Orders* are granted and paid. There is a *receiving box* at Mr. Wm. Bryant's, NEWPORT, which is in Bishop's Tawton parish.

MISCELLANY *of Gentry, Clergy, Partners in Firms, and others, not arranged in the succeeding Classification of Trades and Professions.*

Abbott Miss E., Vicrge. ln
Aldham Byron, supt. of police, 97 High street
Aldred Mrs My., Newport
Amier Mr Wm., Newport
Andrews Mrs E. 8 Salem pl
Annis Mr Mentor,3 Salem p
Avery Mr.J.,Summerland pl
Avery Mr Wm. draper ; h Castle street
Baker James, overseer, 51 High street
Baker Mrs Ann, 62 High st
Barry John, regr., Bear st
Bater Alfred, town crier, Bear street
Bealey Mrs, Bear street
Beard Rev Samuel, (Wes.,) Boutport street
Beer Mrs Mary, Newport
Beevor Mrs E., Bear street
Bencraft Lionel Thos. solr., & town clerk, Castle st
Bencraft Rd. Incledon, solr. Quay
Besley Miss, Bear street
Bidders Miss M., Newport
Blackmore Miss Mary Ann, Pilton
Blackwell Mr Thos., Gammon's lane
Boteler Captain John, Gutterstone
Bowling Mrs Anne, Bellair
Boyne Thomas, accountant, &c., Holland street
Briley Miss E., Newport
Brabazon Captain William, Union terrace
Bray Elias, schoolmaster, High street
Bremridge Mrs A., Newport
Bremridge Rd. Esq., M.P., solicitor & county coroner, Castle street
Brice Henry, coach proptr., Newport
Britton Wm. optician, &c., 140 High street
Britton Miss Alice, Newport
Britton Thomas, sergeant at mace, Boutport street
Brooke Mr T.B.,Litchdon tr

Brown Alexander J., bank manager, Square
Bryan Misses F.&E.,Pilton
Budd R. Esq. Ebberley pl
Butcher Miss Ann, Cross st
Butler Hon. Theobald Fitzwalter, Nelson terrace
Carpenter Wm. registrar, Pilton
Carter Charles, solr., Square
Carter Mr Wm. 26 High st
Carver Mr Isaiah, Bellair
Challis Mr J. H., Barbican
Chanter John Roberts, solr. Square
Chapman Mr Rt. (Plymth. Brethren minister)
Chichester Mrs H., Pill
Chichester Robert, Esq., *Hall*, Boutport street
Churchward Mrs Harriet, Newport
Clarke Mrs E., North walk
Cooke Mrs Ann Maria, Barbican terrace
Cooksley Jas.road surveyor, Pilton
Corsar Mr John, Newport
Culliford Miss J., Bear st
Curtis Mrs C. A., Newport
Curtis Mr Wm., Newport
Cutcliffe Misses,Boutport st
Dallyn Jph. bellows maker, Holland street
Davie Capt. C.,Trafalgar pl
Davie Miss F., Newport
Davis Mr G., 10 Salem pl
Davis Ignatius, Esq. Brdgt.
Davy Jon. land agt., Pilton
Day Mrs LauraL., Newport
Dennis Mrs E., Boutport st
Dennis Mr Ths., Pilton bdg
Drake Mr Charles, Pilton
DraperMr Thomas,Newport
Drummond Captain Henry A., Newport
Duprez Mons. John, teacher of languages, Litchdon st
Dyer Mr Wm. Newport
Edger John, grocer ; house Pilton
Ellis Mrs, Newport
Evans J., bailiff, 54 High st

Exter Mrs E., Newport
Featherstone Samuel, fishing tackle mkr., Newport
Finch Mrs Mary, Pilton
Fisher Misses, Barbican tr.
Fisher John, spirit mert., 92 High street
Flexman Mrs Eliz., Pilton
Free Mr R., Summerlandpl
Freeling Lady, Trafalgar pl
Gabriel Wm., beadle, Sqr.
Geachsias John Geo , acct., Boutport street
Gent Wm. comptroller of customs, Barbican ter
Gidley Miss, Bear street
Gidley Mr Barth., Newport
Gilbert Mrs Jane, Pilton
Gilbert Jno. Pomeroy, bank manager, High street
Gilbert John, tax surveyor, Newport
Glass Misses, Summerld.pl
Gordon Major Frederick, Newport
Gorrell Mr Isaac, Newport
Gotbed Miss, Bear street
Gotbed Wm. gent., Trafalgar place
Grace Mrs Eliz., High st
Graham Mrs Jane, Union tr
Gregory Wm. Weeks, draper, High street
Gribble Mrs Elizabeth, Summerland place
Gribble Henry Ivie, Esq., Boutport street
Griffiths John Rogers,Esq., Pilton
Griffiths Mrs C., Newport
Hall Rev Wm. Cradock, M.A. incbt. of Pilton
Hancock Joseph,supervisor, Bear street
Harding ThomasWrey,Esq. Upcott
Harris John, excise officer, Bear street
Harttree George, glover, High street
Hatherly Lieutenant John, Summerland place
Heathcote Mrs A., Newport

Hiern Miss Eliz., Newport
Hiern-Mrs Hanh., Newport
Hiern Capt. J., R.N., Pilton
Hiern Mr P. W., Newport
Hodge Miss E., Bear st
Hodge Mr J., Victoria st
Hodge Mr S., Salem place
Hole Mrs M., Trafalgar pl
Horden John, gentleman, Rosehill villa
Hunt John Dennis, ironmonger, 36 High street
Hunt Jph. Wingyett, conveyancer, (and member of Inner Temple,) 46 Boutport street
Jackson J., gent. Newport
Jackson Capt. P., Newport
Jeve Eliz., lessee of gas
Joce Thomas, spirit mert. 92 High street
Johnston Rev Geo., B.D., master of GrammarSchl.; house Boutport street
Johnson James, collector of inland rev., Boutport st
Jollyman Rev Wm.(Indpt.) Bear street
Jones Daniel, constable, Tuly lane
Jones Miss E. D.,Castle st
JonesFdk.,insptr. of weights & measures, Newport
Jones Mr Wm. Henry, Barbican terrace
King Miss, Bear street
Kingson John, gent. Bear st
LambertLeut.Wm.,Newprt.
Lang Miss F., Newport
Langdon Mrs My., Bear st
Lansdown Mrs A.,Newport
Latham Wm. Frdk., gent., Trafalgar place
Law Mrs Francis, Square
Law Mr Wm., Bear street
Le Gallais Chas. T., gent., Litchdon street
LeworthyMrHmph., Pilton
List Wm. paper manufacturer, Quay place
Lister Mrs My. E., Broad Meadow
Lock Mrs Eliz., Boutport st
Loundes Mr E., Bear st
Loveday Mr Wm., Newport
Lowis Major Thos. Thornton, Newport
Luxmoore Rev Henry,vicar, Vicarage
Mackerell MrsMy.Union tr
Marsacke Mr Geo., Litchdon terrace
March John King, schoolmaster, Square
Marsh John, govr. Workhs.
Marshall J. Esq., banker, 70 High street
Martin Mr H. Boutport st
Matthews Rev H., Bear st
Mathews Murray Wm.gent Ralegh House

MaunderFred.,woolstapler, Boutport street
May Captain John, Broadgate House
May Miss N., Union ter
May John, lace manager, Barbican
Metherell Mrs E., Newport
Michelmore Miss, Bear st
Miller John,(Exors. of,)lace mfrs., Derby
Mills Mr Benj., Diamondst
Moon James, ironmonger, 76 High street
Munro MajorC.A.,Newport
Newnam Rev Saml.(Bapt.) North walk
Nihil Mrs S., Newport
Northcott Mr Roger, Boutport street
Nott Mr Wm., Newport
NuthallMrsChtte.,Newport
Owen T. Esq., Square
Packer Mr A., Barbican ter
Parker Mrs Chtte., Bear st
Parker Captain Peter,R.N. North walk
Parminter Mr Joseph B., Salem street
Parminter James, draper, Cross street
Partridge Mrs S.,41High st
Passmore Susanna, porter mert. 97 High street
Pawle Mrs A., Newport
Peard G., solr., Castle st
Pedler Mr Chpr., Newport
Petter Mr Wm. postmaster, 88 High street
Phipps Mrs, Bear street
Pinkett Mr E., Trafalgarpl
PrendergastCaptain James, Newport
Pridham & Lake, carriers, Joy street
Purchase Miss E., Joy st
Pycroft Rev James, M.A., incumbent of Mary Mgd. Mount Sandford
Pym Mr Edmd., Newport
Rafarel Wm. gas manager, Bear street
Ratcliff Mr Jas., Newport
Roberts Edward, Fort hill
Rook Mrs E., Pilton
Ross Miss E., Newport
Savile Rev Bouchier Wrey, A.M., incbt. of Newport
SavileEdw.,Bourchier, solr. Boutport street.
Scott Capt J., Trafalgar H.
Servante Miss S., Cross st
Shapland Edwin Hy., mail guard, Sion place
Shephard Mr Saml. Savile, Barbican terrace
Slade Miss E., Newport
Slater Rev Wm. (Indpt.) Barbican terrace
Smith Wm., excise officer, Salem place
Smith Mrs M., Newport

Snell John, police officer, Square
Spurway Mrs A., 63Highst
Squire Miss Mary Ann, Union terrace
Stanley Captain M., Rosehill House
Stark Mr J. R., Raven's cft
Stephens Mr Rd., Salem pl
Stevens Capt. Robert, R.N. Newport
Stiffe Mr Zacharia,Newport
Stribbling Mrs M., Back ln
Tetherley Mrs Eliz., Pilton
Thorne Mr John, Newport
Thorne J., sheriff's officer, Boutport street
Thorne Rd., Esq., Pilton
Thorne Henry King, high bailiff of county court, High street
Thorne Wm.contractor, Sqr
Tinson Jno. relieving officer and regr. Newport
Tinson Wm. lath maker, Litchdon street
Toller Mrs Cath., Cross st
Toller John Henry, solr., and deputy coroner,Boutport street
Tossell Miss Mary, Bellair
Trawin Wm., govr. of Gaol
Tucker Mrs T. H., Barbican terrace
Tucker John, draper, 87 High street
Tucker Mr P.,Gammon'sln
Turner Mr Wm., Nelson tr
Turner John Coham, Dispensary
Venn Mr Hy., Newport
Ville Js., sexton, Anchor ln
Walters Geo., excise officer, Bear street
Ward Mrs My., Boutport st
Webb Mis Eliz., Bear st
Webb Edward, registrar, Boutport street
Webber Mr A., Salem pl
Weeks Mr Josias, Vicrg. ln
White Rd., collr.of customs, Pilton
White Peter, gentleman, Westaway House
Whyte James Esq. Pilton House
Whyte Capt. Wm., Gorwell
Whitefield William, crier, Mallett's row
Widlake Pascal, draper, 64 High street
Wilford Major Jno., Pilton
Williams Miss Eliz., Pilton
Williams Capt. J., Newport
WilliamsCapt. W.,Newprt
Willis Mr John, Litchdon tr
Wills Mrs, Bear street
Willshire Thos., iron fndr., Newport
Wivell Mr Nathaniel, 67 High street

Woodward Capt. Augustine, Newport
Woollacott Miss J., Newprt.
Woollacott Mrs Eliza, 17 High street
Woollacott John, ironmgr., 76 High street
Wrey Sir B. P., Bart., *Tawstock House*
Yeo Mrs S., 56 Boutport st

ACADEMIES.

* *take Borders.*
Blue Coat Schools. William Quince, & Mary May
* Bray & Marsh, 66 Highst
Dalton Charles, Joy street
Dart Sarah Ann, Back ln
Davie Mary, 58 Boutport st
* *Free Grammar School,* Rev Geo. Johnston, B.D.
* Heard Ann, 45 High st
* Henderson Mgt., Newport
Moore Eliz, Pilton
Narracott Mary, Castle st
National Schools, Geo. Hunt, Salem st; Eliz. Ogalbe, Castle st; Susan Brook, Trinity ch.; Wm. & Ann Cann, Newport; & Saml. Parsons, Pilton
* Ralph Hanh., Boutport st
Ratcliffe Ann, Newport
Rice Robt., Vicarage lane
* Sharland Rd., Union ter
Smith E & Misses, Pilton
* Snow Wm., Vicarage ln
Stevens Rd., Nelson ter
* Tanner Eliz., 103 Boutport street
Wills Mary, 93 High street
Workhs. School, John Oliver & Eliza Shapland

AGENTS & SHIP BKS.

Gribble Jonthn. Ivie, Newport terrace
Prust Jph., Boutport street
Worsfold Saml., Castle st

ARCHITECTS & SURVS.

Gould Rd. Davie, Boupt. st
Northcote Geo. & Son, 52 Boutport street

ATTORNEYS.

Bencraft Lionel & Incledon, Castle street
Bremridge, Toller & Savile, Boutport street
Carter & Chanter, Square
Clay John Sherard, (union clerk, &c.,) High street
Dene Chas. Jno. (& proctor) Square
Drake Alfd., (coroner & clk. to borough magistrates,) Castle street
Gribble Wm. (clerk of the peace,) Castle street
Kingdon Jph. F., High st
Law Thomas Hooper, Litchdon street
Mortimer Rt., 53 High st
Palmer C. Edwards, Cross st
Peard & Langdon, Castle st

Wills John, Square

AUCTIONEERS.

Gould John, Joy street
Hearson Geo., Litchdon st
Mogridge John, Cross street
Stanbury John, Sowden
Stevens John, Bear street
Stribbling Wm., High st

BAKERS.

Andrew Jno., Litchdon st
Arnoll Grace, Church lane
Arnoll Robert, High street
Baker Edw. S., Boutport st
Brannam John, Boutport st
Capern Edw., Derby
Conibear George, Newport
Cowell Lewis, Salem street
Day Wm., Pilton
Ford Hy., Aze's lane
Gaydon Agnes, Newport
Hobbs Stpn., 96 High street
Hooper Thos., Derby
Jarman John, Myrtle lane
Jones John, Back lane
Jones Eliz., Joy street
Leach Thomas, Joy street
Marshall J. B., Bear street
Otway Wm., Gaydon st
Pearce Philip, Newport
Phillips Eliz., Boutport st
Porter Wm., Joy street
Rowe Wm., High street
Shapland Wm., Back lane
Stribbling John, Holland st
Todd Wm., Back lane
Warmington Ann, Pilton
Williams Wm. (and plaster manufr.) Anchor lane

BANKERS.

Drake, Gribble, Marshall, & Co. (on Barnard & Co.) High street
National Provincial Bank of England, (on London and Westminster,) J. P. Gilbert, manager, High st
West of England and South Wales District Bank, (on Glyn&Co) Alex. J. Brown, manager, Square.
Savings' Bank, Boutport st. Edwin Risdon Davy, sec.

BASKET MAKERS.

Berry Thomas, Cross st
Dennis Wm., Holland st
Prideaux George, Anchor ln
Prideaux Rd. H., High st
Tucker Wm., Boutport st

BERLIN REPOSTRS.

Bailey Margt. 77 High st
Cook John, 108 High street
McKenzie Ann, High st
Trowbridge C. P., High st

BLACK & W. SMITHS.

Adey George, Newport
Ashton John, Boutport st
Baker Richard, High st
Harper Henry, Newport
Jones Wm., Pilton
King Samuel, Green lane
Morgan Thomas, Tuly lane
Oliver Wm., Silver street

Rowdon John, Litchdon st
Spurway John, Pilton
Squire David, Diamond st
Thorne Henry, (scale beam, &c. manfr.) Joy street
Watts George, Pilton

BONDED WAREHSES.

Cotton John & Son, Cross st
Yeo Wm., Quay place

BOOKSLRS. PRNTRS. &c.

Avery Wm. (printer & pub. of *North Devon Journal,*) 82 High street
Baker John, Boutport st
Brightwell Isaac, High st
Cornish Thomas, Joy street
Evans John, 54 High st
Harris Emanuel, (music and toy dlr.) High street
Hearson Thos. 89 High st
Jones John, (printer only,) Queen Anne's place
Searle Wm. & Son, 15 High st

BOOT & SHOEMAKERS.

Berry Robert, Newport
Blackmore John, Litchdon st
Bridgeman Jno. 91 High st
Bridgeman Rd. 27 High st
Clement Wm., Salem st
Coombes Wm., Newport
Curtis John, 76 High st
Dibble Wm., Pilton
Drew John, Well street
Edwards Brian B. 11 High st
Essery Thomas, Litchdon st
Geen Thomas, Bear street
Hancock James, 48 High st
Heard Thomas, Newport
Hobbs Richard, Bear st
Hunt James, Litchdon st
Jolliffe Orlando, Silver st
Jones Wm., Holland st
Knill Wm., Pilton
Lock Wm. 100 High street
Moore John, Pilton
Nicholls Wm., Gaydon st
Otway Geo. 82 Boutport st
Parminter Thos., Litchdon st
Pedler James, Pilton
Pile Wm., Bear street
Seldon Wm., Newport
Wadham Jas. 32 High st
Wadham Mary, Litchdon st
Ward John, Pilton
Williams Thos. 84 High st
Woolacott Wm , Square

BRAZIERS & TINNERS.

Britton Wm., High street
Chapple & Geen, Anchor ln
Chapple Wm., Joy street
Dinnicombe Robert, Pilton
King Thomas, Joy street
Knill Richard, Litchdon st
Lancey Richard, 17 High st
Mills John, 3 High street
Moon&Woollacott, 76 Highst
Petter John, 68 High street
Seldon Henry, Salem st
Young Wm., Boutport st

BRICK & TILE MAKERS.

Thorne John, Boutport st
Shapland Chpr., Newport

BRUSH MAKERS.
Brown George, Newport
Sanders Richard, Quay

BUILDERS.
Carter Philip, Boutport st
Davy Thomas, Litchdon st
Galliford Edw.81 Boutport st
Galliford Wm., Victoria st
Gilbert Rd., Boutport st
Gribble Richard, Pilton

BUTCHERS.
Ackland Geo. 7 Shambles
Ackland Grace, Anchor ln
Andrews John, 12 Shambles
Bowden Robt. 19 Shambles
Catford Robert, 1 Shambles
Copp Henry, 20 Shambles
Davis John, 23 Shambles
Davis John, Anchor lane
Fisher Fras., Boutport st
Ford James, 27 Shambles
Fry Wm. 13 Shambles
Galliford Wm. 30 Shambles
Gaydon John, 33 Shambles
Grigg James, 17 Shambles
Hancock Rd. 5 Shambles
Hosking John, 11 Shambles
Hussell Wm. 21 Shambles
Huxtable Wm. 3 Shambles
Manning B., Shmbls.& Piltn
Martin Adam, Shambles
Parkin George, 9 Shambles
Parkin Geo. sen. 26 Shmbls
Partridge Thos.28 Shambles
Pugsley Mary, 4 Shambles
Richards Wm. 2 Shambles
Richards Ths. 18 Shambles
Rook Thos. 24 Shambles
Sanders Henry, 8 Shambles
Sanders Thos. 10 Shambles
Snow John, 6 Shambles
Squire John, 15 Shambles
Tucker Geo. 25 Shambles
Ward Wm. 14 Shambles
Westacott Jno. 31 Shambles
Western Wm. 29 Shambles

CABINET MAKERS.
Crook Henry, Nelson ter
Crook John, Boutport st
Hancock John, Boutport st
Hearson Geo., Litchdon st
Jones Nicholas, Boutport st
Ley John, Quay
Skinner Hugh, Boutport st
Stribbling Wm. 50 High st
Symons Philip,(&undertkr.)
Boutport street

CARPENTERS.
Bale James, High street
Bale Wm., Holland street
Bryant Thos., Boutport st
Co] p Wm., Pilton
Dendle Jno. 110 Boutport st
Ellacott Rd., Holland st
Galliford Edw., Boutport st
Gammon Wm. Derby
Hartnoll John, 65 High st
Hartnoll Thomas, Pilton
Hartnoll Philip, Pilton
Oliver James, Cross street
Thomas John, Pilton

Thorne David, Anchor lane

CARVERS & GILDERS.
Darby Hugh, 80 Boutport st
Fewing John, Boutport st
Jewell Wm. 72 Boutport st
Ley John, Quay

CHEMISTS & DRUGTS.
Batcheler Jno.Geo.1 High st
Cann Robert, 99 High st
Cotton Gilbt. Knill, High st
Hall John Hunter, High st
Hayman Alfred, Pilton
Mackrell Thos. 94 High st
Norrington John, 75 High st
Tatham John W., Joy st
Weaver John, 23 High st
Weeks John, Joy street

CHINA, GLASS, &c. DLRS.
Glyde Samuel, 101 High st
Lord Fras. 54 Boutport st
Trestain John, Joy street
Walton Wm. 29 High st

CLOTHES DEALERS.
Arundel Robert, Cross st
Bennett Geo., Boutport st
Hartnoll George, Joy st
Jones Philip, Derby
White Geo., Boutport st

COACH BUILDERS.
Gibbings Wm., Boutport st
Pettle Henry, Diamond st
Symons Richard, Bear st

COAL MERCHANTS.
Arter Wm. & Sons, Quay
Baker John, 2 Boutport st
Bentley John, Castle street
Carpenter Wm., Pilton
Dalling George, Pilton
Densham Thos., Litchdon st
Gibbs Henry, Quay
Hancock John, Salem st
Rawle Samuel, Rolle's quay
Sanders Wm. V., Back ln
Snell Michl., Queen Ann's pl
Tamplyn Wm., Bear st

CONFECTIONERS.
Arnoll Robert, 34 High st
Hobbs Stephen, 96 High st
Jones Elizabeth, Joy st
Lang Wm., Joy street
Newcombe John, Joy st
Rowe Wm. 105 High st
Thornby John, Boutport st

COOPERS.
Barrow Thos., Holland st
Bevan Wm., Hartway head
Carter John, Pilton
Petter James, 39 High st

CORN FACTORS.
Arter Wm. & Sons, Quay
Baker Edw.Setter, Boutpt.st
Balsdon George, Boutport st
CottonJno.Knill&Son,Crs.st
Drake Charles, Holland st
Fisher John M , Boutport st

CORN MILLERS.
Baker Edw. S., Boutport st
Hearneman James, Pilton

CURRIERS.
Adams Samuel, Bear st
Rice Robt. & Son, Cross st

Rude John, Derby
White James, High street

CUTLERS.
Hill Thomas, Bear street
Jones Wm., Salem street
Pearson George, Anchor ln

DYERS.
Jones Wm. Hill, 51 High st
PowningAmbroseT., High st

EARTHENWR. MFRS.
Bannam Thos., North walk
RendellEliasD., Litchdon st

EATING HOUSES.
Lavis Thomas, Joy street
Robins Wm., Quay
Taylor John, Cross street
Weeden Hy. 59 Boutport st

FARMERS.
Bidder Robert, *Yeotown*
Brown Thomas, *Roborough*
Bryant Wm., *Pitt*
Fisher Wm. B., *Pottondon*
Hancock Thomas, Pilton
Harris Wm., *Waytown*
Jones Philip, Boutport st
Lock Osmond Frank, *Marsh*
Marquis Jane, Newport
Northcote George,(and land
    agent,) *Stoneyard*
Parkin Wm., *East Sowden*
Pomeroy Rd., *Maidenford*
Ridd Reuben, Longstone
Sherwill George, Newport
Stanbury Jno., *West Sowden*
Stafford Saml. W., *Tutshill*
Western George, *Westaway*

FIRE & LIFE OFFICES.
Argus, Jno. K. Cotton & Son
Atlas, Wm. Searle & Son,
British Coml., Geo. Hearson
Clerical & Medcl., Hy. Dene
County&Provdt., E.R.Davy
English and Scottish Law,
    Charles John Dene
General, John Weaver
Guardian, Robert Gregory
Great Britain, Thos. Hodge
Hand in Hand, Rt.Mortimer
Imperial, Edger & Carter
Industrial&Deposit, Ths.D.
    Thorne
Legal, &c. Widlake & Gould
London Corporation, John
    Henry Toller
National, Michael Snell
Norwich Union, Moon and
    Woollacott
ProvidentClerks', John Geo.
    Geachsias
Rock, John S. Clay
RoyalExch., Jas. Whitefield
Royal Farmers', Lionel T.
    Bencraft
Standard, Edger & Carter
Star, Thomas King
Sun, Cotton and Son
Temperance Provident, Jno.
    Norrington
West of Engd., H.L.Gribble

FURNITURE BROKRS.
Gribble Charles, Cross st

2 B

578 BARNSTAPLE DIRECTORY.

Lewis Wm., Silver street
Symons Philip, Boutport st
Woodman Samuel, Well st
GAME, &c. DEALERS.
Beer Wm., Quay
Clarke Mary, Cross street
Lavis Thomas, Joy street
Leaker Philip, Boutport st
Prust Joseph, Boutport st
Weeden Henry, Boutport st
GARDENERS, &c.
Allen Anthony, Dahlia cotg
Booth Alex. 55 High st
Burge Wm., Boutport st
Crang James, Newport
Ireland Jno.(nrsrymn.) Pltn
Harris James, Pilton
Mallett Wm. 48 Boutport st
Marshall Thomas, Bear st
Rowland Thomas, High st
Westacott Rt., Boutport st
GROCERS & TEA DLRS.
Berry Samuel, Boutport st
Besley John, 98 High st
Bowden John, 41 High st
Channon John, 6 High st
Edger & Carter, 26 High st
Farleigh Rd., 14 High st
Gregory Robert, 78 High st
Hall Ths.Hunter,63 High st
Manning Benjamin, Pilton
May Thomas, 78 High st
Mills George, 27 High st
Quick James, 102 High st
Quick Wm. Hean, Cross st
Rowe John, 49 Boutport st
Sanders Wm. V., Back ln
Seldon Thomas, Joy st
Souch Jas. S. 28 Boutport st
Thorne Susan, Joy street
Thorne Wm. Hy. 5 High st
Thorne W.H. jun. 30 High st
Veale James, 19 High st
Weeks John, Joy street
Yeo Wm., Quay place
GUN MAKERS.
Bridle James, 69 High st
Fraine Thomas, (and bird
stuffer,) 52 High street
Webber James, Page's ln
HAIR DRESSERS, &c.
Bament John, 1 Boutport st
Dalling Wm. 7 High st
Elson Robert, Joy street
Hill Wm. 69 High street
Laud Abraham, Maiden st
Parkin Wm., Back lane
Rendell John, Joy street
Williams James, Anchor ln
HAT MFRS. & DLRS.
King John, Boutport st
Marshall Thos. 33 High st
Martin Richard, 90 High st
Pickard Jasper, Holland st
Trestain John, Joy street
White George, Boutport st
HORSE & GIG LETTRS.
Bryant Thos., Boutport st
Geen George, Joy street
Hitchcock Wm., Holland st
Paterson Geo. Hy., Quay
Pettle Richard, Back lane

Seldon Wm., Boutport st
Stoneman Hy., Vicarage ln
Thorne George, Boutport st
Waldron John, Boutport st
INNS & TAVERNS.
Admiral Vernon,Chtte. Hill,
Maiden street
Angel, Thos. Avery, Quay
Barley Mow, John Jenkins,
Boutport street
Bear, John Bate, Green ln
Beehive, Js. Smith,Green ln
Bell, John Geen, Quay
Braunton Inn, Rd. Frayne,
High street
Bull, Chas. Widden, Bout-
port street
Castle, Wm.Britton,High st
Chichester Arms, Thomas
Hancock, Pilton
Commercial Inn, John Wal-
dron, Boutport street
Crown and Anchor, James
Hunt, Litchdon street
Ebberly Arms, John Cole,
Bear street
Exeter Inn, Maria Tinson,
Litchdon street
Falcon, Eliz.Gliddon, Joy st
Fortescue Arms, (& postg.)
Wm. Cory, Boutport st
Tap, Jas Parkin, Well st
George & Shakspeare, Benj.
Skinner, Boutport st
Golden Anchor, My. Chap-
ple, Holland street
Golden Fleece,John Otway,
Tuly lane
Golden Lion, (and posting,)
John Marsh, Boutport st
Green Dragon, Philip Pyke,
130 Boutport street
Heart of Oak, John Delve,
Boutport street
Horse and Groom, Wm. Sel-
don, Boutport street
Ilfracombe Inn, Jas. Pris-
cott, High street
King's Arms, Fredk. Jef-
ferey, 30 High street
Lamb, John Hartnoll, 31
Boutport street
London Inn, Wm. Sluman,
Litchdon street
Mermaid, John Baker,
Boutport street
Nag's Head, Thomas Hill,
Anchor lane
Newport Inn, Jph. Perrien
North Country Inn, Sally
Robins, Boutport st
North Molton Inn, Joanna
Irwin, Bear street
Railway Hotel, Geo. Blight,
Boutport street
RedLion,Edw.Hooper,Quay
Ring of Bells, Hy. Knill,
Pilton
Ring of Bells, Dd. Thorne,
Anchor lane
Rising Sun, John Berry,
Boutport street

Rising Sun, Wm. Squire,
Newport
Rolle Arms, Michael Bur-
gess, Bear street
Rolle's Quay Inn, Sl. Rawle
Rose & Crown, Wm. Baker,
Newport
Royal Exchange, Thomas
King, Joy street
Royal Oak, John Easton,
Holland street
Salutation, Peter Camp,
Castle street
Seven Stars, Richd. Beer,
Anchor lane
Sheep Market, Humphrey
Britton, Holland st
Ship, Thos. Bailey, Quay
Shipwrights' Arms, Thos.
King, Square
Smiths' Arms, John Snell,
Diamond street
Star, Geo. Henry Paterson,
(fishmonger,) Quay
Swan, Wm. Slocombe, Hol-
land street
Three Tuns, Jas. Easton,
High street
Town Arms, Hy. Geyton,
Anchor lane
Unicorn, Wm. Copp, Pilton
White Hart, Wm. Parkin,
Joy street
White Horse, Wm. White,
29 Boutport street
White Lion, Rd. Rumson,
Castle street
BEERHOUSES.
Bennett John, Derby
Bowden John, Salem st
Budd Robert, Silver st
Edwards John, Newport
Essery Rt., Boutport st
Featherstone Wm., Newpt
Gaydon Wm., Salem st
Greenslade John, Anchor ln
Grigg Mary, Pilton
Hancock Thomas, Pilton
Jones Charles, Derby
Mountjoy Mary, Silver st
Laramy Wm., Pilton
Norman Thomas, Salem st
Parminter John, Page's ln
Oliver Thomas, Back ln
Petherick John, Back ln
Oatway John, Hartway hd
Richards Eliz., Bear st
Robins Wm., Quay
Seldon Thomas, Salem st
Seldon Robert, Derby
Snow Charles, North walk
Stoyle John, Derby
Taylor John, Cross st
Ward Mary, Newport
IRON BAR MERTS.
Arter Wm. & Sons, Quay
Gibbs Henry, Quay
Hunt and Sons, 36 High st
IRONMONGERS.
Baker Rd., 103 High st
Hunt and Son, 36 High st
King Thomas, Joy st

Lancey Rd. 17 High st
Moon and Woollacott, 76 High street
Murch James, Bear st
Petter John, 68 High st
Williams John, 9 High st

LIME MERCHANTS.
Ballment Hugh, Boutpt. st
Shapland Chpr., Newport
Lauder My., *Pottington Hs*

LINEN DRAPERS, &c.
Alcock Wm. 10 High st
Avery & Parminter, Cross st
Carter My. 107 High st
Clogg Nichs. 24 High st
Gray Isaac, 109 High st
Gregory & Tucker, High st
Harris John, (and stamp distributor,) High st
Haydon John, 1 Square
Hodge Thomas, 73 High st
Lilly Wm. 79 High st
Pethebridge Anty. High st
Smyth Wm., Joy street
Vellacott Wm.& Jno. High st
Widlake & Gould, High st
Williams My. Ann, High st

MALTSTERS.
Baker John, 2 High st
Balsdon Geo., Boutport st
Blight Geo., Boutport st
Carpenter Wm., Pilton
Cotton and Son, Cross st
Dallyn Wm., Back lane
Darke Charles, Holland st
Fisher Jno. M., Boutport st
Gaydon Henry, Newport
Hancock John, Salem st
Lympaney Richard, Quay
Seldon Thomas, Joy st
Slocombe Wm., Holland st
Souch Jas. S., Boutport st
Street Hugh, Boutport st
White Wm., Boutport st

MASONS, &c.
Carter Philip, Boutport st
Bushel Wm., Summrld. pl
Down James, Salem st
Fleming John, Hartway hd
Gould John, (marble,) North walk
Horne Wm. & Son, Back ln
Knill Henry, Pilton
Norman Thomas, Salem st
Oatway Rd., Hartway hd
Parminter John, Page's ln
Pidler Thomas, Castle st
Todd Wm., Back lane
Turner Wm., Silver st

MASTER MARINERS.
Ching Philip, Cross st
Ching Saml., Gammon's ln
Crossman Ths., Somerset pl
Edwards Wm , Holland st
Hawkins Mattw., Pilton
Hearson Henry, Newport
Lake Jas., Boutport st
Marshall Robt., Back ln
Nutt Wm., Back lane
Osborne Wm., Castle st
Williams Thomas, Salem st

Yeo Wm., Bear street

MERCHANTS.
Arter Wm. & Sons, Quay
Ballment Hugh, Boutpt. st
Cotton J. K. & Son, Cross st
Gregory Rt. 78 High st
Snell Michl., Qu. Ann's pl
Yeo Wm., Quay place

MILLINERS, &c.
Avery S. and H., High st
Baker Sus. & Ann, Salem st
Carter Susanna, Joy st
Chugg Ann, 53 High st
Curtis Martha, Pilton
Down Eliza, 3 High st
Ellacott Misses, Holnd. st
Gardener E. S., Boutpt. st
Glover E. & M., Boutpt. st
Fleming H. & S., Boutpt. st
Gammon C. M., Pilton
Gliddon Ann, 16 High st
Gunn C. and E., High st
Greenway Dinah, Boutpt. st
Hancock Eliza, High st
Harris Eliza, High st
Hartnoll Miriam, High st
Hill Ann, Derby
Hobbs Eliz., Joy street
Horne E. and M., Back ln
Kingdon F. & A., 49 High st
Lake H. and M., Back ln
List Mary Ann, Joy st
McKenzie Ann, High st
Moore Ann, Pilton
Parkin Eliza., Aze's lane
Phillip's Eliz., Joy st
Prust M. J., Boutport st
Radmore E. and S., Pilton
Rew Mary Ann, High st
Rowdon A. & J., Litchdon st
Sanders My. A., Square
Stevens A. & E., 77 High st
Thorne Eliz., Hartway hd
Vellacott My., Boutport st
Ward Margaret, Bear st
Webber Penelope, Newport
Westacott B., Litchdon st
Widlake & Richards, Bpt. st

MUSIC TEACHERS.
Edwards John, Newport
Harris Emanuel, High st
Huet Frs. Wm. (and dancing,) Litchdon ter
Huxtable Chpr., Newport
Nicklin Oliver Jph., Sqr
Slater Jas., Hartway hd

PAINTERS & GLZRS.
Allen Theophilus, High st
Baker James, 51 High st
Clarke Jno. Snow, Cross st
Davis Wm., 47 High st
Fleming Edw., Boutport st
Gilbert Wm., Boutport st
Hancock Thomas, Pilton
Hancock Chas., Boutport st
Heale Henry, Castle st
Hill John, Boutport st
Knill Robert, Bear st
Shapland Jno. G., Back ln
Skinner Michael, Back ln
Squire Hphy., Diamond st

Squire Mark, Salem st

PAWNBROKERS.
King Samuel, Green lane
Moon James, Page's lane
Oxenham Sus., Boutpt. st

PHYSICIANS.
Bignell John Beavis, Litchdon terrace
Britton Simon Gage, *King's close*, Newport
Budd Richd., Boutport st
Copner Edwin, Boutport st
Newbolt Wm.Kent,Castle st

PLUMBERS.
Baker Jas. 51 High st
King Thomas, Joy st
Lancey Rd. 17 High st
Mills John, 3 High st
Young Wm. 65 Boutport st

ROPE MAKERS, &c.
Shaddick Pp., Gaydon st
Tossell John, Quay

SADDLERS.
Baltus Jph., Holland st
Bryant Wm., Newport
Clarke Chas., 106 High st
Cowman Emanuel, Joy st
Cridland Edw., Boutport st
Davie Wm., 58 Boutport st
Davolls George, Pilton
Gayton Thomas, Square
Gould John, Joy street
Petter Edwin, 22 High st
Tanner Wm., Pilton

SHIP BUILDERS.
Westacott John and Son, Bridge wharf; h Square

SHOPKEEPERS.
Arter Wm., Cross street
Bate Mary, Newport
Beer Wm., Quay
Bennett Sus., Boutport st
Bowden John, Quay
Brannam John, Boutport st
Buzzacott Eliz., Derby
Cock John, Derby
Courtney John, Newport
Cowell Lewis, Salem st
Essery Robt., Boutport st
Furse John, Pilton
Gaydon Geo., Boutport st
Geen John, Green lane
Glover Thomas, Holland st
Hancock Mary, Anchor ln
Hearn Wm., Castle st
Hoyle Mary Ann, Quay
Hutchings Sar., High st
Isaac James, Newport
Kerswell Thomas, Pilton
Lake Thomas, Back lane
Ley John, Quay
Maldram James, Pilton
Marshall Jno. B., Bear st
Mogridge John, Cross st
Murray Thomas, Derby
Oliver Wm., Silver st
Prust Jph., Boutport st
Quick Wm., Pilton
Reddaway Elnr., Green ln
Redmore Sally, Litchdon st
Rice John, Litchdon st

Rudd Mary, Newport
Snow Wm., Back lane
Squire Mark, Salem st
Steel Thomas, Derby
Street Hugh, Boutport st
Symons Wm., Derby
Tucker Wm., Salem st
Treble John, Back lane
Wadham My., Litchdon st
Westacott John, Derby
Winter Eliz., Quay
Wright John, Wells st
STAY MAKERS.
Carter Susanna, Joy st
Chugg Ann, 53 High st
Ching Eliz.. Cross street
Clatworthy C., Boutport st
Collard Jas. R., Boutport st
Glover E. & M., Boutport st
STOCKING MANFRS.
Howell Wm., Newport
Hutchings John, Bear st
Hutchings Sus., High st
Spurway George, Pilton
STRAW HAT MKRS.
Bater Mary Ann, Bear st
Clarke Caroline, Cross st
Fisher Jane, Boutport st
Goss P., Boutport street
Hunter Eliz., Church ln
Janes Mary, Boutport st
Mallett Sus., Boutport st
Mills Sarah, Back lane
Norman Emma, Back ln
Stevens A. & E. 77 High st
SURGEONS.
Cooke Michl., Boutport st
Curry Wm., Boutport st
Dene Wavell Arundel, Litchdon street
Harding Robt., High st
Hiern Chas. H., Bear st
Joce John, Union ter
Law Thos. Sheppard, Litchdon terrace
March Js. Colley, Boutpt. st
Morgan Mr., *Infirmary*
Parker Wm., Boutport st
Torr Thos. Berry, Boutport st
Winter John, 71 High st
SURGEON DENTISTS.
Blackmore Edward & Son, 129 Boutport street
Borlase Wm. Grenfell, Barbican terrace
Tibbs John. Nelson ter
TAILORS.
(Marked * *Drapers also.*)
*Beer John, 86 Boutport st
Bishop Edward, Pilton
Dennis George, Anchor ln
Fewings Robert, Pilton
Gribble Charles, Salem st
*Harris Michael and Son (Wm.) Holland st
*Hartnoll George, Joy st
*Huxtable Wm., Boutpt. st
Holt Richard, Silver st
Jarvis Wm.. Newport
Lock John, Green lane
Major Geo. H., Well st
*Marsh Wm., 2 High st

Oatway Robt., Holland st
*Rottenbury Geo., High st
*Sanders Wm., Square
Sanders Thos., Vicarage ln
Treble Wm., Silver st
Whitefield Jas., Boutport st
TALLOW CHANDLERS.
Channon John, 6 High st
Greek John, 20 High st
Hancock John, Salem st
Harris James, Pilton
TANNERS.
Adams Samuel, Bear st
King John & Son, Pilton
Sanders Jno. & Sml, Pilton
Smyth Wm. G., Pilton bdg
TEA DLRS. & DRPRS. (TRAVELLING.)
Copland James, Bear st
Cummings Wm., Boutpt. st
Fallace John, 51 High st
Milroy John, Boutport st
Milroy Mary, Boutport st
TIMBER, &c., MERTS.
Ballment Hugh, Boutpt.st
Finch Wm. H., Litchdon st
Gould John, North walk
How John, Rolle's quay
Sanders Wm. V., Back ln
TURNERS. (WOOD.)
Edgecombe Rd., Boutport st
Lee John and Co., Pilton
Manley John, Pilton
Williams John, Quay
VETERINRY. SURGNS.
Brewer Wm.Jno.,Litchdn. st
Hewish John, Quay
WATCH & CLOCK MKS.
Alexander Chas., High st
Delve John, Boutport st
Gaydon John, 97 High st
Hunt John, (silversmith,) Joy street
Jones John Wm., 78 High st
Mallett John, (jeweller,) 4 High street
Pengelly John, 35 High st
Perryman John, 18 High st
Wherly Philip, (German clocks,) Boutport st
WHEELWRIGHTS.
Beard Robert, Anchor lane
Copp John, Potter's lane
Furse John, Pilton
Sargent Thomas, Newport
Steward John, Pilton
Symons Richard, Bear st
Ward John, Pilton
Webber Geo , Godleigh rd
WINE & SPRT. MERTS.
Bowden John, 41 High st
Cotton J. K. & Son, Cross st
Fisher and Joce, High st
Pengelly Olvr. V., High st
Snell Michl., Qn. Ann's pl
Ware Samuel, Boutport st
Wilkinson John, Joy st
Yeo Wm., Quay place
WOOLSTAPLERS.
Abbott Wm., Pilton
Spurway Wm., Pilton
Laramy Joseph, Pilton

Maunder Js.& Sons,Tuly ln
Sanders Jno.& Sml., Pilton
COACHES.
From the Fortescue Arms and Golden Lion.
MAILS to *Tiverton* 45min. past 9 morning, and 4¼ afternoon; and to *Bideford and Ilfracombe* ¼ before 9 morning
To *Exeter* at 8½ morning daily, except Sunday
To *Plymouth* 8 morng. every Mon., Wed., and Fri.
To *Tiverton, South Molton,* &c. daily at 8 morning
CARRIERS.
To *Bideford,* Wm. Barwick's omnibus daily at 5 aftn. from Shipwrights' Arms, and Dart and Parish, 11 morng. from Golden Lion Tap
Bratton Fleming, Jas. Kingdon, (White Horse,) Tue. and Fri. 4 afternoon
Braunton, Charles Robins, (Braunton Inn,) daily 6 evening
Combmartin, James Willis, King's Arms,) Tue. and Fri. 4 afternoon
Ilfracombe daily, Jas. and John Dadd's omnibus from Golden Lion Tap 5 evg., and John Pugsley from Bear st. and Rd. Blackmore from Newport at 9 morning
Lynton, J. Richard's Van, (King's Arms,) Tue. and Fri. 3 afternoon
Plymouth, Pridham & Lake from Joy st. and T. King from Shipwrights' Arms, Tue. and Sat. 8 morng.
South Malton, daily, James Chapple from Golden Anchor, and Wm. Deagon from the Bell, 3 aftn
Tiverton, Thos. Avery from the Angel, Tue. and Sat. 2 afternoon
Torrington, Sml. Copp from the Angel, Mon., Wed., and Fri. 4½ afternoon
STEAM PACKET.
The *Water Witch* from Bristol calls in the river at Penhill Docks *twice* a week in summer, and once in winter
SAILING VESSELS
To *London* once a fortnight; to *Bristol* weekly; and to *Liverpool* monthly

BERRYNARBOR is a pleasant village, on an eminence near the sea coast, overlooking Combemartin Cove, 3 miles E. of Ilfracombe. Its parish contains 899 inhabitants, and 4958A. 1R. 27P. of land, including many scattered farm-houses, &c., and a range of hills in which lime and other stone is got. Westcote says it was originally called Bury, and afterwards *Bury Nerbert,* from the family who held it some centuries ago, but we find it was held by the Berry family till 1708. A. D. Bassett, Esq., who has a pleasant seat here, called *Watermouth,* owns a great part of the parish, and is lord of the manor, which was purchased by J. D. Bassett, Esq., in 1712. Sir P. B. Chichester, Sir P. F. Palmer Acland, and the Executors of the late Charles Cutcliffe, have estates here. Mr. Bassett is also lord of the manors of *East Haggington* and *Woolscott.* The parish has its annual feast or revel on the first Sunday in July, and was the birthplace of the celebrated Bishop Jewel. The *Church* is an ancient structure, with some monuments of the Berry family. The *rectory,* valued in K.B. at £34. 15s. 10d., and in 1831 at £720, in the alternate patronage of the Bishop of Exeter, the Rev. E. W. Richards, and A. D. Bassett and — Fursdon, Esqrs. ; and in the incumbency of the Rev. S. T. Gully, M.A., who has a good residence and about 126 acres of glebe, including 50A. of common. The tithes were commuted in 1841, for £560 per annum. Here is a neat *National School,* built in 1848, and a small *Independent Chapel,* erected about 20 years ago. Three houses and gardens have been long vested for the repairs of the church; but the *Church House* was given by *John Berry,* in 1697, for the residence of poor parishioners.

Bassett Arthur Davie, Esq. *Watermouth*
Dendle George, vict. Globe
Dyer Jane, corn miller
Facey Mrs Joan, *Newbury*
Geer Mr James ‖ Hicks Geo. *school*
Gully Rev Saml. Thos., M.A. *Rectory*
Kent Thomas, vict. Unicorn
White Mr Thos. & Mr John, *Hemstor*

FARMERS.
Bale John, *Woolscott*
Balment Thomas, *New Park*
Berry George ‖ Berry John
Berry Thomas ‖ Berry Wm.
Bowden John ‖ Hicks James
Clark Hugh and Thos. *Ruggaton*
Gammon Thomas, *Stowford*
Hancock John, *Barton*
Hodge John ‖ Huxtable Thomas
Huxtable James ‖ Lewis George
Lovering Geo. Hartnoll, *Ruggaton*
Perrin John ‖ Robins Wm.
Richards John, (lime burner,) *East Haggington*

Skinner Francis ‖ Street Ephm.
Toms Wm. ‖ Western Thomas
Watts Hy. *Thornland* and *Woolscott*
White Richard ‖ Willis John

BLACKSMITHS.
Champ Robert
Harding Thos.
Huxtable Jph.
Leworthy Thos.

BEERHOUSES.
Heddon Francis
Huxtable Joseph
Latham Thomas

CARPENTERS.
Allin Wm.&Thos.
Hasking Anthy.
Heddon Francis
Hicks Ths.&Wm.

MASONS.
Hicks Charles
Hicks Philip
Hicks Richard

SHOEMAKERS.
Harding Richard
Ley Henry
Pile John
Robins John
Snow Richard
Viggers John

SHOPKEEPERS.
Heddon Lovedy.
Kent Thomas
Leworthy Thos.

TAILORS.
Fowles John
Hicks Wm.
Toms Martin

Foot Post: Geo. Burgess, to Ilfracombe, &c

BITTADON is a small parish, 6 miles N. by W. of Barnstaple, containing only about 1000 acres, and 78 inhabitants. The manor was successively held by the Lutterell, Chichester, Acland, and Barbor families. W. A. Yeo, Esq., now owns most of the parish, and is lord of the manor, and patron of the *rectory,* valued in K.B. at £6. 2s. 8½d., and in 1831 at £83, in the incumbency of the *Rev. Francis Mules,* who has 25½A. of glebe, but no parsonage. The tithes were commuted in 1841, for £75 per annum.

The *Church* (St. Peter,) is a small antique edifice, mantled with ivy. The only *farmers* in the parish are, Thomas Brown, *Barton;* Richard Shapland, *Upcott;* and George Smith, *Glebe.*

BRATTON FLEMING, a pleasant village, on an acclivity 6½ miles E.N.E. of Barnstaple, has in its parish 708 souls, and 3940 acres of land, rising in a bold range of hills from two rivulets, and including many scattered farm-houses. It anciently belonged to the Fleming family, and afterwards to the Dillons. The latter sold the manor in the reign of Jas. I., to an ancestor of its present owner, Sir Arthur Chichester, Bart. Part of the parish belongs to Sir P. F. P. Acland, G. B. Kingdon, Esq., and a few smaller owners. *Chimwell,* the ancient seat of the Flemings and Dillons, is now a farm-house. The *Church* (St. Peter,) is a neat structure, in the perpendicular style, with a tower and six bells. The *rectory,* valued in K.B. at £29. 15s. 5d., and in 1831 at £631, is in the patronage of Gonville and Caius College, Cambridge, and incumbency of the Rev. H. S. Pinder, M.A., who has 150 acres of glebe, and a large and handsome Rectory House, recently erected. Here is a National School and a small Baptist Chapel; and a *cattle fair* is held in the village on August 19th.

Brownscombe Wm. vict. White Hart
Champ John, shopkeeper
Conibear Thomas, wheelwright
Darch Thomas, saddler
Gill John, smith ; and Wm. wheelgt
Heal John & Mogridge Jno. shoemks
Hunt Humphrey, beerseller
Huxtable Henry, wheelwright
Jerman Wm. vict. Stag's Head
Kingdon James, *carrier*
Livercombe Wm. blacksmith
Pinder Rev. H. S., M.A., *Rectory*
FARMERS.
Baker John ǁ Beard Thomas, *Stowfd*
Britton John ǁ Burge John
Cottle James ǁ Crang Wm.
Daniel Joseph, *Oxton Park*
Elworthy Richard ǁ Gill John
Gill Jacob ǁ Gill Wm.
Holloway Wm. ǁ Hunt Richard
Hunt Wm. ǁ Hunt Wm. Palmer
Huxtable Anthony ǁ Isaac John
Jerman William, *Mills*
Jones Wm. ǁ Kingdon John
Mogridge Thos. ǁ Pugsley Anthony
Radmore John ǁ Ridd John
Ridd Wm., *Chimwell*
Ridd Thomas ǁ Smith James
Snell Thomas ǁ Tamlyn Henry
Tamlyn James ǁ Tamlyn Wm.
Yandell Wm., *Sprecott*

BRAUNTON, the large ancient village which gives name to this Hundred and Petty Sessional Division, is situated on the banks of a rivulet about 2 miles from the sea coast and the Taw estuary, and 5 miles W.N.W. of Barnstaple. Its extensive parish contains 2274 inhabitants, and 9951 acres of land, extending to the sea coast and the estuary of the Taw, and including the scattered hamlets of *Saunton, Lobb, Nethercott, Knoll, Winsham, Halsinger, Pippacot,* and *Boode.* Near the sea is a large tract of land covered with sand, called *Braunton Borrow,* abounding in rabbits, and having two *light-houses* for the security of mariners navigating the Bristol Channel, or crossing Barnstaple bar. The principal manors in the parish, and their owners are, *Braunton Abbots,* the Earl of Devon ; *Braunton Arundell and Gorges,* A. D. Bassett, Esq. ; *Bere Charters,* Sir B. P. Wrey; *Buckland,* C. H. Webber, Esq., of Buckland House ; and *Saunton,* the heirs of the late Col. Cleveland ; but a great part of the parish belongs to the Executors of the late Lord Rolle, the Dean and Chapter of Exeter, Richard Dyer, Esq., and several smaller owners; Braunton was an ancient demense of the Crown, and was given by Richard I. to Odo, ancestor of the Carews. Henry III. gave two-thirds of it to Clive Abbey, in Somersetshire. In the reign of Chas. I. it belonged to Sir Richard Reynell, from whom it passed to the Courtenays. The *Church* (St. Brannock,) is a large antique structure, remarkable for

having no pillars. Its tower contains six bells, and is crowned by a spire. The *vicarage,* valued in K. B. at £16. 12s. 6½d., and in 1831 at £504, is in the patronage of the Dean and Chapter of Exeter, and incumbency of the Rev. J. W. R. Landon, who has 41A. 1R. 10P. of glebe, and a good residence. The patrons are lords of the manor of Braunton-Dean, and appropriators of the great tithes, which are leased to C. Trelawney, Esq. The tithes have been commuted, the vicarial for £536, and the rectorial for £514 per annum. Here is an *Independent Chapel,* which was rebuilt in 1836, and has a house for the minister, erected in 1848. Schools are attached to the church and chapel. The CHARITY SCHOOL was founded by *Wm. Chaloner,* who, in 1667, left about £450 for that purpose. Of this sum, £400 was laid out in the purchase of a house and 36 acres of land at Georgeham, now let for £33 per annum. The remaining £50 was laid out in purchasing one equal moiety of 32 acres of land at Morthoe, now let for £21, half of which belongs to this school, which has also 10 acres of land, called Goad-gate, left in 1690, by *Arthur Acland,* who also left 40s. a year to a schoolmistress, for teaching twelve young children to read. The schoolroom is near the church, and the master derives upwards of £65 a year from the endowment, and for this he teaches reading, writing, and arithmetic to all the children of the parish sent to him by the trustees. The schoolmistress's annuity is paid out of an estate called Chapel Hill, which is also charged with £3 per annum for distributions of bread among the poor, by the wills of *Arthur* and *Richard Acland.* The poor parishioners have £10. 10s. yearly from one moiety of the above-named estate of 32A., purchased with £50 left by *John Wheak,* in 1702. A schoolmistress has 40s. a year, as the interest of £50 left by *Nicholas Beare,* in 1713, for schooling 12 poor girls. The overseers distribute 48s. yearly among the poor, as the interest of £60 left by *Amos Pollard* and *Henry Incledon.* For the relief of poor widows and orphans *Ann Commyns,* in 1767, left £60, which was vested in the purchase of £100 three per cent. consols. In 1809, *Thomas Bower* left £100, to be invested at interest for the relief of the poor parishioners.

Alven Francis, gent. *Lower Boode*
Brinley Mr Jph. || Dyer Mr Robt.
Chugg Wm. saddler, &c
Darracott James, tanner, &c
Drake Capt Robt. H., *Prospect Lodge*
Dyer Richard, gent. *Bloomfield Cotg*
Fosse Mr Wm. || Harris Mrs E.
Gammon George, carrier
Harris Edward, lime burner
Harris Wm. gent. *Millbrook*
Jennings Thomas, *Buckland Mills*
Kent Rev Samuel C. (Independent)
Landon Rev. J. W. Ready, *Vicarage*
Law Mr John || Parkin Mrs E.
May Thomas, tinner and brazier
Mock Mr Edw. || Mortimer Mr Thos.
Nutt Anthony, edgetool maker
Paddison Wm. corn miller
Pick Josiah P. surgeon
Reed Thomas, nurseryman, &c
Robins Thomas, currier
Robins George, lath render
Rooke Mr John || Pilcher Mrs A.
Squire Ephraim, tinner, &c

Tardrew Thos., Esq. || Symonds Geo.
Tucker J. *warrener*
Vellacott ——, surgeon
Vickery Wm. relieving officer
Warren Henry, cooper
Webber Chas. Hy. Esq., *Buckland Hs*
Webber Arthur, Esq
Western Philip, coal dealer
Widlake and Dummett, maltsters
Willis Thomas, corn miller
Woulds and Kent, serge, blanket, &c. manufacturers, Acorn Mill

INNS & TAVERNS.
Barnstaple Inn, Maria Evans
Black Horse, Thomas Clarke
Mariners' Arms, John Gould
New Inn, Mary Elliott
Red Lion, Wm. Gammon
Beerhouse, Wm. Bale

ACADEMIES.
Cridge Richard
Gregory Amelia
Passmore Eliz.

Passmore John
Sloat Eliz.
BLACKSMITHS.
Edwards Richd.

Evans Robert
Tamlyn James
BOOT & SHOE MKS.
Martin Henry
Mock John
Reed John
Reed Ths. & Wm.
Webber Charles
BUTCHERS.
Drake John
Lane Joseph
Widlake Wm.
CARPENTERS AND
WHEELWRIGHTS.
Atkins John & Ptr.
Dunn Jas. & John
Gammon Edw.
Hartnoll John
Passmore Thos.
Sherwill John
Williams John

FARMERS.
(2 *at Boode ;* 3,
Knoll ; 4, *Lobb ;*

and 5, *at Hal-
singer.*)
Andrew Wm.
Atkins Joseph
3 Avery Berry
Avery Geo., *Upct*
Bidder Thos.
3 Brailey James
4 Chichester Geo.
Conibear John
4 Cousins Geo.
Day George H.
Day Saml., *Bere
Charters*
5 Dyer John
Dyer Richard
Dyer Wm.
Elliott H. *Wnshm*
Evans Robert
Fairchild John
Gordon Robert
Gould Wm.
Hammond John
Harris Wm.
Hartnoll Geo. P.

Hartnoll Robert
Heddon Richard
Hodge Smn. & W.
Howe Ths. & Wm.
Huxtable James,
Saunton
5 Iles Richd. R.
Jones Richard
Jones Wm.
Jury Richard
Lovering J. & W.
2 Passmore Hy.
Peard John
Perryman J. & T.
Pike George
Robins John
4 Scamp Philip
Smith Wm.
2 Snow John
2 Snow J. jun.
Symonds Robt.
Tucker George
Tucker John
GROCERS, &c.
Darracott Thos.

Dummett Robert
Huxtable Wm.
Lock Susan
Milton Thomas
Pettle Geo. baker
MR. MARINERS.
Cory Wm.
Hammond Thos.
Heddon Wm.
Lamprey George
Manley Richard
Reed George
MASONS.
Hammond Saml.
Reed John
Reed Samuel
Reed Wm.
TAILORS.
Clogg John
Darracott Thos.
Gammon Wm.
Hunt John
Webber John
POST - OFFICE
at W. Huxtable's

BUCKLAND, (EAST) a small village and parish, 5½ miles N.N.W. of South Molton, contains 167 inhabitants, and 1384 acres of land, mostly the property of Earl Fortescue, the lord of the manor, and patron of the *rectory*, valued in K.B. at £9. 1s. 8d., and in 1831 at £324, with that of Filleigh annexed to it. The Rev. Henry Hutton, MA., is the incumbent, and has here 40A. of glebe, and a good residence at Filleigh. The tithes of this parish were commuted in 1837, for £144. 10s. per annum. The *Church* (St. Michael,) is an ancient structure, with a tower and four bells. A cottage and 10A. of land have been vested from an early period for the repairs of the church, except £2. 10s. 6d. per annum for the clerk and sexton.

Dadds Wm. carpenter
Holloway John, blacksmith
Holloway John, jun. parish clerk
Rice Wm. shoemaker
FARMERS.
Brealey James || Coles Abraham

Carter James, *Brayley Barton*
Pike Henry, *Crossbury*
Smith Henry || Slader John
Stevens Wm. || Yendell John
Tamlyn John, *Tossel's Barton*

BUCKLAND, (WEST) is a small parish and village, 6 miles N.W. by N. of South Molton, comprising 275 souls, and about 1700A. of land. Jas. George, Esq., is lord of the manor, but a great part of the soil belongs to Earl Fortescue and the Rev. J. Buckingham. The *Church* (St. Peter,) has a tower and five bells, and the living is a *rectory*, valued in K.B. at £13. 3s. 4d., and in 1831 at £220, in the patronage of Lord de Dunstanville, and incumbency of the Rev. Walter Gee, B.D., of St. Mary Week, Cornwall. The glebe is 30A., and the parsonage is a good residence.

Chapple Geo. draper & vict. New Inn
Clatworthy John, blacksmith
Fairchild George, grocer, &c
Pugsley Humphrey, shopkeeper
Ridge Wm. beerseller
Walker Rev Charles Harry, M.A.,
   curate, *Rectory*

FARMERS.
Buckingham John, *Gabbs*
German Nichs. || Rendle Robert
Land John || Miller Wm.
Nott Wm. || Quartly Nicholas
Partridge James, *Studley South*
Thorne George || Vickery Chpr.

COMBE MARTIN, or *Combmartin*, is a decayed market town, in one long, irregular street, in a deep and picturesque valley, about a mile from a fine cove of the north coast of Devon, and 4 miles E. of Ilfracombe.   Its parish contains 1399 souls, and about 3900 acres of land, including 1837 acres of open commons and hilly moorlands.   The manor was given by William the Conqueror to Martin de Tours, ancestor of the Lords Martin, from whom it passed to the Lords Audley. It was dismembered by the Pollards many years ago.   The Barton, or Manor House, with a large estate, now belongs to Sir C. W. Watson, Bart, and the rest of the parish belongs to the Fursdon, Tregonwell, Cornish, Pyke, Gill, and other families.   The market and fair, granted about 1264, were discontinued last century. Hemp was formerly grown in the neighbourhood, and shoemakers' thread was spun from it in the town.   Coal vessels and fishing smacks resort to *Combe Martin Cove*, where pilots for the Bristol Channel are generally to be found.   The houses extend more than a mile along the dale, amid woods and ridges of rocks, tufted with foliage down to the level of the sea.   The scenery is magnificent, and the *mines* in the parish and neighbourhood have long been celebrated for their *argentiferous lead ore*.   In the reign of Edward I., 337 men were brought here out of Derbyshire to work the *silver mines*, which are said to have furnished money for the wars in the reign of Edward III.   They were again worked with success in the reign of Elizabeth, by Sir Beavis Bulmer.   Unsuccessful attempts were made to work these mines with profit about 1800, 1813, and 1817 ; and they were reopened in 1837, and are now worked by a spirited company of adventurers, who have a smelting-house here.   The *Church* (St. Peter,) is a handsome structure, with a tower and six bells, and the living is a *rectory*, valued in K.B. at £39. 8s. 9d., and in 1831 at £435, in the patronage and incumbency of the Rev. H. W. Toms, who has a good residence, and 72A. of glebe.   The tithes were commuted in 1844, for about £400 per annum.   The Independents and Wesleyans have chapels here.   The *Free School* has half an acre of land attached to it, and was founded in 1733, by *George Ley*, who endowed it with 35A. 3R., called Waterlake, subject to 20s. a year for the poor parishioners.   The school was rebuilt about 1820, and is free for 40 children.

Bale Thomas, constable
Bawdon Cornelius, foreman
Brook Thomas, gardener
Burgess John, postmaster, &c
Burgess George, foot postman
Clogg Robert, cooper
Cooke Wm. Henry, surgeon
Cornish Fdk. S., Esq. *Buzzacot*
Cutcliffe Nicholas, jun. quarry owner
Cutcliffe Alice, lodgings
Dovell Wm. maltster
Down John, corn miller
Facey Wm. medicine vendor
Gooding James, collar maker, &c
Handford John, gardener
Harris Thomas, ore smelter
Lerwill Wm. gent || Ridd Mrs
Lewis Betsy and Mary, milliners
Loveridge John, wheelwright
Norman John, gardener
Toms Rev Humphrey Wm. *Rectory*

Willis Mrs Elizabeth

INNS AND TAVERNS.
Barnstaple Inn, Ann Watts
George and Dragon, Wm. Conibear
King's Arms, Thomas Harris
New Inn, Thomas Morcom
Ship and Castle, John Lake

BAKERS.
Robins Henry
Wener Wm.

BLACKSMITHS.
Goss Jas. & Wm.
Thomas John

BOOT & SHOE MKS.
Conibear James
Cutcliffe John
Lancey Wm.
Ley Wm.
Sanders Wm.

BUTCHERS.
Berry Richard

Creek John
Huxtable Joseph

CARPENTERS.
Creek Wm.
Delve John
Fleming James
Irwin John
Rock Chas.

FARMERS.
Adams John
Channing J.
Charley James
Charley Richard
Charley Wm.

2 B 3

Crang Walter	Smalridge John	Sommerville Lws	Hussell Eliz.
Cutcliffe Nicholas	Tucker Wm.	MR. MARINERS.	Robins Henry
Day James	Winzer John	Facey John	Sanders John
Draper Benj.	Willis Wm.	Irwin John	Turner John
Hole Robert	LIME BURNERS.	Lewis Thomas	TAILORS.
Irwin Sarah	Clogg Nicholas	SCHOOLS.	Benham James
Irwin Joshua	Dovell Wm.	Groves Eliz.	Conibear John
Knight Richard	Harris Joshua	Lock John	
Lerwill John	MASONS.	SHOPKEEPERS.	POST *from Ilfra-*
Lovering Maria	Fleming James	Copp Ann	*combe,*and*Car-*
Peak Wm.	Burgess Wm. and	Creek Edw.	*riers* to Barn-
Pugsley Wm.	Henry	Gubb My. beerhs	staple, &c

DOWN, (EAST) a small village, in a picturesque valley, 6½ miles N.N.E. of Barnstaple, has in its parish 473 souls, and 3643 acres of land, rising in bold hills on the north, and including the hamlets of *Churchill, Brockham,* and *Shortacombe.* The manor belonged to the ancient family of Downe, till the reign of Edward III., when it passed to an ancestor of the Coffin family. The late Rev. Chas. Pine Coffin, who died in January, 1850, was lord of the manor and rector of the parish, and his relict resides at the *Manor House.* C. J. S. P. Coffin, Esq., is lord of the manor of East Down, and Sir J. P. B. Chichester, Bart., is lord of the manor of Churchill, formerly held by the St. Aubin and Ley families. Mr. James Harris, John and Rd. Richards, and several smaller owners have estates in the parish. The *Church* (St. John,) is an ancient structure, in the perpendicular style, with a tower and four bells. It has undergone many repairs, and the windows are modern insertions. The *rectory,* valued in K.B. at £18. 13s. 9d., and in 1831 at £383, is in the patronage of C. Chichester, Esq., and has a handsome new residence, and 87A. of glebe. The tithes were commuted in 1843, for £385 per annum. Here is a Wesleyan Chapel. The poor have the dividends of £165. 0s. 8d. three per cent. consols, purchased with £100 left by *Edw. Pine,* in 1802. They have also the interest of £6, left by G. Horwood and W. Lancey.

Burgess Wm. blacksmith
Coffin Mrs C. P. & C. J. S. P., Esq., *Manor House*
Delve Edw. and Hassell J. carpentrs
Harris Jas. Esq. & Mrs E.W. *Viveham*
Mayne Jas. shopkeeper, &c
    FARMERS.   (* *at Churchill.*)
Barrow John || Chugg Wm.
Chugg Walter, *Mills* || Crang Wm.

Davis James, *Lower Viveham*
Garnish Anthony, *Shortacombe*
Jones Geo. Harper, Oakwell
Lerwell Wm. || Passmore Richard
Richards Jas. || Rowe Wm.
Richards John & Richard, *Northcote*
*Smithy Chas. || *Smith Thomas
*Tamlyn Jas. || *Tamlyn Wm.

DOWN, (WEST) a pleasant village, on a bold acclivity, near a rivulet, 6 miles N.N.W. of Barnstaple, has in its parish 637 souls, and 4059 acres of land, including the small hamlets of *Willincott, Dean,* and *Trimstone.* Anthony Loveband, Esq., is lord of the manor of *Bradwell;* and Dr. Yeo is lord of that of *Stowford,* which was the seat of Bishop Stowford, who built Pilton bridge. The Langdon, Parminter, Griffiths, Coats, and other families have estates here. The *Church* (Holy Trinity,) is an ancient fabric, and the living is a *vicarage,* valued in K.B. at £8. 14s. 9d., and in 1831 at £211, in the patronage of the Bishop of Exeter, and incumbency of the Rev. H J. Drury. The tithes were commuted in 1841, the vicarial for £163, and the rectorial for £255. The latter belong to Messrs. G. and J. Langdon, T. Parminter, and J. Menhinniott. The Wesleyans have a small chapel here. The poor have a cottage, garden, and a 3A. field, purchased in 1672, with £20 left by *John Eyre;* and the interest of another £20 left

by the same donor.   For teaching six poor children, a schoolmistress has
40s. a year from *Mrs. Newcommen's Charity.*   (See Bideford.)

Acland Hugh, vict. King's Arms
Brimley Mr Wm. || Chugg Mrs
Davis John, vict. Blue Anchor
Drury Rev Hy. John, *Vicarage*
King John, baker and shopkeeper
May John, saddler
Phillips Mary, schoolmistress
Pile John, shopkeeper
Scamp Robert, mason
Setters Wm. grocer, &c

BEERHOUSES.
Collings Richard
Phillips John
Phillips Wm.
BLACKSMITHS.
Cornish John
Lewis Richard

Phillips Thos. &
ironmonger
CARPENTERS.
Phillips John
Phillips Thomas
Phillips Wm.
Setters John

CORN MILLERS.
Phillips George, *Bradwell*
Thomas Wm.
FARMERS.
Chugg John
Chugg Thomas
Coats Elizabeth
Coats John
Coats Jno. jun
Coats Robert
Coles Richard
Dyer James
Frost James, *Willincott*
Gammon John
Geen John
Hartnoll James

Heddon John
Menhinniott Jno.
Parminter Thos.
Slocombe Thos., *Stowford*
Thomas —
Tucker Robert
Verney John

SHOEMAKERS.
Collings George
Lewis Wm.
TAILORS.
Cornish George
Phillips Henry
Scamp James
Setters Wm.
Vicary Wm.

FILLEIGH, a small village, pleasantly situated 3½ miles W. of South
Molton, and 8 miles E.S.E. of Barnstaple, has in its parish 395 souls, and
2200 acres of land, including about 826 acres in the large and finely wooded
park of CASTLE HILL, the beautiful seat of *Earl Fortescue,* who has
another seat at Ebrington Hall, Gloucestershire.   The grounds, and the
old mansion of Castle Hill, were much altered and improved about 1740, by
Hugh Fortescue, Lord Clinton, who, in 1746, was created *Earl Clinton and
Baron Fortescue,* and died without issue in 1751, when the earldom became
extinct, but the Barony of Fortescue passed to his half-brother, Matthew
Fortescue, who died in 1785, and was succeeded by his son, Hugh, who was
created Earl Fortescue and Viscount Ebrington, in 1789.   The latter died
in 1841, and was succeeded by his son, the present *Right Hon. Hugh Fortescue, Earl Fortescue,* and *Viscount Ebrington,* who is lord lieutenant and
custos rotulorum of Devonshire, and Colonel of the East Devon Militia.
He was born in 1783, and distinguished himself in the House of Commons,
in the debates on Parliamentary Reform.   His eldest son, *Viscount Ebrington,* is now one of the representatives of Plymouth, and was born in 1818.
The large and handsome mansion of Castle Hill stands in the extensive
park, on a well wooded eminence, whose summit is decorated with the
artificial semblance of a ruined castle, and commands a prospect of very
considerable extent.   The grounds in front of the house are disposed into
various pleasing slopes, which gradually descend from the terrace to a fine
sheet of water, and are diversified by stately groves.   Beyond the lake, the
ground again rises, and the view is terminated by a handsome triumphal
arch, on the top of the hill.   Various other ornamental buildings are
scattered through the park.   In the shrubbery are some remarkably large
Portugal laurels; and in the garden is a peach tree of uncommon dimensions.   The *manor of Filleigh* belonged to a family of its own name, in the
reign of Henry II., and it afterwards passed with the heiress of the Densells
to the Fortescues.   It now belongs to Earl Fortescue, who is also patron of
the *rectory,* which is consolidated with that of East Buckland, as noticed at
page 584.   Here is a good Rectory House, and 88½A. of glebe.   The tithes
of Filleigh were commuted in 1839, for £97 per annum.   The *Church* (St.
Paul,) was rebuilt by the first Earl Clinton and Baron Fortescue, in 1732,
and is a neat structure, with several handsome monuments.   The same

nobleman left £100 for the foundation of an *Almshouse*. About 1810, the late Earl Fortescue built four dwellings, at the cost of £300, and gave them, with four gardens, in lieu of the old almshouse. The poor parishioners have the interest of £27, left by various donors. The small river Bray bounds the parish on the east, and near it is *Stag's Head*, in South Molton parish, where there is a school, mill, and post-office.

Earl Fortescue, & Viscount Ebrington, M.P. *Castle Hill*
Anstey Wm. miller, *Stag's Head*
Bowey Philip, shopkeeper
Brewer Daniel Tremlett, land agent
Buckingham Wm. shoemaker
Chapple Abraham, mason
Hutton Rev Hy., M.A. *Rectory*
Pile Rd. *clerk*, & Ferrier Thos. *sexton*
Rutlidge Geo. and Leworthy Mary A., *National School*, Stag's Head

Saul Amaziah, gardener

BLACKSMITHS.
Gratton Richard
Jordan John

CARPENTERS.
Baker Wm.
Clotworthy John

FARMERS.
Anstey Thomas
Bale George
Follett John

Gould Richard
Manning Anthy.

TAILORS.
Ball Jno. shopr., Stag's Head
Odam Jno. Brown

POST-OFFICE at David Bale's, Stag's Head

GEORGEHAM, a small straggling village, in a valley 8 miles W.S.W. of Barnstaple, has in its parish 923 souls and 4650 acres of land, extending westward to *Croyde* and *Morte* Bays, and the long narrow promontory called *Baggy Point*, where the rocky cliffs rise boldly from the Bristol Channel. Most of the parishioners are in the villages and hamlets of *Croyde*, *North Buckland*, *Darracott*, and *Puttsborough*. Croyde is a pleasant sea bathing place, with a fine bay, and much romantic scenery in its vicinity. The manor of Georgeham was anciently the seat and property of the knightly family of *Pickwell*, and now belongs to Earl Fortescue. C. H. Webber, Esq., is lord of the manor of *Croyde*, or *Crede*; but a great part of the parish belongs to John Dunning, W. V. Richards, (of *Incledon House*,) the Rev. F. Hole, and a number of smaller owners, mostly free and partly lease-holders. The *Church* (St. George,) is a fine antique structure, and among its monuments is the tomb of a crusader, supposed to be that of Sir Mauger St. Albyn. In the churchyard are buried *Simon Gould* and his wife *Julian*, who died in March, 1817, each in the 101st year of their age, and having been married upwards of 75 years. The *rectory*, valued in K.B. at £40. 17s. 11d., and in 1831 at £622, is in the patronage of Wm. Hole, Esq., and incumbency of the Rev. Fras. Hole, who has a handsome residence and 35A. of glebe. The tithes were commuted in 1839, for £500 per annum. The poor parishioners have £2. 5s. 7d. yearly, as the interest of £57 left by various donors. In 1778, *John Richards* left £5 a year out of Tucker's and Hartnoll's tenements, for two schoolmistresses, at *Georgeham* and *Croyde*. The poor have also the interest of £50, left by *John Richd. Middleditch*, in 1798; and they ought to have the dividends of £24. 11s. three per cent. consols, left by *Richd. Dean*, in 1805, but they have not been claimed since 1811. *Marked* 1 *are at North Buckland;* 2, *Croyde;* 3, *Darracott; and* 4 *at Puttsborough.*

Bale Mr Gabriel || Pyke Mrs
Chugg Thos. gent. || Heddon Mrs
Conibear Charles, vict. Rock House
Dunning John, Esq. *North Buckland*
Hole Rev Francis, M.A. *Rectory*
2 Prole Wm. gent. || Hill John, *serjt*
Richards Wm. Vellacott, Esq. *Incledon House*
Scamp Rt. maltster&vict. Ring of Bells
Thomas Joseph, vict. King's Arms

BEER HOUSES.
2 Budd James
Lang Wm.
2 Matthew Rd.

BLACKSMITHS.
Clibbitt John
Conibear Charles
2 Gammon Jas.
Goss Wm.
2 Matthew Rd.

Sanders James
BOOT & SHOE MKS.
Butler George
Geen Thomas
Geen Wm.
Lang Philip
Lang Wm.
2 Smith John
2 Tucker Wm.

CARPENTERS.	*1 Boyles Geo.	2 Rowe John	SCHOOLS.
2 Budd James	*2 Brayley John	1 Shapland Eliz.	2 Berry Jane
2 Smith John, *wgt*	*2 Crang Walter	Smith George	2 Butler Eliz.
Thomas Charles	Downing George,	*Smith Wm.	Davies Betsy
Thomas Joseph	*Pickwell*	*Smith Peter	Hooper John
Thorne John	3 Forrest Richd.	*1 Symons Geo.	2 Webber Wm.
CORN MILLERS.	3 Goss Joseph	Trace Wm.	SHOPKEEPERS.
Holcombe Danl.	3 Hancock Wm.	4 Tucker Geo.	Bennett John
Stanbury John	*2 Haydon John	1 Tucker John	2 Howard Jph.
Haydon	4 Holmes Wm.	Tucker Richard	Hunt John
FARMERS.	2 Irwin Wm.	2 Webb Wm.	2 Parkin Betsy
(* *are Owners.*)	*Jones R. Tucker	Webber George	Zeale Richard
*1 Badcock John	2 Lang Wm.	*2 Zeale Geo.&Jn.	TAILORS.
Baggott John	2 Lock James	MASONS.	Breay John
2 Bagster George	2 Moule Agnes	2 Glover Wm.	Goss Philip
and James	*2 Preston John	Gooding John	Menhenniott Geo.
*1 Barnes John	*2 Quick John	Mock John	POST & CARRIERS
4 Barnes Thos.	2 Richards Philip	Pearce Richard	from Barnstaple

GOODLEIGH, a small village, nearly 3 miles E. by N. of Barnstaple, has in its parish 335 souls, and 1180 acres of land, including *Northleigh* hamlet and several scattered houses. The manor belongs to the Misses Incledon, whose family mansion, called *Yeotown*, is now a farm house, and was new fronted in the Gothic style by the late R. N. Incledon, Esq. This house is in the sequestered woody valley of the small river Yeo. Miss Budd and several other proprietors have estates in this parish, which is celebrated for its cherry orchards. The *Church* (St. Gregory,) is an ancient Gothic structure, with a short tower, and some stained glass in its windows. Its screen is richly ornamented. The *rectory*, valued in K.B. at £14. 19s. 4½d., and in 1831 at £302, is in the patronage and incumbency of the Rev. John Harding, M.A., who has a good residence and about 30A. of glebe. The tithes were commuted in 1839, for £184. 19s. 2d. per annum. Here is an *Independent Chapel*, and schools are attached to it and the church. The poor have 26s. a year out of land at Westacott, left by *Hugh Acland*, in 1620; and the interest of £10 left by Richd. Squire, in 1735.

Davie Wm. beer seller
Goss John, smith and beer seller
Harding Rev. John, M.A. *Rectory*
Richards Richard, parish clerk
Shapland John & Jas. vety. surgeons
    FARMERS. (* *at Northleigh.*)
Bell Wm. || *Carter James

Bidder Robert, *Yeotown*
*Davie John, (and tax collector)
*Fisher John || Frayne Thomas
Ireland Philip || Lee John
*Yeo Mary || Watts John, *Dean*

POST *from Barnstaple.*

HEANTON PUNCHARDON, a pleasant village, on an eminence north of the Taw estuary, 4½ miles W.N.W. of Barnstaple, has in its parish 626 souls, and 2300 acres of land, including the hamlets of *West Ashford*, *Chivenor*, and *Rafton*. A. D. Bassett, Esq., is lord of the manor of Heanton, formerly held by the Punchardon family, and afterwards by the Beaumonts, whose heiress carried it in marriage to the Bassetts. *Heanton Court*, now a farm house, was formerly the seat of the Bassetts, and stands near the estuary, forming a conspicuous object in the view from Barnstaple bridge. The Rev. Fras. Hole, C. C. Drake, Esq., G. Langdon, J. Crang, H. Lovering, and a few smaller owners, have estates in the parish. The *Church* (St. Augustine,) has a tower and six bells, and the nave and chancel are separated by a richly carved screen. In the chancel is the finely carved tomb of one of the Coffin family, surmounted by a rich canopy. Here are

also many mural tablets, belonging to the Bassett, Ballyman, and other families.   The *rectory*, valued in K.B. at £22. 7s. 11d., and in 1831 at £431,
is in the patronage of A. D. Bassett, Esq., and incumbency of the Rev.
Fras. Bassett, who has 38A. of glebe, and a large and handsome residence,
built nine years ago.   The tithes were commuted in 1842, for £406 per ann.
Here is a small Independent Chapel.   The *Church Lands, &c.*, have been
held from an early period, for the use of the church, and comprise five
houses and about 3½A., let for only £11 per annum, but subject to fines on
the renewal of the leases.   The *poor* have the dividends of £449. 1s. 5d.
three per cent. consols, purchased with the gifts of John and Fras. Bassett,
and other donors.   *Marked 2 are at Chivenor, and 3 at Rafton or Wrafton.*

Bassett Mrs Mary ‖ Adams Mrs B.
Bassett Rev Francis, *Rectory*
Drake Chas.Cutcliffe, Esq. *Springfield*
Edwards Wm. tailor
Evans Edmund, corn miller
2 Hutchinson Matthew, gent.
Hammond Mrs E. ‖ Langdon Miss
3 Matthews Richard, vict. Exeter Inn
Rogers Betsy, schoolmistress
Thorne Richard, carpenter
Woulds and Kent, woolstaplers and
   blanket and worsted manfrs.

BLACKSMITHS.
Corney Wm.
Tamlyn George
Westcott Jno. (&
   beerhouse)

BOOT&SHOE MKS.
Clark John
Incledon John
Mock Thomas

FARMERS.
Berry John
2 Berry Thomas
3 Boyles Wm.
3 Chichester John
3 Chichester Rt.
Clogg Rd. par.clk
3 Frayne James
Geen Wm.
3 Hammond Hgh.

Hammond My.A.
Hancock George
3 Langdon John
Lovering Hay-
   man, *Horridge*
Martin Edward
Martin Jas.*Hean-
   ton Court*
Priscott Thomas,
   West Ashford
2 Priscott Wm.
3 Reed George
Vellacott Susan

ILFRACOMBE, an ancient *sea port* and *market town*, and the
most picturesque and fashionable *bathing place* on the north coast
of Devon, is distant about 10 miles N. by W. of Barnstaple, 5 miles
N.W. by N. of Exeter, and 200 miles W. by S. of London.   It is
built partly at the bottom and partly on the side and summit of a
steep acclivity, and till about 30 years ago, it consisted chiefly of
one long street, but since then it has risen to great celebrity as a
watering place, and for the accommodation of the numerous visitors,
many rows of neat houses and handsome marine villas have been
built on the terraces; hot and cold baths and a commodious suit of
public rooms have been erected; and tunnels have been cut through
the rocky cliffs to the fine beach and coves of *Crewkhorne*, which affords better and more retired places for sea-bathing than *Wilders-
mouth*, the old bathing place.   Ilfracombe is much indebted to nature and art for a safe harbour, where vessels of more than 200 tons
can ride in safety.   The *harbour* consists of a natural basin, defended from the violence of the sea by a bold mass of rock, stretching nearly half way across the entrance; and an artificial *pier*, upwards of 850 feet long, which was built many years ago by the
Bourchier family, and partly rebuilt and lengthened by Sir Bourchier Wrey, in 1760.   This pier was enlarged and much improved
in 1829 by Sir B. P. Wrey, Bart., the present owner and lord of the
manor.   On three sides, the rocks and hills rise boldly in a semi-
circular sweep, and their craggy steeps are in many places finely
overspread with foliage.   *Hillsborough Rock*, on the east side of the
harbour, rises with a rugged outline to upwards of 500 feet above

the level of the beach. *Lantern Rock*, on the western side, is of smaller dimensions, rising nearly to a point, and having on its conical summit a *light house*, which is 140 feet above low water mark, and was formerly a chapel. A little further to the west is *Capstone Hill*, which rises much higher ; and beyond this are a series of precipitous rocky cliffs and tors, near the higher parts of the town and the beautiful terraces, which command extensive views over the town and the Bristol Channel to the Welsh coast.

The *parish of Ilfracombe* comprises 5583 acres of land, rising in bold hills from the coast, and including many scattered farm-houses, and the small hamlets, &c., of *Damage, Campscott, Slade, Warcombe*, and Lincombe. Its population amounted in 1801 to 1838 ; in 1811 to 1934 ; in 1821 to 2622 ; in 1831 to 3201 ; and in 1841 to 3620, but it has now more than 4000 souls. Sir B. P. Wrey, Bart., is lord of the manor of Ilfracombe, which was formerly part of the barony of Barnstaple, and was held successively by the Martin, Audley, and Bourchier families. The manors of Lincombe and Warcombe belong to C. Cutcliffe Drake, Esq. ; and the Wren, Davy, Meek, and other families, have estates in the parish. Ilfracombe is within the jurisdiction of the port of Barnstaple, and was of such maritime consequence in 1346, that it furnished six ships and 82 mariners for the siege of Calais. It is much resorted to as a harbour of refuge, and has a considerable coasting trade and herring fishery, employing about 70 vessels. Having been a garrison for Parliament, it was taken in September, 1644, for the king, by Sir Fras. Doddington, with 20 pieces of ordnance, as many barrels of powder, and 200 stand of arms. There are *coaches, &c.*, daily to Barnstaple, Exeter, &c., and *steam-packets* ply twice a week to Swansea, Bristol, Cornwall, Bideford, &c. The town is governed by a portreeve, and is described in ancient records as a borough. The *market*, which is now held on Saturday, is well supplied with all sorts of provisions, and was granted in 1278 to Henry Champernowne, to be held on Monday, together with a fair for three days. Here are now two *cattle fairs* on April 14th and the Saturday after Aug. 23rd. The town has now several good inns and numerous furnished houses and lodgings for all classes of visitors. The *Baths* form a handsome building in the Doric order, erected in 1836 ; and the *Public Rooms* form the centre of Coronation square. There are good libraries at three of the booksellers' shops, and the town affords many other accommodations for the amusement and recreation of the numerous visitors who throng to it in the summer season. The town has *gas works* and many good shops, and the walks and rides in the vicinity rank amongst the most picturesque and beautiful in Devon. The CHURCH (*Holy Trinity,*) is a large antique structure, consisting of a chancel, nave, and side aisles, with a low square tower, rising from the middle of the north aisle. It is supposed to have been erected in the 12th century, and has undergone many repairs and alterations. The interior is neatly fitted up, and has room for 1400 hearers. It has a good organ and contains several handsome monuments, one of which is a sarcophagus, erected by government, in memory of *Capt. Richd. Bowen*, who fell at the unfortunate attempt upon Teneriffe, under Admiral Nelson, in 1797. Another is in memory of the mother of John Prince, author of the Worthies of Devon. Ilfracombe is a *prebend* belonging to Salisbury Cathedral, and was held for some time by Camden, the learned antiquary and topographer. The *prebendary* (the Rev. W. Fisher) is appropriator of the rectory, and patron of *vicarage*, valued in 1831 at £150, and now in the incumbency of the Rev. J. M. Chanter, M.A., who has a good residence and 3A. of glebe. The pre-

bendal glebe is 71 acres; and the tithes were commuted in 1842 for £819.
The great tithes are leased to the Carew family, subject to a yearly stipend
of £20 for the vicar. The erection of a Chapel of Ease is in contemplation,
and is much wanted in this now populous parish. A *" Free Church,"* dedicated to Christ, has lately been built in the town, and has room for 800
hearers, under the ministry of the Rev. B. Price. The *Independent Chapel,*
in High street, was erected in 1818, at the cost of about £1400, and will
seat 500. The Rev. Robt. Thomson is the minister, and the congregation
was originally Presbyterian, and was formed in 1715. Here is also a *Wesleyan Chapel,* erected about 15 years ago; and there are in the town large
National and British Schools. The poor have 35s. and the vicar 10s. yearly,
left by *John Toogood* in 1679, out of six tenements at Washfield. As noticed with Poughill, this parish has from *Mrs. Pincombe's Charity* the
yearly sums of £6 for a schoolmaster; £4 for a schoolmistress; and 40s.
each for three poor men. The master of the National School teaches 12
free scholars in consideration of this charity, from which the children have
occasional distributions of bibles, &c. A house, garden, malt-house, &c.,
were given by an unknown donor for the repairs of the *church,* and are
worth £30 per annum, though let for only £3. 10s. on a lease which ex-
pires in 1854. *Richard Harris,* in 1795, left 50s. a year out of a tenement
called Common, for distribution among the poor attending the Dissenting
meeting-house here.

ILFRACOMBE DIRECTORY.

Those marked 1 *are in High street;* 2, *Fore street;* 3, *Broad street;* 4,
at or near the Quay; 5, *Portland street;* 6, *Hillsborough terrace;* 7, *Montpelier terrace;* 8, *Castle terrace;* 9, *Coronation terrace;* 10, *Horn lane;*
11, *Vicarage lane;* 12, *Northfield;* 13, *Regent place;* 14, *Marine terrace;*
and 15, *Meridian terrace.*

The Post-office is in High street, and Mr. Edw. Hearson is the *postmaster;* and Henry Harding *letter carrier.* Letters are despatched at 2½
afternoon, and Money Orders are granted and paid.

Alchorne Evanson, Esq. 7 Montpe-
   lier terrace
Allen Rev Wm., M.A. 9 Montplr. ter
Aston Wm. Clarridge, regr., High st
Atkins Miss My., Caroline House
Bear Geo., policeman, High street
Besley Rev Hy., (Indpt.) High st
Bligh Rd.. Esq. Castle House
Bolton Mrs. 1 Prospect place
Bowen Misses, Borough Lodge
7 Butcher Geo. Lewis, architect
Chanter Mrs Ggna., Coronation ter
Chanter Rev J. Mill, M.A., *Vicarage*
Chanter Rev Wm., M.A., *Langley*
Chiswell Mr John, High street
Chiswell Mr Thomas, High street
Clement Miss Susan, Vicarage lane
Coates Mrs Margaret, High street
1 Colwill John, coffee house
Copner Mrs Cath., Laston House
Crump Rev C. C., rector of *Halford*
Cutcliffe Miss Emma, High street

Dallin J., sail mkr., Britannia row
Davie John, Lighthouse keeper
Davies Edw., gent., Bellemont
9 Davies Miss Caroline Mary
Davison Miss A., Quay
Davy Humphrey Toms, Esq., *Score*
Day Rev Edwin, B.A. curate, High st
De Miere Albt., M.D., Montplr. ter
1 Dennis Chas., ship builder, &c
Dickinson Mrs Susan, Northfield
Down Admiral Edward Augustus,
   Down place
Down Capt. John, Borough cottage
Downes Thos., Esq. Hillsbro' ter
Drake Chas. C., Esq. Lee cottage
Dunn Misses, Hillsborough terrace
Edwards Thomas, music seller and
   professor, 1 High street
Ebrington Mrs H., Montplr. ter
Fosse Miss Eliz., Portland street
Fosse Wm., Esq. Horn lane
Frazier Mr Thos. Castle terrace

Freeman Geo., gent., Castle terrace
Galsworthy Mr James, 15 High st
Gibbs Mr Philip, Horn lane
Gilbert Mr James, Belvidere House
Gillham Robert, Esq. principal coast officer, Victoria ter
Goodlad Mrs Mary, Northfield
Goodwin Mrs Eliz., Hillsborough ter
Gould Rev R. F., 9 Hillsborough ter
Gould Wm., draper, 21 High street
Hayman Rev Hy. (Wes.) Sea-view
Heale Jno., lapidary, Broad street
Hearson Edw., post-master, High st
Hensley Mrs Lydia, High street
Hervest Mrs Martha, Fore street
Hill Mr Hy., currier, High street
11 Hirtzell Capt. Geo. Jno., R.N.
Huxtable Mrs Cath., Horn lane
Huxtable Wm., agnt. for Lloyds and recr. of Droits of Admrlty., High st
Kerr Lieut. John Hy., Vicarage lane
Langdon Wm. Edgar, solr., High st
Lanyon Edw., excise, High street
Lovering Mr Jph., Fore street
Luxmoore Rev Chas., Montplr. ter
Marsh Miss Eliz., Park cottage
3 Martin Jno., steam packet agent
Meek James, Esq. Fore street
Mells Geo. Esq. Broad Park
Metherell Lieut. Richd. Rowe, R.N., Hornbrook Villa
Moore Miss A., Hillsbro' terrace
Newton Miss Eleanor, High street
Nichols Mr Isaac, Church hill
Nickoll Mrs M., Montpelier terrace
Norman Miss A. G., Hillsborough tr
Peak John, gas man, High street
Peard Geo., solicitor, High street
Prevost Miss, 11 Montpelier terrace
10 Price Rev Benj., (Free Church,)
Pyke Mr Geo., Laurel cottage
Reynell Miss, Myrtle cottage
Richards Mrs Maria, High street
4 Rodgman Wm. harbour master
Roget Miss, Northfield
Scriven RevChas., M.A., Belvidere pl
Scriven Mrs R. F., Belvidere place
7 Shawe Mr John Wingfield
Simkin Lieut. John, R.N., Horn ln
Smith Mrs E., Northfield
Spence Miss Eliz., High street
Spalding Mr Chas., Northfield
1 Stap Randal, coast guard
Stanger L. H., gent., Tor cottage
Thomson Rev Rbt. (Indpt.) Horn ln

Thorne Walter Esq. Portland place
Thorold Arthur, Esq. Russell cotg
Thorpe Mrs Fras., Northfield
Tordiffe Thos., Esq. Borough Hs
Tucker Mrs Mary, Vicarage lane
Tyrrell Miss Ann, Wildescott
Vye Nathl., Esq., barrister, and Mrs Eliz., Manor House
Walters Mrs Mary, High street
Webster Wm., commander of the Margt. Revenue Cruizer, Britn. rw
Western Mrs Eliz., Regent place
Williams Mrs Eliz., Northfield
Wren Mrs Ed., Hillsborough terrace
Wyatt Misses, Rock cottage

ATTORNEYS.

Michell John, High street
Peard & Langdon, High street
Turner John Bernard, Portland st

BANKS.

National Provincial Bank of England (draw on London & Westminster,) Hy. Day, manager Fore street
Savings' Bank, Thos. Bowden, High st., *open* from 10 to 11 A.M. daily

FARMERS.

Bament Wm., *Great Shelfin*
Bryant John, *Kellicleve*
Camp James || Challacombe John
Chugg John, *Keypitt*
Clement Wm., *Langley*
Coates Rt. & Wm., *Mullacott*
Conibear Susan, Beacon Bridge
Corney John, *Whitestone*
Cory Thomas, *Lincombe*
Dadds John || Darch Thomas
Denicombe John, *Glebe*
Fisher Charles || Dyer Wm.
Fisher John || Friendship Joseph
Gammon John & Wm., *Warcombe*
Gammon Richard, *Trayne*
Gammon Thomas, *Oakridge*
Gammon Wm., *Hole*
Goss John || Hill Wm.
Heddon George, Campscott
Huxtable Wm., *Lincombe*
Huxtable Mrs || Irwin Wm.
Jewell Richard, *Common*
King John, High street
Ley George, *Lee*
Nugent John, Laston Cottage
Reed John || Reed Richard
Robins John, *Chambercombe*
Shapland George, *Damage*
Sloley Hugh, *Warmscombe*

Snow George, *Warcombe*
Symonds Charles, *Shelfin*
Watts John, *West Hagginton*
Williams John, *Slade*

FIRE & LIFE OFFICES.
1 Alliance, Thomas Bowden
1 County & Provdt., S. Mc. Robert
7 Freemasons, E. H. Lammas
1 Legal & Coml., Thomas Edwards
1 London, Rt. Hy. Moon
1 Royal Exchange, John Banfield
2 Royal Farmers, Henry Day
1 Sun, John P. Barron
7 Temperance, E. H. Lammas
West of England, Wm. C. Aston

HOTELS, INNS & TAVERNS.
3 Admiral Rodney, Wm. Lewis
1 Barnstaple Inn, Ephrm. Lovering
Britannia Hotel, John Martin
3 Crown, George Coates
1 Exeter Inn, Samuel Marks
2 George and Dragon, Wm. Colwill
4 Golden Lion, Hugh Curle
1 Lamb, John Hancock
1 London Inn, Wm. Knight
1 Moon, George Connibear
Packet Hotel, Mary Clark
3 Red Cow, Richard Gammon
1 Ring of Bells, Elizabeth Hancock
1 Rising Sun, James White
Royal Clarence Hotel, James Camp
1 Star, John Badcock
2 Swan, George Bennett
1 Wellington, John King
4 White Hart, Richard Hewitt

ACADEMIES.
2 Glanfield Jas.
1 Goss Elizabeth
1 Harding Wm.
1 Hillman Thos., *British School*
2 Howell Wm.
1 Lewis Jane
National, James S. Catford and Rbca. Lovering
Squire Prisla.
2 Wills Selina
Willis Elizabeth

BAKERS.
* *Confectioners.*
3 Fry Thomas
1 Hookaway Wm.
1 Latham Grace
* 1 Phillips Rbc.
1 Redmore Wm.
2 Rumney M. A.
* 1 Turner G. R.
* 1 Warren Ths.
1 Watts Philip

BATHS.
4 Curle Sarah
12 Scamp J. C.

BEERHOUSES.
Berry Thomas
1 Gammon Pp.
Harding Richd.
2 Lewis Wm.
Ley Richard
Richards Martin

BLACKSMITHS.
1 Avery Joshua
1 Cutcliffe Wm.
Hill John, *Heal*
1 Robins James

4 Rodgman Rt.

BOOKSELLERS, PRINTERS, &c.
1 Banfield J., (& lib. & stmps.)
1 Bowden Thos.
7 Lammas E. H.
2 Wills Jemima

BOOT & SHOE MKS.
2 Barnes John
1 Butler Robert
5 Dalling John
1 Dalling Wm.
1 Davis Edm.
2 Fry John
1 German John
3 Groves Wm.
1 Harding Wm.
1 Hill Robert
2 Jones Thomas
Ley John, *Slade*
Pugsley W., *Heal*
2 Pile George
1 Scamp Thos.
1 Toms John
1 Vickery James
5 Wadham Jas.

BUTCHERS.
2 Andrews Php.
1 Cornish Thos.
2 Dart Peter
1 Knight Thos.
3 Martin Henry
1 Mogridge Geo.
2 Phillips Hy.
2 Smith John
1 Smith Thomas
1 Squire Richd.
1 White James
1 White John

CABINET MAKERS.
1 Chiswell Thos.
2 German James
3 Slocombe Ths.

CARPENTERS.
(* *are Builders.*)
1 Gibbs Wm.
2 German Wm.
* 1 Hancock Ts.
13 Holmes John
* 5 Cole George Jones Wm.
* 15 Knight Ts.
* 6 Marshall Jas.

Pine Wm., Clarence cottage
5 Westlake Ths.

CHEMISTS AND DRUGGISTS.
1 Jones John
1 Moon Rt. Hy.
2 Thomas Thos.

CHINA, GLASS, &c., DEALERS.
2 Fry Thomas
1 Sommers Geo.
1 Walton Wm.
2 Wills Jemima

COAL MERTS.
1 Barnes Wm.
5 Cole Sus. & M.
4 Eastaway John
1 Hodge Wm.
1 Knight Mary
1 Mayne Wm.

COOPERS.
1 Langdon Wm.
2 Tucker Wm.

CORN MILLERS.
Ballsdon Fras.
Hill John, *Heale*
Parkin Jas., *Lee*
2 Thomas John

DYERS.
1 Richards Har.
2 Tucker Eliz.

GARDENERS.
Birmingham Jno., *Ropers field*
2 Camp John
Harding R., *Heal*
1 Ireland George

GREEN GROCERS.
1 Colwill Thos.
1 Thomas Wm.
2 Labbett Mary

GROCERS, &c.
1 German Jph.
1 Hussell Wm.
1 Huxtable Wm.
1 Mc Robert Sl.
1 Turpitt John
1 Wivell T. D.

HAIR DRESSERS.
1 Crocker Eliz.
2 Dalling Wm.

HORSE AND GIG LETTERS.
5 Avery John

2 Dart Peter
2 Hicks John
1 Marks Samuel
1 Mogridge Geo.
1 Picket Robt.
IRONMONGERS.
(* are Braziers.)
1 Avery Joshua,
 (& stove mfr)
1 Aston Wm. C.
1 Rendle Henry,
 (plmbr. & glzr)
2 Turner Wm. T.
L. & W. DRAPERS.
1 Barron John
1 Barron Mary
1Gould&Widlake
1 Huxtable Rd.
1 Wills Prudence
LODGINGS.
6 Alder Isabella
1 Banfield John
2 Barron Susan
8 Blackmore W.
1 Bowden Thos.
Bright John A.
7 Burgess John
1 Chiswell Thos.
4 Cockburn M.A.
ColeMrs, Capstn.
5 Cole Susan
7 Cook Mrs
Cornish James
Crockford Mary,
 Capstone villa
1 Dalling Wm.
1 Davey John
5 Davis Wm.
8 Dendle John
1 Dennis Chas.
1 Dinicombe Js.
Dyer Susan
7 Eastaway Jas.
7 Fleming Grace
1 Fleming Har.
8 Geen John
1 Harding & Stiff
Harding Mary
7 Harding Thos.
4 Harris Chas.
5 Hussell Thos.
Huxtable Mrs
1 Jones John
12 Knight Thos.
7 Lammas E. H.

1 Leeworthy H.
Lovering Eliza
Luscombe Mary
1 Marshall Eliza
8 Parker Peter
1 Parsell Mary
2 Passmore My.
Phillips Mary
14 Pollock Elnr.
4 Pulsford Jane
2 Roberts Ann
7 Rosmond Jph.
5 Scamp Ann
15 Scamp James
14 Smith Ann
1&7 Sommers G.
1 & 7 Toms John
Walters Mary
Widlake John
2 Willis Mary
MALTSTERS.
1 Badcock John
1 Camp James
1 Dennis Chas.
3 Martin John
MR. MARINERS.
1 Barnes Richd.
1 Barnes Nichs.
4 Barnes Wm.
2 ChallacombeG.
Cole Moses
Dallin Wm. C.
4 Dalling Thos.
3 Eastaway Ths.
7 Eastaway Jas.
2 Edwards John
1 Harding John
Harding Robert
13 Harding Rd.
1 Hernaman Rd.
2 Huxtable Thos.
1 Lawrence Rd.
2 Marshall Hy.
Mayne Wm.
4 Redmore Rd.
2 Rumson Wm.
2 Stephens Wm.
4 Street Wm.
11 Tucker Jas.
1 Walters Thos.
3 Williams John
4 White George
MILLINERS.
1 Bowden Ann
13 Dallin Betsy

2 Drake M. & C.
1 Fleming Har.
1 Harding & Stiff
5 Harding Alice
2 Harris Chtna.
3 Hicks Ann
1 Huxtable M. J.
3 Lewis Maria
1 Price Mary
1 Smith Ann
5 Smith Sarah
5 Westlake Ann

PAINTERS AND
 GLAZIERS.
1 Glanfield Wm.
1 Rice Wm.
5 Perry George
SHOPKEEPERS.
2 Barnes John
2 Challacombe J.
3 Clark David
2 ConibearGrace
2 Fry Thomas
3 German Richd.
2 Hartnell Abigl.
3 Holford Har.
1 Litson Saml.
3 Richards Hnra.
1 Snow John
2 Worwell Agnes
STRAW HAT MKS.
1 Burgess Eliz.
2 Gibbs Eliz.
2 Harris Chtna.
3 Lewis Maria
STOCKING&WORS-
TED MANFRS.
2 Border James
2 Lakeman Mary

STONEMASONS
AND PLASTERERS.
7 Burgess John
5 Burgess Wm.
5 Galliford John
1 Gibbs Richard
1Gibbs John
3 Gould John
11 Griffiths John

1 Herapath John
1 Price Wm.
Richards Philip
 and Martin
1 Scamp Robert
1 Scamp Wm.
SURGEONS.
1 Foot Jesse
1JonesJno.,(aph
 & dentist)
1 Moon Rt. Hy.
7 Stabb Thomas
5 Stoneham Pp.
1 Vidal Horace
Vye Edw., Manor
 House
TAILORS.
(* Drapers also.)
1 Baker J. T.
1 Blunt Thos.
1 Challacombe T.
*3 Croscombe J.
13 Harding J. C.
4 Harris Chas.
Perrin H.
* 2 Scamp John
* 2 Smyth John
* 2 Stephens J.
TEA DEALERS.
1 Camp James
2 Wills Jemima
1 Wills Prudence
TIMBER & SLATE
 MERCHANTS.
1 Dennis Chas.
12 Scamp Robert

WATCHMAKERS.
1 Sommers Geo.
1 Webber Henry
WHEELWRIGHTS.
1 Colwill John
2 Colwill Wm.
11 Lovering Rd.
1 Parkin John
1 Redmore Wm.
WINE AND SPIRIT
 MERCHANTS.
1 Camp James
1 Dennis Chas.

COACHES, &c.
Mail to Barnstaple, Tiverton, &c. at
 2½ afternoon, from Britannia Hotel
Coach to Lynton daily in summer,
 from the Clarence Hotel

CARRIERS' OMNIBUSES, *to* Barnstaple ; Jas. & John Dadd's, 9 morning ; and John Pugsley's, from the Star, and R. Blackmore's, from the London Inn, 4½ aft. daily

STEAM PACKETS to Bristol four days a week in summer ; and to Swansea, Bideford, Cornwall, &c. twice a week. The Little Western *sailing vessel* weekly to Bristol

KENTISBURY, a scattered village, in a high situation, 9 miles N.N.E. of Barnstaple, and 3 miles E.S.E. of Combemartin, has in its parish 422 souls, and 3400 acres of land, rising in bold hills, and including the hamlet of *Patehole.* The manor, formerly belonging to the Wolfe, Randall, Richards, and Beavis families, is dismembered, and the parish now belongs to Earl Fortescue, the Misses Incledon, and several smaller freeholders. The *Church* is an ancient structure, with a massive tower and four bells. The *rectory,* valued in K.B. at £12. 10s.7½d., and in 1831 at £303, is in the patronage and incumbency of the Rev. C. B. Sweet, M.A., who has a handsome residence, and about 60A. of glebe. Three of the Richards family held the rectory successively, and the last held it 52 years, and rebuilt the Rectory House in 1761. For teaching poor children the schoolmaster has about £5 a year, out of Griffen's tenement, left by *Mary Jones,* in 1783.

Boyles John, beerseller
Burnell Robert, blacksmith
Comer Alexander, beerseller
Hill Thomas, blacksmith
Sweet Rev Chas. Broadleigh, M.A. *rector ;* and Rev George, *curate*

FARMERS.
Burgess Pp. || Crang Wm. John
Harding Chas. || Lerwell John
Richards Jas. || Richards Richard
Slocombe Richard || Tamlyn Wm.
Turner Richard || Tucker George

MARWOOD, a village on the Ilfracombe road, 3 miles N.N.W. of Barnstaple, has in its parish 1012 souls, and 5596 acres of land, including the scattered hamlets of *Mudford, Milltown, King's Heanton, Guineaford,* and *Prixford.* Part of the parish is in the Earl of Devon's manor of Braunton, and the rest belongs to Chas. C. Drake, Henry Ley, Thomas R. Harding, Thos. Bridges, and John Crang, Esqrs., Dr. Yeo, the Rev. F. Mules, the Rev. J. H. Mules, and several smaller owners. Marwood was the seat and property of the Mervin family, and Whitfield was the seat of a branch of the Bastards. Church Marwood was long held by the Lords Martin and Lords Audley, and afterwards by the Bourchiers ; and Westcote was originally the residence of the Westcote family. The *Church* (St. Michael,) is an ancient structure, with a tower and six bells, and a finely carved screen. The *rectory,* valued in K.B. at £24. 8s. 6½d., and in 1831 at £400, is in the patronage of St. John's College, Cambridge ; and incumbency of the Rev. Richard Riley, B.D., who has a good residence, and 26A. 3R. 36P. of glebe. The tithes were commuted in 1844. Here are *two chapels,* belonging to the Independents and Wesleyans, and the former is a neat structure, in the early English style. The *Parish Land,* about 6A., let for £11, was derived from the gifts of Arthur Acland, and other donors. The rents are distributed among the poor. In 1779, *Richard Harding* left £150 for schooling poor children, and £100 to be invested for the relief of the poor. These sums were laid out in the purchase of £389. 15s. three per cent. consols. The dividends of £100 of the same stock, left by *Wm. Westacott,* in 1810, are paid to a schoolmistress for teaching three poor children.

Berry Thomas, shoemaker
Born Samuel, machine maker
Bridges Thomas, Esq. *Hill House*
Chugg Thomas, beer seller
Crang John, gentleman
Geen John, blacksmith
Hill Henry, parish clerk

Hussell James, cooper, &c
Jones Thomas, schoolmaster
Lerwell Walter, corn miller
Ley Henry, Esq. *Lee House*
Mules John, gent., & Rev Fras. rector of *Bittadon*
Marshall John, tailor and draper

Riley Rev Rd., B.D. *Rectory*
Riley Rev Rd. jun., B.A. curate
Rock John B. corn miller
Slocombe Harriet, shopkeeper
    INNS AND TAVERNS.
Fry's Hotel, James Pearce
Maltsters' Inn, George Richards
Mervin Arms, Wm. Corney, *auctionr.*
North Devon Inn, Fras. Fairchild
Ring of Bells, James Pearce
    FARMERS.
Marked 2, *at King's Heanton ;* 3,
    Metcombe ; and 4, *Warleigh.*
Alford Wm. || Balment John

Balsdon Wm. *Westcote Barton*
Carder Thomas || Clement John
2 Corney Geo. || 3 Delve Peter
Corney Wm. *Milltown*
2 Heywood Wm. || Gammon Philip
3 Irwin Joseph || Isaac Thomas
Joslyn John, *Prixford Barton*
Kelly John, *Blackwell*
4 Kelly Rd. || 4 Kelly Thomas
Lamprey John || Laramy John
Richards Wm. || Smith George
2 Watts Pp. || Smith Jas. *Huish*

MORTHOE is a scattered village, five miles W.S.W. of Ilfracombe, picturesquely seated on the sea coast, where that narrow rocky promontory, called *Morte Point*, juts out more than a mile into the Bristol Channel, between Bockham and Morte Bays, where there is a dangerous reef of rocks, on which vessels have often been wrecked. The parish contains 372 souls, and about 2500 acres of land, rising boldly from the sea cliffs, and including the hamlets of *Horsborough, Shesborough,* and *Estacott.* Earl Fortescue is lord of the manor of Over Wallacombe, and Sir J. P. B. Chichester owns that of Wollacombe-Tracy. The latter was long the seat of the ancient family of Tracy; and Sir Wm. Tracy is said to have lived here secluded from the world after his participation in the murder of Thomas à Becket. The *Church* (St Mary,) is an ancient structure, with a short tower and three bells. It contains the richly ornamented tomb of Wm. de Tracy, a former rector, who founded a chantry in it in 1308. The living is now a *vicarage,* valued in K.B. at £9. 19s. 3d., and in 1831 at £128, in the patronage of the Dean and Chapter of Exeter, and incumbency of the Rev. J. D. Ness, who has a good residence, and about 30A. of glebe. The tithes were commuted in 1840 for £381. The patrons are appropriators of the rectorial tithes.

Barnes Rd., & Butler John, *wheelgts.*
Conibear John, shoemaker
Goss Wm. & Geo. blacksmiths
James John, gent. *Zora Cottage*
Ness Rev John Derby, incumbent
Wakely Wm. vict., Chichester Arms
    FARMERS.
Chugg Geo. || Gammon Thomas

Hartnoll John || Heddon Ann
Irwin Joseph || Lovering John
Langdon John, *Tracy Barton*
Riddell Rt. Andw. || Smith Charles
Sharland Wm. *Shesborough*
Smith Robert || Smith Thomas
    POST *from Ilfracombe.*

PILTON is a pleasant village, on an eminence. about half a mile north of Barnstaple. Its parish contains 1805 inhabitants, and is mostly included in the Borough of Barnstaple, as already noticed at pages 566, 571, and 573. Its principal inhabitants are included in Barnstaple Directory. (See page 574.)

TRENTISHOE is a small village and parish, on the coast of the Bristol Channel, near a rivulet, 8 miles E. by N. of Ilfracombe, and 5 miles from Combe Martin. It has 132 souls, and 1571 acres of land, mostly belonging to Mrs. Griffiths and Mrs. Chichester, the former of whom is patroness of the *rectory*, valued in K.B. at £8. 8s. 4d., and in 1831 at £125, and now held by her son, the Rev. C. Griffiths, B.A., who has 36A. of glebe, and a good residence, in a picturesque valley. The *Church* (St. Peter,) is a small ancient edifice, with a tower and two bells. The tithes were commuted in 1841, for £80 per annum. In the reigns of Edward I. and II., the two

principal estates here belonged to the families of Ralegh and De Trendil shoe, or Trentishoe.

Griffiths Rev Chas., B.A. *Rectory*
Richards Richard, wheelwright
Whiddon Chas. miller and beerhs.
Whiddon Wm. blacksmith

FARMERS. || Dyer Wm.
Flinch John || Hoyles Wm.
Reed Thomas || Squire Thomas
Tucker Henry || Tucker Wm.

HARTLAND HUNDRED

Is a small district, on the north coast of Devon, about 8 miles in length and 5 in breadth, bounded on the north and west by the Bristol Channel, and on the south by a small part of Cornwall and the river *Torridge*, which, though it rises within a few miles of the ocean, runs inland in a very winding course of more than 30 miles to the mouth of the Taw. Hartland is the bold headland which stretches out into the sea between Barnstaple or Bideford Bay, and Bude Bay, and includes only the five *parishes of Clovelly, Hartland, Wellcombe, Woolfardisworthy*, and *Yarnscombe*, which comprises 4966 *souls*, and about 31,000 *acres of land*, rising in bold cliffs from the beach, and in lofty hills from the picturesque valleys of several rivulets and the river Torridge. It is in the Northern Parliamentary Division of Devon, in the Great Torrington Petty Sessional Division, in the Archdeaconry of Barnstaple, and all in Hartland Deanery, except Yarnscombe, which is a widely detached member of this Hundred, and is in Barnstaple Deanery, and Torrington Union. The other four parishes are in *Bideford Union.*

CLOVELLY, or *Clovelleigh*, is a pleasant village and fishing station, occupying a singular and picturesque situation, on the side of a steep rock, adjoining Bideford Bay, about 4 miles E. Hartland, and 11 miles W.SW. of Bideford. It is one of the most romantic places in Devon, and the houses being built upon the precipitous side of the sea cliff, one above the other; the main street ascends in terraces and flights of steps from the beach and pier. Clovelly is celebrated for its *herring fishery*, besides which large quantities of conger, whiting, hake, pollock, and cod fish are caught in the winter; and turbot, sole, plaice, gurnet, and mackerel in summer. Its parish had 950 inhabitants in July, 1841, besides 40 seamen, who were then absent; and contains about 4200 acres of land, mostly the property of *Sir James Hamlyn Williams, Bart.*, who is lord of the manor, and has a large and handsome seat, called CLOVELLY COURT, erected about 1780, on the site of the ancient mansion, which was destroyed by fire. The views from the house and grounds are extremely grand; and above the cliffs, to the south-east of the village, are the remains of an entrenchment, called *Clovelly Dikes*, of a square form, and unknown origin. The *Giffords* were anciently lords of the manor, but in the time of Richard II. it was sold to Sir John Cary, Knight, by whose family a small harbour and pier were made. The manor was purchased about 1730, by *Zachary Hamlyn, Esq.*, whose great nephew was created a *baronet* in 1795. The late baronet assumed the name of *Williams*, in consequence of his father's marriage with the heiress of the Williams family, of Edwinsford, in Carmarthenshire. The *Church* (All Saints,) is a small ancient structure, with a low tower, situated near Clovelly Court. It was made collegiate in 1387, by Sir Wm. Cary, who settled in it a warden and six chaplains, to whom he gave the advowson and the great tithes. The living is a *rectory*, valued in K.B. at £19. 11s. 5½d., and in 1831 at £276, in the patronage of Sir J. H. Williams, and incumbency of the Rev. Z. H. Drake, M.A., who has a good

residence, and about 100a. of glebe. The tithes were commuted in 1838, for about £200 per annum. Here is a small Wesleyan chapel; and a school for 50 girls, supported by Lady Williams. A gallery, built in the church by the Rev.— Prince, is let for £3 a year, which is applied in schooling poor children.

Williams Sir James Hamlyn, Bart.
  Clovelly Court
Drake Rev Zachary H., M.A. *rector*
Dalton Rev Henry, M.A. *curate*
Finch James, beerseller
Grills Nichls., & Bierman P. *shoemks*
Heard Wm. grocer and draper
Hockington Rd. coast guard
Parsons John, tailor
Vine Saml. vict. *Red Lion*
Westlake Mr Joseph
Whitefield Ann, grocer and draper

Whitefield Rt. vict. *New Inn*

FARMERS.

Ashton Wm.
Bartlett James
Bartlett Thomas
Burrows James
Ching Thomas
Ching Wm.
Cleverdon Wm.
Eddy John
Hamlyn Thos.
Hamlyn T. jun
Hackeridge Ts.
Hackeridge T.ju
Jewell Henry
Jewell Joseph
Squires John
POST-OFFICE
  at John Dannell's

HARTLAND, a small decayed market town, spoken of in ancient records as a borough, is situated near a rivulet about the middle of that north-west corner of Devon which juts out into the Bristol Channel, at Bideford Bay, opposite Lundy Island. It is 13 miles W. by S. of Bideford, and two miles from the sea, but its large parish extends to the point, and to both coasts of the promontory, and comprises 2223 souls, and about 16,700 acres of land including many scattered farm-houses, &c., the hamlets of *Millford, Meddon, Cheristow, Elmscott,* and *Pilham,* and the village of STOKE, from 1 to 2 miles W. of the town, where there is a *quay,* on the western coast, where corn, &c., is exported, and coal, limestone, &c., imported. Hartland had a grant for a *market* every Tuesday, in 1280, but it has been obsolete more than sixty years. It has still two annual *fairs,* on the Wednesday in Easter Week, and the 25th of September. This high and bleak parish is bounded on the south by some boggy heights, where the rivers Torridge and Tamar have their sources; and on the west by *Hartland Point,* called by Ptolemy, the *Promontory of Hercules,* and by Camden, *Harty Point.* There is a small pier at the point, near which fishing vessels find good shelter from south westerly winds, under the rocky eminences which skirt the shore. L. W. Buck, Esq., of Moreton, is lord of the manor, and at the court leet and baron, a *portreeve,* and other officers are appointed. *Hartland Abbey,* the seat of George Stuckley Buck, Esq., stands near Stoke village and the church, in the narrow vale, whose sloping sides are richly mantled with hanging woods, and form a spacious deer park, through which a rivulet winds westward to the sea, about a mile below. This abbey, called in ancient writings, the *Monastery of St. Nectan,* was founded by Githa, wife of Earl Godwin, for canons secular; but in the reign of Henry II., Geoffrey de Dinant, then lord of the manor, consented that they should be changed into canons regular, and gave them the church of *Stoke Nectan,* now the parish church. At the dissolution of the abbey, its revenues were valued at £326. 13s. 2½d. per annum. Its site was granted, with the manor, in 1545, to Wm. Abbott, and afterwards passed by heiresses to the Lutterells and Orchards. The mansion was nearly all rebuilt about 50 years ago, by the late Paul Orchard, Esq., and includes the site and some portions of the ancient abbey; the cloisters now forming the basement story of the east and west fronts. When making these improvements, several fragments of richly ornamented mouldings, and a monument of a crusader, were dug up. The *Church* (St. Nectan,) stands more than a mile west of the town, on a lofty eminence near the sea, Stoke village, and the Abbey. It is a

large and handsome building, consisting of a tower, a nave, two aisles, and a chancel; the latter of which is divided from the nave by a richly ornamented screen. It was repaired and beautified in 1849-'50, at the cost of about £800. The *advowson* and the *great tithes* of the parish were purchased in 1615, by the founder of the Charter House, London, and settled as part of the endowment of that excellent institution, to which they still belong. The great tithes were commuted in 1842, for £560 per annum, and are now held on lease by J. H. Furse, Esq. The *perpetual curacy* was valued in 1831, at only £97 per annum. The next presentation has been purchased by Thomas Chope, Esq., of Bideford. The *Chapel of Ease*, in Hartland town, is a small structure, formerly the market house, but converted to its present use in 1839, at the cost of about £400, raised by subscription. Here is a small *Independent Chapel*, built in 1818, and a *Wesleyan Chapel*, erected in 1829. G. S. Buck, Esq., supports a *school*, for 80 children. The *Church Lands*, which have been vested in trust from an early period, for the use of the church, comprise a farm of 54A. 3R. 36P., at West Staddon; and a farm of 16A. 2R. 39P., and a house and garden, at Hartland, let for about £44 per annum, which is carried to the churchwarden's account. Four small dwellings for paupers, have been partitioned off from the two church houses. Here is an *Almshouse* for three poor widows, founded by *Wm. Mill*, in 1618, and supposed to have been endowed with 1A. 3R. 8P. of land, let for £4, which is applied with the poor rates. Adjoining the almshouse is a building, which was formerly the parish workhouse. In 1812, *Paul Orchard* left for the poor parishioners £700 three per cent. consols, and £334. 14s. 7d. three per cent. reduced annuities, and directed the dividends of the former to be distributed in coals or other fuel; and the dividends of the latter in bread.

Addy Mr Giles || Heal Rev A. *Indept*
Bailey Robert, corn miller, *Tosbery*
Buck Geo. Stuckley, Esq. *Abbey*
Carter Daniel D. merchant, Quay
Carter Wm. sen. & jun., gents
Chanter Rev Wm. incumbent
Hockin Edward, maltster
Prust Wm. tanner
Reynolds Rev Jas. Jones, B.A. curate
Rowe Wm. gent. *Down*

INNS AND TAVERNS.
Anchor, John Randall
Hoops Inn, Thos. Colley, Quay
King's Arms, Richard Ashton
New Inn, Charles Prowse
West Country Inn, Wm. Steer
Beer House, Thos. Southwood

BLACKSMITHS.
Clarke John
Johns John
Miller John
Parsons John
Snow John
BOOT&SHOEMKS.
Ashton Wm.
Beer John
Beer Joseph
Burnard Wm.

GoodenoughWm.
Jewell John
Lemon Wm.
Score Thos.
Souch Richard
Souch Wm.
BUTCHERS.
Heard Richard
Randall John
COOPERS.
Downing Wm.

Kellaway Wm.
FARMERS.
Ashton Francis
Avery Ann
Baglole Samuel
Binley John
Bailey Thos.
Barch Richard
Barfitt Charles
Barfitt Philip
BondWm. *Tosbry*
Braund Thos.
Braunton John
Burrow John
Cann Thomas
Carter John
Carter Richard
Ching Hugh
Chope Richard
Chope Wm.
Cleverdon John
Cleverdon Thos.
Coldwell John
Coldwell Wm.
Cook Jno. *Troy*
Cook Rt.*Millford*
Cook Mary, *Mill*
Damond John

Dennis Richard
Foley Pr. *Millfd*
Fulford Richd.
German Samuel
Grills Wm.
Hamlyn John
Hamlyn Thos.
Harris Thos.
Haynes John
Heard John
Heard Richard
Heard Thomas
Hobbs John
Hobbs Richard
Hockin Wm.
Hopper John
Hopper Roger
Howard Joseph
Howard Thos.
Howard Wm.
Jeffrey John
Jeffrey Richard
Jeffrey Thos.
Kellaway John
Littlejohn John
Littlejohn Wm.
Moore Edw.
Moore James

Moore Richard
Moore Wm.
Moss Jno. *Millfd*
Mountjoy Hugh
Mountjoy John
Mountjoy Wm.
Mugford Wm.
Oake Wm.
Pennington Mrs
Pennington Wm.
Pillman John
Prowse James
Prowse John
Prowse Johna.
Prowse Thos.
Prowse Wm.
Pridham Wm.
Prust Daniel
Prust Wm.
Randall John
Randall Joseph
Randall Jph. jun

Rowden George
Rowe Thos. W.
Shepherd John
Shutt John
Shutt Mrs
Sillick Geo. H.
Stone Betty
Stone John
Vine John
Vine Samuel T.
Walter James
Walter John
Watcher Rt. *mill*
Williams John
Williams Richard
Wood Philip
GROCERS, &c.
(* *Drapers also.*)
*Burnard Wm.
*Cann Mary
Cory Thomas
*Dennis John

Heard Richard
Kellaway Philip
Prust Wm.
JOINERS, &c.
Cory Thos.
Curtis Richd.
Evans Wm.
Kellaway Philip
Prust Wm.
MASONS.
Cann Samuel
Cann Saml. jun.
Cann Wm.
Jeffrey John
Jeffrey Wm.
Jeffrey Thos.
Southwood Thos.
PAINTERS, &c.
Cory Thos.
Jenn Thos.
Kellaway Philip
Prust Wm.

SURGEONS.
Carter Dl. *Quay*
Rowe Chas. H.
Vine Wm.
TAILORS.
Avery Wm.
Evans Wm.
Parsons Richd.
Powley Wm.
Westlake Thos.
WHEELWRIGHTS.
Curtis Richd.
Heal John
POST-OFFICE
at Rd. Heard's.
Letters desp. 8
morning
CARRIERS to
Bideford, Tues.
Thu. and Sat.
Cooke Chas.
Williams Thos.

WELLCOMBE is a small scattered village and parish, 3 miles S. of Hartland, adjoining Cornwall and the sea, and near the sources of the rivers Torridge and Tamar. It has only 293 souls, and 751A. 2R. 21P. of land, mostly belonging to L. W. Buck, Esq., the lord of the manor, formerly belonging to the Capra, Merton, Stowell, and Rolle families. The *Church* (St. Nectan,) is a small ancient structure, and the living is a *perpetual curacy*, which was separated from Hartland in 1508, and is valued at only £86, in the patronage of Lord Clinton, and incumbency of the Rev. H. M. Cockshott. The parsonage is small, and the glebe only about 10 acres. The poor have two annual rent-charges, viz., 20s. left by *Henry Rowe*, in 1788, and 6s. left by *Alice Blighe*.

Anderson Rev Wm. D. curate, *Mead*
Parr John, & Prust Thos. *beer houses*
FARMERS.
Bartlett Robt.
Cory James
Damond Wm.

Gefford Thos.
Hamley Philip
Hedden John
Hedden John R.

Hedden Wm.
Heysett Wm.
Hobbs John
Hobbs John, jun
Howard Richd.
Howe Philip

Sanders Wm.
Tremain Thos.
Trick Thos.
Warmington Ts.
Witheridge Thos.
Yeo Philip

WOOLFARDISWORTHY, commonly called *Wolsworthy*, is a large village, 5 miles W. of Hartland, and 9½ miles S.W. by W. of Bideford. Its parish contains 988 souls, and 5960 acres of land, rising boldly from the river Torridge and two of its tributary streams. Sir James H. Williams, Bart., is lord of the manor of *Bokish*, commonly called Bucks, but a great part of the parish belongs to W. W. Melhuish, John Trathen, and B. Prust, Esqrs., (who have neat houses here,) and many smaller owners. The *Church* (St. Michael,) is a small antique structure, containing memorials of the Cole, Hamlyn, Saltren, Duerdon, and other families. Mrs. Loggin is owner of the tithes, which formerly belonged to Hartland Abbey. She is also patroness of the *perpetual curacy*, valued in 1831 at only £91, and now in the incumbency of the Rev. J. W. Smyth, D.D. He has a stipend of £20 out of the tithes, and also about 70 acres of land, partly purchased with Queen Anne's Bounty. The poor have 10s. a year from £10 left by James Burdon, in 1747.

2 c

Andrew Job, tailor
Cleverdon John, carpenter
Cleverdon Richard, butcher
Davy Robert, mason
Friendship Thos. vict. Hotel
Hopgood Richard, blacksmith
Lee Thomas, edgetool maker
Melhuish Walter Wm. Esq
Penington Wm. corn miller
Prust Bartholomew, Esq
Petherick Daniel, mason
Smyth Rev John, D.D. incbt. *Cranford*
Trick Wm. corn miller
Vanstone George, beer seller
Westway Thos. carpenter

BOOT&SHOE MKS.
Eastbrook John
Eastbrook Wm.
Penington Wm.

FARMERS.
Andrew Wm.
Andrew James
Andrew John
Andrew J. jun
Andrew Joseph
Bailey John
Bartlett John
Bartlett Thos.
Beadlick Thos.
Blake Chas.
Bond Grace

Bond John
Boundy Susanna
Britton Wm.
Burrow Jph.
Burrow Jph. jun.
Cann Thos.
Cann Wm.
Ching Wm.
Cory Francis
Cory John
Cory Susanna
Dark Thos.
Daymon Peter
Dunn John
Falley Wm.
Grigg Wm.
Harding Thsn.
Harding Richd.
Heywood Walter
Hewitt John
Lane Josiah
Marquiss Geo.
May John

Moase Philip
Moase Wm.
Prance Saml.
Prance Wm.
Pridham Lnce.
Prouse Chas.
Pyke Samuel
Sanders Thos.
Short John
Short Richard
Short R. jun
Slee Thomas
Stevens Jas.
Sundercock Frs.
Tawin Thos.
Trathen John, *Duerdon*
Vanstone Jas.
Vanstone John
Vanstone Saml.
Vining John
Walkey Saml.
Walter John

YARNSCOMBE, a village and parish, 5 miles N.E. of Great Torrington, and 7 miles S. by E. of Barnstaple, contains 512 souls, and 3047 acres of land. The Trustees of the late Lord Rolle are lords of the manor of Great Yarnscombe; and J. H. Furse, Esq., owns that of Little Yarnscombe. J. P. Blew, Esq., and several smaller owners, have estates in the parish. The *Church* (St. Andrew,) is an ancient structure, with several old monuments. The *vicarage*, valued in K.B. at £7. 11s. 11d., and in 1831 at £132, is in the patronage of the Lord Chancellor, and incumbency of the Rev. John K. Fletcher, D.D., of Callington, Cornwall. The glebe is 30 acres, and the Parsonage is a small stone residence. The tithes were commuted in 1840, the vicarial for £136. 10s., and the rectorial for £152. The latter belong to the Trustees of the late Lord Rolle. There was anciently a chapel at Little Yarnscombe. Here is a small Wesleyan Chapel. The *Parish Lands* comprise 30 acres, called Ashridge, now let for about £20, which is carried to the churchwardens' accounts. The poor have 40s. a year, left by Edward Warren, in 1693, out of North Westcott. They have also the interest of £25 given by Mr. Champneys and Mrs. Nichols.

Dart John, carpenter
Furse Wm. mason, &c
Lander Thomas, shoemaker
Loveland Anty. Esq. *North Church*
Mules Rev Jas., M.A. curate, *Vicarg*
Muxworthy Geo. & John, smiths
Nichols John, tailor
   atway Hy. vict. Hunter's Inn
Stedeford John, tailor
Symons John, vict. Old Bunhouse
Tout Grace, beer seller
Tucker Anthony, shoemaker

FARMERS.
Arthurs Geo.
Bolt John
Chick Wm.
Downs John
Fisher Saml.
Fisher Richd.
Furse Thos.
Gay Thos.
Hayman Wm.
Kerslake Geo.
Kerslake Thos.

Kerslake Wm.
Oatway John
Paddon John
Pengelly Henry
Pengelly Wm.
Petherbridge Ts.
Symons Eliz.
Symons Jno. and Wm. *Cogworthy*
Symons Richd.
Wright James

SOUTH MOLTON HUNDRED

Is generally a fertile and hilly district, bounded on the west by the river
Taw, on the south by the river Mole, and on the east by Somersetshire. It
is intersected by the river Bray and many smaller streams, and is of an irregular figure, averaging about 13 miles in length and 10 in breadth, and extending north-west from the borough of South Molton to that of Barnstaple.
It abounds in *limestone*, and has several *lead and copper mines*, especially on
its eastern side, where it has a lofty ridge of hills, adjoining the mountainous
region of *Exmoor Forest*, in which *Span Head* rises to the altitude of 1668
feet, and some other hills, on the borders of the two counties, to the height
of from 1000 to 1500 feet above the level of the sea. This forest contains
many druidical remains, and gives rise to the Exe, Barle, Mole, and other
rivers. South Molton Hundred is in the Northern Parliamentary Division
of Devon; in South Molton and Barnstaple Polling Districts and Deaneries,
and in the Archdeaconry of Barnstaple. It is all in *South Molton Petty
Sessional Division*, except Bishop's Tawton, which is in Braunton Division.
It includes 14 parishes, of which the following is an enumeration, shewing
their territorial extent, and their population in 1841 :—

Parishes.	Acres.	Pop.	Parishes.	Acres.	Pop.
Anstey, East......	3245	240	Molton, South	6264	4274
Anstey, West	3008	279	Nympton St. Geo..	1684	272
*Bishop's Tawton..	4268	1827	Satterleigh	515	61
Chittlehampton ..	8720	1893	*Swimbridge	7061	1746
Knowstone	4994	578	Twitchen	2918	194
*Landkey	3510	774	Warkleigh........	2414	291
Molland	6168	550			
Molton, North....	14,351	2121	Total ..	69,120	15,100

* The three parishes marked thus * are in *Barnstaple Union*, and all the others are in
South Molton Union. These Unions are County Court Districts. *Newport* and some
other parts of *Bishop's Tawton* parish are in Barnstaple Borough.

South Molton Union comprises the 29 parishes of East and West Anstey, Bishop's
Nympton, East and West Buckland, Burrington, Charles, Cheldon, Chittlehampton,
Chulmleigh, Creacombe, Filleigh, George Nympton, King's Nympton, Knowstone,
Mariansleigh, Meshaw, Molland, North Molton, South Molton, Rackenford, Romansleigh, Rose-Ash, Satterleigh, Twitchen, Warkleigh, Witheridge, and East and West
Worlington ; which extend over an area of 194 square miles, and contained 20,978 inhabitants in 1841, living in 3987 houses, besides which they had 256 unoccupied houses,
and 50 building, when the census was taken. In 1831, their population amounted only
to 18,875 souls. Their total annual average expenditure on the poor during the three
years preceding the formation of the Union was £8655. In 1838, their expenditure was
£7986 ; in 1840, £8190. 13s., and in 1848, £10,806. 18s. The *Union Workhouse*, at South
Molton, is a large building, which was erected in 1836, at the cost of £4379, and has
room for 230 inmates. Earl Fortescue is *chairman* of the Board of Guardians ; Mr. J.
E. J. Riccard is *union clerk and superintendent registrar;* and the Rev. T. Clarke is the
chaplain. Mr. Thomas Redler and Sus. Hamilton are *master and matron* of the Workhouse. Messrs John Cole, of South Molton ; Lnce. Babbage, of Chulmleigh ; and Rd.
Melton, of Bishop's Nympton, are the *relieving officers and registrars of births and deaths.*
Mr. J. E. Cutcliffe, of South Molton, is *registrar of marriages* for the whole Union.

ANSTEY, (EAST) is a small scattered village, among the high hills,
near the borders of Somersetshire, 3½ miles W.S.W. of Dulverton, and 10
miles E. of South Molton. Its parish contains 240 souls, and 3245
acres of land, but only 2500 acres are tithable, and the greater part of the
remainder is open moorland and plantations. The manor was dismembered
many years ago, and the soil belongs to the Rev. John Froude, J. G. Pearse,
A. Smith, T. Hole, J. H. Beadon, and H. Barnes, Esqrs. ; Mrs. Fisher, the
heirs of the late Lord Rolle, and a few smaller owners. The *Barton* is the
seat of the Rev. John Froude, and was built in 1848, on the site of the old

2 c 2

mansion. The *Church* (St. Michael,) is a small ancient building, with a tower and four bells. The *rectory*, valued in K.B. at £10. 6s. 8d., and in 1831 at £180, is in the patronage and incumbency of the Rev. Geo. Poole Norris, of Rosecraddock, Cornwall. The Rectory House is a commodious thatched mansion, and the glebe is 109A. 1R. 9P. The tithes were commuted in 1842, for £168. The poor have the interest of £35, left by various donors.

Bale Jas. and John, carpenters
Froude Rev John, M.A. vicar of Knowstone & Molland, *Barton*
Fulford John, vict. Hare & Hounds
Matthews John, curate of East and West Anstey, *Rectory*
Nott John, corn miller, *Dunsley*
Summers James, blacksmith
Tarr Thomas, parish clerk
Taylor Hy. beerhs. *Waddicombe*

Trick Thos. cooper, *Oldways end*

FARMERS.
Bater Geo. || Cockram Mary
Follett Robert || Hill Wm.
Gibbons Joseph, *Woodburn*
Hoskins Ridwood Wm.
Howe Hy. || Huxtable John
Manning Wm. || Ocock Saml.
Vicary John || Vicary Thos.

ANSTEY, (WEST) is a small scattered village, on the acclivities of a lofty eminence, near the source of the river Yeo, and the borders of Somersetshire, 5 miles west of Dulverton, and 9 miles E. by N. of South Molton. It has in its parish 279 souls, and 3008 acres of land, including more than 1000 acres of open moorland, rising abruptly from the Duns Brook, which divides the two counties. *Yeo Mill* and a number of adjacent dwellings are on the banks of the river, a mile S. of the church. Lord Clinton is lord of the manor, which was held successively by the Le Moigny, Pillond, Cornu, Speccot, and Rolle families. The Hon. Newton Fellowes, Jas. Hill, Esq., Mrs. and Misses Fisher, J. Partridge, A. Smith, Esq., and several smaller owners have estates in the parish. The *Church* (St. Petrock,) is an antique structure, in the perpendicular style, with a tower and three bells, two of which were damaged, and the tower much injured by lightning, about ten years ago. The interior has several neat mural monuments, and a small gallery, erected in 1839. The Dean and Chapter of Exeter are appropriators of the rectory and patrons of the discharged *vicarage*, valued in K.B. at £10. 6s. 8d., and in 1831 at £132. The Rev. G. M. Slatter, B.D., of Exeter, is the incumbent, and has 37A. 2R. of glebe, occupied with the Vicarage House, by a farmer. The tithes were commuted in 1841, the vicarial for £78, and rectorial for £113 per annum. The latter are leased to J. Hill, Esq., and Mrs. Spencer. In 1760, James Handford left two yearly rent-charges out of South Hill estate, viz., £3 for schooling poor children, and £2 for the poor of this parish. The latter have also the interest of £30, given by various donors, and vested with the overseers. The Rev. J. Matthews, of East Anstey, is the *curate*.

Balls Mr John || Burnell Jno. par. clk
Catford Robert, shopkeeper
Elworthy Maria, schoolmistress
Fellowes Hon. Newton, *Churchtown*
Fisher Mrs Grace & Misses, *Badlake*
Heard Edward, blacksmith
Hill James, Esq. *Woodlands*
Hodge John, carpenter & wheelwght
Quick Eliz. & Burnell My. school
Shapcott Thos. vict. Partridge Arms
Shapcott Thos. & Moore Wm. tailors
Sowden John, shoemaker

Venner John, miller, baker, and beer-seller, *Yeo Mill*
FARMERS.
Bawden James, *West Ringcombe*
Bucknell Geo. || Catford Thos.
Cridge John || Elworthy Thos.
Harris Jas. || Hill Thos.
Hill Wm. || Kingdon Geo.
Maunder John || Pearce Geo.
Meed Edward, *Snaily Park*
Pearce Jas. || Quartly John
Tucker John || Veysey Robert
Webber Wm. *Redbrook*

BISHOP'S TAWTON, a small village on the east side of the fertile and picturesque valley of the river Taw, 2¼ miles S. by E. of Barnstaple, has in its parish 4268 acres of land, and 1827 inhabitants, including *Newport*, a populous southern suburb of Barnstaple, and forming part of that borough, as noticed at page 566. Newport is said to have been anciently a borough town. It had formerly a market on Monday, and a fair on the festival of the Nativity of St. John the Baptist, granted in 1294. The Duke of Bedford is lord of the manor of Bishop's Tawton, which belonged at an early period to the Bishops of Devonshire, and was the original Bishop's See; but Putta, the second bishop, removed the See to Crediton. The manor was conveyed by Bishop Veysey, in 1550, to Lord John Russell, afterwards Earl of Bedford, at the request of the King, together with other manors. The bishops had a *Palace* here many centuries after the See was removed, and traces of it are still to be seen. Robt. Chichester, Esq., owns *Accot, Hall, Pill,* and *Halmeston* estates, and is now building a large and handsome mansion, in the Elizabethan style, at HALL, the ancient seat of the Hall family, whose heiress brought the estate to the Chichesters. Sir B. P. Wrey, Bart., and several smaller owners, have estates in the parish. The *Church* (St. John,) is an ancient structure, consisting of a nave, chancel, and north aisle, with a tower and spire. It contains several monuments belonging to the Chichester family, and has recently been repaired and beautified. In restoring the north aisle, in 1849, a series of interesting frescoes, in good preservation, were discovered, covering the whole of the north side, and surrounded by an ornamental border. The principal figures in these antique paintings are ten feet high. During the restoration, three fine painted windows were inserted. In the churchyard are some remains of an ancient building, called the Deanery, belonging, with the rectorial tithes, to the Dean of Exeter. The great tithes of Bishop's Tawton, Landkey, and Swimbridge, were appropriated to the Dean by Bishop Brewer, in 1231. The Dean is also patron of the *vicarage*, valued in K.B. at £21, and in 1831 at £480. The Rev. J. D. Baker, B.A., is the incumbent, and has 25a. of glebe, and a handsome residence, erected in 1841, in the Elizabethan style, at the cost of £1800. The tithes were commuted in 1843, the vicarial for £445, and the rectorial for £350. Thos. Brailey, Esq., is lessee of the latter. *Newport Church* is a modern building, near the site of an ancient chapel, the ruins of which were taken down about the middle of last century. It is a *perpetual curacy*, valued at £87, in the patronage of the Vicar, and incumbency of the Rev. Bourchier Wrey Savile, M.A. The parish has a *National School*, attended by 130 children. The Parish Land (4a.) was purchased with £100 left by *John Berryman*, in 1618, for the poor, who have also the interest of £32, which was expended in enlarging the Church House. They have also the following yearly sums:—26s., left by Hugh Acland; and 10s., left by John Rowley. The vicar has an annuity of 26s. 8d., left by Eliz. Martyn, in 1663, for catechising the children. The poor of Newport have 40s. a year from H. G. Tippett's Charity. (See Barnstaple.) *Newport Borough Lands* were vested in trust in 1691, for the benefit of the inhabitants, and now consist of several tenements, let for only 41s. a year, which is applied in repairing the church.

BISHOP'S TAWTON.
Newport is included with Barnstaple.

Arscott Mary, vict. Three Pigeons
Ashplant Thos.&Edgar Jno. shoemkrs
Baker Rev J. Durand, B.A. *Vicarage*
Brailey Thomas, Esq.
Brealey John, tailor
Chichester Robt. & C., Esqrs. *Hall*
Dart Wm. shopr ‖ Delve Wm. smith
Davis Thomas, carpenter
Ford Mary, corn miller
Harding Robert, gent. *Down Rew*
Quick Thomas, blacksmith
Rawle John, *post-office*

Richards Dorothy, beer seller
Tyte Henry, vict. Three Tuns
FARMERS.
Alford Henry, *Halmeston*
Boatfield Robert ‖ Brown Samuel
Buckingham Wm. ‖ Dennis Edw.
Gaydon Wm. ‖ Hosking Richard

Houle George ‖ Houle Wm.
Huxtable John ‖ Joce Wm.
Marquiss Mrs ‖ Powell John
Rowe Charles ‖ Sanders Joseph
Slade Richard ‖ Tyte Henry
Waldron Henry ‖ Waldron John

CHITTLEHAMPTON, a large and pleasant village, 5½ miles W. of South Molton, and 6½ miles S.E. of Barnstaple, has in its parish 1893 inhabitants, and 8720 acres of land, extending westward to the Taw Valley, and including the village of *Chittleham-holt,* and the hamlets of *Ambow, Bidicot, Brightley, Stowford, Newton,* and *Head,* and many scattered farm houses, &c. There is some beautiful scenery on the banks of the Taw, particularly near Head Wood. A *fair* is held in the village on the third Saturday in March. The manor of Chittlehampton belongs to the heirs of the late Lord Rolle, and was formerly held by the Fitzhamon, Spenser, Dauberry, Pollard, and Venner families. The manor of Chittleham-holt belongs to John Brown, Esq., whose son has a pleasant seat here. *Hudscot,* a neat mansion with pleasant grounds, is the seat of the sister of the late Lord Rolle. J. Tanner, the Rev. P. Johnson, and several smaller owners, have estates in the parish. The *Church* (St. Hieritha,) is a large and handsome structure, in the perpendicular style, with a fine tower and six bells. Its tutelary saint is said to have been interred here. It contains several handsome monuments, and has a finely carved stone pulpit. It was appropriated by Robt. Fitzhamon to Tewkesbury Abbey. The heirs of the late Lord Rolle are now impropriators of the rectory, and patrons of the *vicarage,* valued in K.B. at £34. 18s. 11½d., and in 1831 at £435. The Rev. Rt. Henry Chichester is the incumbent, and has 44¼A. of glebe, and a neat *Vicarage House,* erected in 1844, in the Elizabethan style, at the cost of £1500. The tithes were commuted in 1844, the vicarial for £575, and the rectorial for £675 per annum. *St. John's Church,* at CHITTLEHAM-HOLT, is about three miles S. by E. of Chittlehampton, and is a neat structure, in the early English style, built in 1838, at the cost of £1000. It was founded by the late Lord Rolle, who also built a good house for the minister, at the cost of £900. His heirs are patrons of the *perpetual curacy,* now in the incumbency of the Rev. Edmund Bennett, M.A. The Baptist Chapel, at Chittlehampton, has been sold to the *Wesleyans.* The Plymouth Brethren have a chapel at Chittleham-holt. The *Parish Lands, &c.,* have been long vested for the use of the parish church, and comprise 30A., 15 houses, and several gardens, worth about £40 a year. Belonging to the same trust is an annual rent-charge of £1. 2s. 8d. Here is a National School, partly supported by subscription.

Marked 2, at Chittleham-holt.
Anstey Wm. miller, *Bray Mill*
Ballard Wm. police superintendent
Bennett Rev Edm. *incbt. St John's*
2 Brown John, jun. *Fraynes*
Burgess Mrs Jane, *Langaton*
Chichester Rev Rt. Henry, *Vicarage*
2 Clarke Mary, schoolmistress
Gregory Thomas, miller, *Brightley*
Griffin James, cooper
2 Handford Wm. mason, &c
Holloway James, tailor
2 Nettleship Wm. *curate*

Rolle Hon. Miss, *Hudscot*
Watts Corder, maltster, &c
2 Webber John, mason, &c
INNS & TAVERNS.
Barnstaple Inn, Emanuel Isaac
Bell, Wm. Manaton
Exeter Inn, John Jenkins
Golden Lion, John Rendle
New Inn, Wm. Crocker
Rolle's Arms, James Brailey
BEERHOUSES. | BLACKSMITHS.
Dart Michael | Holloway John
Nott Thomas | Hunt Richard

Seage Wm.	Brailey Amos	Howard Ephm.	2 Sholbrook John
Smith Wm.	Brown Wm.	2 Huxtable John	Skinner Alex.
2 Westacott Wm.	Buckingham Wm.	Joce Eliz. & Wm.	Skinner Thomas
BOOT&SHOE MKS.	Burgess Jane	2 Lake John	Smalbridge Fdk.
2 Baker Henry	Crocker George	2 Lewis John	Vatter Wm.
2 Baker John	Crocker Mary	2 Loosemore Ths.	2 Ward Wm.
Govier Richard	Dunn Henry	Loosemore John	2 Webber Richard
CARPENTERS.	Dyer John	Luxton John	2 Westacott Ths.
2 Huxtable Wm.	Ellicott John	Manning Js. *Head*	SHOPKEEPERS.
Sanders John	2 Ellicott Robert	Manning John	Chapple Judith
Smaldon James	Facey John	2 Manning Thos.	Griffin John
FARMERS.	Gill John	2 Martin Robert	2 Huxtable Emly.
Arthur Thomas	Godbere John	Mildon Wm.	Nott Thomas
Baker James	2 Govier Peter	Mills John	WHEELWRIGHTS.
Baker John	Graddon James	Morris John	2 Heard Wm. &
Barnes Arthur	Graddon John,	2 Phillips Wm.	Edward
2 Bartlett Wm.	*Brattan*	Rendle John	Lock Bartw.
2 Bater John	Graddon Wm.	2 Rowe Peter	Phillpots Thos.
2 Bater Thomas	Guard Philip	Sanders James,	Tinson James
2 Bowman Thos.	Harris Js. *Ambow*	*Langaton*	
Bowman Sarah	2 Hooper John	Sanders George	

KNOWSTONE, a pleasant village, on a bold eminence, encompassed by lofty hills, 9 miles E. by S. of South Molton, has in its parish 578 souls, and 4994 acres of land, including 1219A. of common, 219A. of moorland; the village of *East Knowstone*, about a mile from the church; the hamlet of *Rochill;* and many scattered houses, some of them among the high moorlands near the sources of the river Yeo. Sir Robert Geo. Throckmorton, Bart., is lord of the manor, and owner of the manor-house, called *Knowstone Beaple*, which was so called from its ancient owners, and was long a seat of the Pollards. J. Handford, Esq., Mr. Joseph Hill, and many smaller owners, have estates in the parish. The manor of *Wadham* belonged to Ulf at Domesday Survey, and his descendants took the name of Wadham. *Shapcote* was long held by a family of its own name, and they sold it about 1770 to the Handfords. *Sir John Berry*, an eminent naval officer in the reign of Charles II., was born here at the Vicarage. The *Church* (St. Peter,) is a small ancient structure, with a tower and three bells, and was repaired four years ago. The *rectory* was appropriated to Hartland Abbey, but the great tithes have been mostly sold to the landowners. The *vicarage,* valued in K.B. at £26. 10s. 10d., with that of Molland annexed to it, is in the patronage of Sir R. G. Throckmorton, Bart., and incumbency of the Rev. John Froude, M.A., of East Anstey. The Rev. R. Pole, of Templeton, is the *curate.* The glebe (54A.) and the thatched Vicarage House, are let to a farmer. The vicarial tithes of this parish were commuted in 1842, for £301, and those of Molland for £339 per annum. The poor have £3. 8s. a year out of Edgerley and Bowden estates, left by H. Brooke and others, and the interest of £40 given by various donors.

Bucknell Jacob, maltster and vict., Fox and Hounds	BLACKSMITHS.	FARMERS.
	Elston Benj.	Bray James
Cutcliffe Chas. Newell, surgeon	Elston Wm.	Bray Thos. *East*
Follett Wm. vict. William IV.	Hill Michael	*Kidland*
Hodge Philip and James, carpenters	BOOT&SHOE MKS.	Bray Wm. *Ford*
Moore Misses M. and E. *Estacott*	Boundy James	Buckingham Jno.
Snow John, corn miller	Hill Wm.	*Oulaborough*
Snow Thomas, vict. Mason's Arms	Snow James	

Bucknell John,
  Beaple Barton
Bucknell Robert
Bucknell Wm.
Courtenay Geo. &
  Rd., *Wadham*
Fisher James
Fisher Samuel
Fisher Wm. *Hill*
Follett William,
  Brownsford
Follett W.*Indylk.*
Hill Jph., gent.,
  Moortown

Hill Ths. *Hapson*
Lovern Thomas
Luxton Henry
Mildon Edward
Mogford John,
  Shapcote
Shapland John
Stone Rt. *Weston*
Stone Thomas
Tarr Eliz. *White-
  moor*
Tarr James
Thorne Rd. *Kents*
Tidball Gregory

Webber James
Woodbury Wm.,
  West Kidland
MASONS, &c.
Davie Wm.
Snow Thomas
Steer Wm.
SCHOOLS.
Cockram Har.
Fisher Eliz.
Hernaman Ann
Partridge Mary
SHOPKEEPERS.
Hill Wm.

Snow Thomas
  TAILORS.
Fewin James
Shapcott Wm.
WHEELWRIGHTS.
Battens John
Cole James

POST to *South
Molton*, Mon. W.
Fri. & Sat., Jas.
Snow

LANDKEY is a village and parish, 2½ miles E.S.E. of Barnstaple, containing 774 souls, and 3510 acres of land. The trustees of the late Lord Rolle are lords of one manor, and the Duke of Bedford owns the other, which was anciently held by the Beaples, and afterwards by the Lorings, but part of the parish belongs to Miss Budd and other proprietors. *Acland* is a farm belonging to Sir T. D. Acland, and was the original seat of his ancient family. The *Church* (Trinity,) has a fine tower and six bells, and contains several monuments, one of which has recumbent effigies of Sir Arthur Acland and his lady, who died in 1610. There was formerly a Chapel of St. Mary at Herford. The Dean of Exeter is appropriator of the tithes and patron of the *perpetual curacy*, rated in K.B. at £20, and in 1831 at £179, with that of Swimbridge annexed to it, in the incumbency of the Rev. John Russell. The tithes were commuted in 1846 for £450. After the death of the present Dean, they will pass to the Ecclesiastical Commissioners. The *Wesleyans* have a chapel here. The *Parish Land and Houses* have been vested for the poor from an early period, and are worth about £60, but are let for only £36. 18s. 7½d. per annum, in consideration of fines paid by the lessees. Out of the income £8 is applied in aid of the school, and the rest is divided among the poor, together with the interest of £100, which arose from fines and gifts. The poor have also the following yearly sums:—52s. left by *Sir John Acland* in 1616; 26s. left by *Hugh Acland* in 1620; 52s. left by *Frances Bear* in 1730; and 40s. left by *Rd. Squire* in 1735.

Cook Thos. & Lewis Ann, shopkprs
Gaydon Wm. & Dallin Geo. smiths
Smyth Henry, shoemaker
BEERHOUSES.
Darch Wm.
Davey Wm.
Hoar Samuel

Kemp Wm.
FARMERS.
Bell George
Blake Jno.*Acland*

Bryant Pp. *Pill*
Bryant Thomas
Buckingham Ths.
Buckingham W.
Buckingham William, jun
Ching John

Crocker John
Gammon Thos.
Jones Ann
Pugsley G. *Herfd*
Smith John
Tucker Richard
Vickery Richard

MOLLAND is an irregularly built village, at the foot and on the side of a bold acclivity, 7 miles E.N.E. of South Molton, and W. of Dulverton; and its large parish contains 550 souls, and 6168 acres of land, including about 2275 acres of open common and moorland, rising in lofty hills between and near the sources of the river Yeo and the Duns Brook, the latter of which divides it from Somersetshire. There is a *copper mine* here, but it has been closed during the last three years. Sir Robert George Throckmorton, Bart., owns nearly all the parish, and is lord of the manor of *Molland Bottreaux*, anciently held by the Bottreaux family, and afterwards by the Hungerfords, whose heiress carried it in marriage to a younger

branch of the Courtenays, who were seated here till 1732, when their heiress brought it to the Throckmortons. The Bottreaux family and succeeding owners had a mansion and park at West Molland. The manor house of *Molland Champeaux,* or *Champion,* was long the seat of the Columbs, and afterwards of the Courtenays. These fine old mansions are now occupied by *Messrs. James and John Quartly,* who are noted for their fine breed of North Devon cattle, for which they have obtained many prizes. The parish has much fine grass land, suitable for breeding, though the soil is generally thin, and rests upon rock. The *Church* (St. Mary,) is a handsome structure, in the perpendicular style, with a tower and four bells. It contains several neat monuments, belonging to the Courtenay and other families. The *rectorial tithes* were given by Wm. Bottreaux to Hartland Abbey, and after the dissolution they passed to the Courtenays. In 1721, they were vested in trust by *Thos. Clarke,* for the support of a *lecturer* (or *curate,)* and that office is now filled by the Rev. Joshua Bawden, B.A., of South Molton. The *vicarage* is consolidated with that of Knowstone, as noticed at page 607. The tithes of this parish were commuted in 1841, the rectorial for £99, and the vicarial for £339 per annum. West Molland farm is tithe-free. The above-named Thos. Clarke left two houses, and 15A. of land, called Leddons, for the relief of the poor and schooling poor children, and they are now let for about £20 a year. The poor have also the interest of £33. 10s., left by several donors.

Bale George, vict. London Inn
Dart Wm. vict. New Inn
Frost Wm. gentleman
Gough Edward, land agent to Sir R. G. Throckmorton, *Money Hole*
Milton Wm. miller, *Wade Mill*
Pook James and John, thatchers
Venn Wm. Palmer, miller, *Bottreaux*

FARMERS.
Baker Henry, *Abbot's Park*
Baker James ‖ Brewer James
Bucknell James, *Brimley*
Cockram George, *Little Woods*
Cockram Francis ‖ Cole John
Cole John, jun., *West Bommer*
Elworthy George Hector, *Beere*
Elworthy John, *Gourte*
Fisher John, *Brimblecombe*
Halse John Courtenay, *Pulworthy*
Halse Lewis Courtenay, *Bowchurch*
Halse Philip, *West Lee*
Halse Thos. ‖ Maunder Wm.
Hancock Thomas, *Great Woods*

Mogridge Richard, *Copp Hall*
Moore Robert, *Lower hill*
Pincombe John (butcher,) *Cuckoo*
Quartly James, *West Molland Hs*
Quartly John, *Great Champion*

BLACKSMITHS.
Dart John
Dart Wm.

CARPENTERS.
Baker John
Bale George
Beer John
Greenslade Hh.
Parkin James

DRESSMAKERS.
Greenslade Fs.
Mogridge Mary
Vicary Harriet

MASONS.
Ayre George
Snow John

SHOEMAKERS.
Chapple Robert

Clatworthy Wm.
Gardener John

SHOPKEEPERS.
Kingsland Jas.
Maunder Daniel

TAILORS.
Moore Edward
Pook Pp. & Thos.

WHEELWRIGHTS.
Baker Wm.
Mogford John
Pincombe Thos.

FOOT - POST *to S. Molton, Mon. Wed. and Fri.* Dalbridge Thos.

NORTH MOLTON is a large village on the bold western acclivity of the river Mole, 3½ miles N. by E. of South Molton. It consists chiefly of irregularly built thatched houses, and its extensive parish comprises 2121 inhabitants, and 14,351 acres of land, including more than 2300 acres of commons, most of which are now being enclosed. This large parish extends about 5 miles N. and N.E. of the village, to the sources of the Mole and Duns Brook, among the lofty hills on the borders of Somersetshire and Exmoor Forest. It includes the hamlets, &c., of *Heasley, Ben-Twitchen, Hunston, Walscott, Upcott, Flitton,* and many scattered farmhouses. About ten years ago, a very rich *copper mine* was discovered in

the northern part of the parish, called "*Prince Albert's Mine,*" and containing a mixture of *gold.* The ore is of the purest kind, in large bunches, and pieces of gold of some size have been occasionally found. An old copper mine which had been closed many years was re-opened in 1813, but was soon abandoned; but there are now two mines working in the parish. There is a woollen mill at *Heasley,* and the village has two *cattle fairs,* on the Wednesday after May 12th, and the last Wednesday in October. It had formerly a weekly market and a fair on All Saints' day, granted in 1270 to Roger le Zouch, whose family obtained the manor from King John, and are said to have had a castellated mansion here, the remains of which were to be seen till the middle of last century. A co-heiress of the Zouch family brought the manor to the St. Maurs, and it passed with a co-heiress of the latter to the Bampfyldes. The present owner, the Right Hon. Sir G. W. Bampfylde, was created *Baron Poltimore* in 1831, as noticed at page 201, and resides occasionally at *Court Hall,* a fine old mansion, which was enlarged and much improved about fifteen years ago, and stands in a well-wooded park, east of the church. His Lordship is also owner of *Court House,* a large ancient mansion, finely mantled with ivy, and formerly belonging to the Earl of Morley. Lord Poltimore owns most of the parish; and Court Hall, being in the neighbourhood of Exmoor Forest, was long occupied by his family as a hunting seat; and the few wild red deer which still linger in that mountainous region, render it a desirable abode for the lovers of the chase. A court leet and baron is held twice a year, and the jury are popularly called the council, and the foreman the mayor. The *Church* (All Saints,) is a fine antique structure, with a tower containing six bells, and rising to the height of 100 feet. It stands on a commanding eminence, and the nave and chancel are separated by a richly-carved screen. The whole fabric was thoroughly repaired, cleansed, and beautified in 1849, when two beautiful stained glass windows were inserted, and a new organ erected, at the expense of Lord Poltimore and a parochial rate. It contains several monuments belonging to the Bampfylde and other families, and was appropriated by Alan le Zouch, in 1313, to the monastery of Lilleshull, in Shropshire. Lord Poltimore is now impropriator of the rectory and patron of the *vicarage,* valued in K.B. at £16. 16s. 1d., and in 1831 at £125, with the curacy of Twitchen annexed to it. The Rev. Wm. Burdett, M.A., is the incumbent, and has here 3A. 1R. 16P. of glebe. The Vicarage House was rebuilt after being destroyed by fire in 1801. The living received four augmentations from Queen Anne's Bounty in 1789, 1798, and 1825. All the tithes were commuted in 1842 for £1292. 17s. per annum. Here are two *chapels* belonging to Wesleyans and Independents. There were formerly episcopal chapels at South Radworthy, Holywell, and Ben-Twitchen, in this parish. The *Church Lands* and 21 houses, &c., have been vested for the repairs of the church from an early period, and are worth about £80, but are let for only about £30 a year, in consideration of fines. Here is an old *Almshouse* for six poor parishioners, founded by one of the ancestors of the Earl of Morley, who endowed it with a yearly rent-charge of £5. 4s. The *school and poor* have the dividends of £69. 18s. 2d. three per cent. consols, given by Grace Moorman; and the interest of £50, left by Wm. Moorman in 1780. The *poor* have £5. 4s. yearly out of Nogel's estate, left by Sir Amias Bampfylde in 1625, and the interest of £63. 10s., left by various donors. The *National School* was built about nine years ago; and here are two schools supported by Lady Poltimore. The parish abounds in *limestone,* and is noted for its fine breed of *North Devon cattle,* for which Mr. Davy, of Flitton, and Mr. Merson, of Brinsworthy farm, are highly celebrated. The

POST-OFFICE *is at Mrs. Mary Smith's, and letters are despatched to South Molton at ¼ before 4 in the afternoon.*

LORD POLTIMORE, *Court Hall*, (and Poltimore House, &c.)
Baker John, police officer
Bird John, parish clerk
Burdett Rev Wm., M.A. *Vicarage*
Cook Chas. rope mkr. *Molland cross*
Crook John, thatcher
Dobbs Francis, auctioneer
Fezzey Thos. copper mine agent
Frayne Jas. surveyor of highways
Holloway Rt. sen. & jun. and Peter, thatchers
Hutchings Wm. assistant-overseer
Ley Richard, surgeon
Lyddon Mr Thos. || Hodge Mrs My.
Maunder Edwin, woolstapler and woollen mfr. *Heasley Mill*
Passmore Fras. Burdett, saddler
Slader Mr Thos. || Shapland Richd.
Stranger Rd. land agent, *Court Hs*
Southcomb Mr Jas. || Wilson Andw.
Wright Rev T. H. curate, *Combshd*

FARMERS.
Abbott Roger || Abbott Robert
Avery Charles Davy, North Lee
Avery Wm., North Heasley
Baker John || Bright John
Chapple Robert || Crang John
Collard Royal || Crocombe Richd.
Davy James, *Flitton*
Darch Thomas || Dinsey John
Downs Thomas || Dunn Joseph
Frayne Peter || Frayne Richard
Fry John, Little Heasley
Gibbs Wm., *Higher Fyldon*
Headon Richard || Hill Elias
Hutchings Wm. || Huxtable Thos.
Jarman John || Jarman Wm.
Jutsum Richard || Lake Charles
Lewis John || Ley Nicholas
Lock Wm. & Rd., *South Radworthy*
Loosemore Wm. || Maunder Edw.
Luxton Richard, Lower Fyldon
Merson Richard, *Brinsworthy*
Newton Richard, *Rapscott*
Norrish John, *Stitchpool*
Passmore John, *Higher Fyldon*
Passmore John, *Higher Millbrook*
Passmore Wm. || Parkin Wm.
Purchase Nichls. sen. and jun. and Wm., South Radworthy
Sanders Thos. & Wm. || Rew Thos.
Shapland Ann and Grace, *Walscott*

Shapland George, *Oakford*
Shapland John Terrell, *Popham*
Shapland Richard, *Yardgate*
Shapland Wm. Terrell, *Watscott*
Slader Peter and Wm., *Barton*
Slader Wm., *Eworthy*
Slader Wm. Shapland, *Marsh*
Slader Wm., *Hunnawins*
Smith James || Smith John
Southcomb John, *Yardgate*
Stoneman Richard, Rapscott
Stranger Robert, *Hunston*
Thorne John, *North Radworthy*
Thorne Jno. & Hy., North Heasley
Thorne Jacob & Wm., Ben-Twitchen
Thorne Richd. || Treble James
Trick Walter || Tucker George
Veysey John || Webber John
Way Wm., *Heasley Mills*
Westcott Henry, *West Park*
Westcott John, *South Lee*
Westcott John, Pronsley
Westcott Wm. & Margt., Old House
Westcott Wm., Combshead
Westcott Wm. || Westcott George
Westcott Wm., Lambscombe
Williams Wm. || Yendell Joseph
Yendell Benjamin, Nadrid

INNS & TAVERNS.
Castle, Wm. Jones
King's Arms, Wm. Veysey
Poltimore Arms, John Avery
Swan, Robert Rendle
Somerset Inn, Philip Frayne

BAKERS.
Abbott Roger
Bawden Peter
Bendle Thomas
Cockings John
Collard Hanh.
Lock Mary
Lyddon My. Ann
Treble James
Webber Wm.

BEERHOUSES.
Hill Nicholas
Jones Cphr.
Way Wm.
Webber Martin

BLACKSMITHS.
Bawden Henry, *Heasley*
Bird Peter

Bird Thomas
Dinner John
Gough Wm.
Jones Wm.
Smith John

BUTCHERS.
Moore John
Veysey Wm.

CARPENTERS.
Bawden Hugh
Bird Wm.
Bird Wm. jun
Burgess Hy.
Gillard John
Jarman John
Lock Chpr.
Lock Thomas
Rendle John
Thorne Hy. & Jno.

Westcott Wm.
COOPERS.
Crocombe Jas.
Mole William, *Heasley*
CORN MILLERS.
Baker William, *Heasley*
Ley Nicholas
Squire Rd. *Flitton*
COWKEEPERS.
Bird Robert
Cole Maria
Jarman John
Shapland Nichls.
MALTSTERS.
Avery John
Stoneman John
Veysey Wm.
MASONS.
Bawden Peter
Crang and Lock
Curtis Michael

Gould James
Lock Daniel
Roberts John
Roberts Wm.
MILLINERS.
Abbott Mary
Burgess Ann
Collard Eliz.
Curtis P. and E.
Hutchings Eliz.
Lang Eliz.
Lock Sar. & A.
Moore Mary
Slader My. Ann
Smith Jane
Vickery Harriet
PLUMBERS, &c.
Rendle Robert
Rendle Wm.
SHOEMAKERS.
Bird John
Hodge Wm.
Howe Wm.

Passmore Rd.
Smyth Wm.
Thorne Wm.
Westcott James
SCHOOLS.
Curtis Prscla.
Gould Mary
Passmore Mgt.
Thorne Wm.
SHOPKEEPERS.
Abbott Mary
Baker Wm.
Bird Robert
Bird Wm.
Burgess Hy.
Curtis Michael
Dinner John
Frayne John
Frayne Jno. jun
Huxtable Edmd.
Moore John
Passmore F. & B.

Westcott Hy.
TAILORS.
Burgess John
Passmore Edmd.
Webber Wm.
Westcott Hy.
TAL. CHANDLERS.
Bird Wm.
Burgess Hy.
Charley James
Curtis Michael
WHEELWRIGHTS.
Bird Wm. jun.
Kerslake John
Lang Thomas
Rendle John
Smith John

CARRIER.
Thomas Prescott to Exeter & S. Molton, Mon. and Thursday

SOUTH MOLTON is a *municipal borough*, and well-built *market town*, pleasantly situated on the bold western acclivity of the valley of the river Mole, 11 miles E.S.E. of Barnstaple, 18 N.W. by W. of Tiverton, 16 miles W. by S. of Dulverton, 28 miles N.W. by N. of Exeter, and 181 W. by S. of London. It gives name to a *deanery, hundred, union, county court district, petty sessional division*, and *polling district;* and is the *chief place of election* for the parliamentary representatives of the Northern Division of Devon. It is well supplied with pure soft spring *water*, and has *gas works*, erected in 1836, at the cost of £2200, raised in £10 shares. The principal streets are spacious and well paved, and contain several good inns and neat public buildings, and many handsome and well stocked shops. Its PARISH comprises 6264 acres of land, many scattered farm-houses, the hamlets of *Shallowford, High Bray*, and *Stag's Head;* and the estates of *Bremridge, Freynstone, Hache, North-Aller, Honiton Barton*, &c., extending more than two miles west, north, and south of the town. The soil is generally fertile and well cultivated, and rises in bold undulations from the river Mole on the east, and the Bray on the west. The Mole, from which the town has its name, gives motion to several woollen and corn mills, and is here crossed by a good bridge of one arch, erected after the old one had been destroyed by a flood, in 1841. The parish had 2753 inhabitants in 1801; 2739 in 1811; 3314 in 1821; 3826 in 1831; and 4274 in 1841; but they have since increased to about 4800. The *manor* of South Molton was part of the ancient demesne of the Crown; but in the reign of Edward I., it was held by Lord Martin, under the Earl of Gloucester, by the service of finding a bow and three arrows to attend the Earl when he went a hunting in Gower. It afterwards passed to the Lords Audley, the Dukes of

of Exeter, and the Whitmore and Squier families. In 1700, it was purchased of the latter by the Corporation, who are still lords of the manor; but most of the soil belongs to Earl Fortescue, Sir T. D. Acland, Bart., and many smaller free and leaseholders. The town sent burgesses to parliament in the 13th of Edward I., but it never enjoyed that privilege afterwards. It was incorporated in 1590, by a *charter* of the 32nd of Elizabeth, and this charter was confirmed by one of the 36th of Charles II. The borough comprises the whole parish; and under these charters, the corporation consisted of a mayor, high steward, recorder, and 18 capital burgesses, and an indefinite number of freemen, with a town clerk and other officers, and a court of record and quarter and petty sessions. Under the Municipal Act of 1835, the town council now consists of a mayor, four aldermen, and twelve councillors; and since that year, the borough has petitioned for and obtained a commission of the peace. The style of the Corporation is, the "Mayor and Burgesses of the Borough and Parish of South Molton, in the County of Devon." The income of the borough, in 1840, was £1944. 6s. 8¾d., arising chiefly from rents, tolls, dues, and other manorial profits. Its expenditure in the same year amounted to £2411, the principal items of which were, £987 for renewal of leases; £412 for public works, repairs, &c.; £180, stipends; £98, salaries; £141, lighting and cleansing; £77, charities; and £64 for police and constables. The borough is exempt from county rates, except in cases of prosecution for capital offences. It has *quarter sessions* at the usual periods, and petty sessions weekly, or when required. *Petty Sessions* are also held here on the first Monday of every month, by the magistrates of South Molton Division, to whom Messrs. Pearse, Son, and Crosse are clerks. The *County Court for South Molton District* is held here on the Thursday after the first Monday of every month, and Mr. James Pearse is the *clerk*, and John Manning the *high bailiff*. Its jurisdiction extends to all the 29 parishes of South Molton Union, except Rackenford. (See page 603.) These courts are held at the GUILDHALL, a handsome building of Portland stone, on the south side of Broad street, projecting on arched pillars over the causeway, and having a commodious court room, a council room, and a large and elegant assembly room, where balls, banquets, &c., are occasionally held. The building is crowned by a turret and cupola, containing a bell and clock. The *Borough Gaol*, in East street, was built about twelve years ago, at the cost of about £2000, and comprises dwellings for the gaoler and superintendent of police, and six cells, two large day rooms, and an airing yard for the prisoners. The following are the present Town Council, Borough Magistrates, &c. :—

Mayor, Thomas Brown, Esq. ‖ *Recorder*, W. M. Praed, Esq.
High Steward, Earl Fortescue.
Borough Justices, Earl Fortescue, Viscount Ebrington, and H. J. N. Bawden, Wm. Binford, and Wm. Hole, Esqrs.
Aldermen, Wm. Flexman, Wm. Tapp, Jas. Maunder, and P. Tapp.
Councillors, Messrs. W. G. Smyth, J. E. J. Riccard, J. E. Cutcliffe, John

White, Wm. Binford, Thomas Brown, John Brown, John Tanner, F. M.
Hitchcock, E. J. Riccard, Wm. Thorne, and E. J. Riccard, M.D.
Town Clerk and Clerk to the Justices, J. G. Pearse.
Clerk of the Peace, R. M. Riccard. ‖ *Treasurer,* B. Dunn.
Coroner, James Flexman. ‖ *Deputy-Coroner,* J. T. Shapland.
Gaoler and Crier, Philip Widgery. ‖ *Police Superintendent,* W. H. Fisher.

South Molton was one of the places appointed as the see of a Suffragan
Bishop, by an act of the 26th of Henry VIII., but it did not long enjoy
that dignity. In 1357, Nicholas Fitz Martin, being then lord of the manor,
obtained a charter for a *market,* to be held here on Sunday, and a fair at the
festival of the Assumption of the Virgin Mary. The town has now a considerable market every Saturday, for corn, provisions, &c. The *Market
House,* built by the Corporation in 1810, is a square brick building, standing on pillars and arches. The upper room is used for lectures, concerts,
&c.; and corn, meat, &c., are sold in the basement story; but on Saturdays, the Broad street, or Market place, is lined with stalls of every description. Here are now two annual *fairs,* for cattle, &c., on the Wednesday before June 22nd, and the Wednesday after August 26th; and *great
cattle markets* on the Saturdays after Feb. 13th and March 15th, and the
Saturdays before April 23rd, August 1st, October 10th, and December 12th.
The town has several *wool combing* establishments, and was formerly noted
for the manufacture of serges, shalloons, and pelts. There is still one
large *woollen mill* in the parish, employing about 150 hands; and in the
neighbourhood are several other coarse woollen factories, and quarries of
limestone, flagstones, &c. In the north part of the parish is a *lead mine,*
which yields a considerable portion of silver. The *Church* (St. Mary,) is
a spacious and handsome structure, in the perpendicular style, with a lofty
tower containing eight bells. It was enlarged in 1833-'4, at the cost of
£1400, and has now room for 1500 hearers. The interior was cleansed and
beautified, and a new organ erected, in 1829, at the cost of about £600.
The stone pulpit is of great antiquity, and is richly carved and ornamented.
In the chancel and aisles are several handsome mural monuments, one of
which is in memory of Henry Kerslake and his wife and two sons, who were
burnt to death when their house was destroyed by fire, in 1749. According
to the parish register, Wm. Lake died here in 1754, at the advanced age of
104 years. In 1547, this church was given by Henry VIII. to the Dean
and Canons of Windsor, and they are still appropriators of the tithes and
rectorial glebe, (242A.,) and patrons of the *perpetual curacy,* valued in 1831
at £157, and now in the incumbency of the Rev. T. H. Maitland, M.A.,
who built a handsome Parsonage House about eight years ago. The tithes
were commuted in 1839 for £910 per annum, and are held on lease by the
Corporation. At *Honiton Barton,* about two miles from the town, is *Trinity
Chapel,* belonging to the Southcomb family. It was built in 1730, at the
cost of more than £500, by the Rev. Lewis Southcomb, on the site of an
ancient chapel. It is handsomely fitted up, and the founder endowed it
with £40 a year out of an estate in the parish, and directed that it should
never be made a sinecure; that the stipend should be paid every Lord's-
day; and that when service was omitted, the stipend should go towards the
repairs of the chapel, in which the founder and his father were both buried.
There are four chapels in the town belonging to dissenters. The *Independent Chapel* is a handsome fabric, erected in 1834, at the cost of about
£1000, on the site of the old one, which was built in 1700. The *Baptists*
had a congregation here before 1715; but their present chapel was built in
1843, at the cost of about £900, in the lancet Gothic style. The *Wesleyan
Chapel* was built in 1822, at the cost of about £600. The *Plymouth*

Brethren have a small chapel in South street; and there are in the town a few Mormonites and Bryanites, who meet at private houses. The *Rev. Samuel Badcock*, an eminent critic and divine, was born here in 1747, and was minister of the Independent Chapel, at Barnstaple, from 1770 till 1778, but afterwards conformed to the church, and was ordained by Bishop Ross. He and the late *Judge Buller* were educated at the FREE SCHOOL here, which was built, with a house for the master, in 1682, by *Hugh Squier*, who died in 1709, and bequeathed to the Corporation of South Molton, in trust for this school, and other charitable uses, Upcott farm, (52A.,) at Swimbridge, and the glebe and rectorial tithes of Northam. After paying reserved rent and fines to the Dean and Canons of Windsor, the Corporation derive from this property about £340 per annum. Pursuant to the founder's will, they apply yearly £10 to the support of the schoolmaster; and the rest of the clear income is divided into two equal shares, one of which is expended in repairing the *highways*, and the other is given to the *mayor*, to enable him to defray the expenses of his office. Besides the annuity of £40, the schoolmaster has about £18 a year from stock, money, and turnpike securities, derived from savings of income in former years. He teaches reading, writing, and arithmetic to 30 free scholars, and is allowed to take other day scholars and boarders. The BLUE COAT SCHOOL, in the Church-yard, was established by subscription, in 1711, and afterwards endowed by various donors with £400, of which £200 was given by *Eliz. Squier*, in 1734, and £100 by *Eliz. Northcote*, in 1742. It has received many subsequent benefactions, and its present endowment consists of £2515 new four per cent. stock. The two school rooms, with a house for the master and mistress, were provided by the Corporation. They receive £35 a year for teaching 36 boys and 15 girls, who are clothed in blue once a year. Formerly this charity clothed and educated 45 boys and 20 girls. Here is also a large NATIONAL SCHOOL, built by the Corporation in 1833-'4, at the cost of about £500, and attended by about 100 scholars. *Sunday Schools* are attached to the church and three of the chapels : and there are in the town various charitable and provident institutions; and among the latter is the *North Devon Annuitant Society*, and a branch of the *Devon and Exeter Savings' Bank*. In New road is a neat *Freemasons' Hall*, erected in 1846, at the cost of £450, by Lodge No. 610, which meets on the first Tuesday of every month. *South Molton Union* is already noticed at page 603.

CHARITIES.—By a decree of the Court of Chancery in the third of Charles I., it was determined that the Corporation should provide a *house of correction* for the borough, at their own expense, and should pay a yearly rent-charge of £12 out of the *Common Moor* (6A.,) to the overseers, for distribution among the poor. Two small tenements, left to the poor by *Jane Whittle*, in 1678, are now worth about £5 per annum. The poor of the parish, not residing here, have the interest of £130, derived from £100 left by *Henry Harewood*, in 1629. The resident poor have £12 a year from £200 left by *Eliz. Squier*, in 1734 ; and £100 left by *Wm. Hunt*, in 1642, and now vested in turnpike securities. They have also £12 a year from £300 left by *Mr. Rashleigh*, in 1615, and nine other donors, and now vested in the South Molton turnpike. These sums, and the dividends of £200 three per cent. stock, purchased with the gift of *Nathl. Sprigg*, in 1781, are distributed by the Corporation among the poor parishioners. For a weekly distribution of bread, they have an annuity of £2. 12s. from *Sir John Acland's Charity.* (See Exeter.) Out of the market tolls the poor have 27s. 6d. per annum, pursuant to the bequest of *Robert Brett*, in 1597 ; and about £2 a year from the gift of *Joan Webber*, in 1623. They have also the following *yearly doles,* viz., 20s., left by *Thomas Badcock*, in 1663 ; £2. 12s. left by *Agnes Badcock*, in 1641, out of 2A. 31P. of land ; 28s. from *Mrs. Courtenay's Gift;* £2 from £50 left by *Joseph Palmer*, in 1795 ; 8s. from £10 left by *Wm. Gould*, in 1801 ; £2. 5s. from £50 left by *Thomas Nott, Nicholas Palmer,* and *Joshua Hole;* and 30s. from £30 left by *Mary Jones*, in 1822. The CHARITY TRUSTEES appointed for this borough, under the Municipal Act, are Messrs. W. J. Tapp, Samuel Pearce, Thos. Cunningham, Thos. Brown, and Wm. Flexman.

SOUTH MOLTON DIRECTORY.

The POST-OFFICE is in East street, and Mr. John Thomas is the *post master.* Letters are despatched to London, Exeter, &c., 5 minutes before 6 evening; to the North at 11 morning; to Barnstaple, &c., at 10 minutes past 7 morning, and 35 minutes past 3 afternoon; and to Chulmleigh, &c., at 20 minutes past 7 morning. Letters are delivered at 8 morning and 6½ evening; and there are foot posts every morning to North Molton, Chittlehampton, Filleigh, &c. Money orders are granted and paid.

Allen Misses, Townsend
Anthony Mrs, Townsend
Avery William, thatcher, Back lane
Bawden Humphry John N., Esq., South street
Bawden Rev Joshua, B.A., lectrer. of Molland, East st
Binford Wm., Esq. Broad st
Burgess Frs., gent. Broad st
Burgess Mr John, Broad st
Chant Robert, purser to the *Exmoor Wheal Eliza Copper Mine,* King street
Chapple W., par.clk., East st
Chapple Mrs A., Brnstpl st
Clarke Rev Theophilus, curate, Ivy Cottage
Cock John, brickmaker, &c., Rose Cottage
Cole Jas., relvg. officer, and registrar, Adelaide place
Comins J. & Co., wood turners, sawyers, &c., Molebridge; h South street
Cotty John, gas manager
Crosse Rt. Jennings, Esq., solr., Broad street
Cunningham Thomas, gent. Barnstaple street
Cutcliffe Chas. Jno., gent. Alpha Cotg., Barnstpl. st
Dee Mrs Ann, East street
Dunn Mr John, Church ln
Elworthy Mrs M., South st
Fisher W. Hy., police supt.
Froude Mrs F., South street
Furse Mrs Eliz., East street
Galliford John, clk. East st
Giles Rev Thos., (Indpt.)
Gillard G., poulterer, East st
Gould Josh., organist, East st
Hamilton S., matron, *Wkhs*
Hargreaves Rev Jas., (Wes)
Hartnoll Mr P., East street
Haskings Wm., colt breaker, Back lane
Hearn Jas., farrier, Tnsd
Hill Jas., sergt. major N. D.Y., (late of 10th Royal Hussars,) Albert place
Hill Mr Wm., Madder ln
Hitchcock, Maunder and Hitchcock, woollen mfrs. and merchants, Higher Mole Mills
Hitchcock Frs. Maunder, & Wm. Maunder, mfrs.; house East street
Hodgkin Mrs Chtte., Sth. st
Hole Wm. Esq. Churchyard
Holmes Jas., clk., Albert pl
Huxtable Mrs Eliz., Sth. st

Jones Mrs Eliz., East st
Jones R., superv., Mtplr.ctg
Kay Geo. Ptr., excise, Sth st
Kemp Miss Jane, Duke st
Leatherby Robert, turner, Mole bridge
Leatherby Wm., Prsng. ln
Lethbridge Wm., marine store dlr., East street
Leach Peter, veterinary surgeon, South street
Lyon Pasquell, jeweller, &c. Broad street
Maitland Rev Thos. H., M.A. incbt., Parsonage
Manley Mrs My., South st
Manning John, sheriff's officer, and high bailiff of County Court, Church ln
Maunder Jas., Esq, Duke st
Merson Mr Wm., East st
Mills Mr John, New road
Moseley Mr Wm., Duke st
Nott Mrs Mary, East st
Oram Wm., clk., Albert pl
Paramore Mrs Eliz., East st
Passmore Rev H., East st
Pearce Saml. gent. South st
Pearce Mrs Sarah, East st
Pearse James, Esq., solr. & clerk of County Court, Broad street
Pearse John Gilberd, solr., town clerk, and clerk to magistrates, Broom House
Radley Mrs Mary, Tnsnd
Redler T., gov. of Workhs.
Riccard Jas. Edw. Jackson, Esq. solr. and union clk., Churchyard
Riccard Russell Martyn, solr., (clk. of peace for the Borough,) East street
Sanders Jas. Hooper, woolstapler and fellmonger, South street
Shipley Mrs My., Barstpl. st.
Smith Mrs Grace, East st
Southcomb Geo., road survr. & toll colr., Mill ln. gate
Southcomb L., gent. East st
Southcomb Mrs S., East st
Spencer Mrs Eliz., East st
Sutch Rev James, (Wes.) South street
Tanner Misses, Townsend
Tapp Mr Philip and Mrs, Townsend
Tapp Joanna, worsted dlr., East street
Tapp Wm. Jones, accountant, East street
Tepper Mrs, East street

Tepper Wm., overs., Sth. st
Thorne Mary, pawnbroker, South street
Toms Mrs Mary, East st
Trant Mr Wm., South st
Turner Mrs Eliza, Duke st
Venn John, excise, Albert pl
Vile James, marine store dlr., South street
Webb Mr James, East st
Whitford Capt. Wm. Hall, inspecting agent for South Molton silver and lead mine, and Exmoor Wheal Eliza copper mine, Tnsnd
Widgery John, gent. Brd. st
Widgery Pp., gaoler, &c

ACADEMIES.
*(Marked * take Boarders.)*
Blue Coat School, John and Ann Warren
* *Free School,* John Honey, East street
Hulland Mary, South st
Kingsland Mary A., East st
Maire Eliz., Back lane
National School, Letitia Neil, Back lane
Pearce Mrs & Miss, East st
* Rossiter Wm., East street
* Saunders Sarah, East st
* Stanbury Eliza, Bnstpl. st
Ward Sarah, South street
Webber Jno. & My., South st

ATTORNEYS.
Gillard Edw. K., Church ln
Pearse, Son & Crosse, (clks. to magistrates, and proctors,) Broad street
Riccard & Son, (& proctors,) Churchyard
Shapland John Terrell, (dep. coroner,) Broad street

AUCTIONEERS.
Manning Andw., Broad st
Manning John, Church ln

BAKERS.
Bowden John, Cook's cross
Bowden Wm., Cook's cross
Chapple John, East street
Clark Richard, Barnstpl. st
Hacche John, South street
Harris John, Barnstaple st
Kingdon Oliver, East street
Kingdon Wm., East street
Latey James, East street
Marsden Thos, East street
Thomas James, East street
Vernon John, South street
Vicary Thomas, Townsend
Webb John, South street

BANKS.
National & Provincial Bank of England,(draw on London & Westminster,) Jno. Longworth Dames, mngr. Broad street
Savings' Bank, Edward K. Gillard, sec., Church ln

BASKET MAKERS.
Berry Geo., East street
Bulled John, Cook's cross
Kingsland Robt., Townsend
BLACK & W. SMITHS.
Cardar Wm., South street
Comins James, King street
Dockings Wm., Clapry.Mill
Grattan John, Hill
Griffiths Chas., Broad st
Harris John, Back lane
Harris Wm., South street
Holmes John, Barnstaple st
Moore Richard, South st
Sage James, East street
Sutton Daniel, Parsonage ln
Tepper Thos., Duke street

BOOKSELLERS, &c.
Dunn Bickham, Broad st
Searle George, Broad street
Tepper Amos, Broad street
BOOT & SHOE MKRS.
Adams John, Duke street
Aggott James, South street
Badcock G., Clappery Mill
Bouchier J., Barnstaple st
Cock George, King street
Drake Thos., East street
Eastmond Wm., East st
Hobbs George, East street
Hulland Wm. T., South st
Huxtable Wm., East street
Mairs Thomas, East street
Mairs John, Barnstaple st
Mole John, East street
Nott John, Cook's cross
Nutt Wm., East street
Thomas John, East street
Widgery Wm., New road
Williams John, Cook's cross
BUTCHERS.
Bowden Wm., Adelaide pl
Bright James, New road
Cock George, South street
Cole Wm., East street
Dunn Robert, Townsend
Eastmond John, East st
Fuke Richard, East street
Harris Wm. G., Duke st
Hill Edw., Steppa lane
Skinner Wm., Knight'sBray
Veysey John, South street
CABINET MAKERS.
Hacche John, Cook's cross
Kelly Richard, East st
Kingdon Oliver, South st
Mountjoy Wm., King st
Snow Robert, King street
CARPENTERS, &c.
(* are Builders.)
* Baker Henry, Duke street
† Baker Thomas, Back ln

* Cock Jno., Rose ctg.,Sth.st
Crispin George, Mill lane
Hacche John, Cook's cross
Hacche John, jun. South st
* Smith John, South street
CHEMISTS & DRUGTS.
Attwater A. H., Broad st
Dunn Henry, Broad street
Paige John A., South street
Tanner John, Broad street
COAL DEALERS.
Bentley J. M., Barnstpl. st
Gill Wm., Townsend
Kingdon Oliver, Mill lane
Lewis Thos., Cook's cross
Lewis Wm., East street
CONFECTIONERS.
Fuke Simon, Cook's cross
Latey James, East street
Marsden Thomas, East st
Oram Wm., East street
COOPERS.
Collacott Joshua, East st
Collacott John, Back lane
Leatherby Wm., (& turner) Parsonage lane
CORN MILLERS.
Haskings Joseph, *Bonner's*
Redler John, *Mole mills*
Redler Ts. & Geo. *Hayne's*
CURRIERS.
Bentley Jas. M.,Barnstpl.st
Cole George, Queen street
Reed Wm., East street
Vernon John, South street
FARMERS.
Barnes Wm. *North Cockram*
Buckingham Jno.*Clotworthy*
Burgess Wm. *South Aller*
Bussell Hy. *Daws Blackpl*
Chapple Jas.,Neilds Town
Clark Rd., Barnstaple st
Cridge Richard, Rock
Dale Wm., East street
Densem John, *Townhouse*
Dunn Wm., South street
Dyer Edw., North Woodhs
Eastmond John, East street
Elworthy John, *Freynston*
Elworthy J. *Honiton Barton*
Elworthy John, *Hernamans*
Elworthy Wm.,Sth.Woodhs
Fry Wm., East street
Hancock Robt. *South Hill*
Hancock Wm., Lwr. Blkpl
Harris Eliz. *East Hache*
Lock Mary, *Ford*
Manning Chas., West Hill
Manning Henry, Stone and Combrew
Perryman Wm. *Ford Down*
Phillips Thomas, Coombe
Shapland Geo. *Freynston*
Shapland James, *Snurridge*
Skinner John, *Bremridge*
Skinner John, Meeth
Skinner John Alexander, North Aller
Skinner Henry, West Ford
Skinner Wm. *Knigh's Bray*
Smith Henry, Mill lane

Smith Wm. *W. Clotworthy*
Trix Wm. sen. & jun. *Great Hele*
Tucker John, Ley
Widgery John, Dowerlands
Winnacott John, South st
Yendell Saml, *Mid. Blkpool*
FIRE & LIFE OFFICES.
Atlas, Jno. T.Shapland,B.st
Clerical,Medical,&General, John Gallaford, East st
County Fire and Provident Life, John Comins
English & Scottish Law Life & Loan, Geo. Searle
Freemasons', J. T.Shapland
General, Rt. Sawtell, B. st
Globe, Rd. Tepper, Broad st
Legal & Coml., Alex. H. Attwater
Norwich Union, Jas. E. J. Riccard
Phœnix, George Searle
Palladium, Cstn. Saunders
Royal Exchange,Jno.Cock
Royal Farmer's, B. Dunn
Sun, Wm. Jones Tapp
West of England, Sl.Pearce
GARDENERS, &c.
Leatherby John, Adelaide pl
Rowland Ts., Barnstaple st
Sage Wm. Lucas, Brnstpl.st
Sanders Jas. H., South st
Tapp Joanna, East street
Vernon John, East street
Vicary Thomas, Townsend
GLOVERS.
Kingdon Sarah, South st
SandersJas.Hooper,Southst
GROCERS& TEA DLRS.
Buckingham Ts., Broad st
Chant Robert, Kingstreet
Dakin John, South street
Dale Ann, Broad street
Deagon Wm., Queen street
Hancock Josias, East st
Kingdon Abm., Broad st
Latey James, East street
Radley James, South street
Sheppard Rd., East street
Smith John, South street
Tanner John, Broad street
Vernon Henry, South street
HAIRDRESSERS.
Burgess Francis, Broad st
Chapple Thomas, Broad st
Dunn John, King street
Quick John, East street
HAT MANUFACTRS.
Aggott Henry, Barnstpl. st
Doherty Susan, East street
Pearce Wm., East street
INNS & TAVERNS.
Anchor, Geo. Snow, South st
Barnstaple Inn, My.Mountjoy, Barnstaple street
Exeter Inn, Wm. Vickery, South street
FortescueArms, John Bater, Broad street
George, *(posting,)* Christian Saunders, Broad street

Golden Lion,Jno.Fry, Sth.st
Half Moon, Ann Hill, Sth.st
Hare & Hounds, Thomas
  Barrow, East street
King's Arms, Wm. Thorne,
  King street
New Inn, Philip Baker,
  South street
North Country Inn, James
  Lake, Townsend
Red Cow,W. Aggott, East st
Red Lion, John Graddon,
  Barnstaple street
Ring of Bells, Wm. Gaydon
  Harris, Duke street
Rose & Crown, Hy. Searle,
  South street
Star, Eliz. Dunn, Broad st
Tiverton Inn, John Vernon,
  East street
Town Arms, Jas. Mountjoy,
  East street
Unicorn, Geo. Cole, Queen st

BEERHOUSES.

Dockings John, Cook's cross
Fry Wm., East street
Knill Charles, Cook's cross
Leatherby John, Steppa ln
Osmond John, Back lane
Prescott John, East street
Tout James, Townsend
Wotton Abm., East street

**IRONMONGERS, BRA-
ZIERS, &c.**

Breayley Wm.,Barnstpl.st
Comins James, King street
Comins John, South street
Griffiths Charles, Broad st
Powell Lewis & Son, Sth. st
Thorne Wm., Broad street
Trawin Henry, East street

LIME BURNERS.

Burgess Wm *South Aller*
Cridge Richard, *Rock*

LINEN & WLN.DRAPRS

Brown John, Broad street
Farley John, Broad street
Haydon John, Broad st
Hodge Thomas, Broad st
Radley James, South street
Sawtell Robert, Broad st
Trawin Mary, East street
Webber Mary, King street
White John, East street
Wilmets Wm., East street

MALTSTERS.

Cole George, Queen street
Hooper Grace, East street
Sanders James, East street
Shapland Wm., Duke st
Skinner John & Alexander,
  North Aller
Winnacott John, South st

MASONS.

Bowden Wm., Cook's cross
Collacott Wm., Back lane
Collacott Wm , Churchyard
Gloyn John, East street
Kingdon Wm., East street
Nott John, East street
Phillips Robert, Adelaide pl

Shapcott Henry, Alfred pl
Thomas John, Churchyard
Thomas Wm., Back lane

MILLINERS, &c.

Allen Mary, South street
Carter Jane, South street
Greenslade Eliz., East st
Griffiths Ann, Broad street
Harris Joanna, East st
Hill Jane, Townsend
Holloway Maria, Queen st
Hulland Mary, Cock's yard
Huxtable Sarah, South st
Macey Mary, Cock's yard
Manley & Lockyer, East st
Marsh Eliz., Queen street
Matthews Eliz.,Cook's cross
Mole Eliz., East street
Mole Maria, South street
Nutt Elizabeth, South st
Rowcliffe My. Ann, Broad st
Shapland Eliz., Duke st
Tapp Grace, Duke street
Webb Harriet, East street

**PAINTERS, PLUMBRS.,
& GLAZIERS.**

Comins John, South street
Gillard George, East street
Powell Lewis & Son, Sth. st
Prescott John, East street
Trawin Henry, East street

PHYSICIANS.

Riccard Edward Jackson,
  East street
Thorne James Wilkins,
  Broad street

ROPE & TWINE MKRS.

Bartlett Richard, Mill lane
Bennett Giles, Steppa lane
Bishop Wm., Barnstpl. st
Phillips John, Townsend
Sparkes Robert, South st

SADDLERS.

Flashman Ann, Barnspl.st
Holmes John, South st
Packer John, South street
Smyth Wm., Broad street
Tepper Richard, Broad st

SHOPKEEPERS.

Bishop Wm., Barnstaple st
Blackford John, Mill lane
Bowden Mgt., Cook's cross
Chanter Thomas, South st
Coles Jas. Matthews, East st
Dale Ann, Broad street
Davies John, East street
Drake Robert, Barnstaple st
Dunn John, King street
Kingdon John, East street
Kingdon Wm., East street
Hobbs Elizabeth, East st
Huxtable John, Townsend
Lyddon Wm., Broad street
Manning Mary, Townsend
Mayne Ann, Barnstaple st
Nott John, Cook's cross
Odam George, Church lane
Perry Thomas, East street
Thorne John, Duke street
Tuckett Wm., Barnstaple st

STRAW HAT MAKERS.

Clark Jane, Barnstaple st

Griffiths Ann, Broad street
Matthews Eliz., Cook's crs
Nutt Eliz., South street
Parsons Sus., Steppa lane
Rowcliffe M. Ann., Broad st
Shapland Eliz., Duke st
Webb Harriet, East street

SURGEONS.

Brown Thomas, Broad st
Cutcliffe John Elworthy,
  Broad street
Flexman James, (coroner,)
  Duke street
Flexman Wm., Duke street
Furse Robert, East street
Southcomb Wm. Thomas,
  South street
Tanner Richard Elworthy,
  East street

TAILORS.

Blackford John, Mill lane
Hodge John, East street
Huxtable Wm., Barnstpl. st
Huxtable Wm. jun., Sth. st
Joslin Richard, Steppa lane
Kingdon John, South street
Manning Charles, South st
Moore Samuel, South street
Norman James, South st
Odam George, Church lane
Pearce John, East street
Selley Amos, Churchyard
Sheppard George, East st
Thorne John, Duke street
Vernon Henry, South street
Wilmets Wm., East street

TALLOW CHANDLERS.

Deagon Wm., Queen street
Mogridge (Wm.) & Odgers
  (John Johns,) South st

TANNERS.

Furse George, East street
Smyth Wm. Gould, East st

TEA DLRS. (TRAVLNG.)

Harris Thomas, East street
McKelvie John, East street
McKinnel Rd. (dpr.) East st
Tremeer Joseph, South st

TEMPRNCE. HOTELS.

Bidder John, East street
Bidder Thos., Barnstaple st

WATCH & CLOCK MKS.

Bickell Rd. John, (& jew-
  eller,) Broad street
Foster Henry, East street
Mills Sl. G., Barnstaple st

WHEELWRIGHTS.

Chapple Wm., Barnstpl. st
Griffiths Charles, Broad st
Moor Frank, South street
Moor Henry & Son, South st
Smith James, Clotworthy
Smoldon George, *Hill*
Taylor Wm., Steppa lane

WINE & SPIRIT MERTS.

Chant Robert, King street
Deagon Wm., Queen street
Huxtable Rt., Broad street
Tanner John, Broad street

WOOLCOMBERS.

Goole George, Back lane
Kingdon John, Cook's cross

Parsons John, Steppa lane
Nutt Humphry, New road

COACHES.

Mails, &c. to BARNSTAPLE, Ilfracombe, &c., from the *George Inn*, at 7 morning & 3 & 5½ afternoon ; & to TIVERTON *to meet trains for London, Bristol, & Exeter,* at 9½ & 11½ morning, and at 5½ afternoon.

CARRIERS.

To *Barnstaple*,Jas.Chapple,

from the Unicorn, daily ;
Wm. Deagon, Queen st., daily ; & Pp. Baker, New Inn, Friday.
Chulmleigh, Wm. Shaddick, South st. daily, (on foot.)
Exeter, Thos. Murch, Mill lane, Mon. & Thursday
Exeter, Crediton, Plymouth, &c., Pridham & Lake's Van, from the Union,daily
Plymouth, Wm. Osmond,

Townsend ; and Rt. Leatherby, Mill lane, Mon.
*Tiverton,*Saunders&Hawkes from the George ; & Thos. Avery, from Town Arms, Tues. Thurs. & Sat.; & Philip Baker, (New Inn,) Tuesday
Waggons, &c. to all parts of N. Devon, from the *George Inn,* whence goods are forwarded to *Tiverton Station*

NYMPTON ST. GEORGE, or *Nymet St. George,* commonly called *George Nympton,* is a pleasant village, in the valley of the river Mole, 2½ miles S. by W. of South Molton, and has in its parish 272 souls, and 1684 acres of land. Sir T. D. Acland is lord of the manor, which was anciently held by the Nymet and Hache families. J. G. Pearse, Esq., has an estate here, and a pleasant seat, called *Broom House,* formerly belonging to the Hale and Gay families. The Rev. W. P. Thomas, Mrs. Nott, Jas. Tanner, Esq., and several smaller owners, have estates in the parish. The *Church* (St. George,) is a neat structure, in the perpendicular style, with a brick tower and three bells. It was repaired in 1848. The *rectory,* valued in 1831 at £310, is in the patronage of Sir T. D. Acland, and incumbency of the Rev. Wm. Fortescue, who resides in Somersetshire. The glebe is 118A., and the Rectory House is a good thatched residence, in the Elizabethan style. The tithes were commuted in 1842, for £280 per annum.

	BOOT&SHOE MKS.	
Baker Thos. vict. Castle Inn	May Wm.	Huxtable George
Gould Rev. Geo. James, B.A., curate, &incmbt. of Mariansleigh, *Rectory*	Mills James	Kingdon Joseph
		Ley George
Harris Elizabeth, schoolmistress	BUTCHERS.	Ley James
Pearse John Gilberd, Esq. solicitor, *Broom House,* (& South Molton)	Bawden Robert	Reed Wm.
	Hitchcock John	Russell Wm.
Ridd John, shopr ; & Wm. wheelwgt	FARMERS.	Smith John
Westacott Jas. cooper ; & Jno. sexton	Baker John	Webber John
Wootton John, par. clerk & thatcher	Bawden Robert	TAILORS.
BLACKSMITHS.	Jarman John	Dunn Samuel	Dadds John
Dockings James		Hancock Richd.	Notts George

SATTERLEIGH is a small parish in the Mole valley, 4 miles S.S.W. of South Molton, containing only 61 souls, and 515 acres of land. Mrs. M. F. Byne, of Exeter, is lady of the manor, but part of the soil belongs to Messrs. John Baker and Joseph and James Thorne, and the Rev. James Gould. The latter is patron of the *rectory,* valued in K.B. at £4. 0s. 7½d., and in 1831 at £120. The Rev. W. Thorold, of Warkleigh, is the incumbent, and has here 30 acres of glebe. The tithes were commuted in 1840, for £70 per annum. The *Church* (St. Peter,) is a small antique fabric, with a wooden belfry and three bells. The FARMERS are—John Baker, *Barton ;* John Dennis, Thos. Phillips, John Squire, and Wm. Squire. The latter is also a *maltster.*

SWIMBRIDGE, a large village, 5 miles E.S.E. of Barnstaple, has in its parish 1746 souls, and 7061 acres of land, including the hamlets of *Accot* and *Newland,* and many scattered farm-houses, &c., and several pleasant seats. The Duke of Bedford is lord of the manor ; but John Nott, Esq., R. Chichester, Esq., the Trustees of the late Lord Rolle, and several smaller owners, have estates in the parish. In Risdon's time, there were some remains of the manor house of *Ernsborough,* where that eminent civilian, *Dr. Cowell,* was born, in 1554. The *Church* (St. James,) is a

handsome structure, with a tower, containing five bells, and crowned by a spire. A rich screen, in fine preservation, divides the nave and chancel. The Dean of Exeter is appropriator of the glebe (40A.,) and the tithes, which were commuted, in 1848, for £850 per annum. He is also patron of the *perpetual curacy*, which is annexed to that of Landkey, in the incumbency of the Rev. J. Russell, who has £40 yearly from the tithes of the two parishes, and also an augmentation from Queen Anne's Bounty. J. Nott, Esq., is lessee of the tithes. There is a *Baptist Chapel* here. The *Parish Lands*, &c., comprise 116 acres and 18 houses, let for about £130 a year, of which £20 is applied in repairing the church, £6 in schooling poor children, and the rest in relieving poor parishioners. In the same trust, is a house for the sexton, and a house and garden occupied by paupers. The poor have also the interest of £40, left by three donors; and an annuity of 20s., left by Charity Symons, in 1665.

Berry Thomas, shoemaker
Burgess John, & Norman Hy. shoprs
Clatworthy Abraham, tailor
Darch Wm. vict. Travellers' Rest
Davy Wm. vict. Hare and Hounds
Eastman My. gentwmn. *Yolland Hs*
Galliford Richd. vict. Ring of Bells
Hole Wm., Esq. *Hannaford House*
Hurdon John, surgeon
Ley John, *Post Office*
Nott John, Esq. *Bydown House*
Russell Rev John, M.A., incumbent, *Donniton House*
Shapland Lieut. Henry, R.N.
Shapland Henry, mason
Smallridge John, vict. New Inn
Smith John, tanner, &c

BLACKSMITHS.
Dallin John
Dunn Henry
Harris Robert
Vickery John
Yeo Samuel
BEERHOUSES.
Baker Hmphy.
Bawden Robert
CARPENTERS, &c.
Chapple John
Featherstone Sl.
Warren George
FARMERS.
(* *are Owners.*)
Baxter Sl. *Accot*
Berry Wm.

Brayley John
*Burden George
*Burden Geo. jun
Geen George
*Hartnoll Eliz.
Hartnoll Jane
Hartnoll Thos.
Huxtable Wm.
Martin Alex.
Place Martin
Punchard John
Richards John
Shapland John
*Thorne George
*Thorne Wm.
Willis Richard
Yeo James

TWITCHEN, 6 miles N.E. by E. of South Molton, is a small village in a picturesque dell, encompassed by lofty hills, some of which have flourishing plantations. Its parish contains 194 souls, and 2918 acres of land, extending to the borders of Somersetshire, and including about 310 acres of common. Lord Poltimore is lord of the manor, and owns the great tithes and most of the soil, and the rest belongs chiefly to Sir R. G. Throckmorton, Bart. The *perpetual curacy* is annexed to the vicarage of North Molton. The *Church* (St. Peter,) is a small neat structure, which was rebuilt in 1844, at the cost of £400, except the tower, which contains three bells. The chancel window is enriched with stained glass, and the seats are all open.

Buckingham John, carpenter
Lyddon John, blacksmith
Lyddon Wm. & Thos. blacksmiths
Lyddon Wm. wheelwright
Vicary Jane, schoolmistress
FARMERS. (* *are Owners.*)
Bawden Jph. || Buckingham Jas.
*Buckingham Hugh || Hobbs Geo.

*Buckingham Wm. and Roger
Friendship James, *Ball*
Kingdon John || Lyddon Wm., *Mill*
*Moore Robt. || Pincombe Robt.
Pincombe Thomas, Lower House
Shapland Eliz. || Thorne Richard
*Tapp John || *Tapp Wm.

WARKLEIGH, or *Warkley*, 5 miles S.W. by W. of South Molton, is a scattered village and parish, containing 291 souls, and 2414 acres of fertile land, rising boldly from the Taw and Mole valleys, on the east and west. The heirs of the late Lord Rolle own most of the soil, and are lords of the

manor, which was anciently held by the Raleigh family, and afterwards by the Martins, Audleys, and Bourchiers. J. Gould, Esq., the Rev. P. T. Johnson, and several smaller owners, have estates in the parish. The *Church* (St. John,) is a handsome structure, with a tower and three bells. It has several neat mural tablets, but only part of its richly-carved screen remains. The *rectory*, valued in K.B. at £14. 4s. 7d., and in 1831 at £215, is in the patronage of Jas. Gould, Esq., and incumbency of the Rev. Wm. Thorold, who has 27A. 1R. 12P. of glebe, and a good residence in the Elizabethan style, built in 1844. At *Deason* is a small school, erected in 1846 by Mr. John Stevens, and supported by subscription, and the interest of £37, left by several donors.

Beer Sar. & Manning Ann, schools
Beer Wm. butcher and parish clerk
Burgess Thos. gent. *Warkleigh Cotg*
Heywood John, shopkeeper
Manning James, wheelwright
Marshall Thomas, tailor
Phillips Wm. vict., Hotel
Symons John and Geo. blacksmiths
Thorold Rev Wm. rector of Warkleigh and Satterleigh, *Rectory*
Warren Thos. plough mkr. & butcher

FARMERS.

Beer John, *Shortridge*
Bradford Wm., *Preston House*
Chapple Geo. || Darch John
Cole Philip || Cole Richard
Greenslade Wm. || Heathfield Wm.
Huxtable Roger || Milford Thos.
Mills Wm., *Hill-Town*
Mortimer John, *Warkleigh Barton*
Passmore John || Staddon Samuel
Stevens John || Warren John

TAVISTOCK HUNDRED

Is a small liberty on the south-western side of Devonshire, containing only the three parishes of *Brent-Tor, Milton Abbot,* and *Tavistock,* which comprise 7697 souls, and about 23,000 acres of land, bounded on the south-west by the river Tamar, which separates it from Cornwall, and here receives the small river Tavy, and has a canal to Tavistock, passing through a long tunnel. The Duke of Bedford is lord of the manor and hundred; and the three parishes are in the Southern Parliamentary Division of Devon; in the Archdeaconry of Totnes; and in Tavistock Union, Deanery, Polling and County Court District, and Petty Sessional Division. It has mines of *copper, tin, and lead,* and is generally a fertile and picturesque district, bounded on the east by the mountainous region of Dartmoor Forest.

BRENT-TOR, or *Brentor,* is a parish of scattered houses, from 4 to 5 miles N. of Tavistock, containing 169 souls, and 2180 acres of land, rising in bold hills on the western confines of Dartmoor. The Duke of Bedford is lord of the manor, which formerly belonged to Tavistock Abbey, but part of the soil belongs to the Carpenter, Hoblin, Brandreth, Weeks, and other families. A fair was formerly held near the church, under a grant obtained in 1231. The *Church* (St. Michael,) is a very small and ancient structure, standing on the summit of the conical *tor,* or rocky hill, which rises abruptly on an elevated down. It has a tower and three bells, and has recently been re-pewed. The interior measures only 37 feet by 14½, and on a tablet opposite the door is inscribed "Upon this rock will I build my Church." Tradition says it was built by a merchant, who, being overtaken by a storm at sea, vowed, if he landed safely in Plymouth Sound, he would erect a church on the first point of land he saw. In ancient records, it is called *St. Michael de Rupe.* It stands near the edge of the perpendicular cliff, and its small grave-yard is saturated with moisture, though on the summit of a rock supposed to be an extinct volcano, as implied by the

name—Brent or Burnt Tor. The benefice is a *perpetual curacy*, worth only £66 a year. The Duke of Bedford is patron, and the Rev. E. A. Bray, of Tavistock, is the incumbent, and has yearly about £15 from tithes, £9. 15s. from Queen Anne's Bounty, and £40. 10s. from a farm at Whitechurch.

Arthur John, vict. Herring's Arms
Cudlip John M. mason
Drown Jno. smith & vict. Stag's Hd
Prout James, mine manager

FARMERS. (* *are Owners.*)
*Batton Wm., *Brimsey Batch*
*Bickle Thos. Kinsman, *Holyeat*

Bickle Wm. || Doidge Grace
*Glanville Joseph, *Broad Park*
Glanville Thomas || Mason Jas.
Maunder Wm. || Pengelly —
Petter Thomas || Walter Thomas
Tucker Elias Rowe, *Woodlark*
Westlake John, *East Liddaton*

MILTON ABBOT is a pleasant and well-built village, on a gentle eminence, 6 miles N.W. by W. of Tavistock, and E.S.E. of Launceston, and has in its parish 1256 inhabitants, and 6617 acres of land, generally fertile and in pasturage, and including the hamlets, &c., of *Foghanger, Quither, Edgcumbe,* and *Chillaton,* and many scattered houses. The Duke of Bedford is lord of the *manors* of Milton Abbot, Foghanger, Week-Dabernon, and West Liddaton, formerly belonging to Tavistock Abbey, and granted, at the dissolution, to his Grace's ancestor, John, Lord Russell. The manors of Ford and Chillaton belong to the executors of the late J. P. Carpenter, Esq. Part of the parish belongs to C. Vawdon and Richard Edgcumbe, Esqs., and some of the ancestors of the latter were seated at Edgcumbe from the reign of Henry III. till a few years ago. There is a pleasure fair in the village on Easter Tuesday, and a *cattle fair* on the Wednesday after July 20th. The Duke of Bedford owns the greater part of the parish, and has a beautiful occasional seat here, called ENDSLEIGH COTTAGE, delightfully situated in the picturesque valley of the Tamar, in the midst of sylvan pleasure grounds, through which the river winds in a semi-circular reach, amidst some of the most romantic scenery in Devon and Cornwall. The mansion is an elegant *cottage ornée,* built by the late Duke, in 1810, from the design of Sir G. Wyattville, on the sweetly sequestered site selected by the late Duchess. To produce picturesque effect, it is built in a very irregular manner, and has many ornamental gables, in one of which is a statue of the last abbot of Tavistock. The internal decorations of this ducal residence combine usefulness with taste. The dining room, with its emblazoned window; the library, with its choice selection of books; and the other principal apartments, are elegantly and tastefully furnished, and contain many fine paintings and other works of art. But the beauties to be met with outside the cottage form its chief attractions. The view from the terrace,—the Dairy dell, watered by a running stream; the Alpine garden, with its Swiss cottage; the numerous paths winding along the banks of the Tamar, and the other sylvan attractions, are so enchantingly disposed, as to render Endsleigh one of the loveliest spots in Devonshire. The beautiful lawn, gardens, and pleasure grounds immediately encompassing the mansion, comprise about 20 acres, and beyond them are about 1935 acres of woods and coppices, and 1487 acres of plantations, to which there are private drives, many miles in length, on the Devon and Cornwall sides of the river, which is here crossed by a floating bridge, worked by chains. Permission to view this earthly paradise may be obtained of the Duke's steward, at his office, in Tavistock. The *Parish Church* (St. Constantine,) is a large handsome structure, with a tower and six bells. It is in the perpendicular style, and has lately been repaired, cleansed, and beautified. The Duke of Bedford is impropriator of the great tithes, and patron of the *vicarage,* valued in K.B. at £19. 13s. 6½d., and in 1831 at £557. The Rev. St. Vincent Love Hammick, M.A., is the incumbent, and has a good resi-

dence, erected in 1838, and 87A. 3R. 33P. of glebe. The tithes were commuted in 1839, the rectorial for £374. 11s. 4d., and the vicarial for £455. 8s. 8d. In the village is a small Wesleyan chapel, built in 1835, and a public library. The *churchwardens* have a field and buildings at Tavistock, called Vigo Barn, let in 1817, for 99 years, at only 21s. 1½d. per annum, in consideration of a fine of £50, applied in new seating the church. They have also a house, let for £4. The dividends of £540 navy five per cent. stock, left by *Nicholas Jewell*, in 1738, belong to the poor of this parish and Stoke-Climsland, two-thirds to the former, and one-third to the latter. The *Free School*, built by the Duke of Bedford, in 1829, and supported by him, is a handsome building, in the Tudor style, with room for 100 pupils. The master takes boarders and day scholars, who pay for their education; but the school is free to the sons of labourers, who are instructed in reading, writing, arithmetic, geography, agricultural chemistry, &c. Here is also a *Girl's Free School*, built by subscription and grants.

DUKE OF BEDFORD, *Endsleigh*, (and Woburn Abbey, Bedfordshire)
Baker Mrs Ann, housekpr , Endsleigh
Christie Jas. A. free schoolmaster
Deacon John, painter, &c
Doidge Jno. gamekpr. || Ward Dl.
Forrester John, bailiff to Duke of Bedford, *Harragrove Cottage*
Hammick Rev St Vincent Love, M.A. *Vicarage*
McKay James, gardener
Martim My. A. schoolmistress
Oliver John, parish clerk
Prout Elizabeth, baker
Wedge John, maltster
Williams Mrs Hannah, lodgings
    INNS & TAVERNS.
Bedford Inn, Rd. Chubb, Brickwood
Carpenter's Arms, Charles Hart
Heathfield Inn, Wm. Drown
King's Arms, John Clarke
New Inn, Rd. Gloyne, saddler
    FARMERS. (* at *Edgcumbe*.)
*Badge Wm. || Brendon George
Bickle Wm. || Bickle John
*Bickle Robt., Wm., & Henry
Bickle My. Ann, *Foghanger*
Blanchard Jas., Geo., & Thos. *Leigh*
Chidley John || Creber Charles
*Cole Joseph || *Cole Philip
Cornelius John, *Quither*
Courtice Thomas, *Park*
*Dinnis Thomas || Doidge Edward
Doidge Rd. || Doidge Wm.
Easterbrook John || Grandon Wm.
Edgcumbe Wm. || Hendy Richard
Gloyne John, *Westcott*
Land John || Langman Wm.
Lemon Wm. & Thos. *Hardicott*

Mudge Mary || Martin John
Northey Thos. || Oxenham Wm.
Palmer Roger || Peardon Thomas
*Perry Jno. & Jas. || Prout Samuel
Rowe Wm. || Ryall Oliver
Rowling Robert, *Chillaton*
Ryall John || Ward Daniel
Walters Geo. & Thomas, *Week*
Westlake George, *Broad Town*
Wonnacott John, *Shortaburn*
Wonnacott Nicholas, *Langskerry*
    BLACKSMITHS.   Stacey Jno. *Chillaton*
Ball John
Madaford Roger   MASONS.
Reed John   Coode Charles
Stanton Ann   Dinner John
    BOOT & SHOE MKS.   Martin Wm.
Baker Stephen   Sargant Wm.
Martin John   Wise James
Symons Robert   SHOPKEEPERS.
Stitson John   Deacon Thomas
Wise John   Lee Thomas
    BUTCHERS.   Prout Rt. (&druggist & sdsman)
Cole Roger
Spencer Robert   Satchell Mary
Vosper Francis   TAILORS.
    CARPENTERS.   Deacon Thomas
Davy James   Edwards John
Davy Thomas   Hill John
Davy Wm.   Wise John
Frise Henry   Wise Samuel
Spry John   Wise Wm.
Spry Richard
Spry Rd. jun.   **POST-OFFICE**
Williams John   at Rd. Gloyne's.
    CORN MILLERS.   Letters *via* Launceston
Colling Hy. *Ford*
Daniel John, *Willesley*

TAVISTOCK is an ancient *parliamentary borough* and handsome *market and stannary town*, delightfully seated in the picturesque valley of the small river Tavy, from which it has its name, 33 miles S.W. by W. of Exeter; 15 miles N. of Plymouth; 20 miles W. of Ashburton, and 205 miles W.S.W. of London. It gives name to a large *union, deanery, county court* and *polling district*, and a *petty sessional division*. Its PARISH is all within the borough, except the manor of Cudlipptown, and extends over about 4000 A. of open moorland on the confines of Dartmoor, and includes 10,573 A. of cultivated land, stretching more than 3 miles north, west, and south of the town, and forming a fertile and picturesque district, bounded on the east by the Tavy, and on the south-west by the navigable river *Tamar*, which separates it from Cornwall, and to which there is a *canal* from the town, more than four miles in length, opened in 1817, and passing in a tunnel nearly two miles long, under the rocky hills to Morwellham quay, to which the Tamar is navigable for vessels of 200 tons burthen. The population of the parish was 3420 in 1801; 4723 in 1811; 5483 in 1821; 5602 in 1831; and 6272 in 1841; but it now comprises about 7000, including the numerous scattered farmhouses, &c. The river *Tavy* rises in the mountainous region of Dartmoor Forest, which extends to within a few miles East of the town. In the neighbourhood are the *copper, tin*, and *lead mines*, called the *Devonshire Great Consols*, or *Wheal Maria; Bedford United, Tavy Consols*, and *Wheal Russell*. The first named was opened about five years ago, and belongs to a company, holding 1024 shares, on which only £1 each has been paid, though they are now worth about £200 each. This lucrative mine employs about 1100 hands, and yields about 1350 tons of rich copper ore per month; and its last sale realized £9200. The town has been greatly improved and beautified, during the last ten years, by the Duke of Bedford, who owns most of the parish, and is lord of the *manors of Tavistock, Hurdwick, Morwell, Ogbear, Parswell*, and *Ottery*, formerly belonging to the Abbey; but the manor of *Cudlipptown* belongs to the Rev. E. A. Bray, and was formerly held by the Rolle, Sawle, and Fellowes families. *Kilworthy*, an ancient house, now occupied by a farmer, was long the seat of Judge Glanville and his family, and now belongs to the Duke of Bedford. *Mount Tavy* is the pleasant seat of Mrs. Carpenter, a liberal benefactress of the poor. *Fitzford*, adjoining the town, was anciently the seat of the Fitze family, and afterwards of the Grenvilles, but now belongs to the Duke. Its remains have been converted into a farm-house and outbuildings, but the ancient gateway, mantled with ivy, is still standing. *Morwell House*, occupied by a farmer, is a large and ancient quadrangular building in the Tudor style, which has been completely restored by the Duke of Bedford, who is now rebuilding or enlarging many of the farm-houses on his extensive estates. This house was a country seat of the Abbots of Tavistock, and is situated in the southern part of the parish, overlooking the Tamar valley. TAVISTOCK ABBEY, which stood in the town on the western acclivity of the vale of the Tavy, is said to have been founded in 961, by Orgar, Earl of Devon, or his son Ordulph. Tavistock is said to have been

the seat of Earl Orgar, the story of whose beautiful daughter, Elfrida, is well known. The abbey was destroyed by the Danes in 997, but was soon afterwards rebuilt. It was richly endowed by the founder and subsequent benefactors, and its revenues were valued at the dissolution at £902. 5s. 7d. per annum. It was made a mitred abbey in 1458; and in 1514, Richard Banham procured for himself and successor a seat in parliament. He also obtained from Pope Leo X. a bull which exempted the abbey from episcopal jurisdiction. The abbey had long a flourishing school for Saxon literature, and also a printing press, said to have been the second set up in England. The productions of this press are now extremely rare. In the Abbey Church were buried Edward, brother of Edmund Ironside; Earl Orgar, and his son Ordulph; St. Rumon, to whom the church was dedicated; Bishop Livingus, &c. John Courtenay, one of the abbots, was heir to the earldom of Devonshire, which honor he declined in favour of his next brother. The abbot had the power of inflicting capital punishment in the manor of Hurdwick. The abbey and all its large possessions were granted by Henry VIII. in 1539 or 1540, to John, Lord Russell, an ancestor of the Duke of Bedford, their present owner. The tower and ruins of the Abbey Church, which had been consecrated by Bishop Stapledon, in 1318, were pulled down about 1670, and the materials used in building a school-house. In the early part of last century, the principal remains of the abbey were, "the gatehouse, then used as a prison for captive seamen; the Saxon School, used as a granary, &c.; the walls of the kitchen and chapter-house, uncovered at top; and the abbot's hall, then fitted up as a meeting-house for the Presbyterians," and now occupied by Unitarians. The refectory and some other parts of this once splendid abbey were incorporated into the *Abbey House*, a large and elegant castellated mansion, built about 130 years ago, and enlarged by the late Duke of Bedford, and elegantly fitted up as an inn, under the name of the *Bedford Hotel*. The noble dining-room of this hotel is supposed to have been the refectory, and in it the Duke entertains his tenants and holds his courts. It is also used for balls and other public uses. On removing the ceiling of this spacious room, about 35 years ago, the original vaulted roof was discovered. In 1848, the Duke of Bedford erected on the site of part of the abbey ruins, the handsome new *Guildhall*, which comprises an extensive room, in which the Petty Sessions, County Court, &c., are now held; a magistrates' room and other apartments; under which is the Bridewell, comprising six cells, a dwelling for the police superintendent, a fire engine station, &c. This building, for the free use of the town, cost his Grace about £3000, and is erected in the same style as the venerable remains of the abbey, now mostly incorporated with other buildings. Over the Abbey-Gateway are the rooms of the literary and philosophical society, called the *Tavistoc Institution*, established in 1828; the *Public Library*, established in 1799; and the *Museum*, founded by the Duke for the use of the town. The library comprises about 4000 volumes, and attached is a News and Reading Room. In one of the towers are instruments for registering the state of the weather,

and a large telescope.   Here is also a *Mechanics' Institution*, established in 1832, and now having about 800 members, and a good library.   The site and precincts of the abbey now form the handsomest part of the town, and his Grace intends removing the old walls in front of the Guildhall, so as to open the view from thence to the Bedford Hotel, and the villas in the Abbey Mead.   In 1845, he supplied the town with pure water from a reservoir of 50,000 gallons, at the top of Bannawell street, which is filled by never-failing springs.   The cost of the water-works was about £1400.   In the winters of 1846, '7, and '8, the noble and generous Duke employed a great number of labourers in effectually draining the town, and in carrying the drain waters through Fitzford meadows, which, aided by the fructifying influence of irrigation, now yield three crops of grass per annum.   The cost of this work was about £1500.   His Grace is now erecting a number of improved dwellings for the labouring poor, and has published a pamphlet on the subject. Bedford Hotel was originally intended as a manor-house, for the occasional residence of the Duke of Bedford's family.   *Endsleigh*, the seat of the present Duke, is in the adjacent parish of Milton-Abbot, as noticed at page 622.   William Russell, the seventh Earl of Bedford, was created *Marquis of Tavistock and Duke of Bedford* in 1649.   The present Duke (Francis,) was born in 1788, and succeeded in 1839; and his son, the Marquis of Tavistock, was born in 1809.   Their principal seat is *Woburn Abbey*, Bedfordshire.   In the Vicarage grounds are two ivy-mantled towers, called *Betsy Grimbal's Tower* and the *Still House;* and behind the Bedford Hotel is an elegantly carved porch, with four lofty pinnacles.

Tavistock sent *Members to Parliament* as early as the reign of Edward I., and it has regularly sent two representatives since the time of Edward III. The right of election, until the passing of the Reform Act of 1832, was in the freeholders of inheritance, residing in the borough, who were about 50 in number.   The number of voters registered in 1837 was 329, of whom 300 were £10 householders.   The old borough comprised only the town and its immediate vicinity, but the borough limits were extended by the Reform Act so as to comprise all the extensive parish, except the manor of Cudlipptown.   The present representatives of the borough are the *Hon. Edward Southwell Russell* and *John Salusbury Trelawny, Esq.*   Tavistock is a borough by prescription, but was never incorporated.   It is governed by a *portreeve*, who is the returning officer, and is appointed at the court-leet of the lord of the manor.   A survey and valuation of the borough, made in 1726, says the lord holds courts leet and baron twice a year, at which a portreeve and eight masters are appointed by the lord's steward; that there were lands worth £60 per annum, mostly expended by the masters in repairing the church; and that the lord had a gaol and two sergeants-at-mace, a court of pleas for the manor and hundred, and a weekly court of record, The old Guildhall, being in a dilapidated state, was taken down after the completion of the new one.   *Petty Sessions* are held here every alternate Thursday by the magistrates of Tavistock Division, to whom Mr. R. Luxton is clerk   The *County Court*, for the 24 parishes of Tavistock Union and some others, is held at the Guildhall monthly, and Mr. C. V. Bridgman is the *clerk*, and Mr. John Brownson the *high bailiff.*   Quarter Sessions were formerly held here.   In 1591, when the plague raged at Exeter, the summer *assizes* were held here, and 13 persons were condemned and executed

on the Abbey green. On the breaking out of the *civil wars* of the 17th century, Tavistock was the scene of great confusion and excitement. Whilst the Earl of Bedford and most of the burgesses, with the celebrated Pym, one of their representatives, were warm in favour of the Parliament, many of the neighbouring gentry espoused the royal cause. Fitzford, the ancient seat of the Grenvilles, held out for the King, but was taken by the Earl of Essex, with 1000 stand of arms, and £3000 in money. Prince Charles held several councils here when Plymouth was blockaded by the Royalists, and Exeter by the Parliamentarians ; but the town does not appear to have been garrisoned during that unhappy period, though the royal army marched through into Cornwall, with the King at its head. Henry I. is said to have granted Tavistock a charter for a weekly *market* to be held on Saturday, but it is now held on Friday, and is one of the largest in the county for corn and slaughtered sheep, swine, &c., which are extensively purchased for Plymouth and other towns. The corn market is held in a building on granite arches, erected by the Duke of Bedford in 1839 ; and it is said to be his Grace's intention to erect a commodious *Market House* for the accommodation of the butchers, greengrocers, and the vendors of poultry, butter, eggs, &c., whose shops and stalls are now scattered and inconvenient. Here are nine *cattle fairs*, held on the second Wednesdays in January, March, May, July, September, October, and November; on the first Wednesday in Dec., and the 3rd Wednesday in August. *Races* are held annually on Whitchurch-down. The town has now a clean and handsome appearance, and contains several good inns, and many well-stocked shops. The *Gas Works* were established in 1831, and enlarged in 1835, and now belong to a company holding 750 £5 shares. The manufacture of *coarse woollens* flourished here from an early period, but declined at the close of last century, and is now nearly obsolete. *Mining* operations have been carried on in the neighbourhood from time immemorial, and there are now to be seen several remains of the Phœnician smelting houses, called "Jews' houses." Tavistock is one of the principal stannary towns in Devon, and several profitable mines of copper, &c., are now at work in the neighbourhood, as noticed at page 624. There is a *smelting establishment* at Crowndale, a mile from the town, and the products of the mines have an outlet to the Tamar and the coast by means of the *canal*, which is noticed at page 624, and was commenced in 1803 and finished in 1817, at the cost of £68,000. In the town are two large *ironfoundries* and engine works. John R. Thomas, a working engineer, employed at one of these establishments, has recently completed a *steam carriage*, said to be adapted for travelling on turnpike roads, and having a condensing apparatus which prevents the emission of steam, and reduces the consumption of both coal and water.

The *Church* (St. Eustachius,) is a large and handsome structure, consisting of a nave with a north and two south aisles, a chancel, a south porch, and a lofty tower, containing eight bells, and standing on four arches at the west end. In 1844-5, it underwent a thorough renovation, and has now open carved benches affording 1004 sitting, of which 410 are free. It has a new stone pulpit and altar screen, finely carved ; and some ancient and modern monuments, one of which has effigies of Sir John Fitze and his lady ; and another has the effigy of Judge Glanville in his robes. In the church are preserved some human bones of gigantic size, which were found in a stone coffin when digging for the foundation of the Bedford Hotel, and are said, by tradition, to be the bones of Ordulph, son of the founder of the abbey, whom William of Malmsbury represents as so immense in stature that he could bestride a river ten feet broad. The Duke of Bedford is impropriator of the great tithes, formerly belonging to the

abbey, and also patron of the *vicarage*, valued in K.B. at £10. 17s. 6d., and in 1831 at £302, and now in the incumbency of the Rev. E. A. Bray, who has a good residence, with pleasant grounds. He receives a stipend from the Duke in lieu of tithes. In 1846, the tithes of 3151A. of land, not belonging to the Duke, were commuted for £363. 11s. per annum. There were anciently chapels of *St. Margaret* and *St. John* in the parish; and Tanner says there was here a house of *Austin Friars*, and a *Lepers' Hospital*. There are now in the town four CHAPELS belonging to *Unitarians, Independents, Wesleyans*, and the *Society of Friends*. The Unitarian Chapel occupies part of the abbey buildings, as noticed at page 625, and its congregation originated as Presbyterians, in 1670. The Independent Congregation was formed in 1796, and erected a new chapel in 1820, but it was burnt down and rebuilt in 1833. It is a neat stone building, with an Ionic portico. A small *Cemetery* was made about 16 years ago, on land given by the Duke of Bedford. The ancient GRAMMAR SCHOOL formed part of the old Vicarage premises, which were taken down about 30 years ago to enlarge the church-yard; but the Duke of Bedford furnished the vicar with another residence, and built the present large and elegant school-house and school in 1837, at the cost of £2500. He allows about £50 a year to the head-master, and £20 to the second master, in consideration of which they charge only small quarterages for such boys as are sent by him or his steward. In 1649, *Sir John Glanville, Kt.*, left a house and land at Lamerton, in trust that the yearly profits should be applied in maintaining a boy from this school at one of the Universities. This property is now worth about £20 a year, and is at present in chancery. The *National Schools*, erected in 1847, form a large and handsome building in the Tudor style, and are attended by about 160 boys, 160 girls, and 90 infants. Here is also a large *British School*, erected in 1822 at the sole expense of the Duke of Bedford, and attended by about 300 children. It is supported by subscription, as also is an *Infant School*, attended by more than 100 pupils. Among the charitable institutions of the town are—a *Dispensary*, established in 1832, and *Dorcas* and *Lying-in Societies*. There is a *Freemasons' Lodge* at the Bedford Hotel, and here are several other provident institutions and Friendly Societies. *Tavistock Savings' Bank* was established in 1816, and in 1848 had upwards of £30,000, belonging to 906 individual depositors, 23 Friendly Societies, and 8 Charitable Societies. The Duke of Bedford is its patron and governor. The *West Devon Friendly Building and Accumulation Fund Society*, was established a few years ago, and has now about 100 members. The *Literary Institutions* of the town are already noticed at page 625. *Tavistock and West Devon Agricultural Society* holds its meetings here, and has a numerous list of members. J. Benson, Esq., the Duke of Bedford's land agent, is the secretary. Among the *worthies* of Tavistock may be enumerated the celebrated *Sir Fras. Drake*, said to have been born at Crowndale; *Judge Glanville*, and his son *Sir John*, a political writer; and *Wm. Browne*, the poet, who was born in 1590. Several of the abbots were learned men, and with the aid of their printing press, gave great encouragement to literature. *Mrs. Bray*, the lady of the present worthy vicar, has published several interesting works, descriptive of the romantic beauties of this neighbourhood, and recording much of its history, and the manners and traditions of its inhabitants. The town has several *Almshouses* and *Charitable Bequests* for the poor.

The *Gift House*, an old building, occupied rent free by about 12 poor families, was given by *Oliver Maynard* in 1602 for the residence of poor artificers and handicraftsmen. *Lord Courtenay's Almshouse* is the residence of four poor widows, who are appointed by the Earl of Devon, and have divided among them a yearly rent-charge of £8. 12s. out

of Pitscliffe estate. In 1674, *Nicholas Watts* left, in trust for charitable uses, ten houses and gardens, and about 16A. of land, now let for £64 a year, subject to fines on the renewal of the leases. There is also belonging to the same trust £125 navy five per cents., purchased with a small unapplied portion of the rents intended to be applied in fitting a youth for the University, but there are seldom any applications for this branch of the charity. The trustees, pursuant to the donor's will, pay yearly £10 to four dissenting ministers, and distribute £35. 5s. among 95 poor men in sums of 7s. each. New trustees were appointed, and a new scheme sanctioned, by the Court of Chancery for the application of the four branches of the charity, about 20 years ago. Several ancient *Charities settled by Act of Parliament* in the 3rd of Geo. III. comprised divers small tenements, rent-charges, &c., which were given by the said Act to the Duke of Bedford in exchange for an annual rent of £120, charged on his estate in this parish. The Act directed that, out of the first three years' income, the trustees should lay out £300 in erecting an *Almshouse* for 15 poor persons of Tavistock, who do not receive parochial relief. The annuity of £120 is applied as follows :—£50 for the support of the almspeople and the repairs of the almshouses ; £30 in quarterly distributions among 60 poor parishioners ; £4. 4s. to the master of the Grammar School ; £20 in four marriage portions to poor maidens ; and £15 in apprenticing two poor boys. The Duke of Bedford and the Vicar, Churchwardens, and Overseers, are the trustees.

TAVISTOCK UNION comprises the 24 parishes of Tavistock, Beer-Ferris, Buckland-Monachorum, Bradstone, Brentor, Coryton, Kelly, Dunterton, Lamerton, Lifton, Lidford, Lewtrenchard, Maristow, Marytavy, Meavy, Milton-Abbot, Petertavy, Sampford-Spiney, Sheepstor, Sydenham-Damerel, Stowford, Thrushelton, Walkhampton, and Whitechurch, which embrace an area of 242 square miles, and had 23,995 inhabitants in 1841, living in 4040 houses, besides which there were 157 unoccupied houses, and 36 building when the census was taken. Their total average annual expenditure on the poor, during the three years preceding the formation of the union, was £8547. The expenditure of the union was £6394 in 1838, £8047 in 1840, and £10,083 in 1849. The *Workhouse* is a large building, erected in 1837 at the cost of £7000, and has room for 300 paupers. Mr. John Palmer and Mrs. Heath are the master and matron. John Benson, Esq., is *chairman* of the Board of Guardians, and Mr. John Physick is the *union clerk* and *superintendent registrar.* Messrs. George Kneebone, of Ashleigh, and John Andrews, of Tavistock, are the *relieving officers.* Messrs. F. A. Davis, of Tavistock, and John Percy, of Lamerton, are *registrars of marriages ;* and Messrs. F. A. Davis, Rd. Toop, John Percy, and Geo. Kneebone, are *registrars of births and deaths.*

TAVISTOCK DIRECTORY.

The POST-OFFICE is in Lower Market street, and Agnes Martin is the *postmistress.* Letters are despatched to London, Plymouth, &c., at 40 minutes past 3 afternoon ; to the North at 45 minutes past 7 morning; and to Cornwall at 7 evening. Money Orders are granted and paid.

Contractions :—Hmkt. st. for Higher Market st; Lmkt. for Lower Market st; and Bmkt. st. for Barley Market st.

Andrews John, relvg. officer, Higher Market street
Arkill Rev E., Bannawell
Barratt Isc. supt. *Gas wrks*
Beauford Misses, Bedford pl
Benson John, Esq., land steward to Duke of Bedford, *Manor House*
Blanchard Mary, tanner, Brook street
Bound Wm. fruiterer, Hmkt
Bradney Rev R., West st
Bray Rev Ed. Atkyns, *Vicg*
Bray Mrs., Matthew street
Carpenter Mrs. *Mnt. Tavy*
Carter Mr John, Rock view
Carter Mr Wm., Brook st
Chubb Mr Saml., Exeter st
Colman John, brushmaker, Barley Market street
Colson Rev Henry, M.A. *Grammar School*
Commins Mr John, Canal cottage
Commins Wm. E. clerk, Bedford place

Courtice Nichls. clk., St Jno's
Dingle Thos. clerk, Morwell
Doidge Mr Wm., Brook st
Drew Misses, Exeter st
Durham Benj. patten mkr., Brook street
Flamank Jno. gent. Abbey rd
Gibbons Rev Ts. curate, Bdg
Greenfield Mr John, West st
Gribbell Rd. grocer, Bank hs
Gulley Wm., Gas works
Hambling H. B. gunmaker, West street
Harness Thomas Burnaford, M.D., West street
Heath Mrs. matron, *Workhs*
Hicks Rev H.(Wes.) West st
Hitchins Mrs., Bedford pl
Hitchins Josiah Hugo, Esq. supt. of Wheal Maria copper mine, *Hazeldon*
Honey Mr Wm., Russell st
Jessop John, clerk, Wharf
Job Mrs Selina, West st
Jones Theops. architect to Duke cf Bedford, Bedfd. yd

Kelly Mrs Honor, Bedfd. pl
Kent Rev J., Bannawell st
Lockwood Rev John, B.A., (Indpt) Abbey mead
Luscombe Rd. grocer, Windsor cottage
Luxton Rd. clerk to magistrates, Guildhall buildgs
Martin Mr Hugh, Kilworthy lane
Martin Mrs Mary, King st
Merrifield Geo. tal. chandler, Brook street
Merrifield Wm. *lib.*, Abbey
Merritt Mk. police, Gldhall
Mitchell Jn. Giddey, West st
Moon Jas. pwnbkr., Bmkt. st
Monk Wm. par. clk., Gldhall
Morgan Wm., Esq. *Woodovis*
Northey Mr Gilbert, West st
Northey Sl. coaldlr., West st
Palmer Jno. govr. *Workhs.*
Pearse Mr Edm., Brook st
Phillips John, corn inspctr., Dolvin road

Physick John, union clerk & sup. regr. *Wilmingston*
Price Mrs Eliz., Brook st
Robarts Geo. dentist, Russell street
Rundle Mrs Anne, Exeter st
Rundle Jno., Esq., Ferrum hl
Sims Rev Herbert M. curate
Skinner Miss Mary, West st
Smale Mrs Eliz., Mathw. st
Smale Wm. overseer, Brk st
Stanley Rev George Heap, *(Unitn.)* Abbey mead
Stevens Simon, cattle dealer, Bannawell street
Stone Jph. horse letr., B. st
Thynne Frederick, organist, Mount view
Trickett Geo. dyer, Mattw. st
Truin Rev J., West street
West Rev Jph. *(Ws.)* Bwll. st
Willcocks Mr John, Exeter st
Windeatt Mrs., Bedford pl
Windeatt Ts. gent., West st

ACADEMIES.
British School, Wm. H. Hosier & Miss Maunder
Finn John Saml. Matthew st
Foot Mrs., Highermkt st
Gloyne Wm., Highmkt st
Grammar School, Rev Hy. Colson, M.A., Abbey mead
Hills Misses, Abbey mead
Kelly Misses, Bedford pl
National Schools, Jno. Loam and Fanny Bell
Oates Mrs., West street
Smale Miss, Brook street

AGENTS.
(For Copper Mines, &c.)
Doble Wm., West street
Harvey Wm. B., Exeter st
Hitchins John, Madge lane
Hitchins J. H., Hazeldon
Marrack Rd. (for Belitho & Co.) Abbey mead
Matthews Jph. (mines and canal) Taylor's square
Key John, *Crebor*
Paull John, West street
Penrose Rd., Rock view

Mines and Captains.
Bedford United, Jas. Phillips
Tavy Consols, Wm. Goss
Wheal Maria, Jas. Richards
Wheal Russell, Mr. Barratt

ASSAYERS.
Harvey James, King st
Hitchins Jehu, Lr. Back st

ATTORNEYS.
Bridgman Cphr. Vickery, (clerk of County Court,) Church ln.; h Parkwood
Bridgman Jn. Vickery, Post-Office ln.; h Back street
Carpenter Surrey E.S., Bedford place
Cornish (Hy.) & Chilcott, (Edw.) West street
Robins Rd. Jas., Brook st
Scobell Edw. H., Abbey md

Willesford Chas., Back st.; h *Tavy Cottage*

AUCTIONEERS.
Cerutty Peter, West street
Davis Fras. Adams, West st
Gill and Vigers, *Plymouth,* (attend Tues. & Fri.)
Seccombe John, King st

BAKERS, &c.
Cerutty John, Brook street
Dyer John, Higher Brook st
Ellerey John, Brook street
Horswill Stpn., West street
Long Sl., Higher Market st
Mallett Thomas, West st
Stephens John, Back street
Williams Enoch, Hmkt. st

BANKERS.
Devon & Cornwall Banking Co., West street, (on Barclay & Co.) Jph. Brown, *manager*
Gill & Rundle, Hmkt. st. (on Barnetts, Hoare, & Co.)
Savings' Bank, Bedford office, (open Fri. 2 to 3, & Sat. 6 to 8) John Phillips, *actuary*

BASKET MAKERS.
Shelson Jas., Hr. Brook st
Terrell Jas., Kilworthy lane

BLACK & W. SMITHS.
Cole Wm., Brook street
Doidge Chas., Matthew st
Mason George, Taylor sq
Pearse Jas. & Bros. *Hawkins*
Philp Wm. & John, Paddon's row
Prout Richard, *Lamborn*
Prout Thomas, Brook st
Slocombe Edw., Elbow lane

BOOKSELLERS,
Printers, and Stationers.
Adams Alex., Hr. Market st
Chave Thos. Sml., Back st
Commins Jno. Locke, West st
Feaston Ann, West street

BOOT & SHOEMAKERS.
Blanchard Jonth., Lmkt. st
Brownson John, Brook st
Cook Wm., Bannawell st
Dingle Wm., West street
Down John, West street
Hole Richard, Back street
Jennings Wm., King st
Kingsland Pp., Hr. Back st
Martin Walter, West st
Nichols John, West street
Reynolds Joshua, Hmkt. st
Spurrell Saml., Butcher st
Stevens John, Exeter st
Trudgen Wm., Brook st
Truscott Thomas, Brook st
Walters John, Binkt. st
Webb Richard, Brook st
Willcocks Wm., Pepper st

BRAZIERS & TINNERS.
Babb Wm., King street
Dunn Geo. *(plumber)* Back st
Lamping Thomas, Brook st
Physick Tristram, Matw. st

BREWERS.
Richards John, Pepper st

White John, (& wine, spirit, porter, & hop mert.) Hr. Market street

BUILDERS.
Dennis Richard, West st
Gibbons Richard, West st
Martin Wm. L., Bedford pl
Newton Wm., Hr. Back st
Richards Wm., Brook st
Rundle John, Abbey mead

BUTCHERS.
Doidge Geo., Lr. Market st
Doidge Wm., Exeter street
Gill John, Hr. Brook street
Jackman John, Bannawell st
May Solomon, Hr. Brook st
Minhinnick Hy., Banwl. st
Prout Richard, West street
Skinner Hugh, West street
Turner Edmund, Back st

CABINET MAKERS.
Dennis Richard, West st
Rice Thos., Higher Mkt. st
Winter & Dainty, Banwl. st

CARPENTERS.
Born Thomas, Brook st
Spencer Henry, King st
Walters Richard, Brook st
Walters Wm. W., Bmkt. st
Winter (Edw.) & Dainty, (Isaac) Bannawell street

CHEMISTS & DRUGTS.
Bolt Emanuel, West street
Edgcumbe (Jph.) & Stannes, (Jas.) West street
Gill Wm. (& seeds.) West st
Perry Solomon, Back st

COACH MAKERS.
Parsons John, Brook street
Rendle (George) & Smith, (John.) Vigo Bridge

COFFEE, &c. HOUSES.
Cox Henry, Bedford square
Dunn Thomas, Matthew st
Hill Rd., Barley Market st
Methrell Wm., West st
Pennington Sml., Brook st
Pinhey George, Back st
Spencer Hy., Bannawell st
Symons Thos., Lrmkt. st

CONFECTIONERS.
Connor Hy., Hr. Brook st
Horswill Stephen, West st
Kerswell Edw., Matthew st
Williams Enoch, Hmkt. st

COOPERS.
Cook Thos., Hr. Brook st
Moyse Aaron, Back st
Worthy Rt., Butcher st

CORN MILLERS.
Dawe Isaac S., *Lumborn*
Friend Samuel, *Indiscombe*
Gibbings John, Town mills
Gimblett Wm. *Tavytown*
Robjohns Wm. & Henry, *Two Bridges*

CURRIERS.
Blanchard Hy., Bmkt. st
Drew Edward, Butcher st
Palmer Thomas, West st
Physick Andrew, Back st

DAIRYMEN.

Burley Jno.M.,Kilworthy ln
Cudlip Wm. B., Back st
Dawe Joseph, Bannawell st
Floyd Thomas, Matthew st
Isaac John, Dolvin road
Lavers Henry, Matthew st
Marks Eliz., Barley mkt. st
Polgreen John, Brook st
Richards Wm., Brook st
Stevens John, Exeter st
Stevens Simons, Bannwl. st
Stevens Thomas, Ford st
Vogwill John, Pepper st
Webb Richard, Brook st
Williams Henry, Elbow ln

FANCY DEPOTS.

Davis Fras. A., West st
Searle Eliz., Butcher st

FARMERS.

Allen Samuel, *Heathfield*
Arthur Jonathan, *Nutleigh*
Bickle Thomas, *Blanchdown*
Brooks Mary, *Crelake*
Burn Wm., *Cudlipptown*
Bidgood Mary, *Newton*
Collard Edw., *Morwellham*
Chubb George, *Cudlipptown*
Clifton John, *Romansleigh*
Courtis John, *Crebor*
Creber John, *Hock Lake*
Doidge Charles, *Kingford*
Dingle James, *Lamorn*
Downe John, *Woodovis*
Drew James, *Artiscombe*
Friend John, *Wilminston*
Gill Wm. & John, *Crowndale*
German John, *Gawton*
Glanville John, *Uppaton*
Hill Wm., *Wapisworthy*
Jeffrey Wm., *Langford*
Kinsman Daniel, *Fitzford*
Lethbridge Geo., *Kilworthy*
May Robt. & Wm., *Grendon*
Maunder Jph., *Church Park*
Oxenham Wm., *Grendon*
Oxenham Geo., *Cudlipptown*
Palmer Wm., *Radge*
Perkin John, *Styles Week*
Perkin John, jun. *Ogbear*
Perkin Robert, *Gulworthy*
Prout Thos., *Cudlipptown*
Reddicliffe John, *Cudlipptn.*
Reddicliffe Walter, *Wapiswy*
Reddicliffe Roger, *Broadmr*
Shepherd John, *Rowden*
Skinner Henry, *Down Hs*
Sleman Wm., *Ruby Town*
Snell John, *Indiscombe*
Turner John, *Shillamill*
Vigers Wm., *Crebor*
Walters John, *Mugaberry's*
Westaway Daniel, *Burnford*
Westaway John, *Old Wood*
Ware Samuel, *Hart's Hole*
Witheridge Geo., *Parswell*
Whidburn John, *Wilmingtn*
Williams James, *Gt. Torr*
Withycombe Hy. *Honeys Tor*
Withycombe Roger, *Morwell*
Withycombe George, *Hayle*

FIRE & LIFE OFFICES.

Alliance, E. H. Scobell
Atlas, Edward Pearse
British Coml.,J.L. Commins
Britannia, H. Trehane
Clerical & Medl., H. Terrell
County&Provdt., F.A.Davis
Crown,Joseph Brown
English Widows, &c., R. Luxton
European, C. V. Bridgman
Globe, S. E. S. Carpenter
Hand-in-Hand,Hy.Cornish
Imperial, J. M. Arnold
Indisputable, Gill & Vigers
Legal & Coml. C.Willesford
London Assuce., Wm. Gill
Medical Invalid, R Penrose
Norwich, W. L. Martin
Phœnix, John Physick
Star, Wm. Symons
Sun, Richard J. Robins
West of England, J Phillips
Western, John Seccombe
Yorkshire, Rd. Penwarden

GARDENERS, &c.

Pennington Saml., West st
Welch Wm., West street

GLASS & CHINA DLRS.

Baron Benj., Hr. Brook st
Davis Fras. A., Hmkt. st

GROCERS.

Andrews John, Hmkt. st
Burlace John, Brook street
Burlace Martha, Hmkt. st
Gill Wm., West street
Gribbell & Luscombe,Hmkt
Hamley John, Hmkt. st
Hill Wm., Brook street
Lovis John S., Hr. Brook st
Newton John, King street
Penwarden Rd., Bedford sq
Perry Solomon, Back st
Prout Fras. & Ths., Brook st
Pryer John, Pepper street
Roberts Wm., Bedford sq
Searle Harriet, Matthew st
Skinner John, Lrmkt. st
Turner Edward, Back st
Willcocks Walter, Brook st

HABERDASHERS.

Oates Eliz., West street
Perkin Daniel, Hmkt. st
Searle Eliz., Butcher st

HAIR DRESSERS, &c.

Doidge Charles, Hmkt. st
Doidge Wm., West street
Rowe Wm. (cutler,) Brook st

HATTERS.

Colwill Wm., Barleymkt. st
Doidge Thomas, Hmkt. st
Williams Richd., Hmkt. st

INNS & TAVERNS.

Bedford Hotel, Wm. Rowe
Northway,(posting ;) Jno. Cole, *Top*, Bedford square
Bull and Dog, John Hartop, Back street
Carpenters' Arms, Charles Riddalls, Brook street
Chip-Chop, Jas. Wakham

Commercial, John Courtis, Lower Market street
Corn Market,Wm. Slocombe
Cornish Arms, Jane Down, West street
Cottage Inn, Joseph Langman, Two Bridges
Crown, Ann Rowe, Bmkt. st
Duke of York, Thos. Davis, Ford street
Exeter Inn, Wm. Gribbell, Back street
Fox and Hounds, Michael Whitburn, Pepper st
George, Jph. Rowe, King st
Globe, Elias Bravin, Kg. st
Golden Fleece, Robt. Mashford, King street
Golden Lion,Wm. Richards, Brook street
London Inn, Thomas Floyd, Matthew street
Market House, Jph. & Wm. Ellis, Back street
New Bridge, Thos. Percy
New Quay, John Wills
Ordnance Arms, Thos. Pengelly, Lr. Market street
Plymouth Inn, John Luke, Bedford square
Queen's Head, John Northway, West street
Ship, Pp. Richards, *Morwell*
Union, Sml.TerrellGribbell, Bannawell street

BEERHOUSES.

Nichols John, Hr. Brook st
Pinhey George, Back street
Richards Wm., *Lamborn*
Rowe Benj., Bannawell st

IRONFOUNDERS,

Engineers, and Tool & Implement Manufctrs.

Nichols, Williams, and Co., *Bedford Foundry*
Tavistock Iron Co. (and hammer, tool, &c. mfrs.,) Brook st; Hy.Bullen,*mngr*

IRONMONGERS, &c.

Arnold John Mackrow, Lr. Market street
Baron Benj., Brook street
Dunn George, Back street
Jackson (John,) and Escott (Wm.) West street
Mudge George, Bedford sq
Pearse Wm. (stove & veruvolver manfr.) Bmkt. st
Sims Josiah, Hr. Market st

L. & W. DRAPERS.

Daw Chas. Hy., Butcher st
Flamank John W.,West st
Perkin Daniel, Hmkt. st
Tanton John, Hmkt. st
Trehane Stephen, Hmkt. st
Wescott (Simeon P.) & Stapleton (John,) West st

MALTSTERS.

Chubb Thomas, King st
Cudlipp Wm.Bunney, Bk. st
Paige George, Brook street

MERCHANTS.
(Coal, Timber, Lime, &c.)
Gill and Rundle, Wharf
Northey and Weekes, Quay
Skinner & Son, *Gawton*

MILLINERS, &c.
Ash Ann, Higher Mkt. st
Black Sus., Bannawell st
Cerutty Martha, West st
Cuddaford —,(stay,)Ford st
Doidge Eliz. L., Hmkt. st
Down Mary, West street
Foot Eliz., Hmkt. street
Jenkins Eliz., Brook st
Kerswell Eliz., Matthew st
Rowe Sus., Matthew st
Sargent Mary, Hr. Brook st
Skinner Cath., West st
Symons Jane, West st
Symons Sarah, Hr. Brook st
Tonkin My. Ann, Market st
Walters My. A., Brook st

PAINTERS&GLAZIERS.
Allen Henry, West street
Ellerey Wm., Brook street
Mallett Nichls. Simon, do
Robjohns Wm., West st
Sampson Jas., Hr. Brook st
WilliamsJohn,Bannawell st

PLASTERS. & MASONS.
Collicott James, Brook st
Collicott John, Brook st
Kerswell John, Matthew st
Walters Thomas, Brook st
Yelland Rd., Hr. Back st

ROPE, BAG, &c. MKRS.
Andrews John, West st
Corin Daniel, Pepper st
Cox John, Barleymkt. st
Doidge Thos., Matthew st

SADDLERS.
Andrews Wm., West st
Cross Wm., West street
Hooper Richard, Elbow ln
Mashford Robert, King st
Penwarden Jane, Bedford sq
Start Peter, Taylor square
Worth ——, Matthew st

SHAREBROKERS.
Carter Wm., Bannawell st
Methrell John, Bannawl. st
Ridgman Walter, West st

SHOPKEEPERS.
Backell Thomas, Brook st
Bounsell Frs. Ann, West st
Brown Eliz.& Tsn.,West st
Brown Michael, Brook st
Clemo Jn.(chandler,)Mkt st
Cundy Robt., Barleymkt.st
Dainty Jsa., Bannawell st
Daw Cath., Barleymkt. st
Daw Christian, West st
Down Samuel, West st
Gale Wm., West street
Johns Wm., King street
Kallaway David, Brook st
Kent Eliza J., Brook st
Lovis Francis, Brook street
Marks Mrs., Barleymkt. st
Mason George, Butcher st
Mayne Richd., Bannawl. st
Nelson ——, Exeter street
Pryer Anthony, Pepper st
Staddon Wm., Lmkt. st
Walker J., West street
Webb Richard, Brook st
West J., Brook street
Williams Eliz., Bannawl. st

STRAW HAT MKRS.
Barkell Eliz., Bmkt. st
Hawke My. A., Matthew st
Lang Eliz., Bannawell st
May Eliz., West street
Pryer Ann, Pepper street
Willcocks A., Hr. Brook st
Williams Eliz., Hmkt. st

SURGEONS.
Harness Thos. B. (M.D.) West street
Leamon Edw. Foote, Ford st
Michell and West, West st
Michell Wm. Pryce, West st
Mitchell John Giddey, jun., Ford street
Northey Wm.Cornish, Bfd.sq
Pearse & Northey, Bedfd. sq
Pearse John ; h Abbey Bdg
Sleman Richard, Brook st
West Richd. Elliott, West st

TAILORS & DRAPERS.
Bennett Wm., Hr. Brook st
Dainty John, Bannawell st
Foote Richard, West st
Hill George, Matthew st
Horswill Henry, Brook st
Jenkins Wm., Brook st
Kellaway David, Brook st
Lyons Jph., Lr. Market st
Matters Jonth., Brook st
Nicholls James, Hmkt. st
Prout Wm., Exeter street
Rowell Wm., Hmkt. st
Trist James, West street

VETERINRY. SURGNS.
Lord John Keast, West st
Menhinnick Wm., Brook st
Ridgman Walter, West st

WATCH & CLOCK MKS.
Jackson (John,) & Eastcott, (Wm.) West street
Miles John, West street
Pearse Wm., Barleymkt. st
Snell John Holder, Mkt. st
Stenlake Benj., Market st

WHEELWRIGHTS.
Bennett John, Brook street
Crocomb Edward, Brook st
Dament C., Bannawell st
Jessop Peter, Brook street
Prout Richard, *Lamborn*
Richards Wm., Vigo bridge

WOOLSTAPLERS,
And Fellmongers.
ButchersCs.Barnes,Brook st
Hill John, Thomas, Wm., and Abraham, Dolvin rd
Sargant Gustvs., Brook st

COACHES, &c.
To *Barnstaple*, from Queen's Head, Tue., Thu., & Sat
To *Launceston*, three days a week, to meet *Exeter, Truro, & Plymouth* coaches
Omnibuses to Plymouth and Launceston daily, from Cornish Arms, Exeter Inn, and Proctor & Gillard's
To *Liskeard*, *Bodmin*, &c., Omnibus from Ordnance Arms, Thursday, 9 mng
Pridham and Lake's *Van*, from Queen's Head, to *Barnstaple*, *Exeter*, and all parts, daily
Ford and Co.'s Van, *to all parts*, daily ; P. Cerutty, *agent*

BOROUGHS OF
PLYMOUTH AND DEVONPORT,
THE LATTER OF WHICH INCLUDES
EAST STONEHOUSE, MORICE TOWN, AND STOKE-DAMEREL.

PLYMOUTH, DEVONPORT, and STONEHOUSE, are commonly called "*The Three Towns*," though they adjoin each other, and form one of the largest sea-ports and principal naval and military stations in England, situated at the south-west corner of Devon. They extend about three miles from east

to west, and comprise, with their northern suburbs of *Morice Town* and *Stoke,* about 90,000 inhabitants. Plymouth is on the east, Stonehouse in the centre, and Devonport on the west; and their eastern, southern, and western sides, are skirted and deeply indented by the broad, deep, and extensive *creeks and harbours* in the estuaries of the Tamar and Plym, which meet in *Plymouth Sound,* and take the names of *Catwater, Sutton Pool, Mill Bay, Stonehouse Pool,* and *Hamoaze;* to the latter of which the great naval arsenal of Devonport Dock Yard presents its massive sea wall and numerous docks, slips, &c, in a semicircular range of more than half a mile, exclusive of the Gun Wharf, and the large Government Steam Yard on the north, opposite Torpoint, to which there is a steam ferry across the estuary of the Tamar. Plymouth Citadel and Mill Bay front that broad arm of the English Channel called the *Sound,* in which the force of the Atlantic surges is considerably broken by a stupendous *breakwater,* while the harbours and creeks on either side are shut in from the violence of ocean storms, on the west by that bold peninsular range of hills, extending from Cornwall to Mount Edgcumbe, and that long projection of Stonehouse terminating at the Devil's Point, opposite Mount Edgcumbe; and on the east by the bold promontory of Mount Batten, at the entrance to Catwater, the mouth of the river *Plym,* from which Plymouth has its name. The South Devon Railway extends from Plymouth to Exeter, and connects the three towns with the great railways traversing most parts of the kingdom; but the line intended to pass hence through Cornwall to Falmouth, &c., is not yet made, though an act for its construction was obtained a few years ago. The ground on which the most populous parts of Plymouth and Stonehouse are built, falls towards the centre, making a sort of hollow, extending from east to west; from which the suburbs rise to a considerable elevation on the north, and to the high ground called the Hoe, overlooking the Sound on the south. The site of Devonport is more elevated, but its face has a gradual southern inclination, and on three sides it falls abruptly to the water. The northern suburbs at Higher Stoke rise much higher, and command delightful views of the towns, harbours, headlands, and the castellated mansion and sylvan grounds of Mount Edgcumbe. *Devonport, Morice Town, Stoke,* and *Higher Stoke,* form the PARISH OF STOKE DAMEREL, which had 33,820 inhabitants in 1841, of whom more than 25,000 were in Devonport, 306 in the Parish Workhouse, 1148 in seven Barracks, 478 in the Convict Hulk, and 155 in Stoke Military Hospital. This parish forms the *Municipal Borough of Devonport;* but the *Parliamentary Borough* includes also the PARISH OF EAST STONEHOUSE, which in 1841 had 9712 inhabitants, including 102 persons in the Parish Workhouse, 437 in the Royal Marine Barracks, and 307 in the Royal Naval Hospital. This parish maintains its poor under the provisions of the New Poor Law, and Stoke Damarel Parish is now petitioning to be placed under the control of that act, though neither parish is or wishes to be united with any other for the support of its poor. The BOROUGH OF PLYMOUTH comprises the two *parishes of St. Andrew and Charles the Martyr,* except Pennycross Chapelry in the former, and Compton Gifford tithing in the latter, which are in Roborough Hundred and in Plympton St. Mary Union, as afterwards noticed. The borough parts of these parishes maintain their poor conjointly, under a local act, and their population in 1841 amounted to 36,520 souls, of whom 12,956 were in Charles the Martyr's parish, and 23,564 in St. Andrew's. The latter included 219 persons in the Royal Marine Barracks; 741 in the Citadel Barracks; 332 in Plymouth Workhouse; 79 in the Chatham Hulk; 56 on

Drake's Island; and 320 poor Irish waiting for emigration ships. The total *population* of the two boroughs was 61,212 in 1821; 76,001 in 1831; and 80,052 in 1841, and it may be now estimated at about 90,000 souls. The four parishes in the two Boroughs are in the *Archdeaconry of Totnes* and *Deanery of Plympton*, and in the Southern Parliamentary Division of Devon, and in Plymouth Polling and County Court District. Stonehouse is in Roborough Hundred and Petty Sessional Division, but the municipal boroughs have separate quarter and petty sessions.

PLYMOUTH, as already stated, is the most eastern of the "three towns," and occupies an important maritime situation at the head of Plymouth Sound, which here extends its expansive waters into the noble harbours of Catwater, Mill Bay, Sutton Pool, Stonehouse Pool, and Hamoaze, and receives on the east and west the broad estuaries of the Plym and the Tamar. It is distant 44 miles S.W. of Exeter; 29 miles W. of Dartmouth; 15 miles S. of Tavistock; 5 miles E.S.E. of Saltash; and 216 miles W.S.W. of London. The *Borough* increased its population from about 16,000 souls in 1801, to 36,520 in 1841, and has now upwards of 40,000, including the soldiers in barracks, and others attached to the naval and military establishments. It has now about 5500 houses, of which no fewer than 500 were built in 1846-7. Its *street arrangements* extend about a mile each way, and its site ascends on a bold and broken gradient, back from Mill Bay and Sutton Pool, and the intermediate headland occupied by the Citadel and the Hoe; and is such as to render some of the streets steep, and the entrance from the north-east rather inconvenient; but many of the streets and some of the entrances to the town have been much improved during the last 20 years; and the new buildings in many of the older parts have imparted an air of renovation and beauty to what was before an assemblage of architectural craziness and disorder. There are now in the suburbs many handsome villas and rows of neat houses; and in the *town* are several good streets and many commodious public buildings, well-stocked shops, and large inns and taverns. The large modern town of Devonport which is separated from Plymouth by that of Stonehouse, was called Plymouth Dock till 1824, as afterwards noticed. In the Saxon era, the site of Plymouth was called *Tameorwerth*, but after the Conquest, it acquired the name of *Sutton*, or South Town, in reference to its more ancient neighbour Plympton. In the reign of Edward I., one part of it was called *Sutton Prior* and the other *Sutton Valletort;* the north part of the town being on the lands of the Prior of Plympton, and the south part on the estate of the Valletorts. These names were relinquished in the reign of Henry VI. for the more appropriate appellation of *Plym-mouth.* In the beginning of the reign of Edward II., great disputes arose between the Prior of Plympton and the king, respecting certain rights and immunities, claimed by the former, but always contested by the Crown. At length, by a writ issued from the Exchequer in 1313, a jury was summoned to examine the various claims, and determine the differences between the King and the Prior. By their decision, the Prior, in consideration of a fee-farm rent of £29. 6s. 8d. to be annually paid into the Exchequer for the use of his Majesty, was confirmed in the exercise of various privileges, among which were—the right of granting leases of houses as lord of the fee; of having a manor view of frank-pledge, assize of bread and beer, a ducking-stool and pillory, and the fishing of the waters from Catwater to the head of the river Plym. In the reign of Edward III., the manor was given to John de Eltham, Earl of Cornwall, who had many disputes with the Prior, whose claims were again confirmed by a special jury. About this period, Plymouth, which had been much improved under the liberal building

leases granted by the Prior, became an object of jealousy to the French, who landed here and endeavoured to destroy the town by fire, but were repulsed, with the loss of 500 men, by Hugh Courtenay, Earl of Devon, under whose conduct the surrounding gentry and their vassals had associated with celerity. In a second attempt, in the 6th of Henry IV., the French were more successful. Landing at the head of Sutton Pool, near Britonside, they burnt upwards of 600 houses; but failing in their attempt to destroy the castle and the higher parts of town, they retired to their ships, and proceeded to Dartmouth, where Mons. du Chastel, one of their commanders, and about 400 men, were killed, and 200 others were made prisoners. (See page 487.) From the time of this occurrence till the reign of Henry VI., the town dwindled to a mere fishing village, but it was then improved by the Prior of Plympton, who rebuilt many of the houses at his own expense; and by liberally granting certain privileges, and leases at small fines, occasioned a considerable increase of inhabitants. Trade revived, and the spirit of industry and enterprise being awakened, its capacious harbours were again frequented by merchant and other vessels. About 1438, the inhabitants petitioned Henry VI. for a *charter of incorporation*, and also that they might have a *wall* built round the town, for its better defence against the irruption of an enemy. In the following year, the king granted a charter which incorporated the inhabitants by the name of the *Mayor and Commonalty of Plymouth* and divided the town and borough into four *wards*, called Old Town, High Vintry, Low Vintry, and Looe street Wards; each to have a Captain and inferior officers, but all to be under the control of the Mayor. In the 4th of Edward IV. a confirmation of the liberties and franchises of Plymouth was granted to the Mayor and Commonalty, on condition of their paying a fee-farm rent of £41 to the Prior of Plympton, and one of ten marks to the Prior of Bath; and from this period " the *lordship of the fee of the manor of Sutton Prior and Valletort* (now Plymouth,) was vested in the Corporation of Plymouth, together with the assize of bread and beer, fishery of the waters, view of frank-pledge, tolls of the markets and fairs, and the use of the ducking stool and pillory. In the reign of Elizabeth, a *new charter* was granted to the borough, through the solicitation of the celebrated Admiral *Sir Francis Drake*, by which the former charters were confirmed, and the Corporation declared to consist of a mayor, 12 aldermen, 24 common councilmen, and an indefinite number of freemen, with a recorder, town clerk, coroner, and a number of inferior officers. The above-named gallant Admiral was born near Tavistock, and was the first Englishman that circumnavigated the globe. Through his skill and perseverance, a stream of *water* was brought to Plymouth from the sources of the river Meavy, in Dartmoor, by a winding channel nearly 24 miles in length. This noble undertaking was entirely executed at his own cost, and the channel has ever since been vested with the Corporation, and still supplies the town water-works. The Corporation claims to be by prescription, and has *charters* from eleven monarchs, beginning with Henry VI. and ending with William III. The borough sent *two members to parliament* in the 26th and 33rd of Edwd. I.; in the 4th and 7th of Edward II., and the 4th of Edward III.; and it has regularly returned two members since the 20th of Hy. VI. A *market* is said to have been established here as early as 1253. In the reign of Edward I., the port had 325 vessels. In 1512, an act of Parliament was passed for fortifying Plymouth and other seaports in the west; and in 1520, Bishop Lacey granted an indulgence to all such persons as should contribute to the fortifications at Plymouth. *Leland*, who visited it in the time of Henry VIII., says, "the mouth of the gulph, where the

shippes of Plymouth lyith, is waullid on eche side, and chained over in tyme of necessitie; on the south-west side of the mouth is a block-house, and on a rocky hill hard by it is a strong castle quadrate, having on each corner a great round tower. It seemeth to be no very old peace of worke." The little island of St. Nicholas, or *Drake's Island*, was afterwards strongly fortified, and batteries and block-houses were erected on all sides of the town. On the 20th of July, 1588, part of the English fleet, consisting of 120 sail, under the command of Lord Charles Howard and Sir Fras. Drake, lay at anchor in Plymouth Sound, when the *Spanish Armada* sailed up the channel, and some of its ships looked into the Sound, where the Spanish Admiral is said to have fixed upon Mount Edgcumbe as his future residence; but not liking the company he saw, his fleet passed out to sea, followed by the English, who overtook the enemy on the following day, kept up a running fight till the 24th, and being joined by another squadron off the Isle of Wight, drove the fight to a more general engagement, and continued it at intervals till the 28th, when they assailed the Armada with fire-ships, and in two days saw "the invincible" sea-force totally destroyed or dispersed. To this victorious fleet, Plymouth contributed seven ships and one fly-boat, a quota greater than that supplied by any other port except London. In 1595, twenty-two chests of the *Pope's bulls and indulgences,* which had been taken from a discomfited party of Spanish invaders in Cornwall, were publicly burnt in Plymouth market-place. In 1596, Plymouth Sound was the grand rendezvous of the fleet for the expedition against Cadiz. In 1625, Charles I., with his whole court, a fleet of 120 ships and 6000 troops, remained ten days at Plymouth, and was sumptuously entertained by the Corporation. In the following year, the *plague* carried off nearly 2000 of the inhabitants.

During the CIVIL WAR of the 17th century, Plymouth was in the hands of the Parliament, who retained it even at the time when most of the important places in the west were in the possession of the royalists. Soon after the commencement of the war, the Earl of Ruthen was appointed governor of the town, and Sir Alex. Carew had the command of the fort and island of St. Nicholas. Various attempts were made by the royalists to gain possession of this important post. Sir Ralph Hopton appeared before it in December, 1642, but was driven from his quarters by the Earl of Stamford. It having been discovered in the September following, that Sir Alex. Carew was on the point of betraying his trust, he was sent prisoner to London, and suffered death on Tower hill. In the early part of September, 1643, Colonel Digby was sent with a considerable force of horse and foot to blockade Plymouth, and took up his quarters at Plymstock. The blockading army had batteries at Oreston and Mount Batten, and a guard at Hoo. Early in October they planned an attack on Mount Stamford, a fort so called from the parliamentary general, the Earl of Stamford. Their guard at Hoo was defeated with much loss on the 8th, about which time Prince Maurice, having captured Dartmouth, advanced with his whole army to besiege Plymouth. The Prince's head-quarters were at Widey House, and his army was stationed at Plympton, Plymstock, Cawsand, Egg-Buckland, Tamerton, &c. On the 5th of November, Mount Stamford was taken by the besiegers, and the fort at Lipson attempted. At this critical period, Col. Wardlaw, the governor, required all the inhabitants to take a vow and protestation to defend the towns of Plymouth and Stonehouse, and the fort and island of St. Nicholas, to the uttermost. On the 3rd of December, the royalists took a fort at Lory Point, but were soon repulsed by the garrison, who retook the fort. On the 18th of the same month, an attempt was made to storm the town, but

the besiegers were repulsed with much loss, and the siege was raised on the 25th. Among the Devonshire officers engaged in this long siege, were the Earl of Marlborough, Sir Thos. Hele, Sir Edmund Fortescue, and Sir P. Courtenay. In April, 1644, Sir Richard Grenville advanced with his forces towards Plymouth, but Col. Martin, then governor of the town, marched out with the greater part of the garrison, and defeated him at St. Budeaux, and took two companies prisoners. About three days after, Sir Richard advanced again, but with no better success; and he was again repulsed before Plymouth in July, when Col. Kerr was made governor. About this time, Prince Maurice again attempted the capture of Plymouth, but not succeeding, he left Sir Richard Grenville to blockade the town. The Earl of Essex and his army approached Plymouth about the end of the month, and Sir Richard hastily abandoned the blockade. After the surrender of Essex's army in Cornwall, the King came before Plymouth on the 9th of September, 1644, attended by Prince Maurice. On the 11th, Lord Roberts, the governor, was summoned to surrender the town; but on his refusal, it was determined, at a council of war, not to undertake an assault or close siege; and the blockade was again entrusted to Sir Richd. Grenville. The King lodged at Widey House, but left, with the greater part of his army, on the 14th. In January, 1645, Sir Richard Grenville, having a force of 6000 men, assaulted the town, and gained possession of the four great out-works, but was soon afterwards repulsed, with great loss. Mount Stamford was retaken by the garrison on the 18th of February, and Grenville was again defeated on the 24th. In June, the command of the blockade was entrusted to Sir John Berkeley, and in September to General Digby. Colonel Weldon was made governor of Plymouth in October; but on the 10th of January, 1646, the blockade of Plymouth was finally abandoned. (See pages 31 and 56.) In 1654, a special order was directed from Oliver Cromwell, then Protector, directing that in future all persons who wished to be *married* must be united at the Guildhall, by the Mayor and Justices for the time being. This occasioned a considerable ferment among all ranks, and a sort of remonstrance; but the order was made peremptory, on the ground that marriage was a civil contract. At this time the borough paid its two representatives for their services in Parliament. In 1670, Charles II. visited Plymouth, and was presented by the Corporation with a purse of 150 broad pieces. In 1683, the borough charter was surrendered to the King, on the requisition of Judge Jefferies, and a new one was granted, at the expense of £417. 19s. which vested the power in ten aldermen and twelve assistants only. This continued in force till 1697, when the old charter was restored.

When the combined fleet was in the Channel, in 1779, and the prison-ships were crowded with French and Spanish captives, great apprehensions were entertained for the safety of the place, but a corps of *volunteers* was raised by Wm. Bastard, Esq., and under their escort the prisoners were marched to Exeter. During the alarms of invasion from France, in 1798, 1803, and 1805, great exertions were made for the defence of Plymouth town and dock, but they were not attempted by the enemy. The town, in connexion with its dock-yard, arsenal, and harbours, was the scene of much bustle throughout the last war with France, and rose so rapidly in importance, that its suburb of *Stonehouse* became doubled in population, and its western suburb of *Devonport*, then called Plymouth-Dock, increased from almost nothing to the bulk of a rival town. Though it might have been expected to suffer reaction, and fall into langour and decline after the return of peace, it has, on the contrary, continued to prosper, and has undergone striking improvements, not only in its architecture and the ap-

pearance of domestic comfort, but in the number and character of its
literary and charitable institutions.   Plymouth is supposed to have had
about 10,000 inhabitants in the reign of Edward III., for we find that in
1773, (soon after a great pestilence,) it contained 4837 persons of 14 years
of age or upwards, then rated to the poll tax, from which only clergymen
and mendicants were exempt.   As a sea-port, it has from an early period
been one of the principal rendezvous of the British navy.   From this port,
Edward the Black Prince, after having been detained [forty days in Sutton Pool by contrary winds, sailed in 1355, on his successful expedition to
France, which was crowned with the glorious victory of Poictiers ; and here
he landed on the first of May, 1357, with the French King, and his son, the
Dauphin, as prisoners in his train.   In 1470, the Earl of Warwick, with
the Duke of Clarence, and the Earls of Pembroke and Oxford, landed here
to excite the revolt which caused the temporary restoration of Henry VI.
In 1346, this port furnished 25 ships and 603 mariners for the blockade of
Calais.   The ill-fated Catherine of Arragon landed here in 1501 ; and from
this port were fitted out the vessels of the Earl of Cumberland, Drake, Gilbert, Carlisle, Grenville, Cavendish, Cook, and Wallis, when they set sail on
their respective *voyages of discovery*.   The celebrated Sir Martin Frobisher,
not only sailed from this port, but is said to have died here in 1594.   The
much injured *Sir Walter Raleigh* is said to have been arrested on his
landing here, previous to the enforcing of the fatal but suspended sentence
in 1618.   (See p. 221.)   In 1633, there was so great a flood here that
boats floated into the streets.   During the high tide in 1744, property to
the amount of £3000 was destroyed in the town, and casks and boats
floated about the streets.   The old barbican was washed down in 1762.
The Princess Amelia was at Plymouth and Mount Edgcumbe in 1766, and
in that year the streets began to be paved and lighted.   The Duke of Cumberland was here in 1769, the Duke of Gloucester in 1782, and George
III. and Queen Charlotte in 1789.   Their Majesties were sumptuously entertained at Saltram House, and during their stay there was a naval review
and a grand sham fight, in which the fleet formed into two separate lines of
battle, one being considered French and the other English.   In 1790, two
men were gibbeted for murder, near Stoke church.   In 1796, the Dutton
East Indiaman was wrecked near the Citadel.   In 1791 and 1799, the two
piers which form the entrance to Sutton Pool were erected.   The magnificent Hotel and Theatre were built by the Corporation in 1811, and the colossal Breakwater was commenced in the following year.   On the 5th of
July, 1815, the Bellerophon dropped anchor in Plymouth Sound, having on
board the fallen *Emperor Napoleon*, who for 20 years had filled the world
with his fame, and had pulled down kings and set up princes at his pleasure.   He remained here eight days, and thousands of visitors came from
all parts, and went off in boats and other vessels to behold the man who
had so long been the dread of nations, but was now a fallen enemy, who
had surrendered himself to the protection of Great Britain.   The curiosity
of the crowds which were daily drawn round the Bellerophon was frequently gratified by his condescension in placing himself in the gangways,
conspicuous to every beholder, and returning the respect paid him by the
shouts of the multitude, by bowing to all around.   After waiting the decision of a cabinet council as to his future destiny, which terminated in the
island of St. Helena, he was transferred from the Bellerophon to the Northumberland, which ship and her consorts immediately proceeded on their
long voyage, and arrived at the island after a tedious passage of ten weeks.
The long war, which had cost England so much money and blood, was now
terminated ; the extensive *Prison of War*, (see page 39,) which had been

built in *Dartmoor Forest*, for the relief of the crowded prison ships of Plymouth, gave up its thousands of captives; and the whole world hailed with delight the return of peace. The Grand Duke Michael of Russia visited Plymouth in 1817, and in the same year an act was obtained for settling disputes between the Corporation and the Board of Ordnance. George IV. was proclaimed here in 1819, in the midst of great rejoicings, and a dinner was given to the poor, but there were greater rejoicings, and the poor were much more liberally entertained at his coronation, in the following year, when upwards of 5000 dined in the market-place. The prosperity of the town suffered a severe check during the great panic of 1824, when the Plymouth Bank failed, like many others in the kingdom. During the year there was an extremely high tide; household furniture floated about some of the streets, and many boats were destroyed. *Races* were established on Chelson Meadow, in 1826. Plymouth has received and entertained many royal visitors, and was honoured with the presence of Queen Victoria and Prince Albert in 1843. It has, at various periods, suffered severely from plagues and other maladies, as it did in 1832 and 1849 from *cholera*. This awful scourge swept off 779 of its inhabitants, from June to September, in 1832; and 819 from the 4th of July to the 8th of November, in 1849; and the total number of cases in the former year was 1894, and in the latter 3360. The total number of deaths from cholera in the three towns, from July 4th to October 2nd, 1849, was 717 in Plymouth, 717 in Devonport, and 155 in Stonehouse,—making a total of 1589 during the three months. In the week ending August 16, there were 140 deaths in Devonport alone, and in the following week 112, besides 74 in Plymouth, and 17 in Stonehouse. Some parts of the three towns are very badly drained, but various sanatory improvements have been proposed, and some of them are now being carried out. At present, the drainage of Plymouth empties itself into Sutton Harbour and Millbay, through outlets which are above low water mark, but it has been proposed to collect the drainage into a large culvert, to be carried out into the deep water of the Sound. As noticed at page 59, the *South Devon Railway* was opened to Laira, on May 5th, 1848; and to Plymouth on April 2nd, 1849; when the Mayor invited the Chairman and Directors to a *déjeûner à la fourchette*, at the Royal Hotel, and the arrival of the first train was witnessed by thousands of spectators.

The following general survey of the FORTIFICATIONS, HARBOURS, and NAVAL and MILITARY ESTABLISHMENTS of *Plymouth, Stonehouse*, and *Devonport*, will be followed by a separate description of each town and its public institutions, charities, &c.

The CITADEL at Plymouth is a large fortification on the south side of the town, occupying that bold headland which extends from the western side of Sutton Pool into the Sound, at the confluence of the Catwater. It was erected on the site of an old fort, by order of Charles II., who inspected it personally in the year 1670. It is built chiefly of limestone and granite, and consists of three regular and two irregular bastions; and the curtains of the former are strengthened by ravelins and hornworks. The east, west, and north sides are circumscribed by a deep ditch, counterscarp, and covered way, pallisadoed; and the south side is defended by a lower fort, constructed upon the rocks on the shore, and chiefly intended to defend the Sound. Cannon are mounted both on this fort and on the upper parapets, where there are embrasures for 120 pieces. Two gateways with drawbridges form the entrance from the town; and the second gateway, which opens immediately into the Citadel, displays a sculpture of the royal arms, and other devices. In the centre of the spacious esplanade, where the troops

are exercised, (and round which stand the officers' houses, chapel, magazine, armory, and barracks,) is a bronze colossal statue of George II., in the costume of a Roman warrior, wreathed with laurel. From the ramparts, which are nearly three quarters of a mile in circuit, the views are extensive and beautiful.

The HOE is a commanding eminence, bounded on the east by the Citadel, on the south by the Sound, and on the west by Millbay. It is justly styled "*the lungs of Plymouth*," for here the inhabitants of all grades resort for air and exercise. Great improvements have been made of late years by the formation of carriage drives and public walks, with seats at intervals. The facilities of access from the town to this extensive and delightful promenade have recently been increased by several new avenues. The soldiers stationed in the Citadel frequently exercise on the Hoe; and occasionally may be witnessed a sham fight. The band often enlivens the promenade; and in the central part is an interesting Camera Obscura, and an obelisk which serves as a mark for vessels entering the harbour. The views from this elevated promenade are extensive; embracing seaward, the Sound, Drake's Island, the Breakwater, the Mew Stone, and in clear weather, Eddystone Lighthouse, fourteen miles distant in the English Channel. On the right, the Cornish coast is seen from Penlee Point to the shelving shores of Cawsand,—and from thence over the nearer and well defined groves and lawns of Mount Edgcumbe; and still more westerly, the town of Devonport, with its column and steeples, and the elevated suburbs of Stoke. On the left is seen the line of the coast from Staddon Point to Mount Batten, guarding the entrance to Catwater; and thence, looking inland over the town, may be seen the extensive woods of Saltram, and the more distant hills of Dartmoor. There is a landing place under the Hoe, whence a boat can be procured for a trip to Drake's Island and the Breakwater.

ST. NICHOLAS' or DRAKE'S ISLAND, is near the middle of Plymouth Sound, and comprises only about three acres, strongly fortified, and connected with the south-western shore by a range of rocks, which is uncovered at low water, and is commonly called the *Bridge of Rocks*. Even at high water no vessels can pass these rocks, except those of very small burthen. This small island is surrounded with rocks, and has always been the chief defence of the port. It was strongly garrisoned by the Parliamentarians during the civil wars of the 17th century, but was once or twice on the eve of being treacherously surrendered to the Royalists, as already noticed. The garrison is generally formed by a detachment of troops from the Citadel. The landing place is on the north side, where the rock is ascended by a flight of steps through a vaulted passage. A large portion of the area of the island is occupied by the fortifications, and barracks for about 140 soldiers and 40 gunners. The fortifications have been greatly augmented during the last two centuries, and the principal battery was completed in 1846, and mounts 19 pieces of cannon, ranging from 32 to 68 pounders. In addition to its defences, the fort contains furnaces for heating balls red hot. Some authors consider this island as the site of the *Tamarweorth* of the Saxons, so called from its being "*the river island of the Tamar*," which here mingles its waters in the Sound, after passing the noble harbour of Hamoaze. Westcote says, the island of St. Nicholas was a place of refuge to divers gentlemen in the insurrection of 1549, (see page 56,) when the insurgents plundered and set fire to Plymouth. Before the erection of its fortifications, it had an ancient chapel, which Camden calls St. Michael's. In 1548, the mayor of Plymouth received orders from the Privy Council to convert this chapel into a bulwark.

On the highest point of the promontory on the south side of the entrance

to Catwater, opposite the Citadel, stands MOUNT BATTEN, an ancient circular fort, having no entrance but at a considerable height from the ground, to which access is afforded by a ladder. The interior is arched in the form of a dome, with solid and durable masonry. During the wars between Charles I. and the Parliament, it was the scene of repeated skirmishes and much bloodshed. In addition to the *new fortifications* lately completed at Bovisand, Picklecombe Point, and Drake's Island, a large fort called the *Prince of Wales' Redoubt*, was erected in 1849, on the headland called Western King, near the Victualling Yard. These render the defence of the Sound complete.

The BREAKWATER is a stupendous national work, about two miles south of the Citadel, extending about a mile in length across the central part of the Sound, between Cawsand and Bovisand Bays. The broad and often turbulent waters of the Sound are here about three miles broad, and open into the English Channel about two miles further to the south. From the frequent occurrence of storms from the south-west, which endangered vessels at anchor, it was deemed an object of great importance to make the Sound a safe roadstead; consequently, in 1811, Government determined on the adoption of a plan submitted to them by Messrs. Rennie and Whidbey, of forming this gigantic Breakwater. For its construction they purchased, for £10,000, a mass of limestone rock at Oreston, covering 25 acres. The first stone (a vast block,) was deposited Aug. 12th, 1812; and in the following March, the Breakwater had so far advanced, that parts of its irregular surface were seen above low water. In June, 1847, no less than 3,620,440 tons of limestone had been used in this great work, though 70 yards of the eastern arm, requiring 50,000 tons more, were then unfinished. In addition to this enormous bulk, 2,512,696 cubic feet of granite and other stone were used in the paving and facings. The total cost of the Breakwater was about £1,500,000. The centre part is a straight line, extending one thousand yards, and at each end is an arm or kant, 350 yards long, projecting towards the shore at an angle of 120 degrees; but the low water line extends 70 yards further. The top is 45 feet broad, and is at the ends two feet, and in the centre three feet above the high water of spring tides. Above 500 yards of the centre rests upon shovel rocks and shoals, and the rest stretches out into deeper water, leaving a passage for vessels 1600 yards wide on the west, and another 1000 yards wide on the east. The whole work has a vertical height of from 56 to 80 feet, from the base to the top. In addition to the outer slope is an extensive *berne*, or foreshore, 30 feet wide at the extremity of the east wing, 50 feet wide in the centre, and 70 feet wide at the extremity of the west wing. This foreshore rises from the base of the slope to about five feet above the low water line; and serves to break the force of the waves before they strike the main body of the work, and to prevent their recoil from undermining the slopes of the base, and making a consequent breach in the general structure. The western end of the Breakwater is strengthened by facings of masonry, and finished off in a circular form, to serve as the foundation of a *Light House*, which was completed in 1843, and rises 68 feet above the platform. It is crowned by a lantern eight feet high, supported by gun-metal pilasters, and provided with four refractors, and five tiers containing 118 mirrors. The light can be seen at the distance of eight miles, except in foggy weather, when a bell is struck a certain number of times every minute, by clock machinery. A floating light had been stationed near the same spot since 1813, but was often sent adrift from its moorings. In January, 1817, and November, 1824, the Breakwater (then unfinished,) was much injured by violent storms; particularly in the latter year, when a most tremendous hurri-

cane, acting on an unusually high tide, made vast breaches through this barrier; yet even that tempest demonstrated its great utility, for had not the Breakwater existed, it was supposed that all the ships in the Catwater would have been wrecked, and many of the buildings near the shore swept into the ocean. That it has answered the expectations of its warmest advocates, is evinced by the security it has afforded to ships at anchor,—above 200 sail of vessels having taken refuge within it at one time. On the shore of *Bovisand*, east of the Breakwater, is a large reservoir of water, for supplying vessels free of charge, which is done by means of iron pipes, at the landing place.

EDDYSTONE LIGHT HOUSE is under the control of the Customs' establishment at Plymouth, though distant 14 miles in the Channel, opposite the Sound. This celebrated structure stands upon one of a large cluster of rocks, stretching north and south to the length of about 100 fathoms. The particular form and position of these rocks tend greatly to augment the force of the sea; and previous to the erection of the lighthouse, many fatal accidents happened upon them. Though most important to the port of Plymouth, this lighthouse is highly beneficial to all vessels traversing the English Channel. In 1696, the first attempt to erect a lighthouse on the principal rock, was accomplished by Mr. Henry Winstanley, of Essex, who completed it in three years; but this bold and unfortunate mechanic, perished amidst the ruins of his edifice, in the tremendous storm of November, 1703. Three years after, Mr. Rudyerd, of London, began to erect another lighthouse on the same spot, of stone and timber, and completed it in 1709. This structure, after braving the storms of the ocean for 46 years, was destroyed by fire in 1755. The present lighthouse was erected by that celebrated architect the late Mr. Smeaton, and exhibits a striking triumph of art and ingenuity. It was commenced in 1757, and finished in 1759. With the exception of the lantern, which is of cast iron and copper, the building is entirely of stone, the outside being of granite, and the floors vaulted. It is a circular building, and the diameter of the base is 26 feet, and that of the top 15 feet. The stone work rises 70 feet to the octagonal lantern, which rises 24 feet higher. The stones average a ton weight each, and those on the same level are dove-tailed together, and the successive courses are attached to each other, by means of square blocks of marble, which project one-half of their solidity into the course below, and the other half into the course above. By this means, so firm a bond is maintained, both horizontally and vertically, that the building may be regarded as one entire and perfect substance. Three men are now stationed here, and they are provided with food and other necessaries by a boat appointed for that purpose; but they are always stocked with salt provisions, to guard against the possibility of want, as in winter it sometimes happens that the boats cannot approach for many weeks together.

CATWATER HARBOUR, on the south-east side of Plymouth, is the grand outlet, through which the river Plym falls into the Sound, between the Citadel and Mount Batten. It is capable of receiving a thousand sail of merchant ships, but though protected by high hills, ships have sometimes been wrecked in it, as was the case in the tremendous gales of 1824 and 1828, when 20 vessels were stranded on its rocky shores in the former, and 15 in the latter year. Above Catwater, the estuary of the Plym, assumes a lake-like expanse, called the *Laira* or *Lary*, and skirted by the groves of *Saltram*,—the splendid seat of the Earl of Morley, (see p. 555,) whose predecessor erected at his own expense, the *Laira Bridge*, an elegant structure, consisting of five elliptical arches of cast iron, springing from abutments and piers of stone. The first stone was laid in 1824, and the

bridge was finished in 1827. The centre arch is 100 feet span, and rises $14\frac{1}{2}$ feet above high water mark; and the other arches are two of them 95 and two 81 feet each in span. The roadway is 24 feet wide within the railings, and 500 feet in length.

SUTTON POOL HARBOUR is in the south-eastern part of Plymouth, and is nearly surrounded by the town. The entrance from Catwater is about 90 feet in width, between two large *Piers*, (called the *Barbican*,) that were erected by means of parliamentary grants, in 1791 and 1799. This spacious harbour belongs to the Duchy of Cornwall, but is held on lease by the *Sutton Harbour Improvement Company*, who, during the last four years, have expended large sums in cleansing and deepening it, and in erecting sea-walls, quays, &c. When the contemplated improvements are finished, it will be one of the finest tidal harbours in the kingdom. The railway from Dartmoor granite works terminates at its south-eastern angle, and it is intended to have a communication with the South Devon Railway. New quays, wharfs, cranes, railway slips, storehouses, &c., have been erected by the spirited Company; and a large dredging machine is employed in excavating the muddy bottom, formerly left bare at low water. On the West Barbican pier-head is a fixed light, 29 feet above high water mark.

MILL BAY is larger than Sutton Pool, extending about 500 yards inwards from the Pier, between Plymouth and Stonehouse, and being about the same breadth in its widest parts. *Mill Bay Pier* extends about 500 feet across the eastern side of the Bay, from the vicinity of the extensive limestone and marble quarries on the *West Hoe*, belonging to Thos. Gill, Esq., who, in 1840, obtained an act of parliament for the erection of the Pier, which he completed at the cost of above £27,000. Vessels of 3000 tons burthen may lie safely close to this fine Pier, in the inner harbour, at low water. The *Great Western Dock Company* have lately purchased this pier and the Harbour, and are now constructing at the head of the Bay the GREAT WESTERN DOCKS, which will have a sufficient depth of water, and gates wide enough, for the reception of large steam and sailing vessels. The largest of these docks is now in rapid progress, and will occupy eleven acres, and be 22 feet deep, with a lock entrance for vessels of about 1000 tons, and a gate wide enough for the admission of the largest ships. These extensive docks will be finished in about two years; and along their quays and wharfs will be railways communicating with the adjacent station of the South Devon Railway. Between the docks and the pier there will still be spacious outer harbour, capable of containing a great number of vessels of all classes. It is anticipated that, after the docks are finished, and the other improvements completed, the *Peninsular and Oriental Steam Packets* will start hence, instead of from Southampton; and no doubt merchants trading to *India*, will avail themselves of the great facilities afforded by the docks and railway, and make this the point of debarkation and embarkation, especially for mail bags and passengers;—as much time would be thus saved, and the dangers of the Channel, in a passage sometimes of a week's duration, avoided. On the West Hoe, near Mill Bay Pier, are about to be built a range of large and handsome houses, which will have tasteful grounds, commanding delightful views over the Sound and the adjacent harbours, Mount Edgcumbe, &c. Mill Bay is guarded by several *forts* and *batteries*; and on the eastern side of it is the *Government Prison*, which was rebuilt about 25 years ago, on the site of the old *Prison of War*, but is now used chiefly as a depôt for military stores, and has a spacious yard and barracks attached.

HAMOAZE, the great western harbour of the three towns, is completely land-locked, and extends northward from Mount Edgcumbe to Saltash, a

distance of four miles. It is in some places about a mile broad, and has a number of pools and creeks for the reception of shipping, such as *Stonehouse Pool, Barnpool, Millbrook Lake*, Keyham Lake, &c. Stonehouse Pool branches out of it, between Stonehouse and Devonport, and the tides run up it from the pier called the Admiral's Hard, through Stonehouse Lake and Mill Pool, a distance of 1½ mile. Hamoaze is the estuary of the river Tamar, and falls into the Sound below Devonport. Here are the public establishments and station for the Royal Navy; and a great number of ships of war, of all classes, may at all times be seen lying in ordinary, secured by immense chains, and covered with wooden roofs to protect them from the weather. These floating bulwarks, being stripped of their rigging, and having nothing standing but their lower masts, have a singular, though magnificent, appearance. The depth of this extensive estuary, where a great part of the British navy lies moored in "stern repose," is above 18 fathoms at high water, and 15 at low water. In this harbour, upwards of one hundred sail of the line, besides frigates and small vessels, may safely ride at anchor in severe gales.

DEVONPORT DOCK YARD, one of the largest naval establishments in the kingdom, presents to the broad harbour of Hamoaze, a semicircular wharf wall, more than 1160 yards in length. This Dock Yard, now one of the finest in Europe, is believed to have been commenced soon after the glorious Revolution of 1688, under the auspices of William III. The town of Devonport, to which the Dock Yard gave rise, was called Plymouth Dock till 1824, as afterwards noticed; and in official documents the arsenal retained the name of "*Plymouth Yard*" till the visit of her Majesty and Prince Albert, in September, 1843, when the Queen commanded that in future it should be styled in all documents Devonport Dock Yard. It was commenced on a comparatively small scale, and for a long period the officers and artizans resided at Plymouth, there being then no houses at Devonport. In 1728, government obtained from Sir Wm. Morice, a long lease of 40A. of land, which was then occupied by the Dock Yard, and had been previously rented from year to year. The extent of the arsenal was then 54 acres, and the spot on which the great fire occurred in 1840, appears to have been the original site. William III. constructed the basin and two of the naval docks, and two others were made in 1768. Since then many extensions and improvements have taken place, and this extensive Dock Yard now comprises 70½ acres, and gives employment to from 1400 to 1600 men, as shipwrights, caulkers, joiners, smiths, sawyers, rope-makers, painters, riggers, sail-makers, labourers, &c., besides a large number of apprentices. In time of war, its establishment would be augmented to about 4000. Its peace establishment has recently been reduced, to satisfy the loud cry which has lately been raised for the reduction of taxes and national expenditure; and several new regulations have been established by the Admiralty for increasing the efficiency of this and other naval yards, at a less cost than formerly. The Dock Yard is separated from the town of Devonport by Dockwall street, and they are encompassed on the land sides by a strongly fortified wall 12 feet high. Government own a large space of land on both sides of this long line of fortifications. On entering the Dock Yard from the gates at the end of Fore street, we are struck by the absence of all appearance of labour; but glancing the eye in the vista are perceived long ranges of buildings uniting strength with neatness. Passing hence in a gradual descent to the water's edge, we soon immerge into the bustle of several hundred mechanics. On the right of the entrance is the residence of the director of police; and the next object is the spacious and handsome *Chapel*, which was built in 1816-'17, on the site of the old one, which was

erected in 1700. The interior is handsomely fitted up and has a good organ; and in the tower are six musical bells. The Rev. John Briggs is the *chaplain*, and has a yearly salary of £400. Near the chapel are two reservoirs, from which the establishment is supplied with pure water. Passing from the guard-house and pay office, down a fine avenue, we arrive at the residences of the principal officers, in the centre of which is the mansion of the Admiral Superintendent, approached by two flights of steps. We next arrive at the edge of a terrace or shelf, from whence flights of steps descend into the busy area below. Here almost the whole of the arsenal, before unseen, bursts into view. The noble ships in progress of building, and under repair,—the magnificent storehouses and workshops,—the gigantic sheds protecting the docks; and the neatness and order everywhere apparent, excite the admiration of the stranger. From this point some conception of the vastness of the establishment may be formed. In the engine house and saw-mills it is curious to observe the power of steam, applied at the same moment to the most trifling as well as the most important operations. At one spot, we see it directed to the cutting of wedges; at others cutting screws, drilling, planing, punching, turning grind-stones, and pumping the water out of the superb dock with inexpressible ease. A large fan is driven by it, and air drains, made under the floor of the smithery, convey the blasts to the fires, and thereby supersede the use of bellows. A shaft is carried underground to the saw mills, where immense blocks of wood are changed into delicate planks; and under the steps is a curious machine, called "Jim Crow," for making halyards for vessels of war. In one of the smitheries is one of Nasmith's patent steam tilt hammers, the power of which can easily be increased or diminished to the largest or smallest requirements. The portion of the yard, occupied by locksmiths, carvers, plumbers, masons, &c., is near this smithery. Proceeding to the north jetty, we view the noble Hamoaze, with its bosom dotted with men of war of various ratings, and in different states of equipment. The *new north dock* next claims attention. It is sufficiently capacious for building or repairing the largest man of war, and was first opened in 1789. The next are the *union, double,* and *south or basin docks*. This spot is memorable as the scene of the *great fire*, on September 27th, 1840, when upwards of £80,000 worth of public property was destroyed. On the left are two ranges of buildings, containing the joiners' and carpenters' shops, &c., surmounted by a conspicuous clock, with four dials. We next approach a massive storehouse, which, together with the sail-loft, forms a square of nearly 400 feet, and is built entirely of stone and iron. Near this is the large *new basin*, which has been lately finished and affords space to float ten first rate men of war, exclusive of its two graving docks. On the *anchor wharf* are anchors of all sizes, some weighing 96 cwt. Adjoining the jetty is a graving slip, and near it is a weigh bridge for weighing heavy articles. A swivel bridge crosses the *canal*, which runs into the heart of the yard, and is called the " *Camber*;" and near it is another smithery, where the largest anchors are made, one of which occupies 36 men ten days. Just beyond are three slips, in which the largest men of war are built. The slips for building frigates and smaller craft are at a short distance. The boat and mast ponds and houses are extensive, and near them are the two large *rope houses*, each 1200 feet long, and built entirely of stone and iron. Cables, 25 inches in circumference, and cordage for the navy are manufactured here. There is a pleasant little rocky eminence near the mast house, called the *King's hill*, or *Bunker's hill*. George III., on his visit to this yard, having been so pleased with the charming prospect seen from this rock, expressed a wish that it might be excepted from the general excavation to

which the surrounding site was subjected.   The sides of this rock are thickly covered with ivy and evergreens, and its summit is crowned by a beautiful temple, erected in 1822, in memory of the visit of George III. The docks, slips, canals, basins, &c., are mostly hewn out of the slate rock, and lined with Portland stone.   The extent of the excavations and masonry may be judged of by the following dimensions of the " New North Dock," excavated from the solid rock,—length, 254 feet 2 inches,—extreme breadth, 97 feet—depth, 27 feet 8 inches.   The great diversity of employments, ingenuity, and manual activity, exhibited in the various departments of this Dock Yard, presents a very interesting spectacle, and perhaps no sight is better calculated to enable a comprehensive mind to form a proper estimate of the powers of continued labour than the gradual growth of a few rude pieces of timber into the majestic structure that encounters the wind and waves, and forms the most complete security against invasion that Great Britain can possess.

The Gun Wharf is situated north of the Dock Yard, and occupies nearly five acres, fronting Homoaze harbour, and enclosed by a high wall.   It was planned about a century ago.   After passing from the entrance through a fine avenue of trees, the houses, &c., of the officers are seen on the left. At the foot of a flight of steps are the armory and storehouses.   In the former immense piles of muskets, pistols, cutlasses, &c., are deposited in chests ; and others are arranged about the walls in the forms of stars, circles, fans, and crescents.   Near the storehouses are buildings appropriated as depositories for gun-carriages, and implements of the field.   On the wharfs and around, are a great number of cannon, of different caliber, which belong to the vessels of war moored in the harbour, and also numerous piles of shot, of every size.   At Morice Town, north of Gun Wharf, is the new Government Steam Yard, skirted on the west by Hamoaze harbour, and on the north by Keyham Lake, and occupying about 70 acres. It has two extensive basins, entered from the estuary by locks of such magnitude that the largest ships may enter three hours before high water. The south lock is so constructed as to be converted into a dry dock, when a line of battle ship is brought in to have her bottom examined or cleansed. From the eastern side of the south basin three large dry docks are projected, of such dimensions as to be capable of accommodating the largest steamers afloat.   The north is the fitting basin, and east of it are ranged the storehouses, factories, foundries, smitheries, &c.   This yard has been some years in progress, and is not yet completed.   It will cost about £2,000,000, and there have been employed in its formation upwards of 1200 men, 100 horses, and 70 boats.   South of it is Moon's Cove and Ship Canal, and between the latter and Gun Wharf, is *New Passage,* where the Steam Floating Bridge, a ponderous vessel, conveys passengers, carriages, &c., to and from *Torpoint,* every half hour.   The stage coaches are taken across the broad estuary, without even unhorsing, or the coachmen and guards alighting.

Devonport is the seat of the *military and naval government* of the port, the former being removed here from the Citadel at Plymouth in 1725.   The Government House, comprising the private residence and military offices of the Lieutenant Governor of the garrison ; and the Admiral's House, the residence for the Port Admiral, and offices belonging to his department; are pleasantly situated on the south-east side of the town, upon the fine, open, and spacious parade called Mount Wise, overlooking the harbour of Hamoaze.   Here are held the military parades and inspections ; and on rejoicing days the whole disposable force of the three towns is reviewed, and the parade becomes a scene of great gaiety.   At the east end stands, mounted,

a brass cannon of immense size, taken from the Turks, in the Dardanelles. From the ramparts and the several batteries, (mounted with heavy artillery,) delightful views are seen; and on the summit of the hill, is the *Semaphore*, or *Telegraph Station*, where signals are made with the admiral of all ships that are passing up and down the channel within sight of the coast. The BARRACKS on the east side of Devonport, but within the lines, form four large squares, called *George, Cumberland, Ligonier* and *Frederick Squares*, and have room for 2000 soldiers. The *Laboratory* at Mount Wise is now used as barracks.

The ROYAL WILLIAM VICTUALLING YARD occupies the north side of that large headland at Stonehouse, which projects into the Sound and the spacious harbour of Hamoaze. This magnificent national establishment was commenced in 1826, and completed in 1835, from the designs of Sir John Rennie, at the cost of £1,500,000. The entire premises occupy about 13 acres of land, of which nearly half was recovered from the sea; the material for that purpose being obtained from the excavations made in levelling and preparing the remainder of the site. The entrance gateway is in the Græco-Roman style, and wholly of finely wrought granite. The front exhibits a grand central arch and two side entrances; and on the former is placed a statue of William IV., of Portland stone, $13\frac{1}{2}$ feet in height. It is a most exquisite piece of sculpture, and a good likeness. The ox's heads and anchors over the side entrances, were carved by a rustic sculptor. The general facing of the extensive buildings is of wrought limestone; but the plinths, dressings, cornices, &c., in the principal fronts, are of granite. The doors and window frames are of cast iron, as are the internal columns of all the warehouses, and the girders, lintels, &c. of the Cooperage. The Long Store, Melville Store, and the Cooperage are roofed with iron, copper, and slate. On the right of the entrance is a fine range of buildings, 250 feet by 200, wherein the bread for the navy is prepared by means of a steam engine, of 40 horse power, and 25 pairs of mill-stones, capable of grinding 1000 bushels of corn in the short space of ten hours. The flour is passed from the mill to the story below, where it is kneaded, and the dough cut into biscuits, by curiously contrived machinery. In one part of the buildings appropriated for the preparation of butchers' meat, is the slaughter house, where 70 or 80 head of cattle can be despatched at once. The next buildings, on the left, are called the Melville Quadrangle, and are 240 feet square, with a lofty granite archway, surmounted by a clock. The interior contains spacious apartments for the various stores connected with victualling the navy. In front is a large *basin*, with an entrance for vessels from the harbour, and around it are spacious quays, built of granite. The next building is the Brewhouse, with a steam-engine of 40 horse power; but owing to the discontinuance of serving beer to the navy, it has remained useless. Beyond this is the extensive Cooperage, floored with four-inch York paving. At a short distance are the Clarence Stores, 340 feet long and 50 broad. In front of these stores is a noble wharf, extending 500 feet, and forming a delightful promenade on the margin of the broad waters of Hamoaze, near their confluence with the Sound. The officers' residences are to the right of the entrance. About 150 men are employed here, but in time of war the number would be greatly augmented. The DEVIL'S POINT is the high ground behind the Victualling Yard, where there is a *Reservoir*, holding 7000 tuns of water, and a *Battery*, from which the royal marine artillery practise the firing of heavy shot at a flag fixed on a buoy in the Sound. The ROYAL MARINE BARRACKS front Mill Bay and the Great Western Docks, and generally contain about 700 men, and an excellent band.

The ROYAL NAVAL HOSPITAL is at Stonehouse, opposite Stonehouse

Lake, and occupies about 24 acres, including a verdant lawn of 13 acres. It was opened in 1762 for the reception of sick and wounded seamen and marines, of whom it received no fewer than 48,452 from 1800 to 1814, a great portion of whom were returned to the service as effective men. The buildings range in the form of a square, and will accommodate 1200 patients. The government of the hospital is entrusted to a captain in the navy, and the same officer is superintendent of the Victualling Yard. Every attention is paid to the patients, and the establishment displays much regularity and cleanliness.

The ROYAL MILITARY HOSPITAL is on the opposite side of Stonehouse Lake, near Stoke Church, and was built in 1797. The south front is of grey marble, and has a very imposing appearance, being of considerable length, and having an arcade of 41 arches, forming a fine promenade for the sick. It will accommodate 500 patients, and has extensive grounds enclosed by a lofty wall. The BLOCKHOUSE, at Higher Stoke, is a square fortification, erected in the reign of George II., and intended as a redoubt for the defence of the town and harbour. The views from its ramparts are extensive and beautiful, embracing not only the three towns and their harbours, but a large portion of the adjacent country, in the picturesque vales of the rivers Tamar and St. Germans or Lynher.

The PORT OF PLYMOUTH extends to all the harbours, rivers, and creeks between Looe on the west, and the river Yealm on the east; but its *Pilotage* district extends eastward as far as Start Point, though no master of a vessel is compelled to take a pilot, except going into or coming out of the ports within a line drawn from Rame-Head to the Mewstone. During the late long protracted war, Plymouth was content with its resources as a great naval and military station, and paid but little attention to *Trade and Commerce* with the colonies of foreign countries. Its merchants, at this period, were mostly agents for London, Liverpool, and Bristol houses, and purchased and transported under their directions the vast quantities of prize-goods brought here for sale. Those who withstood the shock caused by the change from warlike to peaceable occupations, gradually extended their connexions with foreign nations and our distant colonial possessions; and the shipping and commerce of the port have been rapidly increasing during the last 20 years. A considerable trade is now carried on with America, the Mediterranean, the West Indies, the Baltic, &c.; and here are now *consuls* or *vice consuls* for about 30 different nations. The port has also an extensive coasting trade with London, Bristol, Newport, Exeter, Newcastle, &c., and has a number of fine *Steam Ships*, which sail once or twice a week with goods and passengers to London, Southampton, Portsmouth, Guernsey, Jersey, Dublin, Cork, Torquay, &c. There is now no port in the English Channel, between London and Land's-End, where so great an amount of business is done as at Plymouth, and where so much *shipping* is employed. The number of vessels which entered the port with cargoes in 1848, was 4106, and their amount of tonnage 399,798. Of the vessels, 538 were from foreign parts, 175 from Ireland, and 3393 were coasters. The number which cleared out in the same year was 2343, including 105 to foreign parts, 328 in ballast, 236 to Ireland; 1585 coasting vessels, and 89 emigrant ships; the latter taking out 8505 passengers. Many vessels make several voyages in the year, and each voyage is counted as a separate vessel in the above statement. The number of vessels registered here in 1849 was 433, of the aggregate amount of 39,657 tons. The gross amount of *custom's duty*, received here, was £100,670, in 1838; £135,930, in 1841; above £116,000 in 1848; and £121,750 in 1849. Here are large bonded warehouses for all sorts of foreign produce. The chief exports are copper and lead ores, manganese, granite,

limestone, clay, fish, &c. Though the coasting trade of Plymouth is more important than its foreign trade, the latter comprises upwards of 50,000 tons annually, consisting chiefly of wine, fruit, corn, timber, &c. The port has several fine vessels engaged in the fruit trade, and receives some of the first importations of early fruits from Denia, Valencia, Zante, &c. Great quantities of coal and culm are imported here for the consumption of the three towns, and the places on or near the navigable rivers, Tamar, Plym, and Lynher. Of late years, Plymouth has become celebrated as a port for *emigration* to Australia, and other parts of the world. In 1849, no fewer than 130 *emigrant ships* left the harbour, with 15,895 *passengers*, of which 109 ships, with 14,118 passengers, went to Australia; 10 ships, with 1171 passengers, to Canada; and the rest went to the Cape of Good Hope, the United States, Port Natal, and San Francisco. In 1847, the number of emigrants who left here in 26 vessels, was 1230; but in the following year, 8505 left, in 88 ships; so that no fewer than 25,730 have sailed from Plymouth during the last three years. Here are several respectable government and general emigration agents, and the vessels are generally of the best description, lying in Catwater or the Sound, always afloat, and sailing quickly and punctually. Plymouth has also about 80 *fishing vessels*, of which about 60 are *Trawlers*, which employ about five men and boys each, and go out to the fishing ground 10 or 12 miles off the coast, where they fish with nets that sweep the bottom of the sea. The others are smaller craft, called *Hooking and Seine Boats*, and usually carry two men and a boy each. When the *mackerel* and *pilchard* seasons arrive, there are large accessions to the Plymouth boats from Brighton, Hastings, Yarmouth, Rye, Cornwall, &c., and in some seasons there are from 200 to 300 boats on the fishing stations. Turbot, soles, brill, cod, hake, mullet, and a great variety of other fish are caught here; and salmon, trout, plaice, &c., in the Tamar and other rivers. Fish is not cured here to any large extent, but great quantities are sent in a fresh state by rails, (as well as by fast sailing cutters to Southampton, and thence by rails,) to London, Bath, Bristol, Manchester, and other markets. The *mackerel fishery* is sometimes amazingly prolific, as many as 500,000 fish having been taken, and brought into Plymouth in one day, and sold wholesale for about £2000, or at 8s. per 120. In the first twelve days of March, 1850, near 400 tons of mackerel left here by rails, and one train took as many as 120,000 of these delicious fish to London, &c. An association of fish speculators call themselves the "Hong-Kong Company," and another company has recently formed an *oyster bed* in Stonehouse Pool, and supplied it with fish and spat of a superior quality from Helford river, Cornwall. The Channel has lately been infested with a species of large fish, called by the fishermen *Blower Whales*, from 20 to 30 feet long, and making a loud and disagreeable noise. One of these whales got entangled in the nets of a lugger which had all her gear out, and took the boat in tow at such a furious rate through the sea, that the poor fishermen were compelled to cut the rope, and let the monster go with all their nets, worth £90. This occurred about 12 miles S.W. of Bolt Head. As already noticed, the three towns still derive a large portion of their prosperity from the naval and military establishments; and it is expected that Plymouth will be made a *mail-packet station* after the completion of the *Great Western Docks*, near the terminus of the South Devon Railway, as noticed at page 643. The *South Devon Shipping Company* has a large number of shareholders, who receive about £10 per share annually.

The CUSTOM HOUSE is situated on the Parade, near Sutton-Pool, and is a large and handsome structure, built of granite, in 1819-'20, at the cost of £8000, in lieu of the old

one, which was small and inconvenient. It contains a long room, 52 feet by 26, and all other necessary offices for the business. Geo. Jones, Esq., is the *collector;* Mr. Wm. Lockyer, *comptroller;* Mr. D. W. Lowe, *landing surveyor;* Messrs. Thomas Page, Richd. Luscombe, W. B. Ramsey, J. H. S. Russell, and W. D. Bickle, *searchers, coast waiters, &c.;* John Steer, John Salmon, Thos. Potbury, Edw. Lawson, Lewis Pode, Rd. Birdwood, and W. G. Slaughter, *clerks;* Robt. French, *jerquer, &c.;* R. M. Parker and Chas. Cuddeford, *warehouse keepers;* Cphr. Rea, *tide surveyor;* and Edwin Langmead, *superintendent of lockers.*

The INLAND REVENUE OFFICE *(late Excise)* is in Duke street. John Mc Culloch, Esq., is *collector;* Mr. John Hannaford, *clerk;* T. Warren, *supervisor;* H. Goffe, *port officer;* and Robt. Tothill, John Makeham, W. Perry, and S. Webb, are the *division officers.*

The BOROUGH OF PLYMOUTH comprises the Island of St. Nicholas, and the two parishes of St. Andrew and King Charles the Martyr, except their out-townships of Pennycross and Compton-Gifford. Its population, charters, and general history are shewn at preceding pages. Under the Municipal Reform Act of 1835, the *Town Council* consists of a mayor, 12 aldermen, and 36 councillors, with a recorder, town clerk, and other officers; and the borough is divided into six wards, and has a commission of the peace, a court of quarter sessions, &c. The paving, lighting, and improvements of the town, and the management of the poor, are vested in separate commissioners, or guardians, under acts of Parliament obtained for those purposes; and the three towns were associated under a local act for the recovery of debts under £5, but the latter has now given place to the new county court. An act for improving the town was obtained in the 51st of George III., and was amended in the 5th of George IV., by "An Act for the better paving, lighting, cleansing, watching, and improving the Town and Borough of Plymouth, and for regulating the police, and removing and preventing nuisances and annoyances therein." The municipal act of 1835, vested the police with the Corporation. In 1849, the *Commissioners of Improvement* received from rates £6860, out of which they expended £2541 in improvements; £1958 in paving and draining; £1443 in lighting; £173 in watering the streets; and £170 in salaries; and paid £600 as interest on debt. In 1833, the entire *Revenue of the Corporation* amounted to about £6782, and their expenditure to £7510, with a debt of £39,000. Their income in 1840 was £10,533, of which £5446 arose from rents, £1157 from tolls and dues, £2677 from borough and watch rates, and £910 from the sale of property. Their expenditure in the same year was £9904, of which £919 was for salaries to municipal officers, £1426 for salaries of police and constables, £1853 for public works, repairs, &c.; £428 for prosecutions, administration of justice, &c.; £155 for charities, £116 for gaol expenses, and £4194 for payments of interest and principal on the borough debt, which has since been considerably reduced. As lords of the manor, the Corporation own the *tolls and dues* of the market and fairs, now let for £3030 per annum, on lease for three years. The rateable property of the borough has recently been assessed at the annual value of £85,393, viz., £56,200 in St. Andrew's, and £29,193 in the parish of Charles. A rate of 6d. in the pound on this rental yields £2134, which is about the sum usually required for the support of the police force. The new BOROUGH PRISONS, which were completed in 1849, are pleasantly situated on the north-east side of the town, and cost about £13,500, of which about £3500 was derived from the freeman's, or prison fund, and £10,000 was borrowed, chiefly from the Exchequer Loan Commissioners. They are handsomely built of blue limestone, relieved by Caen-stone dressings, and the sashes are all of cast iron, glazed with plate glass a quarter of an inch thick. They are generally in the Italian style, and the lofty boundary wall encloses about three acres, divided into airing grounds, &c. The governor's house and porter's lodge are on each side of the en-

trance. The prisons are in the centre of the ground, and are disposed in three large wings, comprising the governor's offices, apartments for the matron, a chapel and surgery, visiting cells, convalescent rooms, a bath room, and cells for 60 prisoners, including six for male and three for female debtors, for whom there are comfortable day rooms and airing grounds. There are four solitary cells, so constructed as to admit air, but no light; and there are 24 airing grounds, radiating from a common centre, and each to be occupied by only one prisoner at a time, whilst an officer is so placed as to be able to see into all the yards,—the arrangements having been so made as to carry out the separate system, in all its completeness, both in the prisons and the chapel. The GUILDHALL, in Whimple street, was built in 1800, at the cost of £7000, on the site of the old one, which had been erected in 1606. It is an incommodious and inelegant building, containing a justice hall, several apartments for the transaction of corporation affairs, the police station, and several cells, &c., which served as the borough prison till the recent completion of the new prisons. The erection of a new Town Hall, on a scale adequate to the present wants of the town and borough, is in contemplation. In the present hall is a fine portrait of George IV., when Prince Regent. Here are held the *Quarter and Petty Sessions* of the borough; but the *Bankruptcy Court*, lately established here, is held at the Hall of Commerce; and the *County Court*, for Plymouth District, is to be held in the new Town Hall, &c., now erecting at Stonehouse, but is now held in the Guildhall, for the three towns, every Tuesday, and also every alternate Wednesday. Mr. Wm. Jacobson is *clerk* of the latter court, and Mr. J. H. Williams, *high bailiff*. The office is at Eldad place. As noticed at page 635, the borough sent *members to Parliament* as early as the reign of Edward I., and has sent two regularly since its incorporation in the 18th of Henry VI. For a long period, Plymouth was considered as an Admiralty Borough, and was generally represented by Lords of the Admiralty, or by Admirals; but when the Prince of Wales (afterwards George IV.) did the Corporation the honour of becoming their high steward, they considered themselves under royal patronage, and two gentlemen of the Prince's household represented them till the election of 1818. The number of *voters* was 1898 in 1837, and is now upwards of 2000. PRINCE ALBERT succeeded the late Duke of Sussex, as *Lord High Steward* of the Borough of Plymouth; and Viscount Ebrington and Roundell Palmer, Esq., are its present MEMBERS OF PARLIAMENT. The following is a list of the *Town Council, Borough Magistrates*, and *Officers*.

MAYOR, John Moore, Esq. || RECORDER, W. C. Rowe, Esq.
BOROUGH MAGISTRATES, Sir Wm. S. Harris, Colonel Dunsterville, and Thos. Bewes, Geo. Coryndon, Wm. H. Hawker, Wm. Prance, John Moore, Thos. H. Bulteel, David Derry, and Geo. T. Shortland, Esqrs.

ALDERMEN.

David Derry	Wm. Burnell	George Coryndon	Alfred Rooker
Thomas Were Fox	Wm.Smith Kerswell	Herbert M. Gibson	Jph. C. Cookworthy
Wm. Prance	James Skardon	Thomas H. Bulteel	Thomas D. Newton

COUNCILLORS.

Frankfort Ward.	John Pope	*Drake's Ward.*	Wm. Luscombe
George Jackson	Wm.Truman Harris	George Venecombe	Wm. H. Hawker,jn.
Wm. Phillips	Samuel Treeby	Thos. Baron Tyeth	James Marshall
Thomas Mitchell	*Vintry Ward.*	Wm. Marshall	*St. Andrew's Ward.*
John Long Colley	Samuel Stanbury	George Frean	John Moore
Alexander Pontey	Thomas Pollard	Ralph Cole	Wm. Baron
John Murch	Wm. Hy. Hawker	John Hallett	John Curgenven
Charles' Ward.	Wm. Fredk. Collier	*Sutton Ward.*	Fras. Freke Bulteel
John Burnell	Robt. White Stevens	Wm. Moore	John Kelly
Wm. Mortimer	Thomas Stevens	Wm. Cuming	George Mennie
Samuel Derry		John W. Sparrow	

2 E 2

MARKETS, FAIRS, &c.—A grant for a market and fair at Plymouth was first obtained in 1253, the former to be held on Thursdays, and the latter on the festival of St. John the Baptist. In 1257, Baldwin de L'Isle had a grant for another market at Sutton, and a fair for three days at the festival of the Ascension. Here are now markets every Tuesday, Thursday, and Saturday, when a plentiful supply of every commodity may be obtained. The *corn market*, on Tuesday and Thursday, is well attended by the farmers and dealers residing within the distance of 15 or 20 miles. There is a *great market*, for cattle, &c., on the second Thursday of every month; and large *fairs*, for cattle, merchandise, and pleasure, are held on the first Mondays in April and November. The *Market Place* occupies three acres of ground, and has three entrances, from Cornwall street, East street, and Drake street. It was built by the Corporation, about 1809, and affords ample room for meat, corn, fish, poultry, and vegetables, as well as for a considerable display of manufactured goods. It might have been made one of the handsomest market places in England, but the *coup d'œil* is much injured by the irregularity of the structure. It is, however, very spacious and convenient, and has a division set apart for corn, and an area for moveable stalls, carts, &c. The cattle market is at the head of Tavistock street. At the fairs, part of the area is occupied by shows, &c. *Races* are held in Chelson Meadow, near Saltram; and during the year there are several *Regattas* and Rowing Matches in the harbours of the three towns.

The principal *manufactures* of the town are those of soap, sail cloth, Roman cement, rope, and twine. Here are also many ship building yards, several iron foundries, breweries, steam sawing mills, a sugar refinery, starch works, &c. *Mr. Wm. Cookworthy*, of Plymouth, was the first person who found out the materials for manufacturing *porcelain*, as now practised at Worcester. His original experiments were made at Plymouth, where a manufactory was for a while established, but it was not successful till its removal to Worcester, after repeated trials here and at Bristol. Here is still a *pottery*, where various kinds of earthenware are manufactured. The *Mill Property* belonging to the Corporation produces about £700, arising from the Higher and Lower Grist Mills; the Mills, &c., in Drake's place and Mill street; the Higher Malt Mill, and the Factory, in Russell street. There is a *Flax Mill* at Stone Park, and a large *patent rope and cordage* manufactory at Teats hill. Here are also a number of *brush makers*.

WATER AND GAS WORKS.—As already noticed, Plymouth is indebted to the skill and liberality of the great Sir Francis Drake, for the *leat*, or conduit (18 miles in length,) which has supplied the town with pure water for nearly three centuries. Formerly, the inhabitants had to fetch the water from a few fountains, in different parts of the town, or from the small reservoir at the head of Old Town street; but about 25 years ago, the Corporation greatly improved the works, by building a weir across the river Plym, at the head of the leat, in Dartmoor, and by conveying the water in iron pipes from three reservoirs to the houses in the principal streets. Fur-

ther improvements were carried out some years afterwards; but the supply is still very deficient, and many of the streets are without water pipes. Measures are, however, in contemplation, for supplying all parts of the town, by extending the course of the leat, and by making large reservoirs at Sheepstor, Manadon, and Torr-House. From 1825 to 1833 the Corporation expended £20,816 in enlarging the water works; and about £6000 in 1849 and '50. The water rents now yield about £3300 per annum. Oil Gas Works were established in Exeter street, under an act passed in the 4th of George IV.; but soon afterwards, the United General Gas Company of London constructed *coal gas works* at Mill Bay, for supplying the three towns. The high price charged by this company, while its monopoly existed, induced the inhabitants of Plymouth and Stonehouse to form a company for a cheaper supply, for which an act of parliament was obtained; and in a few years, the new company compelled the old one to sell them their works. *New Gas Works* were constructed at Coxide, in 1845, at the cost of £25,000, raised in £10 shares.

The EXCHANGE, in Woolster street, near the Custom House, was built in 1813, at the cost of £7000, raised in £25 shares. Until a few years ago, it was only partially occupied, and had a large open area, surrounded by a colonnade; but this area has recently been built upon, and covered with a glass dome, and offices have been built under the galleries. The building is now very spacious, and fully occupied. It comprises a very large room, for sales and public meetings; a *News Room*, 41 feet by 20; the *Hall of Commerce;* and numerous mercantile and public offices. The *Exchange Subscription Reading and News Room Association*, was established in 1848, and has already about 200 members. The " change hour" is from twelve to one o'clock. The Steam Packet Companies have offices in the Exchange; as also have the *Fishermen's Mutual Insurance Society*, established in 1844; the *Port of Plymouth Ship Masters' Society*, established in 1830; the *Board for the Examination of Masters and Mates*, instituted about four years ago, and to which Mr. R. W. Stevens is *clerk;* and the Trustees of the *Merchant Seamen's Hospital Fund*, to which every master of a vessel pays 2s., and the crew 1s. each per month, for their mutual relief in times of sickness and infirmity, and for the relief of the widows and children of such as have died in the service. This fund was instituted by an act of the reign of George II., establishing a Corporation in London, with authority to establish funds for this purpose at the outports. The Plymouth fund was commenced in 1752, and is vested in trust with 15 of the merchants and shipowners of the port. It has now £1500 three per cent. stock, and receives about £760 per annum in contributions. Mr. J. E. Blewett is the *secretary*.

As already noticed, the town has been much improved during the last ten years. The most recent alteration is the widening of Whimple street, at the western end of which stands the new POST OFFICE, a large and elegant building, erected by a company of shareholders in 1848, at the cost of £3000, from designs by Mr. O. C. Arthur, after the style of the Temple of Vesta, at Tivoli, in Italy. Some parts of it are let as offices; but the chief part is occupied as the Post-office and the post master's residence, and is rented by government for 75 years, at £100 per annum. The *Branch Bank of England* was removed from Exeter to Plymouth in 1834, and now occupies a large and handsome building, at George's place, erected in 1844. Here are also three other Banking Houses. The ROYAL HOTEL and THEATRE form an extensive and elegant fabric, which was finished in 1813, at the cost of about £60,000, partly supplied by the Corporation, and partly raised by way of tontine. The north front is 270 feet long, and has in the

centre a magnificent portico of the Ionic order, under which are the entrances to the boxes, and to the great hall and staircase of the assembly rooms. The Theatre is spacious and elegant; and the principal supports and framework of the boxes, and all the interior partitions, are of cast iron, and the roof of wrought iron. The *proscenium* is formed by four beautiful marble columns, with gilt bases and capitals, supporting an elegant entablature, from which rises an arch richly empannelled. The Hotel, which lets for about £750 per annum, occupies all the eastern front, and has in the centre an Ionic portico, corresponding in its proportions with the temple of Ilissus, a choice example of Grecian simplicity. Many of its apartments are spacious, and handsomely furnished; and attached to it is an elegant suite of *Assembly and Ball Rooms*. In Union road is a large room, called the *Central Hall*, belonging to Mr. P. Fisher, and let for exhibitions, meetings, &c. It will hold 800 persons.

The ATHENÆUM is a chaste and classical structure, from designs by J. Foulston, Esq., the architect of the theatre. It is a fine example of the Grecian Doric order, and was built in 1818-'19, for the accommodation of the PLYMOUTH INSTITUTION, established in 1812, for the promotion of science, literature, and the fine arts. In the lecture room are many fine casts from ancient marbles, a colossal bust of Minerva, and other works of art; and the museum contains a large and interesting collection of minerals, fossils, preserved birds, shells, insects, curiosities, &c. There is here an occasional *Exhibition of Paintings*, formed partly by the works of Devonian artists, and partly from the collections of the nobility and gentry of the neighbourhood. Devonshire has given birth to many distinguished artists; and Plymouth claims among its eminent painters, Northcote, Prout, Haydon, Ball, and Bath. Among other *Worthies* of Plymouth may be enumerated *Sir Thomas Edmondes*, the ambassador and political writer; *John Glanville*, author of the well-known "Treatise on Witchcraft," and other works; *John Quick*, an eminent non-conformist divine, author of the "History of the Reformation in France;" *Mrs. Parsons*, authoress of above 60 volumes of novels; *Jacob Bryant*, the learned mythologist; *General Mudge*, who conducted the first trigonometrical survey of the kingdom, under the auspices of Government; and his father, *Dr. John Mudge*, who was distinguished for his skill both in mathematics and medicine. *Sir John Hawkins*, who commanded the rear of the fleet which defeated the Spanish Armada, and ingloriously introduced the slave trade into the West Indies, was a native of Plymouth. In 1675, Charles Fitz-Charles, natural son of Charles II., was created *Earl of Plymouth*. He died without issue, and in 1682, the title was conferred on Thomas Hickman Windsor, the seventh Baron Windsor. It was held by the Windsor family till a few years ago, when the eighth and last Earl of Plymouth died without male heirs. Four *Newspapers* are published here weekly; and in the town are several *News Rooms* and *Libraries*. The PUBLIC LIBRARY, established at the Guildhall, about the beginning of the present century, occupies a handsome building, in Cornwall street, erected in 1811-'12, and comprising a large and well-supplied news-room. There being no windows in the front, the various apartments are lighted by glazed domes, or cupolas, in the roof. The library comprises about 9000 volumes, arranged in a spacious vaulted room, surrounded by a light gallery. The MECHANICS' INSTITUTION, for which a commodious building is about to be erected, was commenced in 1826, and occupies a building in Princess square. It has an extensive library, and a numerous list of members. The *Royal Devon and Cornwall Botanical and Horticultural Society* holds two exhibitions yearly, at the assembly rooms of the Royal Hotel, and Mr. N. J. Easton is its secretary. There is a

Natural History Society, at 16, Princess square; and a *Young Men's Christian Association*, in Bedford street. Here is also a Branch Diocesan *Architectural Society*, and some other institutions for the promotion of literature and the arts and sciences. The ROYAL UNION BATHS, in Union road, occupy a spacious building, and were founded in 1828, by a company of shareholders. They are daily supplied with pure sea water from the Sound, conveyed in iron pipes to a reservoir, which holds 2700 hogsheads. Baths of every description may be had here, including warm, tepid, vapour, sulphur, hot air, slipper, plunge, shower, douche, and swimming baths. Here is also the VICTORIA SPA, which is obtained from a boring in the Artesian manner, 360 feet deep. A comparison of this spa with sea water, from which it is supposed to be derived, by infiltration through the rocks, shows that, while it has lost bromine, iodine, and their acids, it has acquired sulphate of lime, and carbonates of lime and iron, and that it has, in consequence, become equivalent to the saline chalybeates of Cheltenham and Tunbridge.

CHURCHES, &c.—As already noticed, Plymouth was anciently called Sutton, and was a prebendal parish attached to the collegiate church of Plympton, till that church was converted into a priory, when Sutton was appropriated to it. (See page 634.) After the Reformation, the great tithes of Plymouth, with the advowson of the vicarage, were vested with the Corporation, but since the Municipal Reform, they have sold the patronage of both vicarages. In 1640, the borough was divided into *two parishes* by act of parliament, but the new parish church was not completed till after the Restoration, when it was dedicated to the memory of Charles I. The population of the two parishes of *St. Andrew and Charles the Martyr*, is stated at page 633, where it will be seen that they have two out-townships, beyond the limits of the borough. In monastic times, here were several religious houses, but nothing is known relating to their foundation or history. The *Franciscans or Grey Friars* are supposed to have had small monasteries in Palace Court, and on the site of the Distillery in Southside street, where there are some interesting remains of ancient architecture. The *White Friary* is supposed to have been in Friary court, the principal entrance to which is through an antique dilapidated gateway. A *Cistertian Abbey* gave name to Abbey street, and its remains may be traced in the large building, called the Abbey Wine Vaults, which still retains much of its original ecclesiastical character. The White Friary was licensed by Bishop Stapledon in 1324, at the desire of Edward II., and was granted at the dissolution to Giles Iselham. *St. Andrew's Parish Church* is a spacious and venerable structure, which is mentioned in a survey made in 1291, but was evidently mostly rebuilt in the 15th century. It has been thoroughly renovated and much improved since 1824, and has now 2500 sittings, of which 1000 are free. It is chiefly in the perpendicular or early English style, and consists of a spacious nave, chancel, and sides aisles, two small transepts, and a fine lofty tower, which contains a peal of eight deep-toned bells, and was built about 1440, by a merchant of Plymouth, named Yogge. The weight of the tenor bell is $2\frac{1}{2}$ tons, and the tower is surmounted at each angle by handsome and lofty pinnacles. The church being in a very dilapidated state, the parishioners in 1824 determined on its restoration, at the cost of £5000, part of which was borrowed from the Exchequer Loan Commissioners, to be repaid by annual payments of £150. The improvements were continued at intervals, and church rates were annually levied till 1834, when Mr. F. Bone became churchwarden. In 1839, Mr. Bone (without the aid of church rates) having succeeded in completing most of the intended renovations, and also in liquidating the debt, was presented by the parishioners with a valuable service of plate. The interior is divided by

clustered columns and pointed arches, and has now a handsome appearance. Much elegance is displayed in the design and ornaments of the pulpit and reading desk, which, like the pews and seats, are of oak. The unsightly galleries in the aisles were removed, and new ones were erected in the transepts, and at the west end. The beautiful oak roof, with its finely carved bosses, was thoroughly cleansed and restored, and a noble stair-case of teak wood was constructed in the lower story of the tower to communicate with the galleries and the organ loft. The organ is very powerful, and was purchased by subscription in 1735. Saml. Addis, in 1741, gave £400, to be invested in the funds, for the benefit of the organist. The three east windows have been enriched with stained glass, and a handsome altar screen has been erected since 1841. The western windows in the aisles are about to be replaced by new ones, and the north porch is to be rebuilt. The great defect in this extensive church is the want of a clerestory. Its situation was formerly too closely confined by a number of old houses, which belonged mostly to the vicarage, and have lately been removed for the improvement of this central part of the town. In the aisles are many neat mural *monuments*, on one of which is a fine bust of the *Rev. Zachary Mudge*, a late vicar, who died in 1769, and was the author of a volume of sermons. Another monument is in memory of *Dr. Wm. Woollcombe*, an eminent physician, who died in 1822. The principal group represents the genius of medicine supporting indigence. In the north aisle is another monument, on which religion, personified by a female figure, rests upon a medallion bust of the *Rev. John Gandy, M.A.*, a prebendary of Exeter, who died in 1824, aged 85 years, during 55 years of which he held this vicarage, besides previously officiating here five years as curate. This memorial was erected by public subscription, in record of the many virtues of the late venerable vicar. Here is also a tablet in memory of the late celebrated comedian, *Charles Mathews*, who was born in 1776, and died in 1835. The *vicarage*, valued in K.B. at £12. 5s. 5d., and in 1831 at £921, is in the patronage of the Rev. E. Holland, and incumbency of the Rev. John Hatchard, M.A., who derives his income partly from fees and vicarial property, and partly from the small tithes, which have been commuted for the following yearly sums :—£153 from St. Andrew's, £350 from Pennycross, and £65 from Compton Gifford. The vicar of Charles has £525 a year in lieu of tithes, of which he derives £160 from Compton Gifford. The great tithes belong to the land owners, except a few small moduses. The Reverends C. A. Marrett and C. T. C. Trelawny are the *curates*, and Mr. W. P. H. White is the clerk. The PARISH CHURCH OF KING CHARLES THE MARTYR is a large fabric, of mixed architecture, in the eastern part of the town, and was erected under the powers of an act of parliament passed in 1640, but owing to the troubles of the civil wars, it was not completed till 1658, nor consecrated till the Restoration. It consists of a spacious nave, with north and south aisles, a chancel, and a tower, crowned by a spire, which was struck by lightning, and mostly rebuilt about 25 years ago. There are eight bells in the tower, but two of them are broken. The interior of the church has a neat appearance, and contains about 1700 sittings. A new organ, by Beavington and Son, has recently been erected in the east gallery. Here are several handsome monuments, one of which has a finely sculptured bust of the Rev. R. Hawker, D.D., the late vicar, who died in 1846. The *vicarage*, valued in 1831 at £612 per annum, was in the patronage of the late Sir C. Bisshopp, Bart. The Rev. H. A. Greaves, M.A., is the incumbent. The parish of Charles comprises a great part of the town, the village of Lipson, and the tithing or chapelry of Compton Gifford. ST. ANDREW'S CHAPEL, in Lockyer street, is an elegant chapel of

ease to St. Andrew's parish, and was erected in 1822-3, at the cost of £5000, mostly contributed by the Rev. R. Lampen, (the first incumbent,) and H. Woolcombe, J. Pridham, and Thos. Gill, Esqrs.   The front is composed of large blocks of granite, in the Grecian style, with a cupola and bell on the top.   The interior has about 1100 sittings, and is handsomely fitted up. It has galleries and a good organ, and many of the pews are private property.   The benefice is a *perpetual curacy*, valued in 1831 at £115, and now in the patronage of the vicar of St. Andrew's, and incumbency of the Rev. G. Hadow, M.A.   CHARLES' CHAPEL, in Tavistock place, was built by subscription in 1828, as a chapel of ease to the parish of Charles, and has upwards of 1500 sittings.   The living is a perpetual curacy, valued in 1831 at £109, and is in the patronage of Trustees, and incumbency of the Rev. W. Hawker.   To supply that great want of church room which has long been felt in Plymouth, large portions of the town and two parishes have lately been divided by the Ecclesiastical Commissioners into the five DISTRICT PARISHES and perpetual curacies of *Trinity, Christ Church, St. Peter, St. James*, and *Sutton-upon-Plym*, but churches for all of them have not yet been provided.   TRINITY CHURCH, in Southside street, is a substantial structure, in the Doric style, erected in 1841-2, by subscription and a grant from the Incorporated Society.   It has 1082 sittings, of which 636 are free.   The Rev. H. C. Smith is the incumbent, and. the vicar of St. Andrew's is the patron.   CHRIST CHURCH is a handsome structure, in Oxford street, and was built in 1845-6.   It is in the perpendicular style, and has 1080 sittings, of which 536 are free.   The vicar of St. Andrew's is patron, and the Rev. R. Malone, M.A., is the incumbent.   ST. PETER'S CHURCH was formerly *Eldad Chapel*, which was built in 1830, for the late Rev. Jno. Hawker, B.A., but was never consecrated.   It was licensed by the Bishop as St. Peter's Church in 1848, and was altered and improved in that and the following year.   The patronage is in the Crown and Bishop alternately, and the Rev. G. R. Prynne, B.A., is the incumbent.   The District Parishes of *St. James* and *Sutton-upon-Plym* are in the same patronage, and the former is in the incumbency of the Rev. G. S. Hookey, and the latter of the Rev. G. Carrighan.   Churches have not yet been erected for them, but they preach in licensed rooms, the former at the Union Baths, and the latter at Catdown. *Portland Chapel* is a sort of free evangelical church, which was built in 1844 by its minister, the Rev. James Babb, M.A., with a house for his own residence.   He only retains a life interest in the chapel and house, which he has vested with 13 trustees for the future endowment of the "*Poor Saints' Relief Fund*," established six years ago, for the relief of poor and pious applicants.   This fund is intended as the successor to that of the *Corpus Christi Society*, which was founded in 1790 by Dr. Hawker, a late vicar of Charles, but is now obsolete.

CHAPELS.—Dissenters are numerous and influential in Plymouth, for though it has only nine episcopal places of worship, there are in the town about 20 chapels and meeting houses belonging to various sectarians.   The *Independents* are the most numerous, having five chapels in Norley street, How street, Britonside, York street, and Courtenay street.   The latter is called the *Congregational Union Chapel*, and is a handsome building, erected in 1848, at the cost of £2000.   The *Western College*, for educating young men for the ministry among Independents, is at Plymouth, and the Rev. Dr. Alliott, is the president and theological tutor.   There were Presbyterian and Independent congregations here in 1715, and also a French Church. The *Presbyterian Chapel*, in Batter street, was built in 1704, and repaired in 1846.   There is a *Unitarian Chapel* in Norley street; and a *Friends'*

Meeting House, in Bilbury street. The latter was erected on the site of the old one, in 1804, at the cost of £1200. There are *Baptist Chapels* in Princess street and George street, and the latter is an elegant structure, with a colonnade in front, and large schools attached; and was built in 1845, at the cost of £4600. There are *Wesleyan Chapels* in Buckwell lane, (erected in 1723,) Salem street, and Saltash street. The latter is a large and handsome building, which was erected in 1817, at the cost of about £5000, and has a burial ground. The *Plymouth Brethren* have chapels in Raleigh street and Compton street. This sect originated here, and has now congregations in most of the principal towns in England. Among the other places of worship are—*Bethseda Chapel,* in Ebrington street; the *Old Tabernacle,* at Britonside; Park street Chapel; the *Calvinist Chapel,* Octagon street; *Bible Christian Chapel,* Zion street; the *Jews' Synagogue,* Catherine street; the *Second Advent Chapel,* at the back of Eldad, and the *Bethel Union Chapel,* in Castle street. The latter was erected by subscription, in 1833, for the accommodation of sailors and soldiers, and is supplied chiefly by Independent and Wesleyan ministers, and has a large day and Sunday school.

CEMETERY.—The Plymouth, Stonehouse, and Devonport Cemetery Company, was established in 1846, with a capital of £15,000 in £25 shares, for the purpose of supplying an extensive cemetery for the three towns, where the old burial grounds have long been crowded, especially those at the parish churches, and that in Westwell street. This Cemetery is pleasantly situated on a gentle acclivity, about half a mile north of Plymouth, and about two miles from Devonport, and comprises ten acres of ground; more than half of which was consecrated by the Bishop, on June 5th, 1849, for the use of the Established Church, and the rest is appropriated to Dissenters, and was first opened in December, 1848. The ground is well enclosed and tastefully laid out, and has two neat chapels, in the decorated style, one for the consecrated, and the other for the unconsecrated division. About 8A. of land adjoining is to be added to the Cemetery, when required, having been purchased by the Company for that purpose, but now let for pasturage. The Cemetery forms a pleasant promenade, and east of it is a newly made road through the beautiful grounds, called Hyde Park. Mr. J. L. Colley, of 3, St. James' place, is the *secretary ;* and the Rev. Wm. Hocker is *chaplain* of the church portion.

Schools, and Bible, Tract, Missionary, and other Institutions for the instruction and relief of the poor, and for the dissemination of religion, are attached to the churches and chapels, and the town has many *Charitable Institutions,* supported either by endowments or voluntary contributions. Miss Sellon and a few other ladies belonging to the Established Church, associated themselves in the three towns, in 1848, under the name of the PROTESTANT SISTERS OF MERCY, for the purpose of visiting and relieving the poor, and imparting to orphan and other children the blessings of a sound scriptural education. They now occupy a house at Wyndham square; but subscriptions to the amount of more than £14,000 have been raised, in answer to the appeals of the bishop and clergy, for the purpose of erecting them a home in one of the " Five Fields." A *Brotherhood* of Protestant religious zealots has recently been established at Eldad.

The GRAMMAR SCHOOL, in Catherine street, was founded by Queen Elizabeth, who, in the 15th year of her reign, granted the great tithes of Plymouth and the advowson of the vicarage to the Corporation, and directed that they should allow £20 a year to a schoolmaster. The school and master's house belong to the Orphans' Aid Hospital, and are rented by the Corporation, who are the patrons, and allow £50 a year to the master for

teaching 12 sons of resident burgesses; besides whom he is allowed to take a large number of day scholars and boarders. The school is well conducted, and the Rev. Peter Holmes, M.A., F.R.A.S., is the head master, and has six assistants. Here are also several excellent private schools, one of which is called the New Grammar School.

HELE'S AND LANYON'S CHARITY SCHOOL, where 18 poor boys are educated, lodged, fed, and clothed, was till recently held in part of the Workhouse premises, called the Poor's Portion, and will be removed there again when certain alterations are completed. In 1632, *Elize Hele*, the great benefactor of Exeter and other places, (see pages 97 and 98,) gave certain lands, tenements, &c., to his executors, in trust that they should settle them for some charitable and godly uses. In 1658, the surviving executors vested property for the support of a charity school, with certain trustees, by a deed to which the Corporation and the Guardians of the Poor were made parties. This trust property now yields about £500 per annum, which is applied in schooling and maintaining 14 boys, and in giving apprentice fees and out-fits, to such as are apprenticed to trades on leaving the school. They are clothed in blue, and the master is allowed a yearly salary of £80, and has also the care of four poor boys, who are educated and maintained from the charity of *John Lanyon*, who, in 1674, left £2000 to be vested for that purpose. This trust property now consists of several houses, and money in the funds derived from the sale of property; and now yields about £200 per annum, which is expended in schooling, maintaining, and apprenticing four poor boys, who are taken from the Workhouse, formerly called the Hospital of the Poor's Portion.

PLYMOUTH FREE SCHOOLS, in Cobourg street, are supported chiefly by subscriptions and donations, and were established in 1810, on land belonging to Wm. Rowe's Charity, from which they have £25. 2s. 5d. per annum, as the dividends of £841 three per cent. consols. They are conducted on the national system, under the control of members of the Church of England, and are now attended by about 400 boys and 200 girls. Several new class rooms have recently been erected, and some of the higher branches of an English education are imparted to the elder boys, and every facility is afforded for the cultivation of any talent that may be evinced in the scholars. The master has a yearly salary of £80, and the mistress £40.

The GREY SCHOOL, in Hampton street, was commenced in 1714, and is supported partly by subscriptions, and collections at churches. Arising from donations and legacies this charity now possesses £3114. 9s. 7d. Old South Sea Annuities, and £1340 three per cent. consols, of which upwards of £700 arose from benefactions for apprenticing the scholars. The present school rooms, and the house for the master and mistress, were built in 1814, at the cost of £1178. Liberal salaries are paid to the teachers, and the charity now affords education and clothing to 50 boys and 50 girls, appointed by the trustees and a committee of subscribers.

LADY ROGERS' CHARITY SCHOOL, near Bedford terrace, was founded in 1773, pursuant to the will of *Lady Rogers*, who left £10,000 to be vested for the education and maintenance of poor girls of Devon and Cornwall. There is now belonging to this charity £27,872. 15s. 4d. three per cent. consols. About 50 poor girls are now educated and maintained in the school. They are admitted at eight, and are allowed to remain till fifteen years of age, when they are apprenticed, with premiums of 21s., and gifts of £5. 5s. for clothing, agreeable to a new scheme sanctioned by the Court of Chancery in 1787. Sir F. L. Rogers, Capt. Rogers, and others, are the trustees. The HOUSEHOLD OF FAITH, near Charles' Church, was established

in 1787, and consists of a *School of Industry* and a Sunday School, for poor girls, supported chiefly by subscriptions and donations. Among the legacies to this charity are—£500 left by Thomas Hodson, in 1819, and £100 left by James Bruce, in 1814. About 40 of the scholars are clothed at the expense of the charity. The NATIONAL SCHOOLS, at Tavistock place, were established in 1835. They are attended by about 300 boys and 200 girls; and the *Infant School*, in Charles' parish, has about 180 scholars. The *Ragged School Association* was established in 1849, for the purpose of educating and training to habits of industry and piety the children of the most destitute poor; and has already opened two or three schools.

The ORPHANS' AID HOSPITAL was founded in 1625, by Thomas and Nicholas Sherwill, who endowed it with houses, land, &c., now yielding about £200 per annum, and vested with the Charity Trustees of the Borough. This charity now educates and maintains ten orphan boys, who are boarded with Mrs. Hayes, in Catherine street, and educated at the Free School in Cobourg street. *Devon and Cornwall Female Orphan Asylum*, in Lockyer street, was founded in 1834, for the education and maintenance of poor orphan girls, with the view of training them to habits of industry, and fitting them for domestic service. It has now about 47 on the foundation, and 11 boarders, of whom nine are supported by the Naval and Marine Branch Society. The receipts of the hospital in 1849, comprised £280 from subscriptions, and £136 from donations. The *Presbyterian School*, in Batter street, was founded in 1785, by the Rev. Herbert Mends, who left £200 towards its support. It is now called *Batter Street Benevolent Institution* for clothing and educating 50 poor girls. It is supported chiefly by subscription, and children of all religious denominations are admitted, and instructed in reading, writing, needlework, &c.

PLYMOUTH PUBLIC DISPENSARY was instituted in the year 1798, "for the gratuitous relief of the industrious poor with advice and medicines, and, if necessary, attendance at their own houses, in time of sickness." It now occupies a commodious building in Catherine street, which was erected in 1808-9, at the cost of about £1650, including £234 paid for the land. For this building the town is chiefly indebted to the late Charles Yonge, Esq., who, in 1807, bequeathed to the charity £1000, which was preserved entire by the Rev. Duke Yonge paying the legacy duty. In the board room is a fine portrait and a marble tablet in memory of Mr. Yonge. Among the other principal benefactors to this useful and valuable charity are Admiral Vincent, £121; John Maxwell, £100; Mrs. Fox, £100; Capt. Grove, £450; and Mrs. Hirst, Joseph Pridham, Esq., Mrs. King, Miss Bewes, Miss Maxwell, and the late Joseph Whiteford, Esq., each £100. The charity now derives yearly about £165 from three per cent. consols, and £350 from subscriptions; and has in the course of each year about 2000 patients, nearly half of whom are visited at their own houses. Two physicians, four surgeons, and two dentists render their services gratuitously. The ROYAL EYE INFIRMARY, in Mill Bay road, was established in 1821, for the cure of diseases of the eye, and is under the patronage of Prince Albert. In the year 1849 it received 1213 patients, of whom 89 were in-patients. Its receipts during the same year amounted to £355, of which £174 was from subscriptions; £77 from donations; £27 from £933. 6s. 8d. three per cent. consols; and £54 from parishes, &c., for board of patients. The FEMALE PENITENTIARY for the three towns is in Ham lane. It was established in 1832, and has been the means of plucking many brands from the burning, and of restoring many unfortunate females to the paths of virtue. It receives about £170 a year from subscriptions, and about £70 from the work of the inmates, of whom it has sometimes 15 to 20. Here is a *Lying-*

in-Charity, and also several benevolent societies for clothing and feeding the poor. The *Soup Kitchen*, in Green street, was built by the Misses White, of Seven-trees, and supplies soup to the poor in winter at 1d. per quart. *Wash Houses for the Poor* have recently been established by subscription.

ALMSHOUSES.—The *Old Church Almshouses* for twelve poor widows and a nurse, are supported by the Corporation, and were in existence before 1573, but their origin is unknown. There is a large garden for the use of the inmates, and they each occupy separate rooms, and have weekly stipends of 1s. 9d., and monthly allowances of 12 pounds of flour. The Corporation pay the gardener and furnish the seeds. At the back of these are 12 almshouses for poor single women, under the care of the *Guardians of the Poor*, but they have no endowment. Under the same management are the *New Church Almshouses*, in Green street, built about 1680, with £300 left by Jno. Lanyon, and £100 given by John Gubbs. They afford shelter to 36 paupers. Prynne's, Baker's, and Fownes's Almshouses were sold by the Guardians of the Poor, about 50 years ago, for £600, and taken down for the improvement of the town. The £600 was expended on the workhouse buildings. *Alice Miller's*, alias *Baker's Almshouses* were endowed with £10 a year out of 22A. of land at Tamerton Foliott, now belonging to the Guardians of the Poor, and let for £25 a year, which is divided among the inmates of almshouses in the borough. *Jory's Almshouses* at Coxide, were built and endowed by Joseph Jory, Esq., in 1702, for twelve poor widows. They are endowed with 16 houses, &c., in St. Andrew's parish, and a farm of 30½A., at Modbury, let for about £250 per annum. Each inmate has an allowance of 30s. per calendar month. *Victoria Cottages*, in Victoria street, were purchased in 1834 by the late *Mrs. Hodson*, who vested them as almshouses for twelve poor women, and endowed them with £500 three per cent. consols.

The *Borough Charities*, vested with the Corporation, and now managed by the Borough Charity Trustees, (see page 652,) comprise the following, and also the Orphan's Aid, and the Old Church Almshouses, already noticed. At an early period, *Sir John Gayer* left an estate at Torr, in Pennycross, now let for £44. 18s. a year, out of which £8 is paid to the vicar of Charles, for preaching sermons preparatory to the administration of the sacrament; 24s. to the clerk and sexton, and £4 to the Orphans' Aid. The rest of the rent is distributed among the poor of the borough, chiefly in shirts, shifts, petticoats, and other clothing, together with about £90, arising yearly from the following *gifts*, viz., *John White's*, £11. 15s., left in 1584; *John and Thos. Bound's*, £2, left in 1642, out of Thistle Park; *Robt. Hewer's*, £4; and Baron's, Collin's, Hill's, and Ackerman's Gifts, amounting to £9. 12s. per annum. The Corporation have £14. 8s. yearly out of the tithes of Egg Buckland and St. Budeaux, left by *John Burrough*, for providing clothing for the "two town corporals and the governor of the barbican." *Mrs. Joan Bennett's Trust*, for the support of two *exhibitioners* from Plymouth at one of the Universities, yields about £100 per annum, of which about £40 arises from premises in Southside street, and the rest from £1841 three per cent. consols. *Robert Rawling*, in 1626, left £250 in trust to pay yearly £3 for the poor in the almshouses; £2 for the poor of Compton Gifford; 30s. for poor burgesses; and 10s. each to seven other parishes for the poor. He also left two tenements in Batter street, and other property, to the Orphans' Aid Hospital.

WM. ROWE, in 1690, left 3A. 3R. 27P. of land, called Shute Park, in trust to distribute the rent among the poor of the borough. It is now let for £52 per annum, which is distributed by the Guardians of the Poor. The same

donor also left £841, three per cent. consols, the dividends of which are applied towards the support of the Free Schools. In 1727, JAMES MADDOCK left to the Guardians of the poor £1500, in trust to distribute the proceeds yearly in clothing among the poor, one half to those receiving and the other half to those not receiving parochial relief. This charity now consists of £1406 old South Sea Annuities. In 1732, HENRY KELWAY left £1900 bank stock, in trust for the benefit of his relations, or in default of such, for the poor. This stock has since been increased by bonuses, &c., to £4860. 17s. 3d., which yields dividends amounting to about ten per cent. Pursuant to the donor's will, £43 is yearly distributed among his relations, and the rest of the income is applied in educating their children. The two vicars and the master of the Grammar School are the acting trustees.

ST. ANDREW'S PARISH has the following charities, besides its share in the general charities of the borough. The poor have four annuities of 52s. each for weekly distributions of bread, left by *Sir John Acland and Wm. and John Hill*, in the 17th century, and by *John Morshead* in 1750. For the same purpose they have the following yearly sums, viz., 50s. left by Capt. Ackerman, and £2. 2s. 3d. from Huxham's charity. The churchwardens distribute the bread. The poor of *Pennycross* tithing have £4 a year from the gift of John Harris, Johannah Knighton, and Robert Rawling.

The *Parish of King Charles the Martyr* has the following, besides its share of the borough charities. For distributions of bread, the poor have £5. 10s. yearly, as interest of £102. 10s. left by *Mary Collins and John Morshead* in 1750, and lent to the churchwardens. The Vicar distributes £7 yearly in *clothing*, as the gift of Eliz. Chapman and Mrs. Sutton. In 1796, *Eleanor Huxham* left £660 three per cent. stock, in trust with the Vicar, to pay £15 yearly for ten poor women of Plymouth, in equal shares, and to distribute the rest of the dividends in bread at the two parish churches. The dividends of £334. 14s. 6d. three per cent. consols, left by *James Stevens* in 1797, are applied, one-half to the support of the Sunday School, and the other in distributions to the poor. The interest of £150, left by *J. Bruce* in 1841, is divided among three poor tradesmen's families. In 1829, *Mrs. Mary Glanville Hodson* left the dividends of £500 three per cent. stock, to be distributed in bread on the 12th of April and Dec.; and in 1830, *John Morris* left the dividends of £100 of the same stock for distribution in bread among the poor parishioners on the 1st of January. The poor of *Compton Gifford* have 40s. a year from Rawling's Charity; and the interest of £200 left by Rebecca Shaw and Sarah Hancock.

PLYMOUTH WORKHOUSE :—By an act of parliament, passed in the 6th of Queen Anne, (1708,) for erecting a Workhouse in Plymouth for the two parishes, all almshouses belonging to the mayor and commonalty were vested in the *Corporation of the Guardians of the Poor*, established by that act, and consisting of the mayor, recorder, six of the magistrates, six of the common council, 20 inhabitants of the parish of St. Andrew, and 18 inhabitants of the parish of Charles. Among other property transferred to them was the hospital or workhouse called the *Poor's Portion*, built in 1630, and endowed with land and tenements now let for upwards of £20 a year, and given by various donors. This property is let on 99 years' leases, determinable on lives; and subject to fines on every renewal. The Guardians of the Poor are also in receipt of £5 a year in three annuities, left by Php. Francis, Jph. Palmer, and an unknown donor; and they have the management (jointly with the trustees,) of *Hele's and Lanyon's Charities* for the maintenance and schooling of poor boys, as already noticed. The act of Queen Elizabeth was amended by three other acts passed in the 32nd of George II., and the 26th and 53rd of George III., and under them the two

parishes still maintain their poor, without any interference from the New Poor Law Commissioners. The Workhouse has been enlarged at various periods, and comprises an extensive range of buildings, partly ancient and partly modern, but many of the older parts have been altered or rebuilt. It stands in St. Andrew's parish, and has room for more than 400 paupers. The able bodied are employed in teazing oakum, making mats, &c. The guardians are elected annually, on the second Tuesday in May, 14 from the Town Council, 20 from the the ratepayers of St. Andrew's, and 18 from the ratepayers of the parish of Charles. The total cost of maintaining the poor of the two parishes was £11,580, in 1838; £16,529, in 1848; and £15,014, in 1849. The *governor, deputy governor, treasurer,* and *receiver* are appointed yearly by the guardians; and the following are the principal stipendiary officers:—Robert Burnard, *clerk;* H. Wotton, *cashier;* Thomas Scammell, *store keeper;* Eliz. Burnard, *matron;* F. A. Pardon and Thos. Edwards, *relieving officers;* J. P. Williams and Mary Harris, *teachers of the schools;* and Thomas Cole and Rt. Prinn, *collectors of poor rates.* The two parishes form a registration district, and Mr. Wm. Pridham is the *superintendent registrar.* Messrs. J. West and H. H. Heydon are *registrars of marriages;* and James Wyatt and H. H. Heydon are *registrars of births and deaths.*

The PROVIDENT INSTITUTIONS of Plymouth comprise a Savings' Bank; three *Lodges of Freemasons,* held at the Royal Hotel, the Commercial Hotel, and the Golden Fleece; several other Secret Orders, and many Friendly Societies, &c. The FREEMASONS' HALL, at the end of Cornwall street, was built in 1827, at the cost of £2500. It is a handsome stone building, and on the ground floor are the *Commercial News Rooms,* established in 1832. The spacious hall above, is often let for lectures, exhibitions, concerts, and public meetings, and will accommodate upwards of 500 persons. The *Plymouth and South Devon Savings' Bank,* in Cornwall street, was established in 1837, and in November, 1848, had deposits amounting to £90,508, belonging to 4116 depositors, 58 Charitable Societies, and 14 Friendly Societies. It had at the same time invested £12,637 in the purchase of government annuities. In Nov., 1849, the deposits amounted to £97,883, of which £8185 had been deposited in new accounts during the year. The Earl of Morley is *patron;* Lord Seaton, *president;* J. Williams, Esq., *treasurer;* Mr. Wm. Haydon, *secretary;* and W. G. Haydon, *actuary.* Here is a branch of the *Western Provident Association,* noticed at page 119. Mr. Bottomley, of 15, Tavistock place, is secretary to the local board.

COMPTON GIFFORD and PENNYCROSS are tithings and townships; the former ecclesiastically in the parish of Charles the Martyr, and the latter in the parish of St. Andrew; but they are not in the Borough of Plymouth, but in Roborough Hundred, and in Plympton Union. They extend from 1½ to 3 miles N.E. of the Guildhall. COMPTON GIFFORD comprises 1510 acres of land, 271 inhabitants, and several neat houses. It anciently belonged to *Giffords* or *Giffards,* and afterwards to the Whitleigh, Coxe, Northleigh, and Tothill families, but it is now the property of the Earl of Morley. It includes part of the pleasant village of *Mutley,* and Ford Park. PENNYCROSS, otherwise *Western Peverell* or *St. Pancras,* is a chapelry, containing 1310 acres of land, and 276 souls, and includes part of *Mutley* and *Ford Park,* and several handsome houses. The manor was anciently held by the Peverells, and afterwards by the Carew, Hewer, and other families, and is now held by the Rev. J. H. Parlby, of *Manadon,* formerly the seat of the Hewers. The *Chapel* (St. Pancras,) is an ancient building, and the curacy is annexed to the Vicarage of St. Andrew. The following are the principal inhabitants of these small out-townships:—

COMPTON GIFFORD.

Baker Major Thomas, *Ford Park*
Bulcock R., Esq. || Burney G , R.N.
Bremer Lady || Cuddaford Mr Edw.
Farquhar Mr., *Mutley Plain*
Foulston Mrs Elz., *Thornhill Cottage*
Garwood Mrs || Thompson Mrs
Hopwood Rd., Esq., *Thornhill*
Howard Wm., Esq., *Hartley House*
Kingdon G. B., Esq., *Hartley*
Lott Misses, *Vinstone House*
Melhuish Mr. E., Ford Park
Moxon Col. Wm., Ford Park
Rabbidge Mr Edw. || Veale Edw.
Rennie James, Esq., Ford Park
Shepheard Mr Jno., *Townsend Hill*
Spence Hy. Fras., Esq., *Ford Park*
Veale Mr. Geo. & Geo. jun
Whiteford C. C., Esq., *Thornhill*

PENNYCROSS.

Bryant Jas., Esq., *Prospect*
Foote Capt. Geo., *Torr Grove*
Hodge Wm. Chapple, Esq., *Pounds*
Hunt Warwick Augs., Esq., *Burleigh*
King Jas., Esq., *Burrington*
Parlby Rev. Jno. Hall, *Manadon*
Pedlar Colonel Philip Warren, *Mutley House*
Rundle Robt. Esq., *Montpelier*
Scott Edward Henry Orchard, Esq., *Bellair*
Trelawny Rev. C. T. C., M.A. curate

FARMERS.

Body Nichls. || Cox Richard
Boon James, (and corn miller)
Cudlip Mary || Marks Abel
Rowe Thomas, *The Barton*

PLYMOUTH DIRECTORY.

(See also Devonport and Stonehouse.)

The POST-OFFICE is an elegant new building, situate in Whimple street, and Mr. Charles Markes is the *Post-master.* There is a *Branch Post-office* at Mr. George Evan's, 117, Union street, Stonehouse, and there are *Receiving Boxes* at 14, Union street; 11, Exeter street; and 22, Tavistock street. Letters are despatched to Exeter, London, Bristol, &c., every morning and evening, by rails ; to Devonport, 6 morning, 1 afternoon, and 6 evening ; and to Tavistock, Bideford, Barnstaple, Falmouth, Launceston, &c., by mail coach daily. *Money Orders* are granted and paid.

MISCELLANY of *Gentry, Clergy, Partners in Firms, and others not arranged in the succeeding Classification of Trades and Professions.*

Those marked * are Master Mariners.

Abbott Miss E., Frankft. st
Abbott Capt. Jonas Archer, R.N.,'Portland villas
Ackland Mr W.3 Nth.hill pl
Adams Mr. —— 8 Zion st
Adams Mr A. 22 Portlnd. pl
Adams Mrs E. 19 Prtlnd. pl
Adams Major F. Mulgrv. st
Adams Mrs G. 57 York st
Adams P., dpr. Portland vls
Aldridge Mrs L.Wyndm. sq
Alexander Captain J. 20 Buckland street
Allen Misses, 5 Buckland tr
Allen Mr F. 2 North hill pl
Allen J., brewer, Albany pl
Alliot Rev Rd., D.D. president of the Western Indp. College, 7 Wyndham sqr
Alsop Wm., earthnwe. mfr., Coxide Potry. ; h Frhm pl
* Angell W.2 Compton st
Anton Capt. A., Clarence st
Anton Wm., Mutley plain
Arnold Mrs L. 3 Portland pl
Arthur Miss A.2 Hewer's rw
Arthur Rear Admiral Rd. 9 Gascoyne terrace
Atkinson Mrs. Devnshr. ter
Atkinson C. J., clerk, South Devon place
Attrill Miss, 33 Cobourg st

* Aves John, Gibbons st
Babb Rev James, M.A., Portland Chapel, Port. sq
Backhouse Mrs C., Chas.pl.
Baggs Mrs C., Gasking st
Bailey Mr G. 9 Brunswick tr
Baker Mrs Ss. 13 Portlnd.sq
Balkwill Mrs A. Pertlnd. sq.
Balkwill Mr C., Norley pl
Ball Jph. Esq. Tothill cottg
Ball Mr Thos., York st
Bamber Mrs 8. 16 Ham st
Barnes Mrs 3 Ladywell pl
Barnes Capt. Caleb, R.M. 4 Chesterplace
* Barnes Wm. 9 Victoria st
Barnett W. tvlr. Sumlnd. pl
Baron Mr W. 6 Princess sq
Barrable Mr Wm. 16Nth.pl
Bartlett E., clk. 23 Cobrg st
Bartlett Rd., clk. Teats hill
Bartlett Mr W. 29 King st
Bastow W. Esq. 31 Wyndham square
Batchelor Miss A. 1 Windsor street
Bate Mr Hy. 27 Jubilee st
Batten Mrs Eliz. 35 Park st
Batten Mr Jas., Regent st
Baugh Lieut. Js., Provd. st
Bayntun G., *Eye Infirmary*
Bazley Mr J. 11 Hoe street

Bazley Mr J. 14 Prospect st
Beer Mr Jph. 3 Victoria st
Bell Col. Jas. 4 Octagon
Bell Capt. Jas. 25 James st
Bellamy Rev G., chaplain, New Prisons
Benbow J., surg. 32 Oxfd st
Bennett John N., solicitor, 2 Windsor villas
Bennett Mrs My. 13 & Mr Chas. 11 Ladywell pl
Bennett Mr W., Princes sq
BennettMrW.,Claremont st
Bennett W. D. 23Morley pl
Best Mr W. 24 Gibbons st
Betts Miss E. 4 Bellair st
Bewes T.Esq.,BeaumontH.
Bickel Mr. 3 Charles place
Bickham Jn., sex. Finwl. st
Bickle Mr W.D. 26 King st
Bird Mr Jas. 4 Hoe place
Bird Peter, clk. 18 John st
Birdwood Mr R. 7 Mt. Pl.tr
Birkhead Mr H. 2 Albert tr
Bishop Rt., drpr., Regent st
BlackmoreMrsE.,Prospc. st
Blackmore Mr W. G. 3 Windsor place
Blake Mrs Ann, Regent st
Blake Rd. Esq. 3 Windsr.tr
Blake Mr G., 5 Alfred pl
Blatchford J., clk. Notte st

Blewett MrT.E.,Prospect st
Blight Lieut. Emnl., R. N.
  5 Eton place
Blight Mrs S. 3 Garden st
Blyth Mrs E. 3 Belr. cotgs.
Bodley Mr T. 28 Prospect st
Bone Fdk. gent. 30 Oxfd. st
Borlase Mrs A. 4 Victoria st
Borlase Mr W. Cambdg. st
Bosworva J. R. clk. Cobg. st
Botters Miss S. 4 Eldad pl
Bottomley J. sec. toWestrn.
  Provdt. Asn., Tavstck. st
Boulter Mrs F. 11 Row. st
Bovell W. Esq. 11 Northill
Bowden Mr Pp. 2 Wndsr. st
Bowen Mrs. 1 Charles ctgs.
Bowers Miss A. 9 Hill st
Bowers Mrs 3 Prospect rw
Bradbury Mr E. Denhm. tr
Breay W. H., R.N. 5 Port-
  land villas
Breen Wm., clk. to County
  Court, 32 Wyndham sq
Brendon Wm., printer ; h 8
  Melbourne street
Brewer Mr S. W. Morley st
BrewerJ.R.,printer,11Jno.st
Briggs Mr T. 8 Brunswk.ter
Brimacombe Mr J.20 Jno.st
Brimson J. clk. 7 Regent st
Brimson Mr R. 31 James st
Broadrick Mrs. 2 Gibbons st
Brock Mrs Eliz., matron,
  Penitentiary
Broughton Chas. D., Esq.
  Windsor villas
Brown Mrs. 3 South Dvn.pl
Brown Mrs A. Wyndhm. sq
Brown E. R., grocer ; h 4
  Bilbury street
Brown Miss E. 6 Woodside
Brown H., dpr. 8Northill pl
Brown Mrs M., James pl
Brown Mr T. 3 Densham tr
Browne Brothers, coach lace
  and fringe manufacturers,
  32 Buckwell street
Browne A. A. ; h Norley pl
Browne John ; h Jubilee st
Browne T. ; h 32Buckwell st
Browse Mr M. 5 John lane
Bryant Brothers & Burnell,
  sugar refiners, Coxide
Bryant W. Esq. 5 Lipstn.tr
Buckingham Mr R. 7 Nth.p
Bulford Mr J. 3 Portland pl
Buller Mrs S., Mt.Pleasant
Bulteel Rev Henry, (Ind.)
  11 Ham street
Bulteel Thomas Hillersdon,
  Esq. banker, 1 Crescent
Bunce Mrs Col. 11 Union st
Bundock Mrs C. 7 Belle v.pl
Burbey Mr C. 14 Victoria st
Burdwood Capt. Thos. R.N.
  50 Cobourg street
Burford Mr J. 24 James st
Burgess Rev W. C., Wynd-
  ham street
Burgess Mrs M. 1 Eton Ctg.

Burgoyne Mrs A. 32 Wm.st
Burke Mr Peter, Cambg. st
Burkinshaw W., saw mkr.
  4 Richmond street
Burnard E., matron,Wrkhs.
Burnard Rt , clk. Cadman st
Burnell John, grocer ; h 31
  Portland square
Burnell W.,Esq.4 Lipson ter
BurnettMrJn.20Athenm. st
BurnettMrsMy.4Farenm.pl
Bursey Rev Thos. (Wes.)
  24 Clarence street
Burt Mr Thos. 9 Regent st
BussellMrJas.45Tavistk. pl
Bussacott Mr Alexander, 16
  Ebrington street
BuswarvaJohn, clk. 5 Hoe st
ButcherMrH.5Densham ter
Butcher Mr Thomas John,
  52 York street
ButtonMrsMy.14Lockyer st
ByeWm.excise,8Hamptonst
Byham Mrs A., Windsor st
Campbell Lieut. Col. John,
  4 Mount Pleasant ter
Campbell Lieut.Wm.,R.N.,
  29 Prospect street
Cardell G.P., clk. Millbay pl
CardeuCornls.Esq. 14 Cresct
Carden Mrs.2 Athenæum st
Carill Mr Wm. 49 York st
*Carlisle John, 6 Garden st
CarneMissE.27Wyndhm.st
CarrMissA.M.9Windsor ter
Carr Wm. sec.to S.D.Rail-
  way, Buckland street
CarrMrWm.Ogle,7Alfred pl
CarrighanRevG.Greystock,
  M.A. incumbt. of Sutton-
  upon-Plym, & surrogate,
  9 Windsor place
Carter Miss E.10 Albany pl
CartwrightLieut.John,R.N.
  10 Buckland terrace
Casely Hy. clerk, 14 John st
CatorMrThos.3Hewer's row
Chafford Mrs. 11 Regent st
ChanningMrT.39Cobourg st
Chapman MrRt.2Albany pl
Charley Mr Sl.5 Compton st
Ching Mr Wm. Henry H. 18
  North place
Chubb Mrs. 1 Mulgrave pl
Churchill Capt. Edw. Wm.
  9 York street
Churchill Wm. clerk of cus-
  toms, Norley place
Churchward Wm. clerk, 10
  Melbourne street
Clapp Lieut.Wm.,R.N. 39
  Tavistock place
ClarenceG.tvlr.SeaViewHs
Clarke Rt. clk.4 Princess pl
Clarke Mr Thos. 5 Hill st
Clatworthy Mrs A.5 Park st
Cleverton Mr. 7 Boon's pl
Coad Mr Jas. 6 John street
Coad Miss, 8 Mt.Pleast. ter
CoakerJ..R.N.7Denshamter
Coare Geo. Esq. 6 Octagon

Coates and Co. distillers,
  Southside street
Coates Capt. Rd., R.N. 17
  Oxford street
Coath Mrs Rchl. 49 Park st
Coath Mrs Jane, Sutton rd
CoddMrE.S.3Constantin st
Coffin Mr J. N. 4 James' st
Cohen Mrs. 10 Zion street
Colby Capt. Thos., R.N. 12
  Frankfort street
Cole Mr Abm. 8 Bedford ter
Cole Mrs. 22 George street
Cole Mr Jas. 45 Cobourg st
Cole Mrs Jane, 10 North pl
Cole Mr John, 11 Woodside
Cole R. Esq. 29 Portland sq
Cole T. rate collr.Treville st
ColeW.police insp.Morleypl
Collier Miss Jane, 2 Woodsd
Collier Mort. mert.64 Old st
CollierW.mert.13Athenm.st
Collier Wm. mert. Woodside
Collier Wm. F. 64 Old st
CollomPp.clk.23Tavistk.pl
Colley John Long, sec. to Ce-
  metery Co. 3 James' pl
Conning J. J., Union Baths
Coode Lieut. C. P., R.N. 1
  Mount Pleasant terrace
Coode Rear Admiral John,3
  St Andrew's terrace
CookS.sergt.-at-mace,Gldhl
Coombes Mrs. 2 Windsor pl
Coombs Mrs A. 11 Stoke la
*Cooper Geo. C. 6 Regent st
CoramMissE.10Ladywellpl
Cornish Mrs S.31Cobourg st
Cornish J.Esq.Wyndhm. sq
Corser Mr John, Regent st
Cory Mrs Carln. 1 Eldad pl
CoryndouRt.Esq.10Green st
Coryndon Mrs. 9Athenm. st
Cotwell Mr Pp. 3 Mount st
CouchMissH.4Buckland ter
Couch Mr W. 9 William st
Courtis H. Esq. 5 Union ter
Cousens Miss S. 6 Union ter
CousinsMrsM. 9 Compton st
Cowl Mrs. 1 Windsor place
Cox Mr Rd. 3 Hr. Batter st
*CrespinW.4 QueenAnne pl
Crews Mrs. 6 Bellevue pl
Crews Nichls. coach maker,
  2 Twickenham street
Crimp Mrs. 12 Bellevue pl
CrockerMrHy. 20Cobourg st
Croft Mr Cs. W. 21 Portld.sq
Croft MrRd.34Cambridge st
Cross Mrs C. 8 Norley st
CrossRd.tvlr.14Hampton st
CrossmanMrTs.11Morley st
Cuddeford My.tripe dresser,
  80 Cambridge street
Cuddeford Wm. C. clerk, 80
  Cambridge street
Cuming Wm. B., agent to
  Lloyds, 5 Brunswick ter
Cumming Mrs A.,Jubilee st
*Cundy J., Mt.Pleasnt.Cotg
CurgenyenMrsE.Portld.Hs

Curtis Mr Hy.,Richmond ln
Curtis W.clk.5Courtenay st
*Cuthberson D.,Fareham pl
Dabb J.draper,26Athenm.st
Damerel Mr J. 10 James st
DamerelJ.policeinsp.Wm.st
Daniell Capt. Fras.H.E.C.
    12 Wyndham square
*Dart Charles,10 Princess st
Davey Mr S.11Ebrington st
Davey Wm. 19 Gasking st
Davies E.matron, Dispnsry
*Davies Wm. 4 Glanville pl
Davis Mrs Eliz., Norley pl
Davis Mrs J., 25 Union st
Davy P. fellmonger,2Jas. pl
Dawe Josiah Hayne, Esq.
    banker ; h Whimple st
Dawe Mrs P.46Tavistock pl
De Boggee Miss,37Portld.sq
DenisonW. clk. 13 George pl
DennisMiss, 24 Tavistock pl
Dennis Geo. organ builder,
    7 Lockyer terrace
DennisRevS.24Wyndhamst
Derry S. surgn. 8 Mulgrv.st
DerryWm. agt.Glanville st
Dickenson J. clk. 12 Hoe st
DitchamThos.Edw.,Trinity
    agent, Sutton road
DixonLadyCath.9Albany pl
Dixon Miss F. 10 Albany pl
*Dixon Percvl. 1 Camden st
Dobson Mrs E. 4 Eton pl
Dobson J.tvlr. 2 S.Devon pl
Down Mr K. 1 Oxford st
Downing Mrs M.6Morley st
Drake MissE.7 Buckland st
Drake Mr Wm. 14 York st
*Drew John, 10Ebrington st
Drew Mary, upholstress,26C
    Bedford street
Drew Rd. clerk, 2 Bellair st
Driscoll J.mert.8Saltram pl
DrydenT.,R.N.2Portland pl
Duglas Rd., R. N. surgeon,
    2 Buckland street
DuncanMrsG.4 Ladywell pl
DunnisMrsAnn,6Princesspl
Dunsford MrsH.4Saltram pl
Dunsterville Col. James H.
    12 Crescent
Dyer MrHy.23Wyndham sq
EaglesMrsEliz. 28Oxford st
Eales Mr Saml.19Oxford st
Earland MrJohn,3Mount st
Eastham Mrs. 6 York st
Eastlake George, solr. and
    coroner for the waters,
    Windsor Villa
Eastlake Geo. Shute, solr.
    15 Frankfort street
EastlakeJ. solr.28Athnm.st
EastlakeW. solr. 4 Alfred st
Easton Mr Wm. 2 Hoe st
EcclesJ.H.surgn.1Sussex st
Edmonds Misses, 23Oxfd.st
EdmondsDd.master gunner,
    St Nicholas' Island
Edmonds John Gard, solr.
    and coroner, Citadel road

Edwards Thomas, relieving
    officer, Workhouse
Edwards Mr Thos. W. 6
    Summerland terrace
ElliottCol. *BarleyHs.* King st
Elliott Mr J. 48 Cobourg st
Elliott John, inspr. of meat,
    Shambles
Elliott Mr W. E. 5 Wind-
    sor villas
Ellis Mr John, 6 Zion st
Enderwick Mr H. 4 Rowe st
Essery Mr. 18 King st
Evans Mrs G. 25 King st
*Evans W. 12 Ebrington st
Everest Mr G. 18 Devon pl
Everett Mrs E.15 Victoria st
Farley Mr W.,Gloucester st
*Fauckner W.3 Fareham pl
Featherstone Lieut. Saml.,
    R.N. 14 Cobourg st
Filder Mr Edw. sec. to Gt.
    Western Docks, 1 Buck-
    ingham place
Filmer Mr G. 1Albemarle pl
Fishley Mr J. 56 Cobourg st
Fiske Capt., (S.D.M.) 4
    Athenæum street
Fleming Major Julius, 2
    Mulgrave street
Fleming Mr T. 8 Victoria st
Flight Mrs C. 9 Woodside
Fold Mr J. M. 2 Saltram
    cottages
Foote Capt. 22 George st
Foote I. G. clk. 21 Jubilee st
Forsyth Mr J. 17 Cobourg st
Fortescue Geo. F. Esq. 1
    Windsor terrace
Foster J. T. 12 Prospect st
Foster Mrs Judith, 2 Gas-
    coyne cottages
Fouracre Mrs. 7 Regent st
Fowell MrW.13Summlnd pl
*Fowler —, 3 Marine place
Fowler Mrs. 17 Hoe street
Fox Mrs. 10 Portland sq
Fox Miss Dthy. 1 Northill pl
Fox Miss M. 29 Cobourg st
Frampton Lieut. George, 6
    Windsor street
Francis Capt. J. 2 Regent st
Frean G. miller, Drake's pl
FreanG.H.millr.,Skardonpl
Freeman Jno. granite mert.
    5 Lockyer street
Freeman Richd., M.D. sur-
    geon, 11 George place
Freke Mrs B. 3 Buckld. ter
FrowardMiss,4Portld.villas
Furse Cs. clk. 20 Milton st
Gabbs Misses, Elizabeth pl
Gahan Chas., R.N., 33 Ta-
    vistock place
Gandy Mrs. 27 Portland sq
Gandy Misses, 38 Pordld.sq
Gatcombe Richd. Esq. 29
    Wyndham square
Geldard Mr Rd. 4 John st
Gibbons Jph. police supt.
    Portland terrace

Gibbons Mr S. 12Windsor pl
Gibson Herbert Mends.solr.
    4 Bedford terrace
Gibson Mrs J. 9 Gasking st
Gidley Mr Gstvs. Regent st
Gidley Mr J. K. 3 Albert ter
Gilbert Mr J. 19 North pl
Giles J., R.N. 13 Prospect st
Gillard Miss E. 18 Octagon
Gilson Mr Danl. 22 South
    Devon place
Ginder Mr J. 14 William st
Glanville Mr Ths. 31 Rich-
    mond street
Gliddon Mrs M. 8 North pl
Godfrey Peter, bed purifier,
    71 Cobourg street
Goffe H. port officer, South-
    side street
Goldfinch G., R.N. 5 Wind-
    sor terrace
Golding Mrs J. 7 George pl
Gole Mr A. 38 Cobourg st
Gole Capt. J., Clarendon pl
Good Jno. rope mat maker,
    and library, 24 Morley st
Govett MrP. H., Lipson Hs
Granger E.clk.20 Princess st
Grant Capt., R N. 15 Tor-
    rington place
Greaves RevHenryA.,M.A.
    vicar of Charles, 2 Port-
    land villas
Green T.police sergt.Bath st
Greenham Emily, register
    office, 1½ Russell st
Greenway Mr Hy. 11 Mt.
    Pleasant terrace
Greet Mrs My. 13 James st
Grey S. clk. 2 Belle vue pl
Grey Mr Ths. 22 Morley st
Grigg Miss E. 1 Lipson ter
Grigg Miss Jane, Regent st
Grigg Mk. Esq. 14 Ham st
Grosett Miss, 6 Fareham pl
Guard Rd. rope maker, 13
    Wyndham square
Gunpowder Co. (Plymouth
    and Dartmoor,) 15 Tavi-
    stock terrace
Gwatkin Miss,21Princess sq
Haddock Mrs Mgt. 29 Cla-
    rence street
Haddy Mrs. 3 Torrington pl
Haddy John, spirit mert. 6
    Victoria street
Hadow Rev Geo., M.A. in-
    cumbent of St Andrew's
    chapel, Princess sq
Haines Jno. Danl. Esq. 5
    Marine place
Hall Capt. Chas., R.N. 9
    Melbourne street
Ham Capt. Fredk., R.N. 34
    Tavistock place
Hamlyn Misses, 6 Summer-
    land terrace
Hannaford John, clerk, 12
    Tavistock street
Harding Mr J. 1 Bedfd. cots
Hare T. clk. 2 Tavistock pl
Harley Mr Wm. 6 North pl

Harman Mrs Eliz. 4 North Devon place
Harper Mr Geo. 27 Park st
HarrisC.banker; h *Thorncot*
Harris Harry Bulteel, Esq. banker; h *Radford*
Harris Miss A.1 Prospect st
Harris Mr C. 3 Bedford ter
Harris Mr Jas. 36 Park st
Harris Mrs M. 1 Radnor pl
Harris Mr S 22Tavistock pl
Harris Sir Wm. Snow, 6 Windsor villas
Harris Wm. H. spirit mert. 33 Oxford street
Harrison Major Jas. H. 2 Mount Pleasant ter
Harrison Mr J.23Athenm.st
Harvey Mrs E. 14 Alfred st
Harvey John, cement mfr. 9 Morley street
Harvey Mrs M. 1 Union ter
Harvey Thos. cement mfr. 11 Constantine street
Haswell Mrs 22 Cobourg st
Hatchard Rev John, M.A. vicar of St. Andrew's, Westwell street
Hawes W. Esq. 2 Esplanade
HawkerMrs.25Wyndhamst
Hawker Rev Wm. incmbt. of Charles' chapel
Hawker Mrs S. 8 Cobourg st
Hay Mrs Eliz.4Tavistock pl
Haydon Wm. savings' bank actuary, 4 Woodside
Haydon Capt. Wm., R.N., Citadel road
*Hayman W. 3 Cobourg cots
Haynes Capt. John, coast guard, 11 Charles pl
Heale Mr Jno. 8 Ham st
Heath Mrs Har. 12 Gascoyne terrace
Heath Mr Jno. 4 Park st
Heathman John, R.N. 19 Buckland street
HellyerMisses,60Cobourg st
Hellyer Mrs A. 27 Jubilee st
Hembrough Mr P. 11 Jas. st
Henderson Geo. sec. to Gas Co. Millbay road; h 43 George street
Henley Mr E., Qn. Anne's Battery
Henry Mr Jas. G. 1 Upper Buckland terrace
Henwood Mrs A. 8 Exeter st
Henwood Rev O. (Wesleyan,) 33 Park street
Herring MrR.67Cambdge.st
Hetling Rev G. curate of St Peter's, 10 Wyndham sq
Hewitt Mr Jno. 29 John st
Hewlett Misses,13Gascoyne terrace
Hex John, horse letter, 3 Princess street
Heycroft Jas. mert. Hoe pl
Heywood Mr T. 4 Albert ter
Hicks C. police sergt. Claremount street

Hicks Js. Henley, surgeon, 2 Brunswick place
Hicks Mr Saml. 5 Boon's pl
Higham Mrs E. 4 Sussex ter
Hill Mrs A. 87 Cambridge st
Hill Mr E. 1 Summerld. pl
Hill Miss Jane, Regent st
Hill Mr Rd., Skardon pl
Hill W. Esq. 3 Portld. villas
Hilliard Wm., R.N. 29 Cobourg street
Hine Rev Thos C. (Indpt.) 6 Albany place
Hingston A. clk.7Lockyer st
Hingston Mrs.11 Gibbons st
Hingston Mrs.8Ladywell pl
Hingston Lieut. Geo., R.N. 2 Gascoyne cottages
Hingston Mr W. 18 Park st
Hinton MissM.A.9Clarnc.st
Hitley Maj.Fade,3Alfred st
Hoare Mrs E.10 BelleVue pl
*Hoare Wm., Morley pl
Hocker RevWm., B.A.chap. to Cemetery, Hewer's row
Hocking MrsC.12Tavistk.pl
Hodge Miss E. 27 Morley pl
Holman H. J. clk. 14 Gasking street
Holman J. dpr. 7 Nth hill pl
Holmden J. clerk, 2 Eton pl
Holmes Mr E. 19 Octagon
Holmes Rev Peter, M.A., Catherine street
Hook Mrs S. 6 Summerld. pl
HookeyRevGeorgeS., M.A., incumbent of St James's
*Hooper Chas. 9 Charles pl
Hooper Mr Jas., Hoe pl
Hope Mr Geo., Amity pl
Hopkins Evan, printer, &c; house 16 Bedford street
Hopkins Thos. clk. Ham ln
HopkinsonMrsA 10Alfred st
Hopley MrsM.E. Mutleypln
HoppenR.,R.N.2Bedfd ctgs
Horne Misses, 5 S. Devon pl
HoskingMrsSpha.11Park st
Howard Mrs R. 2 Sussex ter
Howell J. bank clk.44 Jas.st
Hoyles Mrs. 8 Charles pl
Hubbard A. clk.8 Albany pl
Hudder Mrs. 37 James st
Hughes Hon Mrs A. M., 10 Athenæum street
HughesJas.tvlr. 10 Flora pl
HuntMisses,15Mulgrave st
Hunt Mrs M.4Torrington pl
Hunt MrW.C. 68 Cobourg st
Hutchinson Jn.clk.Catdown
Hyne Misses, 5 Charles pl
Hyne Miss Sar. 6 Cobourg st
IlesMrsHenrietta,9Greenst
IsbellMrJames,8Clarence st
JacksonS.clk.Blackfriars'ln
JacobsMrSlvs.1Gascoyne pl
Jacobs MrWm. 3 Gibbons st
Jacobson Wm. clrk. County Court, 4 Mulgrave street
JagoMrsAnn,6Athenæum st
Jago Capt Donald, 8 York st
Jago Mr Richd. 34 James st

JagoRt.Stn. Esq.13Crescent
JamesEd.starch mfr.Coxide
James MrJn. Portland villas
Jane Mr John, 15 North pl
Jarvis Mrs M., Skardon pl
Jeffery Wm. gun maker, 22 Briton side&10Lockyer ter
Jeffery Mr Wm. A. 2 Hill st
JenningsMrsHta.8Boon's pl
Jessep Mr., St Andrew's ter
JewittLlewlyn.libn.3Eliz.pl
Jewitt MrTheodr.16 John st
Johns Mr David, 3 Sussex st
JohnsAmbroseBowden,Esq. Tavistock road
Johns Lewis, R.N. 2 John st
Johnson Captain Richard, Gascoyne cottages
JohnstonRevJohn (Indpdt.) 36 Ebrington street
JonesMrsCth.1Densham ter
Jones Rev Eliezer (Indpdt.) 28 Portland square
Jones George, collector of customs, 4 Windsor villas
JonesJohn,nailmaker, Lr. st
JonesMrJonathan,43Yorkst
Jory Miss S. 11 Belle vue pl
Joseph Mr Abm., & Henry, chemist, 6 Mulgrave pl
Joseph Hyam, scrivener, 3 George place
Joseph J. mineralogist, 29 Whimple street
Julian Mrs My. 2 Charles pl
Julian Rd. Esq. Laira Hs
Keast Maria, elastic stocking, &c. mkr. 13 Bedford st
Keen Abel, corn inspector, 4 Mulgrave street
KeenFdk.clk.14Ebringtn.st
Keen Geo. clerk, 2 James st
KellockMrR.15Tavistock pl
*Kendall Jas. 11 Jubilee st
Kenney—,R.N.3Melbrne.st
Kent Mr John, 1 Camden st
Ker David,railway superintendent, 5 Melbourne st
Keys Mr Hy.G.3Saltram pl
Kilroy Mr Alex. 8 Alfred pl
KingMrSml.34Cambridgest
Kingcome Capt John, R.N., 16 Athenæum street
Kingdon Lieut John, R.N., 20 Prospect street
Kingdon Miss Mary Ann,16 Cobourg street
KingdonMrWm.7Victoriast
KingsbearMrJ.4Portland pl
Kinsman Mr Dl. 10 John st
KippenR.,R.N.3Bellevue pl
KiptonMisses,22Wyndm.sq
Kirk Thos. clerk, 7 Amity pl
KirkinEd.carpet mfr.Mill st
Knight Hy. Esq.2 Boon's pl
Knight Mrs Jane, 9 John st
Knight Mrs S. 18 Summerland place
Knight MrWm.12 Nelson st
Lack John, manager of Gas Works, Coxide
Ladd Rev —, Zoar chapel

*Lakeman Wm., Friday st
Lamphey John George, clerk, 13 John street
Lampriere Mr John, 69 Cobourg street
Lander Mr Bj. 10 Cobourg st
Lane Mrs Julia, 1 Hoe st
Lane Mr Wm. 22 Morley st
Lane Lieutenant Wm., R.N., 2 Melbourne street
Lang Mr Rt. 1 Victoria st
Langmead Mr Ab. 44 York st
Langmead Rev Geo. chap. to Citadel, 27 Athenæum st
Langmead Mr J.6 Ebrngtn.st
Lavers Mr Wm. 10 Morley pl
Lawrence Captain Paul, 10 Cobourg street
Lawson E. tvlr. 5 Saltram pl
Lazarus Lyon, curiosity dlr. 27 Frankfort street
Leach Miss J.3 Brunswick ter
Lear Mrs Eliza, 13 Princess st
Le Corney Mrs 1 Melbourne st
Le Cotey Mr John, 36 King st
Lee Jane, cork cutter, Stone-house lane
Lennon Miss, 6 Windsor ter
Leroux Fredk. James, R.N. 8 Oxford street
Lethbridge Wm. clerk, 6 Cornwall street
Levallin Michael, clerk, 2 Tavistock cottages
Levi Mr Fdk. 10 Windsor pl
Lewis Mrs Car. 10 Lockyer st
Lewis Mrs Jane, 23 Prospect.pl
Liddle Mrs C. 4 Portland pl
*Liddle Ths. Fdk.4 Marine pl
Lillicrap Admiral James, 11 South Devon place
Lillicrap Mrs.9 Constantn.st
Lindsay Mrs A. 12 North pl
Lindsell Captain Robert, 3 Windsor villas
Line Mrs My. 7 Woodside
Little Mrs Eliz. 1 Torrngtn.pl
Lobb Mrs Eliz. 40 James st
Lockyer Nicholas, solicitor; house 9 Prince's square
Lockyer Wm. comptroller of customs, 6 Alfred place
Locoy Mr Rt 4 South Devon pl
Lofton Mrs. 18 Charles pl
Lorraine Jn. clk.7 Buckwellst
Loveday Mrs 4 Bedford pl
Lovell Mrs Mgt. 6 Hoe st
Lowcay Captain Henry, R.N. 43 Tavistock place
Lowe David Wm. landing surveyor, 2 Alfred street
Luscombe Mrs H.6 Esplanade
Luscombe John, merchant, Vauxhall street
Luscombe R. clk.20 Jubilee st
Luscombe Thos. coal mert., 9 Saltram place
Luscombe Thos. & Son, cork manufrs. salt merts. &c. Phœnix wharf
Luscombe Wm. merchant, Princess street

Lynch Mrs My.22 Athenm.st
Lyne Mrs. 7 Lipson terrace
Mackey Mr Jno. 15 Wm. st
Maddick Mr Ts.28 Cobourg st
Maddock Mr Jno.20 Oxford st
Maddock Wm. clerk, 25 Clarence street
Mainprise Mrs. 8 Prospect st
Mair Mr Wm. 8 Woodside
Majestie Mrs Ma., Queen st
Makeham J.excise, Princs.st
Mallett Mr Jno.13 Gasking st
Malone Rev Rd., M.A.,incbt. of Christ ch. 1 Eton pl
Mangles Mrs Mary Ann, 15 Lockyer street
Marke S.B.,Esq.17 Crescent
Markes Charles, postmaster, &c. Whimple street
Marrett Rev Clement Augus-tus, curate, St Andrew's
Marris Mr Jno. 12 Athenm.st
Marsh Ts clk.13 Constntn.st
Marsh Wm. clk. Regent st
Marshall Mr Ambrose, 1 South Devon place
Marshall Mrs Elizabeth, 17 Tavistock place
Marshall Col Anthony, 8 Buckland terrace
Marshall Fk.solr.MorleyHs
Marshall Geo.sol.9 Portld.sq
Marshall Mr Jas.7 Athnm.st
Martin Mr Jn..St Michl.'s ter
Martin Capt Henry Clinton, 3 Eton place
Martin Mr Rd.,Tavistock rd
Martin Ths.pier master,Hoe
Martin Mr Rt. 1 Portland pl
Mason Mr James, 9 King st
Massey Mrs E. 24 Union st
Massey J.cattle dlr.4 Flora pl
Mather Mr John, 3 Woodside
Matthews Mr Dd.Chas.cotgs
Matthews J. clk. 10 Notte st
Matthews William, Esq. 11 Portland street
Matthias Col Vt. 5 Bedfd.ter
Maule Mrs 13 Windsor ter
May Mrs. 6 Windsor pl
May Mrs Har. 4 Albany pl
May Mr Jno. 3 Bedford cotgs
McAusland Mr Ptr.5 John st
McCord Jno.drpr.5 Sussex pl
McCreight Duncan, R.N. 26 James street
McCulloch John, colr. of in-land revenue,5 Albany pl
McGeorge Major Wm. 26 Wyndham square
McGinnes Thos. scale beam maker, Stonehouse lane
McKain Wm. F. clerk, 31 Tavistock place
McKeever Mrs J.28 Sthside st
McKellar Captain,R.M.Cla-rendon place
McMoorine Miss C.12 Ham st
McMullan Mrs A.,Morleyst
McOwen Miss S.,Windsor ter
Meheux Mrs My.11 Prospt.st
Mekeham J.excise,Princs.st

Merchant J.L. 5 Belle vue pl
Meuden Chas. 77 Cobourg st
Mewton Mr Dnen.,Lockyerst
Michener Mrs Des.9 Boon's pl
Micklewood Rev Edmond, 3 Compton street
Miles Mr Thos.46 Cobourg st
Miller Mrs Eliz.17 Buckld.st
Millroy Adw.dpr. Denshm.tr
Millroy Ptr S.dpr.5 Sussex pl
Millward Mr John, Cambg.st
Mitchell Mr Ncls.4 Portld.sq
Mitchell Captain Parry, 11 Tavistock place
Moles Cpt.Rd.,R.N. Oxfd.st
Moon Hy.Geo. clk. 5 Hoe pl
*Moon Edw. 22 Hampton st
Moore Capt. Edward, R.N. 9 South Devon place
Moore Mrs Eliz.8 Portland sq
Moore Capt.F.R.7 Albany pl
Moore Robt.Edw.solr.&clerk of peace, Pennycomequick
Morris Mr Dd.2 Tavistock pl
Morris Rev Wm. (Baptist,) 20 Princess street
Morrish Mr Sl. 1 Belle vue pl
Morrison Rev G. (Wes.) 3 Gloucester place
Mortimer Thos.clk.Regentst
Mouchet Miss Sar.7 Cobrg st
Mouxley John,cattle dealer, Millbay road
Mowet Rev Js.(Ws.)Saltshst
Mudge Rd.,R.N.4 Bedfd.ctgs
Mudge Richard Zach. Esq. banker; h Beechwood
Mugford Mr Jn G., Prospt.st
Mundy Capt.J.,R.N.Oxfd.st
Murch Mr John,2 Bedford ter
Murch Wm. clerk,17 John st
Murray Hon. Genl. Henry, governor, Citadel
Nason John Rt.barrack mstr. 5 Athenæum street
Nason Lieut. George, R.N. 1 Mulgrave street
Nason Lieut.R.,R.N.12 Octg
Nathan Mrs Har., Bedford st
Neale Mr Jph., Providence pl
Nelson Mrs Cath 6 Sussex st
Nesham Capt.Ts.2 Mulgv.st
Netherton Mrs.4 Fareham pl
Netherton Mr J.2 Gasking st
Netherton John,jun. excise, 13 Gasking street
Nettleton Edward, printer, &c; h 7 Bedford terrace
Nettleton Fdk.clk 12 Geo.st
Nettleton Lieut. P. J., R.N. 26 Bellair street
Newcombe J.R.,Theatre mgr
Newton Rev Benjamin Wills, 10 Gasking street
Newton Richd. glass cutter, 4 Ebrington place
Nicholas Mr T.P.7 Saltram pl
Nichols Isaac, timber mert. 10 Gascoyne terrace
Nichols Mr Jno.5 Nth Dvn.pl
Nicholson Mr Bnj.67 Cobrg.st

Nicholson Rev Saml.(Bapt.) 20 Portland square
Nicolas James Toup,captain supt. of Victualling Yard
Nisbett Mr Wm. 25 King st
Noel Rev Thomas, M.A. 13 Torrington place
Norman Lieut Masters,R.N. 3 Bellair street
Northcott Mrs My.5 Portld.pl
Norwood Jph.clerk,16 Wm.st
Nott Mrs Cath.E.10 Nthill.pl
Nugent Misses,Portld.villas
Nugent Mrs My.,Hamptonst
Oake Mr James, 51 York st
Oake Capt.Josiah,Cobourg st
Odgers Joseph, harbour mr. 20 Gibbons street
Odgers Rev W. J. (Unitrn.) 3 Mulgrave street
Offord Rev John,9 Torngtn.pl
Oliver Mrs Sarah,6 Radnor pl
Olley Mrs Jane,13 Lockyer st
Ormond Capt.F.3 Endslgh.pl
Ozzard Js., R.N.,Wyndm.sq
Paddon Miss Ann,48 Park st
Page Thos. clerk, 6 James st
Palmer Mr Wm.15 Cobourg st
Palmer Mr Wm.27 Clarnc. st
Pardeu Mr John, 23 Hoe st
Pardeu Arthur,drpr.21 Hoe st
Pardon Fredk.Augsts.relvg. officer, 16 Queen street
Parker Lady Eliz.,Nelsn.vla
*Parker Thos. 27 Gibbons st
Parkhouse Mrs A.9 Princs.st
Parrott Mrs Mary, & Thos. surveyor, 2 Densham ter
Parsons Misses,27 Cobourg st
Parsons Chas. mattress mkr. 9 Buckwell street
Parsons Sophia,mattress mr. 49 King street
Paterson Capt.Wm.L.,R.N. Devonshire terrace
Patey Hy.travlr.3 Albert ter
Payne Alfred,mngr.65 Old st
Payne Mr John,12 Albany pl
Peagam Mrs M.55 Cobourg st
Pearce Mrs Sus.17 Victoria st
*Pearne Richard, Catdown
Pearne Miss Mrs.,Gibbons st
Pearse Rp coachmr.Floract g
Pearse Capt. John, R.N. 21 Tavistock place
Pearse Sml.coalmrt.Alfred pl
Pearse Mr Wm.2 Endsleigh pl
Peck Mr John,14 Sumrlnd.pl
Peeke Mr Nels. 15 Jubilee st
Penn Mrs. 17 Tavistock st
Penson Miss,11 Gascoyne st
Pereira Mrs L. 9 Bedford ter
Perry Miss M. A. 9 Oxford st
Perry W.excise, Fareham pl
Phelps Miss, 2 Eton cotgs
Philips Admiral Jas.Robert, 9 Mount Pleasant terrace
Phillips Thomas,solr.&clerk to magistrts.5 Frankfort st
Pike Mr. 64 Cambridge st
Pike Mrs — 15 Charles pl
Pike John,Esq.8 Sth Devon pl

Pike Mrs Mary A.7 Portld.sq
Pilditch Mrs Eliz.3 Eldad pl
*Pile John, Catdown
Pitchcott John,tvr.24 Oxfd.st
Pitts Joseph,Esq.6 Lockyer st
Plimsaul T.gov.New Prisons
Plummer Wm. Esq.7 Oxfd.st
Plummer Mrs L.13 Princs.sq
Pode Mrs. 3 Arnold point
Polkinghorne Edwn.3 Geo.st
Pollard Miss Eliz.5 Raleigh st
Pollen Lieut. Wm., R.N. 4 Windsor place
Ponisi Dominic, French polisher, 9 Cambridge st
Pope Hy.rope mkr.Teats hill
Pope Mr John, 14 Gibbons st
Pope Jonthn.Cundy, brewer, 23 Portland square
Pope Ts.ropemkr.2 Brunsk.tr
Popham Ths.dpr.5 Woodside
Power Mrs Frs.28 Wyndm.sq
Power Sml.,C.E. Gt Western Docks, 31 Athenæum st
Prance Wm Esq.18 Princs.st
Prance W. H.solr.6 Buckld.tr
Pratt Mr James, 9 Alfred st
Prideaux Mr Geo.8 North st
Prideaux Mr John,Regent st
Pridham G.solr.Nth view hs
Pridham Jph.solr.2 Athnm.tr
Pridham Wm. W.clk.8 Octgn
Pridham Wm. registrar and editor, 7 Norley street
Prinn Rt. tax colr. 6 Hill st
Prowse A. P. acct. Albert pl
Prynne Rev G. Rundle,B.A. incumbent of St Peter's,11 Wyndham square
Pryor Frs.,R.N.41 Tavstk.pl
Puckett Mrs Sus. 25 Oxfd.st
Pullen Miss Emily,5 Susx.tr
Pullen Capt. Wm., R.N. 27 Prospect street
Pulleston Mr John,63 Cobg.st
Pulling Capt. James, R.N. 4 Bellevue place
Putt Mrs Jemima,8 Amity pl
Pye Mr Geo.3 Upr Buckld.ter
Pyle Mrs Lucinda,36 Wm.st
Pym Mrs Eliz. 6 Bedford ter
Quarm Mr Thos. 24 John st
Queade Mrs Philippa, 14 Wyndham square
Quick Mrs Ann, 29 Oxford st
*Quick John, Norley place
Rabbidge Mary, poulterer, 19 Bedford street
Radcliffe Misses,6 Gascyn tr
Radford Mrs E. 12 Woodside
Radford Jno.cik.11 Alfred st
Radford W.drapr. Mt.Drake
Rae Chpr. clerk, Teats hill
Ramsden T.8 billiard table, 3 Old st ; h Princess st
Ramsey Mrs C.47 Gibbons st
Ramsey W.B.clk.3 Alfred pl
Rattenbury Miss E. 35 Gibbons street
Raven Mr Rd. 12 Gibbons st
Rawle Pp.clk. 18 Gibbons st
Rawlins Mrs J. 3 Bedford pl

Ray Mr Sml. F.1 Bedford pl
Reed Miss A. 10 Athenm. ter
Reed Rev Wm. (Bible Ctn.) Zion street
Rees Mrs L. 25 Cobourg st
Reeve Mr Sml. 48 York st
Reeves Mrs A. 34 Cobourg st
Rendle E.surgn.18 Crescent
Rendle Mr H. 3 Tavistock pl
Rendle Mrs R. 5 Summerland place
Rendle Mr Thos. 15 Ham st
Rendle W.,Esq.13 Octagon
Renfry Misses, Tothill Cotg
Rennell Mr P.8 Glanville pl
Riach Jas.,Esq. 2 Lipson ter
Rice Geo. clerk, 12 John st
Rice Robt. clerk,Millbay pl
Richards Mrs J. 18 Tavistock place
Richards Miss My. G. F. 2 Wyndham square
Richards Mr T.39 James st
Richards Rev Wm. (Indt.) 12 John street
Richardson Mrs.7 Torrgtn.pl
Rickard Mr J. 26 Morley pl
Rickard Mr Jno. Nelson, 3 Vennel street
Rickard Sml. clk. of Charles Church, Ebrington Cotgs
Ridley Mr. 32 Portland sq
Ridout Mrs E. 16 Charles pl
Rivell Miss, Lockyer street
Roberts Mrs E. 2 Victoria st
Rochford Capt. Gustvs. Rt., R.N. 2 Sussex street
Rogers Mr C. 5 Princess pl
Rogers Capt. H., R.N., Citadel road
Rogers Mrs M.3 Wyndhm.sq
Rooker Rev Wm. (Indpt.) 2 Princess place
Rorie Jno.J.,R N.6 Boon's pl
Roskelly John B., R.N., Northill place
Rowe Mr Jas. 2 Raleigh st
Rowe Mrs. 21 Gibbons st
Rowe Miss M.30 Tavistock pl
Rowe Mr Thos. 44 Park st
Rowe Thos. town crier, 24 Ebrington street
Rowe Mr T. 3 Ebrington st
Rowell Mrs. 18 Prospect st
Rowland Mr G.Tavistock rd
*Rowland G. 17 Nelson st
Rowse Mrs. 17 Gasking st
Rumble Miss E.,Athenm.st
Rundell Wm. gas rent colr., Fareham place
Rundle Rd.drapr.3 Oxford st
Rusden Mrs D.24 Tavistk.pl
Russell Mr W.8 Torrington pl
Ryall Miss L.18 Summrld.pl
Ryall Mr Wm. 10 Queen st
Saldorf Mr F. 2 Saltram pl
Salmon Mr B. 16 James st
Salmon J. clerk, 21 John st
Salmon Mr Ts. 37 James st
Sambell M.P.naval instructor,15 Wyndham square
Sampson Mrs H.29 Park st

Sanders Mrs R.15Gasking st
Sargent Mrs C.17Devonr.ter
Sargent Mr J.3St Michl's.ter
Saunders J. inst. mkr. 21 Saltash street
Saunders J.clk.14S.Devon pl
Saunders Mr R.12S.Devon pl
Scaife Mrs Sar. 2 Radnor pl
Scales Mrs Jane, 11 York pl
Schow Mrs J.4Devonshr.ter
Scott Hy. Edward Orchard, printer, &c. Hoe Garden House
Scott Mrs. Hoegate street
Scott R. J. brewer, Outland
Seaburn Mr J. 5 Regent st
Seale Capt. Chas., R.N., 15 South Devon place
Searle Saml. 33 Cobourg st
Seccombe Mrs C.6Denshm.tr
Selby Miss, 12 Union ter
Sellon Miss, lady superior of Sisters of Mercy, 1 Wyndham square
Seymour J.,Railway Station
Seymour Mr T.62Cobourg st
*Shapcott H.1Constantine st
Shapto Mr Hy. 2 Alfred pl
Shear Mr C.10 Torrington pl
Shear Mr —, 10 Nelson st
Shepheard Mr Danl. 74 Cobourg street
Shepheard Wm. tax colctr. Whimple street
Shepheard Wm.jun. grocer, 13 Windsor place
Shepherd Mrs.19 Prospect st
Sheppard Mr W. F. 4 Union terrace
Sheppard Thos. Bate,Esq. 9 Buckland terrace
Sherlock J.Esq.7Princess sq
Sherrell Mr Jph. 5 James st
Shewen Mrs E.6 Nth. hill pl
Shillabeer Mrs S.11Queen st
Shilson Dl. 21 Hampton st
Short Mr Edw. 20 Morley pl
Shortland Mrs E. *Lipson Ps*
Silve Mrs. 7½ East street
Skardon Adrw. salt refiner, 26 Briton side
Skardon Chas. auctioneer,40 Tavistock place
Skardon J. auctr. Nth. hill pl
Skowing W.Esq.8 Sussex st
Slater Mrs E.,Chapel House
Slenner Miss, 12Ladywell pl
Sloper Mr G.5 St Michl's.ter
Smale Capt. Jas., R.N. 4 George place
Smale W. travlr. 46 Park st
Smith Mrs A.1Athenæum st
Smith Mr E. J., Raleigh st
Smith Col. C. H.40 Park st
Smith Mrs Eliz.4Gibbons st
Smith Miss E. 1 Portland pl
Smith Mrs C. 29 Athenm. st
*Smith John, 9 Zion street
Smith Rev Hinton C.,M.A. incbt. of Trinity, 5 Princess street
Smith Mrs M. 2 Portland pl

*Smith Peter, 20 Clarence st
Smith Uriah T. *coast gd*. 1 Albert terrace
Smith Mr W. 10 Mount st
Snell Wm. travlr.5 Octagon
Sole Mrs Chtte. 31 Nelson st
Solomon Mrs J. 20 Queen st
Soltau W. H. tract depôt, 5 Cornwall street
Soper Mr Eliœnai,Bellair st
Spark Mr C. 45 Gibbons st
Sparke Mr Ic. 10 Boon's pl
Sparrow Bjn. mert.6 Brunswick terrace
Sparrow Benjn. jun. mert. Catdown
*Spicer Kennett,1 Marine pl
Spinluff Major Genl. Lovell, 13 Charles place
Spry J.sergt.-at-mace, Gldhl
Square Jno. Elliott, solr. *Gilwell House*
Square Mrs S.24 Portland sq
Square W.J.surgn. Coborg st
Squire Misses, 24 King st
Squire Hy. clk. 7 Zion st
Squire Mrs H. 3 Octagon
Stadthagen Mayre,(Hebrew reader,) 21 Queen street
Stannus Mrs M. 30 King st
Stapleton Mrs T.14Athnm.st
Sather W. drapr. Nth.hill pl
Steer J. clk. 29 Tavistock pl
Steer Rev J. (Indpt.) 8 Constantine street
Steere Misses, 8 Gasking st
Stephens Mr G 8Buckland st
Stephens J. tvlr.4Portland tr
Stephens Mr S. 6 Flora pl
Stephens Wm. travlr. 54Cobourg street
Stevens J.srgn.11Princess sq
Stevens Mrs S. 41 James st
Stibbs Mrs Eliz. Zion st
Stidson John, draper, 4 Regent street
Stodart Mr A.6Torrington pl
Stokes Mrs S. 6 Portland pl
Stones Mr—,R.N.,13Frankfort street
Strachan Mrs My.5Alfred st
Strangaway Mrs E. 5 Gascoyne terrace
Stuart William, engineer of Breakwater, 10 Woodside
Stuart Jph. Whidby, engineer, 20 S. Devon place
Stuckey Rt. 12 Bellevue pl
Stumbles Abm. vase and figure mkr. Union Baths
Stumbles Wm.clk.2Nelsonst
Sumpter N., R.N. 5 Bedfdpl
Sutherland Mrs. James' pl
Sutherland Mr.A Frankft ln
Sutton Edw.,R.N.17Northpl
Sweet Mrs. E.Cambridge st
Sweet John, sheriff's officer, Princess street
Symons Capt.,R.N.Skar. pl
Symons Mr J. 3 Windsor pl
Symons Miss M.A.18Vict. st
Symons P.jun.mrt.Catdown

Tanner Chas. tanner, woolstapler, and glue mfr. 36 Portland square
Tanner Miss A. *Sherwell Hs*
Taylor Mr Chas.6 Sussex ter
Taylor Mrs E. 30 Athenm. st
*Taylor Mr J.11 Fareham pl
Taylor Mr Thos 24Cobourg st
Temple Mrs Sus. 1 James' pl
Terrall Mrs M.16Summld.pl
Thomas H.N.,R.N.30Pros st
Thomas Wm. police inspctr. Albert place
Thomas Mr Wm. Bilbury st
Thomas Lieut. Wm., R.N. 17 Charles' place
Thomas Capt. Wm. A.,R.N. 11 Portland villas
Thompson Mr. 58 Cobourg st
Thompson Rd.,R.N.5North hill place
Thomson Mrs J.18Portlnd.sq
Thornton Lieut. Hy. A. D., R.N. 24 Prospect st
Tincombe Misses,Torgtn.pl
Tink Mr C. F. 6 Windsor pl
Tippett Mr J. 2Fareham pl
Tonkin Mr T. 5 Fareham pl
Tolcher Mrs E.9Denshamter
Tothill R.excise,Clarence st
Towell J.tidewtr. Westwl.st
Toye F. writer, 3 Garden st
Tozer Capt. Aaron, R.N. 1 Hewer's row
Treby Jno. clerk, Bellair st
Treby Mr Rd. 12 Saltram pl
Treby S.mert.St Andw.'s ter
Treffry Mr Jph. 30 Park st
Tregellis Mr S.P.6Portlndsq
Trego J. clerk, 11 Green st
Trego Mr W. 5 Gascoyne cot
Trelawny Rev Chas. T. C., M.A. curate, Pennycross
Trelawny C.Esq.28Bedfd.st
Trelawny Jno. S. Esq.,M.P. 8 Esplanade
Trevor Major Edw.16Cresent
Troughton Miss A.3Gascen.p
Troward Rev—Park st Chapl
Trowbridge Wm. travlr. 6 Constantine street
Truscott J.clk.13Tavistk.pl
Truscott Mr T. 28 Morley pl
Tuck Rd. trvlr. 16 Octagon
Tucker Mrs A.11 Gasking st
Tucker H.solr. 15Princesssq
Tucker Mr J. 75 Cobourg st
Tucker Mr Wm. 47 Park st
Tuckett Jno. Debell, *cheese factor*. 4 Constantine st
Turnbull Lieut. Rt.,R.N. 37 Cobourg street
Turner Geo. Wm. cork mfr. 4 Melbourne street
Turner Mr J. 66 Cobourg st
Turner Mr J. 24 Hampton st
Turner J.B.clk.Densham.ter
Turpin Miss L.19 Cobourg st
Twickell Mr Rd .1Windsorln
Underhill Mr R.3Glanville pl
Underhill Mr R.sen.13Hoest

Urrien Capt. G., R.N., Cobourg street
Vaughan Mrs J. 3 Sumlnd. pl
Veale Mrs Sus. 1 Elizabth. pl
Veale Mr Wm. 6 Park st
Vicary Miss M. 17 Queen st
*Vote Wm. 9 Ladywell pl
Wade Mrs Phppa. 8 Union ter
Wahat Mrs E. 3 Windsor pl
Waheb Mrs 2 Upr. Buckld. ter
Walke Miss Mary, Cecil st
Walker Wm. clerk, Portd. ter
Wallace Mrs Eliz. 15 John st
Warren Miss 13 Albany pl
Warren Mrs M. 8 Rowe st
Warren P., Esq. 5 Portland sq
Warren T. supervisor, Park st
Watson Misses 6 Athenm. st
Watterworth Thos. survyr. of taxes, 16 Wyndham st
Weare Miss A. 33 Portland sq
Webb S. excise, 5 Zion st
*Webber John, Gibbons st
Weeks Mr T. 11 Nelson st
Wells Miss, Regent street
Welsford Mrs 22 Princess sq
Welsford Miss Mary, 4 Brunswick terrace
Westcote Mrs, 12 Charles pl
Westcott Mr Jno. 12 James st
Western Mr J. 10 Morley st
Western Mr Wm. Zion st
Westlake Chas. F. agent, 9 Kinterbury street

Westlake Mr Francis Hole, 4 Prospect street
Westlake Jno. clk. 3 James st
Wethered Capt. G. 13 Alby. pl
Weymouth Mrs. 32 Morley pl
Wharton Mrs. 17 Wyndhmsq
Wherry Mr Jas. Queen st
Whipple Miss C. 49 Cobourg st
Whipple Capt. J. 12 Devon. ter
Whipple Mr Wm. 20 Park st
White Misses, 7 Trees House
White Misses, 9 Ham st
White Capt. George, R.N. 3 Queen street
White Mrs J. 7 Gasking st
White Jermh. clerk, Laira
White Mr. P. H. clk. of St Adw.'s 14 Frankfort st
Whiteford Chas. Cobly, solr and town clerk, Thornhill
Whiteford Mrs. 16 Bedford st
Widger Mrs My. 33 Cambdgst
Wightwick Geo. architect, 3 Athenæum street
Wilcocks Mr J. 9 Wyndhm. sq
Wilkey Mr E. 30 Clarence st
Wilkinson Misses, 30 Cobg. st
Williams Mrs. 3 Boon's pl
Williams J. Esq. 13 Ham st
Williams Mr J. 19 Morley st
Williams Mr J. Arnold Point
Williams Mr T 23 Gibbons st
Williams John H. high bailiff, County Court

Willing Mr S. 9 Fareham pl
Willis Mr J. 44 Gibbons st
Willis Mrs Eliz. Chester pl
Willis Mr Hy. 4 Windsor pl
Wills Mrs M. F. 72 Cobourg st
Wills Rt. Hy. Esq. Mt. Lipson
Wills Mr Wm. 43 James st
Wilson Miss, 10 Tavistock pl
Winne Mrs E. 4 Gascoyne ctg
Winter Mrs A. 8 Athenum. st
Wise Capt. C., R.N. Regent st
Wise Mrs Furlong, Holygt. st
Wise Miss M. 1 Athenm. ter
Wood Rev T. (Wesleyan)
Woodley C. Esq. 12 Windsor t
Woodrow Mr D. Hampton ctg
Woollcombe Miss Mary, 7 Windsor street
Wotton A. J. clk. 26 Clarencest
Wotton H. cashier, Workhs
Wright Major T. 21 Wynd. sq
Wyatt Mrs C. 14 Windsor pl
Wyatt Mrs M. 42 James st
Wyatt Saml. deputy regr. 7 Queen street
*Wyatt Wm., Friary st
Yabsly Mrs. Gascoyne cotg
Yeo Wm & Sons, flax spinners, & sail, canvas, linen, & shoe thread mfrs., Stone Park; & rope mfrs. Teats hill; h 40 Gibbons street
Yonge Mrs Duke, 11 Crescent
Youel Lieut. E. 19 Gibbons st
Youle Mrs E. 15 Wyndham sq

CLASSIFICATION OF TRADES AND PROFESSIONS.

ACADEMIES.
(Marked * take Boarders.)

Baker Eliz. 11 Clarence st
Baker Misses, Princess st
Baker John, 25 Hampton st
Baker Robert, Westwell st
*Balkwill My. Athenæum st
Batter st. Schl. Miss Hescroft
*Bennett Wm., M.A. New Gram. School, 1 Princes sq
Bettell Misses, 8 Park st
Blewett Misses, Tavistock pl
*Burt Mrs Fdk., Regent st
*Burt Thos. M., Windsor ter
Catford Jane, Tavistock pl
Cawse Caroline, 12 Union st
Chappell Wm. Thomas, 3 Portland terrace
Clouter Edwin, Queen st ; h 64 Cobourg street
Cluness John Mackintosh, M.A. Mill street
Dennis John, Finewell st
*Endle Sus., Courtenay st
Fleetwood M. 32 Frankft. st
Free Schools, Cobourg st., Geo. Jago & Miss E. Rowe
Glanville Thos. Gibbons st
Greaves Jph. 30 Portland sq
Grammar School, Catherine st. Rev P. Holmes, M.A. & Rev Alfred Swain, B.A.

Grey Coat, Hampton st. Wm. Harris & Miss Page
Grey Chltte. H. Oxford st
Grigg Nath. B., Cobourg st
*Haloran Edw. & Arthur, North Devon place
*Hares J. J. 27 Notte st
Harris Emily & Car. Ham st
*Harvey My. 47 York st
*Haswell Amelia, 1 Portld. sq
Hele's and Lanyon's Charity, Robert Nugent
*Honey Jane, 1 Charles pl
Household of Faith, Elizbth. Bunster, Charles' Church
Jewers Edwin A., Clarence st
Johns Mrs and Misses, Devonshire terrace
Keen Mary, 34 James st
Kelly Misses, 16 Gibbons st
Lady Rogers' Charity, Bedford ter. Susan. Salmon
*Lane Edw. Mt. Pleasant Hs
*Lee Edwin, 7 Windsor pl
*Lobb Eliz. 6 Glanville st
Madge Carol. 13 Gibbons st
Moxey Eliza, 4 Hill st
Michell Saml. 46 King st
Milton Ann, 2 Buckland ter
National, Tavistock pl. Wm. Rose, and Misses Cole and Rowe

Nicholson M. A. 34 Portland square
Pascoe Hanh. Courtenay st
*Penn Sus. 12 Green st
Pennie James, 34 Park st
Pinn Misses, Tavistock st
*Polhill Sarah, 16 Hoe st
Potes James, Coxide
Prout Miss, 41 Park st
*Rattenbury Catherine, 10 North street
*Reeves Rev Henry, M.A. 5 Lockyer terrace
Ross Richd. D. 18 Parade
Snowdon Hy. 28 Buckwell st
Sturgeon Eliz. 5 Sussex st
Taparell Emma, 18 Queen st
*Vallack Maria, Sumrld. ter
Visick Mary and Sarah, 23 Athenæum street
Western Indpt. College, Rev Dr. Rd. Alliott, theological tutor, 7 Wyndham sq
Westcott Eliza, Bedford st
*Weymouth Rd. Fras., M.A. 8 Portland villas
Williams Isaac, Compton st
Wolf Marcus, Catherine st
Workhouse, J. P. Williams and Mary Harris
Wyatt Mary and Lydia, Courtenay street

ACCOUNTANTS.

Cawse Hy. 8 Summlnd. pl
CrockerEbrington,3Rowe st
HarveyThos.Constantine st
Horswill Wm. Octagon st
May Richard, 5 Windsor pl
Roberts George, Catdown
VealeChas.H.S.20Chapelst
WhippleHy.17Summlnd.pl

AGENTS.

(See also Brokers & Merts.)
*(‡ are Navy, § Emigration,
& * Steam Packet Agents.)*
Allen John, *(gunpowder,)*
Stillman street
*Barber T. H., Barbican
Bass Hy. 54 York street
Bellman & Son, Woolster st
*Blewett John Edw., Ex-
change ; h 20 Tavistock pl
Bryant R. J. 7 Gascoyne ter
Burnell Sar. *(Bolting cloth,)*
3 King street
*Clark Rt. Vauxhall st
§Collier & Son, Southside st
Crocker, Clement, and Co.,
33 Whimple
Crocker & Steer, 6 Parade
Derry Wm. *(railway,)* 9
Kinterbury street
DitchamThs.Edw. *(Trinity)*
Sutton road
Elliott Mary, *(lace,)* 2 West-
well street
Filmer Thos. W. *(granite,)*
Laira road
§FouldsWm.Hy.6Marine pl
§Fox, Sons & Co.Hoegate st
Glasson Jno. E. 7 Sussex st
‡Hyman Hyman, 23 Geo. st
Jackson Charles, *(drugs,)* 12
Summerland place
Jarvis John Prideaux, 4
Ham lane
§Johnson S. C., Parade
Keys Joseph, *(mineral,)* 4
Summerland place
Kingwell Rt. *(drain pipes,)*
13 South Devon place
*Langdon Wm. 12 Union st
‡Levy Aaron and Co. 45
Bedford street
‡Levy Markes,50 Bedford st
§Luscombe, Driscoll, & Co.,
Vauxhall street
‡MarkesChas.22Whimple st
Mullins Edw. *(J.&F.Tallis,)*
14 Morley street
*Nicholson Thos. Exchange
Oxland R. *(iron paint,)* 5
Buckland street
Pearse Pollexfen Wm. 14
Oxford street
Parker Mattw.*(Birm. Plate
Glass Co.)* 41 Whimple st
Prout N. Vauxhall quay
Saunders John, *(S. D. Ship-
ping Co.)* Customhs. wharf
Pick E., Sutton Wharf
Skardon & Son, 11Bedford st
Smellie Gordon, *(Geo. Vir-
tue,)* 10 Tavistock street

Smith John J. *(manure,)* 41
Gibbons street
Stephens Thos. 3 Parade
Tarrell Thos. *(Fullerton &
Co.)* 73 Cobourg street
Tucker & Bottomley, (plate
glass)
Tyeth Thos B. *(gunpowder,)*
15 Tavistock street ; house
Northill place
§Walker J., Parade Wharf
Waring Hy. Jas. 11 Octagon
§Wilcocks Jas. B., Barbican
Woodhouse Henry Harper,
Gibbons street

ALE & PORTER MERTS.

Arliss & Co. 6 Woolster st.
and 1 Princess square
BeckfordIsc.White,Unionrd
Derry and Westlake, 9 Kin-
terbury street
Devenish and Co., Sutton
Wharf, C. Child, *agent*
Edgcombe Wm., Martin st ;
h 60 Union street
Hortop Wm. 9 Frankfort st
Mullenay Jas., Vintry st ;
house 5 Windsor street
Postlethwaite J. and Co.
6 Buckwell street
Saunders & Co. 30 Notte st
Tabb Nichls.P.1Whimple st

ANCHOR SMITHS,

And Chain & Cable Manfrs.
Harris John, Catdown
Lougher Wm. and Sons,
Barbican
Putt H. & W., Guy's quay
Putt Hy., Woolster st

ARCHITECTS AND SUR-VEYORS.

(See also Civil Engineers.)
AmbroseJno.jun.Gibbons st
Andrews John, 18 Buck-
well st ; h *Ridgway*
ArthurO.C.,FrankfortChbrs
BallJas.Howell,Portland hs
Dwelley William, jun. 16
Clarence street
Elliott Roger, 5 Princess st
Foster John, 5 Cambridge st
Francis Wm. *(road sur-
veyor,)* Retreat cottage
Skardon James Charles, 11
Bedford street
Wightwick and Damant, 3
Athenæum terrace

ARTISTS.

Burford Mrs. *(wax,)* 16
Union street
Condy Nicholas, 10 Mount
Pleasant terrace
Condy Nchls. Mtw. 2 Grove
Goldsack Chas. 28 King st
Harris Jas. C. 37 Park st
Holmes Geo. 16 Tavistock pl
Johns Hy. 26 Park st
LuscombeHy.A.6Saltram pl
Mitchell Philip, 13 Alfred st

ATTORNEYS.

*(Marked * are Notaries, and
† MastersEx.in Chancery)*
Bayly John, 1Brunswick ter
Bewes Chas. T.,Athenm.ter
Bray Wm. R. 42 Park st
Campbell James, 34 Bedford
st ; h 9 Union terrace
Chapman Fdk. 44 High st ;
h 1 Devonshire terrace
Churchill Jas. 31 Notte st
Cleverton H. W. P., 1 Cour-
tenay st ; h *Saltash*
†Cross Hy. H. 10 Tin st ; h
9 Northill place
*CurgenvenJno.8 Sussex ter
Derry Geo. W., Westwell st
Eastlake Geo. and Co. 15
Courtenay street
Easton Nathl. Jonas, Fin -
well st ; h 2 Hoe st
Edmonds John and Sons, 8
Parade
†*Elliott BenjaminVallack,
1 Octagon
*Elworthy John Edwards,5
Courtenayst;hMnt.Plym
*Fortescue John Faithful,21
George street terrace
Frost Langford, 27 Oxford st
Gibson & Moore, Raleigh st
Gidley Gustvs 17 Saltash st
Gifford John Attersall, 18
Buckland street
Gregg Wm. 16 Queen st
HolbertonWm.,Frankfort st
HopkinsEvan,*(conveyancer)*
Tin st ; h 4 Gascoyne ter
Hunt Warwick Augustus, 4
Frankfort st ; h *Burleigh*
JacksonGeorge,3Princess sq
*†Kelly John, Vauxhall st ;
h Sussex terrace
Lavers Wm., Athenæum ln ;
h 5 George's place
*Lockyer&Bulteel, Prncs.sq
Luxmoore Jnth. 14 North st
Marshall George & Fredk.,
26 Bedford street
MarshallWm.12Cornwall st
Moore John, 1 Buckland ter
Phillips & Son, Frankfort ln
Prideaux Hy.17Frankfort st
*Pridham George & Joseph
10 Union street
Puckford Jacob, 6 Queen st
*Radcliffe Coplestone Lopes,
7Frankfort st;hAthenm.tr
Rooker Alfred, 6 Frankfort
street ; h 1 Sussex ter
Rowse Saml. 23 Princess sq
Tocker Hy. 11 Frankfort st
*Were Nicholas,7 Westwell
st ; h 8 Princess square
Whiteford, Bennett,&Tuck-
er, 16 Courtenay street
Woollcombe, Square, Ste-
phens, & Prance, 7 Athen-
æum terrace

AUCTIONEERS, &c.

Clement Wm. Edwin, Ex-
change ; h Ebrington cotg

Croker Fredk. Wm. & Co. 33 Whimple street
CrossmanJohn,28Gibbons st
Gill & Vigers, 16 George st
Hicks and Ash, Union st
Mennie Rice, 6 Amity pl
Norrish Elias, 19 Union st
SeccombeGregory,Saltashst
Shepheard Jph. 45 Exeter st
Skardon & Sons, 11 Bedford st; h 4 Constantine st
TrickettGeo.jun.Whimplest
WyattJames,7 Courtenay st

BAKERS, &c.
Baker John, 18 Princess st
Barnett John, 27 Love st
Bartlett Mary, Holycross ln
Berry Henry, 14 Exeter st
Bidgood Wm.8Lwr Batter st
BiscuitCo.,Commercial whrf
Blackler Edward, 39Love st
BlackmoreMarkB.,Gibns.st
Blatchford Peter, Britonside
Blight John, Frankfort st
Bridell George, Richmond st
Buchanan Agsts.11 Flora st
Buncehall Joseph, Drake st
Cann Mark A. 26 George st
Carter Mary, 14 Notte st
Chambers Wm. James, 10 Higher Batter street
Cock Theophilus, Bilbury st
Cornelius Pp.,Stonehouse ln
Culverwell Rt., Tavistock st
Davey John, 10 King st
Drew John Henry,Jubilee st
Doble Richard, 9 High st
Doble Robert, 29 Exeter st
Ellis Thomas, 7 Clarence st
Ellis Wm. Stn., Saltash st
Foale John, 59 York street
Foale Robt.Thos.,Armada st
Foley Richard, 9 James st
Fone Fras. 40 Southside st
Friend John, Frankfort st
Gant Wm. 5 King street
GaskingWm.,Stonehouse ln
Gent Wm. 9 Whitecross st
Gilhen John, 8 Stoke lane
Glanville Thos. 2 North pl
Grills Mary Ann, New st
Haddy Jane, 2 Russell st
Hambly Hy.Hele,Exeter st
Hardy Thomas,Vauxhall st
HawkingsJohn,StAndrewst
HawkingsMichl.,41Cobrg st
Hicks John, Richmond st
Hillson Richard,5Britonside
Jacob Jacob, Morley st
James Peter, Millbay road
Jane James, 51 Gibbons st
Kent George, 29 James st
Kent Samuel, Ebrington st
KnapmanEdw.13William st
LethbridgeMrs.,Richmnd.st
Lethbridge Geo., Russell st
Lichman John, Claremont st
Lougher David, 27 High st
Mabin Geo.,QueenAnne's pl
Martin Henry, 27 York st
Matthews Henry,43 High st

May John, 13 Bath street
Millward Daniel, Notte st
Mitchell John, 50 S.side st
Morgan Wm., Claremont st
Morrough John, Millbay rd
NorthmoreWm., Mrkt.alley
Oliver Wm., St Andrew st
Petherbridge Thomas T. 22 St Andrew street
Pike Alfred, Saltash street
Pillar Edmund,Lambhay st
Pillar John, 6 Bilbury st
Polkinghorne&Co.,George st
Potbury Thos., Tavistock st
Ramson Nathl., Higher st
Roberts Arthur, Parade
Rowe Sarah, 13 Britonside
Sanders Peter, 40 York st
Smith John, Bilbury street
Southey Thos., Southside st
Stanbury Fras., Lockyer ter
StanburyWm.77 Cambridge street, & 47 Southside st
Stutaford James, 4 Notte st
Tullidge John,Cambridge st
Uglow Wm., Cambridge st
Vodden Edm., Cambridge st
WakehamTs.,Kinterbury st
Wills Wm., Stonehouse ln
Woodley Agnes, Gibbons st

BANKS.
Bank of England, (Branch,) George pl., Robert Morris, *agent;* C.K.Lee, *sub agent*
Devon & Cornwall Banking Co. 32 Bedford st. (on Barclay & Co.) David Derry, *manager;* AlfredHingston, *sub manager*
Harris, Mudge, & Co. *Naval Bank,* 32 Whimple street, (on Lubbock & Co.)
National Provincial Bank of England, 40 Whimple st. (onLondonJointStockBk.) Colin Robertson, *manager*
Savings' Bank, Cornwall st. (opendaily12to2,&Sat.evg 6 to 8,) Wm. Haydon, *sec*

BARRISTERS.
Daunt Thomas Townsend, 11 Windsor place
Ellery Edw.,Athenæum ter
Peard John Wm., Tothill hs
Shortland George Tonkin,47 Frankfort street

BASKET MAKERS.
Carter John, Cornwall st
Cole Wm. 33 High street
Deacon Thomas, Bilbury st
Munford James C.5Bull hill

BATH CHAIR LENDRS.
Callard Wm., Bath street
Clay Peter, 12 Bath street
Gill Jane, How street
Neal Peter, Eldad place

BERLIN WOOL DLRS.
Garland Eliza, 30 George st
Orley A. M., Tavistock st

BLACK & W. SMITHS.
Allen Joseph, Martin st

Baker Joseph, 12 Drake st
Ball Wm. 4 Tavistock cotgs
Bartlett Henry, Moon lane
Bartlett Wm., Frankfort st
Batho Edward, Stoke lane
BennettGertrude,Bilbury st
Bishop Roger, Chapel st
Callaway Jas.,Cambridge st
Chapple Thomas, Higher ln
Cory John, 25 Bath street
Down Richard, Octagon st
Ellis Wm., Market place
Giles Thomas, Oldtown st
Griffin James, Richmond st
Harris John, Catdown
Hayman Benj., Exeter st
HearderJonth.N.,George st
Hockin James, Sutton road
Kerswell Wm. 13 Barbican
Merrifield Rt. (& axletree & cider press maker,) Mill st
Page George, Westwell st
Pearse Richard, Flora cotgs
Putt Thomas, 24 Parade
Reburn Wm., Lambhay hill
RobertsMichl.,Sutton wharf
Roberts Thomas, 2 Tin st
Roddan (Thomas) & Barter (John), Westwell street
Ross David, Peacock lane
Rouse Joseph, Market st
Rowe Wm. 5 Westwell st
Seccombe Wm., Prince rock
Smith Thos., Buckwell ln
Spry S. W., Whitecross st
Stevens —, 27 Russell st
Vear Wm., Lower lane
Vivian S. C., Tavistock st

BLOCK & PUMP MKRS.
Davies Edw., Southside st
Hingston E., Southside st
Veal Wm., New street

BOARDING HOUSES.
Hardy Jeffrey, 26 George st
Minards Zbdee. 46 Union st
Payne My. 29 George st

BOOKBINDERS.
Gilbert Wm. S. 12 King st
Hayes Robt. 13 York st
Martin John, 2 Norley st
Walker W. 13 Finewell st
Ward John, Oldtown st

BOOKSELLERS AND STATIONERS.
* *have Libraries and* † *are Printers.*
* Albin Edw. 3 Squire's ter
Baggs Cornls. Rickard, 40 Exeter street
Bard Robt. 26 Notte st
†Bates Wm. 38 Oldtown st
Bennett Wm., Ebrington pl
†Bond Rt. jun. 3 Bull hill
†*Bulley Chas. 44 High st. and 21 Union street
Butcher A. 6 Tavistock st
*Dingle Jph., Britonside
†Faning John, 18 George st
†Gilbert Ebr. 12 King st
†*Heydon Hy. Haycock, 1 Tavistock street

2 F

Hooper Wm., Regent st
Hyne Simon, 22 Russell st
Jay Edm., Stonehouse lane
Joll Edw. D. 4 Regent st
†*Keys Isaiah Waterloo Nicholson, 9 Bilbury st
†Lee & Palmer, 22 Bedfd. st
*†Lidstone Roger, 16 Geo.st
Luke Wm. H. 33 Bedford st
Mitchell John, 4 Morley st
Nettleton Edw. 3 Looe st
†*Nicholson Flx.16 Bedfd.st
†Rowe Joshua Brooking, 10 Whimple street
†Sellick Jas. 28 East st
Simms Geo. 30 Whimple st
Smart William Andrew, 12 Buckwell street
†Smith John and Henry, 41 Treville street
†Stevens Rt. White, (and chart pubr.) 15 Parade; h 1 Saltram place
†*ThomasJenkin,Cornwll.st
†*Triggs Wm. Blackler, 32 George street
Tutton Anty. 32 High st
Ward John, 5 Oldtown st
BOOT & SHOE MKRS.
Abbott Edward, Cecil st
Acland Jas. 2 Drake st
Baker John, 29 Jubilee st
Barrett Wm. Quiller, Old st
Bassett W. 23 Frankfort st
Beacon Saml., Buckwell st
Beer James, 30 York st
Bennett John, Saltash st
Bennett Jph. P., York st
Bennett Wm. H., Morley st
Bessell Geo., Ebrington st
Blight Rd. 10 Garden st
Bond James, 24 Exeter st
Bowden Thos. 4 King st
Bowyer Jno. S., Treville st
Bray John, 36 St. Andw. st
Brock Jacob, 10 High st
Burridge John, 39 Looe st
Carvalho J. 37 Richmd. st
Chirgwin Ts., Cambridge st
Coad Sarah, 42 High st
Cole John, Portland cottgs
Commings J., Whitecross st
Conch Wm. 6 High st
Cross John, 21 Oldtown st
Crossing Wm., Tavistock st
Curtis Wm., Cambridge st
Davies Jno., Glanville st
Drake & Cook, 17 High st
Dunning Pp. 24 Parade
Earl Thos., Millbay st
Evans John, 9 Moon st
Faull Chas. 40 Bedford st
Ford Robt. 5 York street
Fowler Mary, 1 Abbey pl
Fox Richd. 12 Britonside
Fraine Jno., Ebrington st
Fraine John, Gasking st
Full Wm. 33 Exeter st
Furze Rt. 19 Cambridge st
Goss Rd. 11 Richmond st
Greenslade G., Vauxhall st
Hackett Jas. 5 Flora st

Hall Jph. Sparkes,Union st
Hardingham Josaphat, 7 Garden street
Harris Hy. 19 Higher st
Harris John, 48 Exeter st
Head John, 42 Treville st
Heath Richd. 2 High st
Hill Thos. 53 Exeter st
Honey Danl. 22 Bilbury st
Hooper Henry, 17 York st
Horwill Wm., Treville st
How John, 35 Buckwell st
Hundry John, Ebrington st
Hunt Wm., Stonehouse ln
Husband T. 33 Buckwell st
Huxham J. 59 Southside st
Jacob Mark, 9 East street
Jamieson Geo., Treville st
Johns Wm., Gibbons ln
Lavers Robt. 49 Exeter st
Lawrence Dd., Southside st
Lethbridge Hy. 8 Tavistock cottages
Lewarn Jas. 17 York st
Lillycrap Wm. Bryant, 24 Treville street
Littlejohn John, New st
Luke Thos. 10 George st
Manley J., Frankfort st
Milton Wm. 4 Green st
Mitchell Js., Frankfort st
Morris Thos. Jph., Old st
Mullins Rd. 44 Union st
Nicholls Peter,Market alley
Northmore John, Exeter st
Pardeu Samuel, 2 Parade
Pearse Richd. 24 York st
Pengilly Rd. 2 Cobourg st
Phelp R. K. 11 Mount st
Quarm Jas., Victoria lane
Quiller Richd., Catdown
Rice John, 5 Tin street
Richmond W. 25 Exeter
Rowe Edw. 16 Woolster st
Rowe Richd. 32 King st
Rowse John, 9 Exeter st
Shepheard John, Bedford st
Sherrell Benj., Cambdg. st
Squire Sml. 13 Buckwell st
Sterling Wm. 20 Parade
Symons John, 8 Bedford st
Thorn Jas. 12 George st
Toogood H., Kinterbury st
Towl John, Southside st
Tremills John, 3 Tin st
Truscott Wm. 24 George st
Tucker Saml. 25 Union st
Tucker Wm. 21 Drake st
Walling Wm., Southside st
Wearing Rd. 21 Looe st
Whitting Thos., Russell st
Widger Jas., Tavistock st
Williams Edw., Gibbons st
Williams Josiah, Tin st
Williams Wm. 5 Exeter st
Wills John, 7 Bilbury st
Wood John, 15 Britonside
Wren Andrew, 7 King st
BRAZIERS & TINNERS.
Arnold Jph. 21 Bedford st
Bennett Rd. 4 Exeter st
Blake Jas. 11 Drake st

Bunker Thos., Treville st
Cornelius Rd., Oldtown st
Dolling Edw. 9 Drake st
Frost Robt. 32 Exeter st
Hawkin Silas, 1 Vintry st
Hill Wm. 8 Tavistock st
Long Robt. 15 Union st
Martin Wm. 18 Parade
Welch Thomas, Stoke ln
Westlake Thos., Russell st
Woolland Jno., Cornwall st
Woolland Rt.., Drake st
BREWERS.
Cumming Wm.,Vauxhall st
Kent Wm. 38 Frankfort st
King Rt. and Son,10 Notte st
Matthews Hy., Manor st
Polkinghorne G. H. and Co. 19 Bedford street
Pope and Allen, Week st
Rew James, 7 York st
Ryall Robt. 4 Russell st
Scott R. and Son, Hoegate st
Skardon Jph. Sml., Green st
Venecombe Geo., Tavistk. st
BROKERS,
(SHIP,INSURANCE,&c.)
(See also Agents.)
Blewett John E., Exchange
Clark Robt., Vauxhall st
Collier & Son, Southside st
Cornbloom Nahum, (bill,) 5 Raleigh street
Crocker H. & Co. 14 Parade
Crocker and Steer, 6 Parade
Fox, Sons, & Co. Hoegate st
Heddon John, 12 Parade
Hopwood & Marris, (share, &c.) 20 Bedford street
Langdon Wm. 12 Union st
LuscombeAgsts.H. 6 Parade
Luscombe, Driscoll, and Co. 7 Vauxhall street
Markes Chs. 22 Whimple st
May (Rd.) and Steer, (Jno.) 19 Parade
Nettleton Jno. 4 Clarence st
Phelps Rd. B. 18 Parade ; h 10 Prospect street
Snow Wm. (bill,) 5 Gloucester place
Stevens Ths. Jones, 4 Windsor street
Stevens Thos. 3 Parade
BRUSH MAKERS.
Cornelius Rd. 41 Oldtown st
Dear Wm. 36 Looe st
Dover Hy. 15 Cornwall st
Martin Rt. & Co. Meeting ln
Pinwill Margt. 1 High st
Rilstone Rd., Claremont st
Watts Cs. & Co., George ln
Weekes Parven, Millbay rd
Wills Brothers, Peacock ln
BUILDERS.
(*See also Carpenters, Masons, &c.*)
Adams (Jph.) & Son, (Hy.) Lambhay hill
Ambrose John, Gibbons st
Barratt Wm., Octagon st
Blackalake A., Russell st

Burgoine Wm. 6 Raleigh st
Clift Thos. 16 Octagon
Clift Wm., Ebrington st
Condy Wm. 53 Cobourg st
Conway W. 22 Britonside ;
h 44 Tavistock place
Corser John, 17 Ham st
Cumming Rd., How st
Drew Wm. 19 Clarence st
Dwelley Chas. 10 Tin st
Dwelley Rd., Hampton st
Dwelley Saml. 3 Regert st
Dwelley Wm., Clarence st
Elford John, Ebrington st
Ellacott John, Victoria st
Elliott Wm., Ebrington st
Evans John, 17 Gibbons st
Evens Rd., Clarence st
Fowler Edw., Princess st
Harvey Wm., Courtenay st
Harvey Wm. Hy. 1 Octagon
Hext Rd. 1 Glanville st
Hicks John, 3 Albany hs
Hortop Wm., Densham cotg
Jarvis Rd. 25 Bilbury st
Line Richd., Sutton road
Marshall John, Alfred pl
Marshall Ths., Brunswk. pl
Nicholson Jthn., Camhdg. st
Oldrey Edw., Norley place
Pawley Roger Haman, Chapel street
Penhall Nicholas Dyer, 3 Courtenay street
Philp Edw. 17 Clarence st
Phillips Wm., 12 York st
Pound Hy. 2 Albemarle st
Roach Geo. 4 Cobourg st
Roberts Stpn., William st
Single Geo. 7 Morley st
Steer Josiah, 26 Parade
Stitson Rt. 10 Sussex st
Symons Jph. 15 Tin st
Symons Rt. E., Tavistk. st
Veale Hy. 14 Green st
Verren N. K. 18 Saltash st
Westlake —, Courtenay st
BUTCHERS.
Marked 1 *have shops in the Mkt, & 2 are Pork Butchers.*
1 Andrews W., Cornwall st
1 Arscott Wm., Claremt. st
1 Atrill Thos., *Wembury*
1 2 Barrett My. 20 Parade
1 Barratt Wm., *Yealmpton*
1 2 Bending G., Gloster pl
1 Borrington J., Stonehs. ln
1 Boundy —, Whitecross st
1 Bowden Hy., Park st
1 Bowden W. H., Park st
1 Bradford Rd., Chapel st
1 Brooks My. 7 Park st
1 Brown Wm. 14 Batter st
Budge Wm. 33 James' st
Burridge Wm., Stonehs. ln
1 Butland Benj., Park st
1 Butland Jph., Park st
1 Butland W., Gibbons st
1 Cambers Ts., Frankft. st
1 Chowne Edm., Drake st
1 Chowne E., St. Andw. st
1 Chowne Edn., Ebrngtn. st

1 Chowne John C., Week st
1 Chowne Wm. 3 Week st
Coad Richd., Armada st
Coad John, 41 Exeter st
1 2 Cocks Sarah, John ln
1 Cole Saml. 37 Old st
1 Cole Wm. 11 Week st
1 Coleman N., *Ermington*
Coram Jas. 41 York st
1 2 Cottle Alice, Kintby. st
1 Cox Jas, 21 Saltash st
1 Crocker Wm., Ebringtn. st
1 Crossing Wm., *Plympton*
1 Cuddeford Edw., Drake st
1 Dewdney Rd., *Ridgway*
1 Elford Thos., *Plympton*
1 EmmettAnnaM.21Wm.st
Emmett Sar. A., Richmd. st
1 Ford Jas. 20 Courtenay st
1 Ford Robt., *Ivybridge*
Fox Rd. 72 Stonehouse ln
1 2 Greenleaf Wm., York st
1 Hake Rd. 41 Richmd. st
Hamlin Fras., Morley ln
Hewitt Cs. F., Tavistk. st
1 Hewitt and Willcocks, 3 Gilwell street
1 2 Hill Geo. & J., Pike st
1 Hillson John, *Plympton*
1 Hington John, *S. Brent*
Hitchcock John, 19 York st
Hoare Wm. S., Southside st
1 2 Honeywill J., Exeter st
1 2 Horswell E., Ebrngtn. st
1 Hooking Jno. 5 York ln
1 Huxham Henry, Thos., and John, *Ivybridge*
1 2 Jenkins W., Russell cots
1 Keals Edw., Stonehouse
1 2 Keals W. H., Ebrngtn st
1 Kent Wm. I., Cambdge.st
1 Kingdon Rd., *Colebrook*
Knapman Geo., Buckwell st
1 Knight Sus. 22 Wm. st
1 Lake John, 6 Park st
Lee John, 20 Southside st
1 Lillycrap Chas., *Tamerton*
1 Little Saml., *Turnchapel*
Luscombe Jno., Vauxhl. st and Southside street
1 Luscombe Thos., New st
1 McDonald J., Compton st
2 Mallett Rt. 6 Russell st
1 Mares John, Bull hill
Martin Jas., Richmond st
1 Oldreive Eliz., Willow st
1 Oldreive Thos., Morley pl
1 Palmer Ann, Compton st
1 Partridge J., Cornwall st
1 Pearse Jph., *Plympton*
1 Penny Mary, *Modbury*
Pile John, 21 Parade
1 Pitts Ths., Ebrington st
Rawlings Wm. 4 Tin st
1 Reed Thos., St. Andw. st
1 Robertson G., Nursery cots
1 Ross Eliz., Gloucester pl
1 Ross John, Ebrington st
1 Rouse John K. 7 Rowe st
2 Rouse Rt. 31 Ebrington st
1 Rundle Michl., Cobourg st
Sambell Wm., Vauxhall st

Sanders John, 5 Looe st
1 Sandover J., *Cornwood*
1 Sandover Pp., *Holbeton*
1 Scoble Richd., *Brixton*
1 Shears John, Richmd. st
1 Shears Rd. 17 Oldtown st
1 Shears Ths., Richmd. st
1 Sleeman John, Britonside
1 Snell Edm., *Landrake*
1 Southwood N., *Yealmpton*
Southwood Wm., Exeter st
1 Southwood Wm. Henry, 14 Clarence street
1 Sprague Wm., Russell st
1 Velvin Geo., *Ermington*
1 Velvin Robt., *Ugborough*
Webber Thos., 8 Britonside
1 Whipple Pp. B., Gaskin st
1 Whipple Wm., 20 Park st
1 Wilcock Hy., *Horrabridge*
1 Wilcocks Jas., *Buckland*
1 Wills Joanna, Week st
1 Wills My. 21 O'dtown st
1 Woods Thos., 7 John st
Woods Wm., Millbay road
1 Wooton Andw., *Plymstock*
2 Worth John, Exeter st
1 Worth John, *Ridgway*
1 Worth Thos., *Underwood*
2 Wright Jph., 6 Notte st
CABINET MAKERS AND UPHOLSTERERS.
Baker Edw. 31 Frankfort st
Beer John, Tavistock cotgs
BrownWm.14 Hr. Batter st
Cousins James, Saltash st
Dyer Adolphs. 31 Union st
Dyer John, 3 Union street
Eyre Geo. 56 Exeter street
Fey Wm. 23 York street, & Holycross lane
Foy Hy. B. 5 Queen street
Full Thos. Kinterbury st
Gay Hy. 1 Raleigh street
Happen John, 14 Gasking st
Harrison Chas. Buckland st
Jacob Wm. 4 Tin street
Jenkins Geo.3Whitecross st
Lane John, 12 Cobourg st
Lane Thomas & Brother, 7 James street
Lane Wm. 5 Clarence st
Madge Jas. C. 18 James st
Madge John Francis & Jas. 24 George street
Puleston Edw. 17 Green st
Rendle My. 21 Buckwell st
Rendle Thos. 52 Oldtown st
Rider Geo. 1 Qn. Anne's pl
Rider Jph. 4 Raleigh st
Sheriff Geo. 8 Week st
Snawdon John, 10 Octagon
StephensWalter,Westwll.st
Tooker John, Kinterbury st
Treman Saml., Amity pl
Westlake Wm. 19 Drake st
Wills Edw. 23 George st
WyattJames,7 Courtenay st
Yabsley Jno. 22 Oldtown st
CANVASS MANUFRS.
Ditcham Edw. Lewis and Co. 16 Drake street

Yeo Wm. & Sons, Mill st

CARPENTERS.
(Joiners, &c.)

Balson John, Constantine st
Barrett Wm. Octagon st
Bidgood Nichls. Providn. st
Cannon Wm. 17 Morley st
Channon Chas. Princess st
Channon Thos. 6 Hill st
Clarke Rd. Saltash street
Conning John, Cecil place
Cox Jas. 41 Richmond st
Easterbrook John, 32 Clarence street
Edgland John, Saltash st
Elford Thos. 7 Flora street
Foale Philip, 26 Looe st
Gorfett Wm. 8 William st
Harding Sml. 1 Princess pl
Hawkins Wm. 29 York st
Hellyer Thomas Knight, 12 Exeter street
Hill John, 9 Milton street
Ireland Jabez, Victoria ln
Line Fras. 13 Higher st
Mc Donald John, 27 Jas. st
Mankin Benj. Moon st
Mark Geo. 9 Basket st
Medler Saml. 30 Wm. st
Murch John, Zion street
Neame G. W. 26 Clarence st
Nicholson Jonathan, 21 Cambridge street
Northcott John Chaplin, 36 Tavistock place
Pain Jas. Stonehouse lane
Parsons Rd. Lipson Vale
Roach Jas. 53 King street
Salmon Wm. Ebrington st
Sanders John, 6 Morley pl
Slade John, Catte street
Steer Josiah, Nichol's court
Symons Jph. 15 Tin st
Turpin John, Bell's lane
Ward James, Coxide green
Waycott Wm. Claremont st
Winter Wm. Hy. 24 Wm. st
Witheridge Arthur, Park st

CARVERS & GILDERS.
Bishop Wm. *(picture gal.)* 44 Union st; h Union ter
Cassin John, Frankfort st
Collins Wm. 8 Basket st
Fry Hy. Lee, 17 Union st
Ivey Hy. 7 Russell street
Leverton John, Jubilee st
Matthews Wm. 1 Lockyer ter
Percy Saml. *(naturalist,)* 2 Ebrington street
Perry Saml. Buckwell ln
Short James, 8 East street
Short Thos. 30 Looe st
Smith Thos. 45 Union st
Watkin — 1 Vennell street

CEMENT MANUFRS.
Harvey John and Thomas, 16 Russell street
Johns and Co. (and paint,) Lambhay wharf
Rattenbury Rd. Freeman, Cambridge st. & 10 Geo. pl

CHAIR MAKERS.
Anthony Robt. Morley pl
Anthony Wm. Richmond st
Brown Wm. 14 Hr. Batter st
Cook Rd., Morley lane
Roan Chas. 22 Union st

CHEMISTS (MANFRG.)
Balkwill & Co., Coxide
Oxland John, 15 James st
Oxland Rt. 5 Buckland st

CHEMISTS & DRUGTS.
Balkwill & Co. 65 Oldtn. st
Ball Rt. Hawker, Octgn. pl
Bazley Jas. 17 Bedford st
Beer Jph. 7 East street
Bellamy Jno. C. 15 George st
Burdwood Jas. Frankfort st
Burt Fdk. Geo. 16 High st
Cornish and Lewin, *(whols.)* 27 Whimple street
Deacon Jno. Edw., 1 Notte st
Densham —, 55 Oldtown st
Finemore William Foot, 14 Union street
Fryer John Hubert, 28 Britonside
Geldard Rd. Kelly, 6 Oldtown st. & 11 Exeter st
Gibbons Wm. 15 Treville st
Hallett John, 4 East st
Hinton Chs. Fox, Oldtn. st
Hollinworth Charles, 22 Tavistock street
Holman John, 1 George st
Loye Philip, 4 Treville st
Mennie Geo. 33 Union st
Mennie and Driscoll, 43 Southside street
Oxland Rt. 5 Buckland st
Palmer Thomas Steele, 17 Richmond street
Parrott Thos. Buckwell st
Richardson Wm. 13 Parade
Rook Robt. 1 Vauxhall st
Rowe John, 32 Tavistock st
Rowe John, 16 Cornwall st
Smith Samuel, 2 East st
Stephens John Harris, 16 St Andrew street
Tracey Wm. 17 Whimple st
Vicary Thos. 30 Bedford st
Wilmot John, 64 York st

CHIMNEY SWEEPERS.
Isaac John, Mooley lane
Steer John, Venecombe ct
Vulcan Co. 2 Britonside
Waller Chpr. Catte street
Westlake John, Mooley ln

CHINA, GLASS, &c., DEALERS.
Chapple Saml. Southside st
Cole Thos. 33 Treville st
Cornelius Rd. 44 Oldtn. st
Eardley John Pearce, 24 Bedford street
Hellyer Josiah, Exeter st
Jarvis Thos. 31 George st
Mills Wm. 3 Treville st

CIDER MERCHANTS.
Edgcumbe Wm., Martin st
Rendle & Co. 24 George ter

CLOG, PATTEN, LAST, & BOOT-TREE MKRS.
Langman John, Tavistock st
Levi Sampson & Benjamin, 24 Buckwell street

COACH BUILDERS.
Collins & Oyns, Squire ter
Luxmoore John, 28 Bedford st; h 38 Tavistock place
Martin Henry and Co. 44 Bedford street
Richmond, Crews, & Pearse, Octagon street

COAL MERCHANTS.
Apter Samuel Youlden, 6 Hampton street
Ash John, Sutton wharf; h 16 Morley street
Bowden Hy. 6 Russell st
Brooking Jas., Bilbury st
Bunce Jno., Lower Batter st
Dunning Robt. 30 John st
Edgcumbe John and Son, 4 Whimple st. & Sutton whf
Findlater Wm. Stuart, 21 Britonside; h 7 Constantine street
Gill Jane, Hoe street
Guswell John, Sutton wharf; house 1 Hoe place
Hill Ferdind. 1 Clarence st
Hitchins Martiu, Sutton wharf; h S. Devon place
Joll John, Morley lane
Langdon Wm. 12 Union st
Luscombe Thomas and Son, Phœnix wharf
Pollard Thos. 22 Parade
Reed Geo. (coke and coal tar,) Sutton wharf
Saunders Saml. Sutton whf; h 5 Tavistock place
Smith John, 1 Bath street
Soper S., Tavistock street
Stephens Thomas Jones, 4 Windsor street
Stevens Thomas, 3 Parade
Waring Hy. J. Millbay pier
White & Pearse, Millbay rd

CONFECTIONERS.
Bonney Rd. 18 Oldtown st
Clase Wm. 27 George st
Congdon Robt. 23 Looe st
Edwards John, Frankfort st
Farquahar Ptr. 62 Oldtn. st
Farwell Wm. 8 Squire's ter
Ford Jas. Mattw. 11 George st
Hawker Eliza & L. Oldtn. st
Holmes John, 21 George st
Lawrence Jas. 12 Union st
Lewis Wm. 14 Drake st
Matthews John, 36 Oldtn. st
Oliver George, 11 Union st
Petrie John, 2 Cornwall st
Pike Alfred, 23 Saltash st
Polkinghorne & Co. 3 Geo. st
Potbury Thos., Tavistock st
Rugg Phœbe, 43 High st
Sturge Alfred, 38 Union st
Sydenham Aaron, Treville st
Tuckett Edw. 19 William st
Vincent Edm. Buckwell st

York Joseph, 9 Britonside
CONSULS AND VICE-CONSULS.
Collier John & Son, *(Sweden, Norway, and Portugal,)* Southside street
Fox, Sons, & Co. *(America, Austria, Bremen, Shili, Greece, Hanse - Towns, Mexico, Rome, Turkey, & Tuscany,)* Hoegate street
Luscombe, Driscoll, & Co., *(Argentine Repbc., France, Hanover, Holland, Naples, Prussia, Russia, Sicily, & Spain,)* Vauxhall street
Treby and Co. *(Belgium and Sardinia,)* Britonside
CONTRACTORS.
Carpenter Jas.,Tavistock pl
Clift Thomas, Octagon
Drew Wm. 5 Torrington pl
Findleter Geo. Mutleyplain
Hart Robert, 7 Bath street
Smith Wm. 9 Prospect st
COOPERS.
Alger John, Britonside
Batchford Wm., St. Adw. st
Corry Thomas, 2 Vintry st
Neil Peter, 4 Eldad place
Skews Mary, Market alley
Walsh John, 55 Southside st
Yeo Thomas A., Vauxhall quay
CORN & FLOUR FCTRS.
(* *are Forage Dealers.*)
Collier Wm. F. and Mortimer, New street
*Congdon Edw., Gasking st
Cridland Edmond Francis, Oldtown street
*Davis Pp. Wm., Oldtn. st
*Dewdney Thos. Cornwll. st
*Gill Wm. Southside st
*Lang Robt. Basket street
Mead Jph. & Jas. 6 Tin st
*Searle Wm. Market place
Smith John, 9 Bilbury st
*White Wm. 6 Drake st
CORN MILLERS.
Blatchford Peter, Tavistock road
Frean & Daw, Drake's mill
Ryder John, *Lipson*
Walke Edw., Mill street
CURRIERS, &c.
Blight Edw. 33 Buckwell st
Burch James, 7 Stoke lane
Chalker Jno., Catherine st
Crews Nels. Geo. 27 Parade
Foale Wm. 58 Oldtown st
Miall and Co. 5 Bilbury st
Taylor John, 7 Bull hill
CUTLERS, &c.
Dyer Danl. 59 Oldtown st
Fraser Wm. George lane
Gribble Jas. 2 Park street
Hoole —, 11 Union street
DAIRYMEN.
Adams George, Regent st
Adams Sampson, *Prince Rock*

Anthony Joseph,*PrinceRock*
Avent Thos. 43 Richmond st
Bambury Rd. 6 North st
Blackler Jno. Hampton st
Cole Thos.Portland cottages
Conybeare John, Oldtn. st
Coram Thos. E. *Lipson*
Cotton Saml. *Little Saltram*
Crute John, 2 Tin street
Daw John, 51 Richmond st
Denbow Wm. 12 Oxford st
Dicker My. 13 Market alley
Evens Jno., Whitecross st
Ferris Mark, 4 George lane
Gloyn Fras. 24 Notte st
Gloyne Wm. 28 York st
Hopper John, 28 Looe st
Inch John, Skardon place
Jones Wm. Millbay road
Lacy John, Claremont st
Lake Fanny, *Mount Gould*
Leathlean Wm., Bath st
Lee Charity, Buckwell st
Lego Moses, *Little Saltram*
Luscombe Grace, Bull hill
Luscombe Jno. Tavistock st
Luscombe Wm. *Mt. Gould*
Luscombe Wm.23 Exeter st
Medland John, Higher st
Medland Wm. *Tothill*
Moore Simon, 25 Mount st
Ormond Benj. 20 Union st
Ormond Benj. 7 George st
Owen James, 7 William st
Palmer My. 9 Claremont st
Penn Thos. 14 Tavistock st
Perriton Wm. George lane
Pike Wm. 40 Frankfort st
Proctor Susan, 7 Bath st
Rabbidge My. 19 Bedford st
Roberts John, Fareham pl
Rundell Richard, *Lipson*
Rundle George, 6 Moon st
Sellick George, 28 High st
Sherle John, 18 York st
Sherrell Josiah, Tin street
Sherrell Wm.18 Morley st
Sherrell Eliz. Basket st
Sherrell Rd. 36 James st
Skinner John, 18-Moon st
Smith M. A., Catte st
Spry Richd. *Prince Rock*
Tamlin John, 5 Vintry st
Taylor John, Morley street
Tozer Thos. 33 High street
Trayes Margaret, *Catdown*
Turner Eliz. Ebrington st
Vanstone Rd. 76 Cambdg.st
Walters Wm. *Mt. Gould*
Watts Jas. 23 Richmond st
Way Robt. 56 King street
Williams John, Squire's ter
DENTISTS.
Bate Charles, 7 Octagon
Bellamy John C. 14 Geo. st
Brendon William Edward, Devonshire terrace
Cawley Geo. Devonshire ter
Coles StrattonJ.,Princess sq
Dicker Wm.Jph.,Princess st
Parrott Thos.16 Buckwell st

Sedmond Rd. 14 Princess st
Stephens John Harris, 16 St Andrew street
Tubbs C. F. 3 Princess pl
DRAPERS, &c.
(*Travelling.*)
Emdon Wolf, 14 Clarence st
Hughan Jno. (tea,) York st
Libby John, 32 Tavistock pl
McBride John, Compton st
Neill Saml. 7 Park street
SpearChristopher,4Queen st
DYERS, &c.
Bellam Abm. 25 Morley pl
Helwig Hy. Ptr., Green st
Hoare Priscla., Oldtown st
Holloway Jno. Octagon pl
Holloway Wm., Week st
Mortimore Rachl. Bedfd. st
Trickett Geo. Bilbury st
Westlake Jno. S 11 Union st
EATING HOUSES.
(*See also Boarding Houses.*)
Biscombe My., Bedford st
Cove Robert, 4 Tavistock st
Elliott John, Britonside
Frost Susan, Bedford street
Gasking J. 21 George st
Harvey Chas. 8 Barbican
Hawke Robert, 25 Parade
Knapton Geo. Buckwell st
Netherton Wm. Oldtown st
Oliver Richd. 24 Tavistk. st
Partridge Geo. Cornwall st
Webber Wm. 23 Parade
ENGINEERS. (CIVIL)
Bampton Agsts. Hamilton, *(town survyr.)* Post Office bldgs ; h 3 Nth Devon pl
Freeman Chas. 1 Hill st
Hodge Rt. 3 Eton cottages
King John, 3 Flora place
ENGRAVERS & PRNTS.
Baggs Cornls.R.40 Exeter st
Brewer Ivilian C., Geo. ln
Harding Soloman, (& lithr.) Oldtown street
Lee George Samuel, (and lithographer) 22Bedford st
Maddock (Wm. Hy.) and Balderson (Thomas), 19 Bedford street
Neame Robt., Catherine st
Niner James, 10 Green st
Patrick Charles, Cecil place
FANCY DEPOTS.
Badham Chas. 2 George st
Bate Catherine, 10 Union st
BlatchfordE. A., Oldtown st
Boggie Athy.23 Tavistock st
Burford Eugene, Union st
Edgcumbe Ann, Bilbury st
Hamper Fdk. 36 George st
Jago Jane & Ann, Union st
Lee & Palmer, 22 Bedfd. st
Levi Phœbe, 35 Bedford st
McKeer Lydia, Treville st
Mendovsky Jonas, Geo. st
Mills Josias, 1 Treville st
Solomon Josiah,Whimple st

2 F 2

Triggs Wm. Blackler, 32 George street

FIRE & LIFE OFFICES.

Agricult. Cattle, G. and F. Marshall, 26 Bedford st

Alliance, H. Prideaux, 17 Princess street

Anchor, J. Odgers, 25 Southside street

Architects' and Builders', J. Foster, Cambridge st

Argus, Jonth. Luxmore, 14 North street

Atlas, B.V.Elliott, Edmond & Sons, & J. E. Elworthy

Australian, Colonial,&Genl. W.H. Luke, 33 Bedford st

Birmingham Fire, E. Hopkins, 19 Tin street

British Empire, J.Holmden, Eton place; &JosephShepheard, Exeter street

British Guarantee, G. & F. Marshall, Bedford st

Church of England, C. L. Radcliffe, Frankfort st

City of London, E. Norrish, Union street

Clerical,Medl.&Genl., Luscombe & Son, Saltram pl

Colonial Life, Edmonds and Sons, 8 Parade

County & Provident, J. M. Carkeet, Woolster st

Crown Life, F. W. P. Cleverton, Courtenay street

Economic Life, Wm. Derry, 9 Kinterbury street

Edinburgh, H. H. Cross, 10 Tin street

Etonian Life, John Kelly, Vauxhall street

European Life, G. Eastlake and Co., Courtenay st

Genl.Annuity&Endmt. Soc. T.G. Pearse, Whimple st

Globe, Skardon and Son, 11 Bedford street

Great Britain, E. Hopkins, 19 Tin street

Guarantee, W.Marshall, 12 Cornwall street

Imperial, Phillips and Son, and Gibson and Moore

Indispensable, Hy. Cawse, 8 Summerland place

Industrial& Genl., F.Chapman, 44 Whimple street

Liverpool & London, J. E. Blewett, Exchange

London Assurance, Lockyer and Bulteel, 9 Prince sq

London Union, Woollcombe & Co. 7 Athenæum ter

Mutual Cattle,F.W.P.Cleverton, Courtenay street

NationalProvident,J.Trego, Green street

North British, H.H. Cross, 10 Tin street

North of England, Jas. Sellick, 28 Whimple street

Norwich Union, Plimsaul Bros. 41 Bedford street

Pelican, Whiteford and Co. Courtenay street

Phœnix, G. Eastlake & Co. and John Collier & Son

Professional, J. W. Rendle, George street

Property Protection,Lockyer and Bulteel, Princess sq

Railway, R.Lidstone,Geo.st

Royal Exchange, W. A. Hunt, Frankfort street

Royal Farmers' & General, F.W.P. Cleverton,Courtenay street

Royal Insurnc., T.B.Pearse, 3 Whimple street

Scottish Equitable, Edward James, Coxide

Scottish Life, T. Saunders, 34 Bedford street

Star, Shepherd and Son, 6 Whimple street

Sun, G.and J.Pridham, and N. J. Easton

United Guarantee and Life, F. Johns, 7 Mulgrave st

Universal, C. L. Radcliffe, 7 Frankfort street

Victoria, J. Postlethwaite, 6 Buckwell street

West of England, Wm.Marshall, 12 Cornwall st

Western Life,W. Rowse, 10 Old street

Westminster Life,Geo.Mennie, Union street; and A. Rooker, Frankfort street

FISHING TACKLE MKS.

Hearder Jonathan Nash, (& galvanist,) 34 George st

Jago Edw. Rd. 4 George st

Terlizzick Wm.N., Union st

FISH MERCHANTS.

Dyer Samuel, New street

Hong Kong Co., Barbican

Miller Wm., New street

Oyster Co.(John Shepheard, agent,) 6 Whimple st

Sambells Wm. 11 Barbican

StanburyThos.,Tavistock st

Wintle Fdk. John, Barbican

FRUITERERS AND GREEN GROCERS.

Abbott John, Southside st

Bolt Wm., Britonside

Bootyman J., Vauxhall st

Briggs Ann, Treville st

Brown Grace, 11 Bedford st

Burgoine Jna., Treville st

Christmas H. 1 King st

Crocker Richd.,Claremont st

Debernam John, 7 High st

Demellweek Jane, High st

Gill Wm. 18 High street

Hine John, 21 Milton st

Kitt James, 8 Squire's ter

Luscombe Philip, 34 Looe st

Luscombe Wm. 23 Exeter st

Palmer John, 1 North st

Puleston Geo. 16 Looe st

Roach Wm. 12 Oldtown st

Santillo Peter, Eldad place

Soper John, 30 Bilbury st

Taylor Eliz. 10 Russell st

Turner Hy. 1 Coburg cotgs

Ward Grace, 10 Bedford st

Westaway My. 22 Exeter st

FURNITURE BROKRS.

Coombs Wm. 12 Bilbury st

Full Thomas, 34 Treville st

Giles Thos. 16 Oldtown st

Northway Thos., Treville st

Oliver Wm., St Andrew st

Skardon John, Bilbury st

Wakeham Wm.,Vauxhall st

Westlake Wm. 19 Drake st

Yabsley Wm. 22 Oldtown st

FURRIERS.

Colling Eliz., Buckwell st

Gill Wm. 8 Union street

Lillicrap John, 26 George st

Thomas Jane, Ebrington st

GINGR.BEER,&c MFRS.

Anstice & Co., Frankfort ln

Clements Mary, Stoke lane

Collins Edward, 22 Bath st

Mackey John B., Russell st

GLASS WAREHOUSES.

(Crown and Plate Glass.)

Ash Samuel, 22 Green st

GrayChs.Worth, Princess st

Gray James Wm.6 Drake st; h 3 Chester place

Hore Wm. 19 John street

Parker Matthew, (plate,) 41 Whimple street

Swinburne G.M.&Co.(&bottle,)19 Britonside;h Mutley

Tucker&Bottomley, (plate,) 41 Whimple street

GROCERS & TEA DLRS.

Acford Eliz. 14 East st

Angier Jas.Hy. 58 Exeter st

AnthonyJohn,33 Oldtown st

Arnold Andw.14 Cornwall st

Baron Jonathan, 2 Ham st

Beedle James. 2 Barbican

Beer Joseph, 6 East street

Blight John, 40 Frankfort st

Burnell,Brown,&Nicholson, (& wholesale,) 4 Bilbury st

Cleave Eliz. 2 Abbey pl

Child Chas. Hy., Saltash st

Crossing Joseph,17 Drake st

Downing Merifield,(&wholesale,) 3 Drake street

Edey Benj. 33 George st

ElliottJosias&Co.20Bedfd.st

Elliott Sml.Hy.30Exeter st

Fackrell James, Armada st

Fawn Geo. 17 Prospect pl

Fole Rt. Thos., Armada st

Foster Samuel,26 Bedford st

French Jph. 17 Vauxhall st

Frost Matilda, 16 High st

Garner Wm. 17 York st

Hallett John, 4 East st

Hammett Wm. and John, 37 Oldtown street

Hardy Thos. 5 Vauxhall st

HillJno.Bray,22Tavistck.st

Hyne John, 12 Drake st

Kelly Jane, 1 Market pl
Kemp John, 18 Ebrington st
Kennard Jas., Kinterbury st
King James, 33 Southside st
Kitt Peter, 47 Treville st
Knight Edwin, Bilbury st
Lougher David, 27 High st
Matthew Rd. 25 Britonside
May John, 13 Bath street
McKeer & Co. 20 Cornwall st
Miles John, 36 Exeter st
Millman —, 12 Barbican
Millward Daniel,32 Notte st
Millward Danl. jun., Abbey
Mitchell John, Southside st
Mitehell Wm. 11 High st
Morrish Thos.&Co.,Bedfd.st
Paull Nicholas, Cornwall st
Penrose Richd. 10 Drake st
Pinhey Henry,28 Treville st
Pitt John, 22 Saltash st
Prettijohn John Pearse, 17
  East street
Saul James, 43 Treville st
Shepheard Wm. and Son, 6
  Whimple street
Shepherd Chas. 1 Norley st
Shepherd Thos., Bedford st
Slade Samuel, 7 Barbican
Snow Robt. 13 Oldtown st
StanburySamuel,16Parade;
  h 11 Saltram place
Stevens Samuel,13 Notte st
Taylor Henry, 19 Exeter st
Tucker Mark, 25 Frankfort
  street and 42 Exeter st
Turpin Matilda & Lavinia,
  17 Southside street
Vivian John, 24 High st
Vivian Thomas, 7 Parade
WadeJn.Quiller,Oldtown st
Wade Robt.&Co.2Frankft.st
Webber J.Wheeler,5High st
Williams Fras. 2 East st
Williams Thos.18 Mount st
Williams Saml.,Cornwall st
Wills Joseph, 18 George st
GUTTA PERCHA DLRS.
Berry Joseph, 8 Lockyer ter
Hearder J. N. 34 George st
HABERDASHERS.
Bastow Sus. 5 George st
Bull Fredk. 26 George st
Cridland My. 45 Oldtown st
Foot Edward, 3 Morley st
Fyfield Rd.Wills, Bilbury st
Godfrey F. Ann, 19 High st
Hannaford E. 10 Exeter st
Hore Rebecca, 32 High st
Jackson Maria, Oldtown st
Jolly Elizabeth, Union rd
Langmead Eliz. U., York st
Mallett & Thomas, Bath st
Moore Louisa, Frankfort st
NileCordelia&E 26George st
Oswald John, Treville st
Parkhouse S. C., Bedford st
Percy Emma, Bilbury st
Radmore Geo·, Cornwall st
Tracy Andrew, Squire's ter
Veale My.&L., Tavistock st
Warren Mary, 5 Oldtown st

HARDWAREMEN.
(*See also Ironmongers.*)
Hyman Lewis, Cornwall st
Isaac Isaac, Bilbury st
LevyAaron&Fdk.,Bedfordst
HATTERS.
(*Marked * are Hat Makers.*)
Adams Wm. 37 Bedford st
*Browning F. J., Oldtown st
*BusbyAnthy.22 Cambdg.st
*Carne Robert, 9 Saltash st
*Carpenter Rd., Bedford st
*Colwell Simon, Park st
Edwards Pascoe, Victoria st
Edwards Stephen,7Cambdg.
  st. and 16 Whimple st
Federick John, Treville st
Honey Daniel, 22 Bilbury st
JenningsSar.40Richmond st
Lott Sus. 8 Whimple st
Margetts G. & Co.,George st
Peagam Geo. 28 George st
Pease John, 3 East street
*Smith Thos., Buckwell st
Stone John, 15 George st
Wilkinson George Thomas,
  2 Whimple street
*Yeo Wm.& Co , Cornwall st
HORSE&GIG LETTERS.
(*See Livery Stables.*)
HOSIERS & GLOVERS.
Bailey Mary, 26 George st
BooldsCornelius,Buckwellst
Down John, Britonside
Gilbert Mary, 5 How st
Hannaford Henry,Exeter st
Hodge Chas. 46 Union st
Holman and Coombes, 48
  Bedford street
May Benj. 46 Bedford st
Norrington Joseph, Bedfd.st
Penhey Ann, 5 Union st
Tucker E. 36 Union street
Tyerman Geo., Whimple st
Wheeler My.S., Buckwell st

HOTELS, INNS,& TVNS.
(* *are Commercial.*)
Admiral Macbride, David
  Smith, Barbican
Albert, Thomas Lougher, 11
  Notte street
Albion, Samuel Bartlett, 52
  Southside street
Anchor and Hope, John Lit-
  tlejohns, 23 New street
Bedford Inn, John Garry,10
  Bedford street
Bedford Inn, George Vene-
  combe, 3 Tavistock st
Black Bull, Thomas Barons,
  11 Britonside
Black Lion,Richard Oldrey,
  35 Exeter street
Boot, John Rowe Crotch, 43
  Bedford street
Breakwater,Bartw. Lavers,
  Queen Anne's place
Brewers'Arms,Jacob Smith,
  Lower Batter street
Britannia, John Roach, 26
  High street

Brunswick, Frederick John
  Wintle, 3 Barbican
Bunch of Grapes, Samuel
  Mitchell, Castle street
Cambridge Inn,Henry Sher-
  man, 24 Cambridge st
Canteen, Charles Couch, St
  Nicholas' Island
Carpenters'Arms, Jph. Cud-
  ridge, 2 Notte street
*Clarence Hotel, Alex. Thos.
  Blake, 44 Southside st
Cobourg Inn,JosiahPhillips,
  46 Cobourg street
*Commercial Hotel,Fras.Hy.
  Chubb, 8 Oldtown street
Compasses, Charles Brooks,
  13 High street
Coronation, Wm. Proctor,
  Martin street
Cornish Inn, John Gribble,
  24 Oldtown street
Country Pink,Wm.Sargent,
  4 Barbican
Crown, John Cann, 56 Cam-
  bridge street
Crown & Anchor, Wm. Sam-
  bell, 11 Barbican
Dolphin, Charles Morgan,14
  Barbican
Duke of York,Emma Wiley,
  Finewell street
Earl Howe, Stpn.Edmunds,
  78 Stonehouse lane
E. & W. Country House,
  Mary Ann Grills, New st
Elephant and Castle, John
  Mares, 1 Bull hill
Exeter Inn, JohnS.Brimson,
  Exeter st ; *Tap*, George
  Courtis, Lower street
ExciseOffice, JamesPardeu,
  29 Notte street
Fawn,W.Neate,17Prospt.st
First and Last, Jeremiah
  Helyer, 32 Jubilee st
Fisherman's Arms,William
  Harper, Lambhay street
Fountain, J.Pearce,Millbay
Fountain,Js.Smith,Castlest
FourCastles, JaneRoss,Old-
  town street
Freemasons'Arms, Jno.Wil-
  liams, Catdown
George, Wm. Hammett, 47
  Oldtown street
George and Dragon, Richd.
  Hodge, 52 Exeter street
*GeorgeHotel,Jeffery Hardy
  26 George street
Globe, Edw. McLaughlin,8
  High street
*Globe Hotel (and posting,)
  Wm.Radmore, 25Bedfd.st
Golden Fleece, Mary Saull,
  15 East street
*GoldenLionInn,Wm.Henry
  Farley, 17 Oldtown st
GreenDragon, Rt.Marshall,
  49 Richmond street ·
Half-Moon, Php.McGinnes,
  Kinterbury street

Hampton Inn, Wm. Drake
  Fox, Gibbons street
Harvest Home,Wm.Chubb,
  18 Tavistock street
House of Lords, Wm. Bart-
  lett, 4 Squire's terrace
Jersey & Guernsey Packet,
  Saml. Brown, Sutton whf
Jolly Young Waterman,
  GraceThompson,Castle st
Jubilee, Richd. Clatworthy,
  38 Jubilee street
King's Arms, Elias Smith,
  Lower Batter street
*King's Arms Hotel (& postg.)
  Sumld.Staniford,Britonsd
*King's Head, John Down,
  13 Bilbury street
King William IV., William
  Ryall, 39 Union street
Lamb, James Bartlett, 17
  Treville street
*London Inn (Old,) Josiah
  Stephens, 16 Vauxhall st
Lord Ebrington, Jas.Elliott,
  4 Ebrington street
Lord Exmouth, Geo.Bustin,
  1 Drake street
Lord Nelson, Geo. Bamsey,
  Castle street
Marine Hotel, Geo. Cockle,
  Queen Anne's place
Maritime Inn, Thos. White,
  19 Southside street
Masonic Inn, Jas. Bowden,
  2 Buckwell street
Mechanics'Inn, Thos. Hors-
  will, 35 St Andrew st
Millbay Pier, Robt. Pearse,
  Millbay road
Modbury Inn, Thos.Adams,
  26 Exeter street
Morley Inn,Wm. Andrews,
  10 East street
*Navy Hotel, Anthy.Harvie,
  34 Southside street
Nelson's Victory,Edm. Jay,
  Stonehouse lane
NewInn, Priscla.Luscombe,
  Catte street
*New London Inn,W. Rowe,
  10 Bilbury street
New Market, My. A. Hodge
  &Car.Palmer,23Cornwl.st
New Town Inn, Wm. Tink,
  39 Cobourg street
Noah's Ark, Pp.Wm. Davis,
  Oldtown street
No Place Tavern, Jno.Dodd,
  1 North place
Old Barley Sheaf, John
  Laskey, 21 Frankfort st
Old Four Castles, JaneRoss,
  Oldtown street
Old Golden Lion, John Gib-
  bons, Kinterbury street
Oxford Inn, Chas. Stitson,
  4 Claremont street
Packhorse,R.Rowe,Week st
Painters' Arms, Wm. Yabs-
  ley, 1 Higher Batter st

Passage House, Elizabeth
  Chapman, Catdown
Pike Street Tavern,William
  Sanders, Looe street
Plough,Zch.Selth,13East st
PlymouthArms,Edw.Lavis,
  58 Northside street
Pope's Head, Jas. Dunstan,
  38 Looe street
Post Office Inn, Jno. Pearse,
  2 Market place
Potters' and Shipwrights'
  Arms, Wm. Coke, Jory st
PrinceAlbert, Ths. Lougher,
  11 Notte street
Prince George, Benj. Cole,
  14 Vauxhall street
Prince of Wales,Robt.Ryall,
  4 Russell street
Prospect Inn, James Heard,
  9 Prospect row
Queen's Arms, Rd. Helson,
  11 Whitecross street
Queen's Head, Jane Boon,
  4 Parade
Regent Inn, John Brown, 1
  Exeter street
RichmondInn,Thos.Madge,
  58 York street
Ring of Bells, John Kins-
  man, 56 Oldtown street
Ring of Bells, Jno.Perriam,
  10 Woolster street
Rising Sun, Wm. Williams,
  Castle street
Robin Hood, Nicholas D.
  Bowers, 12 New street
Rose & Crown, Hy. Hoare,
  51 Oldtown street
Royal Exchange, Thomas
  Taylor, 18 Tin street
Royal Highlander, William
  Cole, New street
*Royal Hotel (&posting)Wm.
  Edwin Elliott, George's
  place ; Tap, John Lee
Royal Mail, John Port, 3
  Bilbury street
Salutation, Wm. Parker,
  Stillman street
Saracen's Head, John J.
  Welchford, Grove
Seventeen Stars, James W.
  Pardeu, Castle street
Ship,Jno.Stevens,14 Parade
Sir Francis Drake, William
  Robins, Camden street
*South Devon Hotel, Henry
  McKeevor Westcott, 20
  Frankfort street
Sportsman's Tavern,George
  Mugford, 5 Higher street
Spread Eagle, Charles Vian,
  13 Treville street
Stone Masons' Arms, Wm.
  Hy. Simmonite, Lower st
Tavistock Inn, Wm. Pillar,
  4 Looe street
ThreeCrowns, Jn.Matcham,
  12 Parade
Three Crowns, Francis M.
  Joslin, Catdown

Turk's Head, Jas. Stevens,
  St Andrew street
Victoria Inn, John Oram, 26
  Gasking street
Vintry Inn, Thomas Angel
  White, 6 Bull hill
Welchman's Arms, Owen
  Williams, New street
WelcomeHome Sailor,Thos.
  Newberry, Castledyke ln
Wheat Sheaf, Wm. Thomas
  Pitchford, 45 King st
WhiteHart,Wm. Pritchard,
  Oldtown street
White Horse, George Wil-
  loughby, 10 Basket st
WhiteLion,Wm.Blatchford,
  26 Tavistock street
White Swan, Isaac Watts,
  17 St Andrew street
York Inn, Charles Sanders,
  10 Stoke lane

BEERHOUSES.

Badcock Wm. 20 King st
Barons Rt., Tavistock Cotgs
Bartlett Richd. Mutley plain
Bartlett Wm., Squire's ter
Beare Richard, 38 High st
BlackborowJno.1 Britonside
Boon George, Flora cotgs
Bovey John, 9 Union st
Brooks Robert, Sutton rd
Brown James, Castle st
Bryant Henry, 8 King st
Burnett Wm., Stonehs. ln
Chambers Wm. 8 Flora st
Charters Alex. 2 Drake st
Chubb Wm. 1 Cobourg st
Clift Henry, Bath lane
Cocker Rt. 60 Richmond st
Collins Wm., Stillman st
Conning John, Cecil place
Crimp John, Richmond st
Crocker Samuel, How st
Cudlip Thos., Claremont st
Davy Joseph, 3 Gilwell st
Densham Thos. 37 High st
Dickers Mary, Market alley
Dickers Har., Market pl
Doble Geo. 6 Richmond st
Down Edw., Stonehouse ln
Down Saml.72 Cambridge st
Dunstan Jno. 22 High st
Earl Eliza, 14 High street
Edwards John, 8 Rowe st
Elliott John, 3 Britonside
Fackrell —, 30 Armada st
Fay Wm. 34 Whimple st
Fry Wm., Stonehouse lane
Geach Wm., Millbay road
Gidley Ann, Cambridge st
Gilhen John, 8 Stoke lane
Glanville Jas.H., Russell st
Hallett Saml., Claremont st
Hall Louisa, 12 Drake st
HarbridgeWm.,Westwell st
HaslettEdw.48Cambridgest
Hawkins John, Tavistock st
Haynes Edm., Millbay rd
Helman Ptr., Lambhay hill
Hill Nathl. 26 Russell st
Hill Robert, Bath lane

Horraton Jermh.,Stonehs.ln
Hosking Joseph, 2 Manor st
Jellard Wm., George lane
Jose Wm. 11 Looe street
Kent Wm. 38 Frankfort st
Kent George, 29 James st
Kent Wm. 11 Russell st
Knapman Geo., Buckwell st
Knight Saml. 27 Russell st
Lidstone Rt., Frankfort st
Lidstone Rt. 27 Bilbury st
Line Wm. B. 9 Salem pl
Lugg John Rt.,Cambridge st
Lugg John, George lane
Luke Henry, 20 Looe st
Macey Wm. 6 Barbican
Madge James C. 5 Notte st
Marshall Jas., St Andw. st
Martin James, 10 Barbican
Martin Wm., Regent st
Martin Wm., Gilwell st
Monroe Wm. 1 Flora street
Oldreive Saml., Exeter st
Oram Wm., Castle street
Ough Saml., Richmond st
Pardeu James, 29 Notte st
Partridge Geo., Cornwall st
Patey James, 15 Higher st
Powell Edw. 13 Union st
Prout John, 46 Frankfort st
Rawlings Eliza, Adelaide st
Rendle John E., Bath lane
Riddell James, Cobourg st
Rowe Grace, Ebrington st
Rundall Geo., Millbay road
Sanders Peter, 40 York st
Searle Conway H. 26 King st
Searle Wm. 13 Vauxhall st
Shepherd Fras., Castle st
Sherrieff Rd. *Prince Rock*
Sherry Jane, Frankfort st
Short John, Cecil street
Short Wm. 13 Tin street
Simmonite Martin, Lamb-
  hay hill
Slade Rd. 9 Flora street
Sluggett Sarah, 8 Garden st
Smith Eliz., Bath street
Smith Jacob, Lr Batter st
Smith John, Castle street
Smith Rd., Stonehouse ln
Soper Samuel, Oldtown st
Soper Robt., Millbay pier
Steer Richard, 18 James st
Steward Rd. N., Princess st
Stuttaford Jas. 4 Notte st
Taylor James, Centràl st
Toll My. 5 Kinterbury st
Toop Archilaus, Millbay rd
Tremer Rd., Lambhay hill
Trennaman Agnes, Bath st
Turner Rt., Ebrington st
Vallack Jas., Richmond st
Vian Eliz. A., Stonehouse ln
Walling Jph., Oram's row
Walter Michl 29 Frankfort st
Ware Thos., Kinterbury st
Webb Robert, 16 Russell st
Webber George, 63 York st
Wiblen James, Amity pl
Wilcocks John, 15 Drake st
Williams Thos., Mount st

Williams Stephen, Castle st
Wills Philip, 5 Russell st
Woodham Fdk., Millbay rd
Wright Joseph, 6 Notte st

IRON& BRASS FOUNDS.
Down Saml. 1 Octagon st
Jay Edm., Stonehouse lane
Lougher W. & Son, Barbican
Mallett John, 11 High st
Mare John Edmnd. (engine
  pump, mill, &c. mfr.) *Ply-
  mouth Foundry*, Russell
  st ; h 19 Athenæum st
Rollin John and Peter, 14
  St Andrew street
Willoughby (Wm.)& Murch
  (Joseph,) 4 Adelaide st

IRON MERCHANTS.
Bayly and Fox, Coxide
Beer Gabriel, Sutton wharf
Lidstone Roger, Oldtown st
Wright Wm. 14 Woolster st

IRONMONGERS.
Adams Jas. 8 Treville st
Arnold Jph. 21 Bedford st
Bayley John, 48 Treville st
Billing Wm. Hy., Parade
Boon Wm.Hy.18 Whimple st
Bunker Thos. 5 Treville st
Cornelius Rd. 40 Oldtown st
Dover Henry,15 Cornwall st
Frost Robt. 32 Exeter st
Harris Fras. W. Treville st
Hawker Silas, 30 High st
Kerswell William Smith, 13
  Barbican
Kibbey Thomas Pickford, 49
  Southside street
Lidstone W. Hy., Oldtown st
Long Robert, 15 Union st
Marshall Pp. Jas. (& stove
  grate mfr) 32 Treville st
Plimsaul Brothers(John and
  Thomas,) 41 Bedford st
Randall Jno. 39 Oldtown st
Rowse Chpr. 11 Oldtown st
Rowse Walter,10 Oldtown st
Stephens Jas., Sutton wharf
Warn Ptr.Adw.5 Whimple st
Welliams Dd. 14 Oldtown st
West John, 23 Bilbury st
Westlake Thos., Russell st
Wolland John, Cornwall st

JUVENILE DRESS
And Ready Made Linen Dlrs.
Budd Eliz. & Sar.,Union st
Challice Sarah, Tavistock st
Harris Eliz. 1 Union st
Ivey Mary, 10 Union st
Jope John, 2 Oldtown st
May Mrs B., Bedford st
Tawton Mary, 8 Union st

LATH RENDERS.
Buzzacott Jno., Britonside
Firks John, 39 Park st
Hine Chas., 4 Exeter st
Martin Thomas, Exeter st ;
  house 15 Ebrington st
Martin Wm. 20 Russell st

LAW STATIONERS.
Barter James, Morley st
Faning John, 16 Bilbury st

LIMESTONE MERTS.
Gill and Son, Millbay road
Sparrow, Simons, and Co.,
  Catdown

L. & W. DRAPERS.
Adams and Channing, 16
  Treville street
Adams & Co. 10 Treville st
Bishop Robert and Son, 10
  Whimple street
Blackler Edward Adams, 12
  Treville street
Bracker (Eliza) & Prickard
  (My. A.) 16 East street
Bull Fredk. 26 George st
Cardell & Co. 38 Whimple st.
  and 32 Buckwell street
Cooper Jno. Aldred,36 Whim-
  ple street
Dabb, Rundle, & Brown, 53
  Oldtown st.&19 Treville st
Dungey Wm. 39 Bedford st
Foot Edward, 3 Morley st
Gent Amelia, 8 Drake st
Holman, Coombes, and Tho-
  mas, 48 Bedford street
Holman & Pardeu, Oldtn. st
Hosking Mary, 5 Drake st
Johns Wm. 7 Treville st
Knight Wm. 29 Prospect st
Lonsdale Jph. 4 Oldtown st
May Benj. 46 Bedford st
Milroy & McCord, Sussex pl
Parkhouse S.C.15 Bedford st
Popham (Hy.) and Radford,
  (Geo.) 27 Bedford street
Radford and Stather, 31
  Bedford street
Radmore Geo., Cornwall st
Rowe Wm. 17 George st
Seaman (Hy.)& Lansdowne
  (Thos. Wm.) 36 Bedfd. st
Spearman Wm.,Whimple st
Spooner Joseph, Whimple st
Stidson and Henwood, 8
  Treville street
Westaway Rt. 31 Exeter st
Wheeler My. Shanks & Co.
  21 Buckwell street
Williams Sus.11 Cornwall st

LIVERY STABLE KPRS.
(Horse, Gig, &c., Letters.)
Delafield Daniel, Martin
Ellis Wm. (cart), Park s
Endle James, 4 Ham st
Endle John, 1 Ebrington st
Gerry Sl., George st. mew
Goodin Wm., Garden st
Greep Geo. 5 Tavistock st
Lavers Arthur, Octagon s
Packer Theodr., Clarence st
Port Wm., Britonside
Roach Wm.(cart,) Sutton w
Rowse Jas. (cart,) King st
Tremills Rt., Athenæum st
Voysey Joseph, 38 York st
Ward (Chas.) & Hex(John,)
  Princess place
Webber & Toms, Bilbury st
Woodman Jas.,Westwell st

LODGING HOUSES.
(See also Boarding.)

Ash John, 16 Morley st
Avery Car. 65 Cobourg st
Avery Wm. Jas. 1 Grove
BaronAmelia,24Athenm. st
Bickford Jas., Devonsr. ter
Bone Henry, Arnold point
Braddock Jph.31Athenm.st
BrookRd.,5Summerland ter
Bunce John, 3 Grove
Butter Kezia, Gascoyne pl
Cannon Wm. 17 Morley st
Chegwyn Jph.Mt.Plsnt. ter
Clouter Edwn. 64 Cobourg st
Coath John, 4 Princess st
Coath Mary, 14 Princess st
Collins Francis, Esplanade
Collins Joseph, Esplanade
Cook Eliz. 16 King st
Copp John, 12 Princess st
Cork My. 57 Cobourg st
Cotton Saml. *Little Saltram*
Cox Mary, 1 Queen street
Curty John, 19 Queen st
Dabb Jemima, 3 Union ter
Dennis Rebecca, John st
Dodd Jas., Wyndham sq
Doidge Mary, 5 Oxford st
Dunning Robt. 30 John st
Dyer Julia, 7 Devonsr. ter
Eadie Eliz. Summerld. ter
Fox Jas. 3 Buckland st
Furse Fras. 18 Cobourg st
Goss Pp. 21 Athenæum st
Hall Charles, Queen street
Harris Ann, 35 Tavistock pl
Harvey Wm. 1 Octagon
Hawkey Thos., Mulgrave st
Hawking Rd. 7 Esplanade
Heath Edw. O. 11 Zion st
Hill Ann, 12 Park street
Hocking Sar. 2 Bedford pl
Hussey Eliz. 7 Mulgrave pl
Hyne Chs., South Devon pl
Jackson Cs., Summerld. pl
Jeffery Eliz. 2 Sussex pl
Johnson Ts., Mulgrave pl
Jones Ptr. 8 Courtenay st
Kastor My. 9 Windsor pl
Kent Eliz. 9 Devonsr. ter
Kernick My. A.8 George pl
Ladd Robert, 1 George pl
Lake Fanny, Mount Gould
Lee John, Summerland pl
Leger Ann, 2 Octagon
Lego Moses, *Little Saltram*
Lemon Rd. 8 Bellevue pl
Littlejohn S., Summerld. pl
Luckraft John, Cobourg st
Mann Grace, 5 Flora place
May Eliz. 3 George place
Mock Janet, 7 Flora pl
Molton Wm., Clarence st
Moore Ann, 26 Cobourg st
Nile Thos. 5 Devonsr. ter
Nott Wm. 9 Bellevue st
Odgers Jas. Sims, 7 Hoe st
Paterson Ann, Windsor ter
Pearce Eliz. 21 Oxford st
Perring Ann, Tavistock pl
Peter Thos. 7 Union terrace

Pomeroy Wm., Sutton road
Porter L. 1 James street
Price Hy. 3 North place
Rich Nichls. 11 Boon's pl
Rickard Mary, 13 King st
Rickard Wm.38 Gibbons st
Sanders Sar. 15 Oxford st
Sanford Mue., Westwell st
Searle Sarah, 9 Queen st
Seccombe Hy. H., Octagon
Shanks My. 8 Tavistock pl
ShortJno.Jph., Densham ter
SmithPrudnc.,Tavistock pl
Snawden John, 10 Octagon
Spinks Chs.Fdk.,Saltram pl
StephensWlr.,St.Michl's ter
Sumpter Cs.,Summerlnd pl
Sutton Wm. 24 Park st
SymonsMy.A.,Devonsr. ter
Tawton Wm., Mulgrave pl
ThompsonJno.6Devonsr. ter
Toll Ann, 9 Gibbons st
Toms Eliz. 10 Charles pl
Toms Sus. 5 Prospect st
Turner My. 13 North place
Tydeman Jas. 16 Lockyer st
Upcott Joshua, 5 Zion st
Westaway Rd. 3 Esplanade,
　and 9 Lockyer street
Weymouth Sus., Bellair st
WhiteShadh.,St.Michl.'ster
WhitfieldJohn,Ebrington st
WillcocksW.,Mt.Pleast.ter
Williams Jane, Alfred st
Williams Louis, George pl
Wills Kitty, 9 George pl
Willson John, Boon's place
Wilson Har.A.,12 Boon's pl
Wimberley Eliz., Oxford st
Wood Levi, 25 Athenæum st
Wyatt Dorcas, Glanville st

MACHINISTS.
Hearder Jnth. N. 34 Geo. st
Jago Edw. Rd. 4 George st
Mare J. E., Plym.Foundry

MALTSTERS.
Allen John, Stillman st
King and Co. 10 Notte st
Pitts Thos. 62 Southside st
Skardon Jph. S., Green st

MANURE MERCHTS.
BurnardC.S.*(Sth. Devon Co.)*
Norrington Chas.,Chester pl
Plymouth Manure Co.,Tre-
　ville street
Pontey, Rowe, and Co.,
　Drake's place
Tamar Co. 2 Glanville st ;
　E. F. Cridland, agent

MARINE STORE DLRS.
Allen S., Woolster st
Bowden Hy. 25 Russell st
Chubb Thos. 12 Oldtn. st
Condy Robt.,Whitecross st
Folley Wm., Catdown
Forest Eliz., Castle street
Gullet Rt., Whitecross st
Harvey Thos., Hr. Batter st
Hunter Wm., Stonehouse ln
Martin Jacob, Claremont st
Pascoe Jas. 37 Looe st
Pedlar My. A. 11 Tin st

Pedlar Thos., Octagon st
Ralph Fredk., Southside st
Sladen Mary, 6 Woolster st
Walkem John, Catdown
Walling Robt., Batter st
Waterfield Mary, Batter st
Warn John, Victoria lane
Watts Matthias and Co.,
　Lower st. and Week st
Wingett Mary, New street

MASONS & PLASTRS.
(See also Stone Masons.)
Coles Robt. 23 William st
Coles Wm. Hy. 16 York st
Crocker Tristram, Jubilee st
Eddy Wm. 10 William st
EdwardsWm.,Cambridge st
Foot Thos. 6 Princess st
Gay John, 25 Jubilee street
Gendle Thos. 13 Park st
Gillard Peter, 15 York st
Harding Thos., Princess pl
Hill John, 28 James street
Hocking John, 17 King st
Hoppell Wm. (and slater,)
　18 Cambridge street
Jenkin Ths.29 Richmond st
Lewis Robert, 3 Ham st
Lewis Rt. jun. Green st
Mallett Hy.,TavistockCttgs
Matters Thos., Clarence st
Parish Hy. 11 King street
Saunders Dnl., Glanville st
Shepheard Rd., Cambrdg.st
Start Thos. 1 Tavistock pl
Steer Wm. 6 Rowe street
Stumbles Hy. 9 Westwell st
Thomas John, Finewell st
Tickell John, Tavistk. Ctgs
Venner John, Catherine st
Verco Wm. 31 Morley pl

MERCHANTS.
(See also Agents & Brokers.)
Avery Robt. 4 Alfred pl
Carkeet John Mills and Co.,
　(& drysalters,)Woolster st
Collier J.&Son,56Southsd.st
Flush Hy. 6 Sth.Devon pl
Fox, Sons, & Co.,Hoegate st
Freeman and Co. (stone,) 6
　Buckland street
Haycroft & Pethick, (*South
　American,*) Woolster st
Henry J. G., Exchange ;　6
　Buckland terrace
Lewis&Veale,(*Irish,*)Exchg
Lindon Hingston, 13 Fine-
　well st ; h 10Sth.Devon pl
Luscombe, Driscoll, & Co. 7
　Vauxhall street
Morice Geo. 4 Charles pl
Norrington Charles, Quay ;
　house 1 Chester place
Parkyn Jas., PortlandVillas
Pope Brothers, Teat's hill
PostlethwaiteJas.9Sussex st
Saunders John Davy & Co.,
　Exchange & Woolster st ;
　house 1 Alfred place
Snell Wm.Westren,5 Octgn
Soper Jph. 7 Woolster st
Sparrow & Symons,Catdown

Sparrow John Wakeham, (stone,) 6 Lipson terrace
TreebySml.&Co.,Britonside

MILLINERS & DRESS MAKERS.

Adams E. M. 3 Cobourg st
Allen J. 10 Westwell st
Bailey Chtte., Richmond st
Bastow Sus. 5 George st
Bennett E. 63 Oldtown st
Body Eliz. 1 Norley st
Brisdon A. E., Lockyer ter
Brook Sar. 4 Courtenay st
Brooking J. 32 Bilbury st
Brooks Maria, 30 Looe st
Cawse Chtte. 12 Union st
Chubb My. A. 9 Cobourg st
Clark Jane, 5 Hill street
Clift U., 38 Ebrington st
Coad Cath. 41 Exeter st
Conway C. 2 Saltram Cotgs
Cridland M. 45 Oldtown st
Crocker E. 74 Cambridge st
Cumming A., Jubilee st
Dapling Sus. 16 Richmd. st
Eastie Eliz., Notte street
Elford E., Ebrington st
Fairfax E., Compton st
Fook Car. 13 Saltash st
Giles Mary, 5 Exeter st
Gray My. A. 57 Cambdg. st
Harben & Pote, 7 Notte st
Hawkins S., Courtenay st
Hellyer M. 12 Exeter st
Hern M. 44 Gibbons st
Hill Sarah, 12 Looe street
Hixon My. 53 York street
Hogan Mary, Westwell st
Horrell Hentta., Bedford st
Hortop Eliz., Britonside
Howard A.J. 43 Oldtown st
Jope John, 2 Oldtown st
Jope Rbca. 17 Devonsr. ter
Jory My. A. 22 Morley st
Kenny Ann, 7 Union st
Kimber A. & S.7 King st
Kingwell E. 44 Exeter st
Lear Mary, 11 Buckwell st
Lee Charity, 20 Buckwell st
Little Mary, 56 York st
Luxon E. 20 Moor street
Macey Eliza, 4 Hill street
Mallard Ellen, 1 Rowe st
Manning Sus. 34 Union st
Martin Sus. 35 William st
Millman T. 31 High street
Moore Eliz., Gibbons st
Moysey Charity, 8 George st
Nankibell K., Gibbons st
Neale E. 3 Garden st
Nicholson M. 21 Cambdg. st
Nile & Stone, 21 George st
Oke N. & M., Ebrington st
Oliver E. 11 Clarence st
Perdeu M. 32 Ebrington st
Pitts Jane, 26 Ebrington st
Purslow Mary, 20 Bath st
Rabbidge M.A. 8 Regent st
Rendle M. 15 Ham street
Roberts Emma, 25 Wm. st
Rowe J. & E. 44 Bedford st
Scantlebury E., Batter st

Seaburn E. 5 Regent st
ShillibeerJ.&M.,Tavistk.st
Sleemin S. 44 Frankfort st
Smale Sus. 29 York st
Snell H., Ebrington st
Stephens E. 28 Ebrington st
Stevens Keziah, 18 Wm. st
Sutton M. 25 Richmond st
Tawton Mrs.32 Frankfort st
Taylor Ann, Clarence st
Taylor Car. 25 York street
Taylor J. 25 Prospect st
Thomas E. 20 Morley st
Truran E., Catherine st
Veale M. & L., Tavistock st
Vivian T. 6 Norley street
Waldron M. A., Queen st
Walters E. 24 Morley pl
Waye M. 7 Drake street
Wearing L. 20 Richmond st
Weeks Rbca. 12 Saltash st
Westlake E. 10 Cambdg. st
White M. & A., Buckwell st
Woolridge E. 23 King st
Wyatt M. A. 5 Nelson st
Yeo Cta. 2 Squire's terrace

MILLWRIGHTS.

Mare J. E., Plym. Foundry
Nason Ephm. 53 Cambdg. st
Wilcocks John, Clarence st

MUSIC & INSMT. DLRS.

Birdsall Thos. 8 Union st
Burford Francis Pearse, 16 Union street
Huntingdon Jph. H. (and tuner,) 14 King street
Moon Edw. 6 Treville st
RowePeterEllison,19 Geo.st
Sellick Jas. 28 Whimple st
Weekes Jal. (flute,) Geo.ln

NEWSPAPERS.

Herald, (Sat.) Nettleton, Evans, Pridham, and Co. 3 Looe street
Journal, (Thurs.)IsaacLatimer, 20 George street
Times, (Sat.) Scott & Hopkins, 16 Bedford street
West of England Conservative, (Wed.) Roger Lidstone, George lane

NEWS AGENTS.

Faning John, 16 George st
HeydonH.H.1 Stonford
Keys J.W. N.9 Bilbury st
Tutton Anthony, 32 High st
West John, 23 Bilbury st

NURSERYMEN, &c.

Anthony Jas. H. 4 York st
Doidge John, 43 Park st
Hill Wm., Sutton road
Hooper Alfred, Gaskin st
Hooper Jas. 1 Finewell st
Kingwell Jonas, Sutton rd
Luxmore Jas., Westwell st
Pontey Alex., Cornwall st
Rendle Wm. E., Union st
Roberts Joel, *Pennycmqck*
Southwood Jas. 6 Ham st
Taylor Thos. 7 Bedford pl
Woods Francis, Tothill

OPTICIANS.

Cox Rd. 3 Hr. Batter st
Cox Wm.Chas.,Southside st
MarkesCharles,Whimple st

PAINTERS&GLAZIERS.

(* are Plumbers also.)

Ash Saml. 22 Green st
Beer Edw., Buckwell st
Bending Jas. 18 Russell st
Brooking John, 12 East st
Burnett & Sons, Athenm. pl
Clare Geo. 4 Kinterbury st
Coliver Edw., Kinterbury st
Cook Saml. 1 Westwell st
Cook (Samuel) and Down (Wm.) 43 Frankfort st
*CorneliusRd.41 Oldtown st
Cox James, 2 Cobourg st
Cummings Rt. 2 Clarence st
Downard George, 14 Parade
Elliott Wm. 4 High st
Gaul John, Cecil place
*Geach John, 39 York st
Gray Geo. 57 Cambrdg. st
Griffin Jonthn. Pp. Wm. 4 Abbey place
Harper Henry, 27 Park st
Harris Henry, 1 Union st
*Hill Wm. 19 Morley pl
Hore Wm. 38 William st
Isaac Thos. 7 Higher st
Ivey Wm. P. 10 Oxford st
Lacey Wm. 21 York st
Matthews Wm., Lockyer ter
Money Wm., Ebrington st
*Parsons Robt. 19 Tin st
Percy Saml. 2 Ebrington st
Probert Eliz., Russell st
*Rowe Thos.3 Ebrington st
Sanders Wm. (coach,) 19 Russell street
Sarah Geo. 12 Richmond st
SaundersJohn,26Cambdg.st
*Smart Argolus, Saltash st
Spiney Andrew, Saltash st
Summers Robt., Southsd.st
*TomsWm.&T.29Bilbury st
Wakeham John, Bedford st
WattsG.Lazrs.14Bilbury st
Widger Geo., Tavistock st
Yalland Wm. 15 Exeter st

PAPER MANUFACTRS.

Allen John, *Stonford*
Tucker (Geo.) & Bottomley, (Jph.) paper hanging manufacturers,41Whimple st

PAWNBROKERS.

Burnett Rd.62 Richmond st
Foster Saml.61 Cambrdg.st
Hall Joanna, 29 High st
Henwood Ann,17 Higher st
HoppenEdw.57Southside st
LevyZipporah,42Southsd.st
Monk Rd. 28 Frankfort st
Nathan Jacob, Treville st
Shepheard Jph., Exeter st
Taylor J. Wm. 36 High st
Toms Rt., Whitecross st
Wilmot John, 38 Looe st
Woolf Wm., Buckwell st

PERFUMERS & HAIR DRESSERS.

Baker Jph., Frankfort st
Ball Geo. Fredk., Union st
Barnes Geo., Buckwell st
Bate Margaret, Norley st
Bickell Robt. 26 George st
Brooking Edw.,Oldtown st
Burford Mrs. 16 Union st
Cowles Rd. 46 Exeter st
Delafield Rd. 11 Union st
Doidge John, 20 Oldtown st
DowningJoseph, Southsd.st
Ellis Wm. 27 Bedford st
Florente Claude, Union st
Gliddon Rd. 2 Batter st
Gregory Fras 37 Exeter st
Hancock Pp. 23 Higher st
Harris Hy. 7 Exeter st
Harris Wm. 21 Tin st
Hartley Saml., Richmd. st
Hennings Geo.34 High st
Hobbs ——, 22 Frankfort st
Hundry Jph. 1 Russell st
Isaac Robt. 42 Frankfort st
Kent John, Russell st
Odam John, 43 Oldtown st
Plank Fredk. 15 Oxford pl
Redhouse Wm., Oldtown st
Rowe Rd. 18 Vauxhall st
SaundersThos.34 Bedford st
Short John, 32 Looe st
Terlizzick Wm. Morris, 18 Union street
Towell John, Russell st
WilliamsJ.Davy,Bilbury st
Williams Thos., Oldtown st

PHYSICIANS.

Armstrong Rt. 5 Esplanade
Bellamy Geo. 14 George st
Budd J. W. 4 Princess sq
Bulteel Jas. 2 Princess sq
Butter J. 7 Windsor villas
Carkeet Wm 8 Frankfort st
Cookworthy Jph. Collier, 20 Princess square
Davie Rd., Tavistock road
Hamilton Wm. 16 Octagon
Hingston Chas. 3 Sussex ter
Magrath Sir Geo.8George pl
Moore Edw. 11 Athenm. ter
Mowatt Jno. 31 Park street
Prance ——, 18 Princess sq
Risk Jno. Erskine, 3 Mnt. Pleasant terrace
Roe Edw. Ts. 12 Princess sq
Soltau W. F. 5 Mulgrave st
Thomson J. 11 Melbourne st
Tripe C. W. 9 Flora place
Yonge Jas. 15 Crescent

PILOTS. (TRINITY)

Blake Jph. || Bigrig W.
Brooks Thos. || Collins F.
Dyer S. || Hill James
Eddy John, Jph. & Saml.
Glynn Edward and Wm.
Hancock Saml. || Hyde Jas.
Hopkins Wm. and John
Lane Saml. || Pierce Isaac
Noble Thos. & Thos. jun.
Parford John and Wm.
Stibbs Jas., Richd. & Wm.

Sulley Geo. || Trigg Geo.
Trelevin Joel
Waller W. || Tucker Chas.
Williams Geo.,Jas.,Rt.&W.

POTATOE DEALERS.

Fox John, Cobourg lane
Kerley and Tomlinson, 10 Vauxhall street
Kerslake Wm., Vauxhall qy
Redding T. S.26Southside st
Roach Wm. 10 Tin street

PRINTERS.

(See also Booksellers, &c.)

Bartlett Geo., Oldtown st
Bond Rt. 9 Cambridge st
Latimer Isaac, 20 George st
Lidstone & Brendon, Geo. ln
Mutton T., Buckwell st
Nettleton & Co. 3 Looe st
Rowe J. B. 10 Whimple st
Scott & Hopkins, Bedford st

PROFESSORS & TCHRS.

Marked * *are teachers of Music,* † *Dancing, and* ‡ *Languages.*

*Adams Miss, 4 Union st
‡Aschfield Ker, Queen st
*Baldy Ann, Buckland st
*Barber ——, 15 Hampton st
Beedell Jas. (artist) York st
*BomyerOtwell, Frankft. ln
*Brown Jane, Jubilee st
*Burford F. P. 16 Union st
*Cross Samuel, 14 James st
‡De Launay Mons. 3 Geo. pl
*Huet Car. 4 Sussex place
†Huet Louisa, Compton st
Inskit Rt. *(naval instr.)* 3 Glanville street
†Isaac Wm. 13 York street
*Jeffery John, Courtenay st
‡Jeslin J. F. 5 Boon's pl
Knapton John, Cobourg st
‡Loyer Aleide, Buckwell st
*Macdonald Austin Thos.13 Union terrace
†Mason R. H., Courtenay st
*Moon Edw. 6 Treville st
*Newcombe Miss & J. R., George place
‡NolletTheodore, Lockyer tr
‡Onffroy A., Buckland st
Parker Geo. *(naval instr.)* 11 Oxford street
Penson J.(artist)22Oxfordst
‡Peters Thos. 10 Union ter
Ralph Geo. 4 York street
*Rowe P. P. 19 George st
Sambell M. P. *(naval,)* 15 Wyndham square
*Tincombe ——, 11 York st
*Toms J., Summerland ter
*Weekes T. E. 8 Flora pl
†WescottW. H.44Bedford st
†Williams Harriet, Octagon

PROVISION DEALERS.

See also Shopkeepers.

Millward D. jun., Abbey
Stanbury Saml. 16 Parade
Vivian Thos. 7 Parade
Wills Jph. (Italian whs.)18 George street

Wyatt Geo. 23 Bedford st

ROPE, & TWINE MFRS.

Bennett Rd. 35 Southside st
Best Wm. F. 29 Teat's hill
Coath J. *(patent)* Sutton rd
Ellis John, Charles place
Gilbert Wm. Mill street
Goodridge Geo., Woolster st
May Wm. 7 Central street
Pope Hy. & Ts., Teat's hill
Reed Rt., Hr. Batter street
Snow Jas., Bellair cotgs
Yeo Wm. & Son, *(patent)* Teat's hill

SADDLERS & HARNESS MAKERS.

Lidstone W., 21 Bilbury st
Maynard Hy. 12 Bedford st
Moysey R. P. 8 George st
Moysey Ts. 48 Oldtown st
Parnall M. & Jno. 35 Treville street
Wills E. R. 4 Market pl. & 9 East street

SAIL MAKERS.

Davies Edward, *(& flag)* 29 Southside street
Gambell Jno. 9 Parade ; h 4 Sussex street
Northmore J.37 Southside st
Odgers Geo. 4 Hoe street
Ord Ralph, Southside st; h Hoe street
Ould H. 21 Parade
Pope Brothers, Teat's hill
Shapcott Jas., Coml. wharf
Yeo Wm. & Son, Mill st

SHIP BUILDERS.

Baker Wm., Catdown
Gent James, Teat's hill ; h 1 Bellair street
Hill Richard, Catdown
Kerswill Wm., Coxide
Moore Wm.& Son, Friary st
Pearn R. & W. *(boat)* Coml. wharf; h 53 King street
Pope Brothers, *Turnchapel*
Routliffe Wm., Mt. Batten
ShilstonJ. Coxide ; h 3 Hill st
Wallis W. H. *(boat)* Teat's hl

SHIP CHANDLERS.

Billing Wm. Hy. 17 Parade
Bromham J. 3 Gascoyne ter
Davies E. 29 Southside st
Johnson Thos. 9 Barbican
Kerswill W. S. 13 Barbican
Kibbey T. P. 49 Southside st
Watts Elias, 31 Southside st

SHIP OWNERS.

Aptor John, 6 Hampton st
Avery Rt. 4 Alfred place
Bromham J., Gascoyne ter
Cuming W.B.,Brunswick tr
Fox Thos. 14 Charles place
Ham Thos. 22 Portland sq
Harris Wm. T., Sutton rd
Haycraft & Pethick, Woolster street
Hill Richard, Catdown
Hitchens M., Sutton wharf; h 7 Sth. Devon place
Johns Fdk., Mulgrave pl

Kerswill Wm., Coxide
Kingwell Rt., Sth. Devon pl
Maddick W., Constantine st
Moore & Son, Friary green
Nicholls Abs. & Isc.,Coxide
Pardeu John, 21 Hoe street
Pope Hy. & Ts., Teat's hill
Pope John, 14 Gibbons st
Postlethwaite J., Sussex st
Rowland T., Queen Anne's
Battery
Saunders Sl., Tavistock pl
Scott E. H.,,Hoe Garden hs
Simons Peter, jun.,Catdown
Soper Joseph, Woolster st
Sparrow Benj.,Brunswick tr
Stevens, Ham,&Co.3 Parade
Stooke Richard, Saltram pl
Treeby Sl. &Co., Briton sd
Trickett Geo. jun., Post-Off
Vivian Thomas, 7 Parade
SHOPKEEPERS.
Abbott Jas. 5 North place
Adams James, Morley pl
Adams Wm. 36 St Adw. st
Ambrose Benj. (bailiff) 16
Tavistock street
Atwill James, 7 Looe street
Barnes Sarah, Mutley plain
Bazeley Frances, Oldtown st
Beard My. Ann, Saltash st
Bell Phœbe, Stonehouse ln
Bird Vincent, 28 Richmd. st
Blackler Jph. 55 King st
Blake George, Stonehouse ln
Bomyer Richd. 12 Regent st
Bracher Eliz., Squire's ter
Brewer Emln. 27 Notte st
Brimblecombe W.,St Adw.st
Brimicombe Ann, Willow st
Brown James, 5 Castle st
Cardell Mary Ann, John st
Cleave Richard, Jubilee st
Colton Wm. 2 King street
Coombes Cath. 7 Higher st
Courtis Mary, Richmond st
Cousins Eliz. Saltash st
Cox John, 43 Oldtown st
Crocker Tristram, Jubilee st
Crowhurst Ts. 30 James st
Cudlip John, 8 Bull hill
Cumming John, 15 Hoe st
Cummings Eliz., Jubilee st
DarlingtonJno.,Claremontst
Davey Mary, 13 Looe st
Dicker Jane, Market alley
Dingle Sarah, Briton side
Doyle Wm., Stonehouse ln
Drew Richard, 9 Moon st
Dyer Betsy, 6 Gibbons st
Edwards Ncls.,Tavistock st
Egg Thos., Cambridge st
Elliott Moses, Sutton road
Foale Philip, 26 Looe st
Folley Wm., Catdown
Frazier Eliz.,Cambridge st
Frost Matilda, 16 High st
Fry My. Ann, 2 Morley st
Gale Saml., Southside st
Garland Wm., 19 Looe st
Giles Susannah, Lower st

Gloyne Fras. 24 Notte st
Greet Chas., Millbay road
Griffin James, Richmond st
Harris Caroline, 5 Higher st
Hart John, 22 Queen st
Harvey Ann, Ebrington st
Hearn W. 11 Cambridge st
Henry My. A. 3 Exeter st
Hicks Chas., Bedford street
Hill John, St Andrew st
Hillman Eliz., Castle st
Hines John, 7 Basket st
Hole Maria, 4 Looe street
Holman Jas. 34 Claremt. st
Hoppins Thomas, Stoke ln
Hughes John, 15 Morley pl
Hyam Geo., Stonehouse ln
Ivey Henry, 7 Russell st
James Peter, Millbay road
Jane My. 20 St Andrew st
Johnson John, Woolster st
Joslin Samuel, Catdown
Keast Robert, 3 Central st
Kelland Ann, 3 High street
Kent Geo. 29 James street
King Honor, Clarence st
Lakeman Eliz. 29 High st
Lavers Hy. 57 Stonehouse ln
Lavers Mary, 6 High st
Lewis Geo., Stonehouse ln
Line Fras., Whitecross st
Lowe Robert, 4 Gasking st
Lucas Wm. 17 Britonside
Luke Thomas, 12 Tin st
Luscombe John, Prospect rw
Luscombe Jno , Tavistock st
Mahony Dennis, 86 King st
Marshall John, 2 York st
Martin Matilda, Tavistk. st
Mead Henry, 3 Russell st
Merchant Maria, Richmd.st
Miller Sus., Hampton st
Mitchell Catherine, New st
Morgan Wm. 18 Exeter st
Musgrave Jph., Jubilee st
Northmore S., Market alley
Owen Wm., Lambhay hill
Packer Sarah, 22 Hoe st
Paine Henry, 4 Morley pl
Pascoe Wm., Stonehouse ln
Pennington My. A., Bath st
Penrose Jph., Millbay road
Phillips My., Richmond st
Pick Jph. 47 Cambridge st
Piddock Geo., Armada st
Pillar Edm., Lambhay st
Pope John, 42 York street
Popplestone E., Richmd. st
Prosser Mary, New street
Quin Hugh,15Cambridge st
Quint Wm., Millbay road
Redcliffe Peter, Armada st
Reed Thos. 10 St Andw. st
Richards John, Gill's Cotgs
Rider J. M. 22 Morley st
Roach Jane, 22 Looe street
Roberts John, 31 Wm. st
Roberts Mary, 2 Rowe st
Roberts Phœbe, Castle st
Roberts Thomas, Millbay rd
Rogers Josiah, Frankfort st

Rogers Ts. Fras., Octagon st
Sanders John, St Andw. st
Sargent Alex. Ts. 22 High
st & 20 Cambridge street
Scamp Wm., Richmond st
Shaptor Gawing, Bath st
Shortridge Ts., Cobourg st
Skinner Joseph, Britonside
Sloggett Edw., Claremont st
Smith Wm., Stonehouse ln
SouthernWm. Qn. Anne's pl
Spear John, 14 Russell st
Stocker Jph. 8 Looe street
Symons J. D., Southside st
Thomas Geo.Hugh,2High st
Thomas Wm. 37 St Andw. st
Townsend Geo., Catdown
Tozer Geo. Wm.,Gibbons st
Treeby My., Whitecross st
Uglow Rd., Cambridge st
Underhill Wm. Blight, 16
Higher Batter street
Underwood W. 2 Windsor ln
Veale Henry, 12 High st
Venning Wm., Lower st
Vian Eml. M., Salem st
Vicary Ann, St Andrew st
Walling Jph., Qn. Anne's pl
Warren T. S. 11 Victoria st
Watts Chas. 22 Green st
Waycott W., Claremont st
Webber Wm., Chapel st
Welch Jane, Stonehouse ln
Welch Wm., Stonehouse ln
Wells Mary, 7 Gilwell st
West Agnes, 3 Bath street
Westcott Grace, Cobourg st
Whipple Pp. 1 Gasking st
Williams Ann, 20 York st
Williams Samuel, Looe st
Williams Sar. 25 Bath st
Willis Sl. 65 Stonehouse ln
Wills John, George lane
Winsborough James, 3 Ta-
vistock Cottages
WoolawayJas.,Richmond st
SILVERSMITHS AND
JEWELLERS.
(*Marked * are Working.)
(*See also Watchmakers.)
*Bastow Thos., Britonside
Cave Saml. 19 George st
Crews C. F., Bedford street
*Ellett Chas. 50 York st
*GilardoneG.34Ebrington st
*Hope Wm. 29 Buckwell st
Hyman Hyman, George st
Joel Ashur, Buckland st
Joseph Jph. 29 Whimple st
Keast Thomas, William ln
Levy Arn. & Co.45 Bedfd. st
Mevy Markes, 50 Bedford st
Lyon Judah, 7 Union street
Markes Chas., Union st. &
Whimple street
Page Jas. Adw. 17 George
street ; h Windsor terrace
*Pope Wm. 3 King street
Shepheard Jabez, 9 Geo. st
Williams Alfred, Oldtown st

SLATE MERCHANTS
Kingwell Rt., Sth. Devon pl
Pearson Thomas, Sutton rd
Veal Hy. 14 Green street

SLOPSELLERS.
Baker Wm. 4 Southside st
Clarke Fras. 5 Tin street
Dadd Sarah, Southside st
Isaacs John, Southside st
Luke John, 16 Tin street
Luke Thomas, 12 Tin street
Mc Donald My., Southsd. st
Pascoe Jas. 37 Looe street
Smith John, Stonehouse ln
Story Cath. 31 Notte street
Terlour Abednego, High st
Wasley Thomas, 17 Tin st
Watson Robert, Britonside
Whitton John, Stonehouse ln

SOAP MANUFACTRS.
Bryant Brothers & Burnells, Sutton road
Gill & Co. (&soda) Millbay rd

SPIRIT DEALERS.
(See also Wine.)
Birkhead Ebzr. 26 Union st
Crotch J. R. 43 Bedford st
Channing J. T. 1 Oldtown st
Gooding Eliz. 31 Looe st
Hambly Phœbe, Buckwell st
Hasby John, 19 Parade
Orchard John, 35 York st
Pick & Co., 24 Whimple st
Rennolls Thos., Treville st
Ryall Wm. 39 Union street
Symons Wm. 1 Ham st
Vennicombe George, 3 Tavistock street

STAY & CORSET MKS.
Abbott E. 1 Bath street
Axworthy A., Tavistk. st
Barter E. 12 Richmond st
Dainty Eliza, 7 East street
Dunning Ann, Looe street
Gliddon Eliz., Whimple st
Mason Car., Growden pl
Nankibell A. K., Gibbons st
Pound My. A., Courtnay st
Yelland & Brooks. Extr. st

STONE AND MARBLE MASONS.
(See also Masons, &c.)
Blowey Wm. 34 King street
Bovey James, *(& statuary,)* 6 Octagon place
Brewer Julian C. *(sculptor,)* Frankfort lane
Crocker Wm., Frankft. st
Greenham Geo. 54 King st
Gullett James. Shepherd ln
Matthews J., Union road
Oldrey Wm., Norley place

STRAW HAT MKRS.
Anstey M. 8 Tavistock st
Brooking Jas., Bilbury st
Colling Eliz., Buckwell st
Crispin Eliz., Clarence st
Down A. D. 30 Oldtn. st
Down Eliz., Hoe street
Down My., Catherine street
Hawker E. & L., Oldtn. st
Hicks Eliz., Exeter street

Hortop Eliz., Britonside
Jennings S., Richmond st
Lee Charity, Buckwell st
Lee Sar. 37 Ebrington st
Lyon Frances, Union street
Miles E., Buckwell street
Mitchell H. 20 Morley st
Mitchell My. 10 Oxford st
Pinwill Jane, High street
Pleace R , 57 Richmond st
Reeby Sar. 20 Higher street
Rowe Agnes, 2 Tavistock st
Rundell Eliz., Claremont st
Salmon Eliza, 4 George st
Saull Ann, Buckwell st
Searle M. 13 Ebrington st
Shaw Eliz. 3 Finewell st
Shillabeer M. & J., Tavis.st
Snell My. 4 Norley street
Spooner J. 26 Whimple st
Terry Jane, 1 Looe street
Weeks R. 12 Saltash street
White L. Compton street
White M. & A. 27 Buckwl.st
Williams E., Cornwall st
Wingrave Jabez, (plat whs.) 9 Frankfort street
Winkley My. 21 Whimple st

SURGEONS.
Andrews Henry John, 7 Buckwell street
Bellamy & Fox, 41 Union st
Bellamy P. F., 15 George st
Braithwaite W., Cobourg st
Carruthers J. M. 3 Sussex pl
Derry & Eccles, Mulgrave p
Eales Wm. Penn Hele, 11 Portland square
Eccles Jno. H. 1 Sussex st
Fox Fras. 41 Union street
Freeman and Stevens, 11 George place
Freeman Richard, M.D. 11 George place
Fuge J. H. 16 Frankft. st
Giles Charles, 1 Gilwell st
Govett P. W. 5 Cobourg st
Hicks & Benbow, 2 Brunswick pl & 32 Oxford st
Jago F. W. P. 6 Lockyer ter
Kimpton John William, 16 Oldtown street
Pearce W. & Son, 1 Flora pl
Rendle & Square, 18 Cresnt.
Richardson Wm. 13 Parade
Sargent D. W. 45 Park st
Smith Henry, Notte street
Spencer W. 17 Gasking st
Stewart Thomas Anthony, 19 Princess square
Thompson Mitchell, 4 Oxfd.st
Wilkinson Js., Courteny st
Whipple John, 14 Devonr.tr

TAILORS & MERCERS.
Abbott Rt. 23 Hoe street
Adams Thos. 27 Bedford st
Alford George, 32 King st
Allen John, 26 John street
Austin Thos. 37 Union st
Axworthy Wm. 17 King st
Braund Louis, Bath street
Browing Wm., Zion street

Channens & Co. 16 Trevl. st
Chubb John, 15 Basket st
Collins W. 23 Richmond st
Colord Wm. 6 Flora street
Colwell Rd. 20 Oldtown st
Davey John, 38 Exeter st
Dawe & Carkeet, 13 Drake st
Dennis John, St. Andrew st
Dennis Wm., New street
Edmonds Wm. 1 Salem st
Fook John, 13 Saltash st
Glanville Rd. 9 Stoke lane
Haison J. C., 21 Wm. st
Harfoot Thos. 6 Union st
Harris Saml. 5 Basket st
Hart Nichls. 55 Exeter st
Hatch Wm., Octagon st
Hayter Jno., 24 Whimple st
Hearn Wm. 23 Union st
Herd John, 3 Market alley
Hicks Rd. & Feather Hy. 43 Bedford street
Huxham H., 59 Southside st
Jope Henry, 19 Devonr. ter
Keast Pp. 13 Bedford st
King Thos. 27 St Andrew st
Lazarus M. & Co.21 Bedfd.st
Lucock John, 21 Southside st ; h 30 Gibbons street
Margetts & Co., George st
Mason Ths. 19 Richmond st
Millman Wm. 12 Barbican
Millman Wm. John Dacres, 27 Southside street
Millroy and Mc Cord, 5 Sussex place
Minola Jph. 5 Westwell st
Mugford W. 4 Cornwall st
Neame W. 51 Cambridge st
Odgers James Sims, Southside street
Oswell John, Treville st
Page Jph. 7 Britonside
Pegam George, George st
Pearse Thomas and Son, 3 Whimple street
Pearse Wm., Millbay rd
Phillips Jas., Kinterbury st
Pleace N. 57 Richmond st
Poole Samuel, Treville st
Pound Jno., 15 Courtenay st
Puckey Jph., Market alley
Quint Wm., Millbay road
Reed Francis, 3 Hoe street
Rogers T. F., Octagon st
Rowe Wm., Southside st
Seccombe Ggy., Saltash st
Shillabeer John, Tavstck.st
Skelton Jph. 1 Vintry st
Skelton Rd. 30 Bilbury st
Stone John, 15 George st
Stone Robt. 53 King street
Stuttaford Elijah, 55 York st
Symons John, Lockyer ter
Toms Andw. 33 Frankft. st
Trounce J. H., Lockyer ter
Vivian Wm. H., Barbican
Watkinson W., Billbury st
Watts Rd. I., Treville st
Watts W. H. 22 Buckwell st
Webb Wm. H. 25 John st
Whittell John, Tavistock st

Willcocks Jno., Southside st
Williams Henry, Regent st
Williams Wm. 33 Clarnc. st
Wilton Jas. 33 Bilbury st

TALLOW CHANDLERS.
Fisher Ponsford, Sussex pl
Hawkes John, 44 Oldtn. st
Lear Ann, Whimple street
Rowse Nichls., Buckwell st
Smerdon Wm. S. 39 High st
Snow Robt. 13 Oldtown st

TEA DEALERS.
(See also Grocers, &c.)
Baggs Corns. Rickard, 40 Exeter street
Halls John, 13 George st
Jago Brothers, 4 North st
Jenkins Eliz. 34 Union st
Knight & Co. 20 Cornwall st
Morrish & Co. 52 Bedford st
Saull James, 43 Treville st
Spurway John, 7 Drake st
Thomas David and Co. 47 Bedford street
Western Tea Company, 16 Bedford st, (J. Baron, agt.)

TIMBER MERCHANTS.
Baker Thomas, Mill street
Bayly & Fox, Sutton road
Bunce T. 22 Lr. Batter st
Collier & Co., Coxide
Endicott Robert and Co., Raleigh street
Hearn Rd. 11 Cambridge st
Maddock Arthur, Notte st
Marshall E. 7 Vauxhall st
Nichols Ambrose and Isaac, Sutton road
Puleston Edw. 17 Green st
Quarme Thos., Sutton road
Rowe Rd. Raleigh st and 33 Cambridge street
Sketon Pp. 2 Rowe street

TOBACCONISTS.
Bewley Henry, 2 Union st

Frost Henry, 16 High street
Hoare Eliz., (mfr.) Hoe st
Schlesinger M., Octagon pl
Smart W. A., Buckwell st

TOY DEALERS.
(See Fancy Depots.)

TRUNK MAKERS.
McKeer Lydia, Treville st
Pedrick Jas., Saltash st

TURNERS. (WOOD.)
Collins Wm. 8 Basket st
Jago E. R. 4 George street
Short James, 8 East street
Short Thos. 30 Looe street
Watkins ——, 1 Vennel st

UMBRELLA MAKERS.
Brooks Walter, Mkt. alley
Hearder J. N. 34 George st
Hedges Wm., Saltash st
Jago Edw. R. 4 George st
Mitchell Bennett, 10 Hoe st
Thompson Wm., Stoke ln

VETERINRY. SURGNS.
Jermon John, Cobourgh st
Raddall Warne, Princess st

WATCH & CLOCK MKS.
Bartlett Wm. 2 Russell st
Bennett Jph , Bilbury st
Crews Chas. F., Bedford st
Fehrenbak and Ketterer, 6 George street
Garland Rd. 41 High st]
Goulding F. H. 13 Bedfd.st
Grigg Hphy. 20 Drake st
Kent Wm. 47 Frankfort st
Levi Markes, 50 Bedford st
Lyon Judah, 7 Union st
Markes Chas., Whimple st
Mitchell R. J. 3 Treville st
Pasmore Sns. 43 Union st
Shepheard Jabez, 9 Geo. st
Walter Michael, Frankft.st
Wyatt Robt. 3 Buckwell st
& 7 Kinterbury st

WHEELWRIGHTS.
Cory Thomas, Russell st
Curno Pp., Russell street
Gay John, Raleigh st
Hill Wm. 9 Jubilee street
Tapson John, Saltash st
Tucker Wm., Raleigh st

WHITESMITHS.
(See Black and White.)

WINE AND SPIRIT MERCHANTS.
(See also Spirit Dealers.)
Broad Alfd. 8 Windsor pl
Collier & Co. 64 Oldtown st & 56 Southside street
Cuming Wm. 4 Vauxhall st
Evens Wm. Hole and Son, 11 East st & 37 Bedford st
Fillis Rd. & Son, (wine,) 45 Treville st ; h Norley Hs.
Halls John, 13 George st
Hammett Wm. 39 Oldtn. st
Hawker Wm. Hy. & Son, (wine,) 18 Britonside ; h 18 Gasking street
Hicks Rd. 2 Bilbury st ; h 27 Tavistock place
May John Brett and Co., Exchange ; and Devonpt.
Picken Sl. 24 Whimple st ; h Skardon place
Postlethwaite Jas. & Co. 6 Buckwell street
Rendle and Harris, George street terrace
Scott Robert and Son, Hoe-gate street
Stephens John, *(agent,)* 5 Hampton street
Tabb Nicls. P., Whimple st
Vivian Thomas, 7 Parade
White Thos. A., Bullhill

WIRE WORKERS.
Arnold Jph. 23 Bedford st
Winter J., 29 Ebrington st

COACHES FROM PLYMOUTH.
From the Royal Hotel and other principal Inns.

To Liskeard, Bodmin, Truro and Falmouth, the *Mail* at 1½ aftn. ; and the *Telegraph* 7¼ morning.

To Tavistock, &c., the *Mail* at 6½ morning and 8½ evening.

To Tavistock, Hatherleigh, Okehampton, Torrington, Bideford, Barnstaple, &c., the *Emerald,* every Tuesday, Thursday, and Saturday at a ¼ before 8 morn. ; and the *Brilliant* (via Launceston,) every Monday, Wednesday, and Friday at 8½ morning.

To *Modbury and Kingsbridge*, the Mazeppa and Great Britain daily at 4½ afternoon, except Sunday.

RAILWAY.
Passenger Trains to Exeter, Bristol, London, &c. leave six times a day, except on Sunday, when only four trains are despatched. *Goods Trains* leave every night, except Sunday. *South Devon Railway Station,* Mill Bay, David Ker, *superintendent ;* W. James, *booking clk.;* Wm. Cuddeford, *parcel clerk;* and John Symons, Wm. Hyett, and Edw. Nettleton, *goods clerks.*

OMNIBUSES
Run from the Royal Hotel and other principal Inns to meet every train, and to *Tavistock, &c.* daily. The *Fairy* Omnibus from the Bedford and New Market Inns, to *Truro, &c., via* Torpoint, Bodmin, &c., at 7 afternoon. Omnibuses run from the King's Arms Hotel, Britonside, to Devonport, every ten minutes, *fare 3d.*

The *Hackney Coach Stands* are opposite the Royal Hotel, in Bedford street, and in Oldtown street, and the fares are

8d. a mile for one or two, and 1s. for three or four persons; or 2s. 6d per hr.

An Act for regulating Hackney Coaches and other Carriages, Boats, and Wherries, in Plymouth, Stonehouse, and Devonport, was obtained in the 6th and 7th of Victoria. It also amended two acts passed for repairing certain roads from Plymouth to Devonport Dock. Boats or Wherries may be hired on moderate terms, for any part of the harbours of the three towns.

STEAM PACKETS.

From Catwater to *London, Dublin, Falmouth, Southampton, &c.,* every Monday and Friday; Rt. Clark, *agent,* Vauxhall street. To *London and Cork* every Friday and Saturday, from Millbay Pier; Thos. Nicholson, *agent,* Exchange. The Brunswick to *Torquay, Southampton, and Portsmouth,* every Thursday, and to *Torquay, Guernsey, and Jersey,* every Monday; J. E. Blewett, *agt.,* Exchange. The *Sir Francis Drake,* from Stonehouse Pool to *Falmouth* every Monday and Saturday, and *direct to Guernsey & Jersey,* every Thursday afternoon; Wm. Langdon, *agent,* 12 Union street. There are small steamers on the river Tamar for conveying marketable commodities, &c., to the three towns; and in summer they make pleasure trips up the Tamar, Yealm, &c., and to Eddystone Light House, &c. The Waterford Steam Screw Boat Co.'s Vessels, occasionally; T. H. Barber, *agent,* Milbay pier.

SAILING TRADERS.

The *South Devon United Shipping Company* despatch one of their eleven schooners weekly from Custom-house wharf Plymouth, to Beal's wharf, London; *agent,* John Saunders. Also, vessels weekly to Bristol. Schooners to *Hull and Newcastle-on-Tyne* once a fortnight; Ths. Stevens, managing owner, 3 Parade. To Catton's wharf, *London,* every ten days; agent, N. Prout, Vauxhall quay. Also, Smacks to Brixham, Torquay, Dartmouth, &c., about twice a week; and cutters and packets occasionally to *Penzance, Charlestown, St. Austle, Guernsey, Jersey, Glasgow, Liverpool, &c.;* apply to the Captains on board, or to the brokers.

CARRIERS

By Rails, &c. to all parts.

Pickford & Co., and Derry and Co., Kinterbury street; Crowley and Co., Frankfort lane; & Ford & Co., Russell street. The latter have also waggons,

&c. to Cornwall every Tuesday, Thursday, and Saturday, at 1 afternoon.

The *Parcel Delivery Company* delivers parcels three times a day in all parts of the three towns.

CARRIERS FROM THE INNS.

Those marked 1 *stop at* Bedford Inn; 2, *Boot;* 3, *Cornish;* 4 *Corn Market;* 5, *Four Castles;* 6, *George;* 7, *Golden Lion;* 8, *King's Head;* 9 *Morley Inn;* 10, *New London;* 11, *Plough;* 12, *Post-office;* 13, *Rose and Crown;* 14, *Spread Eagle;* 15, *White Hart;* 16, *White Horse;* 17, *White Lion;* and 18, *Noah's Ark.*

Places.	Carriers.

Ashburton, 6 Angell, Tuesday and Fri.

Barnstaple and Bideford, 13 Pridham and Lake, Friday, 8 morning; and 5 Proctor, Mon., Wed. and Friday, at 9 morning.

Bodmin, 1 Hancock, Monday; and 2 Lavers, Tues.; Barrett, Wd.; Cayzer & Sowden, Thrs.; and Lapham, Fri.

Boscale, 11 Nichols, Tues. 4 afternoon

Brent, 12 Andrews, Thurs. & Sat. 3 af.

Bude, 12 Cobbledick, Friday

Callington, 1 Oliver, Thurs.; 13 Buckingham, Mon., Tues., Thurs. and Sat. morn.; and Guy, Thurs. 3 aftn.; and 6 Betty, Mon. Tu., Thrs., & St. mrn.

Camelford, 5 Proctor, Tues., Thurs. & Sat.; & 13 Guy, Thurs., 3 aftn.

Chagford, 12 Blanchford, Wed. 9 morn.

Cornwood, 11 Lavers, Tu., Thur. & St.

Dartmouth, 12 Ferris, Tues. & Sat.

Fowey, 13 Crart, Wed. and Saturday

Holbeton, 12 Ball, Tues., Thurs., and Saturday; 10 Clark, Mon., Tuesday, Thursday, and Saturday.

Holsworthy, 18 Sanders & Seccombe, Thurs. and Sat. at 1 afternoon.

Ivybridge, 10 Blight, and 14 Stevens, Mn., Tu. Th. & Sa.; 8 Savery, daily; Atwill, from the Lamb.

Kingsbridge, 12 Cobbledick, and 13 Sawyer, Tues. & Fri. morn.

Launceston, 17 Broad and Chapman, Tu. & Sat.; 12 Carwithen, Fri.; 5 Procter, daily; 1 Newson, Wed. and Sat; 13 Wilton, Tuesday.

Lifton, 5 Proctor, Tues. & Friday.

Liskeard, 1 Stanton, and 16 Roberts, Tues. and Fri.; 9 Elford, Wed. and Sat.; 2 Lavers, Cayzer & Lapham, Tue., Thrs. and Sat.; 1 Kellow, daily, 4 afternoon.

Looe, 1 Hill, Tu. and Fri.; 13 Crart, Wed. & Sat.; Courtenay, Tues. and Friday, from 65 Oldtown st; & 4 Snell, Friday.

Menheniot, 1 Ough, Wed. & Saturday.
Milton Damerel, 17 Jenkins, Sat.
Modbury, 8 Field, Tus., Thurs. & Sat. ;
    12 Luscombe, Tues. & Friday ; 13
    Fox, Tuesday & Saturday.
Newton Ferrers, 13 Winter, Tuesday
    and Saturday.
North Tawton, 3 Mattaford, Thurs ; &
    5 Taverner, Tues. & Friday.
Okehampton, 5 Taverner, Tu. & Fri.
Padstow, 2 Barrett, Wed. and Sowden,
    Thursday.
Plympton & Ridgway, 2 Goss, daily ;
    and 13 Beavis, daily.
St. Cleer, 2 Ough, Wed. & Saturday.
St. Columb, 2 Cayzer, Thursday.

St. Kew, 2 Oliver, Thursday.
South Molton, 3 Mattaford, **Thurs. &**
    4 Letherby, Thursday.
Stratton, 12 Cobbledick, Friday.
Tavistock, 5 Proctor, Orchard & Tabb ;
    7 Isaacs, 13 Butcher, 2 Webber, and
    6 Down, daily. Several of them have
    Omnibuses.
Truro, 1 Kellow, daily, 4 afternoon.
Ugborough, 12 Tolchard, Thur. & Sat.
Underwood, 15 Willis, daily.
Wadebridge, 2 Barrett, Wed. ; & Cay-
    zer & Sowden, Thurs. 4 afternoon.
Yealmpton, 8 Chaff, and 12 Jones, Tu.,
    Thurs. & Saturday, 4 afternoon.

STONEHOUSE.

EAST STONEHOUSE, commonly called *Stonehouse*, is a populous town-ship and parish, forming the centre of the "three towns," lying between Devonport and Plymouth, and separated from the former by Sutton Pool and Stonehouse Creek and Lake ; and from the latter by Mill Bay, and a boundary line running behind the Gas Works, across the middle of Union street, and up Twickenham place, Manor street, and Eldad road, to Mill pool,—a little east of Mill Bridge, opposite Stoke. More than half of Union street is in Plymouth, and also one side of Twickenham place, Manor street, and Eldad road. Stonehouse, though to all appearance form-ing part of Plymouth, is a separate township. It was added by the Reform Act of 1832 to the Parliamentary Borough of Devonport, but it is still in the Hundred and Petty Sessional Division of Roborough, and forms an Union of itself, under the new poor law, as noticed at pages 633-'4. It was anciently called *Hepeston* or *Hippeston*, and in the reign of Henry III. had but one house, which was the seat of Joel de Stonehouse, then lord of the *manor*. Before this time, it obtained the name of East Stonehouse, in con-tradistinction to the hamlet of West Stonehouse, which stood on the opposite shore of the harbour, near Cremill and Mount Edgcumbe, until burnt by the French, some centuries ago. The manor passed from the Stonehouse family to the Durnfords, with whose heiress it passed to the Edgcumbes. The Earl of Mount Edgcumbe is now lord of the manor, and owner of all the land, except what has been sold to Government for the Royal William Victualling Yard, &c. Most of the land is built upon and let at moderate rents, on leases, subject to perpetual renewal on the payment of small fines by every succeeding tenant. Stonehouse had become a con-siderable place when Risdon wrote, about 1620, and it increased rapidly in *buildings and population* during the first 30 years of the present century. Its number of inhabitants amounted in 1801, to 3407 ; in 1811, to 5174 ; in 1821, to 6043 ; in 1831, to 9571 ; and in 1841, to 9712 ; including 102 persons in the Workhouse, 437 in the Royal Marine Barracks, and 307 in the Royal Naval Hospital. In the latter year, it had 1069 inhabited houses, 42 unoccupied, and 8 building, when the census was taken ; and its number of *males* was then 4145, and *females*, 5567. It owes its prosperity chiefly to its convenient situation for naval and military depôts, and the large Govern-ment establishments connected with the victualling, sanatory, and medical service. During the late war there were maintained here several barracks, capable of containing more than 3000 men. The principal of those now

occupied are the *Royal Marine Barracks*, which have room for about 700 men, and were built about 1783. They are near the head of Mill Bay, opposite the *Great Western Docks*, now in course of formation, as noticed at page 643. From these docks the town extends southward along that bold and strongly fortified neck of land, which juts into Plymouth Sound and Hamoaze harbour, between Mill Bay and Sutton Pool, and is terminated on the south-west by that extensive and elegant establishment the *Royal William Victualling Yard*, already described at page 647, and by the forts and batteries of *Devil's Point* and *Western King*, (see page 641;) and on the south-east by the forts, &c., of *Eastern King*, where there is a large new battery. The spacious *harbours* of Mill Bay, Sutton Pool, and Hamoaze, are noticed at page 643, and the *Royal Naval Hospital*, at pages 647-'8. Stonehouse participates largely in the trade and commerce of the Port of Plymouth, (see page 648,) and its streets are generally spacious and well built, running in straight lines, crossing each other at right angles, and having many handsome houses and well stocked shops, and several commodious inns and hotels. The Prince George and Brunswick Hotels are large and well conducted establishments, and in Edgcumbe street is a convenient Market place, which is well supplied on Tuesdays and Saturdays, but many of the inhabitants frequent the neighbouring markets of Plymouth and Devonport. Here are two annual *fairs* on the first Wednesday in May and the second Wednesday in September. *Stonehouse Bridge*, which crosses the creek between Stonehouse Pool and Lake, forms a direct communication between this town and Devonport, and was built about 1773, by the lords of the two manors, whose successors, the Earl of Mount Edgcumbe and the St. Aubyn family, have equal shares of the tolls, which now yield about £2500 per annum. Foot passengers pay a half-penny, horses, 1d., and carriages, 2d. to 3d. each. Before the erection of this bridge the passage was by a ferry boat. It is matter of surprise that the inhabitants of the three towns have not taken means for the abolition of tolls on this bridge, so as to make it free, like the *Mill Bridge*, (nearly half a mile above,) which was rebuilt about 20 years age. A large and handsome TOWN-HALL, with accommodations for the *County Court*, and weekly *Petty Sessions*, and apartments for the "*Stonehouse Literary and Scientific Institution*," was erected in 1849-'50, at the cost of £3700, raised in £1 shares. It is in the Italian style, and contains, besides the court room, the police station, and the apartments of the Institute, a handsome *Ball Room*, 85 feet by 45. The Institute was established many years ago, and has a good library, and a well supplied reading room, and the Earl of Mount Edgcumbe is its patron and president. Here is also a *Mechanics' Institute*, and various societies for the instruction and relief of the poor. The *Royal Western Yacht Club* has its house near Millbay, and has among its numerous members Prince Albert and many other royal personages. The Queen is its patroness, and the Earl of Mount Edgcumbe is its commodore. The town is well lighted with *gas* from the works, noticed at page 652, and has a plentiful supply of *water* from the works noticed with Devonport.

CHURCHES AND CHAPELS.—East Stonehouse was formerly a chapelry, in the parish of St. Andrew's, Plymouth, but was constituted a separate parish by act of Parliament. ST. GEORGE's, the parish church, was built by subscription in 1789, on the site of the ancient chapel. It is a plain stone fabric, with a disproportioned tower, but the interior is neatly fitted up, and has about 700 sittings. The living is a *perpetual curacy*, valued at £197 per annum, in the patronage of the Vicar of St. Andrew's, Plymouth, and incumbency of the Rev W. H. Nantes, B.A. ST. PAUL's CHURCH, at the end of Durnford street, was built by subscription and grants in 1830-'1

at the cost of about £2700, and is an elegant structure in the lancet pointed style, with 1100 sittings, the greater part of which are free.   The benefice is a perpetual curacy, in the patronage of the incumbent of St. George's, and is now held by the Rev. R. W. Needham.   Part of the eastern side of town has been formed into the new ecclesiastical district of *St. Peter's.* (See page 657.) There is an episcopal chapel at the *Royal Naval Hospital,* of which the Rev. W. R. Payne is chaplain.   The *Roman Catholic Chapel,* in St. Mary's street, was opened in 1807.   There is a *Baptist Chapel,* in Union street ; a *Wesleyan Chapel,* in Edgcumbe street ; and *Independent Chapels,* at Emma place and Union place.   Here is a large National School, which was established many years ago, and has since been considerably enlarged.   It is now in three departments, attended by about 200 boys, 180 girls, and 200 infants.   The poor parishioners have 30s. a year from *Rawlin's and Lanyon's Charities,* (see Maker and Plymouth,) and they participate in the benefits of the *Dispensary* at Devonport.

Stonehouse Parish Workhouse, was erected in 1801, when the old one was taken down.   It has room for 130 paupers, and the parish forms an union and registration district under the new poor law; and in 1838, expended £3005. 14s. in maintaining its in and out door poor.   Mr. Richard Rodd is the *union clerk* and *superintendent registrar ;* Mr. J. Capron is the *relieving officer* and registrar of births and deaths ; and Messrs. Charles Chapple and Thomas Tapp, jun., are the registrars of marriages ; Mr. Joseph and Mrs. Piercy are master and matron of the Workhouse.

STONEHOUSE DIRECTORY.

The Post Office is at 117 Union street, and Mr Geo. Evens is the postmaster.   It is a branch of the Plymouth Post Office, as noticed at page 664.

Miscellany *of Gentry, Clergy, Partners in Firms, and others, not arranged in the succeeding classification of Trades and Professions,*
      Those marked * are Master Mariners.

Adair Mrs Sarah, Emma pl
Adamson Lieut. John, R.N. 7 Hobart street
Alms Mr Geo. 83 Union st
Amos Capt. Jas. Wm., R.N. 27 Hobart street
Anderson Mr Wm., Hobart st
Archer Jas.clk.3 Nelson ctgs
Bailey Mrs Mary, 33 Fore st
Baker Mr Adw.C., Hobart ter
Barnard Cpt.Edw., Emma pl
Barnes Capt.John, Emma pl
*Barratt John, Hobart ter
Bate John, rate collector, Edgcumbe street
Baylis Mr. 3 Union street
Bayly Wm. mercht. Fore st
Beamish James C., Esq. 63 Durnford street
Bedford Mrs., Stone Hall
Beer John, colr. 5 Phœnix st
Belam Mrs. 56 Union st
Benson Mr Wm.31 Hobart st
Besly Chas. clk. Caroline pl
Besly Rev John, Durnford st
Billing Edward, gent. 15 North Caroline place
Bleazby Mrs., Durnford st
Blight Capt. Willm., R.N. Emma place
Boardman Capt.Robert Ball, 9 Emma place

Boger John Hext, solr. and manor steward, 5 Lower Durnford street
Boger Mrs S. 1 Emma pl
Boulter J.J.clk. Manor office
Boyle Mrs. 7 Durnford st
Boyle Mr John & Mrs B. 10 South Caroline place
Branson Jeremiah, acentnt. Buckingham place
Brooking Thomas B. tailor ; h 2 Twickenham place
Brooks Mrs M. 2 Hobart st
Brown Mr Jph. 13 Hobart st
Brown Mr P. 123 Union st
Bulley Barbara, furrier, 23 St Mary street
Busk Mr Wm.5N.Caroline pl
Burnley Mrs. 12 Emma pl
Bushell Mr Edw.32Hobart st
Bassell Mrs. 33 Hobart st
Butters Mr Wm.106Union st
Capron John, relvg. officer & registrar, 4 Clarence pl
Carrington Mrs Caroline, 9 Phœnix street
Charles Mr. 17 Union st
Chown Mr Fredk. James, 34 Union street
Clarke Capt. James, R.M. 33 Durnford street
Clouter Jonathan, Esq. 6 Buckingham place

Clymo Misses, Hobart cotgs
*Coaker Rd. 7 Windsor pl
Cock Edw. acct. 16 East st
Coles Misses, 56 Durnford st
Conner Lieut. Ross, R.N. 7 North Caroline place
Conway Rt. agt.73 Dunfd.st
Cook Mrs Fanny,5Hobart st
Cookson MrsC.M.,Durnfd.st
Cooper Wm. engrvr. Union st
Corfield Mrs., Durnford st
Cotgrave Lieut. Rd., R.N. Preventive Station ; h 21 Emma place
Cotgrave Lieut.Rowland B., R.N. 51 Durnford st
Cridland Henry,woolstapler, seed mert.&tanner,Fore st
Cross Thomas, lock and gun smith, Fore street
Davey Rev Philip Gibbs, M.A. 42 Durnford st
Davis Wm. boat builder, Newport street
Davis Miss, 43 Durnford st
Dawe Rd. dyer, Edgcmb.st
Devonshire Miss Eliz. W. *Alvrington House*
Digby Lieut.Edw.,Emma pl
Dixon Lady Agnes, 2 Edgcumbe square
Dowdney John,forage dealer, Little Durnford street

Drew Gideon, naturalist, 73 Union street
Duffin Mrs L.,N.Caroline pl
Dyer Lieut. Robert,R.M. 4 Hobart cottages
EdeCapt.John,6Durnford st
EdwardsThos.,Hobart cotgs
Elliott MrJohn,122 Union st
Elliss Mr Chas.14Emma pl
Errington MajorArnoldChs. 5 Emma place west
Evens Mrs Ann, 42 East st
Evens Mr Wm. 24 East st
Eyre Mrs Ann, Emma pl
Fanshawe Captain Arthur, R.N. 4 Lr Durnford st
Farmer Mrs. 10 N.Carln.pl
Field Mr John, 16 Emma pl
Folds Mrs. 46 Durnford st
Foley Timothy Edw. clerk, Durnford lane
FooteCapt.John,LrDrnfd.st
*Fox Charles, Nelson cotgs
Fox MrsJaneL.12 Emma pl
FreemanWm. George, stone merchant, 68 Durnford st
FullerChs.,R.N.Durnfd.st
Gammell Major Wm. 1 Victoria place
Gloyn Rt.clk.13 Clarence pl
Godden Rev George Henry, (Indept.) 3 Hobart st
Griffith Robert Edward, excise, 2 Union place
Hall Mrs Eliz. 10 East st
Hancock Abraham, Esq. 47 Durnford street
Hands Mr Jph. 62 Union pl
Hare Mrs. 31 Emma pl
Hare Hon. Capt. Richard, 57 Durnford street
Harris Mr Rd. 68 Union st
Hele Rd.Esq.28 Durnfd.st
Herbert Capt.Pp. Emma pl
Hicks Wm. boat builder, Strand street
Hilton Misses, 10 Emma pl
HockerCapt.Edward,R.M. 36 Emma place
Hocking Richard and Son, *ship builders*, Newport st
Hoggett James, pipe maker, George street
Hoof Francis, conveyancer, Edgcumbe street
HorswellJames,corn miller, 8 Mill Pleasant
HunterMrAndw.,Durnfd.st
IngleJohn,Esq.1Edgcmb.st
James Mrs., Clarence pl
Jean Mrs. 26 Emma pl
Jennings MrsL.6 Hobart st
Jervis Capt. Wm. Henry, R.N.38Emma place east
Johnson Mr P.,Twicknm.pl
JohnstonMiss,34Durnford st
JonesMrsM.A.,Hobart ctgs
Kein Mrs My.I.7 Emma pl
KentCapt.W.G.C.,Emma pl
Kiddell Lieut. 26 Hobart st
Kitt Arthur, contractor, 6 Emma place

KirbyWm.blacking manfr. 7 Fore street
Lamoureux John,par.clerk, 17 South Caroline place
Langdon Jas. 14 Hobart st
LawMisses,11N.Caroline pl
LemonMajorThs.22Union st
Lemon Capt.Thomas,R.M. 4 North Caroline place
Lennock Capt.54 Durnfd.st
LeonardMajorRt.,Emma pl
Lewis MajorGeneralGeorge, C.B. 63 Durnford street
Lilburn Lieut., Buckgm. pl
Lillicrap Admiral James, 11 South Caroline place
Lillicrap Wm.wheelwright, 37 Union street
Loney Capt.,R.N.,Emma pl
Loudon John,Esq.Durnfd.st
Lowe Mrs. 16 N. Caroline pl
Lower Mr Charles, Union pl
Luckraft Capt. Wm., R.N. 12 North Caroline place
Lugher Mrs. 64 Durnford st
Luscombe Miss,Durnford st
MadgeWm.,R.N.31Unionst
Makenzie Mrs. 9 Hobart st
Mallock Mrs. 27 Emma pl
Malony Madm., *Convent*, 28 Union street
Mann John P. professor of languages, 25 Hobart st
Marsh MrsA.3 LrDhrnfd.st
Marshall Mr. coast guard, Fore street
Martin Mrs. 58 Union st
Mason Wm. G. purser, 8 Emma place
May Mrs. 75 Union street
Maynard Mr James,15 Clarence place
McCallum Colonel John, 53 Durnford street
MeathrellJnthn.lathrender, Brownlow street
Mercer Mrs. 37 Emma pl
Meredith Mr.38 Durnford st
Miller Lieut.G.6 Phœnix pl
Millman Mrs Har.,Union st
Molesworth Col. Richard C. 10 Emma place
Moir(Jno.)&Baker(Andw.), ironfounders, Phœnix st; h 81 Union street
Morris Admiral James, 4 South Caroline place
Mountstevens Capt. Wm., Emma place
Nantes Mrs. 22 Emma pl
Nantes Rev Wm.Hy.,B,A. incumbent of *St George's*, 9 Emma place
Nathan Aaron, police supt. St Mary street
NeameMrW.J.R.,Winds.pl
Needham Rev Rd.W. incbt. of *St Paul's*,39 Durnford st
Nelson Capt.37 Durnford st
NicholsonCol.ThomasWm. 17 North Caroline place

NicolasJohnToup,C.B.capt. supt. of Naval Hospital & Victualling Yard
NorcockJno.purser,Drnfd.st
O'DonoghueMisses,Hobrt st
Oleron Rev Mark, *(R.Cath.)* 2 St Mary street
Ommanney Adml. Hy.Manadon, 6 Emma place
Opie Richard, 39 Chapel st
Ormsby Lieut.17 Hobart st
Pallowe Mrs., Durnford st
Palmer MrSml.9Clarence st
Parker Peter Perlee, naval accmpt. 8 Phœnix place
PascoeAdml.41 Durnford st
Pascoe Lieut.John E.,R.N. 5 Adelaide place
Pascoe Capt.Richard,R.M. 8 Durnford street
Pasmore Misses,24Emma pl
PaulHenry,R.N.,Battery st
Pawley MrWm.60 Union st
Payne Mrs. 45 Durnford st
PayneRevWm.R.chaplain, *Naval Hospital*
PearseCapt.Jph.,Buckgmpl
Pengally Misses, Durnfd.st
PengelleyLieut.John,R.N. 6 Emma place
Perkin Lieut. John, R.N. 30 East Emma place
Pettingal Capt. Fras. Wm. engineer, 4 Emma place
Phillips Mrs My. Durnfd.st
Phillips Thomas, Esq. 62 Durnford street
Piercy Joseph & Ann,master and matron, *Workhouse*
Pigow MrsMgt.LrDurnfd.st
Pitfield Lieut. 3 Emma pl
Pole Lady Charlotte,1 Lower Durnford street
PollardN.colr.Edgcumbe st
PostlethwaiteRevThs.Geo., M.A. 24 Emma place
Preston Mr Ntl.80 Union st
Protherhoe Rev J. *(Indept.)* Nelson cottages
RaeWalter,Esq.2 Emma pl
Randle Wm. 116 Union st
Rattenbury Mrs., Hobart st
*Renny Thos.1Nelson cotgs
*Richards Thos., Hobart st
Risk Lieut. John, Emma pl
Roberts Mr Rt., Adelaide st
Robertson Mrs.3 Caroline pl
Robertson Mrs., Windsor pl
Rogers Rev Chas.(*Baptist,)* 3 Phœnix place
Rogers Wm.,R.N.35 Durnford street
Russell Lieut. Jas. T. and Wm. 30 & 20 Hobart st
Russell Mrs., Durnford st
*Sadler W. S. 15 Emma pl
Sands Rev Edn.50 Union st
Sargent MrsC.E.,Emma pl
Saunders Wm. constable, 6 Barrack street
Saundry Edw. 9 Union pl
SergeantMrP.L.13Union st

Sheppard Mrs.9N.Carln.pl
Simpson MrChs.100Union st
Simpson Jno.Esq.3Emma pl
Slaughter Capt. Wm.,R.N.
  7 Buckingham place
Snell Wm. land surveyor,21
  Chapel street
Snow Rev Wm.M.31 Durn-
  ford street
Soady Major Thomas Eales,
  24 Emma place
Somerville Misses,Emma pl
Speed John, R.N., Emma pl
Spry Capt. 3 Clarence pl
Stephens Capt.72 Durnfrd st
Stevenson Robert, R.N. 8
  Hobart street
Sullaven Mrs. 7 Phœnix pl
Sumpter Miss, 69 Union st
Symons Mrs.,LrDurnford st
Symon Peter, stone mercht.
  19 North Caroline place
Tancock Lieut. 10 Hobart st
Taylor Mrs. 16 Hobart st
Taylor Jas. clk.Windsor pl
Thomas Admiral Rd., Lwr.
  Durnford street
Thompson Misses, Bucking-
  ham place
Thompson Capt.,Durnford st
Thompson Mr Nichls. 104
  Union street
Thring Mrs. 66 Durnford st
Thuell MrThy.,Brownlw.st.
Toby Capt. 55 Durnford st
Townsend Mrs.2 Victoria pl
Tremlett Admiral Wm. 9
  Buckingham place
Trop Mrs. 101 Union st
*Turnbull Wm.,Brownlowst
Turner Wm. cork cutter,
  Clarence place
Twysden Capt. Henry, 11
  Lower Durnford street
Veitch Lieut. 11 Hobart st
Vivian MrJohnR.4Emma pl
Vosper Saml. ale and porter
  merchant, 110 Union st
Walsh Capt. 4 Durnford st
Waddon Mrs. 8 Clarence pl
Waring Mrs. 6 Windsor pl
Warn Mrs M. 2 Phœnix pl
Watson Capt.G.29 Emma pl
Watson Rt. clk.29Hobart st
Way Mr Rd. 37 East st
Webster Rev John, (Bapt.)
  25 Clarence place
Welch Misses,32Durnford st
Westbrook Lieut.5Emma pl
Westlake Mrs.16 Caroline st
White Mr Robt. 20 East st
White Mrs. 32 Emma pl
Wiggins MrMtw.,Durnfd.st
Wilcox Mrs. 26 Emma pl
Williams Mr. 12 Battery st
Williams Vinct.4 Hobart st
Winter Mrs., Strand street
Wofandale Wm. town crier,
  Newport street
Wolridge Mrs.,N.Caroline pl

Wood Rev Thos. (Wes.) 3
  Adelaide place
Wyngett Wm.clk.Caroln.pl
Youle Miss My. 49 Union st

ACADEMIES.

Drew Mtlda., Hobart Cotgs
Furse Wm. A., Battery st
Hooking Robt. 35 East st
Howe Jemima, 36 East st
Infant School, Wm. Hardy
Mackenzie A.,9N.Caroln.pl
National School, John Glan-
  ville and Mrs Budge
Prout My. A. 2 Union st
Rowe Chalwell, 95 Union st
Slater Gabriel, Union st
Steel Cath. 5 Phœnix st
Sturgeon Misses,1Phœnix pl
*Workhouse School,*W. Davis
  and Mary Leworthy

ARCHITECTS.

Lemon Saml. 22 Union st
Chapple Cs.24 Edgcumbe st

ATTORNEYS.

Boger, Boger, and Bewes,
  Manor Office, Emma pl
Elworthy Henry John R.29
  Union street
Gill Henry, 14 Union pl
Rod Rd. (supt. regr. & clk.to
  magistrates,)48Durnfd.st

AUCTIONEERS.

Bishop John&Son,41Union st
Hoare John, 28 Edgcumbe st

BAKERS, &c.

Bone John, 53 George street
Bovey Thos. 56 Fore street
Burt John, 32 Edgcumbe st
Cole James, 11 Union st
Friend Richd. 85 Fore st
Keep Thos. 23 Union st
Lambell Rd. 39 George st
Lord Stephen, 16 Barrack st
Piper Jas. 48 Adelaide st
Ryder John, 32 Chapel st
Ryder John, 26 Edgcumbe st
Stanbury Hy. 108 Union st
Tapp Ths.R.9Edgcumbe st
United Bread & Flour Co.,
  Newport st; H. Pickard,
  secretary
Weaboarn Thos.3Newport st
Willey James, 9 Barrack st

BATH CHAIR LETTRS.

Palk Jas. 16 Lr. Durnford st
Stevens R. 27 Clarence pl
Stratford Thos., Quarry st

BLACKSMITHS.

Blight John, 14 Market st
Cross ——, 8 Chapel st
Dodridge Silas, 35 Fore st
Pike Geo. (and stove grate
  manfr.) 41 Edgcumbe st
Stepp Thos. 10 St Mary st
Tink Rd. 23 Brownlow st

BOOKSELLRS. PRNTS. AND STATIONERS.

(* *have Libraries.*)
Blackwell Fredk. & Thos.
  59 Union street
*Cole Edw.W.12Edgcmb.st

Cornish W.Pike,6Edgcmb.st
Doidge J. Sweet, 32 Union st
Gilbert P.(bindr.)88Union st
*Huss My. *Stamp Office,* 29
  Chapel street
Langford W.Hy.47 Union st
*Pollard Wm. Nisbet, 38
  Edgcumbe street

BOOT & SHOE MKRS.

Allen Wm. 37 Chapel street
Braginton Wm.45 George st
Brent Jph. 22 Edgcumbe st
Brookes ——, 31 Chapel st
Browning John, 17 St.My.st
Collard Pp.,Ltle.Durnford st
Collins Uriah, 36 Chapel st
Crowl John, 20 Market st
Harris Hy. 23 Chapel st
Harris Wm. 5 Union st
Harvey (Abm.) and Morris,
  (Thos.) 4 Edgcumbe st
Jarvis John, 7 Barrack st
Keast Wm. 34 Edgcumbe st
Mullins Rd. 42 Edgcumbe st
Neale James, Chapel lane
Palmer Chas., Battery st
Smith Jas. 1 Newport st
Trebilcock Thos.96 Union st
Trebilcock Wm. 89 Union st
Truscott Wm.7Edgcumbe st
Underhill Rd. 4 Union st

BRAZIERS, &c.

Daniel John, 34 Fore st
Toms John, 82 Fore st

BREWERS.

Butchers Thos.6 St.Mary st
Clarke Jas. Edw.1Durnfd. st
Hare & Son, 3 Durnford st
Jasper Fredk., Brownlow st

BUILDERS.

Chown John, 8 Hobart ter
Deacon Josiah, Brownlow st
Goodyear & Son,Adelaide pl
Hearn Fras.Lovis and Son,
  17 Brownlow street
Langman John, 33 East st
May Wm.&Thos.Mill plsnt
Morgan Edw.21 Clarence pl
Prouse Thos. 15 Market st
Roberts Walter, 65 Union st
Taylor Thos. 1 Adelaide pl
Thuell Geo. 128 Union st
Thuell Henry, Quarry st

BUTCHERS.

Cleave John, Edgcumbe st
Dicker John, 66 Union st
Dingle Wm. 54 Union st
Goss Jas. F. 3 St. Mary st
Hyne Simon, 4 Chapel st
Joyce John, 76 Union st
Pike Rd. 15 Edgcumbe st
Pike Wm. 7 Chapel street
Pike W. Saml. 98 Union st
Pinches Fras. 78 Fore st
Poole Wm. 25 George st
Roberts Daniel, Market st

CABINET MAKERS.

Bishop John&Son,41Union st
Bolson Margt.26 St.Mary st
Bulley Wm. 20 Chapel st
Hancock John, 27 Union st

Hoare John, 28 Edgcmb. st
Hodge Saml. 24 Union st
Kinton Ths.36 Edgcumbe st
Lott Ann, 17 Edgcumbe st
Moorcombe Ths.67 Union st
Were James, 13 Chapel st

CARPENTERS.
Harris John, 5 Barrack st
Mortimore Jas.109 Union st
Pilditch Thos. 37 East st
Roberts Ann, Durnford lane
Rogers James, Hobart ter
Saunders Jno. 58 George st
Stevens Thos. 64 George st

CARVERS & GILDERS.
Blackwell Fredk.& Thos.59
   Union street
Culverwell Chas.39Union st

CHEESEMONGERS.
Lang John, 1 St Mary st
Matthew John, 36 Union st

CHEMISTS & DRUGTS.
Hambly Geo. 79 Union st
Leadbeater Geo. & Co. 33
   Chapel street
Martin Wm. 125 Union st
Snell Harry B. 92 Union st
Wey Wm. 8 Edgcumbe st
WilliamsGeo.19Edgcmb. st

CHINA & GLASS DLRS.
Brotherton Rt. 8 Chapel st
Stevens Thos. 64 George st

**COAL MERCHANTS
AND DEALERS.**
Ellis Hy. 7 Emma place
Langdon Rd. 7 Hobart ter
Langdon Wm. 12 Union st
Lucas Wm., Strand street
Payne Wm. 27 St Mary st
Russell Thos., Strand st

CONFECTIONERS.
Brewer Cath. 20 Chapel st
Coleman Robt. 19 Union st
Cormick John, 48 Union st
Granville Hy. Walker, 129
   Union street
Oldridge Hy. 54 George st

COOPERS.
Cook John, 7 Phœnix st
Ford Edm. 12 Market st
Narracott Val., Market st

CURRIERS.
Bate John, 39 Edgcumbe st
Gribble Jph. 16 Market st

DAIRYMEN.
Crouch Stpn. 10 Market st
Dawe Richd. 53 Union st
Penwarn Rd. 37 Union st
Stephens Benj. 15 Chapel st
Symons Peter, 8 Battery st
Tolchard Hy. 121 Union st
Williams Chs. 61 George st
Wills John, Ltle. Durnfd.st

DENTISTS.
Jewers Fredk. 42 Union st
Snell Harry B. 92 Union st
Tarratt Wm. 87 Union st

DRAPERS, &c.
   (Travelling.)
Banks Andw. 16 Union pl
Bissey Wm. 4 Phœnix pl
   Adelaide st

HughamWm. 1 Adelaide st
McCallumRt.51Adelaide st
Scott Hugh, 53 Union st
Shear Wm. 5 Adelaide st
Wilson (Jas.) & McCubbin,
   (John,) 14 Union street

EATING HOUSES.
Ashton Jane, 43 Edgcmb.st
Davys Ann, 10 Chapel st

FIRE & LIFE OFFICES.
City of London, Geo.Evens,
   117 Union street
Clerical&Medl.,A.Narracott
Eagle & Protector, Payne &
   Wrentmore,27 Edgcmb.st
Etonian, Wm. Wey, 8 Edg-
   cumbe street
Family Endowment, Chas.
   Chapple, 24 Union st
Guardian, Richd. Rodd
Imperial, Thos. Hoof, 54
   Edgcumbe street
Star,Ts.Mayne,111Union st
United Kingdom, Wm. Ver-
   coe, 106 Union street
Yorkshire, G. Leadbeater &
   Co. 33 Chapel street

FURNITURE BROKRS.
Bishop John, 41 Union st
Hoare John, 28 Edgcmb. st
Morris Davis, 14 George st

GREEN GROCERS.
Abbot Eliz. 41 Chapel st
Blachmore Jph., Chapel st
Jarvis Louisa, Edgcumbe st
Stentiford Edw., Chapel st
Titherleigh Bj.C.,Chapel st

GROCERS, &c.
Brotherton Rt. 43 Chapel st
Brown Ths.13 Edgcumbe st
Buchanan Hy., East street
Kent Herbt. 2 Edgcumbe st
Ladbury Ths. Fdk.,Union st
Langdon Wm. 12 Union st
Pennell Rd.44 Edgcumbe st
Richmond Geo. 22 George st
Sambell Thos. 90 Union st
Tobilcock Fras.127 Union st
WalkhamNchls.27Chapel st

HABERDASHERS, &c.
Clark Cath. 29 Clarence pl
Dawe Thos. 12 Chapel st
Drew Jas. 42 Edgcumbe st
Snell Jane & My.,Chapel st

HAIRDRESSERS.
CornishWm.P.6Edgcmb.st
Glober Hy. 10 Union st
Kent Alfd. 25 Edgcumbe st
Twitt Wm. 2 George st

HATTERS.
Kidney Thos. 107 Union st
Rue Jas. 97 Union street
Yeo John, 7 Union street

HORSE, GIG, &c.LETRS.
Barons Rd., Dunford lane
Couzens Dvd., 70 Union st

INNS AND TAVERNS.
Brunswick Inn, Richard B.
   Nightingale, 4 Fore st
Builders' Arms, Jph. Wil-
   liams, 27 George street

Canteen, Ward West Arliss,
   Marine Barracks
Commercial Inn, My.Wills,
   Newport street
Crown,Jn.Cornish,Chapel st
Earl Grey, Walter Geake,
   45 Edgcumbe street
Edgcumbe Inn, Jno. Morti-
   mer, 16 Edgcumbe st
Exmouth Arms,Rd.Netten,
   63 Union street
Freemasons' Arms, Jemima
   Beale, 22 Chapel street
Half Way Inn, Hy.Pardeu,
   30 Claremont place
Hospital Inn, Jas. Gosden,
   46 Fore street
Long Room, Jph. Nooks, I
   Pound street
London Inn, My.A.Bartlett,
   3 Fore street
Lord High Admiral, Jane
   Facey, 1 East street
Navy and Army Inn, John
   Pengelly, 82 Fore street
Prince George, J. Killingly,
   Chapel street
Queen's Arms, Geo. Pike,14
   Edgcumbe street
Red Lion, Jas. Downing, 15
   Chapel street
Three Kings, Wm. Wilk-
   ings, 63 George street
Victualling Office Tavern,
   Wm. Dunning, Durnfd.ln
Victualling Office Tavern,
   Eliz. Please, 6 Fore st
Vine, Js. Warren, Strand st
White Lion, Wm. Holyoak,
   11 Clarence place
York Inn, John Blewett, 76
   Fore street

BEERHOUSES.
Bickford Stpn., Market pl
Bissitt John, 30 Fore st
Bradley Jas. 1 Barrack ope
Bridgeman Wm. 1 Fore st
Cary Jas., 10 Barrack st
Chipman Eliz., Durnfd. ln
Clissold Dl. 17 Barrack st
Cough Jane, 11 Battery st
Croker Mattw. 80 Fore st
Dolan My. Ann, 79 Fore st
Drown Thos., 77 Fore st
Edwards Jno. 26 Barrack st
Ellis Saml. 25 St. Mary st
Ellis Thos. 2 Adelaide pl
Foale Robt., Durnford ln
Foster Jph. 55 Fore street
Garden John, 3 Pound st
Gardiner Saml. 83 Fore st
Gerrard Wm., Barrack st
Harvey Andw. 62 George st
Hawke Robt. 4 Phœnix st
Hellyer John, 5 George st
King Thos. 44 Union st
Lashbrook Wm. 74 Fore st
Line George, Battery st
Long Wm., Brownlow st
Mitchell John. 55 Union st
Mudge Jno. 25 Newport st

Nile Rd. 42 George st
Pennary Chas. 5 Fore st
Penwarn J., Adelaide pl
Peters Maria, Barrack st
Phillips Thos. 50 George st
Pound George, Quarry st
Prout Fras. 15 Fore st
Quartermain John, 27 Barrack street
Reeby Rd. 10 Newport st
Rendle John, 69 George st
Rogers J. 6 Twickenham pl
Rosevear Jno., Barrack st
Rowe Wm. 5 East street
Shepheard Ths., Clarence pl
Thompson Wm., 50 Fore st
Treneman Rt. 82 Union st
Turner Leonard, 10 Fore st
Viner Chas. 66 George st
Wagstaff Wm., Barrack st
Wallace Thos. 11 Fore st
Weekes Simon, Hobart ter
Welsford John, Barrack st
Willis Thos., Barrack ope
Wilmot Wm. 18 Barrack st
Young Thos. 8 Barrack st

IRONMONGERS.
Gliddon Jas. 120 Union st
Pomeroy Richd. Sethard, 1 Edgcumbe street
Upton Geo. 45 Union st
Weekes Fredk. Wm., Edgcumbe street

L. & W. DRAPERS.
Eads Jno. 11 Edgcumbe st
Kidney Thos. 28 Hobart st
Meadows Sar. 2 Chapel st
Payne (Jas.) & Wrentmore (Abm.) 27 Edgcumbe st
Rue Jas. 97 Union st
Saundry Wm. 1 Union st
Wyatt John, 70 Union st

LODGING HOUSES.
Arnold Ebzr. 11 Durnford st
Atwill Mk. 20 Durnford st
Barron Geo. 57 Union st
Churchward E. 6 Caroline pl
Gooding Mgt. 5 Hobart cots
Greet Jph. 30 Edgcumbe st
Hitchfield J. 19 Dunford st
Horwell Ann, Emma pl
Hughs Eliz. 86 Union st
Jeffery Nancy, Durnford st
Jenkins Stpn., Durnford st
Johnson Hy. 20 Edgcmb. st
Knowling Miss, Union st
Lakeman Rd. 35 Durnfd. st
Leddra Rebca. 52 Union st
Mitchell Hy. 103 Union st
Moore John, 2 Windsor pl
Palk Jas. 16 Durnford st
Parish Ann, 51 Union st
Pavey Wm. Hy. 15 Durnford street
Penhey Probert, 5 Emma pl
Pike Wm. Geo. 13 Durnfd.st
Price Cath. 15 Hobart st
Sanders Fras., Durnford st
Southey Chas. 24 Hobart st
Thompson E. 84 Union st
Thuell John, 126 Union st
Walker Saml. 25 Durnfd. st

MARINE STORE DLRS.
Edgecombe Hy. 75 Fore st
Patch Wm. 9 George st
Pennick John, Brownlow st
Pennick J. jun. Brownlow st
Powell Chas. 34 Union st

MASONS, &c.
Brownlow Wm. 3 Phœnix st
Gliddon John, 23 Fore st
Goodfellow W., Brownlow st
Harvey & Son, 91 Union st
Parker John, Hobart cotgs
Perkins Wm. 44 George st
Thuell Geo. 128 Union st

MILLINERS.
Batchelor J. 94 Union st
Bray E. 7 Adelaide street
Bray E. 21 St. Mary st
Brooks E. 4 Ltle. Durnfd. st
Burnett A. 28 Chapel st
Cato Eliz. 12 Adelaide st
Chase My. 25 Union st
Chown Eliz. 4 Adelaide pl
Collins My. 3 Edgcumbe st
Corse E. 4 Brownlow st
Craggs Mrs. 77 Union st
Dalley C. 28 Catherine st
Daniel My. A. 34 Fore st
Dunstone C. 45 Fore st
Friend E. 40 Edgcumbe st
Goss My. Ann, 3 St. My. st
Hodge Emma, 9 Union st
Hopkins A. 15 S. Carolinepl
Jeffery M. 19 Clarence pl
Lapthorne Ann, 36 East st
Lander A. & E., Twickm.pl
Macfarlane B. 40 Union st
May Louisa, 6 Union st
McCormick S., Clarence pl
Nathan H. 24 St. Mary st
Nicholson C. 6 Chapel st
Pope Emily, 7 Clarence st
Restalic C. 39 Chapel st
Spry Sus. D. 78 Union st
Triggs A., Twickenham pl
Turner C. & M. 71 Union st
Willcocks &Taylor,Union st

MUSIC PRECEPTORS.
(* are also Music Sellers.)
Brown Wm. 41 East st
*Cole Edw. W., Edgcmb. st
Dennis Thos. 30 Union st
Hoof Miss, 34 Edgcumbe st
Kilbee Gilbt. 2 Brownlow st
*Prout John, 2 Union st
Prout Edwin Hy., Union st
Purton John, 18 East st
Richards Wm. 8 Emma pl
*Stockham Thos. 16 East st
Turner Jas. 35 Chapel st

PAINTERS & GLZRS.
Buchanan Jno. 102 Union st
Bussell Wm. 6 Battery st
Collins M. 20 St. Mary st
Dawe Thos. 12 Chapel st
Hudd Jph. 93 Union st
Northey Jas. 118 Union st
Philp Thos. 72 Fore st
Thomas Saml. 6 Battery st
Thuell John, 126 Union st
Toms Eliz. 1 Edgcumbe st
Trego Chas. jun. 8 Union st

Weekes Rt. 25 Chapel st

PAWNBROKERS.
Atwill Wm. 22 Fore st
Hooper Chas. 71 Fore st
Lane Wm. D. 8 Fore st
Southey Eliz., Adelaide st
White John B. 1 St. Mary st

PHYSICIANS.
Sheppard Jas. 15 Union st
Turner Wm. 35 Emma pl

POULTERERS.
Goss Saml. 14 Chapel st
Thomas Mark, 119 Union st
Wilkes Eliz. 19 Chapel st

ROPE & TWINE MRS.
Brewer Jas. 6 Union pl
Harvey Thos. 63 Fore st

SHOPKEEPERS.
Anstice John, 60 Fore st
Barratt Geo. 46 George st
Bonear Jph. 11 Chapel st
Buchanan Jane, 51 Geo. st
Burge Thos., Adelaide st
Burrows Wm., Adelaide st
Cann George, 31 Fore st
Carr Mary A. 19 Barrack st
Clero Eliz. 70 Fore st
Coombes Jph. 65 Union pl
Cresswell My. 26 George st
Dawe Henry, 40 Fore st
Hatherleigh S. 52 Geo. st
Heard Jas. 13 George st
Henderson Eliza, Chapel st
Hill Chas. 68 George st
Hoskins John, Phœnix st
King Grace, Barrack st
Langman John, 33 East st
Marshall Peter, Barrack st
Mutton Chas. 51 Fore st
Parsons Edw., Barrack ope
Partridge John, Chapel st
Perkins John, Hobart st
Pilditch Rd. 49 Adelaide st
Powlesland Wm., Union pl
Rowlands Rd. 19 Fore st
Seymour Thos., Adelaide st
Sloggett Edw. 109 Union st
Stephens My. 48 Fore st
Stevens Jph. 82 Fore st
Thomas Grace, 38 Geo. st
Trute Rt. P., Battery st
Waits Grace, 16 Fore st
Whitaker Wm. 14 Fore st
Wills My. 4 Newport st

SILVERSMITHS, &c.
Boreli D., Edgcumbe st
Mayne Thos. 111 Union st
Roberts Wm. 34 Union st
Turner —, 67 Union st

SLOPSELLERS.
Easterbrook J., 37 Fore st
Lyons Jacob, 13 Market st
Newton Emln. 81 Fore st
Thompson Dthy. 66 Fore st
Williams Thos., Chapel st

STAY MAKERS.
Francis Rebecca, 19 Geo. st
Harper Mrs. 23 Union st

STRAW HAT MKRS.
Bolt Selina, 12 Market st
Eascott Louisa, 64 Union pl
Halliday Martha, 58 Geo.st

Hurley Ann, 9 Brownlow st
Kelly A. 19 Adelaide st
Rider Louisa, 85 Union st
Rowe Eliza, 12 Adelaide st
Seymour and Wallace, 62 Union street
Sleep M., Twickenham pl
Soper M. & E. 6 Adelaide pl
Uren Eliz. 24 George st
Williams M. A. 34 Chapel st

SURGEONS.
Burrows Isaiah, 9 Emma pl
Isbell Warren John, 14 Durnford street
Kay W. T., Marine sq
Little John C. 23 Emma pl
Millar A., Marine Barracks
Perry Hy. 65 Durnford st

TAILORS.
Bartlett J. Fdk. 72 Union st
Bate Hy. 42 Adelaide st
Bennett Thos. 49 George st

Brooking and Cox., Twick- enham place
Cross Benj. 105 Union st
Daniel Pp. 18 St. Mary st
Daniel Rt. 124 Union st
Doyle Fdk. 107 Union st
Eads John, 11 Edgcmb. st
Evens Geo. 117 Union st
Fox Edw. 7 Emma place
Griffith Thos. 47 Fore st
Isum Jas. 19 George st
Nickols John, 38 East st
Williams John, Windsor pl

TEA DEALERS.
(See Grocers, &c.)
Vercoe Wm. 106 Union st
Viney Robt. 21 Hobart st

TIMBER MERCHTS.
Lambrell Wm., Water ln
Peake & Son, Caroline pl
Wood John, Fore street

Woolridge John, Market st
UMBRELLA MAKERS.
Kent Wm. B. 5 Edgcmb. st
Marshall Ths. 112 Union st

WATCH & CLOCK MKS.
Boreli Domnc., Edgcmb. st
Brissington W., St. My. st
Mayne Thos. 111 Union st
Searle G. Elliot, Edgcmb. st

WINE AND SPIRIT MERCHANTS.
Bray W. Harvey, 61 Fore st
Narracott Val., Caroline pl
Simmons Wm. 112 Union st
Trayes Hy. 26 Union st

COACHES, CARRI- ERS, STEAM- PACKETS, AND RAILWAY.
See Plymouth & Devonport.

BOROUGH OF DEVONPORT.

DEVONPORT, the most western of the three towns which form the port of Plymouth, is bounded on the east by Stonehouse Pool and Creek, on the north by Morice Town, and on the south and west by the spacious harbour of *Hamoaze*, to which *Mount Wise*, the great *Naval Dockyard*, the *Gun Wharf*, and the *Government Steam Yard* present their extensive sea walls and fortifications, as noticed at pages 643 to 647. Devonport is in the parish of *Stoke Damerel*, and owes its origin as a town to the foundation of the Naval Dockyard, in the reign of William III., about 1690. So late as 1700, not a house was to be seen here, except the *Barton of Mount Wise*, which stood on the spot now occupied by the Semaphore, and was built by Sir Thomas Wise, whose descendant, Sir Edward Wise, sold the manor of Stoke Damerel, in 1667, to Sir Wm. Moris, for £11,000. On the death of Sir Wm. Moris, Bart., in 1749, this now valuable estate passed to his nephew, the late Sir John St. Aubyn, Bart., whose devisees now own it, and are lords of the manor. The first house in the town is said to have been a wooden building, at the landing place called North Corner; and the seat of business and the principal residences were for some years confined to that locality; but during the late war, the town increased rapidly, and it now occupies all the extensive oblong space between the Dockyard and Gun Wharf on the west, and the lines of fortifications on the north, east, and south. The population within the lines comprises above 25,000 souls; but including the suburbs of *Morice Town*, and the rest of the parish of *Stoke Damerel*, the total population of the municipal borough of Devonport amounted to 33,820 in 1841, as noticed at page 633. The *municipal borough* comprises all Stoke Damerel parish, and was incorporated by royal charter in 1837; but the *parliamentary borough* includes also East Stone- house, and was created by the Reform Act of 1832, and vested with the privilege of sending two members to Parliament. In the reign of George II., immense barriers and fortifications around the town were raised, and in 1725, the town became the *seat of the military*, as well as the *naval government* of the port of Plymouth. The "King's Boundary Walls" con- stitute lines of fortifications, 12 feet high, on the north and south-east. The walls of the Dock Wharf are in some places 30 feet high; and those of the Gun Wharf protect the town on the north-west. The heavy *batteries,*

on the delightful parade called *Mount Wise*, were designed to protect the entrance from the sea; and the redoubt and block house on Mount Pleasant, to command the capital of the lines, within which are extensive *Barracks*, the *Government House*, the *Port Admiral's House*, &c., as noticed at page 646. There are other fortifications, among which, without the walls, is a breastwork, with a ditch from 12 to 20 feet deep, excavated from the solid slate and limestone rock. About 1810, Government commenced the expensive work of remodelling and strengthening these fortifications, but, on being inspected by the Duke of Wellington, in 1816, he pronounced them to be useless as a means of defence, and they were consequently left in an unfinished state. In the lines are two *barrier gates*, one leading to Morice-Town, and the floating bridge which crosses the Tamar; and the other leading to Stoke. There are guard houses and draw-bridges at these gates, but the approach from Stonehouse, which is the principal thoroughfare, is without gates; being left unfinished when the works were relinquished, in 1816. The streets being all modern, are generally straight, spacious, and well-built. Fore street, St. Aubyn street, Duke street, and many other of the principal thoroughfares are lined with good houses and neat and well-stocked shops; and the footpaths being paved with limestone from the neighbouring quarries, the pedestrian literally walks on marble, which speedily becomes so much polished as to have a beautiful variegated appearance, when washed by heavy rain.

The town is well supplied with water, and lighted with gas, and was called *Plymouth Dock* till 1823, when the inhabitants sent a petition to George IV., praying that the name of the town might be changed to *Devonport*, or such other appellation as his Majesty might deem proper. In answer to this petition, the King directed that on and after the 1st of January, 1824, the town should be called Devonport, and on that day the inhabitants paraded the streets in triumphal procession, and proclaimed the new name in all public places. A general subscription was also entered into, for the purpose of erecting a COLUMN, commemorative of the event. This handsome column cost £2750, and stands near the Town-Hall, upon a rock, which rises 22 feet above the pavement, and is ascended by a flight of steps. Including the plinths and foundation rock, the entire elevation of the column is 125 feet. On the upper plinth, which is nine feet high, are panels for inscriptions; and within the shaft, which is fluted, and of the Grecian Doric order, is a spiral staircase, leading to a balcony on the summit of the capital, which is surrounded by elegant iron railing, and commands extensive views over the town, the harbours, and the adjacent country. The whole is constructed of granite of a very superior quality, and was intended to have been crowned by a colossal statue of George IV., which would be a grand finish to the structure. The town is much higher than Stonehouse and Plymouth, but descends to the shore of the broad and extensive harbour of Hamoaze, through which the waters of the river Tamar fall into Plymouth Sound. (See pages 643-'4.) Though generally considered clean and healthy, it suffered severely from cholera in 1849, as noticed at page 639. It is well supplied with water, in connexion with Stonehouse, Stoke, &c., by the *Water Works Company*, which was incorporated by Act of Parliament, in 1723. It had been previously attempted to obtain water from the Plymouth Leat, but this being refused, the Devonport Leat was formed, and may be occasionally seen in close companionship with that of Plymouth, as it pursues its winding course of 37 miles, from its source in the wild region of Dartmoor. The principal reservoir is at Higher Stoke, whence an abundant supply of water is sent in iron pipes to Devonport, Stonehouse, the Dockyard, Gun Wharf, &c. The *Devonport*

Gas Plant Leasing Co. have their works at Keyham, and lease them to the *Devonport Gas and Coke Company*, who now hold them at the yearly rent of £650, which yields an annual dividend of six per cent. to the owners of the works.   In the 21st of George III., an act was obtained for paving, cleansing, and watching the streets, and for removing nuisances, and regulating coaches, &c., in the town and suburbs.   This act gave place to another act, obtained in 1814, which vested the *paving, cleansing,* and *lighting ; the regulation of coaches, porters, &c. ;* and also the *maintenance of the poor* of the parish of Stoke Damerel, in a body of 150 *commissioners,* to be chosen from amongst the inhabitants.   The *Market Place* is in the heart of the town, and belongs to the lords of the manor, to whom it yields a considerable annual rent.   It is abundantly supplied with butter, poultry, flesh, fish, fruit, vegetables, &c., especially on the three market days—Tuesday, Thursday, and Saturday; but it is not a mart for either corn or cattle, though the Market Act, passed in 1835, has a clause for the establishment of a grain market.   The poultry and butter market is in an extensive loft over the shambles.   A pleasure *fair* is held in the town on Whit-Monday. The *Customs' and Inland Revenue* establishments here are branches of those at Plymouth.   (See pages 648-'9.)   The large *Bonding Warehouses* on the Quay at Mutton Cove were erected in 1846-7, by a company of merchants and traders, at the cost of about £1450.   There are excellent wharfs at Richmond walk, North corner, and Morice Town.   A *Coal Association* has large stores here, and vessels are in constant communication with London, Wales, &c.   The *United General Bread and Flour Company* has many members here, but its office is in Stonehouse.   There are in the town three banks, a large ironfoundry, several breweries and malting-houses, boat yards, roperies, &c.; but the chief scene of bustle is the great Naval Dockyard, as noticed at pages 644-'5.   The *Rowing Regatta,* in summer, is a source of great attraction, and a large number of finely built boats usually compete for the valuable prize cup, presented by her Majesty, as well as for the premium of £5, presented to the builder of the best rowing gig.   The *Royal Hotel* and the *London Hotel,* in Fore street, are large and commodious establishments; and the former has a spacious *Assembly Room,* in which balls, concerts, and exhibitions are frequently held.   Here are also several other large and well-conducted inns, and many respectable lodging-houses.   The POST-OFFICE is a chaste and handsome building, erected in 1849, from the designs of that eminent architect, G. Wightwick, Esq., to whose skill the three towns are indebted for the beauty and convenience of several other public edifices.   This Post Office belongs to a company of shareholders, and cost only about £1700, though it has an elegant semi-circular portico, or rotunda, after the Tivoli example of the Corinthian order, and forming a complete circle within.

The TOWN-HALL was erected in 1821-'2, at the cost of nearly £3000, raised by subscription, in shares, which have been nearly all paid off by a sinking fund.   It was designed by Mr. John Foulston, after the style of the Parthenon at Athens.   The portico exhibits four massive columns, of the Doric order; and on the entablature, over the entrance, has been placed a fine figure of Britannia.   In the recess is a flight of steps, leading to the hall, which is 75 feet long, 45 broad, and 31 in height; and is finished by a handsome cornice, and provided with suitable benches, &c., for the magistrates, all of which can be removed when the room is required for any large public meeting.   It is decorated with several fine portraits, including those of George I., II., and III. ; Queens Charlotte and Caroline, Wm IV., and Sir Edw. Codrington.   The building also contains the overseers' office, the council chamber, police station and prison, committee rooms, apart-

ments for the town-serjeant, &c. The Quarter and Petty Sessions for the borough are held here, and the Town-Council are about to erect a large new *Prison*, at the cost of about £11,000, with cells, &c., for 44 male offenders, 12 females, and 14 debtors. Prisoners from Stonehouse will also be sent to it by the magistrates of Roborough Division, who hold petty sessions here, and to whom Mr. A. B. Bone is clerk. As already noticed, the Municipal Borough of Devonport was incorporated by royal charter in 1837, and divided into six wards, and placed under the control of a *mayor*, 12 *aldermen*, and 36 *councillors*, with a recorder, town clerk, and other officers, of whom the following is the present list, together with the Borough Magistrates :—

MAYOR, Edward St. Aubyn, Esq. || RECORDER, John Greenwood, Esq.

BOROUGH MAGISTRATES : Edward St. Aubyn, John Beer, jun., Wm. Hodge, Wm. Hancock, Jonth. Ramsey, sen , Cornls. Tripe, G. F. Somerville, Edw. Abbott, Thos. Sanders, Timothy Carew, Geo. Glasson, Saml. Kerswill, and Jno. Williams, Esqrs.

ALDERMEN.

Edw. St Aubyn.	Uriah Row	Wm. Chapman.	James Willing.
Robert Rundle.	Matthew Scott.	Henry T. Smith.	J. W. W. Ryder.
John Beer, sen.	Thos. Husband.	John Beer, jun.	Peter Best.

COUNCILLORS.

Morice Ward.	John Symons.	*Clowance Ward.*	Frederick Row.
Thomas Rutter.	Samuel Oram.	James Halse.	Richard B. Oram.
W. Greenwood, jun.	Wm. Richards.	Joseph Arnold.	Samuel Brooking.
Thomas W. Ryder.		Thomas Rundle.	
Joseph C. Gill.	*St John's Ward.*	Henry V. Harris.	*Stoke Ward.*
Albert Smith.	Cornelius Tripe.	Saml. P. Jackson.	John Williams.
Geo. Reuben Bush.	Henry K Bamber.	Alex. Haldane.	Wm. Hole Evens.
St. Aubyn Ward.	Edward Abbott.	*Tamar Ward.*	Timothy Carew.
M. W. Jeffery, sen.	John Little.	Wm. O. Cox.	Edward W. Foster.
John C. Hancock.	John Weary.	Abm. Beard.	Wm. Hancock.
Thos. H. Hawker.	Robert Bridgeland.	Rd. E. Knowling.	T. W. Liscombe.

Town Clerk, Thomas Woollcombe, Esq.
Clerk of the Peace, George Henry Ellery Rundle, Esq.
Coroner and Clerk to the Magistrates, Allan Belfield Bone, Esq.
Treasurer, A. C. Bone || *Sergeant at-Mace*, James Day.
Police Superintendent, Wm. Brockington.

The *Municipal Borough* comprises only the Parish of Stoke Damerel, but the PARLIAMENTARY BOROUGH includes also the Parish of East Stonehouse, and is one of the new boroughs created by the Reform Act of 1832. The number of parliamentary *voters* is about 2000, and their present *representatives* are Sir Jno. Romilly and Hy. Tuffnell, Esq.

CHURCHES, &c.—The *Parish of Stoke Damerel* comprises about 1816 acres of land, mostly belonging to the devisees of the late Sir John St. Aubyn, and let on liberal building leases, as noticed at page 696. It had 23,747 inhabitants in 1801, and 33,820 in 1841, and comprises the town of Devonport, and the handsome and populous suburbs of LOWER and HIGHER STOKE, on the north-east, and that of MORICE TOWN on the north, near the extensive Government Steam Yard. (See page 646.) These suburbs are only separated from Devonport by the lines of fortifications, and the government ground in front; and they comprise many streets, rows, and terraces of neat houses and villas, as well as some large mansions, of more than ordinary architectural character. Higher Stoke occupies an elevated site, and both it and Lower Stoke have greatly increased in buildings and population during the last ten years. Many of the inhabitants in these pleasant adjoining suburbs are naval and military officers, on retired or half-pay; and others are retired merchants and tradesmen. Morice Town derived its name from the Morice family, who were formerly lords of the manor of Stoke, which at Domesday Survey belonged to the Damerels, and afterwards passed to the Courtenay, Wise, and Morice families. From the latter it passed to the St. Aubyns, its present owners. The PARISH CHURCH is at

Lower Stoke, near the Military Hospital, about three-quarters of a mile from Devonport. It is an ancient structure, which seems to have originally consisted only of one aisle, with a tower of handsome workmanship. The increase of population occasioned a second aisle to be erected in the early part of last century; and a third aisle was added about 1750. By these additions, what was at first the breadth has now become the length of the building. The interior is conveniently fitted up for a large congregation, and on the west side is a spacious gallery, furnished with an organ. On the walls are many neat monuments, and the churchyard is crowded with grave stones, &c., though it is very spacious, and was considerably enlarged about 30 years ago. The *rectory*, valued in K.B. at £18. 8s. 9d., is in the patronage of the Devisees of the late Sir John St. Aubyn, and incumbency of the Rev. W. J. St. Aubyn, who has a good residence. The tithes were commuted, in 1840, for £628 per annum. The advowson was granted by Charles II. to Sir Wm. Morice, from whom it passed to the St. Aubyns. St. MICHAEL'S CHAPEL OF EASE stands near the junction of Stoke and Morice Town, at Navy row, and is a handsome structure, in the lancet Gothic style, erected in 1843, at the cost of £4000, raised by subscription. The stone was given by Government. The interior is neatly fitted up with 1200 sittings, many of which are free. The curacy is in the patronage of the Rector, and incumbency of the Rev. R. Gardner, M.A. *St. James's in Morice Town* is a new district church, now building at the west end of Navy row. The first stone was laid July 25th, 1849, and the building will cost about £6000, of which £4000 has been contributed by the Lords of the Admiralty, in consideration of a great number of sittings being free for the use of the numerous workmen employed in the Government Steam Yard, &c. It will consist of a nave, two aisles, and a porch, with a handsome tower and spire on the south side; and will be in the decorated pointed style, from designs by James Piers St. Aubyn, Esq., the architect. The perpetual curacy was established by the Ecclesiastical Commissioners in 1846, and is in the patronage of the Crown and Bishop alternately, and in the incumbency of the Rev. W. B. Killpack, M.A. The following five churches are in Devonport, and the three last-named are district churches. St. AUBYN CHAPEL, in Chapel street, is a large and handsome building, which was erected under the powers of an act of Parliament, in 1771, at the cost of £7000, raised by subscription. It forms an oblong square, and contains three aisles, with galleries at the sides and west end. The entrance is beneath a well-designed portico, above which rises an octagonal spire. The interior is neatly fitted up, and most of the pews are private property. The benefice is a perpetual curacy, valued at £117, in the patronage of the Rector of Stoke Damerel, and incumbency of the Rev. S. Rundle, M.A. St. JOHN'S CHAPEL is a large fabric, in Duke street, and ranks as the second episcopal place of worship erected in Devonport. It was built under the authority of an act of Parliament, in 1779, at the cost of about £7700, raised by subscription. The tower, which is surmounted by a cupola on granite pillars, is heavy and disproportioned; but the neatness and elegance of the interior in a great measure compensate for these defects. It has about 1500 sittings, mostly private property. The ceiling, 90 feet long and 70 broad, is remarkable for its ingenious construction, being unsupported by a single pillar. The Rector of Stoke Damerel is patron of the perpetual curacy, which is now held by the Rev. James Lampen, M.A. *St. Paul's District Church* is now building in Morice square, by subscription and grants, and will be smaller than St. James', but in the same style. The first stone was laid July 25th, 1849, and the building will have sittings for about 400 adults and 320 children. The perpetual curacy is in the alter-

nate patronage of the Crown and Bishop, and the Rev. John Adams, M.A., was inducted as the first incumbent in 1846. *St. Mary's District Church,* now building by subscription and grants, in James street, will have about 800 sittings, and will be in the decorated pointed style, with a tower and spire, rising at the west end of the south aisle, to the height of 122 feet. The living is a perpetual curacy, in the patronage of the Crown and Bishop alternately, and now in the incumbency of the Rev. T. C. Childs, B.A. *St. Stephen's District* now occupies a licensed room in Clowance street, and is the fourth ecclesiastical district formed in the parish of Stoke Damerel in 1846, under the statute 6 and 7 Vic., cap. 37; and it is hoped that it will not be long without a church, since the pressing appeals which the Bishop and Clergy have lately made to the public in behalf of the " spiritual destitution of Devonport," have been so liberally answered in the other districts. St. Stephen's District has about 3000 inhabitants, half of whom are too poor to pay for church accommodation. The Crown and Bishop have the alternate patronage of the perpetual curacy, now enjoyed by the Rev. G. W. Proctor, M.A. There is a handsome *Chapel in the Dock Yard,* as noticed at pages 644-5. There are in Devonport and the rest of the parish of Stoke, seventeen DISSENTING CHAPELS, viz., four belonging to the *Wesleyans,* in Morice street, Monument street, Morice Town, and Higher Stoke ; two to *Independents,* in Princess street and Mount street; three to *Calvinists,* in Ker street, Granby street, and South street; two to *Baptists,* in Morice square and Pembroke street; the *Unitarian Chapel,* in Granby street; the *Moravian Chapel,* in James street; *Tabernacle Chapel,* in Gloucester street ; *Providence Chapel,* at Stoke ; the *Bible Christian Chapel,* in King street; and *Salem Chapel,* in Navy row. *Sunday Schools,* and *Bible, Tract, Missionary,* and *other Religious Institutions,* are supported by the congregations of the churches and chapels.

Devonport Mechanics' Institute was established in 1825, and had so prospered in 1843, that it erected a handsome building in Duke street, at the cost of about £1400 ; to which it added a larger building in 1849, at the cost of nearly £2500. The twin buildings are in the Italian style, and comprise a lecture hall which will hold 1000 persons ; a large subscription news room, a number of class rooms, a museum, and a library of more than 3000 volumes. The institution has about 800 members, and has weekly lectures during eight months of the year, and various evening classes. One of its late vice-presidents, *Mr. John Thomas Towson,* has lately rendered essential service to navigation by his " *Tables to facilitate the practice of Great Circle Sailing,*" published by the Admiralty in 1848; and by the means he afterwards devised of applying these Tables to the computation of azimuths. These valuable tables are now extensively used by most maritime nations, and the use of them has been the means of greatly shortening the voyages to Australia, New Zealand, &c. The *Public Library and News-room* occupy a handsome building in Ker street, erected in 1823, in the Egyptian style, at the cost of about £1500. The library comprises more than 4000 volumes of useful and valuable works ; and the news room is spacious and well supplied. The institution has a valuable mineralogical collection, presented by the late Sir John St. Aubyn, Bart. There is a news room at Mr. Colman's, in Fore street ; and there are in the town several circulating libraries. Three weekly *newspapers* are published here. The *Assembly Rooms* are at the Royal Hotel, and the *Theatre* is a large plain building in Cumberland street. The *Royal Clarence Sea Baths,* on the pleasant beach, near Richmond walk, were established many years ago by Mr. R. O. Backwell, but now belong to Mr. Applin. Hot, cold, shower, vapour and swimming baths, and also improved machines on the beautiful

beach, in front of Mount Edgcumbe, are always ready. There are in the town and suburbs several highly respectable and ably-conducted *Boarding and Day Schools*, one of which is the Classical and Mathematical school, formerly supported on the proprietary system, and now conducted by J. G. Jonas, B.A., Esq.

SCHOOLS AND CHARITIES :—The *National Schools* in St. John street were built in 1809, and are now attended by about 200 boys and 80 girls, the latter of whom are partly clothed. In various parts of the town and suburbs are several other public schools, supported by members of the established church ; and others supported by dissenters; and in Cornwall street are *Ragged and Evening Schools*. Devonport United Mathematical and Commercial School was established in 1830, by the artizans of the Dock Yard, and its pupils pay from 3d. to 7½d. each per week. The *Royal Naval and Military Free Schools*, for the education of the children of seamen and soldiers, are in King street, and are in three department for boys, girls, and infants. They are liberally supported by subscription, under the patronage of Her Majesty, who is also patroness of the *Royal British Female Orphan Asylum*, which now occupies a large building, lately erected for its use, at Stoke, at the cost of £3200. This excellent charity was established in 1839, and is supported by subscriptions and donations, for the instruction and maintenance of about 60 female orphan children of sailors, soldiers, or poor civilians. It receives and expends annually upwards of £1000, part of which is received for the board of children sent by the subscribers to the *Dock Yard Orphan Fund*, established in 1848. *Devonport and Stonehouse General Dispensary, and Institution for Diseases of the Eye and Ear*, was established in 1815, when a building was erected for its use in Chapel st., at the cost of £800, of which £100 was the gift of Ann Spearing. It is supported by subscriptions, donations, and the gratuitous services of two physicians and six surgeons. Here is a *Lying-in-Charity*, a *Benevolent Society*, a *Humane Institution*, and various other charities for relieving the distressed poor. In 1834, Mr. R. T. Spearman left £12,000 to be applied, after the death of certain parties, in founding an *Almshouse* for poor women above the age of 60, and members of the established church. Four poor widows of shipwrights have the dividends of £600 three per cent. consols, left by *J. Chambers*, in 1787. The poor parishioners have 10s. yearly from *Rawlin's Charity*, and also the dividends of £555 three per cent. consols, purchased with £500 left by *John Williams*, for a distribution of food and clothing at Christmas. In 1829 *Mr. T. Crapp* left £5000 to be vested in trust after, the death of certain persons, (some of whom are still living,) for the following uses, viz., the interest of £4000 to be divided yearly among six poor men and six poor women; the interest of £500 to be applied in aid of the Lancasterian School ; and the interest of the other £500 to be applied at the discretion of the trustees. The *Military Hospital*, at Stoke, is noticed at page 648.

The UNION SAVINGS' BANK was established in 1818, and now occupies a handsome building in Chapel street. It is under the patronage of the Earl of Mount Edgcumbe, and in November, 1849, had a surplus fund of £9345, and deposits amounting to £372,811, belonging to 11,601 depositors. It has also invested about £74,000 in the purchase of government life annuities. The *Royal Naval Savings' Bank* has about £40,700 belonging to 1048 depositors, 7 Charitable Societies, and 3 Friendly Societies. It is held in a large and elegant building in Ker street, belonging to the *Royal Naval Annuitant Society*, which was established in 1823, and has branches in Portsmouth, London, and Bath. Since its establishment this annuitant society has received £277,000, and has paid in annuities £118,740. Capt.

G. F. Somerville is the actuary. There is a *Savings' Bank in the Dock Yard,* of which Mr. R. Scott is the actuary; and at 39, St. Aubyn st., is a Branch of the *Western Provident Association,* (noticed at page 119,) of which Mr. W. R. D. Gilbert is secretary. Here are also two *Investment and Building Societies;* two *Lodges of Freemasons;* several *Friendly Societies,* &c.; and in Fore street is a *Temperance Hall,* erected in 1849.

The WORKHOUSE *for the parish of Stoke Damerel,* which includes Devonport, is under the control of the Commissioners of the local act of Parliament, as noticed at page 698. It is an old building, in the centre of the town, and has been enlarged at various periods; but being very inconvenient and too small for the present wants of the parish, it is about to give place to a commodious *New Workhouse,* now building on the Saltash road, nearly two miles from the town. This building will have room for 500 paupers; and attached to it will be a *Lunatic Asylum,* large enough for 35 inmates. There have been as many as 470 paupers crowded in the old workhouse. The expenditure of the parish for the maintenance of the poor was £10,358 in 1838, and £9841 in 1848. The *Commissioners* are numerous, as already stated, and Mr. John Beer, jun. is their *clerk*; Mr. James, and Mrs. Lancaster, are *governor and matron* of the Workhouse; James Babb, *assistant overseer;* James Lancaster, jun., *relieving officer;* and Miss A. C. Bone *treasurer.* Many of the inhabitants have recently petitioned to have the parish placed under the provisions of the New Poor Law. Mr. J. Elms is *superintendent registrar;* and W. Stonelake and J. T. Towson are registrars of marriages. The registrars of births and deaths are Messrs. J. T. Towson, P. Pascoe, J. Gedye, J. Bath, and W. M. Rickard.

DEVONPORT, STOKE DAMEREL, AND MORICE-TOWN DIRECTORY.

The POST-OFFICE occupies an elegant building, erected in 1849, at the junction of Fore street and Chapel street. Letters are received and despatched three times a day, *via* Plymouth; and money orders are granted and paid. Mr. J. W. Coffin is the postmaster. There are receiving boxes at Morice-Town and Stoke.

MISCELLANY of Gentry, Clergy, Partners in Firms, and others, not arranged in the Classification of Trades and Professions.

☞ *Those marked* s, *are in Stoke;* m, *Morice Town; and the others in Devonport, or where specified. Marked* * *are Master Mariners.*

Abel Mrs. 56 Mount st
Ackman Mr Rt.,Glostr. st.M
Adams Mrs.,St Michl's. tr.s
Adams Col. Jas. 3 St Jean D'Acre terrace, s
Adams Rev John,incbt. of St Paul's, 11 Tamar ter. s
Adams Mr John, 44 Fore st
Ady W. gent.,Tamar ter. s
Anderson Mrs.,Portland pl.s
Angeor Mr Sl. 4 Ross st. M
Angier Ezkl., Union ter. M
Applin Fdk.,Clarence Baths
Archer Mr T.W.,Chtte. tr.M
Ashton Mr T.,Homepark, s
Askett Rd. police inspr. 44 Pembroke street
Avery Mr J., Glcstr. st. M
Aylmer Capt.H.,Tamar tr.s
Babb Jas. asst. overseer, 16 Charlotte terrace, M
Babb Mr Jno., Glostr. st. M
Badcock Mrs., Nelson ter. s
Bailey Mr J., Homepark, s
Bailey T.S. acct.18 Chapel st
Baker Mr Chas. 17 Fort st

Baker Hy. Esq. *St Michael's Lodge,* s
Baker Mr Rd. 11 George st
Bamber Hy. K.R.N. 8 Ker st
Banks H. R.N. Portld. pl. s
Barnes Mrs.,Clarence pl. M
Barrett Mr C., Baker's pl
Bartlett Arthur, *fringe mfr.* 110, Fore street
Bartlett Mr T., Lambert ope
Bartlett Wm. Edwards,town surveyor, 15 Ker street
Bastard Mr W. South hill, s
Bateman Mrs., D'Acre tr. s
Bath Jno. tax colr. & regr. 11 Portland place, M
Bawden Mrs., Coalrckt. ope
Bayley Mr T. 30 Princess st
Beard Mr A. 65 Navy row,M
Beer Mrs.,Mt.Pleasant pl.s
Beer Mrs Eliz. 17 Mount st
Beer John,jun. solr. & clk.to comissrs. of poor, streets, &c. 30 St Aubyn street
Belcher Mrs.,Clarence pl. M
Benjamin Mr S., Sth. hill, s

Berryman Mrs.,Traflgr.pl.s
Billing Geo. Wilcox, solr. ; h 32 Ker street
Billing Mrs. 28 George st
Bird Mrs. 3 Ross st. M
Bishop Mr G.52 Clowance st
Bisshopp Col.Cecil,8 St Jean D'Acre terrace, s
Blackford Mrs.86 Navy rw.M
Blatchford Wm. & Son, *corn millers,* Swilly mills
Blight Mrs M.29 Portld .pl.M
Bolton Hy. artist, 88 Navy row, M
Bone Mrs. 33 Ker street
Bone Mrs. 8 St Aubyn st
Bond Sarah, *soap boiler,* 28 Marlborough street
Boon Mr John, 26 John st
Bowden Mr Ts. Glostr. st.M
Bowden Mr John, Sth. hill buildings, s
Bowey Mrs., Trafalgar pl. s
Bowyer W. *copper nail mkr.* Broad backway
Braddon Mr W.,Trafalgar pl

Brain Mr Geo., Navy row, M
Bray Mr J., Wellington st. s
Brent Mr J., Union ter. M
Bridgeland Mr R 45 Geo. st
Briggs Rev. J. M. A. Dockyd. chaplain, 5 Tamar ter. s
Brock Mrs E., Hompark, s
Brockington Wm. police supt. 36 Clowance street
Brooking Mr S., Portld. pl. M
Brown Mr J. 16 Wellington st
Brown J. clerk, 9 George st
Brown Mrs., St Michl.'s ter. s
Brown Mr S. 12 Chtte. st. M
Brown W. R.N. 10 Napier st
Brownrigg Lieut. Marcus F R.N. 9 Napier street, s
Bryant Hy. police inspr. 41 Monument street
Buchan J. agent, Somerset pl
Buckthought Ts. inspr. of market, 3 James street
Budge Mrs., Portland pl. s
Budge Mrs. 34 Princess st
Bullen Rt. Hy. R.N. Monument street
Burdwood Jno. clk. 7 South hill buildings, s
Burley Mrs L., Brunswick Cottages, s
Burnett Mr T., Clarence ldg
Byde Rev John, rector of Edworth, 5 Homepark Ctgs. s
Byerlee Mr Geo. F. 32 Portland place, M
Cardell Parminter, draper; h Pennycomequick
Carew Mr T. 18 Stoke ter
Carlyon Mr J. 137 Navy row
*Carne Rd. 9 Stopford pl. s
Chaff Mrs E. 50 Chapel st
Channon Mr G., 56 George st
Chard Capt. Fras. R.N. 16 Baker's place
Chasman Mrs J., Homepk. s
Chidley Mr G., Stopfd. pl
Childs Major, Paradise row
Childs Rev Thos. Cave, B.A. incbt. of St Mary's, 58 James street
Christopher Mr D. 52 Geo. st
Christophers Rev S. W. (Wes) 4 Clarence place, M
Churchward Sml. clerk, 16 Gloucester st. M. & Mr W. 10 Stopford place, s
Clarke P. C. bank manager, 38 Fore street
Clark W. mert. 40 James st
Clifton Wm. Esq. 13 Penlee crescent, s
Clouter Mr Jno., Morice sq
Cobeldick Mr R., Chatte. st
Collier Capt. Edwd. R.N. 5 Penlee crescent, s
Collins Mr Rt. Hy. 11 Higher Portland place, s
Collings Misses, 20 Chtte. tr
Condy Mr Rd., Trafalgar pl
Cook Geo. police inspector, James street

Coombe Edw. bed warehouse, 25 James street, ope
Coombe Jph. feather cleaner, 78 George street
Coombs Jas. bank manager, 10 Brunswick terrace
Coram Mrs., Brunswk. Ctgs
Coram Lieut., Portland ter
Cornish Mr Jas., Trafalgar pl
Couch Capt. 3 Homepark bgs
Couch Isaac, excise, John st
Courtis Mrs C. J. 59 Mount st.; & Mr S. 47 Clowance st
Cox Mr G., Wellington st
Cox Wm. R.N. 121 Navy row
Crabb Mr Jas., Clowance st
Cradick Mrs 45 Chapel st
Cragg Capt. John B. R.N. 6 Higher Portland place, s
Crapp Miss A. 18 George st
Crealock Wm. Stapley, clk. 15 Sth. hill buildings, s
Creed Mr Jas. 43 Ker st
Creyke Mrs., Albemarle vils
Crocker Mr Jno., Glostr. st
Crosby John, naval instctr. 25 Clowance street
Crossing Misses, Church st. s
Cuddeford Mr R. Union pl. M
Cudlip Mr. Jas. 35, & Mr Jph. 73 Gloucester st. M
Cumming Mr Ts. 2 York pl.; & Mrs A. 5 Windsor ter. s
Curgenven Mrs E. 27 Geo. st
Curry Admiral R. 2 Belmont place, s
Darling Mr Wm. 21 Duke st
Darton Thos. police insptr. 4 Cannon st.; & Mrs M. 21 Granby street
Davey H. R.N. Trafalgar pl. s
Davey Mr W. 4 Clowance st
Davis Mr J. 54 Gloucester st
Davis Ts. 1 Trafalgar pl. s
Dawe Jas. actuary, Savings' Bank, Chapel street
Day James, sergt.-at-mace, Town-Hall
Deagon Mr E., Windsor ter
Dean Mr J. 62 Glostr. st. M
Dent Mr Douglas, 5 St Michael's terrace, s
Deseret Mrs., Homepk. bldgs
Dickerson Mr John, 2 Portland terrace, s
Dingly Mr Wm., Traflgr. pl
Dodridge Mr W., Richmd. wk
Doidge Mr Geo. Jas. 9, and Mr Thos. 34 Portland pl. M
Dominy Mr Geo. H. 14 Morice sq. and Geo. 20 Navy row
Domville Mr Henry J. 9 Homepark buildings, s
Dorrington Mr Fras. 62 Geo. st
Drake Mr J., Waterloo st. s
Driscoll Mr P. 95 Navy row
Dunning Mr Richd. 8 Albemarle Villas, s
Dymond Mr Geo. J. 41 Geo. st
Eager John, clk. Glostr. st
Earle Mrs Jane, 50 Duke st
Easterbrook Mr J., Navy row

Easterbrook Rev R. (Calvinist,) South street
Easto Capt. Richmond, R.N. 16 South hill bldgs. s
Eaton R. storekpr. Gun Whrf
Edey Jph. Esq. Swilly Lodge
Edgcumbe Mr Elijah, 51 Gloucester street, M
Edge Mrs. 2 Somerset pl. s
Eliwell Mrs. 10 St Aubyn st
Ellery Miss Eliz. 51 Geo. st
Elliott Edw. farmer, Keyham Barton
Ellis Chas. store keeper, 9 Brunswick terrace, s
Ellis Mr Rt., Paradise row
Elwes Mr Wm., Wellngtn. st
Evans Mrs Eliz., Stoke ter
Evens Wm. R.N. 8 Brunswick terrace
Faber Wm. Esq., Penlee cres
Facey Mr John, 45 Navy row
Faunter John, shirt manfr. 23 James street
Flaxman John, draughtsman, 4 Mary place, s
Flower Rev W. B., B.A. curate of Stoke, Paradise row
Foster John, R.N. Traflgr. pl
Foster W. Edw. Esq. Outland
Fox Benj. mert. 5 Stoke ter
Fox Chas. Jas., Brunswk. ter
Francoe Dnl. lastmkr. Boot ln
Franklyn Mrs Eliza, 6 Brunswk. Ctgs. and Mrs M. 1 Windsor terrace. s
French Rev R. W. (Calvinist,) Ker street
Frost Edwin, tract, &c. depôt, 54 Duke street
Fry Mr Saml. 9 Stoke ter. s
Fry Mrs Sar. 1 Clowance st
Furneaux Mr Hy. 35 John st
Furneaux Jas. Esq. & Capt. John, R.N. Swilly House
Furze Mr John, 8 Clarence pl
Gardner Rev Richd., M.A. incumbt. of St Michael's, Navy row, M
Gaul John, billiards, Ker st
Gay Mrs J. 57 George st
Gedie John, clk. 12 James st
Genower Mr Chs., Napier st
Gilbard Mrs. 8 Stoke ter
Gilbert Mr Rt. 66 George st
Gilbert W. R. D. sec. to Western Provident Assn. 39 St Aubyn street
Gill Capt. R.N. 3 St Aubyn st
Gillies Mrs Eliz. 17 Geo. st
Glanville Mrs. 1 York pl. s
Glencross Mr James, Penn Tamar Cotg; & Mr Josiah, 34 Ker street
Gloyn Mr Wm. 38 Glostr. st
Goddard Mr W. 2 Clowance st
Good John, lib. 31 Lambert st
Goodall Major Geo. 5 St Jean D'Acre terrace, s
Goodall W. Esq., Penlee cres
Gormully Miss, 12 Stoke ter
Goss Mr Thos., Trafalgar pl

Gowings Mr John, Stoke ter
Graham Major, Stopford pl
Grant Mrs., Portland ter. s
GrantCapt.R.N.2Park pl. s
Gray Mr Dd. 68 Gloster. st
Greaves Mrs Chtte.17 South
hill buildings, s
Greenslade Jph., French po-
lisher, 2 Fore street
GregoryMrG.,Canterburyst
Grills Mr. 7 Stopford pl. s
Grose Mr Wm. 3 Traflgr. pl
GuardWm.clk,Garden st.M
Hall Mr Geo. 73 James st
HallCapt.19Sth.hill bldgs.s
Halse Jas. R.N. 35 Geo. st
HamptonMrW.H.,21Johnst
Hancock MrW.,Charlotte st
Hancock MrW.,Somerset pl
Hannaford Mr W., Mill st
Harris Miss, Coalrckt. ope
Harris MrT. S., Gloster. st
Harry Miss, Paradise row
HarveyMr Sdny.,Traflgr.pl
Hay Lord John, C.B. *Capt.
Superintdt. of Dockyard*
Hayne Mr W., Glostr. st. M
HaywardMrT.,Glostr.st. M
Heard Mr John, 2 *Rosehill*
Heavyside RevRobt.curate,
George street
Hedley Thos. A. engineer,
Gas Works, *Keyham*
Hellyer Mrs. 19 John st
Henderson James, Dockyd
HennaMrWm.5Clowancest
Henry Mrs., Somerset pl. s
HensleyMrs.,Brunswk.tr.s
Herbert Rev T. W. assist.
curate, Tamar ter. s
HeyshamMrs.,Homepk.cts
Hicks Misses, 81 Navy row
Hicks Edw. agent to Water
Co. 44 George street
Hicks MrJno.27Clarence pl
Hicks Mr Jph.1 Stopford pl
Hill Mr Jas., Milehouse rd
Hillas Mr Sml.,Union pl. M
Hillyer Mr J. P.18Garden st
Hillyer Capt., Somerset pl
Hoar Eliz. pipe maker, 94
Pembroke street
Hobling MrHy.20 Stoke ter
Hobson Mrs., Penlee Cotgs
Hock Mr E.,Homepk. bldgs
Hodge Wm. Chappel, Esq.
banker, 37 Chapel st
Hodson Alderson, gent. 4
Penlee crescent, s
Holdermess Mrs. 13 Stoke ter
•HoltonRd.,Gloucester st. M
Honey Mr John, Glostr. st
Hoare Major, Trafalgar pl. s
Horton Rev Thos. (Bapt.) 4
Stoke terrace
Horwell Mr Thos. Richard,
York place, s
Hosking Mr. Wellington -st
Hughes Mr Chas. 14 St
Jean D'Acre terrace, s
Hughes J. J. vety. surgeon,
17 Market street

Hunt MrWm. 69 Navy row
HusbandMrH.3 Milne pl.M
Hutchins Mr Jno. N., Port-
land place
Hutchison Rev Æneas B.
curate, Clarence lodge, M
Isbell Rev G. Home park, s
Jackman Mr Wm. 11 St
Jean D'Acre terrace, s
Jackson MrEdw.8Morice st
Jago Mr Rt. Charlotte ter
James Mr John, Princess st
Jeffery MosesWm. chemist,
31 Ker street
JefferyMrWm. Portland ter
JenkinMrS.*Pennycomequick*
Jennett Fras. Fdk. clerk, 4
Windsor terrace, s
Jewell MrMarkW.,56 Clow-
ance street
Johns Mr John, 19 Glostr. st
Johns Mrs Sus., Princess st
Joll Mrs Ann, 19 Fort st
Jones Mrs., Dispensary
Joll Jas., lime burner, bone
crusher, and cement mfr.
Tamar whf; h Union pl
Jones Mrs Eliz. 3 Portld. pl
Jones Capt. 4 Stopford pl. s
Joues Lieut. Waterloo st. s
Jorey Mrs. 61 George st
Jorey Mr John, Rosehill, s
Keene Mr Hrto., Ross st M
KellockJno. R.N.14 Homepk
KendallMrSl.48Clowance st
Kennedy Adw. R.N Saltash
road, & Capt. Wm. H. 13
Tamar terrace, s
Kent MrIsc.69 Navy row, M
Kett John, contr. Princess st
Killpack Rev Wm. B. M.A.
incbt. of St James', 7
Tamar terrace, s
Kingdon Mr Jno. Coalrkt. op
Kitto Mr Saml. 9 Quarry st
Knapman Mrs. 25 Geo. st
Knight Mr Sl., Vine cotg. s
Knight Mr Wm. 46 Navy
row, M
Lacy Mr Jno. Ordnance st
Laddick Mrs Susanna, 32
Cannon street
Lampen Mr John, James st
Lampen Rev John, M.A.
incbt. of St John's, and
surrogate, Homepark, s
Lancaster Jas. & Mrs. gov.
and matron of *Workhouse*
Lancaster Jas. jun. relvg.
officer, 57 James street
Lawrence General Elias,
C.B. 10 Tamar terrace, s
Laws R. sectry. Dockyard
Lawson Mr Gilbt. Garden st
Lee Mr Jas. 103 Navy row
Lidstone Mr Jno. 3 Glostr.st
Little Miss Eliza, 13 St
Jean D'Acre terrace, s
Litle John, 135 Navy row
Little Mrs My. 23 Ker st
Little Pp. Moysey, solr. 2
St Michael's terrace, s

Little Wm. Jph. solr. 4 St
Michael's terrace, s
Llewellyn John, naval inspr
Dockyard ; h 14 Traflgr. pl
Loring Mr Wm. Alexander,
Navy row
LoryLieut.Wm.16Tamar ter
Loughborough Rev Ralph
L. curate, 13 Brunswick
terrace, s
Lowe A. landing surveyor,
Customs
Lowe George, gent. 1 St
Michael's ter; and Mrs.
35 Clowance street
Luck Sarah, canvass dlr.
Francis alley
Luke Mrs. 30 Chapel st
Luke Mr John, Charlotte st
Lunn Mr Wm. 21 South
hill, s
Luxmore Mr Wm. 21 Prin-
cess street
Mactyre Mr Alx., Stopfd. pl
Maddick Mrs Eliz. Milne pl
Maingay Mrs. Albermarle
villas
Maitland Capt. Sir Thos.,
R.N. 38 George street
Manicom Mr John, 41 Ker st
Martin Jno., R.N.Portld. ter
Massengbird Chas., Esq. 1
Penlee crescent, s
MatthewsMr.3Brunswk.ter
May Miss, 19 Stoke terrrce
May Mr Jno., Waterloo st ;
& John, 72 Gloucester st.M
May Mr John Brett, 6
Albermarle villas, s
May John R. clk. 24 South
hill bldgs. and John, 32
Chapel street
May Mrs My. 7 Portland
place, & Mr S. 1 Garden
street, M
May Rd. acct. Fellow's pl
May MrWm. 11 Clarence pl
Mayning Mr James, 20
Garden street
McKer MrSml.Prospect row
McKenzie Mrs.18Baker's pl
McQueen Capt.18Tamar ter
Mead Mr Thos. 16 Fort st
Medder Mr Samuel C.,
Pennycomequick
Melrose Mr Jas.Wellgtn. st
Mends Admiral Wm. 9 St
Jean D'Acre terrace, s
Milford Mr Jas. 13 South st
Millar Mr Chas., Stoke ter
Miller Mrs. 23 Navy row
Miller Mr Chas. Navy row
MillroyMr Alex.,Pennycmk
MillsEdw.B.Esq.3Penlee cr
Millward Mr A.17Chapel st
Milton Mrs. 18 Sth. hill blgs
Milton Mr Thos., Traflgr. pl
Mogg Mr Thos R.,Union ter
Moncrieff Miss,Portlnd.blgs
MooneRt.E. solr.Pennycmk
Moore Lieut.Wm. Hy. R.N.
Penn Tamar cottage

Morcombe Mrs.74 Navy row
Morell John, clk. 85 Jas. st
Moses Mr Geo., Prtland pl
Munton Mrs. 70 Navy row
Neil Mr Wm. 21 Charlotte st
Nevile Capt. 1 Somerset pl
Newton MrGeo.,Portland pl
Nichols Lieut. J., Home-
park cottages
Nicholas Mr J., Charlotte st
Nooth Lieut. Col. Henry, 3
Albermarle villas, s
Norman Miss, 74 James st
Norman Alfred, architect,
&c., 24 St Aubyn street
Northam Elias, clk. York pl
O'Driscoll Mr Wm.Navy row
O'Neil Mr., Brunsk. cotgs. s
Oram Mr John,3 Portland pl
Oram Mr Saml.27 Market st
Ormsby Mrs., Trafalgar pl
Ovenden Rd. scale beam
mkr. 40 Marlborough st
Paddon Capt. Silas, R.N. 1
Brunswick terrace, s
Palmer Mr John, Stoke ter
Paramore Sl.clk.93Navy row
Parker Capt. Hy. Dickson,
R.N. 4 Hr. Portland pl. s
Parker P.P. naval accompt.
49 George street
Parramore Mr Dd.43 Geo.st
*Parry John, 12 Fort street
Patey Chas. R.N. 1 St Jean
D'Acre terrace, s
Patrick Miss, 1 Morice st
Pawley Mr Geo. 11South hl
Peacock Mrs L. 3 Park pl.s
Peake Hy.F.R.N.8 Penlee cr
Peake Mrs J. 78 Navy row
Pearce Mr Rd., Charlotte st
Pearce Mr Wm. 52 Glostr.st
Pearse Mr Jno. Windsor ter
Pearse Rd. mert. Penny-
comequick, & John, news
agent, Marlborough st
Penfold J. L. clk. Homepk
Perring Mrs Jane, 18Fort st
Perry Mr Rd. 38 John st
Pett Mr Rd. 10 Baker's pl
Phillpot Mrs., Trafalgar pl
Philp Miss 57 Mount st ; &
Mr Thos. 20 Sth. hill blgs
Pickard Lieut. Somerset pl
Pike Mrs Ann, 56 Navy rw
Pincombe Abm. naturalist,
24 Market street
Pinny Rev J. (Bib. Chistn.)
King street
Pinsent Mr Rd. S. 40 St
Aubyn street
Ponton Mr Sl.136Navy row
Poole Mrs , Paradise row, s
Pope Chas. R.N 22 Ker st
Pope Mr Wm. 42 Glostr. st
Portugal Mr. 3 Somerset pl
Pote Mr Sampson,13 Fort st
Pote Mr John, 45 Garden st
Potts Mrs.4 Brunswick ter.s
Potts Lieut., Wellington st
Pridham Lieut., Belmont pl

Proctor Rev Geo. Wm. M.A.
incbt. of St. Stephen's,10
George street
Proctor Geo. R.N. 10 Geo. st
Purdon Simon, gent. 4
Tamar terrace, s
Purner Mrs., Trafalgar pl
PyeWm. Esq. 15 Tamar ter
Pyer Rev John, (Indpt.) 19
Trafalgar place
Radford MrI.C.,Dockwall st
Radford Mr Wm.4 Napier st
Radmore Mrs J.39Navy row
Rae Rt. H. Dockyard school;
house Keppel place
Ramsay Jonathan, gent. 9
Penlee crescent, s
Randall Mrs., Charlotte ter
Ratcliffe Mr John, 72Geo.st
Raven Mrs. 15 Clowance st
Reece MrJohn,4 Somerset pl
Reeve Mrs. 51 Monument st
Remington Capt.41 Duke st
Rendle Mr Rt. Coalrkt. ope
Rendle MrThos. Clarence st
Rennie Alex. reporter, 19
Cannon street
Renolds MrJph.48Navy row
Restarick Mr Jas.,Chtte. ter
Restarick James and Wm.
gents. 85 James street
Restarick Mrs., Portland pl
Richards Capt. Harry L.,
R.N. 3 Stopford pl. s
Richardson Major, 45 Ker st
Rickard Mr Jas., Morice sq
Rogers Rev C. (Baptist,)
Pembroke street
Rogers Mr Wm. 17 Portld. pl
Rolston Mrs. 24 Barrack st
Ross Capt. Roht. 6 George st
Ross Stpn. clerk,Portland pl
Row MrJ.H.,Portland bldgs
Row Uriah,mert.4 Morice sq
Row Mr Wm. 14 Stoke ter
Row Mrs. 41 Chapel st
Rowland Rev Thomas, (Cal-
vinist,) Granby street
Rowlings Mrs Susanna, 1
Higher Portland pl. s
Rudd Mrs.13 Homepk.bldgs
Rundle George H. solicitor,
7 Napier place
Rundle Richd. colr. of water
rent, 6 South street
RundleRevSaml.M.A.incbt.
ofStAubynChap.6Napierst
Rundle Thos. spirit mercht.
Richmond walk
Ryder A. furrier, Chapel st
Sampson Mr Wm. 63 Geo.st
Sanders MrJas.,Charlotte st
Sanders Mrs.,Portland bldgs
Sanders Capt. 84 Navy row
SargentGeo.R.N.Clarence pl
Sawdye Mr Edw.7 Stoke ter
Scott Matthew, R.N. 24 Cla-
rence place, M
Scott Mr Rd., Brunswick ter
Scott Robert, Esq. Outland
ShanksThs.R.N.Somerset pl

Shapcote Lieut.Thos. R.N. 4
St Jean D'Acre ter. s
Sharp James, surveyor, 14
Waterloo street
Shatton Lieut.Wm. R A. 10
South hill buildings, s
Shepheard Wm. H.B.clerk,
2 Upper Somerset pl. s
Short John, hide merchant,
Marlborough street
ShortMrW. 27Waterloo st.s
Shuttleworth Capt. A. A. 3
Portland terrace, s
Simpson Mrs., Paradise row
SimpsonMrEdwin,15Geo.st
Slade Mr Hy.,Sth.hill bldgs
Smart Richard, seedsman,
Princess street
Smith Mrs., Portland pl
Smith Lieut., Donegal pl
SmithMrs.,Albemarle villas
Smith Rev J. (Moravian,)
James street
Smith Rev J. 19 StAubyn st
Smith Rev Richard C. 68 St
Aubyn street
SmithwickMrRt.,Tamar ter
Snell Lieut. John C. R.N. 6
St Jean D'Acre ter. s
Snodgrass Rt.trvlr.Homepk
Snowden Mrs. 15 Chapel st
Solfleet John Charles,R.N.31
Portland place
Somerville Capt. Geo. Field,
R.N. 7 Homepark cotgs. s
Sowden MrS.53 Clowance st
Sparrow Mrs. 13 St Jean
D'Acre terrace, s
SpenceChas.clk.Trafalgr.pl
Spencer Rev Wm. (Indept.)
10 Paradise row, s
Spicer Mr Henry, 27 John st
Spiers Mrs. 48 Pembroke st
Spiller Mr Wm., Portland pl
Spiller Mr Wm. 1 Stoke ter
Spratt Capt. 21 Trafalgar pl
SpryMrWm.8Coalrackt. ope
Spurling Miss, 12 South hill
Stanford MrLuke,Navy row
StapleyCapt.,Brnswk.ctgs.s
Stapley MrW.12Brnswk.ter
St. Aubyn Edward, Esq.,
Nelson terrace
St. Aubyn Rev Wm. John,
M.A.rector ofStoke,Rectory
Stehelin Capt., Trafalgar pl
Stevenson Mr John D. 17
John street
Stewart Capt., Somerset pl
Stokes Mrs E. 1 Napier st
Stokes MrsL.,StMichael's tr
Stone Mr Edw. 53 George st
Stone Mrs. 71 Navy row, M
Strong Lieut., Somerset pl
Swain Thos. R.N. Baker's pl
Sweet Mrs. 15 Baker's pl
Sweet Mr Rt. 71 James st
Sykes Mr Wm. 4 Pym st.M
Symons MrJohn,Homepark
Symons J.E. sweep,Wm.st
Szyrma Col. L. 24 Ker st
Tayer Mrs., Tamar ter

TaylorMrWm.,Coalrckt.ope
Temple Mrs. 1 Park pl. s
ThaneJas.,R.N.Fellow's pl.s
Thomas Mrs. 23 Ross st. M
ThomasMrJohn,47Glostr.st
Thorn Mr G.,Hr Portland pl
Tissat Mrs. 6 Brunswick ter
Tizard Mr Pp. 24 Morice sq
Toms Mr John, 58 Mount st
Townsend MrA.,Wellgtn.st
TownsendRd.Esq.,Tamar tr
Townsend Mr Thomas,Wellington place
Townshend MrThomas,Clarence place
Towson Mr John Gay, and J.T. 12 Trafalgar place, s
Tozer Mr C., Clarence pl. M
*Tozer Wm. 37 Clowance st
TrannickMrRd.,Chrltte.ter
Trant Mr A. 3 Chapel st
Treleven MrJ.53 Princess st
TremearMrW.102Navy row
Trickry MrS.7 Paradise row
Trounsell Mrs., Trafalgar pl
Truscott MrGeo.24 Chtte.ter
TruscottMrJohn,21Navy rw
Truscott Mr Rd.15 Chtte.ter
TruscottMrWm.13 Chtte.ter
Tucker Mr Hy. 7 Morice sq

Tuson Miss, 74 James st
Usherwood Rt.tvlr.Napier st
Vallence Mr Wm., Coalracket ope
Veale MissM.A.,Trafalgr.pl
Veitch Miss My.6South hill
VigorWm.gent.11Penlee crs
Vivian John, crier, Ker st
WakehamMrA.55Clownc.st
Walker Mr John,Princess st
Walker Wm. R.N. 2 St Jean D'Acre terrace, s
Walters MrSml.29 Glostr.st
Warren Mrs. 11 South hill
Warren James Low,R.A.surgeon, 1 Albemarle villa, s
Warren Mrs L.37Portld.pl.s
Warton MrG.S.22 Morice sq
Watts MrMats.,Brunswk.tr
Watson Mrs. 3 Church.st.s
WaymouthMrJ.,Waterloost
Webber Mrs M.22 George st
Wellington Mrs M., South hill buildings, s
Wharton Mr.33 St Aubyn st
White MrFras.43 Glostr.st
White Mr Geo. 32 Garden st
White MrJohn, 60 Mount st
White Miss, 36 St Aubyn st
Wilcocks JamesB.solicitor & emigration agt.82Navyrw

Williams Mrs. 3 Belmont pl
Williams Edw.R.N.Milne pl
Williams Mrs Eliz., Fort st
Williams Miss, 4 Park pl
Williams MrHto.,Navy row
Williams Mr John, 7 Penlee crescent, s
Williams Mrs.13Portland pl
Williams Cpt. Montgomery, 19 Tamar terrace, s
Williams Lieut. Richard N. R N. 4 Somerset pl. s
WilliamsMrWm.,Princss.st
Willing John, clerk to Gas Co. 58 St Aubyn street
Wills Lieut. 6 Milne place
Wilson Mrs Car. 8 Napier st
Winchester Mr Wm. 12 St Jean D'Acre terrace, s
Wood Mr Ebenz., Morice sq
Woods Rev J.C.(Unitarian,) Granby street
Woollcombe Thomas, solr; h Ker street
Wymond MrJno.6 Clarnc.pl
Yelland MrEdw. 5 George st
Younge Rev Henry, (Wes.) 22 Morice street
Younge Wm. R.N. 9 Fellows' place

CLASSIFICATION of TRADES & PROFESSIONS

In Devonport, Stoke Damerel, and Moirce Town.

ACADEMIES.
(1 take Boarders.)
1 Aikenhead Rchl. & Eliza, 8 Morice square
1 Avent (My.) and Gibson (Ann, 54 Chapel st
1 Barrett Chtte. and Jane, 5 Stopford place, s
Beadle Mrs. 15 Ross st. M
1 Borlase Emily, 3 Mary pl
1 Braund Eliz. K. 46 Charlotte street, M
1 Bruce A. & L. 65 Geo. st
Burnett M & C., Cumbld.st
1 Classical & Mathl. School, 11 Tamar ter. s; John G. Jonas, B.A. & E.W. Jonas
1 Cole Belina, 49 George st
Cole Jas. 5 Ross st. M
1 Coles Rt. Wm. 26 Trafalgar place, s
Collins Betsy, James st
Cossentine W., Morice sq
1 Creft My. and Isabella, 3 Tamar terrace, s
Davie John, 43 Granby st
Devonport United Mathl. and Coml. School, J. H. and Mrs Lemon, John st
1 Elwin M.A. 58 Navy row
Ford Misses, 16 King st
1 Gabriel Sarah, 35 Ker st
Gilbert W. Rt., Union ter.M
1 Hussey Jane, 21 Chapel st

1 Jonas Jno. St. Aubyn st
Kallansee A., Princess st
Kemp Hy. 9 Milne pl. M
King Jesse, 7 Milne pl. M
Marles H. & L H ,Morice sq
1MathewsM.H.85 Navy rw
May Athalia, 32 Duke st
Moor My. 11 Union place
Morris M. 6 Homepark cots
National, J. Underhill, John st. & Miss Toney, Duke st
Ragged School, Cornwall st
Roberts —, 37 St. Aubyn st
Royal Naval and Military, King st; Mr Good, Miss Hackwell, & Mrs Smith
Thomas Hy. 36 John st
Walker Eliz. 2 Chtte. ter. M
Wise John H. 10 Mount st
Yelland Edwin, John st

AGENTS. (NAVY)
Levi Phineas,15 Catherine st
Oliver Rt. Moon,36Chapel st
Smart Herbert James, 5 Portland buildings

ATTORNEYS.
(1 Masters ex. in Chancery.)
1Beer & Rundle,52Chapel st
1 Berryman Wm. Rd. 58 St. Aubyn st; h 6 Tamar ter.s
1 Bone Allen Belfield, 26 Barrack street; h 11 St. Michael's terrace
1ChapmanW.60St.Aubyn st

Elms Jph. (and supt. regr.) 69 St. Aubyn street
1 Foot Josiah, Chapel gn; h 10 Penlee Crescent, s
Gard John Methrell, (conveyancer,) 17 St.Aubyn st
1 Gard Edw. Oram, 17 St. Aubyn st;hWoodld.villa,s
1 Gilbard Js. (stamp office,) St. Aubyn street
Gill H.Husband,4Chapel st
1Hawker Ts. 50St.Aubyn st
1 Jeffery Jno. W. 42 Marlborough street
1 Little and Woollcombe, 26 Ker street
1 Little and Billing, 52 St. Aubyn street
Oram Richd. Bennett, (conveyancer,)23 St. Aubyn st
Penberthy H. 49 Barrack st
Ramsey Bj. May, Cumberland ope ; h 23 South hill
Shapland Wm. 14 Barrack st; h 3 Trafalgar pl. s
1 Smith Hy. Trefusis and Albert, 12 Morice sq; h 8 Tamar terrace, s
Sole Edwd. 67 Duke st; h 23 George street
1 Tillman Wm. Treby, 28 Market street

AUCTIONEERS.
vent Robt., St. Aubyn st

Ayres Jno. 10 Cumberld. st
Blake —, 18 Catherine st
Elms Jph. 69 St. Aubyn st
Hainsselin D. H. 21 Fore st
Wood Chas. 3 Catherine st.
  and 5 Stafford hill
Wood Wm. 55 Fore st
Yeo John, 51 St. Aubyn st

BAKERS.
Adams Hy. 20 King st
Almond W. H. jun. Pond st
Angear Saml. 2 Chapel st
Bate Robt. 21 John st. M
Bate John, 25 Market st
Bates Thos. 95 Pembroke st
Berry Hy. 46 Gloucester st
Bickley John, 24 Navy row
Blackwell Sml. L., Duke st
Butcher John, 17 James st
Chaff Thos., Monument st
Chowne Wm., Pembroke st
Coleman John, 33 James st
Couch Jph. B. 17 Granby st
Davis Wm. 32 Pembroke st
Dinnis John, 119 Fore st
Dodridge Wm., Catherine st
Drew My. 26 Cumberland st
Edgcumbe Wm. 32 King st
Ellis Jph. 47 Queen st
Eyres John, Cumberland st
Gartrell Saml. 53 Navy row
Gover John, 31 Tavistock st
Grant John, 30 Cumberld. st
Hancock Joshua, 23 Wm. st
Harvey Jno. 20 Church st.s
Hawkings Js., Tavistk.st.s
Hawkings Ts., Canterby.st
Heals John, 1 John st
Hicks Ann, 23 Duke st
Hifley John, 84 Pembrk. st
Hoar James, Cornwall st
Hooper Jane, 17 Pembrk. st
Jackman S. P., Clowance st
James Peter, Granby st
Johns John, 25 Marlboro' st
Land Jas. 49 Tavistock st
Millington Ts. 36 Queen st
Mugford Jas. 12 Fore st
Northey Jno. 16 Chltte. row
Oliver Thos. 21 Wm. st. M
Paine Geo. 1 John st. M
Pawley Wm. 108 Pembrk. st
Pearn Jas. 1 Portland pl. M
Philp Peter, 5 Pembroke st
Pike N. M. 61 Tavistock st
Pillar Ths. 12 Navy row, M
Polkinghorne E.,Princess st
Pridham Geo. 68 George st
Proctor Thos. 6 Charles st.M
Prout Warwick Guy, 47
  Cornwall street
Rudd Wm. 66 Duke st
Ryder Ths. Wm., Cornwl.st
Sambells Benj. 27 Queen st
Sargent John, 44 Keith st
Sherriff Jane, Barrack st
Sleeman Jno. 61 Pembrk. st
Sowden J. 21 Francis alley
Squire Ann, Hood st. M
Stanbury Saml., Dockwalls
Symons W. H., Pembrk. st
Thorne Sus. 24 Chapel st

Thorne Wm. 7 Marlboro' st
Townsend Wm.,Waterloo st
Treeby Sml., Cherrygdn. st
Underhay Har. 27 Navy rw
Underhay Wm. Chas. 16
  Charlotte street, M
Webber John Frost,60 Glou-
  cester street, M
Whenmouth Saml. 27 Wil-
  liam street, M
Whittle Geo. 35 Duke st
Wood John, Doidge's well
Wollacott Eliz., Pembrk. st

BANKERS.
Devon and Cornwall Bankg.
  Co. 38 Fore street; P. C.
  Clarke, manager, (on Bar-
  clay and Co.)
Devonport Bank, (W. & W.
  C. Hodge and Co.) Fore
  st. (on Lubbock and Co.)
Dockyard Savings' Bank, R.
  Scott, actuary
National Provincial Bank
  of England, Fore st ; W.
  Pleadwell, manager, (on
  London & Joint-Stock Bk)
Royal Naval Savings' Bank,
  Ker street ; Capt. H. D.
  Parker, R.N. actuary
Union Savings' Bank, Chapel
  st ; Jas. Dawe, actuary,
  (open Tues., Thurs., and
  Saturday)

BASKET MAKERS.
Boon Thos. 2 Barrack st
Deacon John, Cumberld. st
Deacon Wm. 34 Market st

BLACKING MAKERS.
Jury Mary, 6 Boot lane
Osborn Sar., Cherrygdn. st

BLACK & W. SMITHS.
Allee Saml. 17 Quarry st
Allen Saml. 6 Granby ope
Brimblecombe John & Ths.
  80 Princess street
Colwell Nichls. 4 Moon st
Crocombe Wm.38 Tavistk.st
Davey John, 5 Baker's pl
Dodridge Sar., Spiller's ope
Doney John, 39 Marlboro'st
Dyer Wm., Princess st. ope
Grills Hy. 35 Marlboro' st
Leeby Richd., Mutton Cove
Potham Ths., Cumberld. st
Radford Hy. 21 Market ln
Rickard Wm. 124 Fore st
Stoneman Geo. 21 Mkt. st
Weekes Hanbl.17 Wm.st.M
Weekes John. 40 Chapel st

BLOCK & PUMP MKS.
Davies Wm. 8 Spiller's ope
Hingston Jas. Mould, Rich-
  mond walk
Tucker Wm., Prospect row

BOAT BUILDERS.
Flower Wm. Tamar, Wharf;
  house 29 John street
Wallis John, Baker's place
Willis & Son, 14 Baker's pl

BOOKBINDERS.
Lampen Geo., Tavistock st
Lewis John, 16 Cumberld.st
Marshall Chas 8 George st

BOOKSELLERS, STA-
TIONERS, &c.
(* *have Libraries*.)
Barnacle Lewis, Prospect. rw
Brend Sml. 68 St. Aubyn st
*Colman Wm. 51 Fore st
Farl Wm. (old,) Mrlboro'.'st
Harris H.Vinton,15 Fore st
*Hearle Geo.W. 118 Fore st
*Heydon John, 104 Fore st ;
  h 3 Lambert ope
Keys Elias, 6 James st
Lewis John, 16 Cumberld.st
Lidstone Roger, 107 Fore st
Mennicom Edw. 3 Tavistk.
  st ; h 3 Portland bldgs. s
O'Neil Adw. 7 Navy row, M
Pengelly Thos. Hodge, 91
  Fore street
Roberts Jph., Navy row
Wood Chas. 3 Catherine st.
  and 5 Stafford hill
Wood Wm. (and news agt.)
  52 Fore street

BOOT & SHOE MKRS.
Adams John, Granby st
Addiscott Rd. L. 113 Fore st
Andrews Jno. 5 Market ln
Andrews Wm.38Garden st M
Axworthy Pp. 102 Fore st
Baker John, 27 Morice st
Baker Wm. 65 Princess st
Banbury Rd. 4 William st
Bastard Thos., Princess st
Bateman Jno., Tavistk. st
Barley Saml., Prospect row
Best Hy. John, 25 Navy rw
Bray Geo. 25 William st.M
Brooks A. E., James st. ope
Cary Wm. 6 Boot lane
Ching Wm. Hy. 47 Jas. st
Clemence John, 10 Mt. cove
Collier John, 10 Pembrk. st
Collier Wm. 17 Pond lane
Collins Wm. H. 28 John st
Cook Nichls., Charlotte st
Cornish My. 7 Market ln
Couch Ths. 19 Marlboro' st
Davies Sml., Cherrygdn. st
Dawe Rd. 38 Tavistock st. s
Doddridge Wm., Cathrn. st
Drake Hy. 2 Bragg's alley
Dukes Jas. 16 Chapel st
Dyer John, 11 Church st
Easterbrook Jas., Mount st
Edwards Chas., Ker st
Elliott John, Francis alley
Ellis Jph. 47 Queen st
Elworthy Ts., St. Aubyn st
Faul Wm., St. Aubyn st
Gribble W. 41 Cherrygdn.st
Grose Hy. 29 Tavistock st
Harvie & Morris, Cumbld.st
Heath Wm. 44 Fore st
Hill Wm. 8 Princess st
Hockett Jas., Bragg's alley
Hockett Thos. 2 Pym st

Hodge Jane, 38 Queen st
HooperThos.N.,Marlboro'st
HutchinsSaml.16 Market st
Jones Peter J., Tavistock st
King Wm. 11 Tavistock st
Lane Thomas, 26 Duke st
LetherbyRt.Ptr.9 Navy row
Leonard John, 29 Navy row
Limpenny Ths.,Canterby.st
Moorman Rd., Tavistock st
Nettle Jph. 104 Pembroke st
Oldfield Chpr., Marlboro' st
Orchard Jnthn.,1William st
Palmer D. 38 Cornwall st
Parish John, 20 Marlboro' st
Payne John, 13 Princess st
Pearce Wm. 7 Morice st
Pengelly Saml. 19 Pond ln
Perkins Thos., Cornwall st
Perry John, 54 Charlotte st
Philps Thos.,Cherrygrdn. st
Philps Wm. 23 Cornwall st
Picken Jas. 27 Tavistock st
PitmanChas.73Pembroke st
PyleFras.Wm.,Pembroke st
Quance&Sleep,106 Navy rw
Quick Thos. 77 George st
Quick Wm. 3 Tamar ter
Rawling Edw.,StAubyn ope
Reed Richard, 117 Fore st
Reed Thomas, 5 Duke st
Reed Thos. 81 Pembroke st
Reed Wm. 8 Market st
Rockett Wm. 20 Cannon st
Rogers Richd. 57 Queen st
RundleHeury,3Pembroke st
Sawdye Edw., Tavistock st
Sherriff Thos., Francis'alley
Sincock Hy. 80 Pembroke st
Snell Benj. 4 Ker street
Spry John, 9 Tavistock st
Spry John, 95 Fore street
StanburyGeo.,William st.M
Stroud Joseph, 84 Fore st
Swanson Wm. 59 George st
Symons John, 36 Pembrk.st
Taylor John, 42 King st
Thomas Jas. 126 Navy row
Toms Wm. 36 Gloucester st
Tregellis Edw. 7 South st
Tremlett Wm.58 Pembrk.st
Triggs John, 39 Fore st
Uglow Wm. 4 Navy row
Vosper Jas. 43 Cornwall st
Warn Rd. 13 Monument st
Warren John, 19 Duke st
Warren John, 46 Granby st
Weston Chas. 42 Pembrk.st
Wheeler Jas. 8 James st
Whitford Hy. 49 James st
Whitell Geo. 35 Duke st
Wilson Wm. 44 Tavistock st
Woods Jas., Bragg's alley
Worley Ths. 57 Clowance st
Yabsley Rd. 70 George st
BRAZIERS & TINNERS.
(are Plumbers.)*
*Barfitt John, 48 Queen st
Downing Amos, Cathrn. st
*Heath Jno. and Wm. Hy.
  23 Catherine street

Jewell Wm., Fort street
Reed Rd. 35 Pembroke st
Rickard John, Bragg's alley
*Rider Hy. 21 John st
BREWERS, &c.
(are only Porter, &c., dlrs.)*
*Butcher Edwin, Market st
*Dymond Ths. Kitte, Gran-
  by st; h 22 St. Aubyn st
Gist Wm., Clowance st
Haldane Alex., Canterbury
  st; h 55 Mount street
*Hawker Chas. and Co. Bar-
  rack street
Husband Ths., John st. M.;
  h Stoke villa
Knowling R. E. 41 Queen
  street; h Morice sq
Liscombe Thos. W., Tamar
  st; h Trafalgar pl. s
Matthews Thos. 13 Cross st
Sargent & Co. 54 Princess st
White Jno. Jph., Canter-
  bury st; h 47 Ker st
BRUSH MANUFRS.
Hinvest Wm. 69 Duke st
Poor Thos. 105 Pembroke st
BUILDERS.
(See also Carpenters.)
Bartlett John, 1 Ker st
Bartlett W. Edwards,Ker st
Blake (Jph.)& Pope(Matw.)
  Edgcumbe place, s
Carne Jph. 32 Granby st
Cornish Wm., Tamar st. M
Crocker Hector, South st
Deacon Thos. 13 George st
Elliott Saml., Garden st. M
Greenwood John, (and brick
  mkr.) Brunswick cottages
Greenwood Ths. 21 Cannon
Hockaday Lnc., Marlboro'st
Mallett Wm. 33 Chapel st
Moule Hy. 28 Navy row
Percy Edw. 30 King st
Perkins Thos. 1 Ross st
Rawling M. 24 Princess st
Spriddle John, 18 Cannon st
Symons (Jph.) and Hoskin
  (Jno.) Hood street, M
Taylor Thos. 3 Wood st. M
Worth Jas. 14 George st
Worth Richd. 36 Ker st
BUTCHERS.
(1 have Shops in Market.)
1Barnacott Martha,Duke st
1 Binney Edw., Duke st
1 Body Sophia, Cathn. st
1 Brimacombe John, Monu-
  ment street
Budge Wm. 12 Pembroke st
Budge Wm. 8 Boot lane
1 Camh Wm. 4 Barrack st
Clegg Thos. 108 Fore st
Cole John, 6 Cornwall st
1 Coombs Wm. 4 Barrack st
Copp Jas. 11 Marlboro' st
1 Cornish Eliz. 39 Cross st
1 Cory Wm. 33 Barrack st
1Cowling Eliz.28 Barrack st
1 Cross John, 6 Barrack st

Cull John, 54 Tavistock st.s
Dawe Wm.G.34 Pembrk.st
1Easterbrook Chs.,Barrck.st
1 Easterbrook Rd.17Pond ln
1 Easterbrook Saml.,Boot ln
1Easterbrook S jun.Chapl.st
Easterbrook Wm., Pmbrk.st
1EasterbrookWm.,Barrck st
Elliott Rt. 71 Princess st
1 Fox Peter, 29 Barrack st
1 Goad Wm., James st
GombeWm.101 Pembroke st
Hancock Geo., Chtte. st. M
1 Harvey Daniel, Granby st
1 Harvey Richard & Wm.,
  Granby ope
1HeardRd.,Cherrygarden st
HockingEdwin,76 George st
Hoeking Wm. 48 Shambles
1 Horswell Rt., Princess st
1 Husband Jas.,131 Navy row
1 Jope My.Ann,Pembroke st
1 Joyce John, 76 Union st
1 Lee Catherine, 49 Ker st
Lee Thos. 13 Tavistock st
1LuscombeJohn,Cornwall st
1 Luscombe John, Pond ln
1 Madge M. 14 John st
Mares John, 3 Cornwall st
1 Medland Sarah, South st
1 Medland Geo., 10 Mill st
1 Mogg John, 6 Barrack st
1 Moore John, Market st
1 Moore J. jun.Bragg's alley
1 Moorshed Thos.17 Duke st
PattersonJane,22William st
Paige Thos. 1 Tavistock st
1 Pearse Eliz., Gloucester st
Pearse John G., Union ter
1 Petherbridge Edward, 22
  Tavistock street
1 Pike John, 29 Barrack st
Pinches Fras., Dingle's ope
Piper Jas. 47 Tavistock st
Pomworthy Eliz.,Pembrk.st
1 PriorEliza, Cumberland st
Quance Rd. 16 Navy row
Richard Abm. 20 Cannon st
1ReddawayWm.,Barrack st
1 Sambells John, Fore st
1 Screech Pp. 6 Market ln
1 Short Jane, 104 Fore st
1 Smith Jas.17 Tavistock st
1 Smith Wm. 12 Barrack st
1 Spry James, 13 John st
1 Spry John, 62 Duke st
1 Stanbury John, Barrack st
1 Stanbury Wm., Barrack st
Stevens Wm. 33 Cannon st
1 Sutton Geo. 20 Chapel st
1 Sutton John, 20 Navy row
1 Sutton Wm. 30 Barrack st
1 Warren Joseph, Mill st
1 Webber John, 2 Morice sq
1 Weeks Eliz. 5 John st
1 Weeks John, 46 Duke st
Williams Wm. 33 Garden st
CABINET MAKERS, &c.
Alger Fras. 24 Marlboro' st
Bonuey John, Pembroke st
Boolds Jas. 45 Marlboro' st

2 H

Ellis Thos. 104 James st
Fittock Peter, 58 George st
Gormully Wm., Marlboro'st
Granville Rt. 85 Fore st
Mewton Wm. 88 James st
Morcombe Edw.B.,James st
Morcombe Saml., Duke st
Richards John, 27 Market st
Rickard Fras., St Aubyn st
Thompson Sidney Smith, 66
　St Aubyn street
　Upholstresses.
Greenslade Ann, 2 Fore st
Harvey Eliz. 47 Navy row
Mackay Ann, 9 Princess st
Mortimore L. 27 Clowance st
Pike Emma, Mount st
Rowe Mary, 4 Cumberland st
　CARPENTERS.
Carne John, Granby st
Downing Ptr. 11 Clowance st
Edgcumbe John, Marlboro'st
Foale Robt., James st. ope
Harper Wm., UprSomersetpl
Head James, York place, s
Hernaman Sml. 19 Union pl
Hitchings Wm., Pembroke st
Jenkin Thos., Marlboro' st
Perkins John, Charlotte st
Perkins Thos. 17 Navy row
Richards Rd. 8 Granby ope
Rogers John, 55 Mount st
Bow Wm., Trafalgar st
Stivey John, King street
Stivey Wm., Catherine lane
Tratton —, 26 King street
Triggs Chpr. 24 Tavistock st
Tryscott Rd. 12 York pl. s
Wale Thos. 5 Marlboro' st
　CARVERS & GILDERS.
Blackmore Hy. 106 Fore st
Gaul John, Ker street
Hill John, 12 Duke street
Lamb Francis, 10 James st
Lane John, 25 Tavistock st
Mitchell John, 43 Fore st
Smith Wm. Hy. 21 Fore st
　CHAIR MAKERS.
Cook John, 7 Phœnix st
Ellis Thomas, 4 James st
Every Jas. 42 Marlboro' st
Hare Cath. 16 James st
Phillips My. A. 95 James st
CHEMISTS & DRUGTS.
Bush Geo. Reuben, Cornwl.st
Cleife Henry Holditch, 46
　St Aubyn street
Dickerson Hy. 14 Cumbld.st
Evans John, 45 Pembroke st
Glencross Jas.&Co.62 Fore st
Gumm John, 109 Pembroke st
Hamond Saml.,Trafalgar pl
Hayward Wm.H., Market st
Jeffery & Co. 5 Market st
Johns Thos. I.R. 49 Fore st
Lory(Jacob)&Burt(F.Geo.),
　98 Fore street
Mackay John, Catherine st
Martin Wm. Brown, 56 St
　Aubyn street
Pollard Wm. 30 Catherine st
Row Charles, 90 Fore st

Rowe Wm. 32 William st. M
Ryder Jas. Benj., Navy row
Singleton John, 1 Morice pl
　CLOTHES DEALERS.
Almond Jas. 60 James st
Barrett Jph. 43 James st
Billing Isachar, 2 Boot lane
Costallo Jane, 4 Boot lane
Crocker Wm. 1 Moon st
Evans Mary, 52 Cornwall st
Evens Eliz.,Cherrygarden st
Gale John, 39 Cornwall st
Granville Gr., Broad bkway
Hamond Maria, 5 Pond ln
Hill Cath. 76 Princess st
Jewell C. 12 Chapel st
Jewell Isaac, 6 Pond lane
Johns Reuben R. 83 James st
Knight Saml. 54 Queen st
Lobb Gregory, 51 James st
Maddock Wm., Cornwall st
Nutbean Sarah, 16 Boot ln
Oaff Wm. 30 Tavistock st
Parsons Jas. 2 Francis alley
Peek Wm., Cornwall st
Petherick John, Cornwall st
Ryder Mary, 20 Cornwall st
Smith Thos. 57 James st
Stephens Ann, 8 Queen st
Ussell John, 61 James st
Walters Thos. 15 Cornwall st
Warren Mary, 5 Boot lane
Yelland Eliz., Broad bkway
　COACH BUILDERS.
Elliott Thomas Edmund,
　Tamar wharf
Pawlyn Rt. 38 St Aubyn st
　COAL MERCHANTS.
Beer John & Walter, James st
Greenwood Wm. 9 Morice sq
Tapson Ebsworthy, Tamar
　wharf; h 79 Navy row
Winlow & Son, 21 Ker st
　CONFECTIONERS.
Bright Jph., Catherine st
Granville Brnd., St Aubyn st
Granville Jas. 68 Fore st
Granville Mary, 53 Queen st
Lawrence Ann & Son, 54 St
　Aubyn street
Mugford James, 20 Fore st
Thomas Wm. 44 St Aubyn st
　COOPERS.
Almond John, Mutton cove
Beasant Wm. 17 Ross st
Cook John, 7 Phœnix st
Jordan Jph., Duke st. ope
McLeon Michl. 10 Ordnance
　st; h 28 Portland pl. M
Marks Jph. Rd. 45 King st
　CURRIERS.
Bennett Edw.Stpn.,Jamesst
Blight Jane, (and tanner,)
　2 Princess street
Cannon Geo. 10 Marlboro' st
Harvey Wm. 12 James st
Miall & Co. 28 Market st
Peek Wm. 11 Princess st
Philp John, Cherrygarden st
Sambell Fdk. 3 James st
　CUTLERS.
Price Jas. B., Catherine ln

Price John, 11 King street
　DAIRYMEN, &c.
Axford My. Ann, *Swilly*
Bassett Wm., Monument st
Batten John, 2 Pembroke st
Bishop Edwd. 79 George st
Blatchford Jas., Charlotte st
Botterell Wm. *Millbrook*
Brooking Mary, 20 James st
Brown Nancy, Russell st
Budge John, 51 Chapel st
Cundy Robert, 11 Fore st
Davy Wm. 35 John street
Dyer Wm. 1 Plym street
Eastcott Wm. 8 Granby st
Elliott George, *Swilly*
Fogwill My., Old Saltash rd
Hancock Rd. 108 Navy row
Hancock Wm. 120 Navy row
Harvey John, Tavistock st
Hodgson Wm. 43 Plym st
Honey Richd. 12 Garden st
Jenkins Wm. *Outland*
Knight James, 49 Navy row
Lakeman Wm., Church st. s
Luscombe Eliz., Glo'ster st
Mabin Wm., Saltash road
Osborn Richd. 5 Moon st
Parnell Richd. 33 John st
Pascoe Wm., Old Saltash rd
Penwarn Sus. 4 Princess st
Petherbridge E.,Tavistockst
Rosevear Rt. *Rose Farm*
Rowe Richard, *Homepark*
Searle Thos., Francis alley
Smith Hy., Cherrygarden st
Stevens Rt., Francis alley
Sweet Wm. 25 Plym st
Tope Eliz. 18 George ln
Trays Samuel, *Swilly*
Vogwell Ann, Doidge's well
Webber Jas., Mount Cottage
Weekes Richd. *Mile House*
Weekes Wm. 56 Duke st
Wheeler Esther, Croft st
　DYERS & SCOURERS.
Baker Geo. 6 Marlbro' st
Ball James, 94 James st
Burt Fdk. 17 Market st
Burt Harriet, 36 King st
Hazlewood Thos. 5 James st
Kennard Wm. 39 King st
Mortimore Rachel,109 Forest
Williams Wm. 90 James st
　EATING HOUSES.
Cary Margt. 23 Cornwall st
Chambers John,15 Pembk.st
Emmett Rd., Cornwall st
Ford James, 14 Duke st
Hall Agnes, 9 Duke st
Hanger My., Mt Cove pl
Hyde W. B., Cornwall st
Jones Owen, 67 Fore st
Markham Jas.,Teetotal rms
Moody Jno. A. 9 Boot ln
Restarick Josiah, Duke st
Soper Sarah, 39 Queen st
Sopp My. A., Cornwall st
Southey Chas. 36 Geo. st. s
Squance Jas. 97 Fore st
Staddon Fanny,74 Pembk.st
Thomas Rd. 55 Queen st

Wall Richard, Mutton cove
Wearn Thos. P. 1 Duke st
White Wm., Tavistock st

ENGRAVERS & PRNTS.
Clark John, 61 Duke st
Dorning Robert, 37 Ker st
DallingerJph.S. 62 James st
Sloggett Hy. 37 Chapel st

FANCY DEPOTS.
Cox Helen, 47 St Aubyn st
Daws Richd. 88 Fore st
GodfreyEmmeline,88Forest
Oxland Wm. 31 William st
Levi Phineas, Catherine st

FIRE & LIFE OFFICES.
Argus, R. M. Oliver, 35 Chapel street
Atlas, Josias Foot, Chapel gn
British Commercial, W. Shapland, 14 Barrack st
Church of England, Alex. Rennie, 19 Cannon st
City of London, W. C. Cox, 89 Fore street
Clerical and Medical, W Byers
Colonial, J. B. Restarick, 87 James street
County & Provident, N. R. Hoare, 8 Coal racket ope
Crown, Rundle and Sons, 75 George street
Eagle, Wm. Chapman, 60 St Aubyn street
Economic Eliz., Little & Billing, 52 St Aubyn st
Globe, John M. Gard, 17 St Aubyn street
Great Britain, and India and London Life, J. W. Jeffery, 42 Marlbro' street
Guardian, Benj. M. Ramsey, Cumberland street
Indispensable, Jno. Heydon, 104; and J. M. Bamford, 61 Fore street
London Assurance, J. M. Rickard, 16 Waterloo st
Minerva, James Gilbard, 7 St Aubyn street
National and Mercantile, R. Lidstone, Fore st
NorwichUnion, R.C. Smith, 68 St Aubyn street
Palladium, A. B. Bone, 26 Barrack street
Pelican Life, Thos. Hawker, 50 St Aubyn st; and W. Shapland, 14 Barrack st
Phœnix, A. B. Bone, W. Shapland & W. Chapman
Railway, R. Lidstone, 108 Fore street
Reliance, Wm. Gard, 13 Garden street
Royal Exchange, J. & H. T. Smith, 12 Morice square
Royal Farmers', W. Wood, 55 Fore street
Royal Naval Annu itnt. Society, Ker street; Capt. G. F. Somerville, *actuary*

Scottish Life, H. Penberthy, 49 Barrack street
Sovereign, C. Rowe, 90 Fore st
Star Life, Wm. Stonelake, 63 St Aubyn street
Sun, W. R. Berryman, 58 St Aubyn street
West of England, Edward Sole, 67 Duke street

FISHING TACKLE MKS.
Shaw John, 42 Catherine st; house Fellows' place
Terlizzick Wm. 20 Fore st

FURNITURE BROKRS.
Braund Geo. 26 Tavistock st
Brimblecombe J., Princess st
Churchward Jas. 45 Queen st
Clarke S. 16 Tavistock st
Davis Eliz. 44 James st
Ellice Robt. 43 Chapel st
Ellis John, 45 James st
Evans Wm. 43 Queen st
Fisher George, 14 James st
Fisher Wm. 9 Cornwall st
Garland Eliz. 97 James st
Luscombe Hy. 66 James st
Marks Jph. 13 Marlbro' st
May Richd., St Aubyn st
Netting Rd. 61 Cornwall st
Pickin Ann, 22 James st
Rickard Jph. 9 James st
Rogers Nichls. 63 Duke st
Stephens Ann, 8 Queen st
Wadelton Chas. 2 James st
Wadelton Eliz., Duke st
Webb John, 44 King st

GARDENERS.
Brown Jno ,Mkp & *Tamerton*
Dustow John, *Milehouse*
Harvey Jno. *Underhill Cottage*
Martin John, *Underhill*
Moore Richd., Keppel st
Moule Saml. 11 York pl. s
Parsons Sus. 46 Marlbro' st
Roberts Thos., Trafalgar pl
Ross Eliz. 14 Ross st
Webb James, *Deadlake*

GINGER BEER MKRS
Bennet J. S. 30 Market st
Coleman Chas. 92 Pembk. st
Dingle Rd. 15 James st

GLASS, CHINA, &c. DLRS.
Booth Geo. 28 Cherrygdn. st
Burt Jno. Stokes, 86 Fore st
Jory Mary, 20 Catherine st
Lacey George, 12 Cross st
May Mary, 11 Catherine st
Moore Richd., Keppel st. M
Quance Thos. 106 Navy row
Sanders Wm. 30 Moon st. M
Warner Thos. 13 Pond ln

GREEN GROCERS.
Biggin Robt. 58 Queen st
Dreedon Ann, 58 George st
Hearn Cath. 10 Gloster st. M
Hooper Jas. 51 Cornwall st
Hyne Henry, 23 Princess st
Pearson Emma, 27 King st
Smith Jane, 3 George st
Treleven Jane, 130 Navy rw
Wivell Jas. 12 Cornwall st

GROCERS & TEA DLRS.
Abel Israel, 55 Cornwall st
Avery Sampson Coombe, 9 Market street
Best Peter, 13 Cumberld. st
Bond Thos. & Co. 78 Fore st
Bray Edward, 3 Duke st
Bush Geo. Reuben, 13 Cornwall street
Clatworthy Thos. 24 Cathn. st
Codd Francis, 51 Queen st; house 2 Morice square
Collard Thos., Cornwall st
Coombe Edw. 25 James st
Coombe Jno. Cornls. Gloster st
Denham Rd. 68 Duke st
Doubtfire Jas. 10 Market st
Elliott Josias and Co. 55 St Aubyn street
Elliott Jph. 29 Cumberld. st
Elliott John, 14 Fore st
Elliott Saml. 18 Tavistock st
Emmott Wm. G., Princess st
Evans Samuel, 12 Pond lane, and 29 Catherine st
Fittock George, Catherine st
George Florence, 46 Queen st
Gosling Jas. 32 Cherrygarden street, and 13 Tavistock st
Gribble Richd. 16 Geo. s
Hancock William Kemp, 29 Cumberland street
Heath John, 7 Duke st
Hutchens Geo. 23 Market st
Hutchens Hy. 8 Catherine st
Isreal Abel, 55 Cornwall st
Jackson Sml. P. 39 Clownce. st
Jeffery & Co., Market st
Jory Thomas, 105 Fore st
Jory Michl. 16 Catherine st
Kemp James, 4 Morice pl
Mackay Jno. 14 Catherine st
Morrish and Ladyman, 60 Fore street
Oxford Chas. 27 Cornwall st
Pitcher Jonth. 53 Cornwall st
Pollard Wm. 30 Catherine st
Powlesland Wm. 66 Union place, s
Short Wm. 19 Navy row. M
Soper Thomas, 35 Market st
Sowden Wm., Granby st
Spiller Jno. 35 William st. M
Thomas David, 2 Market st
Tremeer Jno. 16 Tavistock st
Tucker W. Cotton, 119 Fore st
Watter John, 1 Cross st
Williams Sml. 48 Cornwall st
Windsor Jas. 3 Marlbro' st
Youlton Eliz. 12 Ker st

GUN MAKERS.
Edwards Wm. & Son, 63 St Aubyn street
Heard Hy. 33 Barrack st

HABERDASHERS.
Abbott Benj. 98 Pembrk. st
Allen Lavinia, Cross st
Barrable Cath. 51 Princess st
Bennett J. S. 3 Market st
Billing Mgt. & E. 59 Fore st
Boolds Har., Catherine ln
Catcliffe My. B. 144 Fore st

Cowser Hanh., Cumbrld. st
Dikes Mary, 24 James st
Dingle Sus. 18 William st
Dunn Jane,92&115 James st
Earle Jane, Duke street
Fox M. & J. F 29 Market st
Furneaux Jas. 29 King st
HendryConstnce.,19 Pond ln
James Ellen, 45 St Aubyn st
Johns Thos. B. 47 Granby st
Keen John, 9 Queen street
MarshallLucy,33Tavistk.st
May Mary, 2 Duke street
Pascoe Peter, 19 Cumbrld. st
RickardsElz.19Pembroke st
Roberts Mary, 64 Duke st
Rogers Jas. Cooper, 33 Cum-
   berland st ; h 6 Stoke ter
Satterley Ann & Co. Mkt. st
Seal Henry, 35 Queen st
Stephens Mary Ann & Eliz.,
   Pembroke street
Swanger Wm. 45 Queen st
Sweetman Caroln., Duke st
WadlingWm Jn.StAubynst
Warren Thos. 13 Pond ln
Whitford My. 7 Wm. st. m
Williams Ann, 91 James st
Williams John, Bragg's aly
Worth Jas. 20 Tavistock st

HAT MFRS. & DLRS.

Carpenter Rd. 74 Fore st
Crook Geo., Catherine ln
CumingJane,42 Cherrygn.st
Herring Robt. 56 Fore st
Lee James, 112 Fore st
McKenzie Saml. 15 Cross st
Mayne Thos. 1 Catherine st
Sparke Andrew Kinsman,
   30 Fore st & 43Catherine st
Waugh Geo. 27 Tavistock st
Willing & Davis, 39 Cath. st

HORSE, GIG, &c.LETRS.

Avent John, 74 George st
Dunn John, Barrack st
FurneauxJohn,3 Princess st
Jones Eliz. 8 Church st. s.
Jordan —, Cumberland st
NorthmoreGe.2Lambert ope
Popham Cies, 4 Lambert ope
Seldon Thos. 19 Market st
Wills Thos., Trafalgar ln. s

**HOTELS,
INNS, AND TAVERNS.**

Anchor & Hope,My.Northy,
   17 Cornwall street
ArtilleryArms,Chtte. Samp-
   son, 1 Marlborough st
Barley Sheaf, Thos. Martin,
   19 Catherine street
Barnstaple Inn, Fras. War-
   ren, 17 Princess st
Blue Anchor, Alex. Ash,(&
   cork cutter,) 63 James st
Bristol, Jane Copplestone,
   51 Pembroke street
Britannia, Edwd. Bennett,
   Milehouse
Brown Bear, John West, 19
   Chapel street
Bull's Head, Geo. Radford,
   49 Queen street

Butchers' Arms, Thos. Ma-
   thews, 13 Cross st
Carlton Inn,Edwin Butcher,
   16 St. Aubyn street
Castle and Keys, Samuel
   Bazley, 15 Prospect row
Clarence Inn, Saml. Lane,
   13 Catherine street
Clowance Inn, John Scott,
   45 Clowance street
Commercial Inn, Rt. Mar-
   shall, 36 Fore street
Cornish Arms, Wm. Hor-
   rell, 37 Pembroke st
Cornish Tavern, John Lap-
   thorne, 11 Ordnance st
Cross Keys, Jas. Guskitt,
   40 Queen street
Cross Keys, John Perne,
   Tavistock street
Crown and Column, Geo. P.
   Harrison, 46 Ker st
Crown Hotel, Thos. Sheall,
   5 Cumberland st ; *Tap*,
   Rd. Vicary, 2 George st
Dartmouth, John Earle, 53
   James street
Dock Gates, Henry Creber,
   Fore street
Dolphin, Thomas Shute, 52
   Granby street
Eagle, Jno. Collins,39 Cum-
   berland street
Exeter Arms, Ambrose Col-
   lin, 41 Cumberland st
Falmouth Tavern, Nichls.
   Brown, 60 Queen st
Ferry Inn, Jane Ellen Kent,
   Tamar street, m
Fountain (Naval Rendez-
   vous,) Thos. Skinner, 63
   Fore street
Freemasons' Arms, Betsy
   Vanstone, 26 John st. m
George, Anthy. Facey, 13
   Pembroke street
George and Dragon, Leond.
   Philp, 77 Duke street
Globe, John Braund, 11
   Market street
Gloucester Arms, John A.
   Tregear, 37 Gloucester st.m
Golden Lion, Benj. Axford,
   97 Fore street
Half Moon, Rt. Goodman,
   17 George street
Horse & Groom, Jas. Doel,
   8 Cumberland street
India Arms, Geo. Mitchell,
   18 Cornwall street
Jolly Bacchus, Peter Earle,
   30 Pembroke street
Jolly Sailor, Elizth. Cock,
   Cornwall street
King and Constitution, Jno.
   Peek, 19 James st
King & Queen, My. Evans,
   25 Cornwall street
King's Arms, Fdk. Butcher,
   60 Pembroke street
King's Head, John Blight,
   38 Clowance street

Lamb, Richard Easton, 1
   Queen street
London Hotel, (& posting,)
   Thos. Rd. Townsend, 47
   Fore street
Lord Hood, Geo. M. Frost,
   28 King street
Market House, Ebenezer
   Collins, 36 Market st
Marquis of Granby, Wm.
   Lapthorne, 21 Barrack st
Masonic Tavern, Jno.Brock,
   62 Navy row, m
Masons' Arms, Jno. Arscott,
   70 Pembroke street
Military Arms, Hy. Ter-
   rell, 22 Fore street
Military Hospital, My. Ax-
   ford, 1 Paradise row
Mount Edgcumbe, Thomas
   Flemen, Mutton Cove
Mutton Cove Tavern, Eliz.
   Wall, Mutton Cove
Naval Hotel, Benj. Moon,
   31 Fore street
Navy and Army Inn, John
   Mitchell, 41 James st
Navy Arms, My. Bradmore,
   44 Charlotte street, m
Newcastle Tavern, Edward
   Bennett, 50 James st
New Star, Ann McGugan,
   31 Queen street
Old Globe, Thos. Sercombe,
   Cornwall street
Ordnance Arms, Rt. Moore
   Burt, 8 Fore street
Oxford Inn, Har. Symons,
   67 Fore street
Pear Tree, Wm. Sweet, 32
   Tavistock street
Pilot Boat, Sus. Perkins, 9
   Pembroke street
Plymouth Inn, Jas. Prout,
   25 Fore street
Portmouth Passage House,
   G. Ryder, 30 Cornwall st
Post Office Inn, Jph. Har-
   ris, 20 Market street
Prince of Wales, Martha
   Restarick
Prince Wm. Henry, James
   Pollybland,18Cumbrld.st
Queen's Arms, John Gaul,
   Ker street
Queen's Head, Rd. Taylor,
   13 Duke street
Red Cow, Jno. Taylder, 1
   Barrack street
Richmond Walk Inn, Hy.
   Doddridge, Richmond wk
Rising Sun, Wm. Hillson,
   Fore street
Rose and Crown, Hy. Hor-
   rell, 26 Pembroke st
Royal Exchange, Jno. Sim-
   monite, 56 Pembroke st
Royal Hotel, (and posting,)
   Robt. N. Moorshead, 84
   Fore street
Royal Standard, Pp. Jas.
   Rogers, 33 Wm. st. m

St. Aubyn's Arms, R. Hortop, 141 Navy row, M
Shakspeare, Sarah Benoy, 3 Cumberland street
Sirus Frigate, My.Thomas, 16 Pembroke street
Sportman's Arms, Thomas Hewlett, Saltash road
Sunderland & Liverpool,W. Shepherd, 5 Tamar st. M
Swan, Wm. Maddock, 34 Cornwall street
Tamar Inn, Chs. Ts. Smith, 10 Tamar street, M
Tavistock Inn, Ts. Hockin, 23 Tavistock street
Three Tuns, Peter Jessop Down, Catherine st
True Blue, Jno. B. Metters, Cornwall street
Turk's Head, Dd. Holland, 4 Prospect row
Two Trees, Jas. Halls, 4 Fore street
Union, J. Hancock, 23 William street, M
White Hart, Saml. Coombe, 76 Pembroke street
White Lion, R. Burt,King st
William IV., Richd. Hockridge, 31 Cornwall st

BEERHOUSES.
Adams Ts. 51 Tavistock st
Adams Wm. 16 George st
Alee Ann, 17 Quarry st
Bailey Emma, 116 Navy rw
Baker Wm. 1 Navy row
Ball Ann, Fort street
Beer Hy. 30 Granby st
Bath James, 1 Mount st
Best Hy. John, 25 Navy rw
Blake Jas. 7 Cornwall st
Bomyer Peter, 6 King st
Bond Robt. 15 Duke st
Bond Saml. 12 William st
Bonney Jno. 65 Pembrk. st
Burgess Geo. 116 Navy row
Burke Hy. 32 Barrack st
Carline My. A. 112 Navy rw
Cary John, 13 Queen st
Caunter Jane, 9 Baker's pl
Caydon Sml. Cumberld. st
Cayzer John, 1 Keith st. M
Chapple Wm.8Waterloo st.s
Chiswell John, 7 Quarry st
Chubb Robt. 48 Granby st
Claddick Jane, Mount st
Clemence Wm. 20Wm. st. M
Clutterbuck, Ts. 16 John st
Colmer Ann, 18 James st
Cook Fras. 97 Pembroke st
Cook Rd. 8 Trafalgar pl
Craddick Abm., Francis aly
Crapp John, 38 Navy row
Crispin Jph. 139 Navy row
Crispin My. 97 Pembroke st
Crocker John 2 Tamar st
Cudlip Matw. 29 Pembrk.st.
Cumming Js.18 Pembrk. st
Curry Edw. 10 James st
Dart Mary, 23 Morice st
Dole Jas. 9 Cumberland st

Downe Chas. 5 Dockwalls
Dumick Jas. 30 James st
Easterbrook John, 83 Jas. st
Edgcumbe Benj. 4 King st
Evans John, 8 Marlboro' st
Facey Anty. 13 Pembrk. st
Farthing Ts. 40 Tavistk. st
Fisher Eliz.,Broad backway
Fouracre Jph. 48 Duke st
Gitsham Jas. 33 Queen st
Grills Chas., Garden st. M
Grogeet John, 64 Duke st
Hall James, 14 Duke st
Hannaford J., Fellow's pl.s
Hawkey Sus.16 Cumberld. st
Heard Sar. A., Gloster st
Heyes Thos. 13 Wm. st. M
Hoggarty Ty. Cherrygdn. st
Honey Jas. 16 Prospect row
Howe Eliz. 8 Ross st. M
Howell Wm. 6 Pembrk. st
Jago My. 1 Charlotte st. M
Jasper Rd. 13 King st
Jefferys Wm., Hood st. M
Jenkins John, 10 Queen st
Jenkins My.A.11 Dockwalls
Johnson Wm. 86 Pembrk. st
Jones Wm. 17 William st.M
Jope Ann, 35 Navy row
Jose Jph. 1 Boscowen pl. M
King Mary, 6 Quarry st
Knight Wm. 14 George ln
Lawrence A. 24 Pembrk. st
Leathleman Eliza,35 Marlborough street
Little Geo. 19 William st. M
Luckes Hy. 58 Duke st
McPherson Mary Ann, 68 Navy row
Marks John, 58 Cornwall st
Marshall Wm.,Waterloo st s
Martin John, 50 Navy row
Matters John,40 Cornwall st
Meather Ann, 5 William st
Medlin Jph. 78 Princess st
Mitchell Nancy, 19 John st
Murch, Edw.31 Marlboro'st
Netting Rd. 4 Moon st. M
Newberry W. 16 Dockwalls
Newcombe Jno. 22 John st
Nicholls John, Canterby. st
Nicholson Fras. 3 John st
Northcote Thos., Fort st
Parsons Saml., Pembrk. st
Payne Rd. 13 Granby st
Pearce Selina, 2 Garden st
Poole Geo. 2 John st. M
Pope Wm., Tavistock st
Pottam Hy. 8 Mill st
Punder Wm. 22 Dockwalls
Rider Adw. 22 Pembrk. st
Riley Thos. 68 James st
Rocket Wm. 51 Cornwall st
Ryalph My., Catherine ln
Skinner Martha Jane, 3 King street
Sloggett J.Ford, 28Chltte.st
Smith Geo. 9 Tamar st. M
Smith John, 24 John st. M
Soper Richd. 39 Queen st
Splatt John, Cherrygdn. st
Taylor My. 8 Pembroke st

Thomas Rd. 55 Queen st
Thomas Wm., Bragg's alley
Tooker John, 7 Catherine st
Tozer John, 2 Market ln
Treliving Rlph. M.,Cross st
Tucker Wm., Cornwall st
Turner Pp. 7 John st. M
Uglow My. 10 Granby st
Uglow Wm. 64 Princess st
Underhill Jane, Pembrk. st
Wall Richd. Mutton Cove
Warne Fras. P. 1 Dnke st
Welman Danl. 67 James st
Wicket Rd. 38 Pembroke st
Wicks Hgh.H.11Glostr.st.M
Wicks Sar. 13 Navy row
Williams Grace, *Milehouse*
Williams Jno., Pembrk. st
Williams Thos., *Deadlake*
Yeo Wm. 6 Cumberland st

IRONMONGERS.
Andrews W.P., Catherine st
Arnold Jph.&Sons,13Fore st
Backwell Richd. Oliver and Son, 40 Fore street
Barfett John, 48 Queen st
Bawden Jas. 3 Morice pl
Date Fdk. & Edw.81Fore st
Disten & Chafe, 72 Fore st
Facey John, Catherine st
Gould Edw. 4 Cornwall st
Harry Jno. 50 Queen st
Heath Jno. and Wm. Head, 23 Catherine street
Lobb Chas. 3 Navy row
Marshall Thos. S. and Rt. 43 St. Aubyn street
Pengelly Wm. 7 James st
Pike Geo. 41 Edgcumbe st
Ramsey Jthn. jun. Duke st
Roberts Geo. 106 James st
Treseder Fras. 1 Market st
Winnicott Rd. 37 Cathrn.st
LACE & FRINGE MFR.
Myers Saml. 47 Duke st
L. & W. DRAPERS.
Bissey Wm. 4 Phoenix pl. s
Braddon Wm. 32 Tavistk.st
Butters Isaiah T.41Cathn.st
Davey Wm. and Chas. 35 Catherine street
Dawe Wm. 2 Morice pl. M
Dawe Wm. Ts. 36 Cathn.st
Every Ths. 27 Catherine st
Foster John, 18 South st
Greenwood Wm. 31 Fore st
Grose Jno.Wm. 75 Fore st
Hatch Thos. 31 Catherine st
King Robt. 82 Fore st
Knight Wm. & Co.4 Mkt.st
Littleton Philip Arthur, sen. 12 Catherine street
Moon Benj. 31 Fore st
Pinsent and Co. 32 Mkt. st
Richards Michl. Stevens, 22 Fore street
Rowe John, 21 Catherine st
Sargent Digory Warn, 33 Catherine street
Tippetts Geo. 22 Navy row
Treleven Thmsn., Tavstk.st
Willing & Davis,39Cathn.st

Willing Herbt. and Edwin, 58 Fore street

LODGING HOUSES.
Arnold Wm. 5 Paradise rw.s
Atwill Ann, 13 Baker's pl
Baker Benj.5 Chltte. ter. M
Brook Wm. 7 Waterloo st
Brown Ann, 9 Clarence pl
Bullock Benj. 31 George st
Chapman Ann, 29 George st
Cradick My. A., Chapel st
Cutler Thos. 42 George st
Fittock Har. 27 St. Abn. st
Fowl John, 33 George st
Gill John, Pennycomequick
Head John, Charlotte ter
Herbert Jph. 40 George st
Herring Dd., Paradise row
Hodgkins Eliz., Pards. row
Holmes Cath. 32 George st
Jarrard Jas. 67 George st
Jeffrey John, South hill
Jorey Thos. 18 Ker st
Knight Thos., Paradise row
Knighton Ths., Paradise rw
Long Grace, 24 George st
Lindsey My. A., Stoke ter
Luke Mrs. 30 Chapel st
Lyne Amelia, 64 George st
McKer Sml. 19 Prospect rw
May John, 32 Chapel st
Morlow Wm. 6 Pym st. M
Naylor Eliz. 7 George st
Niles Peter, 30 George st
Palmer Jane, Clarence pl
Pengelly Sarah, 15 Stoke ter
Penson Eliz., Paradise row
Perriton Rebc. 36 George st
Polkinghorne Jeb., Navy rw
Prior Louisa, Trafalgar pl
Ratcliff Jane, Navy row
Richards Chs., Paradise rw
Richards Har., Paradise rw
Rockett Robt., South hill
Rogers Thos. 73 George st
Rundle Mary, 34 Chapel st
Russell Chari'y, Waterloo st
Sims Saml. 12 Cumberld. st
Snow Sar. Ann, 19 Ker st
Stout Ann, 31 Chapel st
Symons Tmpnc., Granby st
Taylor Matw., Trafalgar pl
Tucker Sar., Wellington st
Tuckett Thos. 2 May pl. s
Watson Jph. 75 Navy row

MALTSTERS.
Gist Wm., Clowance st
Husband Thos., John st
Knowling Rd.E.41 Queen st
Liscombe Ths. W.,Tamar st

MARINE STORE DLRS.
Baker Eliz., Mnt. Cove pl
Brimblecombe T.,Princess st
Callicott J. 3 Ordnance st
Ferguson J., Cherrygdn. st
Gately Michl.15 George ln
Hockaday Jas.,Francis alley
Lacy Wm., Pembroke st
Lawson Thos., Cornwall st
Limpenny Ts., Francis alley
Lishman Mttw. J. 20 Geo. ln
Luscombe Hy. 66 James st

Maddock Wm., Cornwall st
Nathan Laz.102 Pembroke st
Restarick Thos.87 James st
Vincent John, 22 Market st

MASONS & SLATERS.
Callicott John, Ordnance st
Carne Jph. 33 Princess st
Carne Wm., Granby st
Dell Chas. 9 George sq
Dyer John N., Chapel st
Easterbrook John, 79 Jas.st
Easton Jas. 33 Cumbrld. st
Godfrey Rd. 6 Mt Pleasant
HawkingThs.37Tavistk. pl
Horswell Wm.,Jessamine ln
Lake John, 14 South st
Nancollis John, Chapel st
Rickard Ptr.45)Marlboro' st
Sheppard Wm., Princess st
Smith Rd.15 Tavistk. st. s
Smith Wm. 5 Church st. s
Taylor James and Son, 41 Pembroke street
Williams John,12 Princess st

MERCHANTS.
(See also Plymouth.)
Clark, Row,&Co.70 James st
Restarick Thos. 87 James st
Short Jno.(hide,)Marlbro' st

MILLINERS, &c.
Allen J. and F. 57 Fore st
Anthony J. A. 29 Duke st
Bates A., 46 James street
Betty & Curtis, Princess st
Blackmore Mrs. 106 Fore st
Brush My. 28 Duke street
Callard A. 121 Fore st
Cannon Ann, 6 Duke st
Carter M. 31 Cumberland st
Cawse Chtte., Princess st
Chalk Mercy, 46 Mount st
Channon M.64Tavistk.st. s
Clatworthy M. 11 James st
Cox Helen, 48 St Aubyn st
Clines Eliz. 19 Clowance st
Cummings S. 42 Navy row
Davies E. 12 Clowance st
Fox M. & J. 29 Market st
Frost F. 54 Duke street
Gardener M.A. 15 Cross st
Garland Ann, 12 Mount st
Gormilly M.&S. 92 Fore st
Harding S. & M. 9 Ker st
Harris M. A. 95 James st
Hawell L. 33 Barrack st
Head Misses, Coalrckt. ope
Hobbs Caroline, 5 Fore st
Hodge Eliz., Pembroke st
Holman A.& E. 36 Chtte.st
Hoskin Eliz. 49 Ker st
Lapthorne E. H.125Navyrw
LuscombeChtte.66 James st
McCurdy M. 15 Waterloo st
Marshall L.33 Tavistock st
MartinMy.A.,Cherrygdn.st
May Ann, 3 Pembroke st
May A.& M. 20 Charltte. st
May D. & M. 5 Clarence pl
Page Mary, 48 Duke st
Palmer C. 25 St Aubyn st
PenfoundM.A.15Boscwn.pl
PincombeL.&C.34Market st

Prior Eliz. 25 Cumberld. st
Rickard C. 25 St Aubyn st
Rickard F. & L. 20 Duke st
Robins A.1 Coalracket ope
Satterley Ann, 26 Market st
Sleep My. S. 56 Cornwall st
Stephens Eliz. 103 Fore st
Symons Agnes, Waterloo st
Tozer Eliz., Clowance st
TresederE.&M.,Cumbrld. st
Wade M.& E., Pembroke st
Wallis J.&A.71 Pembroke st
Walter P. 59 Navy row, M
Williams E. 36 Princess st
Wood Hanh. 16 Duke st
Wood M. 30 Princess st

MUSIC DEALERS.
Hunt Saml. 53 St Aubyn st
StonelakeWm. 62 St Aubyn st; h 6 Waterloo street

NEWSPAPERS.
Independent, (Sat.) Wm. Byers, Fore street
Telegraph, (Friday,) Wm. Richards, 12 St Aubyn st
West of England Conservative, (Sat.) E. Lidstone,Fore st

OPTICIANS.
Cox Wm. Chas. 89 Fore st
HeathWm.&Thos.Cornish, 46 Fore street
Ramsey Edw. 54 Fore st

PAINTERS & GLAZRS.
(Marked 1 are Plumbers.)
1 Andrews Wm .25 Cathn.st
Atwill John, 96 James st
Aunger Smpsn.4 Tavistk.st
Bastion John, 35 Duke st
Bird Saml. 26 Gloucester st
Bowden John, 5 James st
Brook Wm. 7 Waterloo st
Brown John, 12 George st
Chapman Thos. Wood, 2 Tavistock street
Clark John, 86 James st
Clark JohnA. B. 4 James st
Dell James, 48 James st
Earl Thomas, Granville st
EvansThs.,Cherrygarden st
Fielder Hy. 7 King st
Guard James, Tamar Whf; h 5 Portland place, M
1 Heath J. and W. H. 1 Catherine street
MabryW.&Son,45 Mount st
May Wm. 31 King st
1 Murch Jph. 1 Waterloo st
Nicholls Jno. R.69George st
Pitcher Robt.44 Cornwall st
1 Roberts John, Portland pl
Seldon Thos. 19 Market st
1 TruscottJosiah,111 Fore st
Warren Rd. 58 Cornwall st
WeymouthJ.&H.19King st

PAWNBROKERS.
Badge Jas. 5 Princess st
Beal Eliz., Boot lane
Bulford John Rodgers, 14 Marlborough street
Bush Geo. 10 Cornwall st
DowningG.20 Monument st
Emdon Abm. 14Ordnance st

Goodridge J. M. 20 Pond ln
Harvey Thos. 1 Cornwall st
Knight Chas. 12 Tavistk. st
Palmer Geo. 10 Pembroke st
Pearse Ths. 91 Pembroke st
Ryder Augusta, Cannon st
Ryder John, 34 William st
Ryder Rd. 6 William st
Treliving Eliz., Pembrk. st

PERFUMERS & HAIR DRESSERS.

Annis Wm. 15 Princess st
Babb John, 13 James st
Bennett John D. 26 Fore st
Brush Wm. 4 Duke st
Budge Robt. 13 Market st
Doherty Hy. 17 Pembroke st
Gardiner James, 11 Cross st
Gitsham Jas. 12 Queen st
Harris Wm., Cornwall st
Hennings Wm., Union ter
Holland Geo. 96 Fore st
Jago Jph. 12 Tavistock st
Lamb John, 64 James st
Leman John, 6 Lambert ope
Manley Jas. 2 Wm. st. M
Rider Andw. 8 Navy row
Scott John, 1 St Aubyn ope
Terlizzick Wm. 24 Fore st
Wakeham Jas. 60 George st
Wakeham Wm. 99 James st
Wakeham W. jun. 71 Geo. st
Watts Wm. 53 Fore st

PHYSICIANS.

Cocks John, 4 George st
Glasson Geo. 2 St Aubyn st
Rowe Fredk. 28 Ker st

PLUMBERS.

See Braziers & Painters.

POULTERERS.

Brent Nichls. 34 Cumbrld. st
Budd John, 12 Cross st

PRINTERS.

(See also Booksellers.)

Byers Wm. 116 Fore st
Colman Wm. 51 Fore st
Harris Hy. Vinton, Fore st
Hearle Geo. W. 118 Fore st
Heydon John, 104 Fore st
Keys Elias, 6 James st
Lidstone Roger, 107 Fore st
Pengelly Ths. H. 91 Fore st
Rattenbury Edw. Jas. 52 Queen street
Wood Chas. 3 Cathrn. st., and 5 Stafford hill
Wood Wm. 55 Fore st

PROFESSORS & TCHRS.

Burn Dd. Wm. *(music,)* Rose-hill; & Louisa, *(drawing,)* Rosehill, s
Burnard Rd. L. *(navigation,)* 6 Portland buildings, s
De la Rue P. *(French,)* 40 Ker street
Hunt Saml. 53 St Aubyn st
Lancaster Wm. 57 Geo. st
Row Wm. H. *(music,)* Trafalgar place
Towson John Thos. *(naval instr.)* 71 Fore street

Wollacott & Marshall, *(dancing,)* 8 George street

PROVISION DEALERS.

See also Shopkeepers, &c.

Avery S. C. 9 Market st
Palmer Thos., Duke st
Wyatt Fras. 18 Duke st

REGISTER OFFICES.

(For Servants.)

Aunger Smpn. 112 Fore st
Barrett M. 9 Fore street

ROPE, & TWINE MFRS.

Pellew Peter, 1 Bragg's alley
Squance Wm. 7 Tavistk. st
Squance Wm. 5 & 12 Fore st

SADDLERS, &c.

Beard Wm. Edwards, Fore st
Maynard Hy. 64 St Aubyn st

SAIL MAKERS.

Brockington Thos., Mutton cove; h 49 Clarence pl
Jervis & Banks, Richmd. wlk
Rider Hy. 3 John st. M

SAW & TOOL MFRS.

Lee Wm. 115 Fore street
Shaw John, 42 Catherine st

SHIP OWNERS.

(See pages 684-5.)

SHOPKEEPERS.

Allen Jph. 75 James st
Barratt Mary, Granby st
Ball Philippa, 25 John st
Beer My. A., Ordnance st
Bennett Rd. 15 Queen st
Biggins Robt. 58 Queen st
Bird Mary, 15 Granby st
Bradley Allen, 12 Market ln
Bradgate Hy., Cornwall st
Brook Betsy, 14 Princess st
Bunker Hy. 11 Queen st
Buss John, Prospect row
Chamber Edw., Moon st
Chown Louisa, Tavistock st
Chudleigh Wm. 97 Navy row
Clemens Thos., Tamar st. M
Coe J. J. 28 William st. M
Coke Rd. 87 Pembroke st
Collings Rt. 62 Tavistock st
Congdon M. C. 23 Marlbro. st
Cooke Nichls. 100 Pembrk. st
Courteys Chas., Pembrk. st
Crapp Roger, Doidge's well
Curtis Saml., Cornwall st
Davies Eliza, Pembroke st
Davis Richd. 13 Mount st
Edgeland Ann, Cherrygdn. st
Fielder Hy. 40 King st
Ford Wm., Doidge's well
Fox Saml. 52 Tavistock st
Freeman Wm. 39 Pembrk. st
Gay Margt., Pembroke st
Geaton Wm., Cornwall st
Giles John, 20 Quarry st
Glanville Wm., Fore st
Gordon Daniel, 15 Queen st
Halse Eliz. 1 Cumberld. st
Higman John, Ordnance sq
Hill Charles, 50 James st
Hockin James, 23 Granby st
Hodgkiss Saml. 38 Cornwl. st
Holland Chtte. 17 Marlbro' st
Holt Fredk. 11 Market st

Honey Jas. 16 Prospect row
Hooper Ann M., Princess st
Hooper Sarah, Princess st
Hoskin Agnes, 11 King st
Hoskin Hy. 57 Cornwall st
Hoskin Reuben, 20 Fore st
Jenkins Grace, Princess st
Jewell Geo. 79 Pembroke st
Joce Maria, 106 Pembrk. st
Johnson Wm. 74 Pembrk. st
Jory Hy. 10 Fore st
Julien Cath. 37 Chtte. st
Kendall Jas. 61 Glostr. st
Kitto Wm. 72 Pembroke st
Lacy Wm. 59 Princess st
Lacy Wm. 4 Pembroke st
Lamb Mary, Gloucester st
Lee Jph. 41 Queen st
Light Richd. 37 Keith st
Long Wm. 71 James st
Martin Wm., Boscowen pl
Mazzey Jane, Pembroke st
Mitchell Eliz. 3 St Aubyn ope
Morrell Wm. 14 Market st
Nepean My. 29 Wm. st. M
Norton Saml. 20 Cannon st
Paul Wm. 72 Navy row
Peard John, 42 Tavistk. st. s
Penrose Chas. 25 Dockwalls
Philp P. E. 5 Pembrk. st
Picken Edw. 65 James st
Pitcher Jthn., Cornwall st
Randall Sus. 11 Mt Cove st
Redwood Hy., Waterloo st. s
Rendell Ebnzr. 36 John st
Roberts Jthn., Cornwall st
Rogers Wm. Hy., Granby st
Rowe John, 14 Chapel st
Ryder Hugh, 37 Queen st
Seal Eliz. 37 Queen st
Shedwick John, 37 John st
Skinner P. 99 Pembroke st
Smeath John, 10 Boscowen pl
Sorlie Ann, Cannon st
Squire Thos., Francis alley
Stentiford Martha, South hl
Stephens John, 35 Pembrk. st
Stephens Jno. 16 Cornwall st
Stephens Wm., South hill
Street Henry, 14 King st
Stroud John, 14 William st
Sweet Chas. 3 William st
Sweet John, 13 Dockwalls
Symons Wm. 23 Chtte. st
Tapp Sarah, 1 George st
Tapper Sus. 16 Garden st. M
Taylor Jas., Wellington st
Thomas Geo., 8 Charlotte st
Thomas John, 31 Pembk. st
Tucker Sl. 12 Canterbury st
Vigars John, Monument st
Ward James, Dockwalls
Ward John, 74 Glostr. st
Warren Jph. 38 Cumbld. st
Webb Wm. 12 Marlboro' st
Weekes John, Cherrygdn. st
Western John, 1 George ln
Whitford J., Monument st
Willcocks My. 14 Wm. st
Williams Car. G. 89 Jas. st
Williams Mary, Dockwalls
Williams Sar. 10 Welngtn. st

Winter John, 13 Keith st. M
Yabsley Jno. 62 Pembrk. st
Yeo Isaac, 83 Pembroke st
Yoel Cath., George lane

SILVERSMITHS, &c.
Granville Saml. 48 Fore st
Ramsey Edw. 54 Fore st. s
Row Wm. H. 34 Fore st
Skerrett Geo. 37 Fore st

STAY MAKERS.
Budge Emma, 13 Market st
Coupland&Gilbard,Queen st
Durham M. A., Granby st
Hodgson M. 26 James st
Nicholl J. 31 James street
Pascoe Eliz., Tavistock st
Rowe Mrs., St Aubyn st
Walters Eliz. 49 Granby st

STONE AND MARBLE MASONS.
Hanger Saml., Mt. Cove pl
Taylor John, Pembroke st
Yelland John, Navy row

STRAW HAT MKRS.
Alger L. 24 Marlborough st
Avery Jane, 57 Navy row
Banbury Eliz. 4 Wm. st. M
Brooks Sarah, Mt. Cove pl
Buckingham C.,Tavistk. st
Bulford Har. 51 Ker st
Clements Ann, 3 Chtte. st
Cullum Jane, 7 Pym street
Dalman H., 26 George st
Davis & Tuckerman,15Market street
Downing C.23 Charlotte row
Gombe Eliz., Pembroke st
Gould Cath. 123 Navy row
Gould S. 8 Morice street
Gruzelier L., Waterloo st. s
Hayes L. 39 Charlotte st
Head Jane, 42 Mount st
Heard Jas. 11 Navy row
Mallet Eliz. 21 Gloucester st
Medlen Sus. 13 Ker street
Pearce Ann, 8 Moon street
Penfound Eliz. 15 Queen st
Perkins Eliz. 100 James st
Pincombe E. J. 24 Mkt. st
Powe Ann, 41 Navy row
Rundle S. J. 44 Navy row
Scobell & Trent, 2 Pond ln
Sleep My. S. 56 Cornwall st
Stevens Eliz. 103 Fore st
Thomas A. & M., Navy row
Treneman J. 18 Monumt. st
Wren Selina, 32 Mount st

SURGEONS.
Baldy John Patey, 23 Pembroke street
Bennett Jas. 54 George st
Cole Wm. 104 Navy row
Crossing (Thos.) & Little, (Jno.) 10 Morice sq. & 52 St Aubyn street
Dansey G.9St Michl.'s ter.s
De la Rue —, 40 Ker street
Evans Wm., Queen street
Folds Wm., Dockyard
Hallett John, 12 James st
Harrison Garland Foley Bayly, 29 Ker street

Kerswill Saml. 34 King st
Laity Rd. 9 St Aubyn st
May Jph. 5 St Aubyn st ; h 32 Trafalgar place
Moore Michl.38 Portld.pl.M
Proctor Geo. 10 George st
Reid John, Dockyard
Rolston Geo. 31 St Aubyn st
Rowe Frdk. 28 Ker st. & 5 Navy row
Rutter Ts. 13 St Aubyn st
SloggettWm.H. 86 Navy rw
Swain Paul Wm. 20 Ker st
Tripe Cornls. 27 Ker street
TripeLorenzoP.4StAubynst
Watson Robt. Mather, 7 St Jean D'Acre terrace, s
Welch Wm. 32 St Aubyn st

SURGEON DENTISTS.
Mould Thos. 21 St Aubyn st
Stephens Jas. C 35 St Aubyn st ; h 9 Tamar terrace

TAILORS.
(* are Mercers also.)
Axworthy Abel, 36 King st
Babb Wm. 34 Gloucester st
*Bastard John, 28 Fore st
Bate Henry, Market street
*Batten & Adams,50 Fore st
Blight&Dennaford,Chapel st
*Bowden Wm. 33 King st
Bradbury Wm. 28 Moon st
Bray Peter, Cherrygdn. st
Brimacombe Wm., Monument street
*Chinnock Rt. 46 Chapel st
Copplestone Jno. 2 Navy rw
Cowlyn Frns. 91 Fore street
Cowlyn Wm. 12 King st
Crapp John, 38 Navy row
Dawson Rd., Canterbury st
*Edmonds Rd. 70 Fore st
*Egg Edw. 32 Cathrn. st
Frost Edwin, 54 Duke st
German Rd. 93 Fore street
Goodridge Jas.,Jessamine ln
*Griffin John, 37 King st
Gubbs Rd. 52 Chtte. st. M
Hobb Jas. 46 Duke street
Hockins Chas. 99 James st
Hodge Jas. 55 Tavistock st
Hoyten Wm., Waterloo st. s
Husband Jas., Cornwall st
Huxtable John, Granby st
Jones Henry, 13 James st
Jones John, 17 Catherine st
Jones Thos. 64 Fore street
*Kemp Rd. 29 Fore street
*Knight Sl. 54 Queen st
*Lazarus & Co. 28 Cathn. st
Littleton Wm. 52 Fore st
Lobb Gregory, 48 James st
*Mackay Jas., Catherine st
Martin John, 76 James st
Merrifield J. 18 Princess st
Moon Benj., 52 Fore street
Morris Jas. 20 Princess st
*Nickols Wm 32 James st
*Olver Geo. 93 James st
Oram Edm. 39 St Aubyn st
*Pascoe Chas. 89 Fore st
Pearse John, Tavistock st

Pile Wm., James st. ope
Polkinghorne H.29Chapel st
Potam John, 59 Queen st
*Pote Rt. 47 King street
Rogers John, 49 Charlotte st
Scorey& Stephens,87 Fore st
Sims Sl. 12 Cumberland st
Spiller Thos. 41 Fore street
Stephens Jnthn., Cornwl. st
Stevens Wm. 3 Cross street
Stivey John, James st. ope
Stroud Rd. 12 Morice street
Swinhoe Rd. 10 Catherine st
*Symons John, 76 Fore st
Symons Peter, 45 Duke st
Wallworth Ts. 103 James st
Waycott Wm. 42 Ker street
Welham Danl. 67 Fore street
Welman Michl. 29 James st
Whitford James, 10 Ker st
Wilman Danl. 67 James st
Wilman Jph. 98 James st
Woollington John, Duke st

TALLOW CHANDLERS.
Hyne Saml. 80 Duke st
Jones Wm., Cornwall street
Miller Thos. 9 Pond lane
Pool Jas.&Wm.64Pembk.st
Snow Rt. 12 Market street
Tucker George & Sons,Pembroke street

TIMBER MERCHANTS.
Bird Vincent, Moon street
Collings John, Cumberld. st
Dyer Geo. 47 Chapel street
Gormully Wm. (mahogany) 32 Marlborough street
Hoar Hy. T. 41 James st
King Wm. 19 Mount street
Shaw John, 8 Fellow's pl. s
Webber John, Mount st
Wood Wm. 25 Mount st

TOBACCONISTS.
Crossman Thos. 46 King st
Gibson John, (mfr.) 9 Catherine street
Hoar Eliza, (mfr.) 94 Pembroke street
Levi Jacob M. 85 Fore st

TURNERS.
Gaul John, Ker street
Lane John, 25 Tavistock st

UMBRELLA MAKERS.
Crocker Eliz. 101 Navy row
Heard Hy. 33 Barrack st
Manning Rd. 8 Duke st

WATCH & CLOCK MKS.
Almond Rd. P. 14 Pond ln
Ching Wm. 10 Duke street
Croydon Chas. 27 Fore st
Dodd Edw. 33 Marlboro' st
Dorning Rt. 37 Ker street
Dymond Chs.27 St Aubyn st
Edwards Wm. & Son, 63 St Aubyn street
Gorfin Hy. 2 Marlboro' st
Gormully Pp. 92 Fore st
Kallansee Chas. 71 Fore st
Lancaster Thos. 56 Queen st
Leddra John, 43 King st
Libbey Danl. 42 Fore st

Mosser & Wehrle, *(German)*
10 Tavistock street
Ramsey Edw. 54 Fore st
Sheppard Ts. 14 Morice st
Skerrett Geo. 37 Fore st
Treliving Jno., Catherine st

WHEELWRIGHTS.

Bews Wm., Tamar st. M
Northcott J., Brunswk. Ctgs

Sleep Elijah, *(& millwgt.)*
40 Granby street

WINE AND SPIRIT MERCHANTS.

Banfield Jno. Maberley & Co. 61 Fore street
Cundy My. A. 109 James st
Dean Wm. 78 Princess st
Devonport Wine Co.,Mkt. st
Fox Bnj. & Sons,6 Cathrn. st

Franklyn G. 57 Gloster st. M
Franklyn Thos. 45 Fore st
Hawker & Co. 12 Barrack st;
h 3 Trafalgar place, s
Jasper Eliz. 46 Cherrygdn. st
Moon Benj. 31 Fore st
Pool Wm. 112 Fore street
Rundle & Sons, 75 George st
Woollacott John, 77 Fore st

COACHES, OMNIBUSES, STEAM PACKETS, &c.,

Noticed with Plymouth, at pages 687 to 689, convey or forward passengers, &c. to and from Devonport; and an Omnibus runs through the "three towns" every ten minutes, and calls at the principal Inns.

OMNIBUSES *to Tavistock,* Newson's daily, from Market House Inn, 8 morning; and Avent's, from Carlton Inn, Mon. Wed. & Fri. 6½ mg. To *Looe & Fowey,* from the Fountain Inn, Wed. & Sat. 6 evening.

To *Boscastle,* Gilbert's, every Wed. 8 morning, from Portsmouth Passage House.

COACHES *to Kingsbridge,* at 4 aftn. from the Royal and London Hotels; and to *Cornwall,* through *Liskeard, &c.,* at 7½ morning, and 2 afternoon.

STEAM PACKETS leave North Corner every Tues. Thurs. & Sat., at 4 aftn., for *Calstock, &c.,* calling at the intermediate quays on the river Tamar; and *Market Boats* ply on the same afternoons to *Beer, Forder, Morwellham, Tideford, &c.* There are *sailing vessels to London* every eight days from Mutton Cove.

CARRIERS from the Inns.

Marked 1, *stop at Dock-Gates;* 2, *Fountain;* 3, *Golden Lion;* 4, *Oxford Inn;* 5, *Globe;* 6, *Market House;* 7, *Portsmouth Passage; and* 8, *Tavistock Inn.*

Barnstaple, 5 Pridham & Lake, Wed. & Fri.; & King, Thursday
Bideford, 6 Newson, Mon Wed. and Friday; and Brook, Saturday

Bodmin, 4 Lapham, Fri.; 2 Levers, &c., Tues. Wed. & Thurs.; & Hancock, from 10 Navy row, Monday
Boscastle, 7 Nichols, Tuesday
Brixham, 5 Shears, Thursday
Bude, 5 Cobbledick, Friday
Callington, 7 Dawe, Betty, Guy, &c., Mon. Tues. Thurs. & Sat. Vans every Friday from several houses
Chagford, Guskett, from Barrack st., Tuesday
Hartland, 8 Jenkins, Saturday
Kirkhampton, 6 Mountjoy, Thursday
Kingsbridge, 5 Luscombe, Tues. and & Fri.; & 6 Sawyer, Tuesday
Launceston (see Tavistock)
Lifton, 6 Paddon, Saturday
Liskeard, 1 Roberts & Elford, Tues. Wed. Fri. & Sat.; 2 Stanton & Levers, Tues. & Fri.; 2 Kellow, daily, to all parts of *West Cornwall*
Looe, 6 Hill, Tues.; 3 Snell, Wed. and Sat.; and Courtenay, from 10 Princess st., Tu. & Fri.; & 8 Searle, Thu.
Menheniot, 6 Ough, Thursday
Moreton, 8 Wills, Thursday
Okehampton, 6 Maddeford, Wednesday
St Austle, 2 Kellow, daily
St Clear, 6 Ough, Thursday
St Teath, 7 Oliver, Thursday
Tamerton, 5 Tremeer, Monday
Tavistock, Newson's Omnibus daily, 8 morning; Maddeford, Wed.; & Paddon, Sat. Vans every Friday, at 5½ evening, from several places
Thornberry, 8 Yeo, Saturday
Torquay, Paignton, &c., 3 Tozer, Thu.
Truro, 2 Kellow, daily
Wadebridge, 2 Cayzer & Body, Thurs.

NORTH TAWTON AND WINKLEIGH HUNDRED

Is a fertile and long narrow district, in the Northern Parliamentary Division of Devon, stretching about 18 miles from north to south, and varying from 7 to less than 4 in breadth. The river Taw flows through a picturesque valley on its eastern side, and receives here several tributary streams. The whole Hundred is in the Archdeaconry of Barnstaple, and in the Deaneries of Barnstaple, Chulmleigh, and Torrington; and comprises 21 parishes, of

2 H 3

which the following is an enumeration, shewing their territorial extent and their population in 1841:—

Parishes.	Acres.	Pop.	Parishes.	Acres.	Pop.
§Ashreigny	5586	1088	§Dowland	1700	244
‖Atherington	3425	629	*Down St. Mary	2229	407
§Bickington, High.	3993	895	*Eggesford	1217	168
*Bow, or Nymet Tracey	2962	973	*Lapford	3750	706
			*Nymet Rowland	595	102
*Brushford	1000	144	†Tawton North	5328	1728
†Bondleigh	1784	342	†Nymet Broad	451	50
‡Burrington	5330	1244	*Wembworthy	1934	418
*Chawleigh	5478	850	§Winkleigh	9118	1650
*Clanaborough	800	69	*Zeal Monachorum	2946	649
*Coleridge	3670	677			
§Dolton	3476	922	Total	66,672	13,955

UNION:—*Those marked * are in Crediton, + in Okehampton, § in Torrington, ‡ in South Molton, and ‖ in Barnstaple Union.*

Petty Sessions are held monthly at Chulmleigh and Winkleigh, alternately, and Messrs. Pearse, Son, and Crosse, of South Molton, are *clerks* to the magistrates.

ASHREIGNY, or *Ring's Ash*, is a village and parish, 4 miles W. by S. of Chulmleigh, and contains 1088 souls, and 5586 acres of fertile land, including the hamlets of *Riddlecombe* and *Hayes*. The Rev. P. T. Johnson, B.D., is lord of the manor, formerly belonging to the Reigny and other families, but part of the soil belongs to the Hon. Newton Fellowes, Mrs. Pyncombe's Trustees, Miss Carew, the Rev. S. Alford, the Rev. W. P. Thomas, and a few smaller owners. Here is an annual fair on the Wednesday after January 30th. The *Church* (St. James,) is an ancient structure, with a tower and six bells; and the living is a *rectory*, valued in K.B. at £24, and in 1831 at £402. The Rev. P. T. Johnson, B.D., is patron, and the Rev. G. Johnson is the incumbent, and has a good residence and 78A. of glebe. The tithes were commuted in 1841 for £460 per annum. Here is a Wesleyan Chapel, and the parish has £10 a year from Mrs. Pyncombe's charity, for schooling poor children.

Barlow Rev George, curate
Bird Wm. wheelwright
Boundy James, beer seller
Boundy Sml. shopkeeper & schoolmr
Callard Robt. & Eddy Thos. *smiths*
Cruwys Mr Geo. ‖ Lane T. shopkpr
Featherstone John, vict. Union Inn
Johnson Rev George, rector

FARMERS.
Babbage John
Bolt David
Cole Samuel
Fishleigh Fras.
Hancock John
Harris Wm.
Kelland John
Ley John

Mitchell Philip
Pippin Wm.
Sheere Christphr
Short Bernard
Skinner Wm.
Tout John
Turner Jph.
Ware Richard

ATHERINGTON, a village and parish in the Taw valley, 8 miles W. by S. of South Molton, and E.N.E. of Torrington, has 629 souls, and 3325 acres of land, including the hamlets of *Langridge* and *Eastacombe*. A. Bassett, Esq., is lord of the manor of *Umberleigh*, which extends over this and High Bickington parish, and had an ancient *chantry chapel*, which was pulled down in 1800. *Buriate* is an estate belonging to Gonville and Caius College, Cambridge; and *Wootton* belongs to the representatives of the Melhuish family. The *Church* (St. Mary,) is a fine old structure, with several ancient monuments and brasses, and a carved oak screen, which was brought from Umberleigh chapel. The *rectory*, valued in K.B. at £26. 2s. 1d., and in 1831 at £459, has a manor attached to it, and is in the patronage

and incumbency of the Rev. James Arthur, B.A., who has 205a. 3r. 21p. of glebe, and a good residence, erected in 1837, at the cost of £1000. The tithes were commuted in 1839, for £416 per annum. In the parish are two small chapels belonging to Wesleyans and Baptists.

	FARMERS.	Jones Richard
Arthur Rev Jas., B.A. *Rectory*		King James
Beer Wm. vict. Carpenters' Arms	Arthur George	Lemon John
Clarke John, & Losemore Wm. *smiths*	Beer Thomas	Ley John
Down John, maltster	Bowden Thos.	Norman Robert
Eastman Robt. vict. White Hart	Brownscombe Ts.	Sage John
Groves Thos. gent. *Umberleigh Hs.*	Cawsey J. & R.	Slowman John
Lang John, vict. New Inn	Down H. & W.	Tucker Wm.
Scoyne John, vict. Bell	Harris Isabella	Webber John
Stedeford Geo. shopkpr. *Post Office*	Hunt Thomas	

BICKINGTON, (HIGH) 8 miles E. by N. of Torrington, and N.W. of Chulmleigh, has in its parish 895 souls, and 3993 acres of land, including *North and South Hele, Stowford*, and other scattered farms. It had formerly a *market* every Wednesday, which was discontinued about 1725, and it has still a cattle fair on the Monday after May 14th. The parish is in several manors, and belongs A. Bassett, Esq., Mrs. Pyncombe's Trustees, the Rev. W. P. Stowell, John Bremridge, Esq., the Rev. P. Johnson, and a few smaller owners. The *Church* is an ancient structure, with a tower and six bells, and the *rectory*, valued in K.B. at £39. 7s. 7d., and in 1831 at £532, is in the patronage and incumbency of the Rev. W. P. Stowell, who has a pleasant residence and 157a. 3r. 34p. of glebe. The Baptists have a chapel here, and the poor have the interest of £40 left by Joshua Tucker, in 1721. The parish school has £10 a year from Mrs. Pyncombe's Charity.

	FARMERS.	Richards Henry
Bealey Thos. vict. Black Horse	Alford Henry	Richards Thos.
Bremridge John, gent. *Nether Grove*	Alford Mary	Slee Richard
Brownscombe Chas. maltster & vict. Golden Lion	Cann Thomas	Squire Samuel
Darch John, carpenter	Cook Ml. *Langley*	Webber John
Davey Wm. schoolmr. & shoemaker	Cowman John	Webber Richard
Gibbs Henry, vict. Commercial Inn	Dunn Sl. *Deptford*	Woollacott Rt.
Jones Charles Richard, surgeon	Friend Wm. *Hele*	SHOPKEEPERS.
Stowell Rev W. P. *Rectory*	Gooding Eliz.	Clemett Thomas
Turner Wm. shoemaker	Harris Thomas	Smith Wm.
BLACKSMITHS.	Matthews Richd.	Turner John
Heal John	*Stowford*	
Heaman John	Parker Thomas	

BLACKSMITHS.	BUTCHERS.	
Heal John	Moore John	
Heaman John	Moore Richard	

BOW, or NYMET TRACEY, is a small, decayed market town, on the banks of a rivulet, 7½ miles W. of Crediton. Its parish contains 973 souls, and 2962 acres of land. The manor anciently belonged to the Tracey family, and afterwards passed to the Martin, Audley, Fitzwarren, Bourchier, and Lethbridge families. S. C. Hamlyn, Esq., Samuel Wreford, Wm. Hill, and several smaller owners, have estates here. About 80 houses and cottages were destroyed by fire in the parish in 1833 and 1835. The weekly market, formerly held on Thursday, is now obsolete; but here is a great *cattle market* on the second Thursday in March, established in 1815; and also two *fairs* for cattle, &c., on Holy Thursday, and on November 22nd, when that date falls on Thursday, and when not, on the Thursday after. The *Church* (St. Bartholomew,) stands nearly a mile south of the town, and is a fine antique fabric. The *rectory*, valued in K.B. at £19. 8s. 9d., and in 1831 at £402, with that of Broad Nymet annexed to it, is in the patronage of F. Vandermeulen, Esq., and incumbency of the Rev. F. Vandermeulen, who

has a good residence and 68A. of glebe. The tithes were commuted in 1840, for £335 per annum. The church land and houses let for about £29 a year. The *Free School*, founded in 1682, by John Gould, has 2½A. of land, and the master teaches 10 free scholars. The poor parishioners have about £24 a year from tenements left by *John Hoyle*, in 1636; and about £7. 10s. per annum from the gifts of *Christopher Lethbridge* and other donors.

Bibbings John, schoolmr. & agent to Royal Farmers' Ins. Co. & Provident Building Society
Ellacott James, vict. White Hart
Harvey Grace, vict. King's Arms
Harvey John, vict. Tradesmen's Inn
Hatherley Hy. & Geo. blacksmiths
Hill Wm. jun. auctioneer, &c.
Jackman Wm. saddler, &c.
Madge Thomas, glazier, &c.
Martin John, butcher
Parish John, sen., mason, &c.
Rowden John, blacksmith
Rowden James, baker, butcher, and chandler
Sanders Jas. Lee, tanner, &c.
Sanders Mr Jas. || Packer Wm.
Stuckey Wm. vict. *Post Office*
Tolley Wm. seedsman
Tucker Geo. vict. Ebrington Arms
Vandermeulen Rev F. *Rectory*

Warren Wm. Rt. surgeon, *Gratton*
Watts Wm. cattle dealer
Webber Wm. cooper
Wreford Saml. Esq. *Gratton House*

CARPENTERS.
Ellacott George
Ellacott John
Tucker George
Ward Wm.

FARMERS.
Ellworthy Thos.
Elworthy John
Faylor Wm.
Heard John
Henderson John
Hill Wm. sen.
Hole John
Kelland Cphr.
Partridge John
Stone Rd. *miller*

MALTSTERS.
Arscott Richard
Bawdon Thomas
SHOPKEEPERS.
Jerman John
Parish John, jun.
Parish Grace
Webber Wm.
TAILORS.
Alford John
Stuckey John
White John

POST OFFICE at Ann Stuckey's. Letters *via* Exeter

BRUSHFORD, a small parish in the Taw valley, 5 miles S. by W. of Chulmleigh, has only 144 souls, and about 1000 acres of land, nearly all the property, and in the occupation of the *Luxton family*, to whom it has belonged since the reign of Elizabeth, previous to which the manor and tithes belonged to Hartland Abbey. The *Church* (St. Mary,) is a small structure, with a tower and three bells. George Luxton, Esq., is impropriator of the tithes and patron of the perpetual curacy, valued at £51, and now held by the Rev. John Luxton, B.A. The other principal residents are Robert Luxton, gent., *Barton;* Robert G. and George Luxton, *corn millers;* George and Lawrence Luxton, gent., *Higher Reeve;* and Samuel Pope, blacksmith.

BONDLEIGH, or BUNDLEIGH, a small village in the Taw valley, 7 miles S. by W. of Chulmleigh, and N.N.E. of Okehampton, has in its parish 342 souls, and 1784 acres of land, mostly the property of the Trustees of the late Earl of Egremont, who are lords of the manor and patrons of the *rectory*, valued in K.B. at £10. 17s. 8½d., and in 1831 at £232. The Rev. G. Stone is the present rector, and has 55A. 2R. 33P. of glebe, and a thatched residence. The tithes were commuted in 1842, for £200 per annum. The *Church* (St. James,) has a tower and four bells, and here is a small chapel occupied by Baptists and Bible Christians. The poor have the interest of £18, left by several donors. DIRECTORY,—John Baker and George Tancock, *blacksmiths;* George Burridge, *shopkeeper;* Jno. Crocker, *shoemaker;* Christopher Routley, vict. *Wyndham Arms;* Catherine Seldon, schoolmrs.; Rev. George Stone, *Rectory;* and Cpr. Brook, Joseph Burridge, Wm. Dart, Wm. Ellacott, Jph. Goss, Jonas Isaac, John Kelland, Ann Potter, John and Rd. Raymont, Rd. Seldon, John and Thomas Stoneman, and Henry Western, *farmers.*

BURRINGTON, a pleasant village, 4 miles N.W. by W. of Chulmleigh, has in its parish 5330 acres of land, including *Halsbury, Callard, Northcote*, and other scattered farms. The parish had 1244 souls when the census was taken in 1841, but they included 196 visitors at the village *fair*, on Trinity Monday. The Hon. Newton Fellowes has a manor and estate here, but a great part of the parish belongs to the Rev. P. Johnson, L. W. Buck, Esq., R. Chichester, Esq., and the Rev. James Buckingham, B.C.L. The latter is patron and incumbent of the *vicarage*, valued in K.B. at £13. 11s. 3d., and in 1831 at £301. The tithes were commuted in 1838, the vicarial for £260, and the rectorial for £308. 10s. The latter belong to Mr. Tout. The vicar's glebe is about 90 acres. The *Church* (Holy Trinity,) is an ancient structure, with a tower and six bells, and a handsome screen. The Wesleyans and Baptists have small chapels here. The poor have £2. 10s. yearly from Pyncombe's and Tossel's charities.

Arscott Wm. vict. Portsmouth Arms
Buckingham Rev Jas., B.C.L. vicar
Cole Thos. and Pickard Jas. shoprs
Davis Rev Samuel, curate
Dillon John, druggist, &c
Eastmond Wm. vict. London Inn
Headon Jas. vict. Barnstaple Inn
Woolway Giles, schoolmaster

BLACKSMITHS.
Bendley John
Harris John

CARPENTERS.
Govier J. L. G.

Thorne Wm.

FARMERS.
Alford George
Alford James
Babbage Gilbert

Babbage James
Cole Jno. sen
Cook Richard
Dillon James
Down Thomas
Heaman Jane
Heaman Robert
Kingdon John
Lock Wm.
Manning Chas.
Maynard Cath.
Middleton Robt.
Pickard Jnth.

Prowse Robert
Richards Wm.
Rippon John
Rowe John
Shobrook Thos.
Shopland Wm.
Snell James
Snell John
Webber John
Westaway John
Wright John
Wright Robert
Wright Wm.

CHAWLEIGH, a parish and village on the south side of the Little Dart valley, 2 miles S.E. of Chulmleigh, contains 850 inhabitants, and 5478 acres of land ; and has two *cattle fairs*, on May 6 and the Tuesday before the last Thursday in October. L. W. Buck, Hy. Reed, Cpr. Northcote, and the Rev. J. Russell have estates here, but about three-fourths of the parish belong to the Hon. Newton Fellowes, who is also lord of the manor, and patron of the *rectory*, valued in K.B. at £25. 14s. 2d., and in 1831 at £501, and now in the incumbency of the Rev. P. F. Clay, M.A., who has an ancient residence and 95 acres of glebe. The tithes were commuted in 1849 for £470 5s. 10d. per annum. The *Church* (St. James,) has an embattled tower, six bells, and a handsomely carved screen. The Independents and Bible Christians have chapels here. The parish has 24a. of land, ten houses, and several gardens let for about £90, which is mostly applied in the service of the church. The *Free School* and master's house are vested with the trustees of the parish lands ; and here is another school supported by the rector. The poor parishioners have about £6 yearly from various bequests.

Alford Saml., schoolmr. and shopr.
Anstey Wm. & Hooper Saml.,shoprs.
Clay Rev Pelham F., M.A. *Rectory*
Dilling Geo. & Webber Wm., smiths
Edworthy Rd., wheelgt. & vict. Oak
Edworthy Thomas, wheelwright
Gough Richard, schoolmaster
Luxton Thos., vict. Schoolmr's Arms
Middleton J., saddler and grocer
Reed Thos., vict. London Inn
Saunders John, shoemaker
Webber Giles, shopkeeper

FARMERS.
Cann J. and R.
Cole Wm.
Drake John
Ford Edmund
Kemp T. and W.
Lewis Henry
Phillips H. & Rt.
Stone Mill
Reed Henry
Reed Edward

Reed Richard
Saunders Antny.
Saunders Jeffrey
Saunders Wm.
Snell Edward
Snell Wm.
Stone Richard
Vickery John
Woolway John
Wreford Matw.

CLANABOROUGH, 5 miles W.N.W. of Crediton, is a small parish, containing only 69 souls, and 800 acres of land, belonging to W. and S. Wreford, J. Sillifant, Esq., and a few smaller owners. The *Church* (St. Petrock,) is a small antique structure, with a tower and three bells. The *rectory*, valued in K.B. at £5. 17s. 3½d., and 1831 at £171, is in the patronage of the Lord Chancellor, and incumbency of the Rev. Peter Glubb, of Little Torrington. The glebe is 50A., and the tithes were commuted in 1839 for £95 per annum. *Directory :* Rev. H. A. Hughes, *curate ;* Wm. Wreford, Esq., *Barton ;* and John Gibbings and Thos. Stone, *farmers.*

COLERIDGE, or COLDRIDGE, 5 miles S. of Chulmleigh, and east of Winkleigh, has in its parish 677 souls, and 3670 acres of fertile land, including the hamlet of *Leigh,* and a number of scattered farms. A fair is held in the village on the first Tuesday in March. The Hon. Newton Fellowes is lord of the manor, and owns a great part of the soil, and the rest belongs to the trustees of the late Earl of Egremont, Mrs. Parker, and several smaller owners. The *Church* (St. Mary,) is a fine antique fabric, with a beautifully carved screen, and six musical bells. In the chancel is an effigy of one of the Evans family. The *vicarage,* valued in K.B. at £7. 8s. 9d., and in 1831 at £142, is in the patronage of the Bishop of Exeter, and incumbency of the Rev. J. S. Townshend, who has 17A. of glebe, and a good residence, built about 12 years ago, at the cost of £500. The tithes were commuted in 1844, the vicarial for £155, and the rectorial for £200. The latter belong to the Hon. Newton Fellowes, who partly supports the parish school. The Plymouth Brethren have a small chapel here. A tomb in the church records the death of three brothers, who were killed by lightning.

Collins Ann, shopkeeper
Dart John, blacksmith and victualler, Ring of Bells
Hancock Wm., shopr. & carpenter
Hancock John, carpenter
Harris John, vict. Taw Bridge
Kentisbeare J., vict. Stag's Head
Mashford Joseph, schoolmaster
Mashford Josiah, shoemaker
Simmons John, blacksmith
Townshend Rev. J. Smith, *vicar*
Webber Thos. vict. Ancient Inn

FARMERS. (* *are Owners.*)
Dart Samuel
Densham Rd.
Fisher Wm.
Gibbings Rd.
Harris John
* Isaac Fras.
Kelland W. F.
* Kingdon John, *East Leigh*
Lang Edward
* Luxton Robt.
* Luxton Thos.
Partridge Reed
Partridge Wm.
Reed John
Reed Richard
Rice Joseph
Routley James
Western Henry
* Wreford Wm.

DOLTON, or DOWLTON, 6 miles N. by E. of Hatherleigh, and 4 miles N.W. by W. of Winkleigh, has in its parish 922 souls, and 3476 acres of land ; and has two cattle *fairs,* on the Wednesday before the 25th of March, and the Thursday before the 1st of October. Mr. Thos. Owen is lord of the manor, anciently called *Duellone,* but the soil belongs to many proprietors. *Halsdon House* is the seat of J. H. Furse, Esq., whose family has been seated there since 1680. The *Church* (St. Edmund,) is a venerable structure, with a tower and five bells, and the living is a *rectory,* valued in K.B. at £20. 16s. 8d., and in 1831 at £363. The Rev. Peter Johnson, B.D., is patron, and the Rev. Wm. Karslake is the incumbent, and has a fine old residence, and 121A. of glebe. The tithes were commuted in 1844 for £338. 7s. 7d. per annum. The Baptists and Plymouth Brethren have small chapels here. The poor have the dividends of £117. 19s. 10d. four per cent stock, left by Grace Jenn in 1809, and the interest of £24. 10s. left by unknown donors.

Arnold Mr Wm. || Collins Mr
Budd Daniel, shopkeeper
Budd Robert, grocer and draper

Bright John, tinner and brazier
Burdon George, relieving officer
Chambers Robert, shoemaker

Cox Richard, shoemaker
Friend Henry, maltster
Furse Jno. Hy., Esq. *Halsdon House*
Hancock John, parish clerk
Heaman George, wheelwright
Heard Eliz., smith & vict. Royal Oak
Heard Rt., smith & vict. Union
Karslake Rev Wm. rector & r. dean
Lyne Samuel, blacksmith
Lyne Thomas, vict. New Inn
Owen Geo., surgeon, and Miss E.
Parker John, excise officer

Risden Wm., surgeon and registrar
Tardrew Lieut. George, R.N.

FARMERS.

Bissett Nathl.
Brook John
Budd John
Budd Robert
Budd Wm.
Friend John
Harris Wm.
Heamen Wm.
Hodge R. *Stoford*

Hooper John
Hooper Thomas
Lyne John
Sloman Mark
Stanbury John, *Cherubeer*
Stanbury Rd.
Trick John
Wadland Henry

DOWLAND parish, 4½ miles N.N.E. of Hatherleigh, comprises 244 souls, and 1668 acres of land, including *Upcott*. Sir S. H. Northcote, Bart., is lord of the manor, owner of most of the soil, impropriator of the tithes, and patron of the perpetual curacy, valued in 1831 at only £81, and now held by the Rev. J. R. Ruse, of Monk's Okehampton. The *Church* is a Gothic fabric with a tower and five bells. The poor have 50s. a year out of the great tithes, left by Hugh Stafford in 1671. An old building, called the Church House, is occupied by paupers.

Ash Alexander, beer seller
Batter Simon, shopkeeper
Hill John, wheelwright
FARMERS.
Brook Philip | Folland James

Crocker Samuel, *Upcott*
Hooper Henry, *Barton*

Hooper William, *Eastacott*
Lethern Thos.
Lyne George

DOWN ST. MARY, 6 miles N.W. by W. of Crediton, has in its parish 407 souls, and 2229 acres of land. Henry Charles Sturt, Esq. is lord of the manor and owner of most of the soil, but Bradford Barton belongs to B. Radford, Esq., the patron of the *rectory*, valued in K.B. at £12. 13s. 4d., and in 1831 at £275. The Rev. W. T. A. Radford, B.A. is the incumbent, and has 50a. of glebe, and a neat Gothic residence, built in 1846, at the cost of £1600. The *Church* is an ancient structure, with a curious Norman tympanum over the south door.

Avery John, beer seller
Bushell Samuel, schoolmaster
Dunn Wm. vict. Union
Partridge Andrew, vict. Sturt's Arms
Radford Rev Wm. T. A., *Rectory*
Slee Richard, shopkeeper

FARMERS.
Cheriton Joseph
Cheriton J. jun
Cheriton Wm.
Kelland John

May Roger
May Robert
Moon Thomas
Morris John
Searl John

EGGESFORD parish, in Taw vale, 2½ miles S. of Chulmleigh, has 168 inhabitants, and 1216 acres of land, nearly all the property of the *Hon. Newton Fellowes*, the lord of the manor, who is son of the late, and brother and heir of the present Earl of Portsmouth. On coming to this and other estates, formerly belonging to his mother's family, he assumed the name of Fellowes, in place of Wallop, his paternal name. Old *Eggesford House* was the seat of the Lords Chichester in the 17th century, and was rebuilt by W. Fellowes, Esq. in 1718, but was taken down about 26 years ago. The present seat of the Hon. Newton Fellowes is a neat mansion, standing in the adjoining parish of Wembworthy. He is patron of the *rectory*, valued in K.B. at £7. 18s. 9d., and in 1831 at £132, and now enjoyed by the Rev. P. F. Clay, M.A., of Chawleigh. The *Church* (All Saints,) is a small structure, with a tower and two bells. The poor have the interest of £30, left by the Rev. John Churchill. The Parsonage is a new building, and the glebe

is about 75A., of which 29A. is woodland. The tithes were commuted in 1847 for £61. 16s. 6d. per annum.

Davey Rt., tailor, and Ann, schoolms.
Reed Ann, shopkeeper
Roberts Rev Wm. P., B.A. curate

FARMERS.
Powell Thomas
Reed Geo. & Rd.

Ruddall George
Shopland John
Snell John

LAPFORD, a pleasant village and parish in Taw vale, 5 miles S.E. of Chulmleigh, has 706 inhabitants, 3750 acres of land, and a *fair* on the Monday after the festival of St. Thomas-a-Becket. It includes the hamlet of *Eastington*, and a number of scattered farm houses, some of which are fine old " bartons," especially Bury and Kelland Bartons, the former of which was long the seat of the ancient family of Bury. The manor was parcel of the honour of Torrington, and was dismembered many years ago. The soil now belongs to many proprietors. *Irishcombe*, near East Worlington, is a detached member of this parish, at the distance of about 6 miles, and belongs to the Keats family, but was formerly the seat of the Notts. The [*Church* (St. Thomas-a-Becket,) is a fine old structure, with a tower and six bells, and an ancient screen and rood loft. The *rectory*, valued in K.B. at £15. 1s. 10½d. is in the patronage of W. Tanner, Esq., and incumbency of the Rev. J. A. Radford, who has a good residence, and 158A. of glebe. The tithes were commuted in 1840 for £404. 16s. 2d. per annum. The Wesleyans and Independents have chapels here, and the poor have a yearly rent-charge of 20s. left by Alex. Arundel in 1627.

Challice George, blacksmith
Clarke Wm., machine maker
Cork Rev Edward, (*Indpt.*)
Delve Richard, seedsman
Ellis Rd. vict. Maltsters' Arms
Hoard Wm. wheelwright
May Wm. tailor ; & Harriet, shopr.
Northcott Roger, vict. Malt Shovel
Partridge Mrs Sarah, *Wood House*
Radford Rev J. A., *Rectory*
Richards Wm. wheelwright, and P. parish clerk

Rouncefell James, beer seller
FARMERS. (* *are Owners.*)
Balman Edward
* Balman Thos.
Challice Richd.
* Croote Wm. & Son, *Higher Ml.*
* Densham Wm. *Bury Barton*
Gown John
* Hosegood John
* Kelland John

* Kelland J. jun
* Kelland Pp.
* Kelland P. jun
Lavis Edward
* Moon John, *Kelland Barton*
Pike Richard
Raymont Rd.
Saunders Josias
* Snell John

NYMET ROWLAND, or *Rowland's Leigh*, is a small parish in the Taw valley, 4 miles S. by E. of Chulmleigh, containing only 102 souls, and 591A. 1R. 25P. of land, mostly belonging to Mr. Jas. Partridge, of the *Barton*, and Mr. John Wreford, of *Cleavehanger*. The *Heal farm* is occupied by Wm. Cann. The manor was dismembered many years ago. The *Church* (St. Bartholomew,) is a small structure, with a tower and three bells. The *rectory*, valued in K.B. at £6. 1s. 3d., is in the patronage of Wm. Tanner, Esq., and incumbency of the Rev. T. R. Dickinson, M.A., who has 71 acres of glebe, but no parsonage. The tithes were commuted in 1842 for £71 per annum.

NORTH TAWTON, a small ancient town, pleasantly situated on the east side of Taw valley, 6½ miles N.E. of Okehampton, and 10 miles W. of Crediton, has in its parish 1728 inhabitants, and about 5350 acres of land, exclusive of *Ilton Moor* and *Stone Moor*, now being enclosed and cultivated. It was anciently a market and borough town, and is still governed by a portreeve elected annually, who has a small field during his year of office. From its ancient appellation of Cheping Tawton, it is evident that it had a market long before the grant of John Valletort in 1270, of a market on Wednesday and a fair for three days at the festival of St. Nicholas. The market, which was afterwards held on Friday, was discontinued about

1720; but in 1849, a small *Market House* was erected in the town at the cost of £750, raised in £5 shares, and the market was re-established, to be held on Thursday. Here are three annual *fairs*, on the third Tuesdays in April and December, and the second Tuesday in October. In the town is a large *tan yard* and a *woollen factory*, the latter of which has been employed in the manufacture of *serges, &c.*, from a very early period. Most of the modern brick and slated houses occupy the sites of old thatched *cob* buildings, which were burnt down during the last 30 years. The manor was an ancient demesne of the Crown, and was held successively by the Valletort, Champernowne, St. Leger, and Fellowes families, the latter of whom purchased it in 1718. The Hon. Newton Fellowes is now lord of the manor and owner of a great part of the parish, and the rest belongs to the Trustees of the late Lord Rolle, and several smaller owners. *Ashridge House* is the seat of Wm. Orchard, Esq.; *Crook Burnell*, alias *Stone*, belongs to the Sturt family; and *Nicholls Nymet Barton* belongs to John Wreford, Esq. Near the church is a moated site, supposed to have been the ancient seat of the Valletorts. The *Church* (St. Peter,) is an ancient structure, with a tower containing six bells, and crowned by a wooden spire. The *rectory*, valued in K.B. at £32. 4s. 7d., and in 1831 at £884, is in the patronage and incumbency of the Rev. G. Hole, B.C.L., of Chulmleigh, whose son officiates, and occupies the *Rectory House*, a good residence in the Elizabethan style. The glebe is 95A., and the tithes were commuted in 1844 for £797. 15s. 10d. per annum. The Independents and Bible Christians have small chapels here. The *Church Lands and Cottages* are let for about £28 a year. The *Free School* was endowed in 1746 by the Rev. Rd. Hole, with a house and 10A. of land at West Newton. The poor have about 26s. 8d. yearly from the gifts of Cphr. Kelland and Edmund Rowland.

Blight Samuel, tailor and stationer
Budd Christian, M.D. surgeon
Bulleid Samuel, maltster
Chapple John, land surveyor, and agent to the Sun Fire office
Collihole Wm. saddler, agent to West of England Insurance Co., &c.
Day Wm. blacksmith
Durant Captain John
Durant Wm. draper, & John, saddler
Ellis John, schoolmaster
Fulford Robert, solicitor
Gill John, watch and clock maker
Gillard George, solicitor
Gowman Ts. & Pyke Jno. shoemkrs
Hole Rev. G. jun. curate, *Rectory*
Ho er John, blacksmith
Letnern Wm. timber merchant
Lethern John M. auctioneer, &c.
Morris John Wm. surgeon
Orchard Wm. gent. *Ashridge House*
Pedler Wm. draper, &c.
Pillman Jonas, cooper
Ponsford John, grocer
Pyke Hugh, assistant overseer
Rodd Francis, schoolmaster
Skinner John, gent. *Westacott*

Stanton Jph. H. R. druggist
Stoneman Rt. & John, butchers, &c.
Sweet Mr Chas. S|| Tucker G. tailor
Tamlin Thomas, ironmonger
Taylor Lanct. and Pp. shoemakers
Vicary Gilbert, serge & flannel mfr
Vicary Wm. tanner &c.
Vilven Geo. and Richd. tailors
Western James, currier, &c.
White Robert, cabinet maker
Wreford John, Esq., *Nicholls Nymet*
Wilkey Mary, grocer, &c.

INNS AND TAVERNS.
Fountain, Wm. Hawkins
George Inn, Wm. Durant
Gostwyck Arms, John Bickham
Ring of Bells, Wm. Fisher.

FARMERS.
Born Cphr.
Croote Geo. H.
Drake Fras. D.
Fisher Henry
Lethern Robt.
Luxton Thos.
Partridge Jas.
Salter Wm.
Seaward Wm.

Shillson John
Skinner John
Snell James
Snell Wm.
Wensley Anthy.
POST OFFICE at W. Collihole's
CARRIERS to Crediton, Exeter, &c.

NYMET, (BROAD) on one of the tributary streams of the river Taw, 8¼ miles W. of Crediton, is a small parish, which contains only 50 inhabitants, and 451 acres of land; and until lately, it claimed exemption from county and highway rates, but a recent decision in the Court of Exchequer declared it liable to both.   It pays church and poor rates, &c., to North Tawton, its small antique church having been long used as a lumber room. Its sinecure rectory, valued in K.B. at £2. 4s. 2d., and in 1821 at £48, is in the same patronage and incumbency as Bow, or Nymet-Tracey.   The manor anciently belonged to the family of De Brode Nymet, and is now nearly all in one *farm*, belonging to Mr. Rd. Dunning, and occupied by Thos. Prickman.

WEMBWORTHY, a pleasant village and parish, 4 miles S.S.W. of Chulmleigh, has 418 inhabitants, and 1934 acres of land, mostly the property of the *Hon. Newton Fellowes*, who has lately erected a neat mansion on the site of the old barton of *Heywood*, in lieu of his former seat of *Eggesford House*. (See page 723.) Heywood was anciently the seat of the Espeke, or Speke family, and was leased by Sir George Speke to Sir John Doddridge, one of the justices of the King's Bench, in the reign of James I. and Charles I.   J. H. Mayne, Esq., has an estate in the parish.   The *Church* (St. Michael,) is a small antique structure; and the *rectory*, valued in K.B. at £11. 13s. 4d., and in 1831 at £146, is in the incumbency of the Rev. Peter Johnson, B.D., and in the patronage of himself and others.   The Parsonage is a neat and pleasant residence, and the glebe is 55¼A.   The tithes were commuted in 1845 for £166 per annum.

Fellowes Hon. Newton, *Heywood House* and West Anstey
Grubb Jno. Geo. schoolmaster
Hosegood John, miller, *Rashleigh*
Johnson Rev. Peter, B.D. *Rectory*
Line Eliz. beer seller
Pearen John, wheelwright
Snell Wm. blacksmith
Symons Wm. wheelwright

FARMERS.
Darke Richd.
Davy John
Cole Samuel
Grendon John
Hellyer John

Saunders George, *Rashleigh*
Shillson Wm.
Underhill Betsy
Underhill Robt.

WINKLEIGH is a large ancient village, situated on a lofty eminence, on the Crediton and Torrington road, 6 miles S.W. of Chulmleigh and E.N.E. of Hatherleigh, and 22 miles W.N.W. of Exeter. Its parish contains 1650 inhabitants, and 9118 acres of land, including a large tract of barren, moory ground; but some parts are woody, and the remainder is tolerably good corn and grazing land.   It forms a *Hundred* of itself, together with some estates in Lapford, Coleridge, and Zeal Monachorum parishes, now called Loosebeare tithing.   The Rev. Peter Johnson is lord of the manor, and had a borough court, or view of frankpledge, which gave place to the new county court held at Torrington, in 1848. *Petty Sessions* are held here monthly, by the magistrates of South Molton Division; and here are two annual *fairs*, one on the second Wednesday in October, and the other on the Monday after the 7th of July, unless that date falls on a Sunday, in which case the fair is held on the Monday se'nnight.   The manor belonged to the Crown at the Domesday Survey, when it was settled on Matilda, the Conqueror's consort, and the park-keeper had a virgate of land. Risdon speaks of two *castles* at Winkleigh, on the east and west sides of the town, where their sites still retain the names of Court and Croft Castles.   The manor was for a long period divided between the Keynes and Tracey families, and was afterwards held by those of Holland and Lethbridge.   The Court Barton was purchased of the latter by the late Rev. J. T. Johnson, from whom it passed to the Rev. P. Johnson.   The Hon. Newton Fellowes owns *Southcote* estate; and that of *Holcombe* belongs to Robt. Luxton, Esq.

Part of the parish belongs to J. H. Tremayne, Esq., and several smaller owners. Wm. de Portu Mortuo was lord of the manor of Holcombe in the reign of Henry III., and in 1260 had a charter for a weekly market, and a fair for three days at the festival of the Ascension. In 1361, Richard Inglish had the King's charter for castellating his mansion at Up-Holcombe. The *Church* (All Saints,) is a fine antique structure, with a tower, containing five bells, and commanding from its summit extensive views, in which are seen the hills of Dartmoor, and the steeples of 24 parish churches. The Dean and Chapter of Exeter are appropriators of the rectorial tithes, and patrons of the *vicarage*, valued in K.B. at £21. 8s. 9d., and in 1831 at £215, and now held by the Rev. Henry Wright, B.A., who has a good residence, and 8A. 3R. 26P. of glebe. The tithes were commuted in 1846, the vicarial for £312, and the rectorial for £427 per annum. The Wesleyans, Independents, and Bible Christians have chapels here. The *Church Lands* have been vested for the repairs of the church, from an early period, and comprise about 25A. in East Chappel farm, let for £19. 10s., and a garden let for 5s. 3d. per annum. The churchwardens have also 6s. yearly from chief rents; and a house occupied by paupers. The poor parishioners have £2. 12s. yearly from *Sir John Acland's Charity,* (see Exeter;) and the interest of £30, left by unknown donors. Here is an *Almshouse* for five poor women, founded in 1681, by *Bartw. Gidley,* who endowed it with a cottage and half an acre of land, worth £4 per annum.

Bulleid Thomas, cooper
Collihole Thomas, maltster
Collihole Rt.&Wm. carriers to Exeter
Crocker John, butcher
Dingley Thos. K. surgeon
Dunning Rd. tanner, *Wood-Terrell*
Dunning Miss || Watts Mr John
Hellyer Saml. plumber and glazier
Keenor Robt. cooper, &c
Keenor Henry and John, masons
Luxton Wm. surgeon
Miller John shoemaker
Miller Wm. & Nathl. cattle dealers
Newcombe Chpr. baker, &c
Thorne John, cattle dealer
Westaway Nathaniel, shoemaker
Wright Rev Hy., B.A., *Vicarage*

INNS AND TAVERNS.
Barnstaple Inn, Robt. Williams
Clotworthy Arms, Geo. Edwards
King's Arms, Mary Williams
Ring of Bells, Walter Williams
Seven Stars, Nathl. Hammett, *butchr*

BLACKSMITHS.
Lethern John
Mitchell Robt.
Mitchell Saml.
Raymont Robt.
Raymont Wm.

CARPENTERS.
Davey Alex.
Davey Saml.

FARMERS.
(* *are Owners.*)
Bear John
Brook Tphna.
Bulleid John
Chambers John
Chambers Saml.
Cock Scipio
*Collihole Rd.

Collihole Thos.
Cowle John
Darch Richard
Dart Richard
Dufty Samuel
Dunn Samuel
*Dunning Rd.
Down Simon
Ford Wm.
Grendon Wm.
Harris Jeremiah
*Haywood Btw.
*HaywoodWalter
Hawkins Wm.
Isaac Richd. R.
Keenor Henry
Kimp John
Kimp Philip
*Lethern John
*Luxton George
Luxton Henry
*Mullen Wm.
Newcombe Cphr.
Packer George
*Raymont Rd.
Rodd John
Snell Robert
Stevens Francis
*Stevens John
Stevens Saml.
Thorne Benj.
Trick John

GROCERS, &c.
Cock Sarah
ColliholeEliz.&J.
Friend Arthur,(& registrar)

SADDLERS.
Jerrett Wm.
Lethern John
Williams Chas.

TAILORS.
Dulling James
Lake Richard
Turner John

WHEELWRIGHTS.
Collihole Richd.
Hill Wm. & John
Newcombe Shdh.

POST-OFFICE at Richd. Collihole's. Letters by *Exeter and Bideford mail coach,* daily

CARRIERS pass to all parts; and Rd. & Wm. Collihole,toExeter, Mon. and Thursday

ZEAL MONACHORUM is a village and parish in Taw vale, 8 miles W.N.W. of Crediton, and contains 649 souls, and 2946 acres of land, including the hamlets of *Loosebeare* or *Loxbeare*, *Burstone*, and *Tuckingmill.* It was anciently called Sele Monachorum, and had the latter part of its name from its being long held by the monastery of Buckfast, to which it was given by King Canute. J. H. Ley, Esq,, is now lord of the manor; but Loosebeare belongs to the Kelland family, and Burstone to J. and W. Wreford, Esqrs. Messrs. J. and R. Pedler, John Sweet, and a few smaller owners, have estates in the parish. The *Church* (St. Peter,) has a tower and five bells; and the living is a *rectory*, valued in K.B. at £17. 8s. 9d., and in 1831 at £401. The Rev. John Comyns, M.A., of Bishop's Teignton, is the rector, and has sold the patronage to Mr. Tombs. The glebe is 52¼ acres, and the Parsonage is a neat residence, with tasteful grounds. The tithes have been commuted for £419 per annum. The poor have £10, and the rector and trustees £2 yearly, from the bequest of *Fras. Hole*, in 1730. For schooling poor children, *Weekes Hole*, in 1768, left £100, now vested at interest. The poor parishioners have £3. 1s. 8d. per annum, in four rent-charges, left by Andrew Davy, Richard Hole, Robert Packer, and Edmund Rowland.

Bibbings Joseph, wheelwright
Bibbings Wm. farming implement maker, and registrar
Clotworthy Wm. vict. North Star
Cooper Rev Edw. curate, *Rectory*
Hill Geo. gent. *Laurel Cottage*
Hill Wm. gent. *Foldhay*
Hooper Wm. blacksmith
Mitchell Wm. machine maker and vict. Golden Lion

Staniford George, blacksmith

FARMERS.
Cheriton Saml.
Hern James
Homyard Saml.
Moon Edward
Pedler John
Pedler Robt.
Snell George

Snell Wm.
Sweet John
Wreford John
Wreford Wm.
SHOPKEEPERS.
Slee Charity
Slee Thomas
Vanstone Ann

ROBOROUGH HUNDRED

Adjoins the Boroughs of Plymouth and Devonport, and forms the south-western extremity of Devon, bounded on the west by the broad estuary of the river Tamar; but including Mount Edgcumbe and part of Maker parish, on the Cornwall side of the harbour and Plymouth Sound. It extends about 14 miles northward from Plymouth, to the wild and hilly district of Dartmoor Forest, where there are several *lead and tin mines*. It is skirted on the east by the river Plym, and traversed by the navigable river Tavy, and the railway from Dartmoor granite quarries. It is in the Southern Parliamentary Division of Devonshire, in Tavistock and Plymouth Polling Districts; in the Archdeaconry of Totness, and in the Deaneries of Tamerton and Plympton. It forms a Petty Sessional Division, and comprises 15 parishes, &c., of which the following is an enumeration, shewing their territorial extent, and their population in 1841.

Parishes, &c.	Acres.	Pop.	Parishes, &c.	Acres.	Pop.
§Compton Gifford *tp.*+	1510 ..	271	.*Meavy	3351 ..	361
§Pennycross *chap.*+ ..	1310 ..	267	*Sampford Spiney ..	1721 ..	443
*Beer Ferris ‖	5888 ..	2142	*Sheepstor	3469 ..	127
§Bickleigh	2980 ..	469	§'Tamerton Folliott ..	4641 ..	1214
*Buckland Monchrm.	6839 ..	1411	*Tavy St. Peter.... ⎫	6000 ..	496
§Budeaux (St.)	2507 ..	790	*Willsworthy *ham.* ⎬	2450 ..	91
§Egg Buckland	3198 ..	1296	*Walkhampton....	10,501 ..	717
‡*Part of Maker par.* ⎫ ‡Vaultershome-*tyth* ⎬ ‖	1320 ..	1156	*Whitchurch	6450 ..	918
			Total	64,135	12,169

☞ UNIONS :—Those marked thus * are in *Tavistock Union;* § in *Plympton St. Mary Union;* and ‡ in *St. Germans Union;* the latter of which is mostly in Cornwall. Upwards of 10,000 acres are *unenclosed lands* in Dartmoor.

† *Compton Gifford* is a tithing and township, in the parish of Charles the Martyr, Plymouth ; and *Pennycross,* or *Weston Peverell,* is a chapelry and township, in the parish of St. Andrew, Plymouth, as already noticed at pages 663-'4.

‖ Beer Ferris includes the disfranchised borough of *Beer Alston* ; Maker includes *Mount Edgcumbe ;* and Egg Buckland includes *Laira Green.*

BEER FERRIS, or *Beer Ferrers,* commonly called *Beer Town,* is a small village on the western bank of the navigable river Tavy, about two miles above the confluence of the estuary of the Tamar, about 8 miles N. by W. of Plymouth, and 9½ miles S. of Tavistock. Its parish includes the ancient disfranchised Borough of Beer Alston, and many scattered farm houses, &c.; and contains 2142 inhabitants, and 5888 acres of fertile land, bounded on the east and west by the tidal waters of the Tamar and Tavy, and terminating in a point at their confluence. It is noted for producing immense quantities of apples, cherries, strawberries, gooseberries, currants, &c., and the finest cider ; and at Gawton is a large tree which, in a good season, has borne 1000 lbs. weight of cherries. At *Weir Quay* are extensive *smelting works,* and in the neighbourhood are several *lead and tin mines,* yielding a large portion of silver, and employing above 1000 hands. The *manor* of Beer Ferris was given by the Conqueror to Alenson, from whom Beer Alston took the latter part of its name ; but in the reign of Henry II. it belonged to the ancient family of Ferrers. In 1337, Sir Wm. de Ferrers had a license to castellate the manor-house, in which the Lords Willoughby de Broke afterwards resided, and had a park here. The Earl of Mount Edgcumbe is now lord of the manor, and owner of a great part of the parish. The manor of *Ley,* or *Legh,* was long held by the Ley family, but now belongs to Sir T. T. F. E. Drake, Bart., and part of the parish belongs to a few smaller freeholders. The *Church* (St. Andrew,) is an ancient structure, mostly in the decorated style, and has an embattled tower. It contains some antique monuments of the Ferrers and Champernownes, and others of more modern date. One is a beautiful double-recessed Easter sepulchre, with effigies of Sir John Ferrers and his lady. Many of the old oak benches remain, heightened into modern pews. The large east window was enriched with ancient stained glass, which is now deposited in a chest. The late C. E. Stothard, F.S.A., lost his life by a fall when copying this fine window. The *rectory,* valued in K.B. at £24. 1s. 0½d., and in 1831 at £800, is in the patronage of the Earl of Mount Edgcumbe, and incumbency of the Rev. Fdk. Shelley, who has 148A. 3R. 1P. of glebe, and a large and handsome *Rectory House,* built in 1837, in the Elizabethan style. The tithes were commuted in 1842 for £750 per annum. Twelve houses and gardens, worth £60 a year, have been long vested for the repairs, &c., of the church. The parish *Free School,* for 16 poor children, was founded in the 17th century, by Sir John Maynard, who endowed it with a house and garden for the master, and with 15A. of land, worth about £21 a year.

BEER-ALSTON, a small ancient town and disfranchised borough, in the parish of Beer Ferris, is pleasantly situated on a gentle eminence, overlooking the vales of the Tamar and Tavy, on the east and west, and distant about 3 miles N. of the parish church, and 6½ miles S. of Tavistock. It has been much improved during the last 20 years by the erection of new houses, and has now about 1400 inhabitants, many of whom are employed in the lead and tin mines of the neighbourhood. It first sent two members to Parliament in the 27th of Elizabeth, and was disfranchised by the Reform Act of 1832. The right of election was in those who had land in the borough, and paid 3d. acknowledgment to the lord of the manor, who varied

the number of electors at his pleasure, by granting burgage-tenures to as many of his own partizans as might be necessary. These newly made burgage-tenures were usually resigned as soon as the election was over. The portreeve, elected annually at the lord's court, was the returning officer. In the neighbourhood are the Tamar, the East and South Tamar, and the Valletort Consols *lead mines*, and two large smelting works, which yield a profitable proportion of silver. The lead mines here are said to have yielded 16 cwt. of silver during three years in the reign of Edward I. The *market* is now only held on Saturday evenings, for the sale of provisions, &c. In or about 1294, Beer-Alston had a grant for a market every Wednesday, and a fair at the festival of St. Andrew, but they have long been obsolete. A chapel, built here in the reign of Edward III., was afterwards used as the parish workhouse, and is now a coal store. A neat *Chapel of Ease*, in the early English style, was erected here in 1848, by the Earl of Mount Edgcumbe, but it is not yet consecrated, though service is performed in it on Sunday evenings. Here is an *Independent Chapel*, built in 1809; and also a small *Wesleyan Chapel*. Schools are attached to the three chapels, and here is a small parochial library. *In the following Directory, those marked 2 are at Beer Ferris, and the others at Beer Alston, or where specified.*

Barnicoat Rev Humphy.Lowry,curate
2 Code Philip, painter
2 Cudlip Robt. market boat owner
Davy Thomas, saddler
East Tamar Mining Company
Frise Mr Thos. || Drake John,sexton
James Rd. miller, *Denham Bridge*
2 Jasper Wm. rate collector
Johnson Percival Norton, Esq. *Ward*
Johnson&Co. *WeirQuay Smelt Works*
2 Knill Thomas, parish clerk
Martin James, brewer
Mullard Wm. police officer
Northy Thos. coal merchant, *Quay*
Richards John, basket mkr. & Mr Jas.
Robins Bartholomew, mining agent
Smith Geo. Esq. *Cleveland Cottage*
2 Shelley Rev Frederick, *Rectory*
Whillan Rev Wm. (Independent)

FARMERS.

Ball Mary, *Barn*
Bloye Charles, *Tuckermarsh*
Bloye James, *Mewton*
Brighton Charles, Leaches
Brighton George, Newhouse
Brighton George, jun. *Lower Ley*
Brighton Henry, *Collins*
Bragg Mary, Maria, & Ann, *Colyton*
Borley Jas. *Hewton;* & Geo. *Hooe*
Channon Sampson, Higher Pounder
Cleave John, *Main;* & Wm. *Knatm*
Clifton Wm., Glebe Farm
Coram Wm. *Hallwell*
Courtis Thomas, *Little Gawton*
Creber John, *Anderton*

Cudlip Rd. *Battens;* & Wm. *Hole*
German John, *Higher Gawton*
German Wm., Ward Farm
Hamlyn John, *Ley*
Jackson John, *Henberries*
Johns John || Jose Nicholas
2 Lane John, (ferryman)
Langham Wm. *Slymford*
Lipson Richard, *Higher Ley*
Matthews Rt. *Down;* & Rd. *Walcomb*
Matthews Jane, *South Birch*
Metters Joseph || Mills Edward
Oliver Mary, Egypt Farm
Pode Samuel || Repath Agnes
Rich George || Rich John
Rowe Richard || Rowe Oliver
Stephenson John Wills, *Whitsun*
Toll Rd. Humphrey, *Liphill& Norton*
Watters Thomas || Williams Jthn.
Westlake Mrs. *Great Braunder*
Westlake John, *Lockridge*
Wills Nicholas || Wills Thomas
Withycombe Henry, *Hole*

INNS AND TAVERNS.

Commercial, John Goddard
Cornish Arms, Wm. Burrow
2 Devonport Inn, Wm. Robins
Edgcumbe Arms, John Ball
Holes Hall, Henry Caunter
2 Plough, John Fuge
Victoria, Nathaniel Robins

BAKERS.

Ball Henry
Oliver Thomas
Radford Eliz.

Stevens Edward
Weekes Edward

BEER HOUSES.

2 Dawe Roger

Jewell Richard	2 Hamlyn John	Courtis John	TAILORS.
Langman Henry	Maynard John	Goddard John	Goddard John
Langman Nichls.	Maynard Peter	2 Goddard Chas.	HoskyngThomas
Wills Thomas	Richards John	Hamlyn Betsy	Maddeford Rd.
BLACKSMITHS.	Wilcocks Thos.	Langman Robert	WHEELWRIGHTS.
Foote Jacob	MASONS.	Luxmore James	Richards John
2 Walters Richd.	Corner Wm.	Pode Peter	Westlake Wm.
Walters Wm.	Pode Wm.	2 Procter Jos.	
Westlake James	Spear Wm.	Skews Daniel	POST.OFFICE
Williams Walter	SHOEMAKERS.	Thomas Ann	at John Rowe's.
BUTCHERS.	2 Alfred Thomas	SCHOOLS.	Letters desp.8mg.
Coram John	Bishop Robert	Burke Edm. *free*	
Langman James;	Brooming Wm.	2 Jasper Sarah J.	CARRIERS.
Henry; Nichls;	2 Foote John	Tresise Mary	Rowe, to *Tavi-*
Robert; & Wm.	Jewell Richard	SURGEONS.	*stock*, Tu.& Fri.
Luxmore James	Sleep John	Honey Wm.	*Market Boats* to
CARPENTERS.	SHOPKEEPERS.	Jackson Richard	Devonport, Tu.
Bishop Wm.	Ball Mary		Thur. & Sat.

BICKLEIGH is a small village on the western side of the river Plym, in the picturesque vale to which it gives name, six miles N. by E. of Plymouth. Its parish contains 469 souls, and 2980 acres of land, including the village of *Jump*, and many scattered houses. *Bickleigh Vale* is much resorted to by anglers and the lovers of woodland scenery, who find excellent entertainment at Maristow Inn. The Plymouth and Devonport *leats*, and Dartmoor Railway, cross this parish; and at Jump are two annual *fairs*, on the third Wednesdays in April and September. The manor was long held by Buckland Abbey, and afterwards by the Slannings, Modyfords, and Heywoods, the latter of whom sold it to S. M. M. Lopes, in 1798. Sir Ralph Lopes, Bart., is now lord of the manor, owner of most of the soil, impropriator of the rectory, and patron of the *vicarage*, valued in K.B. at £11. 7s. 4d., and in 1831 at £300, with the perpetual curacy of Sheepstor annexed to it. The Rev. J. D. Cork, M.A., is the incumbent, and has a good residence, recently enlarged. The *Church* was rebuilt by Sir R. Lopes, in 1839, except the tower, which contains six bells. The interior is neatly fitted up, and the east window is enriched with stained glass. The poor have £100 three per cent. consols, purchased with the gifts of Elizabeth Modyford·and John Herring.

*Marked * are at Jump.*	BEER HOUSES.	Mason Lawrence
*Clemens Thomas, wheelwright	Towl Elizabeth	Mumford Wm.
Cork Rev Jph. Duncan, M.A. *vicar*	Weeks Walter	Peeke Joshua
Gent John, miller, *Roboro' Mill*	BOOT& SHOE MKS.	Peeke Thomas
*Giles George, land agent	*Box James	Southall Gad
*Hamley Joseph, blacksmith	*Oates George	Waycott John
*Lane Jacob, vict. Lopes' Arms	FARMERS.	Westlake Wm.
*Lethbridge Robt. ‖ Ward Wm. M.	Atwill John	Widdicombe W.
*Parnell John, saddler	Blake John	SHOPKEEPERS.
Reed Wm. vict. Maristow Inn	Brock Wm.	Cole John
*Symons John, mason	Hanaford Wm.	*King Wm.
	Hodge John	*Weeks Walter
	Lillicrap Fras.	

BUCKLAND MONACHORUM is a small, pleasant village, in a picturesque valley, 4 miles S. by E. of Tavistock, near *Roborough Down*, an elevated tract of 1877 acres of moorland, which is about to be enclosed and cultivated. Buckland had the latter part of its name from its monastery,

and is sometimes called *Buckland Drake*, from the Drake family, who have held the manor since the reign of Elizabeth.   Its parish contains 1411 inhabitants, and 6838 acres of land, including about 2000 acres of open moorland, woodland, &c.; the romantic hamlet of *Milton*, and a great part of the large village of *Horrabridge*, which is partly in the parishes of Sampford-Spiney, Whitchurch, and Walkhampton; being on both sides of the small river Walkham, and on the western side of Dartmoor, where there are two *copper mines* and a *tin mine*, employing about 400 hands, and a *woollen factory*, employing about the same number.   The parish comprises also many scattered farm-houses, &c., and several neat mansions, and is bounded on the west by the river Tavy, and traversed on the east by Plymouth and Dartmoor Railway.   A *cattle fair* is held in the village on Trinity Monday, Tuesday, and Wednesday; and it had formerly a weekly market on Tuesday, granted to one of the abbots in 1317. A large and well-endowed ABBEY was founded here in 1278, by Amicia, relict of Baldwin, Earl of Devonshire, for monks of the Cistercian order.   When it was dissolved in the reign of Henry VIII., its revenues were valued at £241. 17s. 9½d. per annum, and the site was granted to Richard Grenville, who built upon it a "fair new house," which afterwards became by purchase the seat of the celebrated circumnavigator, *Sir Francis Drake*, who, having no issue, bequeathed it to his nephew, of the same name, who was created a *baronet* in 1622.   The late baronet, Sir Francis Henry Drake, left it to his sister's son, the late Lord Heathfield; and at his death, in 1813, it passed to a younger son of his sister (Mrs. Fuller, of Sussex,) the present *Sir Thomas Trayton Fuller Eliott Drake*, who was created a baronet in 1821, and resides at Nutwell Court, as noticed at page 254.   He owns a great part of the parish, but Sir Ralph Lopes, Bart., is lord of the manor, which was granted to the Crymes family after the dissolution of the abbey.   Sir A. Buller, Knight, J. H. Gill, Esq., G. Leach, Esq., and several smaller owners, have estates in the parish. *Buckland Abbey*, a neat mansion, with tasteful grounds, is now occupied by Thomas Gill, Esq.; and there are still preserved in it many interesting articles which belonged to the great circumnavigator, such as his sword, drum, the bible which accompanied him in all his voyages, a shield of Queen Elizabeth, several portraits of the family, &c.   It appears to have been a castellated mansion, and some remains of the abbey church were incorporated in the building.   Sir Richard Grenville made it his occasional residence during the blockade of Plymouth, and had a garrison here, but he left it after the capture of Dartmouth.   In a garret are the four great arches of the church tower, and in the dining room is a large Gothic window. *Bickham*, which was long the seat of the Elford family, is now the residence of J. H. Gill, Esq.   *Pound*, the pleasant seat of Sir Anthony Buller, Knt., was rebuilt about 30 years ago, and was the residence of the late Sir Herbert Sawyer.   *Crapstone*, the seat and property of George Leach, Esq., was long the residence of the Crymes family, and was afterwards sold to the Elfords.   Mr. Leach has lately erected a handsome new house, near the ancient mansion.   The *Church* (St. Andrew,) is a handsome cruciform structure, in the perpendicular style, with a tower and six bells.   The fine old oak benches, beautifully carved, still remain, but are much disfigured by high-backed pews of deal.   The roof is ornamented with bosses at the intersection of the ribs; and at the extremity of the hammer-beams are singularly curious corbels, consisting of angels, each bearing a musical instrument of antique form.   The great east window is very fine, and contains a few fragments of ancient painted glass, which, when complete, represented the life and martyrdom of St. Andrew.   There are also remains of stained glass in the south transept window, and in the Drake aisle is a

handsome modern monument by the elder Bacon, to the memory of *Lord Hathfield*, the gallant defender of Gibraltar, whose nephew, Sir T. T. F. E. Drake, Bart., has recently presented a powerful organ to the church. The *vicarage*, valued in K.B. at £19. 8s. 9d., and in 1831 at £430, is in the patronage and incumbency of the Rev. Wm. L. Nichols, M.A., who has a good residence, and 49A. 2R. 39P. of glebe. The tithes were commuted in 1842, the vicarial for £304. 10s., and the rectorial for £174. 18s., of which £163. 6s. 6d. belongs to Sir T. T. F. E. Drake, and the rest to four small impropriators. A small *Chapel of Ease* was erected at *Horrabridge* in 1835, at the cost of upwards of £700, raised by subscription. It is in the early English style, and has about 300 sittings. The Rev. S. H. Walker, M.A., is the curate. The *Wesleyans* have a chapel at Horrabridge, built in 1832, and a smaller one at Milton, erected in 1847. The parish *Free School* was founded in 1702 by Lady Elizabeth Modyford, who endowed it with a house for the master, and £10 a year out of an estate now belonging to Sir R. Lopes, who pays £7. 10s. to the master, and expends the remainder in clothing the free scholars. Four of the scholars are clothed out of the dividends of £200 New South Sea Annuities, purchased with £120 left by *Matth. Elford, Esq.*, in 1723. The poor parishioners have the dividends of £161. 1s. 6d. and £126. 10s. 9d. three per cent. consols, purchased with the gifts of *Catherine Ilbert and John Burrows ;* and also the interest of £50 left by *Lady Mody-ford,* and vested with the overseers. Schools are attached to the Episcopal and Wesleyan Chapels at Horrabridge, and at the former, Miss Buller and Mrs. Collier pay for the education of 22 poor children, and the master teaches four free, for the use of the school, which was built in 1848, at the cost of about £90.

Marked 2 are at Horrabridge, and the others in Buckland village, or where specified.

Buller Sir Anthony, Kt., *Pound*
2 Chapple John, painter, &c.
Edwards Richd., capt. of the *Wheal Franco and Yeoland copper and tin mines*
2 Gard John, schoolmaster
Gill John Hornbrook, Esq., *Bickham House*
Gill Thos., Esq., *Buckland Abbey*
2 Hamlyn and Co., fellmongers and woollen manufacturers
Leach George, Esq., *Crapstone*
Martin Alexander, capt. of the *Wheal Lady copper mine*
Nichols Rev Wm. L., M.A., *Vicarage*
Palmer Joseph, free schoolmaster
Venner Samuel, veterinary surgeon
2 Walker Rev. Samuel Hy., curate
Worthy Wm., bone mert., *Coombe*
FARMERS. (** are Owners.*)
Bartlett Fras., *Sanguines*
2 Bowden John || Blowey Philip
Carns James, *Ludbrook*
Cawker John, *Upton*
Chapple Richard || Chowne John

Corber John, *Milton*
Corber Benjamin, *Leys*
* Cortor Samuel, *Cudgeford*
* Dawe Joseph, *Lower Hellington*
* Dawe John, *Higher Yeoland*
Dawe Chtte., *Lower Elford Town*
Fairweather Jarvis, *Barton*
Giles John Edmund, *Axtown*
Glanville Wm., Tor
Hamlyn John, *Bickham*
* Hamlyn John, *Jessop's Sawton*
Joachim Wm., *Elford Town*
Knapton Wm. || Lakeman Wm.
Leamon Wm. || Luscombe John
2 Moses Mark and Elias || Mudge R.
Northmore Jacob || Nattle Wm.
Peters Thos. & Hy. || Palmer Wm.
Pryn John || Wilcocks Walter
* Reed Jph. and Rd., *Chubbaton*
* Sims Saml. || * Wilcocks Wm.
* Wilcocks Ambrose, *Denham*
    INNS AND TAVERNS.
Crown, John Blowey
King's Arms, Rt. Newcombe, *Bedford Bridge*
2 London Inn, Rd. Toop, (and auctioneer, surveyor, and regr.)
Roborough Inn, Wm. Knight

2 I

BEERHOUSES.	CARPENTERS, &c.	MILLERS.	2 Chapple James
Cundy John	2 Foote James	Harris J., *Hatch*	Gill Wm.
Kinsman John, *Milton*	Goss J., *Milton*	2 King John	2 Golsworthy Sl.
	Lethbridge Cpr.	Tregellis Willm., *Lopwell*	2 Palmer Jph.
Pearse Mark	Newcombe Rt.		Shillabear Wm.
	Petherwick Smn.	White J., *Milton*	TAILORS.
BLACKSMITHS.	Shortridge Jas.		Jutson J., *Milton*
Chowne W. C.	MASONS.	SHOEMAKERS.	Parsons John
Gill Wm.	Blowey John	2 Blowey James	
Helson John	2 Chapple Wm.	2 Hodge John	POST-OFFICE
Keagle Richard	2 Foote Thomas	Symons Joseph	at Rt. Camp's,
2 Westlake Rt.	2 Fuge Wm.	Trood Thomas	*Buckland*, and
BUTCHERS.	Pearse Mark	Westlake Wm.	Jas. Chapple's,
Collard Edwin	Spry Thomas	SHOPKEEPERS.	*Horrabridge.*
2 Oyns Richard	Worthy Wm.	2 Broadlick John	Letters via Tvstk.

ST. BUDEAUX, a pleasant village on an eminence, overlooking the broad estuary of the river Tamar, 4 miles N.W. of Plymouth, has in its parish 790 souls, and 2507 acres of land, including the hamlets, &c., of *King's-Tamerton, Henieknowle, Whitleigh, Saltash Passage, Kinterbury,* and part of *Knacker's-knowle,* or *Knoll,* the latter of which is partly in Egg-Buckland parish. A small part of the parish of St. Budeaux is in Cornwall. Lord Graves is lord of the manor, but a great part of the parish belongs to E. H. Gennys, T. Pollard, W. W. Chard, W. J. Clarke, and C. T. C. Trelawney, Esqrs.; Lord Ashburton, and several smaller owners; some of whom have neat houses here. The manor was anciently called Budockshed, and was long held by a family of its own name, who resided in the castellated manor house, of which an ivy mantled tower still remains. Sir Harry Trelawny, aid-de-camp to the great Duke of Marlborough, lived here some years in retirement, and amused himself with planting and ornamental gardening. St. Budeaux church and churchyard, having been strongly fortified by the royalists when blockading Plymouth, were taken by the Parliamentarians in January, 1646, when Major Stuckley, with 20 other officers, and above 100 men, were taken prisoners. The *Church,* dedicated to St. Budeaux or Budock, is a handsome structure, which was erected in the 8th of Elizabeth, by Roger Budockshed, partly with the materials of the original church, which was of great antiquity, and stood in an unhealthy situation near the Tamar estuary. Among its numerous monuments is one to Sir Thomas Byard, of Mount Tamar, who devoted the greater part of his life to the service of his king and country. The living is a *perpetual curacy,* valued in 1831 at £114, in the patronage of the Vicar of St. Andrew's, Plymouth, and incumbency of the Rev. B. W. S. Vallack, B.A., who has a good residence, mostly rebuilt about 20 years ago. The small tithes were commuted in 1843, for £60, and the great tithes for £325. The latter belong to J. Wills, Esq. The *Rev. Thomas Alcock,* who officiated here more than 60 years, was a very eccentric and penurious character, and his sermons abounded in Latin and Greek quotations and passages from the English poets; even the treasures of private epistolary correspondence contributed to the instruction of his congregation. His Memoirs of Dr. Nathan Alcock, his brother, is a well written piece of biography. Here is a *Charity School* for educating and clothing 12 poor boys and 12 poor girls, which was endowed in 1767 with £400 stock, given by Peter Madock Docton, in satisfaction of an annuity of £10 left by his father. This stock was sold in 1770, and the proceeds laid out in the purchase of 17A. of land. There are also belonging to the school £375 three per cent. consols, which arose from savings of income; £100 left by Elizabeth Mary Docton; and two yearly rent-

charges of 20s. each, left by John Harris and Joanna Knighton. Two cottages for the residence of poor widows, were given by John Ernesettle, and endowed with 26s. 8d. per annum out of Ernesettle Barton. The poor parishioners have 30s. a year from Lanyon's and Rawling's charities, and one-third of the dividends of £100 three per cent. consols, left by Joanna Knight. *Those marked 2 are at Knacker's-knowle, and 3 at King's Tamarton.*

Avent Rt. auctioneer, *Prestons*
Braim Thomas, quarryman
Chard Wm. W., Esq. *Mount Tamar*
Fortescue Mr John, *Saltash Passage*
2 French Mrs S. || Gregory Mr
Gennys Edm. Henn, Esq. *Whitleigh*
2 Hancock Mr John || Jolley Wm.
Oldfield Mr. manager of the Govmt. *Powder mill*, Kinterbury
3 Patey Capt. Charles G. E., R.N.
Pollard Tobias, Esq. *West Whitleigh*
Pryor Joseph, free schoolmaster
Smith Mrs Elizabeth, *Leamons*
Stoyles John, cooper, &c
Toll William, tailor
Vallack Rev Bnj. Wm. Sol., B.A. incbt

FARMERS.
2 Abbott Edward || Brock Samuel
Aubridge Wm. *Agaton*
3 Bradford George || Bonney Peter
Bradford Wm. *Weston mill*
Brooking John || Davis John
Corber Richard || Clarke James
Hancock Richard, *Ernesettle*
Hatherleigh Henry, *Agaton*
Hatherleigh Wm. *Kinterbury*
Hicks Francis || Jarvis Jonathan

Peeke Richard || 2 Pollard Misses
2 Rowe John || Symons Richard
Stephens Peter || Stephens John
2 Toms Wm. || Tolchard Henry
Truscott Francis || Yates Charles

INNS & TAVERNS.
Castle Farm Inn, Saml. Corber
Devonport Inn, Wm. Honey, *Saltash Passage House*
New Inn, James Pengelly
St Budeaux Inn, Francis Martin
Beerhouse, Richard Hancock

BLACKSMITHS.
Body Wm.
Bond Wm.
Rundle Nicholas
3 Waldron Jph.

CARPENTERS.
Martin Francis
Pengelly Wm.
Penny Thomas

MASONS.
3 Bond Joseph
Hoskin Wm.
Skinner John
Soby Thomas

SHOEMAKERS.
3 Bonney Wm.
2 Foote John
Curtis R. H.

SHOPKEEPERS.
Glanville Thos.
Palk Thomas
3 Stoneman Wm.

CARRIERS *to Plym. & Devonport, Tues. Thu. & Saturday*
Glanvill Thomas
3 Truscott Fras.

EGG BUCKLAND, a large village, 3 miles N. by E. of Plymouth, has in its parish 1297 souls, and 3197 acres of land, including part of the village of *Knacker's Knowle*, many scattered houses, and the extra-parochial place called *Laira Green*, near the river Plym and Dartmoor Railway. A fair is held in the village on the second Wednesday in June. C. Tolcher, Esq., is lord of the manor of Egg-Buckland; and E. Clarke, Esq., is lord of the manor of *Efford;* but the greater part of the parish belongs to the Earl of Morley, the Countess Rothes, the Misses Morshead, Colonel Elliott, G. W. Soltau, Esq., Mrs. Revell, the Trustees of the late Sir J. St. Aubyn, R. A. A. Julian, Esq., T. Briggs, Esq., and several smaller owners, some of whom have pleasant seats here. *Widey Court House*, now the seat of the Misses Morshead, was the head quarters of Prince Maurice, when he besieged Plymouth, from the beginning of October till Christmas, 1643; and the King was there in September, 1644. *Derriford House* was rebuilt about 30 years ago, and belongs to W. L. Langmead, Esq. The *Church* is an ancient structure, with a tower and five bells, and contains several monuments of the Hals, Collins, and other families. It was appropriated to Plymouth Priory. The *vicarage*, valued in K.B. at £8. 4s. 4d., and in 1831 at £474, is in the patronage of the Lord Chancellor, and incumbency of the Rev. George Hunt, M.A., who has a good residence and glebe. The tithes have been commuted, the vicarial for £512. 10s., and the rectorial for

£205 per annum, The latter belong to Miss Wise. In 1790, the *Rev. Vincent Warren* left £800 three per cent. consols to the Vicar, in trust to apply £12. 10s. yearly in clothing ten poor children, and to distribute 20s. among twenty poor children of Plymstock. The Parish School has £100 of the same stock, given by Peter Culme, in 1778, and the poor have 30s. a year from Lanyon's and Rawling's charities. *Marked 2, are at Knacker's Knowle; 3, at Crabtree; 4, at Laira Green; 5, at Longbridge; and the rest at Egg-Buckland, or where specified.*

2 Adams Mr John; & Benj. tailor
2 Bowden Jeremiah, cattle dealer
2 Bright Mrs My. || Coleman Mrs
Briggs Rev John, *Bircham*
Briggs T. gent. *Fursdown*
4 Brucks Capt. || Chalker Mr John
2 Bulley Rd. coach builder, &c
Clarke Irving, Esq. *Efford House*
Derry David, Esq. *Marsh House*
4 Edmonds John, Esq. || Hawker Mrs
Elliott Col. E. *Leigham House*
Glanville —, Esq. *Derriford House*
Hamlyn Mr J. || 4 Luddington Mrs
Hunt Rev Geo., M.A. *Vicarage*
Julian R. A. A., Esq. *Eastover*
Knight John, wheelgt., Crown hill
4 Margery Misses || 2 Maunder Mrs
3 Medland John, carpenter
Morshead Captain & Misses, *Widey Court House*
2 Nosworthy James, saddler
Revell Mrs J. *Widey House*
2 Revell Mr || 4 Smith Mrs
Robinson J. D., Esq. *Fancy House*
4 Scott Rt. J. gent. || 5 Stumbles W.
Soltau Geo., Esq. *Little Efford*
2 Stuttaford Jno. & Wm. *masons*
Tolcher D., Esq. *Colwell*
Tolcher Edward, Esq. *Forder*
5 Tremills Mr Joseph

FARMERS.
Anthony Wm., Little Efford
Atwill John || Balke John
Beer John, Derriford
Bone Henry, *Efford*
Bowden Wm. || Brooking John

Butland Jph. & Benj., Little Efford
Cole John || Crews James
Cornish John, *Leigham Mills*
Cropman John, Gossehill
Cuddeford Thomas || Dawe Wm.
Dinner Richard || Distin John
Gloyn Francis || Gordon John
Grant Martin || Hillson Henry
Kelland John, *Buckland Down*
Kills Wm. || Knight Wm.
Moyse John || Neale John
Moore Simon, *Broom Park*
Pengelly Jas. *Outer Cross Park*
Rabbage Edw. || Revell Rd. *Widey*
Saunders John || Sparkes Thomas
Spurrell Wm. *Derriford*
Stoyles Wm. || Taylor Samuel
Tozer John || Willey Henry
Wills John || Williams Robert

INNS & TAVERNS.
Crabtree Inn, Robert Selmon
4 Laira Inn, Thomas Martin
New Inn, A. I. Stuttaford, *mason*
3 Rising Sun, John Jones

BEERHOUSES.	DRESSMAKERS.
Markes Jermh.	2 Cross S. A.
2 Randle G. S.	2 Pengelly M.
BOOT &SHOE MKS.	MILLERS.
2 Foote John	2 Bartlett John
2 Purdy Charles	Gullett Mrs
Spry Edward	Horswill Mr
COOPERS.	SHOPKEEPERS.
2 Down Thomas	3 Hughes Edw.
3 Medland John	Stuttaford Ach.
2 Stoyles John	2 Stuttaford Ann

MAKER parish, which occupies a great part of the bold promontory and peninsula, which juts into the English Channel on the west side of Plymouth Sound, and the south side of the Harbour of Hamoaze, opposite Stonehouse and Devonport, is partly in Cornwall, and contains 2725 inhabitants, and 2260 acres of land, of which 1156 souls and about 1320 acres are in VAULTERSHOLME tithing, which is in Devonshire, and includes the beautiful seat of *Mount Edgcumbe*, the parish church, the village of *Kingsand*, and part of *Millbrook*. The whole parish is in the Archdeaconry of Cornwall and Deanery of East, and the Union of St. Germans. *Makerton* was one of the manors of the ancient family of the *Valletorts*, from whom *Vaultersholme* had its name. Mount Edgcumbe had for-

merly a village called *West Stonehouse*, as noticed at page 689, and was the property of the ancient family of Stonehouse, whose heiress brought it to the Durnfords. *Sir Piers Edgcumbe*, who died in 1539, married the heiress of the Durnford family, and the estate has since remained in his family. His son, *Sir Richard*, built a castellated mansion on the hill, to which he gave the name of Mount Edgcumbe. Richd. Edgcumbe, Esq., the immediate descendant of Sir Richard, having filled several important public offices in the reigns of George I. and II., was created *Baron Edgcumbe*, in 1742. His grandson, George, the third baron, was created *Viscount Mount Edgcumbe and Valletort* in 1781; and in 1789, was raised to the dignity of *Earl of Mount Edgcumbe*. He died in 1795, and was succeeded by his son, Richard, the late Earl, who died in 1839, when he was succeeded by his son, the present *Right Honourable Ernest Augustus Edgcumbe*, EARL OF MOUNT EDGCUMBE, and *Viscount Valletort*, who was born in 1797, and married the daughter of the late Admiral Fielding. He is an aid-de-camp to the Queen, and colonel of the Cornwall Militia.

MOUNT EDGCUMBE, the delightful seat of the Earl of that name, occupies that towering promontory of verdant lawns, groves, parks, rocky cliffs, and sylvan terraces, which overlooks the spacious harbours of Hamoaze and Plymouth Sound, and the towns of Plymouth, Stonehouse, and Devonport; and is approached from thence by the *Cremill ferry boat*. The beautiful grounds are about three miles in circuit, and the mansion is an extensive and handsome castellated building, which was erected in the reign of Queen Mary, by Sir Richard Edgcumbe, whose father obtained the estate by marrying the heiress of the Durnford family; but it has at various periods undergone considerable alterations. It occupies an elevated situation on the side of a beautifully wooded hill, in a spacious lawn, bounded with rich old timber trees, growing down to the water's edge. The house is built chiefly of red limestone, obtained near the spot, and covered with stucco; but the doors and window cases are of moor-stone. Its form is nearly square, with a tower at each corner, and battlements on the top. The towers were originally round; but about 80 years ago, they were rebuilt in an octagon shape, and of a larger size. The hall occupies the centre of the house, and rises to the height of the second story. This spacious and elegant room was newly fitted up by the first Lord Edgcumbe, in the Grecian style, and is handsomely decorated with Doric columns and pilasters of Devonshire marble, surrounded by an Ionic entablature. At each end of the hall is a gallery, in one of which is an organ. The chimney-pieces, tables, and *termini* supporting the busts, are of different varieties of Cornish granite, highly polished. Among the numerous family portraits which decorate the mansion, is one of Margaret Edgcumbe, maid of honour to Queen Elizabeth, painted in the 68th year of her age, and the 48th of her widowhood. Here are also full-lengths of Charles II., James II., William III., and Prince Rupert; and also finely executed heads of Charles I. and his natural grandson, the Duke of Monmouth. The northern windows command a noble vista, irregularly bounded by trees of various species, extending down to the broad harbour of Hamoaze, near its confluence with Plymouth Sound. Of the modern additions which have been made to this edifice, that of a wing, containing a library well stored with books, and other rooms, is not the least important. The grounds surrounding the house are laid out in the most pleasing and diversified manner. They rise on the east in precipitous acclivities from the rocky shore of the Sound; but those parts which stretch along the shore of Hamoaze and Millbrook Lake, on the north and north-west, slope to the water with a gentler inclination. " Throughout the whole demesne, an agreeable al-

ternation of lawn, grove, and garden scenery, gratifies and relieves the eye; yet the prevailing style is of a richly varied woodland character. The general impression which an examination of its beauties leaves on the mind, is that of a magnificent Italian landscape, with its thick umbrageous woods rising proudly above each other." To walk round and view this beautiful mount, it is necessary for strangers to make application to Mrs. Huss, bookseller, Stonehouse, when a guide may be obtained for a party not exceeding six persons ; but on Mondays free admission is given to the public, without more trouble than entering names at the lodge gate. On the left of the entrance are pleasure grounds or gardens, which skirt the entrance to the harbour, and are laid out in the respective styles of the English, French, and Italian horticulturists : the latter enriched with a noble conservatory, statues, urns, fountains, and long avenues of oderiferous orange trees. In the French garden is an octagonal room, opening into conservatories. At the back of this apartment a pleasing illusion is created by the removal of a picture;—a small antique statue of Meleager is then discovered, behind which is a mirror that reflects most of the various objects within the garden. In this division, opposite a beautiful magnolia tree, is a votive urn and tablet, inscribed to the memory of the late Countess of Mount Edgcumbe, who died in 1806, and to whose genius these grounds owe many of their improvements. The English garden is larger than the others, and contains many majestic and beautiful trees, including several magnolias, Libanian and Virginian cedars, &c. Here, likewise, is a neat pavilion, of the Doric order, the marble basin of which is supplied with hot and cold water, from the mouths of bronzed dolphins. A walk leading from this garden descends into a deep excavation or quarry, which, from being embosomed amidst lofty evergreens, overspread with parasitical plants, and interspersed with antique urns, sarcophagi, and other funeral emblems, assumes the character of an ancient cemetery. At one extremity, to increase the interest from association, amidst a heap of architectural fragments, lies a fine capital of the Corinthian order, brought from the ruins of Alexandria. Near this spot, on the margin of Barnpool, is the block-house, now partly in ruins and mantled with ivy. This, with a similar fort at Devil's Point, the opposite promontory, was erected in the reign of Elizabeth, for the defence of the harbour. Near Barnpool is the " amphitheatre," a noble assemblage of trees, rising with symmetrical curvature, rank above rank, to a great elevation, and displaying an endless variety of form and foliage. Among the exotics are some beautiful tulip trees, a majestic cedar of Libanus, several vast plane trees, and a Caroline poplar of extraordinary height. Near the beach is a neat Ionic rotunda, in which is a bust of Milton, and an inscription quoted from his Paradise Lost, in apposite allusion to the umbrageous mantling of the contiguous acclivity. The next object of attraction is an artificial ruin, representing the remains of a Gothic tower, the summit of which commands a panoramic prospect of great beauty. Near this ruin is a cottage, romantically situated near the cliff, and having a neat garden plot, teeming with shrubs and flowers. The southern side of the hill, towards the sea, is an abrupt rocky cliff, planted with almost every kind of evergreen tree and shrub, many of them of extraordinary size. Midway up the hill, through these plantations, extends the great terrace; and walks cut in zig-zag directions have been carried from thence upwards towards Redding Point, and downwards to the very brink of the precipitous cliff. These walks lead to numerous points of view, affording an extraordinary variety of wild and romantic scenery. The imitation Indian cottage, on the summit, overlooks the Sound. In Picklecombe is a little secluded valley,

in which stand the imitative ruins of an ancient Gothic chapel, mantled with ivy. In Hoe Lake valley is a keeper's lodge, and a deep ravine, which forms the western boundary of the park, which is enlivened by numerous herds of fine deer. From the loftier points of the park, and especially in the neighbourhood of Maker Church, at its western extremity, the more distant landscape presents a series of prospects of the most varied description. In front, and right and left, are the towns and spacious harbours of the Port of Plymouth, and beyond them the horizon is bounded by the lofty and rugged hills of Dartmoor. The far-famed beauties of Mount Edgcumbe have elicited the admiration of the most illustrious personages both of this and foreign nations; poets have been lavish in its praise, and the Admiral of the Spanish Armada fixed his longing eyes upon it from the Channel, and declared that it should be his future residence, after the partition of England among the *dons*, but as John Bull and his jolly tars were not parties to this arrangement, the Spanish Duke's elysian dreams were never realized. (See page 636.) It was occupied as one of the royal garrisons, to act as a check upon Plymouth, during the civil wars of the 17th century, and was the last fortress in Devon, except Salcombe, that held out for the King. The *Parish Church of Maker* is dedicated to *St. Macra*, and the living is a *discharged vicarage*, valued at £233, in the patronage of the Lord Chancellor, and incumbency of the Rev. Edward Trelawney, M.A. The great tithes were appropriated to Plympton Priory, but now belong to the Earl of Mount Edgcumbe, together with most of the parish. The church occupies a commanding eminence between Mount Edgcumbe and Rame Head, and its tower serves as a land-mark, and in the late wars was used as a signal station. A house at Plympton, let for £12 a year, has been long vested in trust for the repairs of Maker church. Several tenements at Plymouth, left to Maker parish by Joan Bennett, in 1650, are let for £20 a year, of which £14 is divided among the poor, and £6 is paid to the vicar for monthly sermons. The poor parishioners have about £14. 10s. per annum, left by J. Trevill, J. Lanyon, J. Kerley, and other donors. There are several schools and a Wesleyan chapel in the parish.

MAKER PARISH.
(Vaultersholme, Kingsand, &c.)

Earl of Mount Edgcumbe, *Mount Edgcumbe House*
Banks Jph. ship builder, *Cremill*
Blight John, tanner, *Millpool*
Bowey Mrs || Vallack Miss
Chapple Richd. ferryman, *Cremill*
Elliott Mrs || Treville Mrs
Gillard Mr Wm. || Gifford Mrs
Gray Mr Francis || Row Mr Henry
Gregory Mr Wm. || Rowe Miss
Ham & Son, watch & clock makers
Kerns My. housekeeper,*Mt Edgcmb.*
Kingdon Ann, baker
Laye Peter, house steward,*Mt Edgcb.*
Little John, surgeon, *Millpool*
Nepean Captain Edmund, R.M.
Prowse Wm. surgeon
Sang Andrew, hairdresser
Thomas Rev Joseph N. Houghton, incumbent of *Millbrook*
Tidy Mr || Napton Richard
Toms Daniel, Esq. *Millpool*
Trelawney Rev Edward, M.A. vicar of *Maker*

INNS AND TAVERNS.
Devonport Inn, George Odgers
Edgcumbe Inn, Eliz. Graves, *Cremill*
King's Arms, John Nicholls
London Inn, Jane Eddey
Prince George, Nicholas Wills

BEER HOUSES.
Avery George
Lee John
BOOT & SHOE MKS.
Hill Stephen
Stanton Richard
FARMERS.
Harris John
Lee John
Matthews Thos.
Pearn Joseph
Prince Wm.
Skardon Thos.
Stephens Wm.
Veale John
Veale Wm.
Willcocks Edw.
SHOPKEEPERS.
Coath Joseph
Hocken John
Langler George
Oliver John
Webber Wm.

MEAVY is a scattered village and parish, near the sources of the river Plym, and near Dartmoor Railway, from 6 to 7 miles S.E. of Tavistock. It comprises 361 souls, and 3351 acres of land, a large portion of which is on the uncultivated hills of Dartmoor, near *Ringmoor Down, Brisworthy,* and *Loveton,* the latter of which is a small village. Sir R. Lopes is lord of the manor and owner of a great part of the parish, but the manor of *Good-a-Meavy* belongs to E. Scobell, Esq., and those of *Callisham* and *Durance* belong to Sir T. T. F. E. Drake. It has its name from the small river *Mew* or *Meavy,* one of the sources of the Plym. The *Church* (St. Peter,) is an ancient structure, with a tower and six bells, and the living is a *rectory,* valued in K.B. at £13. 5s., and in 1831 at £238, in the patronage of the Lord Chancellor, and incumbency of the Rev. John Abbott, M.A., who has a small residence, and 23A. of glebe. The tithes were commuted in 1839, for £224. 10s. per annum. A *Baptist Chapel* was built here in 1850, and land was given for the site and burial ground by Mr. John Dawe. The National School, built in 1837, is attended by about 40 children.

Abbott Rev John, M.A. *Rectory*
Adams Mr Jesse, *Fancy dale*
Brown Edmund, blacksmith
Dingle John, baker & carpenter
Pedler Jno., Esq. *Hoo Meavy House*
Rundle Philip, vict. *Royal Oak*
Scobell Edwin, Esq. *Good-a-Meavy*
Tregillus Mary, baker and shopr.
Tregillus Edw. corn miller
   FARMERS. (* *at Loveton.*)
Andrews Walter | Andrews Henry

*Atwill John
Atwill Wm.
Bowden Robert
*Chapple Mary
Creber James
Damarell Thos.
Dawe Wm.
Dawe John
Helyer Richard
Lillicrap John
*Luscombe Sml.

*Matticott John
*Moses Geo., Rd., and Wm.
Northmore Rd. & Mark
Northmore Wm.
Rowe Joseph
Rowe Wm.
Rundle Philip
Williams James

SAMPFORD-SPINEY parish, on the west side of Dartmoor, and in the valley of the small river Walkham, 4 miles S.E. of Tavistock, has 443 souls, and about 1800 acres of land. It includes part of the village of *Horrabridge,* (see p. 733,) and a number of scattered farm-houses, &c. The manor anciently belonged to the family of Spinet, or De Spineto, and afterwards to the Drakes, Bidgoods, and Hals. John Parlby, Esq., is now lord of the manor; but the Cornish, Cole, and other families, have estates here, mostly freehold. The *Church* has a tower and three bells, and the living is a *perpetual curacy,* valued at only £54, with that of Shaugh annexed to it. The Dean and Canons of Windsor are appropriators of the tithes, and patrons of the living, now held by the Rev. S. W. Pearse, B.A., of Cadleigh. The tithes were commuted, in 1841, for £172. 10s. per ann.

*Marked * are at Horrabridge.*
Cole James, Esq. *Lr. Eastentown*
Cornish Henry, Esq., *Woodtown*
*Hamlyn and Co. woollen manfrs
*Hancock Sar. wheelwright, &c
*Harding James, tailor
*Harding John and Wm. smiths
Mashford John, vict. Fox Inn
Morrish George, carpenter
Shillabeare Amos, land surveyor

*Toop Hy. shopr. & vict.White Hart
   FARMERS.
Andrews Thos.
Burgoyne Wm.
Foote James
Gosling Wm.
Lillicrap John
Mashford Walter
Nichols Richd.

Northmore Jas.
Perkins James
Spry John
Spurr Joseph
Spurrell Thos.
Tozer Aaron
Tozer Giles
Worth George

SHEEPSTOR, or *Shipstor,* anciently written *Schitestor,* or *Shittor,* is a small village, in the picturesque valley of the little river Mew, or Meavy, on the western side of Dartmoor, near several rocky hills, and the Dartmoor Railway, 7 miles S.E. of Tavistock. Its parish has 127 souls, and 3469 acres of land, partly open moorland, on Ringmoor Down, &c., near

the sources of the river Plym. John Bayly, Esq., is lord of the manor; but a great part of the soil belongs to Sir R. Lopes, the Northmore family, and several smaller owners. *Longstone*, the ancient seat of the Elford family, is now a farm-house. The *Church* is a small antique fabric, with a tower and five bells; and the living is a *curacy*, annexed to the vicarage of Bickleigh. A house, left for repairing the church, is let for £4. The poor have two cottages, and also 5A. of land, let for £11. In the parish are two large *rabbit warrens*.

Bayly John, Esq. *Narrow Tor*		Chapple John	Northmore Rd.
Lavers John, *Legeston Warren*		Creber John	Northmore Smn.
Were Nichls. *Ditsworthy Warren*		Jackson John	Northmore Wltr.
FARMERS.	Andrews Wm.	LiscombeJohn L.	Reed Peter
Andrews Robt.	Atwill John	Maddock Henry	Shillabear Wm.

TAMERTON FOLIOTT is a large and handsome village, pleasantly seated at the head of a creek, from the confluence of the Tamar and Tavy, 4 miles N.W. of Plymouth. It has a fair on the third Tuesday in July, and had formerly a market, granted in 1269. It was one of the quarters of Prince Maurice's army, when besieging Plymouth, in 1643. Its parish contains 1214 inhabitants, and 4641 acres of land, but only 3805 are titheable. It gives name to the Deanery of Tamerton. The manor of Tamerton Foliott was anciently held by the Foliot family, and afterwards by the Gorges, Bonville, Coplestone, and Bampfyldes, the latter of whom sold it to the Radcliffes, in 1741. It now belongs to the Rev. Walter Radcliffe, who resides at *Warleigh*, the ancient manor-house, near the mouth of the Tavy. *Maristow*, more than two miles north of Tamerton, and 7 miles S. of Tavistock, is delightfully seated on the east bank of the Tavy, and is the seat and manor of *Sir Ralph Lopes*, whose father was created a *baronet* in 1805. The mansion has tasteful and well wooded grounds, and stands near the site of the ancient chapel of *St. Martin*, which belonged to the canons of Plympton, and from which the manor was originally called Martinstow. After the dissolution, it was granted to the Champernownes, from whom it passed to the Slannings and Heywoods, the latter of whom sold it to the late *Sir Masseh Manasseh Lopes, Bart.*, in 1798. It was visited twice by George III., Queen Charlotte, and three of the Princesses, during their sojourn at Saltram, in 1789, and they were delighted with the romantic scenery of the grounds and woods. The ancient chapel was rebuilt by the late baronet. A great part of the parish belongs to several smaller owners, some of whom have seats here. The *Church* (St. Peter,) is an ancient structure, with a lofty tower, and contains some antique monuments, one of which has the effigy of one of the Gorges, in plate armour. The *vicarage*, valued in K.B. at £17. 7s. 8½d., and in 1831 at £315, is in the patronage of the Lord Chancellor, and incumbency of the Rev. G. F. Arthur, who has a good residence and 3A. of glebe. The tithes were commuted in 1839, the vicarial for £339. 10s., and the rectorial for £155. 10s. per annum. The latter belong to P. M. Little, Thomas Woollcombe, and a number of smaller impropriators. Here is a small Wesleyan chapel. The *Almshouse*, for four poor widows, was founded in 1669, by Lady Bampfylde, who endowed it with an adjoining field. The *Free School* was founded in 1734, by Mary Dean, who endowed it with the interest of £480, and with Radge Farm, (108A.,) now let for £100 per annum, out of which the master has £37 for teaching 37 free scholars, who are clothed at the expense of the charity. The poor have the dividends of £235. 19s. 3d. three per cent. stock, which arose from the gifts of Lady Modyford and other donors. 2 I 3

Ardagh Major, *Wadlands*
Arthur Rev Geo. Fredk., Vicarage
Bowden Charles, vict. Seven Stars
Briggs Wm. Esq. *Down House*
Brown Mrs ‖ Chubb Mrs
Du Pre Duckworth, surgeon
Ellis Walter, Esq. *Looseleigh*
Ewing Mrs ‖ Haytor Wm.
Fellowes Admiral Sir Thomas, Kt., *Harwood*
Francis Wm. tailor
Griggs Mark, Esq. *Cann Cottage*
Jackman John, Esq. *Powisland*
Johnson Capt., R.N.‖Pearse Mrs
Lillicrap Charles, butcher
Lopes Sir Ralph, Bart., and M. L., Esq. *Maristow*
Mc Kenzie Wm., Esq. *Denmark*
Maddocks John, glazier, &c.
Northcott Jas. vict. King's Arms
Needham Mrs. ‖ Reeve Mary
Pearse John & Philip, shoemakers
Prideaux Chas. & Hy., Esqrs. *Brook*
Radcliffe Rev Walter, *Warleigh*
Reed Joseph, Esq. *Upland*
Shaw Wm., Esq. *Haxtor Lodge*
Smith Sidney, wheelwright
Smith James, gent. ‖ Walker Mrs.
Ward Joseph May, gent.
Winchester Wm. Hy. surgeon

BEERHOUSES. | Roberts Pethk.
Pepperell James |

BLACKSMITHS.
Calloway Wm.
Gregory Matthew
CARPENTERS.
Bawden Richard
Gloyne John
Hacker John
Roberts John
Symons Thomas
FARMERS.
Avery Richard
Bradridge Henry
Brown Wm.
Chesterfield Rt.
Dawe Joseph
Fairweather Ths.
Fowler George
Fowler James
Giles John, *Jump*
Glanville Chas.
Gregory John
Hamlyn Thos.
Hamlyn Wm.
Hill John
Horswill James
Hull Mark
Hyne Henry
Leamon Geo.
Legassick Wm.
Lethbridge John
Luscombe Philip
Maddock Wm.

March James
Maynard Edward
Poppleton Saml.
Scott Richard
SpurrellWm.jun.
Williams Richd.
MASONS.
Ellis John
Gloyne Wm.
Northcott Jas.
Roberts John
MILLERS.
Meathrell John
Taylor George
NURSERYMEN.
Brown John
Hull Wm.
Williams Robert
SCHOOLS.
Vellacott Miss
Warn Richard
SHOPKEEPERS.
Fone Thomas
Full George
Houghton Ann
Pepperell James
Smith Sidney

FOOT POST to *and from Ply- mouth, daily*

TAVY ST. PETER, a scattered village in the Tavy valley, on the western borders of Dartmoor, 4 miles N.N.E. of Tavistock, has in its parish 587 souls, and about 6000 acres of land, of which 91 souls, and about 2450 acres, are in *Willsworthy* hamlet, a high moorland district in Lifton Hundred, 6 miles N.N.E. of Tavistock. The parish also includes *Godsworthy*, and many scattered farm houses. The Duke of Bedford is lord of the manors of Peter Tavy and Huntingdon; but Willsworthy belongs to the Buller family; and the Rev. W. Radcliffe and several smaller owners have estates in the parish, mostly freehold. The *Church* (St. Peter,) has a tower and five bells; and the living is a *rectory*, valued in K.B. at £17. 1s. 8d., and now in the patronage of the Bishop of Exeter, and incumbency of the Rev. Wm. Macbean, M.A., who does not reside here. An ancient chapel at Willsworthy has been long used as a cowhouse.

Bayly John, Esq. *Old Mead*
Prout Robert, blacksmith
Spry Thomas, Esq. *Sortridge*
Ware Thos. vict. Peter Tavy Inn
BOOT&SHOE MKS.
Grennen Philip
Teed John
CORN MILLERS.
Quick Samuel
Williams Richd.

FARMERS.
(* are Owners.)
*Arthur John
*Arthur James
Bolt Thomas
*Bray Elias G.

Burley John
Burley Wm.
Cole Thomas
*Crossing Jas. P.
Dawe Thomas
Doidge Wm.
Fuge John
*Gill James
Harvie Ann
Holmes Peter

Kennard John
Mudge Wm.
Palmer Wm.
*Paul John
*Peek Richard
Pentecost L. B.
Phillips John
Reep Wm.
Rice James
Roskilly J. M.

Slocombe Wm.	Vogwill Jno. jun	SHOPKEEPERS.	WHEELWRIGHTS.
Spear Wm.	MASONS.	Date Samuel	Bickle Thomas
Vallance David	Bray Elias G.	Fuge Wm.	Creys Isaiah
Vogwill John	Bray Thomas G.		

WALKHAMPTON, a scattered village, in the valley of the little river Walkham, on the western borders of Dartmoor, 5 miles S.E. of Tavistock, has in its parish 717 inhabitants, and 10,501 acres of land, including 6602 acres of open common and wastes in Dartmoor; part of the village of *Horrabridge*, and many scattered farms. Sir Ralph Lopes, Bart., is lord of the manor, owner of a great part of the soil, and of the barton of *Gnatham*, impropriator of the rectorial tithes, and patron of the *vicarage*, valued in K.B. at £9. 14s. 7d., and now in the incumbency of the Rev. D. S. Stone, M.A., who has a good residence and 18A. 2R. 14P. of glebe. The small tithes were commuted in 1839, for £141 per annum. The *Church* is a neat structure, in the perpendicular style, with a tower and six bells. The FREE SCHOOL was founded in 1719, by *Mrs. Eliz. Modyford*, who endowed it with 162A. of land, now let for about £160 a year. There is also about £1100, which arose from surplus school income, and is now vested at interest. The master and mistress teach 40 free scholars, who are partly clothed at the expense of the charity. The poor have the interest of £50, left by the foundress of the school.

Deacon J. H. Esq. *Kingseat*
French John, miller, *Huckworthy*
Greep Thomas, vict. Church House
Pearse John, blacksmith
Spurrell John, shoemaker
Stone Rev David Smith, M.A. *vicar*
Thorne —, vict. Manor House
Vanstone John, miller, Phœnix Mill
Worth John, tailor

FARMERS.
Adams Richard
Andrews John
Andrews Wm.
Blackford James
Brian John

Creber Eliz.
Creber John
Creber Richard
Dawe Joseph
French George
Giles John E.
Giles Abraham
Gosling Wm.
Hamlyn Samuel
Hannaford Saml.
King Walter
Legassick George

Mortmore Elias
Pearse Henry
Stancombe Isaac
Thorn Richard
Tuckett Joshua
Tuckett Thomas
Vogwill Thomas
Williams James
SHOPKEEPERS.
Reed James
Worth John

WHITCHURCH, a small scattered village, on an eminence, 2 miles S.E. of Tavistock, has in its parish 918 souls, and 6450 acres of land, of which 2523 acres are open commons and wastes, on the borders of Dartmoor, where there are several lead and tin mines, the largest of which is the *Wheal Anderton Tin Mine*, which has long been successfully managed by Mr. James Carpenter. Colonel Harris is lord of the manor of Whitchurch; and that of *Walreddon* belongs to Wm. Courtenay, Esq. The parish has a few neat mansions, and many scattered farm houses, mostly small. *Grenofen* is beautifully situated among romantic scenery, and was rebuilt by J. M. Knighton, Esq. *Halwell House* was for 300 years the seat of the Glanvilles. The *Church* (St. Andrew,) is a venerable structure, in the perpendicular style, with a tower and six bells. In the chancel are several handsome monuments, belonging to the Pengelly and Mooringe families. The *rectory*, valued in K.B. at £16. 5s. 5d., and in 1831 at £240, is in the patronage and incumbency of the Rev. Richard Sleeman, B.A., who is also impropriator of the rectory, and has 80A. 3R. 25P. of glebe, and a large and handsome residence. The tithes have been commuted, the rectorial for £260, and the vicarial for £192. 10s. *Fras. Pengelly*, in 1719, left for the poor £100, and also £6 a year out of the great tithes, for schooling poor children. The poor have also the interest of £10, left by Peter Sleeman, in 1778.

Collier Mrs. *Grimston*
Carpenter Jas. mine agent, *Anderton Cottage*
Courtenay Wm., Esq. *Walreddon*
Deacon Jas. Henry, Esq. *Halwell*
Gorman Wm. shoemaker
Hannaford Peter, *Dartmoor Inn*
Morris Thomas, Esq. *Grenofen*
Sleeman Rev Richard & Mr Thos.
Toop Walter, shopr. and innkeeper

BLACKSMITHS.
Creber John
Moore Walter

CARPENTERS.
Dobson Richard
Hunn Samuel

CORN MILLERS.
Cocker Samuel
Harris John

Taverner Edwd., *Grenofen*

FARMERS.
Arthur John
Blatchford Thos., *Longford*
Blatchford Jas., *Moortown*
Berribell Wm.
Bickle Wm.

Chubb Roger
Cocker Samuel
Cudlip W. B.
Dawe Wm.
Dodd Wm.
Edmunds James
Foot John
Gidney John
Giles John
Glanville Henry
Glanville Nichls.
Goddard Edw.
Jope John
Karslake Richd.
Knight Henry
Knight John
Mortimore Wm.
Mudge Roger
Nicholls Jane
Oxenham John

Oxenham Philip
Page Eliz.
Palmer Charles
Peek Richard
Pengelly John
Price Percival
Radcliffe James
Rickard Thomas
Rowe Thomas
Slocombe Wm. *Crowndale*
Smith John
Smith Samuel
Spry John
Warn George
Westaway Ann
Wilcocks J. R.
Witheridge J.

FREMINGTON HUNDRED

Is in the Northern Parliamentary Division of Devon, and extends about eleven miles southward from Barnstaple to Great Torrington and the vale of the river Torridge. It is bounded on the north by the estuary of the Taw, and on the north-west by the estuary of the Torridge; and is mostly in the Petty Sessional Division of Braunton, and partly in that of Torrington. It is in the polling districts of Barnstaple, Bideford, and Torrington; and is all in the Archdeaconry of Barnstaple, but extends into the Deaneries of Barnstaple, Torrington, and Hartland. It contains eleven parishes, of which the following is an enumeration, showing their territorial extent, and their population in 1841:—

Parishes.	Acres.	Pop.	Parishes.	Acres.	Pop.
§Alverdiscott	2244	.. 332	*Leigh (West) ..	2456	.. 526
*Fremington	6810	.. 1326	*Newton Tracey..	340	.. 125
§Giles (St.) in the Wood........	3330	.. 915	§Roborough	3000	.. 588
			*Tawstock	6500	.. 1489
*Horwood	746	.. 118	§Torrington	3640	.. 3419
§Huntshaw......	1962	.. 296			
*Instow	1360	.. 557	Total	32,388	.. 9631

UNIONS.—Those marked thus * are in *Barnstaple Union*, and § in *Torrington Union*.

ALVERDISCOTT, or *Alscott*, is a pleasant village and parish, 5 miles E. by S. of Bideford, containing 332 souls, and 2244 acres of fertile land, including the hamlets of *Bullworthy* and *Stonecross*. Richard Preston, Esq., is lord of the manor, formerly held by the Fleming, Bellew, and other families; but A. W. J. Dene, Esq., and several smaller owners, have estates in the parish. The *Church* (All Saints,) has a tower and three bells, and the living is a *rectory*, valued in K.B. at £13. 3s. 11½d., and in 1831 at £168. W. Lee, Esq., is the patron, and the Rev. W. M. Lee, M.A., is the incumbent, and has a good residence, and 39A. 2R. 10P. of glebe. The tithes were commuted in 1844 for £140 per annum. Three tenements and an acre of land have been vested from an early period for the reparation of the

church. Wibbery, or *Webbery*, was anciently the seat of a family of its own name, and was successively held by the Lippincots and Cutcliffes, the latter of whom rebuilt the house about 30 years ago.

Capel Hon. Capt. A. H. C., R.N.
Cloak Thomas, blacksmith
Cooper Geo. land survyr. &c. Barton
Hutchinson Mr C. F. ‖ Warry Capt

Lee Rev Wm. M., M.A. *Rectory*.

FARMERS.

Henry Copp, John Fry, and John Petherbridge

FREMINGTON, a large village, pleasantly seated on an acclivity south of the estuary of the Taw, 3 miles W. of Barnstaple, has in its parish 1326 inhabitants, and 6810 acres of land, including the village of *Bickington*, and many scattered farm-houses, &c. It was anciently a borough, and sent members to the parliament at Westminster in the reign of Edward III. In 1547, it was considered as part of Instow parish. Merchant vessels trading with Barnstaple usually anchor in the small creek of the Taw estuary, called *Fremington Pill*, or *Pen-hill;* and coal vessels discharge cargoes there. The manor and hundred of Fremington were held by Earl Harold, but were given by William the Conqueror to Geoffrey, Bishop of Constance; and afterwards passed to the Tracey, Holland, Sloly, Hawkins, Acland, and Barbor families. *Wm. A. Yeo, Esq. (high-sheriff of Devon in 1850,)* is now lord of the manor, and owner of a great part of the parish. He resides at *Fremington House*, a large handsome mansion, with extensive gardens, green-houses, hot-houses, &c., containing a valuable collection of exotics. *Brynsworthy* is the seat of S. T. M. May, Esq., who is lord of the manor of Colybeare. C. Roberts, Esq., of *Bickington House*, and the Crocker, Quartly, Petherbridge, and other families, have estates here. The *Church* (St. Peter,) has a tower and five bells, and the *vicarage*, valued in K.B. at £20. 0s. 5d., and in 1831 at £430, is in the patronage and incumbency of the Rev. W. C. Hill, B.A., who has 83A. 3R. 26P. of glebe, and a handsome residence, built in 1831. The tithes were commuted in 1842, the vicarial for £359, and the rectorial for £421 per ann. The latter belong to W. A. Yeo, Esq., subject to the yearly payment of £50 for the support of a lecturer, and £10 for a scholar at one of the Universities, pursuant to the bequest of *John Doddridge*, in 1658. The poor have about £24 a year from land and money derived from the gifts of *John Penrose and others*, and £4 in three rent-charges left by Grace Tew, Eleanor Thorne, and Samuel and Elizabeth May.

Marked 2 are at Bickington.

2 Ayres Mrs ‖ Braund Henry, joiner
2 Chapple Mr Wm. ‖ Cook Charles
Crocker Anthony L. *Muttle Bridge*
Crocker Stephen, gent. *Brookfield*
Crocker Thomas, vict. New Inn
2 Drew Wm. tailor
Dey Mr Wm. *Victoria Cottage*
2 Fishley Edmund, pot & tile maker
Hill Rev Wm. Chas., B.A., *Vicarage*
2 Hooper Mr Rd. ‖ Ley Wm.
2 Jewell Gideon, vict. Greyhound
2 Ley Wm. cabinet maker, &c
2 Luxton John, cattle dealer
4 May S. T. M., Esq. *Brynsworthy*
Roberts Charles, gent. *Bickington Hs*
2 Rattenbury Mr W. ‖ Johns Mrs
2 Sargent John, machine maker
2 Sheere Cphr. vict. Royal Exchange

Smallcorn Saml. tailor, & Thos. clerk
2 Thorold Edw. S. gent ‖ Tythe Mr
2 Townsend Rev Jno. H., M.A.,*Lodge*
2 Watts Wm. carpenter, &c
Yeo Wm. Arundell, Esq. *Fremington House*

BEERHOUSES.

Buckingham D.
2 Ridge Robert

BLACKSMITHS.

Tremlett John
Walter Joseph
2 White John
2 White Thos.

FARMERS.

Adams Wm.
Blake John
Dullan George
Dullan John

Cann Mary
Copp Henry
Fairchild Wm.
2 Gibbings Saml.
Gill John
Green Wm.
Harding Samuel
Heal Abel
Hill John
Holland John
Hookway Geo.
2 Hutton Eliz.
King Hugh

Lee Wm.
Lock Eliz.
Lovering Fras.
Moore Thos.
Moule Henry
Parker Thomas
Petherbridge Ts.

Phillips Henry
Pudicombe W.
Quartly W. B.
Shapley Cphr.
Sussex Wm.
Tupland Thos.
Vellacott John

2 Williams Jno.
SHOEMAKERS.
Dennis Geo. shop
2 Easton Saml.
2 Sargent John
SHOPKEEPERS.
Dennis George

2 Easton Eliz.
2 Gibbet Geo.

STONE MASONS.
Hern John
Rattenbury Geo.

ST. GILES-IN-THE-WOOD, or *Stow St. Giles*, a pleasant village
and parish, 3 miles E. by S. of Great Torrington, contains 915 souls, and
3330 acres of land, including the hamlets of *Kingscot, High Bullen*, and
Healand. A great part of the parish is in the manor of Stevenstone, which
belongs to the trustees of the late *Lord Rolle*, who resided occasionally at
Stevenstone House, but chiefly at Bicton, as noticed at page 218. Stevenstone is a fine old mansion, with a deer park, and is occasionally occupied
by Lady Rolle. Sir S. H. Northcote is lord of the manor of *Winscot*, which
was held by Risdon, the antiquary. *Way* belongs to J. H. Furse, Esq.,
and other parts of the parish belong to several smaller owners. The *Church*
was built in 1309, as a chapel to Torrington. The benefice is now a *perpetual curacy*, in the patronage of the incumbent of Great Torrington, and is
now held by the Rev. John Francis, who has 50A. of glebe. The Dean and
Chapter of Christ Church College, Oxford, are [appropriators of the tithes.
Here are four *Almshouses*, founded by Sir Henry Rolle, and endowed with
£5 a year. The parish has several tenements for the poor, and two cottages for the clerk and schoolmaster. The poor have the interest of £200,
given by various donors, and an annuity of 20s., left by Charles Beer.

Bragington Geo. Esq. steward to trustees
  of the late Lord Rolle, *Rose Moor*
Brinsmead Hy. & Thos. machine mkrs
Brinsmead Thos. brewer, maltster, &c
Clarke Robert, joiner, & Wm. butcher
Cock Wm. schoolmr. & parish clerk
Cock Thomas, shopkeeper
Francis Rev John, B.A. incumbent
Rolle Lady, *Stevenstone House*
Squire Francis, beer seller
Thorne Francis, vict. Red Lion
Ware John, corn miller
BOOT&SHOE MKS. | Folland Isaac
Ashplant Thos. |

BLACKSMITHS.
Clemens Thos.
May John
May Wm.

FARMERS.
Blackmore Rd.
Clark Jno. & Rd.
Clemens Mary
Ellis Wm.
Hooper John
Hookway John
Judd Francis
Judd Thomas

Leigh Wm.
May Isaac
Matthews John
Rowe J. & L.
Shapland Geo.
Squire F. & R.
Snell Jno.
Snell Wm. owner
Symons Edw.
Tanton T. & W.
Thorne Ann
Turner Thos.
Vodden T. & W.

HORWOOD, a small village and parish, 3 miles E.N.E. of Bideford, has
only 118 souls, and about 750 acres of land, nearly all belonging to the
Rev. John Dene, M.A., the Trustees of the late Major Hogg, and Earl Fortescue. The Rev. J. Dene owns the estates called Church and Pen Horwood, and is patron and incumbent of the *rectory*, valued in K.B. at £7. 8s.
4d., and in 1831 at £157. The tithes were commuted in 1848, for £127
per annum, and the glebe is 36 acres. The *Church* (St. Michael,) has a
tower and three bells, and contains memorials of the Denes, Rolles, and
Pollards. The Rev. John Dene, M.A., has a pleasant seat, called *Horwood
House*, and the other principal residents are—Thomas Copp, Joshua Downing, and Wm. Jenn, *farmers*, and Edw. Lee, *blacksmith*.

HUNTSHAW, or *Hunshaw*, 3 miles N.E. of Torrington, has in its parish
296 souls, and 1962 acres of land, mostly belonging to Lord Clinton, the
lord of the manor and patron of the *rectory*, valued in K.B. at £11. 7s. 1d.,
and in 1831 at £200. The Rev. C. D. M. Drake is the rector, and has 36A.

of glebe, and a good residence, in a picturesque valley. The tithes were commuted in 1844, for £151 per annum. The *Church* (St. Mary,) has a tower and three bells, and the parish sends two boys to the Free School at Wear Gifford. The *Church Lands, &c.*, comprise 3 gardens, 2 orchards, 4 houses, and a blacksmith's shop; and the poor have about £2 yearly from *John Lovering's Charity*, and an annuity of 20s. left by Edm. Dennis.

	FARMERS.	Fisher Samuel,
Drake Rev Chas. Digby Mackworth, *Rectory*	Brownscombe J.	*Barton*
Priscott Thos. blacksmith	Clark Francis	Phillips George
Short Joseph, beer seller	Dinnis Ann	Snell Esther

INSTOW, a much improved village and bathing place, pleasantly situated on the shore of the broad estuary of the river Taw and Torridge, opposite Appledore, 3½ miles N. by E. of Bideford, has in its parish 557 souls, and 1360 acres of land, and is famous for cockles. A. Clevland, Esq., is lord of the manors of Instow, Bickleton, and Fullingcote, and patron of the *rectory*, valued in K.B. at £12. 17s. 3½d., and in 1831 at £320, in the incumbency of the Rev. A. F. Lloyd, who has 30A. of glebe and a good residence, erected in 1825, at the cost of about £800. W. A. Yeo, Esq., and several smaller owners, have estates in the parish. A garden and a field of 1½A., left to the poor by *Joan Tucker*, are let for £2. 10s. per annum. The *Church* (St. John,) is an ancient structure, in the perpendicular style, and has a tower and three bells. [*Directory, see Appendix.*]

LEIGH, (WEST) a village and parish, on the east side of the estuary of the Torridge, 2 miles N. by E. of Bideford, has 526 inhabitants, and 2456 acres of land, including *East Leigh* and Southcott hamlets, and many scattered houses. Mrs. Torr, of *Torville*, is lady of the manor of West Leigh, and owner of the Barton of East Leigh. *Tapley*, or Taplegh, a handsome mansion, with tasteful grounds, is the seat of Mrs. Clevland, and belongs to her son, Archibald Clevland, a minor. L. W. Buck, Esq., and several smaller owners, have estates in the parish. The *Church* (St. Peter,) is an ancient structure, and the living is a *vicarage*, valued in K.B. at £8. 2s. 1d., and in 1831 at £170, in the patronage of the Dean and Chapter of Exeter. The Rev. D. Lang, B.A., is the incumbent, and has a neat residence, erected in 1837, and 45A. of glebe. The Wesleyans have a chapel here, built in 1841. The Church Land is 2A., and the poor have the interest of £50 given by John Berry. The great tithes are in the appropriation of the Vicars Choral of Exeter, but are leased to Miss Incledon.

	Prescott Wm.	Maule Wm.
Allen Mr W. ‖ Wood James, gent.	Stevens John	Pillafent John
Boatfield Rt. C. vict. New Inn	CORN MILLERS.	Puddicombe Rt.
Clevland Mrs Caroline, *Tapley*	Kent John	Sleeman Thos.
Hackridge John, butcher	Richards Thos.	Taylor John
Lang Rev Dashwood, B.A., *Vicarage*		
Pyncombe Thomas, tailor		
Stevens Capt. N. coal merchant	FARMERS.	MASONS.
Torr Mrs Jane, *Torrville*	Balsdon Richard	Hill Richard
Torr James B., Esq. *Westleigh Hs*	Brailey Thomas	Jones Thos.
BLACKSMITHS. ‖ Lemon John	Brown James	Sleeman John
Lee John ‖ Mullis Thomas	Holman Aaron	
Oliver Wm.	Holman John	SCHOOLS.
BOOT&SHOE MKS. ‖ CARPENTERS.	Hookway Saml.	Cann Wm.
Dyer Robert ‖ Hackridge Sml.	Laramy James	Mullis James

NEWTON TRACEY, a small parish, 5 miles E.N.E. of Bideford, has only 125 souls, and 340 acres of land, belonging to the Trustees of the late T. Hogg, Esq., and a few smaller owners. The *Church* (St. Thomas-

a-Becket,) is a small Gothic structure, and the benefice is a *rectory*, valued in K.B. at £5. 8s. 1¼d., and in 1831 at £69. The Lord Chancellor is patron, and the Rev. John Dene, of Horwood, is the incumbent, and has 38A. 3R. 10P. of glebe. The tithes were commuted in 1848, for £50 per annum.

Adams John, farmer	Priscott George, schoolmaster
Campbell Sir Alex., Bart., *Newton Cross House*, (and Scotland)	Sussex John, shopr. *Post Office*
Clark John, vict. Hunter's Inn	Westacott John, farmer

ROBOROUGH, 5½ miles E. by S. of Torrington, has in its parish 588 souls, and about 3000 acres of land, including the hamlet of *Ebberley*, and a number of scattered farms. Henry Hole, Esq., is lord of the manor, and owner of a great part of the soil, and resides at *Ebberley House*. The Trustees of the late Lord Rolle own *Owlacombe*, and several smaller proprietors have estates in the parish. The *Church* (St. Peter,) has a tower and six bells, and the living is a *rectory*, valued in K.B. at £10. 9s. 8d., and in 1831 at £244. The Bishop of Exeter is the patron, and the Rev. W. W. Gurney is the incumbent, and has 60A. of glebe, and a handsome residence, in the Elizabethan style, erected some years ago, at the cost of about £1500. The tithes were commuted in 1842, for £271 per annum. The poor have the interest of £50 left by the Rev. Saml. May and John Alford.

Bealey John & Richard, blacksmiths	Rockey Thos. wheelwright	
Clark Robert, blacksmith	FARMERS.	Page John
Ford James, vict. George Inn	Allen Eliz.	Passmore John
Gurney Rev Wm. Walter, *Rectory*	Copp Wm.	Squire Wm.
Harris Andrew, vict. New Inn	Down Wm.	Wadland Sarah
Hole Henry, Esq., *Ebberley House*	Lemon Wm.	Wedlake William,
Isaac John, shoemaker	Millward Sus.	*Cliston*

TAWSTOCK, a pleasant scattered village and parish, from 2 to 4 miles S. of Barnstaple, has 1429 inhabitants, and 6500 acres of land, including the neighbouring hamlets of *East Combe*, *West Combe*, *Hiscott*, *Prustacott*, *Chapeltown*, and *St. John's Chapel*, in the fertile vale of the river Taw. The manor was successively held by the Brewer, Tracey, Martyn, Audley, Fitzwarren, Hankford, and Bourchier families. The eldest daughter of Edward Bourchier, Esq., Earl of Bath, carried it in marriage to *Sir Chpr. Wrey*, who was created a *baronet* in 1628. It now belongs to *Sir Bourchier Palk Wrey*, *Bart.*, of TAWSTOCK HOUSE, a large and handsome mansion, delightfully situated in an extensive and well-wooded park, on the western side of the river Taw, 2½ miles S. of Barnstaple, near the line of the intended Taw Vale Railway. The house was nearly burnt down in 1787, but was soon afterwards rebuilt from a design by the late Sir B. Wrey. An ancient gateway, dated 1574, is all that remains of the old mansion of the Bourchiers. The park abounds in beautiful scenery and fine aged oaks, and the high grounds command rich and extensive views over the bay and town of Barnstaple. Chas. Sturt, Esq., is lord of the manor of Templeton. The *Church* (St. Peter,) is a fine Gothic structure, with a tower rising from the centre, and contains several monuments of the Bourchiers and Wreys. The *rectory*, valued in K.B. at £69. 12s. 1d., and in 1831 at £997, is in the patronage of Sir B. P. Wrey, and incumbency of the Rev. H. B. Wrey, M.A., who has 112A. of glebe, and a large and handsome modern residence. The tithes were commuted in 1848 for £837 per annum. Here are two chapels belonging to Roman Catholics and Independents. The *Poor's Lands*, purchased with the benefactions of various donors, comprise about 56 acres, let for upwards of £70 per annum. The

poor have also £12 a year from Sir B. P. Wrey, as compensation for some old poor's land; the interest of £120, left by Margaret Pyne and another donor; and two yearly rent-charges of 13s. 4d. and 5s., left by Lawrence Gibbons.

Gill George, vict. Hotel
Jones John, shopkeeper
Lewis John, tailor and draper
Maunder James, schoolmaster
Perrien John, *Post-office*
Pristacott Richard, blacksmith
Weld Edw. Esq. || Walters Lieut. G.
Williams Rev. John, (Catholic)
Wrey Sir Bourchier Palk, Bart. *Tawstock House*, (and Holne Chase)
Wrey Rev. Henry, Bourchier, M.A. *Rectory*

FARMERS.
Andrew James
Andrew Philip
Brailey Wm.
Cann John
Cawsey Robt.
Crispin Philip
Darch Richd.
Dennis John
Fisher Thos.
Jones Thomas
Lovering Geo.
Lovering John
Lovering Thos.

Moore Robt.
Packer Richd.
Parsley Wm.
Petherbridge Rd.
Petherbridge W.
Shapland John
Small Samuel
Smallridge Geo.
Smallridge Thos.
Somers Henry
Symons Noah
Symons Jph.
Ware John
White John

TORRINGTON, (GREAT) is an ancient *borough*, and clean and well-built *market town*, pleasantly seated on a bold eminence, on the north-east side of the picturesque valley of the Torridge river and canal, 34 miles N.W. by W. of Exeter; 6 miles S.S.E. of Bideford; 10 miles S.S.W. of Barnstaple; and 196 miles W. by S. of London. It is the head of a large union, and its parish contains 3419 souls, and about 3640 acres of land, including *Moortown, Norwood, Staple Vale, Beam*, many scattered farm-houses, and some extensive *commons*, the enclosure of which is opposed by the inhabitants. The Trustees of the late Lord Rolle are lords of the *manor and barony*, and owners of most of the soil; and the rest belongs to J. H. Furse, Esq., Archdeacon Stevens, Mrs. Stevens, and a few smaller owners. The barony of Torrington belonged anciently to a family of its own name, and after being for some time divided among their co-heiresses, it passed to the Crown, of which it was subsequently held by the Hollands. Queen Mary granted it to Jas. Bassett, Esq., whose son sold it to Sir John Fortescue, from whose family it passed to the Rolles. The celebrated Gen. Monk, Duke of Albemarle, was created *Earl of Torrington* in 1660, but the title became extinct on his death in 1668. In the following year, Arthur Herbert was created Earl of Torrington, but dying without issue in 1716, the title again became extinct. In 1716, Thomas Newport was created *Baron Torrington*, but the title died with him in 1719. Sir George Byng was created *Viscount Torrington* in 1721, and the title has since been enjoyed by six of his descendants, and is now held by the *Right Hon. George Byng, Viscount Torrington, and Baron Byng*, who resides at Yorkes Place, Kent. *Torrington Castle*, which appears to have been erected in 1340, by Richard de Merton, who married an heiress of the Torrington family, stood on the south side of the town, near the edge of a high and steep precipice, overlooking the river Torridge. Its site is now a bowling-green, and near it is a column, commemorative of the battle of Waterloo. There are now but few vestiges of the castle, and its chapel, which had been converted into a schoolhouse, was taken down in 1780. *Beam House*, which was formerly a seat of the Rolles, is now occupied by A. R. Hole, Esq. Torrington was formerly a parliamentary borough, but the burgesses were exonerated from the burden of sending members to parliament, at their own request, in 1368. They stated in their petition that they had never been subject to this burden till the 21st of the then king's reign, when the sheriff, to their great injury, summoned them to send two members to parliament. Their

prayer was granted, but it is recorded that the borough sent members to parliament sixteen times before the 21st of Edward III., although they had not been summoned from the 15th till the 21st of that reign.   Torrington was incorporated by Queen Mary, and a charter of the 15th of James I. It received another charter in the 2nd of James II.   The CORPORATION formerly consisted of a mayor, 8 aldermen, 16 capital burgesses, and an indefinite number of freemen, with a recorder, town-clerk, and other officers. At the period of the municipal enquiry in 1833, the court of record had been disused for 50 years, and the view of frankpledge was also in disuse. The gaol was then an insignificant building, containing five cells, with unglazed windows.   Under the Municipal Reform Act of 1835, the borough is included among those not to have commission of the peace, and is governed by a Town-Council, consisting of a mayor, 4 aldermen, and 12 councillors.   The mayor and ex-mayor are justices of the peace, and the borough comprises the whole parish. The income of the Corporation in 1840 was £271, of which £100 was derived from the borough rates. It is a polling place for the Northern Division of Devon ; and *petty sessions* are held here every third Monday, by the magistrates of Great Torrington Division, to whom Mr. W. G. Glubb is clerk. *Torrington County Court District* comprises all Torrington Union, and the court sits here on the Friday after the first Monday in every month, at the Guildhall. Mr. W. A. Deane is the *clerk*, and Mr. Frederick Holwill is the high bailiff.   In 1484 a sessions was held here, at which Bishop Courtenay and others were indicted for treason against Richard III.   In 1590 the Michaelmas quarter sessions for Devon were held here on account of the plague being at Exeter. Torrington was visited by the plague in 1591, and in the 17th century it was the scene of some of the important actions of the *civil war*. In 1643, Colonel Digby took up his quarters here for the king, and was reinforced by some of the Cornish royalists.   After several skirmishes, he took the forts of Appledore, Bideford, and Barnstaple. About the middle of February, 1646, Lord Hopton had scarcely stationed his army here and fortified the town, when he was attacked by Sir Thomas Fairfax, and totally defeated, after a severe action, in which both himself and Lord Capel were wounded. The famous Hugh Peters, who was then chaplain to Fairfax's army, preached in the market place after this victory, and made many converts to the parliamentary cause. On the 19th of February the General left Torrington, the quarters being inconvenient on account of the church having been blown up. There was formerly a considerable manufacture of *woollens* carried on at Torrington, and here are still many *glove makers*. In 1823-'4 a small *Canal* was cut by the late Lord Rolle, from this town to the navigable part of the river Torridge, below Wear Gifford. It is about five miles long, and in one place crosses the valley by a lofty stone viaduct of five arches, which harmonizes with the surrounding romantic scenery. The town has been much improved during the last 20 years, and is lighted with *gas*, from works erected in 1836, at the cost of £2000, raised in £10 shares.   In 1841-'2 a commodious *New Market House* was erected by a company of proprietors at the cost of £2990, on which three per cent. interest is paid.   The tolls, dues and stallages produce about £180 per annum, out of which £30 is paid yearly to the borough fund, as compensation for the old market. Over the butchers' shops, &c., is a large *hall*, let for exhibitions, lectures, &c. The *market* is held by prescription every Saturday, and is well supplied with provisions, corn, &c. Here are *cattle fairs* on May 4th, July 5th, and October 10th, and a *great cattle market* on the third Saturday in March. Balls, concerts, &c. are occasionally held at the Guildhall and the Market Hall, and here is a *newspaper club*, consisting of many of the respectable tradesmen of the

town. The *Town Council, Borough Officers,* &c. are as follow :—

Mayor, Charles W. Johnson, Esq. Ex-Mayor, George Braginton, Esq.
Aldermen, George Braginton, Richard Braginton, C. W. Johnson, R. B. Rouse.
Councillors, James Rude, Thos. Reed, J. F. Williams, W. C. Hunt, George Doe, Robert
Martin, Lewis Tapley, George Toms, John Sloley, Wm. Evan Price,
Thos. H. Lake, and Wm. Anthony Deane.
Town Clerk, W. G. Glubb. Inspector of Weights and Measures, T. H. Lake.
Serjeants at Mace, Charles Chambers and Thomas Williams.
Beadle, James Lugg. Crier, T. Williams.
Charity Trustees, Peter Glubb, C. W. Johnson, Bryan Reed, W. E. Price, Wm. Collan,
E. H. Caddy, R. B. Rouse, W. H. Rouse, H. A. Vallack, Geo. Braginton,
Thos. Snell, John Adams, Thomas Cowdry, and James Rude.

The PARISH CHURCH (St. Michael,) which was mostly rebuilt in 1651, after being nearly destroyed during the civil wars, is a large and handsome structure, with a lofty tower, containing six bells, and crowned by an octagonal spire, the latter of which was erected in 1830, when the curious old spire was taken down. The interior is neatly fitted up, and has a good organ and a well executed altar-piece, the latter of which was given by Lady Rolle. The Dean and Canons of Christ Church, Oxford, are appropriators of tithes, and patrons of the *perpetual curacy,* which was valued in 1831 at £162, and is now in the incumbency of the Rev. Samuel Buckland, M.A., who has a good residence, built in 1844. The *Independents, Baptists, Wesleyans,* and *Bible Christians* have chapels here, and attached to them and the church are Sunday Schools, and associations for the propagation of religious knowledge.

The *Blue Coat School,* in Well street, with a house for the master, was given by Denys Rolle, Esq., who endowed it in 1709 with £220, to which £730 was added by the donations of the Rolle family. As interest of this £950, the Trustees of the late Lord Rolle pay £47. 10s. 0d. per annum, out of which the master has £16 for teaching 22 poor boys, who are provided with blue clothing once a year. The *National School* was built about 15 years ago, by the late Lord Rolle, and is attended by about 150 children. The TOWN LANDS, &c., have been vested from an early period for the repairs of the church, and other public uses, and in 1815 they were conveyed by Lord Rolle to the mayor and 22 other trustees. They now comprise a great number of houses, cottages, gardens, fields, &c., let to 136 tenants at small rents, amounting to only about £82 a year, on leases for three lives, subject to fines on the renewal of the leases. The feoffees also receive about £30 a year from the tolls of the markets and fairs. A large portion of the income is expended in the service of the church, and in paying salaries to the organist, clerk, sexton, town clerk, and serjeants-at-mace. The MAGDALEN LANDS, granted to the Corporation, for the relief of the poor of the borough, by *Tristram Arscott,* in 1665, had previously formed part of the endowment of the lepers' hospital at Taddiport. They comprise 13A. and three houses, let for only £30, subject to fines payable on the renewal of the leases. The ALMSHOUSES, on the north side of the churchyard, were founded at an early period, and vested with the feoffees of the Town Lands, for the residence of 10 poor people. John Huddle erected or rebuilt one of the houses, and their endowment was augmented by him and other benefactors, and now consists of about 118A. of land and 7 houses, &c., let for only about £80 a year, but subject to fines on the renewal of the leases. The poor parishioners have upwards of £30 a year from 13 *benefactions,* mostly bequeathed in the 17th century. Staple Vale Woollen Manufactory was built about 50 years ago, on 50 acres of common land, which was let under the sanction of an act of parliament in 1777, at 50s. per annum, on lease for lives, subject to a fine of 21s. on every renewal. The rent and fines are applied in apprenticing poor children. The poor have still common right on about 300 acres of open land called *Hatchmoor, Wester, and South Commons.*

TORRINGTON UNION comprises the 23 parishes of Great and Little Torrington, Alverdiscott, Buckland Filleigh, Frithelstock, Huntshaw, Langtree, Petersmarland, Shebbear, St. Giles in the Wood, Wear Gifford, Yarncombe, Ashreigny, Beaford, Dolton, Dowland, High Bickington, Huish, Merton, Petrockstow, Roborough, Sheepwash, and Winkleigh, which comprise an area of 122 square miles, and 18,188 inhabitants. The total average annual expenditure of the 23 parishes on their poor, is now about £9500, but before they were united it was only about £7500. The *Workhouse* is a neat stone building, which was erected in 1837, at the cost of £4000, and has room for 250 inmates, but has seldom more than 180. Mr. W. G. Glubb is the *union clerk and superintendent registrar;* Mr. and Mrs. Luard are *master and matron* of the Workhouse; and the Rev. G. W. T. Carwithen is the *chaplain.* Edward Wills and John Mills are the *registrars of marriages;* J. Coplestone Hole, Wm. Risdon, Chas. R. Jones, and Robert Rudall, are the *registrars of births and deaths;* and Charles Heale and Geo. Burden are the *relieving officers.*

GREAT TORRINGTON DIRECTORY.

The POST OFFICE is at Mr. James Rude's, High street; and letters are despatched at 1½ afternoon and 6 evening. Money orders are granted and paid.

Those marked 1 are in Bidnawell street; 2, Calve st; 3, Castle st; 4, Fore st; 5, High st; 6, Mill st; 7, New st; 8, Potacre st; 9, South st; 10, Well st; and 11, at Staple vale.

3 Bastard John, fishing tackle mkr
9 Bishop James, solicitor's clerk
Braginton George, Esq. banker and merchant, High st; h *St Giles'*
5 Braginton Rd. and W. D., Esqrs.
Brinsmead Robert, canal agent
10 Brown John, horse, &c. letter
7 Bryant Wm. revenue officer
Buckland Rev. Saml., M.A. incmbt
3 Buckpitt Rev James, (Indept)
3 Caddy Edmund Hy. surgeon
Callon Mr Wm. || Chapple Mrs
6 Canston Rev John, B.A. curate
10 Cawsey Nancy, dyer
Chambers Chas. sheriffs' officer
7 Craig Robert, bank clerk
9 Doe Mary, earthenware dealer
3 Friendship Wm. and John, rope, &c. makers
7 Fry Wm. veterinary surgeon
7 Fussell John, police officer
10 Harper Thos. parish clerk
Haverfield Mrs || Heanes Miss
10 Heale Chas. relieving officer
Hole Alfred Robt. Esq. *Beam House*
Holwill Frederick, high bailiff of County Court
Humphreys Mr John || 8 Kemp Smn.
Johns Mrs || Lovering Mrs
9 Johnson Chas. Wm. union auditor
Kingdon Mr John || Morgan Mrs
Kingdon Mr Thos. and Mrs Eliz.
6 Langdon J. B. gardener
Luard Peter Shaw and Mrs. master and matron, *Union Workhouse*
7 McCartney Capt. James Nixon
Martin Robert, corn miller
9 Mollard Rev John, (Wesleyan)
8 Morfill Jas. professor of music

7 Palmer Rev John Nicholas, M.A.
6 Palmer Capt. John, R.A.
Perry Mrs Eliz. || Pettle Mrs
2 Pow Thomas, basket maker
Risdon Miss || Stoneman Mrs
7 Salter Wm. organist, &c
6 Sanford John & Robt. gardeners
Sanford Mr Thos. || Snell Thos.
9 Sloley John, bank manager
Snell Mr Thomas || Thomas James
StokerSergt.MajorN.D.Y.C. *Staple Vl*
7 Thompson Rev David (Baptist)
Tree Geo. inland revenue officer
Vicary Chpr. edgetool maker, &c
Walker Mr George and Miss Eliz.
10 Wills Mrs S. and 4 Mrs Ann

ACADEMIES & SCHOOLS.
Blue Coat, Thomas Harper
5 Elsworthy Thos. || 8 Friend Mrs
4 Jackson Thos. || 11 Gawtry Misses
8 *National,* Chas. Mountjoy and My. Henberrow
Workhouse, Wm. Chudley

ATTORNEYS.
Caddy Harrington, Castle street
Deane Wm. Anthony, (clerk of County Court,) South street
Doe George, South street
Glubb Wm. Gill, (town and union clerk,) Fore street
Price Wm. Evan, South street
Snell Silas, New street
Tapley Lewis, New street
9 Vallack Hy. Adoniah, (& coroner)

BANKS.
Braginton, Harding, & Co. (Agricultural Bank,) High st; (on the Commercial Bank)

National Provincial Bank of England, High st; J. Sloley, manager; (on London & Westminster Bank)

Savings' Bank, Fore street; Henry Fowler, actuary

FIRE & LIFE OFFICES.
7 Alliance, Silas Snell
9 Atlas, W. E. Price
7 Clerical & Medical, L. Tapley
Crown, Edwin Handford
7 Legal & Commercial, S. Snell
9 National Provident, J. Lake
5 Royal Farmers', G. Braginton
9 Star, Wm. Sellick
9 Sun, H. A. Vallack
5 Temperance, Chas. Veysey
4 United Kingdom, W. G. Glubb
9 West of England, George Doe

INNS & TAVERNS.
7 Barnstaple and Bideford Inn, Wm. Wilson Walkey
5 Bell, Mary White
5 Black Horse, Wm. Brown
8 Black Swan, Wm. Furse
9 Boot, Mary Bowden
3 Exeter Inn, John Lake
4 *Globe Hotel*, Edward Willis
10 Hunters' Inn, Henry Lewis
9 New Market, Margaret Dart
10 New Inn, Jane Williams
10 Old Inn, John Lloyd
4 Plough, Mary Cock
9 Rising Sun, Wm. Lake
9 Rolle Arms, John Holwill
6 Torridge Inn, Wm. Sanford
7 Tradesman's Arms, James Bastard

SURGEONS.
4 Caddy (E. H.) & Cawdry (Thos.)
7 Hole John Coplestone (registrar)
7 Hole Richard Lewis and G. L.
Holmes T. J. *Warren House*
Owen John, Potacre street
Rouse Rd. Batten, South street
Tapley Thomas Knight, New st

AUCTIONEERS.
5 Ashton Thos.
9 Lee John
3 Rodd Wm.

BAKERS.
7 Evans Thomas
8 Furse Wm.
8 Lake Wm.
8 Youatt John

BEER HOUSES.
3 Cross Eliz.

7 Rattenbury Rd.
6 Sanford John

BOOKSELLERS.
5 Fowler Mary
9 Sellick Wm.

BOOT & SHOE MKS.
5 Bower R. H.
9 Davy Chas. H.
4 Gayton John
5 Gould Wm.
5 Hackwill Wm.

10 Norman Chas.
9 Page John
3 Passmore H. S.
10 Sanford Hy.
7 Shaddick John
7 Slee John
7 Slee Richard
10 Simmons Rt.
9 Tanton James
7 Thorne Richd.
3 Williams Thos.
6 Williams Wm.

BUTCHERS.
10 Brown John
9 Fry Roger
10 Moore John
10 Penhorwood H.
6 Sussex Wm.
8 Youatt John

CARPENTERS, &c.
2 Barrett John
6 Beer John
10 Blight Robert
10 Cook Walter
7 Coombe Wm.
10 Darke Wm.
6 Haywood Thos.
9 Lee John
6 Pearse Samuel
6 Vicary James
7 Williams Danl.

CHEMISTS AND DRUGGISTS.
4 Fowler Henry
5 Handford Edn.
9 Row John

COOPERS.
10 Fowler Thos.
10 Werry Wm.

CURRIERS.
9 Adams & Son
7 Chapple Natl.
10 Ruddicombe Abraham
5 Rude James

FARMERS.
Andrews Samuel
Bennett John
Bolt John & Mary
Brown J. & W.
Davis Joseph
Davis Samuel
Downing James
Gent Wm.
Goss Andrew

Goss John
Hole Alfred
Hunt James
Judd Anthony
Judd John
Martin Robert
Moore Thomas
Reddaway John
Reed Thomas
Stone Joseph
Thorne Thomas
Wadland James
Walkey John
Walkey Wm. W.
Ward Thomas
Williams John F.
Williams Joseph

GLOVE MANFRS.
7 Bageshot Sus.
7 Banham Jph.
6 Banham J. jun.
9 Barrow John
10 Chapple John
7 Chapple Michl.
10 Chapple Thos.
6 Keen Thomas
Lake Thos. H.
7 Long John
10 Pettle Thos.
3 Toms George
6 Vaughan Thos.

GROCERS, &c.
9 Adams John
8 Bastard John
5 Brookes Sarah
9 Burnell Jph.
10 Burridge Wm.
5 Gempton Jas.
5 Handford Edn.
5 Harper Eliz.
6 Hawkins Mrm.
5 Pickard Wm.
9 Pidgeon Henry and Son
8 Mallet Wm.
9 Sanford Eliz.
5 Veysey Chas.

HAIRDRESSERS.
9 Chambers Sml.
8 Ladd James
8 Nickells Jph.

HATTERS.
5 Burridge Hy.
8 Smith John
6 Wonnacott F.

IRONMONGERS.
5 Bartlett Eliza
5 Dennis John
9 Lake John

L. & W. DRAPERS.
5 Ashton Thos.
9 Doe Mary Ann
6 Hawkins Mrm.
4 Friendship Hy.
9 Luxton Thos.
10 Mallet Wm.
9 Pidgeon & Son
5 Veysey Chas.

MALTSTERS.
9 Bowden Mary
4 Cock Mary
3 Fry Sl. brewer
7 Grant Wm.
9 Holwill John
10 Lloyd John
Martin Rt. *Mills*
3 Walkey George
Williams John F.

MILLINERS, &c.
9 Bishop Mrs
7 Elsworthy A.
5 Elsworthy Rbc.
3 Fry Mary

5 Gould S. & E.
10 Mallet Mrs
4 Martin Isbla.
8 Walkey L.

NAIL MAKER.
1 Allen John B.

PAINTERS, &c.
8 Bartlett Rd.
9 Lake John
9 Petherick John

SADDLERS.
9 Blatchford G. B.
9 Holwill John

SHOPKEEPERS.
9 Bowden Mary
4 Brown Ann
10 Cooper Rd.
7 Fielden Wm.
9 Gribble Jane
10 Jones Ann
9 Luxton Grace
7 Lythaby Eliz.
8 Moorman M. A.
6 Nation Thos.
5 Thorne Eliz.
6 Ware Eliz.
6 Williams Fras.

STONEMASONS.
10 Cock Walter B.
6 Pearse John

TAILORS.
6 Blight Robert
9 Bowden Saml.
3 Clarke Thomas
3 Courtice John
3 Essery Joseph
8 Hellings John
10 Lake Wm.
6 Mills John
8 Stoneman Wm.
9 Tucker John
3 Tucker Stephen
7 Werry Wm.

TANNERS.
Adams & Son
6 Kingdon Jno. B.
5 Rude James

WATCHMAKRS., &c
5 Dennis John
5 Gaydon Fredk.
9 Saunders Wm.
8 Williams John

WHEELWRIGHTS.
6 Beer John
10 Cock Robert

6 Haywood Thos.
7 Langbridge Ts
10 Squire Henry

WOOLSTAPLERS.
9 Pidgeon & Son
11 Reed Thos. mfr

COACHES.
Mail to *Bideford*,
9¼ morng. & to
Exeter, 6½ evg.
Coaches to *Bideford, &c.* Tues.
Thu. & Sat; &
to *Plymouth*,
Mon. Wed. & Fr.

CARRIERS
from Exeter,
Barnstaple,
Plymouth, &c.
call at the Inns.
10 Copp Saml. &
9 Handford G.
to Barnstaple,
Mn. Wed. & Fri;
& to Bideford,
Tues.

SHEBBEAR HUNDRED,

In the Northern Parliamentary Division of Devon, and in the north-western part of the county, is skirted on three sides by the winding stream of the river Torridge, and bounded on the north-west by Bideford Bay and Hartland Hundred. It averages about 12 miles in length and eight in breadth, and is a picturesque district; having the Borough and Port of Bideford within its northern limits, and the towns of Torrington and Hatherleigh near its borders. It is in the petty sessional divisions of Great Torrington, and Black Torrington and Shebbear; in the Archdeaconry of Barnstaple, and in the Deaneries of Hartland and Torrington. It contains 26 parishes, of which the following is an enumeration, shewing their territorial extent, and their population in 1841 :—

Parishes.	Acres.	Pop.	Parishes.	Acres.	Pop.
*Abbotsham	2090	.. 414	‡Meeth	2479	.. 314
*Alwington......	5330	.. 392	§Merton	3738	.. 763
§Beaford........	3335	.. 713	*Monkleigh	2177	.. 699
*Bideford *Borough*	4510	.. 5211	*NewtonSt.Petrock	1556	.. 261
*Buckland Brewer	5656	.. 1103	*Northam +......	2700	.. 3578
§Buckland-Filleigh	3037	.. 275	*Parkham	5808	.. 995
*Bulkworthy	6050	.. 196	§Petrockstow	4030	.. 616
§Frithelstock	2380	.. 705	*Putford (East)..	3230	.. 197
§Huish	923	.. 141	§Shebbear	5826	.. 1160
‡Iddesleigh......	2952	.. 545	§Sheepwash	1771	.. 497
*Landcross......	331	.. 120	§Torrington(Little)	2880	.. 588
§Langtree	4028	.. 941	§Wear Gifford....	1587	.. 576
*Littleham	1290	.. 390			
§Marland Peter's	2200	.. 351	*Total*	81,894	..21,741

☞ UNIONS :—Those marked thus * are in *Bideford Union*, § in *Torrington Hundred*, and ‡ in *Okehampton Union*. These unions are also County Court Districts.

+*Appledore* is a large village in Northam parish.

PETTY SESSIONS are held on the last Wednesday of every month, alternately at Petrockstow and Hatherleigh; at Great Torrington every third Monday; and at Bideford weekly.

ABBOTSHAM, a scattered village, nearly two miles W. of Bideford, has in its parish 414 souls, and 1758 acres of land, extending westward to the shore of Bideford or Barnstaple Bay, and including the hamlets of *Shepperton, Coombe Walter,* and *Rickersdown.* E. H. Vidal, Esq., is lord of the manor, but Dr. Heywood, Mr. Richd. Turner, Rd. Best, Esq., and a few smaller owners, have estates here. The *Church* (St. Helen,) is a small antique structure, with a low tower, containing four bells. The *vicarage,* valued in K.B. at £16. 4s. 7d., and in 1831 at £170, is in the patronage of the Lord Chancellor, and incumbency of the Rev. Edw. A. Sanford, who has 36A. of glebe, and is about to erect a new vicarage house. He is impropriator of nearly all the great tithes, which were commuted in 1840, with the small tithes, for £123. 12s. per annum. The *Poor's Land* is 10A., and the poor have also £4. 10s. a year, left by Robert Shee, in 1627, out of Bartonmoor close.

Best Rd., Esq. *Abbotsham Court*
Fulford Wm. parish clerk
Heywood Dr. *Kenwith Lodge*
Holmes Thos. vict., New Inn
Moss Edw. wheelwright
Sanford Rev Edw. A. *Vicarage*
Steer John, vict., Heart of Oak

FARMERS.
Bale Edw.
Burdich Wm.
Cork John
Heywood Jph.
Hunt Thos.

Pettle John
Pickard Jasper
Steer John
Turner John
Turner Richard

ALWINGTON, a pleasant village, on the banks of the little river Yeo, four miles S.W. by S. of Bideford, has in its parish 392 souls, and 5330 acres of land, including the hamlets of *Fairy Cross, Ford, and Woodtown.* The Rev. J. T. P. Coffin, M.A., is lord of the manor of Alwington, and has a handsome seat here, called *Portledge,* which has been the seat and property of the Coffins nearly from the time of the Conquest. Chas. Bruton, Esq., is lord of the manor of South Yeo, and owner of the pleasant seat called *Yeo Vale,* and of the Barton of *Winscott.* Mr. S. Rolstone and a few smaller owners have estates in the parish. The *Church* (St. Andrew,) is a small antique structure, with a tower and four bells, and contains monuments and memorials of the Coffin, Pine, and other families. The *rectory,* valued in K.B. at £17. 4s. 2½d., and in 1831 at £282, is in the patronage and incumbency of the Rev. J. T. P. Coffin, M.A., who has 60A. of glebe, and an old Parsonage, let to a farmer. The tithes were commuted in 1837, for £243 per annum. The remains of an ancient chapel at Yeo Vale, formerly stood near the mansion, but have been removed to a more distant part of the grounds. The Parish School was built by the Rector and Mrs. Morrison, in 1836. Here is a small Wesleyan chapel, and an *Almshouse* for three poor people, founded in 1667, by Richd. Coffin, who endowed it with ten acres of land, vested with the successive heirs of his family. The poor have 2½A., purchased with benefaction money, and the interest of £25, left by Richard Coffin, in 1795.

Coffin Rev J. T. Pine, M.A. *Portledge*
Dayman Humphrey, schoolmaster
Eastman John, vict., Swan
Hole Lewis S., registrar, &c
Johns David, blacksmith
Morrison Mrs. *Yeo Vale*

Pennington Rd. and Wm. carpenters
Poe Wm., carpenter
Prowse Robert, corn miller

FARMERS.
Ashton Ann
Crealock Wm.

Clement Charles
Delve George
Downing Dmnr.

| Ford George | Hanford Amos | Vale Richard | Walter Richard |
| Grigg Edward | Haywood Thos. | Wakeley James | |

BEAFORD, a pleasant village, on the eastern acclivity of the Torridge valley, 5 miles S.E. of Great Torrington, has in its parish 713 souls, and 3335 acres of land, including *Kiverley, Woolly, Upcott,* and a number of scattered farm houses, &c.   J. H. Furse, Esq., is lord of the manor, but Woolly belongs to Sir T. D. Acland, and several smaller owners have estates in the parish.   The *Church* (All Saints,) is an ancient structure, with a tower and four bells; and the *rectory,* valued in K.B. at £11. 15s. 7½d., and in 1831 at £233, is in the patronage and incumbency of the Rev. Charles Wood, B.A., who has 77A. 2R. 15P. of glebe, and a handsome residence, built in 1850.   The Baptists and Bible Christians have small chapels here. The parish clerk has the free use of a house and 6 acres of land, given at an early period.   There were formerly chapels at Upcott and Woolly. [*For Beaford Directory, see Appendix.*]

BIDEFORD, a pleasant and well-built *market town, sea port,* and *muni-cipal borough,* is picturesquely seated upon two acclivities, rising from opposite sides of the broad and majestic river *Torridge,* which is here crossed by a stone *bridge* of 24 arches, and of excellent masonry, 677 feet in length.   The river is navigable up to Torrington, with the aid of a small canal from Wear Gifford; and below the town it expands into a broad estuary, which falls into Bideford or Barnstaple Bay, with that of the Taw, about three miles below.   Few places excel in romantic scenery this beau-tiful little seaport town of North Devon, which is the head of a large *Union,* and *Polling and County Court Districts,* and is distant nine miles S.W. of Barnstaple, seven miles N. by W. of Great Torrington, 52 miles N. of Ply-mouth, 42 miles N.W. of Exeter, and about 200 miles W. by S. of London, being 50° 2' north latitude, and 4° 3' west longitude.   Its *Parish* com-prises about 4510 acres of land, and had 5211 inhabitants in 1841.   Its population amounted to only 2987 souls, in 1801; to 3244, in 1811; to 4053, in 1821; and to 4846, in 1831.   The *town* is mostly on the western side of the river, and being on a bold acclivity, and within three miles of the sea, it is highly salubrious, and the streets are clean and well drained; descending to the bank of the river, where there is a commodious quay, and where the long bridge, with its numerous arches, has a very picturesque appearance.   The name of Bideford is a corruption of its original appella-tion, *By-the-ford.*   The manor was settled by William the Conqueror on his consort Matilda, and was given by William Rufus to Sir Richard de Gren-ville, whose descendents resided here and at Kilkhampton, in Cornwall, for many generations; and three of them represented Devon in Parliament. *Sir Richard Grenville,* of Bideford, distinguished himself in the reign of Elizabeth, as an adventuring navigator, and was, with Sir Walter Raleigh, the joint discoverer of Virginia and Carolina, of which he published an account.   In 1521, being then vice-admiral of England, he sustained with his single ship, the most glorious but unequal conflict that is recorded in naval history, against the whole fleet of the enemy; and after having re-pulsed them fifteen times, yielded not till his powder was all spent.   He died of his wounds two days afterwards, on board the Spanish Admiral's vessel.   His own ship, reduced to a hulk, sunk before it could be got into port.   His great-grandson, *Sir John,* who first wrote his name *Granville,* is well known for the active share he had in bringing about the restoration of Charles II., who, in 1661, created him *Baron Granville of Bideford, Earl of Bath, &c.*   After the death of the last Earl of Bath of the Granville family, in 1711, their Devonshire estates were divided.   The *manor of Bideford* was purchased in 1750, by John Cleveland, Esq., and it now belongs to

Archibald Clevland, Esq., and is vested in trust during his minority; but a great part of the parish belongs to L. W. Buck, Esq., G. B. Hart, Esq., J. S. Ley, Esq., and many smaller freeholders. *Daddon* is the property of *Lewis Wm. Buck, Esq.*, one of the parliamentary representatives of North Devon, who has a handsome seat called *Moreton House*, pleasantly situated in a spacious and well-wooded lawn, about a mile S.W. of the town. The Bucks came from Ireland, and settled in Devonshire in the latter part of the 17th century. George Buck, who died in 1743, married the heiress of the Stuckleys, of Daddon and Afton Castle.

Bideford is called a borough in ancient records, but it does not appear to have ever returned members to parliament, except twice, in the reigns of Edward I. and II. A market day on Monday, and a fair for five days at the festival of St. Margaret, were granted to Richard Grenville, in 1271. The gallant Sir Richard Grenville procured a *charter* from Queen Elizabeth, which incorporated the town, made it a free borough, confirmed the market and fair, and granted two other fairs. This charter was confirmed and extended by other charters, in the 7th and 16th of James I. Under these charters, the government of the borough was vested in a *mayor*, 4 *aldermen*, and 10 *capital burgesses;* with a recorder, town clerk, two sergeants-at-mace, and other officers. By the Municipal Act of 1835, the government is vested in a mayor, 4 aldermen, 12 councillors, a recorder, and several borough magistrates. The borough has a separate *court of quarter sessions ;* and petty sessions are held here once a fortnight, both for it and the division of Great Torrington. The *County Court* is held monthly, at the Guildhall, for the parishes in Bideford Union, as well as those of Horwood, Instow, and Westleigh. Mr. J. Rooker is clerk of this court, and Richard Buse is the high bailiff. Early in 1643, a *fort* was erected on each side of the river, and a small one at Appledore. A parliamentary garrison was then placed at Bideford, but it surrendered to Col. Digby in September. *Chudleigh Fort,* on the eastern acclivity of the valley, is said to have been built by order of Major-General Chudleigh, and its site is now enclosed by a stone wall. In consequence of the patronage of the Grenville family, a trade with Virginia and Carolina, then recently discovered, was established at Bideford in the reign of Elizabeth, and the town continued to enjoy a considerable share of American commerce till the breaking out of the war, which ended in the independence of the United States. In the reign of Charles I., the merchants here imported large quantities of wool from Spain; and afterwards, besides their commerce with France, Holland, and the Mediterranean, had so large a share of the Newfoundland trade, that in 1699, they sent out more ships than any port in England, except London and Topsham. In some years of last century, Bideford imported more tobacco than London. The *trade* of this port is still very considerable; large quantities of timber, hemp, tallow, &c., are imported from the Baltic and America; wines, fruits, &c., from the Mediterranean; cattle, &c., from Ireland; coal, culm, iron, flag-stones, &c., from Wales; and marble and slate from Cornwall. The Newfoundland trade is again revived, and bids fair to equal its former importance. The number of registered vessels belonging to the port is 150, of the aggregate tonnage of 12,436 tons. The exports consist chiefly of agricultural produce. Four first-class *emigrant ships* (belonging to Mr. Richard Heard,) sail from Bideford to America, &c. Passengers find this a very desirable port to start from for the western shores; and it is remarkable, that no accident has happened to any of the ships which have left Bideford with emigrants during the last twenty years. Ship building is carried on here to a considerable extent; and during the

late war, several frigates, bombs, and gun brigs, were built here for the royal navy. Steam and sailing vessels ply to Bristol, in connexion with steamers to Liverpool, London, &c. Here are three large *potteries*, which employ many hands in the manufacture of coarse earthenware. Here are also several *malt-houses*, two *breweries*, a number of *lime-kilns*, and an *iron-foundry*. Brown and grey paint and mineral black are got in the neighbourhood; and at *Chapple Park* is the valuable CULM MINE of the *Bideford Anthracite Mining Company*, lately established, and now employing a considerable number of hands. A tram road, more than a mile in length, is being made underground to the heart of the mine. The *Port of Bideford* includes Appledore, Clovelly, Hartland, and all the north coast of Devon, extending westward from the estuary of the Taw and Torridge. The *Quay* was constructed in 1663, and belongs to the lord of the manor. Ships of 500 tons burden may lie safely at the quay, and those of 300 tons can get up to the bridge. Small craft go up the river to Wear Gifford, whence there is a canal to Torrington. The amount of *customs* received here in 1840 was £5648; and in 1847, £3750. The CUSTOM HOUSE OFFICERS are, H. Rodd, Esq., *collector;* Jas. John Paxton, *comptroller, &c.;* Wm. Martin, *harbour master;* and John Courtis, *locker*. The MARKET, held every Tuesday and Saturday, is well supplied with meat, vegetables, fruit, &c.; and on the former day with corn, cattle, swine, &c. Here are *great markets*, for cattle, &c., on the second Tuesday in March, the last Tuesday in April, and the third Tuesday in September. FAIRS for cattle, &c., are held on Feb. 14th and 15th, July 18th, and November 13th. There is a spacious market-place in the centre of the town, but much business is done on the Quay. The town has been much improved during the last twenty years, and in the principal streets are many neat houses, good inns, and well stocked shops. The *New Inn* was enlarged and superbly fitted up a few years ago, and contains excellent accommodations for families and commercial gentlemen. The paintings alone cost upwards of £700; and a large and elegant portico and verandah extend across the whole front of the building. The town is now well paved, and has *Gas Works*, erected about 16 years ago, at the cost of £2800, raised in £10 shares. Within the last few years, many respectable families have settled in the town, which, in point of cleanliness, salubrity, convenience, and comfort, is surpassed by but few places in England. The *Guildhall*, where the Town Council meet, and where the courts are held, is an old, inconvenient, Elizabethan building; but the erection of a new hall and prison is in contemplation. The receipts of the Corporation in 1848 amounted to only about £300, of which £170 was derived from borough rates, and £53 from the rent of property. The following is a list of the present TOWN COUNCIL, PUBLIC OFFICERS, &c.:—

Mayor, Thomas Evans, Esq. *Recorder,* W. M. Praed, Esq.
Justices, H. R. Glynn, J. S. Ley, C. Carter, T. G. Harding, H. O. Ley.
Aldermen, James Smith Ley, Thomas Ley, Thomas Wickham, George Richards.
Councillors, Arthur Ley, Thomas Parramore, T. Mc'Kenzie Smith, Wm. Wickham, H. O. Ley, T. Evans, W. Cadd, T. Pethebridge, Richard Buse, John Narraway, Chas. Carter, Robert Taylor.
Town Clerk, Charles Carter, Jun. *Treasurer,* W. H. E. Burnard.
Clerk of the Peace, James Rooker. *Coroner,* T. L. Pridham.
Auditors, Wm. Moase, Francis Ash. *Assessors,* R. Gilbert Giddy, Edw. Lethbridge.
Inspectors of Weights and Measures, John Cooke, William Gilbert.
Police Constable, Denis Sullivan. *Beadle and Crier,* William Major.

The CHURCH (*St. Mary,*) is a large antique structure, which has been enlarged, repaired, and altered at various periods, and has now sittings for more than 2000 hearers. It is supposed to have been built in the 14th century, and was originally in the form of a cross, but is now extremely irregular. It has three large galleries, and a good organ; the latter was

given by the Corporation, about 1728.   The tower contains six musical bells, on which chimes play every four hours.   Among the monuments is one to the memory of *John Strange*, a benevolent merchant, whose humanity and fortitude were remarkably conspicuous during a dreadful visitation of the plague in 1646, when " the Mayor deserted the town through fear." The names of 229, who died of that fatal malady, are inserted in the parish register, and among them is that of Mr. Strange, whose bust is placed in a niche in the upper part of the monument, which is said to have been erected by a sea captain, through gratitude for relief afforded him after shipwreck. Though the plague was so fatal here in 1646, the town was not visited by cholera in 1832, nor in 1849.   The church is now being repaired at the ex- pense of a rate of 2d. in the pound; and it is hoped that another rate will soon be obtained for the enclosure of the church-yard.   The *rectory*, valued in K.B. at £27. 7s. 6d., and in 1831 at £777, is in the patronage of L. W. Buck, Esq., and incumbency of the Rev. R. H. K. Buck, M.A., who has a good residence, and 60A. of glebe.   The *Independents, Baptists, Wesleyans*, and *Bible Christians* have CHAPELS here.   The Independent Chapel is called the " *Great Meeting House*," and is a spacious building, which was erected in 1696, by a congregation formed by the Rev. Walter Bartlett, and his son, the Rev. John Bartlett, who were ejected from the benefices of Bideford and Fremington, for non-conformity, in 1662.   The pious and *Rev. James Hervey*, was curate here in 1738 and '9, and while here wrote a great part of his " Meditations and Contemplations."   In 1841, the Feoffees of the Bridge Trust appropriated a field of 1½ acre, as a *Public Cemetery*, half of which is consecrated for the use of members of the Established Church.

Dr. John Shebbeare, author of the "Practice of Physic," but better known for his political writings, for which he was sentenced to stand in the pillory, in 1758, and was afterwards pensioned, was born at Bideford in 1709.   He was put in the pillory, but was attended by a servant, who held an umbrella over his head; and the sheriff was prosecuted for not enforcing the sentence. Mr. Abraham Down, and his brother Benjamin, both ingenious mathe- maticians, and the latter the publisher of maps of Cornwall and Devon, were natives of this town.

The BRIDGE TRUST comprises property which yields an annual income of about £380, and has been vested with feoffees from an early period, for the reparation of the bridge and for other public and charitable uses, in the parish of Bideford.   This property comprises 92 houses and other buildings, with gardens, &c., in the town and suburbs, let for only £55 a year, in consideration of fines paid when the leases were granted ; and about 155A. of land and many houses, &c., in this and other parishes, let at rack-rents, amounting to £329 per annum.   There is also belonging to the charity upwards of £1400 three per cent. consols, purchased with savings of income.   In 1810, the feoffees expended above £2500 in repairing and widening the *bridge*, and rebuilding the parapet walls.   After providing for the repairs of the bridge, the large surplus income is appli- cable for " *charitable, necessary, and reasonable uses and purposes ;*" and is consequently applied in supporting a school and fire engines, relieving the poor, repairing the Guild- hall, Bridge Hall, &c., and in paying small salaries to the bridge-wardens, hall-keeper, scavenger, &c.   The Mayor always acts as one of the feoffees, and executes the leases of the trust property.   In 1848, the feoffees contributed largely towards the improve- ment of Meddon street.   The *Bridge Hall* was built for the use of the feoffees, in 1758, and the *Bridge* is said to have been built and endowed by Sir Theobald Grenville, in the early part of the 14th century.

The GRAMMAR SCHOOL is held in a room which belongs to the Bridge Trust, and is kept in repair by the feoffees.   In 1689, *Susannah Stucley* left £200, to be laid out in lands for the support of a Grammar School in Bideford provided the town would raise £400 more for the same purpose.   Towards the latter sum, £100 was left by John Thomas.   The money thus raised was laid out in the purchase of an estate, called Bushton, in West Buckland parish, consisting of a farm of 57A., now let for £50 per annum ; and a wood of about 20½A., which is in the hands of the trustees.   Falls of timber in this wood yielded to the charity £204 in 1799, and £439 in 1813. The trustees,

2 K

in 1817, laid out £420 in the purchase of a house in Bridgeland street, for the residence of the schoolmaster, for a term of 99 years. The schoolmaster is required to teach the Greek and Latin languages, and the elements of history, geography, astronomy, mathematics, &c., gratuitously to three boys sent to him by the trustees ; and not to charge more than £6. 6s. per annum for any of the other day scholars. The school has been long in high repute, and was ably conducted by the Rev. Henry Alford, M.A., from 1826 till 1849, when he resigned, and the Rev. Hugh Fowler, the present master, was appointed. The NATIONAL SCHOOL is a large building, erected by the Bridge Feoffees, in 1825, and attended by about 200 children of both sexes. An *Infant School*, erected by subscription in 1845, has about 120 pupils. Here is also a large *British School*, built in 1835, and attended by about 110 boys and 90 girls. The *Subscription Rooms*, are neat and commodious apartments on the Quay, where assemblies are held, and where there is a good library and well supplied news room. A *Literary and Scientific Institution* was established here in 1846, and has now a numerous list of members, and a library of 500 volumes. In the town are several circulating libraries ; hot and cold baths ; a savings' bank, and other provident institutions ; a lodge of free masons ; and various friendly, charitable, and religious societies.

BENEFACTIONS.—The poor parishioners have the rent of 2A. 2R. 23P. of land, left by *John Andrew* in 1605, and now let for £10. They have a yearly rent-charge of 20s., left by *John Andrew*, out of property held by the Corporation. The *Poor's Stock*, consisting of £300 three per cent. reduced annuities, arose from various benefactions, and the dividends are applied in relieving the poor and schooling poor children. *Poor Man's Meadow and Field* (about 4A.) are held by the overseers, and the rents are carried to the poor rates. In 1681, *George Baron* left a yearly rent-charge of £6 out of an estate called the Commons, for the relief of poor old seamen or their widows. The same estate was charged by *Wm. Pawley*, in 1728, with the yearly payments of 21s. for the poor, and 21s. for the rector for preaching a sermon on St. Paul's day. The poor have a yearly rent-charge of 13s. 4d., left by *Alex. Arundell*, in 1627, out of land at West Morchard. *Henry Young*, in 1789, left £100 for the minister and poor of the congregation of the *Dissenting Meeting-house* in Bridgeland street. This legacy now forms part of £584. 11s. 11d. new four per cent. stock, purchased with this and other gifts to the said Meeting-house. In 1810, *Margaret Newcommen* left in trust with the dissenting ministers of Bideford, Barnstaple, Tavistock, and Appledore, £960. 19s. 6d. new four per cents., and £176. 15s. 7d. of the same stock, in trust to apply the dividends of the former in relieving the poor, and of the latter in schooling poor children of this and other parishes.

STRANGE'S ALMSHOUSES, in Meddon street, form a row of seven tenements for the residence of seven poor families, placed in them by the overseers. They were founded in 1646 by the before-named *John Strange*. The almspeople have each a small garden, and there is a large garden belonging to the charity, let for about £6 per ann., which is applied in repairing the buildings. AMORY'S ALMSHOUSES, in Old Town, consist of six small dwellings, occupied by poor families, placed in them by the parish officers. They are said to have been given by Henry Amory, in 1663, for the reception of the widows of seamen. Small gardens are attached to each dwelling, but there is no endowment.

BIDEFORD UNION comprises the 18 parishes of Abbotsham, Alwington, Bideford, Bradworthy, Bulkworthy, Buckland-Brewer, Clovelly, East-Putford, Hartland, Landcross, Littleham, Monkleigh, Northam, Newton St. Petrock, Parkham, West Putford, Welcombe, and Woolfardiswarthy, which comprise an area of 122 square miles, with a population returned in 1831 at 17,787, and in 1841 at 19,568 souls. The total average annual expenditure of the 18 parishes on their poor, during the three years preceding the formation of the Union, was £7333, but in 1838, it was only £5225, and in 1849-50, £6428. 17s. 1½d. The *Workhouse* was erected in 1835-6, and has room for 200 paupers. H. A Harvie, Esq., is the *union clerk and superintendent registrar ;* the Rev. H. Alford, M.A., *chaplain ;* Mr. and Mrs. Stevenson, *master and matron* of the Workhouse ; Messrs. J. S. Burrow and L. Ashton, *relieving officers ;* and Messrs. Jas. Lee, C. E. Pratt, L. S. Hole, Wm. Fry, and D. D. Carter, are the *registrars of births and deaths.*

BIDEFORD DIRECTORY.

The POST-OFFICE is in High street, and Mr. John Lee is the *post-master.* Letters are despatched at 7 morning, and 17 minutes past 2 afternoon. Money Orders are granted and paid.

In the following Directory, those marked 1 *are in Allhalland street ;* 2, *Bridgeland street, or Bridge street ;* 3, *Bull hill ;* 4, *Buttgarden street ;* 5, *Chingswell ;* 6, *Cooper street ;* 7, *East-the-Water ;* 8, *Grenville street ;* 9, *Gunstone ;* 10, *High street ;* 11, *Honestone lane ;* 12, *Market place ;* 13 *Meddon street ;* 14, *Mill street ;* 15, *New street ;* 16, *Quay ;* 17, *Strand ;* 18, *Tower street ;* 19, *Potters' lane ;* 20, *Queen street ; and* 21, *in Old Town.*

Adderley Mrs Sarah, *Northdown*
2 Alford Rev. H., M.A. union chapln
Ash Francis, auditor, Quay
13 Balch Richard, surveyor
Baller Mr Edw., *Orchard hill*
7 Baller Mr Jno. || 5 Balsdon Capt.
10 Barratt Samuel, bank clerk
17 Bartlett Rd. Esq.|| & 10 Mrs Eliza
2 Baxter James, customs' clerk
2 Bayly Mrs and Miss Sar. J.
7 Beer Philip, mineral agent
Beighton Mrs Abigail, Strand
13 Beighton Rev. Jno. T. (Indpt.)
7 Bideford Anthracite Mining Co. culm and black paint owners, &c. Wm. Skews, agent
14 Bishop Capt. Thos. ship owner
Blanchard Mrs., Abbotsham road
10 Bowen Mr Walter||2 Brayley Geo.
Braithwaite Rev. Wm., M.A. curate, *Coldharbour*
17 Braund Thomas, tax collector
Brayley Mr Wm., *Coldharbour*
Brewer Capt. Fras., Cooper st
Buck Lewis Wm. Esq. M.P. *Moreton*
Buck Rev. R. H. K. *Rectory*
4 Burrow Jas. S. relieving officer
14 Buse Rd. high bailiff of county ct
2 Call Capt. Geo. I||6 Burdon Nathl.
14 Capern Edward, postman
14 Carter Chas. sen. Esq.
13 Chanter Miss E.||Chaplin Misses
Chanter Thos. B. Esq. *Glenburnie*
Church Mr Rd. N., Marine gardens
10 Clandinnan Rev. John, (Wes.)
12 Clotworthy John, coffee hs. kpr
Cochet Admiral John, Mill street
7 Coldwell W. postman||2 Clide Mrs
Cole Mr Rt., Tower hill || 19 Mrs
13 Cole Rt. M. inland revenue officer
13 Colmer Mr Geo.||20 Congdon Mrs
Cook Capt. Chas., Market place
13 Cook John, glove cutter, &c.
17 Cooke Mrs Eliz. || 7 Mrs Mary
Cooke Owen, Esq., Strand cottage
10 Corin Jacob, revenue officer
2 Courtis John, locker
17 Crocker Samuel, lodgings
Crowe Col. John, Northdown
10 Day Capt. Wm.||11 Dobrie Mrs
2 Dodds Mrs Han. || Eastman Sar.
6 Dyer John, serjeant at mace
Dyer Robt. and Lewis, clerks
20 Ellis Thomas, *(Seaman's Fund)*
Ellison Misses G. & H., High street

2 English Miss Dorothy A.
Farmer George, Esq., Strand
2 Forester Mr Hy. || 14 Forbes Miss
Fowler Rev Hugh, M.A., Gram. school
7 Gilbert Wm. gaoler
Glynn Capt. Hy., R.N., The Cottage
7 Glynn Admiral Henry Richard
Glynn Captain John, E.I.C.S. *Rockmount Cottage*
2 Glynn Mrs Sus.||17 Greening Miss
Gould James, Esq., *Knapp*
Grant Miss Fanny, Abbotsham rd
13 Gregory Ts. Davis, vetnry. surgn.
10 Grossard Mrs || Hayman Mrs A.
10 Hamlyn John, *emigration agent*
6 Handford Mr. Jno. || 10 Heath Mrs
10 Heath Ellis Chilcot, gent
16 Heywood Miss Har. || Holmes Mrs
Hillman Mr Wm., Providence row
5 Holman Robert, clerk
Hooper Capt. Geo., Victoria terrace
16 Hooper Wm. pawnbroker
Horden Miss Rebecca, Mill street
Hutchins Capt. Ts., Marine gardens
14 Huxham Thomas, road surveyor
10 Illman Wm. and John, gents
14 Isaacs Mr T.S.||10 Jenkins Capt.W.
4 Jennings Mrs Margaret
8 Joce Jas. secretary to Gas Company
Keats Capt. Wm., R.N. *Porthill*
10 King Miss My. & Miss Dorothy
14 King Miss Eliz.||14 Lamping Miss
Lang Capt. F. *Retreat*
Lee Jas. registrar, Victoria terrace
10 Lee John, agent
2 Lendon Thomas, pawnbroker
16 Ley Hy. Oliver, bank manager
Ley Jas. Smith, Esq. *Durrant House*
16 Mackenzie J ph. music professor
13 Maine ——, supervisor
10 Maine Mrs F. || 16 Marshall Capt. W.
Major Mrs R., Woodland terrace
Major Wm. town crier, Union street
Manning Mr Ts. E. & Miss, Bridge st
2 Marshall Jas. N. bacon factor
4 Marshall Wm. mariner
16 Martin Richard, harbour master
16 Martin Wm. ship agent, &c
2 Maxwell Rev John Goodman, B.A.
McNamara Capt. John, Silver st
Morrison Miss Ann, Northam road
13 Moorshead John, revenue officer
14 Murphy Thos. carver & gilder
11 Narraway Wm. clerk
6 Parkhouse Mrs || 13 Pasker Mr W.

4 Parsons Fras. veterinary surgeon
4 Patey John, coffee-house keeper
2 Paxton Jas. John, comptroller
14 Peakhorne Miss || 10 Pearson Mrs
5 Perryman Charles, mate
14 Pinckney Mrs Mary || PlimleyMrs
7 Pollard Thos. paint, &c. merchant
2 Pridham Mrs || 7 Raddon Miss
Pyke Capt. John, R.N. *Ford House*
2 Rawle Capt. Rd., R.N. || 10 Reed Mrs
Richards Geo. actuary ; h *Wooder*
2 Rodd Henry, collector of customs
15 Salter Wm. herbalist
7 Saunders Mr. John, & 4 Mr Jph.
Scott Mr John, Marine gardens
20 Shopland Misses Jane & M. A.
2 Shaxon Capt. Ts. || Smith Mrs
13 Short Wm. pipe maker
Small Mr John, Marine gardens
Spencer Miss Sarah, Willett street
7 Squire Capt. N. || 10 Stone Gregory
Stevenson Jas. master of *Workhouse*
2 Sullivan Denis Ts. police officer
Tardrew Wm., Esq. *Annery House*
2 Thomas Capt. W.N. || 10 TaylorMrs
Thorold Fdk., Esq. *Cleveland*
Trender F. S., Esq., Northam road
7 Tucker Miss || 13 Turton Miss
Vanstone Jas. gent., Terrace
2 Vinson Mr Wm. || 17 Weekes MrR.
2 West Mrs Sar. || 16 WheelerMr Rd.
13 Westcott Wm. marine store dealer
2 Whale Rt. artist || Walter Misses
13 Williams Rev. John, (Wes.)
7 Willison Mrs A., & Mr John C.
4 Woodman Richd. coach builder
Wren Major T. *Lenwood*
17 Wren Mrs Sarah, Bath House
1 Yelland Robt. Easton, banker and
ship broker
6 Yeo Capt. Rd. || 17 Wise Mrs
ACADEMIES.
*Marked * take Boarders.*
2 Blackwell Charles ; h Strand
10 Blight Wm. || *Clandinnan Chtte.
British, Chas. Hy. Witherington, &
Hannah Burnett
2*Croscombe Har. || 2*Forbes Miss
Elliott Jph. & Mrs. *Workhouse*
1 *Grammar School*, Rev Hugh Fowler, M.A., & Wm. Shortridge Blight
Hatherley Misses, Mill street
10 *Infant*, Emma Ogilbee
Main Misses, High street
National, Chas. Ellin, & J. Trick

Pickard John, Market place
ATTORNEYS.
Brayley George, High street
14 Burnard Wm. Henry E. (regr. of
marriages, boro' treasurer, &c ;) h
Queen street
Carter Chas. jun. (town clerk, bridge
steward, & notary,) Willett st ; h
Bridgeland street
Harvie Harry Arthur, (proctor and
union clerk,) Church yard
14 Hatherly Wm. Fortescue Wells,
(clk. to comssrs. of taxes)
4 Jennings Rd. Fras. ; h Meddon st
Ley Arthur, Bridge street
2 Rooker James, (clerk of peace and
county court)
12 Smale Chas. ; h Victoria ter
BANKS.
1 Agricultural & Commercial, (Harding, Braginton and Co.) *on Commercial Bank*
16 National Provincial Bank of England, *(on London and Westminster
Bank,)* Hy. Oliver Ley,*manager*
Savings' Bank, Quay, open Tuesday,
Thurs. & Sat. from 10 to 3 ; Geo.
Richards, *actuary*
FARMERS.
Bayley David, *Ford farm*
12 Beer John || 12 Brook Henry
Brook Wm., *Upcott*
14 Bray Saml. || 13 Chubb Rd.
Call John, *Upcott*
14 Ching Richard
13 Colwill Pp. || 13 Daniel James
1 Fry Thomas || 11 Gilbert Jame
13 * Grant John Henry
9 * Holman Richard
1 Holman Thos. || 10 Holman Wm
9 Kivall John || 14 Martin Thomas
Lee John, *Saltern* || 10 Taylor Rd.
Shepherd Wm., High street
Turner Rd. and Wilton Jno. *Grang*
FIRE AND LIFE OFFICES.
1 Albion, Rt. E. Yelland
10 Argus, Thomas Griffiths
14 Cattle Asrnc., W. F. W. Hatherly
14 Church of Engld., Wm. Blight
14 Colonial, W. F. W. Hatherly
10 County & Provdt., Hy. Tardrew
12 Etonian & Genl., Wm. Cadd
16 Family Endowment, Thos. Ley
Guardian, Geo. Richards, *Wooder*
5 Indisputable Life, Rt. Holman

1 Legal & Commercial, Cole & Son
14 London Assurance, Marine, and Royal Farmers, W. F. W. Hatherly.
14 Lothbury, W. S. Blight
10 Minerva, W. H. Fry
5 North Devon and Bideford Annuitant, Rt. Holman, secretary
10 Palladium, John Lee
Norwich Union, H. A. Harvie, and C. Smale
Phœnix; Thomas Hogg, Bridge st
2 Provident Clerks, &c. Society, T. G. Woollacott
Royal Exchange, 10 Charles Veysey, and 2 James Rooker
Sun, 1 R. E. Yelland, and 12 Thos. Trewin
10 United Mutual, Wm. Reed
10 West of England, J. Hamlyn
2 Western Anntnt., James Rooker
2 Yorkshire, Edward Dingle

HOTELS, INNS, & TAVERNS.

12 Angel, Wm. Perkins
5 Appledore Inn, Ann N. Lang
14 Barley Mow, Wm. Fry
7 Blacksmiths' Arms, Thomas Lile
2 Bridge Inn, Elizabeth Harvey
1 Castle Inn, Wm. Denbow
15 Commercial, John Aishton
3 Cornish Arms, George Giddy
9 Dove, Wm. Mc Cullum
12 Farmers' Exchange, John Beer
11 Horse and Jockey, Wm. Radford
12 Joiners' Arms, Charles Cook
15 King of Prussia, James Harris
16 King's Arms, Rt. Stafford
11 Lamb, Wm. Roberts
16 London Tav., Wm. Bartholomew
Malt Scoop, Philip Brownscombe
6 Mariners' Inn, Grace Lyle
12 New Inn, (postg.) Ths. Parramore
7 New London Inn, John Daniel
11 New Ring of Bells, Wm. Johns
16 Newfoundland Inn, Jno. Maunder
11 Old Portobello, James Gilbert
11 Old Ring of Bells, Bartw. Fishley
12 Peacock, Wm. Ellis
11 Plough, John Grant
7 Railway Inn, Wm. Lake
11 Red Lion, John Johns
7 Sailors' Arms, Wm. Coldwell
12 Ship, Thomas Jewell
6 Ship, John Colley
7 Ship on Launch, Geo. Sluman

16 Steam Packet Hotel, P. Freeman
7 Swan, James Plucknett
14 Swan, George Lock
16 Three Tuns, James Prance
4 Torridge Inn, J. A. Houston
6 Tradesman's Inn, Eliz. Hookway
14 Union, James Friendship
7 Welcombe Inn, Wm. Lake
White Hart, Samuel Balch, Queen st
White Pack Horse, Lewis Cawray

SURGEONS.

5 Acland Wm. and Wm. Hy.
Cooke Wm. Owen, *Strand Cottage*
16 Jones Arthur Newell
2 Pridham Thomas Lnce. (coroner)
2 Smith Thos. Mc Kenzie
Thompson John, Buttgarden street
4 Turner Charles Colwill

AUCTIONEERS.
10 Heard Rd.
Husband Thos., Old Town
10 Lee John
17 White Ed. M., (architect, &c)

BAKERS.
(* *Confectioners.*)
10 Allan Wm.
13 Balch Stpn.
14 Barnacoat Cs.
7 Blake Wm.
11 * Boyns My.
14 * Bridgman G.
10 * Friendship A.
6 Gloves Wm.
15 Gribble Wm.
14 Heay Mary
15 Haddon Alfd.
11 Jenkins John
9 Jordan Robt.
3 Martin Eliz.
1 * Ocock James
4 Pady Philip

BASKET MAKERS.
Baker Wm.
1 Berry Geo. H.
14 Berry Joseph
Berry Wm.
Pearse Wm.

BEERHOUSES.
13 Bragg John
Cawsey Lewis
6 Colley John
7 Colwill Wm.
13 Drew John

7 Lile Thomas
12 Tucker John
7 Watts Henry

BLACKSMITHS.
Chalk John
10 Down Robert
7 Galliver Saml.
10 Jenkins Wm.
May Henry
1 Mock John
10 Palmer Rd. L.
13 Parsons Hy.
11 Stevens Thos.

BLOCK MAKERS.
7 Griffey Thos.
7 Johnson Robt. and Son

BOOKSELLERS, &c.
14 Bishop John
14 Blight Wm. S. (parish clerk)
1 Cole Wm. & Son
10 Griffiths Thos.
8 Hayman J. G.
2 Hogg J. J.
10 Jacobs Sarah
1 Wilson John

BOOT & SHOE MKS.
15 Adams Richd.
14 Bale James
7 Dark Wm.
15 Davey Wm.
1 Galsworthy Jn.
7 Geaton John
11 Haycroft Wm.
14 Hoare John
14 Hookway Jas.

14 Jenkins Hy.
14 Jenkins Thos.
2 Lendon Thos.
14 Major Wm.H.
10 Maynard Jas.
14 Mayne Wm.
10 Middleton Rt.
14 Otway Wm.
8 Prescott James
15 Prince Thos.
14 Prouse Hugh
10 Rendle Jnthn.
13 Swain Wm
14 Whitaker Geo.
9 Wickatts Jas.
  BREWERS.
10 Abbott Wm.
6 Brownscombe P.
11 How John
13 Parramore Ts.
14 Prust Michael
  BUTCHERS.
7 Blake Wm.
1 Holman Thos.
1 Holman Rd.
Marshall James
14 Penrose Jas.
  CABINET MAKERS.
Ashton Henry
13 Hawkesley Geo.
10 Heard George
10 Lee John
14 Lock John
14 Lock George
  CARPENTERS, &c.
  (* *Wheelwrights.*)
14 Bale James
Braund Jesse
12 Ellis Wm.
7 Embery Wm.
10 Heard George
13 Jones Thos.
*10 Lamerton Jno.
*9 Lamerton Ths.
Lee Rt.,Pimlico pl
11 Moase Peter
Moase Wm.
13 Radcliff James
10 Sanders Thos.
16 Taylor Robt.
2 Trace John
*14 West Wm.
17 White Edw. M.
Yeo Wm.,Silver st

CHEMISTS & DGTS.
12 Cadd Wm.
2 Dingle Edward
10 Fry Wm. Hy.
10 Griffiths Thos.
2 Hogg Thomas
8 Joce James
14 Quicke Wm.
16 Saunders John
  Cornish
  COAL MERTS.
7 Anthracite Mining Co.
7 Blake Wm.
7 Daniel John
9 Fewings John
11 Fishley Bartw.
10 Heard Richd.
6 Heard Thos. S.
13 Houston A. J.
15 How John
1 Hutchings P. H.
11 Johns Wm.
7 Lake Richard
16 Ley Thomas
16 Martin Wm.
Oliver Ann
14 Prust Michael
7 Stanbury Thos.
Walker John
  COOPERS.
1 Hutchings P. H.
2 Pillefant Saml.
10 Werry Robert
CORN MERCHANTS.
14 Carter John
Ellis Thomas
13 Giddy Richard
15 How John
16 Ley Thomas
16 Norman Thos.
14 Prust Michael
9 Richards Thos.
9 Long George
11 Narraway John
13 Petherbridge T.
12 Sanguin Thos.
White Wm. Penny,
  Westcombe
  DYERS.
10 Ellis James
15 Gribble Eliz.
15 Richards Mary

EARTHENWARE
MANUFACTURERS.
7 Ching Bryant
17 Crocker Saml.
7 Cole John
10 Green George
19 Tucker John & Son
  GARDENERS.
13 Cann Edward
10 Cann James
14 Carter John
6 Craggs Wm.
13 Gibbs Thomsn.
9 Jordan Robert
1 Slocombe Jane
13 Thorn Richard
GLASS, &c., DLRS.
14 Bale James
16 Ching & Co.
10 Green George
12 Phillips John
GROCERS, &c.
13 Balch Stephen
12 Cadd Wm.
16 Ching & Co.
10 Clarke Betsy
2 Dingle Edward
10 Doidge Simon Carder
10 Fry Wm.
12 Grigg John
11 Heard Peter
6 Heard Thos. S.
16 Hooper Wm.
1 Hutchings Peter
12 Phillips John
4 Mallett Tmsn.
14 Prust Michael
7 Pollard Wm.
14 Quicke Wm.
2 Rigsby Thomas
12 Trewin Thos.
10 Trick Ann
  HAIRDRESSERS.
15 Bowen George
10 Lee Wm. Yeo.
1 Nicholls John
10 Outway Geo.
  HATTERS.
12 Brend Jph.
7 Dannell Edn.
8 Hornabrook P.
HORSE, &c. LETRS.
15 Aishton John

Balch Samuel
Chalk John
11 Fishley Brtw.
5 Friendship Jas.
14 Fry Wm.
1 Hale Robert
9 Holman Rd.
4 Houston J. A.
12 Parramore T.
16 Penfound&Co.
16 Stafford Robt.
IRONMONGERS,&c
12 Chope Walter
14 Lendon Wm.
2 Lethbridge Wm.
14 Martin Wm.
12 Richards Dhy.
10 Saunders W.P.
10 Tardrew Pp. & Son,(&foundrs.)
10 Tardrew Wm.
10 Yeo Thomas
L. & W. DRAPERS.
8 Pedler Chpr.
10 Reed Wm.
10 Vellacott W. L.
  Stamp office
10 Veysey Chas.
10 Vinson & Son
10 Wyatt Joseph
  MALTSTERS.
10 Abbott Wm.
6 Brownscombe P.
Ellis Thomas
13 Giddy Rd. G.
13 Grant John H.
11 Heard Peter
15 How John
7 Lake Richard
4 Ley Stephen
16 Ley Thomas
16 Maunder John
14 Prust Michael
11 Radford Wm.
10 Trick Charles
  MERCHANTS.
Chanter Ts. Burnard, Queen st; h Glentor
4 Chope Thomas
4 Evans Thomas
10 Heard Richd.
15 How John
16 Ley Thomas
7 Pollard Wm.

MILLINERS, &c.
Burnard Mary
14 Capern Jane
14 Carter Mary
2 Coull Ann
10 Davies Mary
10 Doidge Mary A.
13 Jenkins Fras.
7 Jones E.
3 Martin E. B.
2 Matthews Mary
4 Monkley Ann
4 Payne Miss
Pill Harriet
14 Penrose My. A.
10 Prust Eliz.
14 Prouse Chtte.
2 Sweet Emily
14 Turnbull E. A.
7 Waters Mary
11 Young Maria
PAINTRS. & GLZRS.
10 Bartlett Bryt.
14 Carter John
14 Clark George
14 Daniel Bartw.
14 Hernaman Jno.
11 Husband John
14 Lendon Wm.
7 Lile John
14 Murphy Thos.
14 Prior & Pound
2 Sweet John
1 Sweet Edm. F.
14 Whitaker John
ROPE MAKERS.
21 Barns Richd.
4 Evans Thomas
Williams Joshua
2 Watkins Rd.
SADDLERS.
11 Chope Henry
8 Pridham Thos.
12 Richards Drthy.
10 Yeo Thomas
SHIP BUILDERS.
Cox George
7 Johnson Robert
and Son
7 Waters Thomas
SHOPKEEPERS.
10 Allen Wm.
14 Bale Thomas
13 Backway Ann

2 Baker Edward
13 Balch Stephen
14 Carter John
7 Chapple John
13 Curtis Grace
13 Cook John
10 Cutland Sarah
21 Dark Samuel
13 Drew John
21 Fowler Hugh
7 Geaton John
7 Harvey George
14 Harwood Thos.
13 Hawkesley Geo.
14 Hernaman Jno.
21 Hookway Wm.
7 Huxtable John
21 Isaac John
14 Jenkins Hy.
11 Jenkins John
11 Jewell Hugh
7 Lee Wm.
4 Mallett Thos.
7 May Wm.
11 Moase Peter
13 Oxley George
4 Pady Philip
Palmer Maria
21 Phillips Susan
12 Pickard John
14 Pickard Sarah
7 Pollard Wm.
15 Prince Thos.
14 Prust Thos.
19 Purchase Fras.
1 Richards Thos.
11 Rook Fanny
1 Sweet Jane
7 Symons Sarah
7 Thorne Richd.
4 Turner Eliz.
STONE MASONS.
15 Baker Isaac,
(statuary & slate
merchant)
14 Bale Thomas
4 Boyns John
13 Glover Wm.
9 Jeffery Nicholas
7 Lee Wm.
Moase Wm., Cold-
harbour
4 Monkley Thos.

STRAW HAT MKRS.
11 Betty Susan G.
3 Boyns Ann
14 Capern Jane
7 Huxtable Misses
14 Maunder Sus.
14 Prouse Chtte.
11 Rook Fanny
10 Stone Sophia
Stone Ann
2 Sweet Emily
TAILORS.
10 Beer James
13 Braund John
19 Clark John L.
11 Cutcliffe Geo.
14 Davies Wm. G.
14 Elson Edw.
10 Grant Robert
11 Huxtable Edn.
9 Lloyd Lewis
10 Oatway Wm. V.
19 Purchase Fras.
11 Roberts Wm.
14 Turnbull Rd.
10 Vinson Thos.
and Son

14 White John
TALLOW CHNDLRS.
14 Down Edw. H.
10 Down Samuel
9 Hornabrook Ptr.
7 Huxtable John
TIMBER MERTS.
Chanter Thos. B.
10 Heard Richd.
15 How John
16 Taylor Robert
WATCHMKRS. &c.
10 Down Robert
10 Mill Wm. Jewell
14 Organ Wm.
8 Short Samuel
10 Tucker Robt.
14 Webber Henry
14 Williams John
WINE & SP. MERTS.
11 Bailey Wm.
10 Doidge S. C.
10 Trick Ann
10 Wickham Thos.
and Co.
10 Willcocks Stpn.
Cleverly

COACHES, &c.

From New Inn, the Quay, &c.

The *Mail* to Exeter, at 7 morning.

Emerald, to Plymouth, every Mon., Wed., and Friday, at 9 morn., and to Barnstaple, Tues., Thurs., and Saturday, at 5 afternoon

OMNIBUSES to *Plymouth,* Tues. 10 morn.; to *Barnstaple,* daily, at 9 morn. and 5 evening; and Tues., Thurs., and Sat. noon; to *Torrington,* Tues., Thurs., and Sat. 6 evening; and to *Hartland,* Tues., Thurs., and Saturday, 5 evening

CARRIERS.

Pridham and Lake's and the other Omnibuses noticed above, convey goods to *Plymouth, Torrington, Tavistock, Barnstaple, &c.*

To *Clovelly,* Jewell, from the Ship, Tues., Thurs., and Saturday

To *Exeter,* Penfound, from Allhalland street, and Pridham & Lake, from the Quay, Mon., Wed., & Fri

To *Bude, &c.,* Cobbledick, from the King's Arms, Tues. & Sat. morngs

2 K 3

To *Hartland*, Williams, from the Steam Packet Inn, Tues., Thurs., and Saturday, 5 afternoon —
To *Launceston*, Penfound, Wed. and Sat., and Robert Tredinnick, from the Steam Packet Inn, Thursday

CONVEYANCE BY WATER.

The *Water-Witch Steamer*, to Bristol,

Ilfracombe, Lynmouth, &c., every Monday ; John Lee, *agent*

Sailing Smacks, with goods and passengers, weekly, to Bristol ; Richd. Martin, *agent*

Regular Traders, every fortnight, to Griffin's Wharf, London ; Wm. Martin, *agent*

BUCKLAND-BREWER, a large village, 5 miles W. by N. of Great Torrington, has in its parish 1103 souls, and 5656 acres of land, including the hamlets of *Bilsford, Galsworthy*, and *Tithacot*, and many scattered houses. It had formerly a weekly market on Wednesday, granted to the abbot of Dunkeswell in 1290, but it has long been obsolete. Two *fairs* are held in the village, on Whit-Tuesday and the third Monday in November. The trustees of the late Lord Rolle are lords of the manor, which was given by the Brewer or Briwere family to Tor and Dunkeswell Abbeys. Mrs. and the Rev. J. M. Stevens, J. H. Lee, Esq., and several smaller owners, have estates in the parish. The *Church* (St. Mary and St. Benedict,) is a large antique structure, with a lofty tower and five bells. It stands on an eminence, commanding a view of the Bristol Channel. The *vicarage*, valued in K.B. at £25. 17s. 3½d., and in 1831 at £244, with the chapelries of Bulkworthy and East Putford annexed to it, is in the patronage of the Crown, and incumbency of the Rev. T. A. Colling, B.A., who has 9A. of glebe, and a good residence, built in 1846. The tithes were commuted in 1843, the vicarial for £235, and the rectorial for £240 per annum. The latter belong to the Rev. J. M. Stevens, and were formerly held by Tor Abbey. There was a fraternity or guild in the church, dedicated to St. Michael, and valued at £8. 7s. 4d. per annum at the dissolution. The poor parishioners have £134. 13s. 7d. three per cent. consols, purchased with £100 left by Hester Turner, in 1787.

Coll Mr Bayley, *Orleigh Court*
Colling Rev Thos. Adams, B.A., vicar
Gard John, corn miller
Lake Thos. vict., Coach & Horses
Norman John, sen., maltster
Norman Thos. corn factor
Pinhale John, farrier
Saunders Nicholas, vict. Bell
Saunders Wm. corn miller
Squire Robt. & Joshua, plumbers, &c
Stapledon Mrs E. and Mr Joseph

BLACKSMITHS.
Dennis Richard
Mounce John
Prouse John
Stapledon Josh.
BOOT &SHOE MKS.
Cole John
Martin Wm.
Matthews John
Morrish James

BUTCHERS.
Brend Wm.
Clarke Robert
CARPENTERS.
(* *Wheelwghts.*)
*Born John
Pasker & Squire
Saunders Robert
Smale Frederick
Withecombe Wm.

SHOPKEEPERS.
Cole Catherine
Evans Mary
Richards John
FARMERS.
Abbott James
Abbott Thomas
Bartlett Bryant
Bartlett James
Clement Joseph
Cleverdon Thos.
Courtice John
Crang James
Fry Thomas
Fulford Barthw.
Fulford Philip
Furze Wm.
Glass Thomas
Golsworthy Ambs
Hamlyn James
Heal Elizabeth
Heal John
Heal Laurence

Jenkins Wm.
Lashbrook Wm.
Littlejohns Thos.
Martin Henry
Mounce Sarah
Norman John
Norman J. (Hele)
Oxenham Richd.
Passmore John
Phillips Thomas
Phillips Richard
Prouse Eliz.
Reed Thomas
Seldon Wm.
Shapton Samuel
Skinner Robert
Stapledon Thos.
Trather Wm.
Tucker Robert
Veal Edmund
Walter Eliza
Ward Wm.

BUCKLAND-FILLEIGH is a village and parish, 6½ miles W.N.W. of Hatherleigh, containing 275 souls, and 3037 acres of land, nearly all the

property of Lord Ashburton and Lord Clinton, the former of whom owns the manor of Buckland-Filleigh, and has a pleasant seat here, formerly the residence of the Filleigh and Fortescue families. Lord Clinton owns the manor and barton of *Hartleigh*, by inheritance from the Rolles. This estate includes part of Heanton deer park. The *Church* (St. Mary,) is a beautiful little structure, standing close to Lord Ashburton's mansion, and containing several handsome monuments of the Fortescue family. The *rectory*, valued in K.B. at £11. 16s. 0½d., and in 1831 at £238, is in the patronage of the Bishop of Exeter, and incumbency of the Rev. Stephen Nosworthy, B.A., who has a good residence, and 87A. 3R. 37P. of glebe. The tithes were commuted in 1842 for £210 per annum. The poor have the interest of £20, left by the Rev. Wm. Walter and another donor.

Lord *Ashburton*, Buckland House, (and *The Grange, Hants*.)
Nosworthy Rev Stphn., B.A., *Rectory*
Braund John, carpenter
Gilbert Rd. parish clerk and tailor
Martin James, blacksmith and vict., *Ashburton Arms*
• Nollys James E., land steward

Vanstone James, machine maker

FARMERS.
Crocker Hugh
Heard Samuel
Hooper Wm.
Lane James
Reddeway J.

Risdon James
Piper John
Walsh Thos.
Warmington Jno.
Whitelock Hy.

BULKWORTHY, a small scattered village, 7 miles S.W. of Great Torrington, has in its parish 196 souls and 6050 acres of land, including *Heytown* hamlet, and a large tract of waste. The trustees of the late Lord Rolle are lords of the manor; but the barton of *Hankford* belongs to the Rev. J. M. Stevens, and several other proprietors have estates in the parish. The *Church* was built by Chief Justice Hankford, as appears by an inscription on the window; and the curacy is annexed to the vicarage of Buckland Brewer.

Avery Joseph, farmer
Beer John, blacksmith
Ching John, farmer, *Stowford*

Daniel James, corn miller
Newcombe Henry, farmer, *Hankford*
Newcombe Wm. farmer

FRITHELSTOCK, a village and parish 2 miles W. of Great Torrington, comprises 705 souls and 2380 acres of land, including the hamlets of *Frithelstock Stone, and Milford*. There was a small *Priory* of Austin Canons here, founded by Sir Roger Beauchamp, in the reign of Henry III. It was valued at the dissolution at £127. 2s. 4½d. per annum, and was granted to Viscount Lisle. The estate now belongs to Lord Clinton, but the Rev. P. Thomas is lord of the manor, and Mrs. Stevens, and a few smaller owners, have estates in the parish. The *Church* (St. Mary and St. Gregory,) is an ancient structure, and the living is a *perpetual curacy*, in the patronage of Mrs. P. Johns, and incumbency of the Rev. G. W. T. Carwithen, M.A. Part of the Priory church, with lancet shaped windows, still remains. The *Poor's Land* comprises 8 acres, and a right of common over 200A. of waste. The poor have the interest of £32, and the parish has a yearly rent-charge of 50s. left by Mary Melhuish in 1794, for schooling poor children.

Beer Joseph, shopkeeper
Carwithen Rev George Wm. T., incumbent
Durant John, corn miller
Earl Mr. *Green Cottage*
Friendship John, wheelwright
Lee James, vict. New Inn
Morris John, blacksmith

Perkin Saml. & Benj., shoemakers
Sandford Geo., vict. Clinton Arms
Short Thomas, tailor
FARMERS.
Ball Giles & Jas.
Bartlett Wm.
Beer John
Curry Daniel

Dark Wm.
Dullam Rt.
Dullam Wm.
Fisher John
Frain Samuel

Freeman Saml.	Norman Sarah	Phillips John	Snell James
Mann Joseph	Parsons Joseph	Shopland Cphr.	Squire Wm.
Moase Hannah	Perkins George	Smale Wm.	Walters George
Moase James			

HUISH, a small scattered village on the west side of the Torridge valley, has in its parish 141 souls and about 1100 acres of land, of which 722 acres are in the extensive parks of *Heanton Sachville*, which are partly in the parish of Petrockstow, where the old mansion was burnt down about forty years ago. HEANTON HOUSE, the present elegant modern mansion, stands in this parish, and is the seat of *Lord Clinton*, the lord of the manor, and owner of most of the soil, who has lately made great improvements in the mansion and its beautiful grounds. Huish was anciently held by a family of its own name, and afterwards by the Tresilian, Yeo, and Innis families. Sir James Innis, afterwards Duke of Roxburgh, purchased the estate in 1782, and built a new house for his own residence; but he sold the estate to Richard Eales, Esq., of whom it was purchased by the late Lord Clinton, who was succeeded in 1832 by the present *Right Hon. Charles Rodolphus-Trefusis*, BARON CLINTON AND SAY, who was born in 1791, and whose son the *Hon. Henry Rolle*, one of the heirs of the late Lord Rolle, was born in 1834. (See page 218.) His Lordship's other seat is Trefusis Castle, Cornwall. Heanton House was re-modelled by the late Lord, and the old deer park in Petrockstow is still preserved. Huish parish includes the hamlet of *Newbridge*, and the barton of *Lovistone*, where that eminent oculist, J. Cunningham Saunders, was born. *Huish Church* is a small antique structure, with a tower and three bells, and the living is a *rectory*, valued in 1831 at £194, in the patronage of Lord Clinton, and imcumbency of the Rev. J. C. Kempe, of Merton, who has 66A. 2R. 25P. of glebe. The tithes have been commuted for £117 per annum.

Lord Clinton, *Heanton House*
Archer Rev Samuel Haywood, B.A. curate, *Rectory*
Anderson Alexander, farm steward
Brooks John, farmer
Carpenter John, blacksmith
Cato John, gardener, *Heanton Hs.*
Bickham Mrs. housekeeper, *do.*
Wright Charles, butler, *do.*
Rockhey Thomas, corn miller
Stanbury Richard, farmer

IDDESLEIGH or IDSLEIGH, on the east side of the picturesque valley of the river Torridge, 4 miles N.N.E. of Hatherleigh, is a village and parish, containing 545 souls and 2962 acres of land. Sir S. H. Northcote, Bart., is lord of the manor, and owner of about 2000 acres, formerly held by the Sully and Bingham families. *Ash* is the seat and property of Hugh Mallett, Esq., and has been long held by his family. The mansion is a handsome modern building, more than a mile from the village, on the banks of the river Okement. The Rev. P. Johnson, Wm. Arnold, W. Parker, and a few smaller freeholders have estates in the parish. The *Church* (St. James,) has a tower and four bells, and has lately been renovated and partly rebuilt at the cost of about £400. In the chancel is the effigy of a crusader, supposed to represent Sir John Sully. The *rectory*, valued in K.B. at £17. 1s. 3d., and in 1831 at £350, is in the patronage and incumbency of the Rev. Frederick Pitman, M.A., who has 145A. 2R. 3P. of glebe, and in 1849-'50 erected a large and handsome *Rectory House*, in the Elizabethan style, at the cost of about £2000. It stands on a commanding eminence, and has tasteful grounds. The tithes were commuted in 1847 for £332. 10s. per annum. The *Parish Houses* are ten ancient tenements, which have long been vested with the overseers of the poor; together with £50 left by a Mr. Potter, about 1586.

Anstey Bartw. parish clerk
Anstey Wm. vict. Northcote Arms
Mallett Hugh, Esq. *Ash House*
Manning Aaron, vict., Duke of York
Pitman Rev Fdk. M.A. *Rectory*

FARMERS.
Arnold Wm.
Arnold Thos. O.
Arnold Robert
Arnold Jane&My.
Brook Philip
Brook Tphna.
Channing Cornls.

Cox Samuel
Goss Thomas
Lethern John
Paddon George
Parker Wm.
Piper Samuel
Ward John
Ward Wm.
Weekes Wm.

BOOT&SHOE MKS.
Avery Wm.
Simmons Saml.
SHOPKEEPERS.
Clatworthy Thos.
Westcott Thos.
TAILORS.
Ansty George
Hale Wm.

LANDCROSS or LANCRASS, a small village and parish in the Torridge valley, 2½ miles S.S.E. of Bideford, has only 120 souls and about 500 acres of land, mostly belonging to the trustees of the late Lord Rolle, who are lords of the manor, and patrons of the *rectory*, valued in K.B. at £5 4s. 9½d., and in 1831 at £84. The Rev. E. H. Furrington, B.A. is the incumbent, and has 9A. of glebe and a small residence. The *Church* (Holy Trinity,) is an ancient structure, with a wooden belfry. The celebrated General Monk was born here in 1608. The FARMERS are John Abbott, Simon Crang, John Ford, Henry Guard, *(miller,)* and Wm. Partridge, *Watertown.*

LANGTREE is a considerable village, 3½ miles S.W. of Great Torrington, and has in its parish 941 souls, and 4028 acres of land, including the hamlets of *Stowford* and *Week.* The Trustees of the late Lord Rolle own most of the soil, and are lords of the manors of Langtree and Stowford, and patrons of the *rectory*, valued in K.B. at £29. 1s. 3d., and in 1831 at £523. The Rev. John Guard, M.A., is the incumbent, and has 66A. of glebe, and a good residence. The tithes were commuted in 1838 for £470 per annum. The *Church* has a tower and five bells, and contains several neat monuments. There was anciently a chapel at Cross hill. The *National School*, built in 1840, is supported by the rector. [*See Appendix.*]

Bassett John, schoolmaster
Clements John, vict. Green Dragon
Cleverdon Wm. vict. New Inn
Gabell Mr || Dark Wm. clothes dlr
Guard Rev John, M.A. *Rectory*
Osborne James, corn miller
Perdon John, corn miller
Slade Capt. Adolphus, R.N. *Week Hs*

BEER HOUSES.
Kivell Wm.
Parnicott John

BLACKSMITHS.
Blight Wm.
Blight Humph.
Thorne Wm.

BOOT & SHOE MKS.
Call Jame
Palmer John
CARPENTERS.
Hadger Thos.
Saunders Thos.
Vanstone John
FARMERS.
Ackwill George

Andrews John
Barkwell Isaac
Beer Wm.
Bullivant Jas.
Bullivant Saml.
Bumberry John
Clements Saml.
Copp John
Copp Wm.
Copp Henry
Hearn Henry
Johns Thomas
Ley James
Madge John
Mallett Humph.
Netherway Hy.

Saunders Robt.
Symons Thos.
Tucker John
Vanstone John
Ward Thomas
Whitelock Geo.
Whitelock Rd.

SHOPKEEPERS.
Call James
Ford John
Thorne John
TAILORS.
Ford John
Lang Wm.
Thorn John

LITTLEHAM, a village and parish, 2 miles S. by W. of Bideford, has 390 souls, and 1290 acres of land. Mrs. and Miss Anthony are ladies of the manor, owners of a great part of the soil, and patrons of the *rectory*, valued in K.B. at £14. 16s. 10½d., and in 1831 at £241, and now held by the Rev. J. L. Harding, B.A., who has 97A. of glebe, and an elegant residence, in the Grecian style, with a beautiful lawn, &c. The tithes were commuted in 1841 for £204 per annum. The *Church* (St. Andrew,) is a small antique fabric, with a tower and four bells. Its windows are enriched

with stained glass, and the fabric was repaired and beautified in 1848-9, at the cost of about £200. J. Heal, Esq., and a few smaller owners have estates in the parish. The poor have the interest of £16. 10s., and there is in the village a small Wesleyan chapel.

Crealock Jas. shoemkr. & vict. Hoop
Harding Rev. John Limebear, B.A. *Rectory*
Marshall Wm. tailor
Shutt John, mason, &c.
Sing Thomas, shoemaker
Touchet John, gent. High Park
BLACKSMITHS. | Hearn Wm.
Dennis Alex.

CARPENTERS.
Dennis Richd.
Grigg John
FARMERS.
Ball Wm.
Clarke Henry
Copp John
Dennis Wm.
Dullam John

Ford Michael
Heywood Wm., *Court*
Jones George
Morrish John
Morrish Richd.
Prouse Thos.
Tucker Thos.

MARLAND, (PETER'S) or *Petermarland*, 4 miles S. by W. of Great Torrington, is a village and parish, containing 351 souls, and 2200 acres of land, mostly belonging to the Rev. J. M. Stevens, M.A., archdeacon of Exeter, and partly to G. Oldham, Esq., the latter of whom owns the small manor of Twigbear. *Winscott House* has been long the seat of the Stevens family, and is now the residence of the Archdeacon's son. The *Church* (St. Peter,) is a small antique structure, and the benefice is a *perpetual curacy*, worth only about £60 a year. Archdeacon Stevens is patron and impropriator of the tithes, and the Rev. Peter Glubb, M.A., of Little Torrington, is the incumbent. The *Church Land*, left by John Harvey, is a farm of 54A., let for £32. Upon it are four cottages, built by the parish, and occupied by paupers. The poor have £5 a year, left by *Eliz. Clevland*, in 1785.

Banbury James, parish clerk
Eyre John, vict. New Inn
Holman Lewis, carpenter and vict. Sheepwash Inn
Stevens John C. M. Esq. *Winscott*
BLACKSMITHS. | Hutchins Thos.
Stacey John
Stacey Richd. | BOOT & SHOE MKS. | Eyre John

Mills Wm.
Stacey Lewis
FARMERS.
Balkwill Jane
Balkwill John S.
Eyre Mary
Passmore Saml.
Passmore Wm.

Quick Cphr.
Shepherd Robt.
Taunton John
Taunton Pp.
Taunton Thos.
Taunton Wm.
TAILORS.
Liverton Robt.
Palmer Richd.

MEETH, near the confluence of the Torridge and Okement rivers, 3 miles N. by E. of Hatherleigh, is a scattered village and parish, containing 314 souls, and 2170 acres of land, in the manors of Meeth and Fryes Hele, the former of which belongs to R. Preston, Esq., and the latter to the Earl of Morley; but part of the soil belongs to the Acland, Mallett, Bowden, and Owen families. The *Church* (St. John,) is an ancient structure, with a tower, four bells, and a fine Saxon door-way. Among its monuments is a very handsome one, erected in 1848, in memory of the late Mrs. Lamb. The figures represent an angel ascending with the deceased. The *rectory*, valued in K.B. at £9. 7s. 6d., and in 1831 at £250, is in the patronage of the Rev. F. D. Lemprière, and incumbency of the Rev. E. Lemprière, who has 25A. 3R. 27P. of glebe, and a good modern residence. Here is a *National School*. The poor have the interest of £5, given by one *Madge*, and of £100, left by *Samuel Jerman* in 1758, except 10s. for a sermon.

Beare Lawrence, machinist
Lemprière Rev. Edward, *Rectory*
Madge Mr Thomas Acland
Norman Mary, vict. New Inn

Vanstone Benj. carpenter, &c.
Vanstone John, carpenter, &c.
West Wm. saddler

FARMERS. (** are Owners.*)

*Acland Hugh
*Bowden Saml.
Brook Mrs B.

Lock John
Madge Philip
Mallett John

Powlesland Geo.
Sleeman John
*Taunton Rd.
Ward Samuel

Weekes Saml.
Weekes Thos.
Wright Wm. (&
maltster)

MERTON, a neat village near Lord Clinton's park, 7 miles N. by W. of
Hatherleigh, has in its parish 763 souls, and 3738 acres of land, including
the hamlets of *Smithacott* and *Little Potheridge*, and many scattered houses.
Lord Clinton is lord of the manor of Merton, and owner of a great part of
the parish. The Trustees of the late Lord Rolle hold the manor of *Potheridge*, where the Monks were long seated, and where the mansion was
rebuilt by *Gen. Monk, (Duke of Albemarle,)* about 1670, but was mostly
pulled down after the death of the Duchess in 1734, though the magnificent stables are still standing. Archdeacon Stevens, and a few smaller
owners, have estates in the parish. The *Church* (All Saints,) is a handsome structure, which was restored and beautified about four years ago.
One of the windows is richly emblazoned with stained glass, and a new
organ has been erected. The *rectory*, valued in K.B. at £29. 15s. 7½d., and
in 1831 at £424, is in the patronage of Lord Clinton, and incumbency of
the Rev. J. C. Kempe, B.A., who has 65A. of glebe, and a handsome residence. The tithes were commuted in 1843 for £365 per annum. A neat
National School was built by Lord Clinton, about four years ago. The
rector has 20s. and the poor 5s. per annum, left by Thomas Langdon,
in 1727.

Burnett Alex. steward to Ld. Clinton
Down Wm. wheelwright & smith
Gordon John, shopkeeper
Kempe Rev. Jas. Cory, B.A. *Rectory*
Lewis Geo. shopr. & vict. Malt Scoop
Mills John, schoolmaster
Smith Thomas, cooper, &c.
Stanbury Wm. miller, *Westmoor*
  BLACKSMITHS.
Folland Michael
Luxton Samuel
Reed Wm.

  BOOT&SHOE MKS.
Elliott Samuel
Smith John
  FARMERS.
Anstey Thos.

Ashton Joseph
Ashton Thomas
Chummings Jno.
Collihole Wm.
Coplestone Sml.
Ford John
Ford Robert
Goldsworthy G.
Gordon James
Gordon John
Leverton Geo.
Lewis George
Luxton John

Neno Charles
Pope Wm.
Routcliffe Andw.
Snell Wm.
  MALTSTERS.
Ashton Samuel
Snell Thomas
Ward Bartw.
POST-OFFICE
at Jeremiah
Smith's. Let-
ters desp. 1½
afternoon

MONKLEIGH, 3 miles W.N.W. of Great Torrington, is a village and
parish, containing 699 souls, and 2177 acres of land, formerly belonging to
Montacute Priory, in Somersetshire. The Rev. J. T. P. Coffin is now lord
of the manor, which was given to his family after the Reformation; but a
great part of the parish belongs to Wm. Tardrew, Esq., and John Saltren
Willett, Esq.; the former of whom resides at *Annery*, a fine old mansion
which has been much altered and modernized, and was for a long period
the seat of the Hankford family. J. S. Willett, Esq., resides at *Petticombe*,
and here are several smaller landowners. Sir Wm. Hankford, who died at
Annery, in 1422, is said to have been the Lord Chief Justice who committed
Prince Henry to the Tower, for striking him a blow on the bench. The
Church (St. George,) is an ancient structure, and the living is a *vicarage*,
valued in K.B. at £14. 14s. 7d., and in 1831 at £180. J. S. Willett, Esq.,
is the patron, and the Rev. Chas. W. Willett, M.A., is the incumbent. The
great tithes belong to the patron, and were commuted in 1845. The Wesleyans have a chapel here built in 1834.

Chapple John, butcher
Cleverdon James, beer seller

Dennis Thomas, wheelwright
Ellis Jas. vict. Hunter's Inn

Martin Henry, corn miller
Padley Rev. C. J. A. curate
Pike Lieut., R.N. *Chantry*
Rigsby John, vict. Bell
Shute Wm. schoolmaster
Tardrew Wm. Esq. *Annery House*
Willett Rev. Chas. W., *Vicarage*
Willett J. S. Esq. *Petticombe*

BLACKSMITHS.
Dennis Rd. & Jno.
Ellis Wm.

BOOT & SHOE MKS.
Ashplant John
Ellis Thos.

FARMERS.
Branton Thos.
Brown James
Coates Richard
Crang Simon
Guard Wm.
Heal Charles
Huxham Thos.
Lack John
Lewis Mrs.

Newcombe Thos.
Newcombe Jas.
Newcombe Eliz.
Peard Sarah
Petherick Daniel

SHOPKEEPERS.
Cann Richard
Dennis Richd.
Ellis Wm.

NEWTON ST. PETROCK, 7 miles S.W. of Great Torrington, is a village and parish, containing 261 souls, and 1556 acres of land, including *West Hole*, and several scattered farm houses, &c. L. W. Buck, Esq., is lord of the manor, and owner of a great part of the soil, and the rest belongs to several smaller owners. The *Church* is a small antique structure, and the *rectory*, valued in K.B. at £8. 5s. 9½d., and in 1831 at £277, is in the patronage and incumbency of the Rev. F. D. Lemprière, of London. The glebe is 70A. 3R. 31P., and the Parsonage is an old residence. The tithes were commuted in 1840, for £151 per annum. The poor have 2s. a year, left by John Beccles. DIRECTORY—Rev. O. Z. O'Neill, curate, *Rectory;* Wm. Eyre, carpenter; Richard W. Cobbledick, miller; and John Blake, John Ball, Rt. Bean, Wm. Cobbledick, Jno. Fishley, John Gorvatt, Hugh Jeffery, Hugh King, Gideon Moor, *Mills;* John Osborne, Edw. Palmer, Rd. Quance, Thos. Reid, Wm. Saunders, Thos. Stapleton, John Tanton, Jas. Walters, and John Western, *farmers.*

NORTHAM, a large and well built village, is pleasantly seated on the peninsula between Barnstaple Bay and the river Torridge, from 1¼ to 2½ miles N. of Bideford. Its parish contains 3578 inhabitants, and about 2700 acres of land, including the pretty little seaport town of *Appledore; Northam Ridge* hamlet; many neat villas and scattered houses, and a large plain of turf common, called *Northam Burrows*, on which the inhabitants have common right. The manor of Northam was long held by Frampton Priory, and one of the priors had a grant for a fair here in 1252, but it has long been obsolete. Queen Elizabeth granted the manor to the Dean Canons of Windsor, to whom the fee still belongs, together with the tithes and the advowson of the *vicarage*, valued in K.B. at £10. 10s., and in 1831 at £138, and now held by the Rev. I. H. Gosset, M.A., who has a good residence, an augmentation from Queen Anne's Bounty, and a small stipend from the tithes, which have been commuted for £525 per annum, and are leased to the Corporation of South Molton. Captain Keats, Jas. Ley, Esq., Miss Lloyd, Robt. Barton, Esq., and many smaller owners have estates here. The *Church* (St. Margaret,) is a large and handsome structure with a lofty tower, and contains several neat monuments belonging to the Melhuish, Downe, Bevy, and other families.

APPLEDORE, in two divisions, called *East and West Appledore*, is a small sea-port town, in the parish of Northam, delightfully seated on the coast of Barnstaple Bay, at the mouths of the rivers Torridge and Taw, 3 miles N. of Bideford. It is the first harbour within the bar of the broad estuary of the two rivers, and is subordinate to the port of Bideford. Its principal trade is coasting and fishing, and in the town are many lodging houses, and several good inns and taverns for the accommodation of the numerous visitors, who throng hither in summer to enjoy the sea breezes, and the beautiful scenery of the neighbourhood. The town stands on an acclivity, commanding extensive marine views; and the fine beach is of great extent, and has a remarkable bank of pebbles, about a mile long, resembling the Chevil-bank, near Weymouth. Hubba the Dane landed here in the reign of Alfred the Great, and was discomfited and slain, with about 2000 men, before Kenwith Castle, which stood near Kenwith Lodge. The town has been much improved during the last 20 years, and has now upwards of 2500 inhabitants. It has two provision markets, on Wednesday and Saturday, mostly held in a small building erected in 1828. The *Chapel of Ease*, built about ten years ago, is dedicated to St. Mary, and is an elegant stone building, surrounded by lofty trees, and standing on the site of an ancient Roman Catholic Chapel. The living is now a *perpetual curacy*, valued at £150, in the patronage of the Vicar of Northam, and incumbency of the Rev. E. Reynolds, B A. Many old relics were found in digging the foundations of the chapel, and behind it is the site of an ancient *fort*, supposed to have been built during the civil wars of the 17th century. Here are three small chapels belonging to *Baptists, Wesleyans*, and *Independents*. The Presbyterians had a Meeting-house here as early as 1715, but the congregation are now Independents, and built their present chapel in 1816. The parish of Northam has large *National and Infant Schools*, and various charities for the poor.

Northam Parish Charities:—At Appledore are four small *Almshouses*, for as many poor families, purchased in 1695, with £60 given by Richard Branton, and other donors.

Here are various benefactions for the poor parishioners, among which are the following yearly *rent-charges*,—16s. left by *John Strange*, in 1626, out of Bennett's farm ; £5 out of Nethercote, purchased with £100 left in 1622, by a *Mr. Berriman ;* 36s. out of South-cote, purchased in 1674, with £30 left by *Anne Britton ;* 14s. 4d. left by Alex. Arundell, out of land at Bishop's Morchard ; and four annuities, amounting to £1. 12s. 4d. per annum, given by *W. and T. Leigh, J. Beare,* and others. In 1691, £50 left to the poor by *John Berry*, and £60 left by *Richard Cholwill*, for schooling poor children, were laid out in the purchase of three-fourth parts of a house, and 15½A. of land, at West Putford, now let for about £15 per annum. Two legacies, left for the poor parishioners, viz., £200 by *James Cocke*, in 1700, and £100 by *Eliz. Langdon*, in 1702, were vested in the purchase of four cottages, and about 11A. of land, now let for about £49 per annum. *Thos. Melhuish*, in 1702, built an *Almshouse*, for four old maids or widows, and endowed it with 40s. a year, out of 10A. of land, called Cox. He also charged the same estate with a yearly payment of 30s. for schooling poor children. The vicar has 30s., and the poor 20s. yearly, from £50 left by *Lady Ann Berry*, in 1716. Two annuities of £4 each, were given by *David Best*, in 1791 and 1806, for schooling poor children. Near the church is an *Almshouse* for four poor widows, supposed to have been given by William Leigh, and endowed with two annuities, viz., 10s. left by *Ann Smith*, and 14s. from £14, given by an unknown donor.

NORTHAM PARISH.

Those marked 2, are at Northam ; and the others at Appledore, or where specified.

Post-Offices at Rt. Yeoland's, Northam ; and at Susan Sarah's, Appledore

2 Allen Jph., Esq. || Baller Edward
Ball Rev John E. (*Baptist*)
Barratt Capt. || Blackmore Capt.
Beara & Cook, rope, &c. manfctrs
Beara John, ship chandler
Benyon Capt. || Blithe Mrs
2 Benson Ts. gent. || Berry Capt.
Blackmore Capt. || Bowden Capt.
Boon Captain || Bowen Moses
Brooks Capt. || Brooks Mrs
Brown W. J. gent. || Chapple Jas.
Channon Captain John
Chanter Thomas B., Esq.
Clapp Rev J. (*Independent*)
2 Davison Jas. || Day Captain
Dunsford Mrs || Eaton Captain
England Capts. John and Richard
Evans Mr. Richard & Capt. Wm.
Facey Capt. Wm. || Fishwick Capt.
Fisher Thomas, ship master
Fisher Capts. Wm., Jph., & John
Fursey Samuel, ship master
Gibbs Mr Saml. || Gilley Miss
Gorbin Capt. || 2 Gould Mr James
Gosset Rev Isaac Hy., M.A. *Vicarage*
Gowman Wm. plasterer
Hall Capt. Hy. || Ham Capt. J.
2 Harding Thos. G. || Harris Capt.
2 Herman Benj. surveyor, &c
2 Hewitt Mr B. || Lewis Major
Hillman Capts. Pp. and Thomas
Hooper Jas. || Jones Capt. John
Jackson Mrs || Kelley Captain

Jones Thos. revenue officer
Keats Capt. Wm., R.N. *Port hill*
Large Wm. traveller
Lawton Capt. || Larney Captain
2 Ley Jas., Esq. || Ley Capt. Pp.
Limbrey Capt. || Lowther Mrs
Mead Captain || Marshall Captain
Morton Dr Thos. || Morgan Misses
2 Nicholls Col. || Peel Jph. gent
Popham Capt. || Peace Lieut.
Quance Rd. || Russell Matthew
2 Reynolds Edw. & John, gents
Reynolds Rev Edw., B.A. incumbent of Appledore
Sleeman Mr John || Scott Capt.
Squire Capt. || Strange Miss
Smith Captain Owen
Stapledon James, ship master
Tatham Capts. James & Wm.
Thorold Frederick, Esq
Tucker Capt. Wm., R.N. & Mrs
Tucker Mr Thos. Wills Thomas
Williams Capts. Jph. and Edward
Williams Capts. Rd., Jno., Geo. & Ts.
Wincott Capt. || 2 Yeolland Robert
2 Wren Mr Thos. || Wills Mrs

INNS & TAVERNS.

2 Bell, John Plucknett
Champion of Wales, My. A. Lovering
Coach and Horses, F. Prout
Full Moon, Elizabeth Evans
Globe, Thomas Lang
2 King's Head, John Kelly
Prince of Wales, Francis Screech
Royal George, Richard Perry
Red Lion, John Fisher
Royal Hotel, Wm. Bolt
Ship, Hannah Gowman
Shipwright's Arms, Thos. Bloor
Swan, Wm. Cann

Swan, Philip Guy
Tavern, Wm. Cocks
Unicorn, Thomas Halls
ACADEMIES.
Baker Miss
England Ann
Hake W. & T.
Hooper John D.
Moore Mr
BAKERS.
Beer John
Hamlyn Grace
BEERHOUSES.
1 Diamond Thos.
1 Halls John
Kelley Wm.
Kelley John
Nichols David
1 Paddon Henry
BLACKSMITHS.
1 Braund Thos.
1 Davis Wm.
Evans Wm.
Lemon Robert
Ley Wm.
1 Rooke Wm.
1 Saunders John
BLOCK MAKERS.
Cook Thomas
Fisher John
1 Haynes W. C.
Hincks Henry
1 Lang Pp. jun.
BOAT BUILDERS.
Clibbett Wm.
Cook Peter Ts.
Geen Thomas
Hincks Henry
Williams Geo.
BOOT & SHOE MKS.
1 Bassett John
Channon James
Cole Wm.
England James
Fursey Samuel
1 Hartnoll Chas.

1 Hartop Thos.
Mayne Thomas
1 Mugford John
1 Oke Wm.
1 Yeo Thomas
BRAZIERS, &c.
Burnecle Wm.
Cock James
BUILDERS.
1 Burch Richard
Cock James
Dart Richard
Dennis Thomas
1 Lock Thomas
1 Williams Jsa.
BUTCHERS.
1 Causey Thos.
1 Fulford John
Martin Henry
Pickard B.
CHEMISTS, &c.
Howes Cphr.
1 Penney Wm.
COOPERS.
Cook Thomas
Craig Wm.
Lemon James
FARMERS.
Balsdon John
Bassett Wm.
2 Bellew Thos.
Berry Richard
Carter George
Causey Henry
2 Cock Thomas
2 Crelock J. & W.
2 Ford Samuel
Gordon Wm.
2 Hoare Thos.
2 Hoare Wm.
2 Hockridge Sml.
2 Irwin John
2 Lashbrook W.

2 Lethern Rd.
2 Lemon Thos.
2 Lock George
Mill John
Mill George
Partridge James,
  Burrow
Penhorwood Wm.
Pickard James
Pickard John
2 Rickard Btw.
2 Rickard Geo.
Sage John
2 Tucker George
2 Williams Wm.
GARDENERS.
Cole Wm.
1 Dowell Thos.
1 Willis John
GROCERS.
Dennis Thomas
1 Down George
Gritt Mary
Howes Cphr.
Palmer J. E.
1 Penney Wm.
Rodd Misses
1 Williams Hy.
Williams Thos.
JOINERS, &c.
Bartlett Stn.
Bridgman John
Evans Richard
1 Lock John
Nichols George
Owen George
1 Perkin Wm.
1 Williams Geo.

LINEN DRAPERS.
Fisher Jane
Gritt Mary
1 Serjeant Jas.
Swindale Eliz.
Wyatt James

MALTSTERS.
1 Kelly Wm.
Williams Henry
Williams Isaac
MASONS.
Bowden George
Bowden Thomas
Gowman Pp.
1 Lemon Richard
Lemon Thomas
MERCHANTS.
Cook Thomas
Darracott John
Limbery Richard
1 Rodd John
Yeo Wm.
PAINTERS, &c.
Nicholls Geo.
1 Serjeant Robt.
1 Williams Thos.
SAIL MAKERS.
1 Popham Thos.
Williams Wm.
SHOPKEEPERS.
Craig Wm.
Gibbs Thdsa.
Lamey Mary
Lang Peter
Hartnoll M. A.
Holman Mary
Townsend Ann
SURGEONS.
Ashwood J. N.
1 Limbery Thos.
1 Pratt Chas. E.
TAILORS.
Beara Wm.
1 Burdon James
Cutland John
Day Arthur
Heard James
1 Sanders Robt.

CARRIERS
& *Boats* daily
to Bideford

PARKHAM, a scattered village, near the source of the small river Yeo, 6½ miles S.W. of Bideford, has in its parish 995 souls, and 5808 acres of land, bounded on the north by Barnstaple Bay, and including the small hamlets of *Ash, Horncross, East Goldsworthy, Buckish Mills, Newhaven,* and many scattered farms. The Trustees of the late Lord Rolle are lords of the manor ; but most of the soil belongs to the Buck, Kekewick, Coffin, Lee, and other families. *Ash Moor* was enclosed in 1850. The *Church* (St. James,) is a large ancient structure, with a tower and six bells. The *rectory*, valued in K.B. at £20. 6s. 8d., and in 1831 at £738, is in the patronage and incumbency of the Rev. F. W. Thomas, who has a good residence, and 119A. of glebe. The tithes were commuted in 1841, for £730 per annum. In the parish are three chapels, two belonging to the Wesleyans, and one to the Bible Christians. The National School was built in

1849-'50. The *Poor's Land* is 5A., and the poor have 40s. a year, left by Rt. Wonnacott and Mary Cholwill.

Ashton Lawrence, relieving officer
Braund Wm. corn miller
Briton Chas., Esq. *South Yeo*
Ching Mr John || Martin J. school
Eastman Jas. vict. *Hoop*
Grigg Reuben, vict. *New Inn*
Lane James, glazier and painter
Sanders Daniel, tailor
Thomas Benj. M., Esq. *Foxdown*
Thomas Rev Fras. W., *Rectory*
Wood Thomas, Esq. *Peppercombe*

BEERHOUSES.
Eveleigh John
Harris Samuel
Lane Lewis

BLACKSMITHS.
Andrew Thomas
Chalke Michael
Grigg Richard
Veal Henry

BOOT & SHOEMKS.
Dyer Robert
Gill Wm.
Kivell Thomas

Martin James
Moase John

BUTCHERS.
Bate Wm.
Becalick Samuel
Heal John
Lane John

CARPENTERS.
Cloak S. & J.
Heal Robert
Heydon John
Lott Robert
Moase John

CORN MILLERS.
Metherall Thos.
Sanders Thomas

FARMERS.
Andrew Ann
Andrew Edmund
Austin James
Boundy Richard
Caddy Elizabeth
Ching Thomas, *Goldsworthy*
Clement Abm.
Coy Wm.
Dark Rebecca
Downing James
Downing Thos.
Dunn Bartw.
Dunn Richard
Edwards George
Furse George
Grigg Thomas
Harding John
Hartop Ann
Heal John

Heywood Joseph
Heydon Richard
Hockridge T.&W.
Jeffery Richard
Kivell Wm.
Lane Wm.
Lang J. & W.
Lemon Thomas
Lewis Wm.
Littlejohn John
Moase James
Mugridge Chas.
Norman Robert
Norman Samuel
Pickard James
Pickard Wm.
Pridham My. A.
Robins Thomas
Shortridge James
Squance John

MASONS.
Jewell Thomas
Jewell Henry
Viggars Wm.

PETROCKSTOW, or *Stow St. Petrock*, is a pleasant village and parish, 4 miles N.N.W. of Hatherleigh, containing 616 souls, and 4030 acres of land, including 210A. of woodland, 1360A. of open moor, and the deer park of *Heanton Sachville*, (136A.) where the ancient mansion was burnt down many years ago, as noticed at page 768, where it will be seen that the present handsome mansion, called *Heanton House*, stands in the adjoining parish of Huish, and is the seat of Lord Clinton, the lord of the manors, and owner of most of the soil of both parishes. The old house was for some time a seat of the Rolles, and afterwards of the Earls of Orford. *Merland* belongs to Mr. John Bonifant, and formerly belonged to the Zouch and Fitzwarren families. The *Church* is an ancient fabric, with a beautiful stained glass window, and a much admired Norman font. It has several monuments belonging to the Rolle and other families. The *rectory*, valued in K.B. at £17. 0s. 2½d., and in 1831 at £285, is in the patronage of Lord Clinton, and incumbency of the Rev. Louis Woollcombe, M.A., who has a good residence, and 49A. of glebe. The tithes have been commuted for £271 per annum. The *Parish School* was built by Lord Clinton, in 1844, at the cost of about £700. The Wesleyans and Bible Christians have *chapels* here, and the poor have £2 a year, left by several donors.

Adams Rd. tanner (& *Torrington*)
Bonifant John, gent. *Merland*
Gill James, carpenter
Moon Wm. gamekeeper
Smale James, shopkeeper
Trace Wm. vict., White Hart, *(post)*
Woollcombe Rev Louis, *Rectory*

BLACKSMITHS.
Bird Samuel
Luxton John

BOOT&SHOE MKS.
Bissett George

Lyon Thomas
Trace Wm.

FARMERS.
Ash George
Bissett Richard

Clay John
Dart John
Doble Henry
Freeman John
Freeman Samuel
Freeman Wm.
Hopper John
Madge Philip
Palmer Richard
Piper Wm.
Risdon Joseph
Sanders Robert

Squire Mary
Taunton Thos.
Taunton Wm.
Vivian James
Weare Robert
Williams Edw.
Williams Richd.

WHEELWRIGHTS.
Hawking George
Seldon Wm.
Tucker Pp.

PUTFORD, (EAST) a small village in the Torridge valley, 8½ miles W.S.W. of Great Torrington, has in its parish 197 souls, and 3230 acres of land, mostly belonging to the Trustees of the late Lord Rolle, and partly to John Dayman, Esq., and a few smaller freeholders. The *Church* is considered a chapel to Buckland Brewer, its curacy

having been long consolidated with the vicarage of that parish. The principal residents are John and Wm. Fry, Wm. Furse, and Wm. May, *farmers*; and George Beer, *blacksmith*.

SHEBBEAR, the village which gives name to this hundred, is on the northern acclivity of the Torridge valley, 7½ miles W.N.W. of Hatherleigh, and has in its parish 1160 souls, and 5826 acres of land, including many scattered farms, and the hamlet of *Cott*. Lord Clinton is lord of the manor, but most of the soil belongs to the Rev. T. H. Kingdon, and the Hearn, Heyset, Reed, Walter, Stevens, Coham, and other families. The *Church* (St. Lawrence,) is a small structure, with a tower and five bells, and was appropriated to Tor Abbey. The *vicarage*, valued in K.B. at £11. 8s. 4d., and in 1831 at £285, with Sheepwash annexed to it, is in the patronage of the Lord Chancellor, and incumbency of the Rev. P. D. Foulkes, B.A., who has a thatched residence, and 3A. of glebe. The tithes were commuted in 1846, the vicarial for £288.11s. 8d., and the rectorial for £216. The latter belong mostly to the freeholders, and the Heyset, Brent, and Braund families. The Baptists, Wesleyans, and Bible Christians have *chapels* here, and there is a National School in the parish. The *Parish Lands*, for repairing the church and relieving the poor, comprise about 100 acres, and 20 tenements, let for only about £30 a year, subject to fines. The poor have 23s. a year, left by *Thomas Walter*, and one Smallacombe.

Bale Mrs. *Shebbear Grange*
Besley Francis, surgeon
Edmunds John, parish clerk
Foulkes Rev Peter D., B.A. *vicar*
Herring Miss ‖ Gressell Edward
Mills George, maltster
Thorne Samuel, printer

BLACKSMITHS.
Crocker John
Crocker Hugh
Larkworthy John
Paige Robert
Still James
White Charles

BOOT &SHOE MKS.
Acland George
Acland Wm.
Hocking Wm.
Most Wm.
Underhill Richd.

CARPENTERS, &c.
Balkwill Isaac
Callaway John
Callaway Robert
Pett Wm.

White James

CORN MILLERS.
Damarel James
Slade Wm.

FARMERS.
Abraham Isaac
Abraham John
Abraham Thos.
Adams Wm.
Ball John
Balkwill Isaac
Balkwill Thomas
Balsdon Daniel
Balsdon James
Berry Matthew
Bird Samuel
Blackford Grace
Bridgman John

Bridgman Wm.
Callicott Wm.
Cobbledick Hugh
Copp Thomas
Dunn John
Durrant John
Fowler Bartw.
Frain Mary
Hearn John
Hearn Pp.
Hocking Wm.
Jeffery Wm.
Johns Samuel
Larkworthy Wm.
Leach George
Ley John
Locke Richard
Mills George
Mills Robert
Millman Wm.
Moore John
Paige George
Paige Robert
Parsons J. & R.
Penhall Wm.

Quance Richard
Reed John
Sherwin John
Spear Isaac
Spear Wm.
Spearman Abm.
Still John
Taylor John
Thorne Samuel
Walkin David
Walter Edward
White John
Williams George

MASONS.
Acland John
Blight Robert

SHOPKEEPERS.
Balkwill Thos.
Griffin Edward
Mills Robert

TAILORS.
Mountjoy John
Spear James

SHEEPWASH, or *Shipwash*, formerly a market town, is a long village in the Torridge valley, 5 miles W.N.W. of Hatherleigh. Its parish contains 497 souls, and 1771 acres of land, including 182A. of woodland, and 391A. of common. A market was held here every Monday, till the latter end of last century; and here are still two annual fairs, on the second Thursday in March, and the first Thursday in October. The two market houses, after being long neglected and dilapidated, were converted into dwellings some years ago. Several houses in the town were destroyed by fire in 1743. Lord Clinton is lord of the manor, formerly held by the Avenel, Metstead, Holland, and other families. *Upcot Avenel* is the pleasant seat of G. L. Coham, Esq., and was formerly the property of the Hortons and Thornes. The *Church* (St. Lawrence,) is a small antique structure, with a low tower and one bell; and the benefice is a curacy, annexed to the vicarage of Shebbear. The tithes were commuted in 1839; the vicarial for £99, and the rectorial for £110. The latter belong to Charles Burdon, Esq. The Baptists and Bible Christians have chapels here.

Coham Geo. Lewis, Esq.*Upcot Avenel*
Feild Rev Jas. Meyrick, B.A. curate
Finnamore Rd. vict. Half Moon
Hooper Thos. shopkpr. and draper

Longman Mr John
Rudall Robert, surgeon
Southcombe Wm. & Arthur, tailors
Spear John, inland revenue officer

Wonnacott Geo. vict. White Hart		FARMERS.	Herring Edm.
BLACKSMITHS.	Essery Wm.	Chapman Jph.(&	Hooper Thos.
Steer Thos.	Johnson Saml.	timber mert)	Luxton John
Steer Gabriel J.		Chapman J. jun.	Paige Wm.
BOOT&SHOE MKS.	CARPENTERS.	Clemett George	Snell Charles
Essery Henry	Beere Joseph	Clemett James	Tucker Wm.
Essery Joseph	Braund Wm.	Davy Thomas	Vanstone Stphn.

TORRINGTON, (LITTLE) a pleasant village, nearly 2 miles S. of Great Torrington, has in its parish 588 souls, and 2880 acres of land, including the village of *Taddiport*, on the south-west side of the river Torridge, opposite Great Torrington. The manor of Little Torrington belongs to the Stevens family, and that of Potheridge to the Trustees of the late Lord Rolle; but several smaller freeholders have estates here. *Cross House*, which was long the residence of the Stevens family, is now the pleasant seat of *Sir Trevor Wheler, Bart.*, whose baronetcy was created in 1660. The *Church* is an ancient structure, and the benefice is a *rectory*, valued in K.B. at £14. 18s. 11½d., and in 1831 at *£452*. The Trustees of the late Lord Rolle are the patrons, and the Rev. Peter Glubb, M.A., is the incumbent, and has a plain old residence, and about 50A. of glebe. The tithes were commuted in 1839, for £400 per annum. The *Magdalen Lands*, which now belong to the poor parishioners, were anciently part of the endowment of a *lepers' hospital at Taddiport*. They comprise two fields, (8A.,) several gardens, and 13 cottages, let for about £34 a year. There are also 2 acres, called Chapel field, which are held by the rector in consideration of preaching 12 sermons yearly in *Taddiport Chapel*, which belonged to the hospital, and is now finely mantled with ivy. This chapel is repaired out of the rents of the Magdalen Lands belonging to Great and Little Torrington, and service is performed in it once a fortnight. The poor of this parish have *£7* a year out of Grey Friars' estate, at Canterbury, purchased with £120 left by John Hart. The *parish school* was built in 1840, by Sir T. Wheler and Mrs. Stevens.

Blake Andrew, schoolmaster		FARMERS.	Judd Wm.
Copp Wm. beer seller		Arnold Nichls. F.	Nicholls Wm.
Glubb Rev Peter, M.A. *rector*		Ball Richard	Pengilly Richd.
Sillifant Richard, mason		Banbery Fras.	Quance Ann
Wheler Sir Trevor, Bart. *Cross House*		Banbery Wm.	Routcliffe Saml.
Wilson Ann, vict. Buckingham Arms		Channings Geo.	Snell Anthony
Wilson George, butcher		Clement Henry	Ward Wm.
BLACKSMITHS.	Vodden John	Cole John	Wilson Wm.
Gribble Wm. &G	CARPENTERS.	Copp Edmund	
Parr Wm.	Broad John	Hackwill E.	TAILORS.
Thorne Richard	Broad Thos.	Heal Philip	Blake Samuel
BOOT&SHOE MKS.	Broad Wm.	How James	Gloyne John
Elliott Saml.			

WEAR GIFFORD, a pleasant village and parish, on the eastern side of the river Torridge, 3 miles N.W. of Great Torrington, contains 576 inhabitants, and 1587 acres of land, including the hamlet of *Clifft*, and a number of scattered farms. The river is navigable to this village for small craft, and by means of a canal, barges, &c., go up as high as Torrington. A large earthenware manufactory has lately been established here; and in the parish is a small woollen factory. The manor of *Weare* was held by the Giffords at an early period, and afterwards passed to the Fortescues, who were seated here for several generations, in an ancient mansion, now occupied by a farmer, and containing a profusion of richly carved old wainscot, said to have been brought from various parts of the kingdom. Earl Fortescue is now lord of the manor, but part of the parish belongs to the Trustees of the late Lord Rolle, and a few smaller owners. The *Church* (Holy Trinity,) is a plain structure, containing monuments of the Fortescue, Rolle, and other families. The *rectory*, valued in K.B. at £13. 5s., and in 1831 at £180, is in the patronage of Earl Fortescue, and incumbency of the Rev. Wm. Fortescue, of George Nympton. The parsonage is a small building, and the glebe is 17 acres. The Wesleyans have a small chapel here. In 1671, *John Lovering* left £100 for the endowment of a Free School for 16 children of this parish; £50 for the poor of this parish; £40 for the poor of Great Torrington; and £10 for the poor of Huntshaw. These legacies were laid out in the purchase of 8A. 11P. of land at Barnstaple, now let for about *£30* a year, half of which belongs to the school, and one-fourth to the poor of Wear Gifford.

Bate John, butcher	Edgworth Mr Thos. ‖ Lamerton Mrs
Braginton Geo. lime merchant, &c	Fry Susan, corn miller
Chapple Wm. shoolmaster	Mitchell Rev Henry, M.A.

Palmer Rev Chas. E. curate, *Rectory*
Saunders Sarah, shopkeeper
Short Wm. tailor
Turton John, woollen manufacturer
Warman Jph. vict. Fortescue Arms
Watts Thos. || West Miss
Wear Gifford Pottery Co. earthenware
  manufacturers
    BLACKSMITHS.
Ford Wm. | Tucker Adam

BOOT & SHOE MKS.
Cole James
Isaac George
Parr John
  CARPENTERS.
Downing George
Lamerton Wm.
    FARMERS.
Alford Wm.

Ashton John
Balsdon John
Channings Danl.
Downing Thos.
Harris Wm.
Kidwell Ann
Kidwell Wm.
Newcombe Wm.
Tout Edward

BLACK TORRINGTON HUNDRED

Is a large and picturesque district, averaging about twenty miles in length, and 15 in breadth, It is bounded on the north by the river Torridge; on the east by the small river Okement; on the south by Dartmoor, and Lifton Hundred; and on the west by Cornwall, from which it is divided by the river Tamar, which rises near the sources of the Torridge, at the north-western extremity of this Hundred, within five miles of the sea. The whole Hundred is in the Northern Parliamentary Division of Devon, and in Holsworthy and Hatherleigh Polling Districts. It is mostly in the Arch-deaconry of Barnstaple, and partly in that of Totnes. The following enu-meration of its 37 parishes, &c., shews their territorial extent, and their population in 1841 : —

Parishes.	Acres.	Pop.	Parishes.	Acres.	Pop.
*Abbots Bickington	1034	75	§Inwardleigh	6059	715
§Ashbury	1650	65	§Jacobstowe	2836	309
*Ashwater	8587	1046	*Luffincott	990	93
§Beaworthy	6270	405	*Milton Damerell	4252	813
§Belston	1756	208	§Monk Okehampton	1488	259
*Black Torrington	6595	1252	§Northlew	5300	1051
*Bradford	3469	530	*Pancraswick	3782	540
+Bradworthy	9586	1081	‡Petherwin North	8000	1066
*Bridgerule (part of)	2970	221	+Putford West	2620	490
§Broadwood Kelly	2666	471	§Pyworthy	5020	758
*Clawton	5358	639	§Sampford Courtenay	7962	1239
*Cookbury	1833	301	*Sutcombe	3593	523
§Exbourne	2280	593	*Tetcott	1885	300
*Giles (St.) in Heath	3044	375	*Thornbury	2000	524
*Halwell	3426	319	‡Werrington	5070	685
§Hatherleigh	7041	1882	*Northcott, ham. ||	660	100
§High Hampton	3200	365	§Kigbear, ham. ||	1460	—
*Hollacombe	1218	132			
*Holsworthy	8870	1857	Total	144,260	21,351
§Honeychurch	500	69			

☞ UNIONS.—Those marked thus * are in *Holsworthy Union;* § in *Okehampton Union;* ‡ in *Launceston Union;* and † in *Bideford Union.* These Unions form County Court Districts.

|| *Northcott* is in *Boyton Parish,* which is mostly in Cornwall; and *Kigbear* hamlet is in Okehampton parish.

ABBOTS-BICKINGTON, a small parish, 9 miles S.W. of Torrington, has only 75 souls, and 1034 acres of land, formerly belonging to Hartland Abbey. The Trustees of the late Lord Rolle are now lords of the manor, owners of most of the soil, impropriators of the great tithes, and patrons of the perpetual curacy, valued at £96, and now held by the Rev. P. D. Foulkes, of Shebbear. The *Church* (St. James,) is a small fabric, with three bells. The *farmers* are, John Allen, *Youldon;* Arthur Petherick, *South Place;* and Thomas Reed, *Barton.*

ASHBURY parish, 5 miles S.W. of Hatherleigh, has only 65 souls, and 1650 acres of land, nearly all the property and manor of John Morth Woollcombe, Esq., of *Ashbury House*, a fine old mansion, with tasteful grounds, where his family has been seated since 1685. The *Church* (St. Mary,) is a small structure, which has lately been repewed, at the expense of Mr. Woollcombe. The *rectory*, valued in K.B. at £5. 13s. 4d., and in 1831 at £109, is in the patronage of the Crown, and incumbency of the Rev. H. Woollcombe, who is also rector of High Hampton and Pillaton. The *farmers* are, Stephen and John Palmer and John Wood.

ASHWATER, 7 miles S.E. by S. of Holsworthy, is a large village and parish, containing 1046 souls, and 5870 acres of land, including the hamlet of *Quoditch*, and many scattered houses. It has *fairs* on the first Tuesday in May and the first Monday in August. Richard Preston, Esq., is lord of the manor of Ashwater; Sir Wm. Molesworth is lord of the manor of *Hunscott*, and owner of *Henford Barton ;* and W. B. Coham, Esq , owns the manor of *Greenworthy.* The *Church* (St. Peter,) has a tower and five bells, and contains a rich monument in memory of the last of the Carminow family ; one to John Short, and another to Peter Spoure, Esq. The *rectory*, valued in K.B. at £26. 6s. 8d., and in 1831 at £491, is in the patronage and incumbency of the Rev. Thomas Melhuish, who has a good residence, and 94A. of glebe The tithes were commuted in 1842 for £469 per annum. The Baptists and Bible Christians have small chapels here.

Beer John, corn miller
Clifton Richard, vict. New Inn
Cory John, schoolmaster
Davey John, postman
Hill John, ironmonger and draper
Melhuish Rev Thomas, *Rectory*
Sanders Samuel, machine maker
Wickett John, blacksmith
Wilcocks Walter, shopr. & ironmgr

FARMERS.
Baskerville Sdh.
Baskerville Ts.
Baskerville Rd.
Beale Shadh.
Beale Sampson
Beer Clement
Cole Wm.
Colwell Charles
Davey Michael

Facey Alex.
Facey Thomas
Geary Richard
Metherell Wm.
Palmer Richard
Parsons Elntr.
Scoines John
Veale Cotton
Veale Oliver
Veale Wm.

BEAWORTHY, a village and parish among the hills, 8 miles S.W. of Hatherleigh, contains 405 inhabitants, and 6270 acres of land, mostly belonging to Sir Wm. Molesworth, and partly to J. M. Woollcombe, Esq., J. Smale, C. Brown, and a few smaller owners. The *Church* (St. Alban,) is a small antique structure, with a tower and three bells. The *rectory*, valued in K.B. at £6. 6s., and in 1831 at £146, is in the patronage of Sir Wm. Molesworth, and incumbency of the Rev. Wm. Molesworth, M.A., of St. Breock, Cornwall. The Rectory House was rebuilt about four years ago. The glebe is 80A. of poor land, and the tithes were commuted in 1843 for £105 per annum. The Bible Christians have a small chapel here ; and the poor have the interest of £16. The *farmers* are, John and Richard Bailey, Chas. Brown, Rd. Down, Brian Duffty, Fanny Glass, John, Josias, Robert, Seth, and Wm. Harry ; Jeremiah James, Sus. Metherell, Wm. Rowe, John Smale, Stephen Voddan, and Joseph Walters.

BELSTON, or *Belstone*, is a small village, picturesquely seated, 2 miles S.E. of Okehampton, at the northern extremity of Dartmoor Forest, between and near the sources of the rivers Taw and East Okement, where there are many rocky tors and highly interesting druidical remains. Its parish contains 208 inhabitants, and 1756 acres of land, including 784 acres of open commons and wastes, and the hamlet of *Prestacott.* The parishioners enjoy the right of pasturing cattle and sheep, and cutting turf, &c., in the forest, on the payment of a small acknowledgment to the Duchy of Cornwall, under the name of *Venville* (or fenfield) money, as noticed at page 38. The name of Belston is supposed to be derived from *Bel's-ton*, the town of Bel or Belus, where the Druids had a temple for the worship of the sun; or from *Bel-stone*, or *Bel-tor*, the rock of Belus. In support of the latter derivation, there is in the adjacent part of the forest a large *logan stone*, which can be made to vibrate with the pressure of a single finger. In support of the former derivation, there is upon Watchet hill a small *idol temple*, formed of a double circle of erect stones, the inner one referring to the phase of the moon, and the outer to the sun. The river *Taw*, which rises in the northern part of the forest, derives its name from a deity of the Druids, called *Tu-autos*, or the thunderer. The old *Roman road*, between Exeter and Launceston, passed through this parish, entering it at the ford, near the serge mills, and leaving it by the steep hill, west of Sticklepath. The *manor of Belston* belonged to an ancient family of its own name till the reign of Henry III., when their three co-heiresses married into the families of Specot, Chamberlayne, and Fulford. Two shares of the manor now belong to the Trustees of the late Lord Rolle ; and the other share, with the *advowson*, belongs to the Rev. H. G. Fothergill, the present *rector*, who has held the living since 1836, and has a good residence, and 75A. of glebe. The *rectory*, valued in K.B. at £9. 0s. 1d., and in 1831 at £166, has now £110 a year in lieu of tithes, pursuant to a commutation in 1841. The *Church* (Virgin Mary,) is a small but interesting specimen of Anglo-Saxon architecture, with a tower and five bells. The interior was newly seated with deal a few years ago, but still retains some of the ancient

oak seats, with carved ends, and a finely carved old oak screen. The chancel has two windows, a sedilia, and a few panes of painted glass. The fabric is built of granite, and an ancient cross, formerly belonging to it, is now placed in the wall of an adjacent stable. There is a small *chapel* in the parish, used by Baptists and Wesleyans.

BELSTON DIRECTORY.

Bowden John, blacksmith
Fothergill Rev Hy. George, *Rectory*
Reddaway Geo. vict. New Inn

FARMERS.
Brookland Wm.
Langmead John
Langmead Wm.
Reddaway Robt.

Reddaway R. jun.
Reddaway Wm.
Reed Wm.
Westaway Henry

BLACK TORRINGTON, which gives name to this large hundred, is a considerable village, in the picturesque valley of the river Torridge, 5½ miles W. by N. of Hatherleigh. It has in its parish 1252 souls, and about 7200 acres of land, rising in bold hills on the south, and including 400A. of woodland, 708A. of wastes and commons ; the hamlets, &c., of *East and West Chilla, Middlecott,* and *Gorford Ley ;* and many scattered houses. The manor has been held by the Mayne, Zouch, Harris, and other families, and is now the property of Lord Ashburton. *Coham* was for many generations the property and seat of the Cohams, and now belongs to W. B. Coham, Esq., who occasionally visits the ancient mansion, which is encompassed by fertile pastures and rich woodland. The Risdon, Hayne, Braund, Molesworth, Woollcombe, and other families, have estates in the parish, mostly freehold. The *Church* has a tower and six bells, and the living is a *rectory*, valued in K.B. at *£*22. 8s. 9d., and in 1831 at £303. Lord Poltimore is patron, and the Rev. John Penleaze is the incumbent, but resides abroad. The Rectory House is a commodious mansion with pleasant grounds, and the glebe is 191 acres. The tithes were commuted in 1843 for £450 per annum. The Baptists and Bible Christians have chapels in the village ; and the latter have another at East Chilla, nearly 3 miles from the village. Here is a *National School ;* and in 1849, John Daw, Esq., left a house and garden for the occupation of the master. *West Chilla Moor* was enclosed in 1849, at the cost of only £108. Other commons are about to be enclosed. In 1665, *Peter Speccott* gave £180 to be invested in land for the poor of Holsworthy and Black Torrington; fiveninths for the former, and four-ninths for the latter. The property purchased consists of a cottage and 16A. 1R. 1P., let for about £20 a year. The *Church Lands,* &c., comprise 6A. and six houses, let for only £29. 4s. per annum, subject to fines. *Marked* 2, *are at East Chilla ;* 3, *West Chilla ;* 4, *at Middlecott ; and* 5, *at Gratten.*

Braund John, schoolmaster
Chapman Edw. maltster ; & Mr Jph.
Dart John, blacksmith
Gilbert James, auctioneer, registrar, and agt. for Globe & Naval Ins. Cos.
Hockin Richd. vict. Pack Horse
Osborn James, vict. Union Inn
Owen —, surgeon
Peacock Misses, gentlewomen
Risdon Geo. S. corn miller, *Haynes*
Vanstone James, carpenter
Vanstone Elizabeth, *Post Office*
Veale Rev Westcott Harris, B.A. curate, *Rectory*

FARMERS.
Arscott Wm.
Balsdon Jas.
Balsdon John
Braund Geo.

Duffty John
Duffty Mrs.
Gilbert James, *Coham House*
Horn Wm.

2 Horrell John
Hunkin Saml.
Hutchings John
Hutchings Saml.
3 Hutchings Wm.
Jeffery Thos.
Johns John
5 Johns Thos.
5 Knight John
Leach Elias
Leach Robert
3 Littlejohns Ts.
Luxtons James
Paige George
2 Parsons John
Quick James
Risdon Jph.
Rogers James
Scott James

Sparkes Jas.
Squance John
Tanton J., *Totley*
Tucker Anty. C., *Totley*
3 Walter John
4 Ward Geo.
4 Ward Stpn.
Woolridge Benj.
2 Yelland Jas.
SHOEMAKERS.
May Samuel
Trott Wm.
SHOPKEEPERS.
Chapman Wm.
Hall Wm.
TAILORS.
Burley Wm.
Davey George

BOYTON, a village and parish, 5 miles N.W. of Launceston, has 600 souls, and about 4200 acres of land, all in *Cornwall*, except NORTHCOTT hamlet, which has 100 inhabitants, and 740 acres of land, in the valley of the river Tamar, occupied by the following *farmers :*—Digory Downing, John Downing, John Martin, Thos. Stapleton, and Wm. Walters. Northcott supports its highways with Werrington. The Rev. Edw. Rudall, M.A., is the *vicar.*

BRADFORD, in the Torridge valley, 8 miles W. by N. of Hatherleigh,

is a village and parish containing 530 souls, and 3468 acres of land. The manor of Bradford, anciently held by the Dabernon and other families, was sold by the late Geo. Cary, Esq., to Messrs. Vivian, Grylls, and Kendall, bankers, of Helston. *Dunsland*, a large and ancient mansion, with an estate of about 1000 acres, is the seat and property of W. H. B. Coham, Esq., who is also lord of the manor of Lashbrook. Dunsland was successively held by the Cadiho, Arscott, and Bickford families. The mother of the present owner was heiress of the latter family. *Hengescot*, formerly belonged to a family of that name, and is now the property of Earl Stanhope. *Bovacott* is the residence of L. R. Heysett, Esq., who also owns *Gidcott*, where there was anciently a chapel, and the lands at Flares and Rightdown. Several smaller freeholders have estates in the parish. The *Church* (All Saints,) is an ancient structure, with a tower and five bells, and contains several neat monuments. The *rectory*, valued in K.B. at £13. 8s. 4d., and in 1831 at £310, is in the patronage of the Rectors of East-Down, Bratton-Fleming, and Goodleigh, as Trustees of Bampfield's Charity; and is now in the incumbency of the Rev. J. C. Yule, M.A., who has 70a. of glebe, and a fine old residence, lately repaired. The tithes were commuted in 1842 for £305 per annum. The poor of Bradford and Cookbury have the dividends of £459. 9s. 5d. three per cent. consols, purchased with £400, left by Eliz. Bickford in 1821. They have also the interest of £25, left by Wm. Wills in 1808.

Coham Wm. Holland Bickford, Esq. *Dunsland House*
Gilbert James, machine maker
Heysett Lewes Risdon, Esq. *Bovacott House*
Hutchings Ts. vict. Bickford's Arms
Wills Wm. vict. Highstead Inn
Yule Rev. John, C.D., M.A., *Rectory*

FARMERS.
Arscott Matw.
Furse Joseph
Hole John
Hutchings Thos.
Isaac Abm.
Mason Chas.
Parnacott John

Sanders John
Trick James
Wills John
SHOPKEEPERS.
Damerell Grace
Longman Wm.
Page Joseph

BRADWORTHY, a scattered village, near the sources of the small river Waldon, 6½ miles N. by W. of Holsworthy, has in its parish 1081 souls, and 9586 acres of land, including a large portion of hilly moorland, and the small hamlets of *Denworthy, Alfardisworthy, Kimsworthy,* and *Youlston.* A *fair* is held in the village on September 9th. The manor, with a fair on St. John's day, was granted to Lord Brewer by King John. After passing to various families, the manor was sold in severalties, and it now belongs to C. H. Hotchkys, Esq., the Trustees of the late L. S. Ashton, A. B. Wren, Esq., and a few smaller freeholders. The *Church* (St. John,) is an ancient structure, with a tower and five bells, and the living is a *vicarage*, valued in K.B. at £25. 5s. 5d., and in 1831 at £283, with the perpetual curacy of Pancrasweek annexed to it. The patronage is in the Crown, and the Rev. J. B. Clyde, B.A., is the incumbent, and has a good residence, and 25a. 2r. 3p. of glebe. The tithes were commuted in 1842, the vicarial for £195, and the rectorial for £381. The latter belong to the Trustees of the late L. Ashton, Esq.

Clyde Rev. Jas. B., B.A. *Vicarage*
Hotchkys C. H. Esq. *Cleverdon Hs*
Lee Samuel, wheelwright
Oke Wm. blacksmith
Walter Athaliah, shopkeeper
Walter Jno. maltster & vict. New Inn
Wren A. B. Esq. *Berrydon House*
FARMERS.
Allen Roger

Ashton John
Aston Wm.

Buckler Nichls.
Caseby Wm.
Ching John
Ching Wm.
Cleverdon Thos.
Grylls John
Harding John
Hockin Joseph
Hopper John

Jewell Thos.
Moore John
Osmond Thos.
Routley John
Short Richd.
Veale George
Walter Chas.
Walter Wm.
Wickett Peter

2 L

BRIDGERULE, a village and parish on both sides of the Tamar valley, 5½ miles W. by S. of Holsworthy, has 497 souls, and upwards of 3000 acres of land, of which 221 souls and about 2000 acres are in Devon, and the rest are in *Cornwall*, being on the west side of the river, near the Bude Canal. It was anciently called Bridge Reginald, from Reginald Adobed, who held it at Domesday Survey. The Church and the hamlets of *Tines* and *Dux* are in Devon. Sir Wm. Molesworth is lord of the manor, but most of the soil belongs to Mrs. E. Usherwood, T. H. Kingdon, and a number of smaller owners. The *Church* is an antique structure, with a tower and five bells. The *vicarage*, valued in K.B. at £14, and in 1831 at £152, is in the gift of the Rev. T. H. Kingdon, B.D., and incumbency of the Rev. S. N. Kingdon, B.D., who has 33a. of glebe, and a good residence, erected in 1842. The Church House, built in the reign of Henry VIII., is partly occupied as a school and partly by paupers.

Cole Philippa, vict. Bridge Inn
Coomb John, post-office
Cornish Samuel, wheelwright
Goodman Sus. shopkeeper
Kingdon Rev. Saml. Nicholson, B.D. *Vicarage*
Luxton Simeon, wheelwright

FARMERS.
Badcock Wm.
Bailey John
Hayman Wm.
Honey John, *Dux*
Northey E. L.

Rogers Thos.
Tubb Henry
Webb Henry
Wickett Wm., *Tines*
Wood John

BROADWOOD-KELLY is a village and parish, 5½ miles E. by N. of Hatherleigh, containing 471 souls, and 2666 acres of land, including the hamlet of *Splats*. Benj. Cleave, Esq., is lord of the manor, formerly held by the Kelly, Belston, Gilbert, and other families; but a great part of the parish belongs to the Davie, Hole, Arnold, Sampson, and Parker families. The soil is freehold, and generally poor. The *Church* stands on an elevated site, and was thoroughly repaired, repewed, and new roofed about 16 years ago, when five new bells were fixed in the tower. The *rectory*, valued in K.B. at £19. 7s. 6d., and in 1831 at £257, is in the patronage and incumbency of the Rev. N. J. B. Hole, B.C.L., who has a neat modern residence, and 73a. of glebe. The poor have the interest of £24, left by several donors, and vested with the overseers.

Bolt Thos. vict. New Inn
Down Wm. & Erland B. wheelwgts
Hole Rev. Nathl. Jno. Brassy, B.C.L. *Rectory*
Luxton George, gent. *Romsey*
Stevens John, tailor and shopkpr

FARMERS.
Arnold John
Baker Richard
Bulleid John
Channings Cphr.
Kemp John
Lang Thomas

Paddon Bartw.
Parker John
Raymond Jonas
Sampson John
Sampson Saml.
Sampson Wm.
Summershay Wm

CLAWTON, a village and parish on the small river Claw, 4 miles S. by E. of Holsworthy, has 639 souls, and 5358 acres of land, mostly the property of Sir Wm. Molesworth, the lord of the manor of *Affaland*, formerly held by the Arscotts. The *Church* is an ancient fabric, with a tower and three bells, and the living is a perpetual curacy, valued at £75, in the patronage and incumbency of the Rev. Thos. Melhuish, of Ashwater, who is also impropriator of the tithes, which were commuted in 1842 for £377. 18s. 9d. per annum. There is neither glebe nor parsonage. The Wesleyans and Bible Christians have chapels here. The poor have 28s. a year from several benefactions.

Abbott Jas. tailor and shopkeeper
Baskerville John, wheelwright
Baskerville Ts. & Cole Wm. smiths
Melhuish Rev. Thos. Warren, curate
Penwarden Robt. vict. Dolphin

FARMERS.
Bayly Daniel
Bishop Wm.
Braund Arscott
Braund Geo.

Marshall B. M.
Maypowder Jno.
Skinner Jno. and Wm.

COOKBURY, 4 miles N.E. of Holsworthy, has in its parish 301 souls, and 1833 acres of land, mostly belonging to the Earl of Devon, Lord Stanhope, W. H. B. Coham, Esq., and the Misses May; the latter of whom own the manor of *Stapledon.* The *Church* (St. John,) is a small fabric, and the benefice is a perpetual curacy, annexed to the rectory of Milton Damerell. The glebe is 24 acres, and the tithes were commuted in 1842 for £118. 2s. 6d. per annum. The *Church Meadow* (3A.) was given at an early period, on condition that the owners of Dunsland should have the use of two pews. The poor have a share of two *charities*, noticed with Bradford. DIRECTORY:—Richd. Gilbert, blacksmith; John Penwarden, beerseller; and Wm. Harris, Emanl. Hole, John Penhale, and Richard Sanders, *farmers.*

EXBOURNE, a pleasant village and parish, on the east side of the picturesque valley of the river Okement, 5 miles E.S.E. of Hatherleigh, has 593 inhabitants, and 2280A. of land. Here is a cattle *fair* on the 3rd Monday in April. The assignees of Joseph Risdon, Esq., are lords of the manor, but most of the soil belongs to John Tattershall, S. and R. Westlake, and other freeholders. The *Church* (St. Mary,) has a tower and five bells, and the *rectory*, valued in K.B. at £27. 11s. 8d., and in 1831 at £299, is in the gift of John Hudson, Esq., and incumbency of the Rev. H. Brailsford, LL.B., who has a good residence, built nine years ago. The tithes have been commuted for £275 per annum. The *School* was built in 1839. The poor have the interest of £48, left by several donors.

Brailsford Rev Hodgson, LL.B., *rec.*	*Haithaman Wm.	Ward John
Cawker Samuel, vict. Red Lion	Hooper John	TAILORS.
Drew Chas.surgeon‖Merrifield Miss A.	Luxton Fras.	Brock Moses
Payne John, solicitor	Madge Fdk.	Easterbrook Wm.
Piper Samuel, *Post Office*	*Merrifield John	THATCHERS.
Westlake Mr. Thomas, *Woodhall*	*Tattershall Jno.	Easterbrook Ths.
Ward Wm. vict. New Inn	Weeks Henry	Medland Moses
BLACKSMITHS.	Westlake John W.	WHEELWRIGHTS
Netherway Wm.	Skinner George	Westlake Richard	*and Carpenters.*
Shobrook Thos.	FARMERS.	MASONS.	Brock Wm.
BOOT & SHOE MKS.	(* are Owners.)	Coombe Wm.	Cawker Samuel
Keener John	Arnold E.(&maltr	Newcombe Cpr.	Fairchild John
Rattenbury Sth.	Dart Theodore	SHOPKEEPERS.	Fairchild Jph.
BUTCHERS.	*Garrett Robt.	Luxton Fras.	Ward John
Madge Walter	Gibbings Eliz.	Madge Fdk.	Ward Thos.
	Gibbings Saml.		

ST. GILES IN THE HEATH, a village and parish, 5 miles N.N.E. of Launceston, and 9 miles S. by E. of Holsworthy, has 375 souls, and 3044A. of land, including the hamlets of *Panson, Hoggadon,* and *Sitcott.* Part of it is in the Duke of Bedford's manor of Werrington. Sir Wm. Molesworth is lord of the manor of Panson, or Paunston; and the Misses May, and several smaller owners, have estates in the parish. The *Church* is a small structure, with a tower and five bells, and was formerly in the appropriation of Tavistock Abbey. The living is a *donative*, valued at £97, in the patronage of the Earl of Mount Edgcumbe, the Marquis of Lothian, and the Dowager Countess of Suffield; and in the incumbency of the Rev. Edward Rudall, M.A., of Boyton. The patrons are impropriators of the tithes, which have been commuted for £129. 8s. 8d. per annum. The poor have the interest of £22.

Box Wm. blacksmith	FARMERS.	Harris John
Chubb Jas. vict. Arscott Arms	Banbury Thos.	Kittow Jonth.
Chubb Rd. & Wm. wheelwrights	Botterell S. & W.	Lillicrap Wm.
Veale John, shopkeeper	Chubb James	Palmer Wm.

HALWELL, a small village, in a hilly district, 7 miles S.E. by E. of Holsworthy, has in its parish 319 souls, and 3426 acres of land, including *Stronds, Upcott, Stowford, Landhill, Foxhole,* and other scattered farms. Sir Wm. Molesworth is lord of the manor, and owner of great part of the soil. The *Church* has a tower and five bells. The *rectory*, valued in K.B. at £12. 3s. 9d., and in 1831 at £210, is in the patronage of the Lord Chancellor, and incumbency of the Rev. Ambrose Stapleton, of East Budleigh. The glebe is 125 acres, and the Parsonage is a good residence, built in 1849, at the cost of £600.

Cole Rev. E. Hearle, curate, *Rectory*
Down Richard, wheelwright
Fice John, blacksmith
Hill Francis, shopkeeper
Symons Oliver, vict. Hare & Hounds

FARMERS.
Beale Mgt. & W.
Box Richard
Durant John
Ham John
Harry Seth

Harry John
Price Wm.
Soby Benj.
Soby Josias
Soby Thomas
Soby Thos. D.

HATHERLEIGH is a small ancient market town, pleasantly situated on the banks of a rivulet, about a mile S. of the river Torridge, 8 miles N.N.W. of Okehampton, 29 miles W.N.W. of Exeter, and 16 miles S.S.E. of Bideford. Its parish contains 1882 inhabitants, and 7041 acres of land, including a moor of 430 acres; and *Stapleford, Fishley, Upcott,* and other scattered farms. The town suffered severely from fire some years ago, but most of the houses were soon afterwards rebuilt, and the principal street widened and much improved. A new Market House was built in 1840, at the cost of £280, and the *market*, now held on Tuesday, was then re-established, after being disused more than half a century. Two *Public Rooms* were built by a number of shareholders in 1821. Four cattle *fairs* are held here, on May 21st, June 22nd, Sept. 4th, and Nov. 8th, or on the Tuesday following when any of these dates fall on a Saturday, Sunday, or Monday. *Petty Sessions* are held at the George Inn, on the last Wednesday of every alternate month, by the Magistrates of Black Torrington and Shebbear Division, to whom Mr. H. Hawkes, of Okehampton, is clerk. Jph. Lang Oldham, Esq., is lord of the manor of Hatherleigh, which formed part of the endowment of Tavistock Abbey, and was afterwards held by the Arscotts and Molesworths. A portreeve and other officers are elected yearly at the manor court. The *manor of Fishley*, which belonged to the same abbey, was afterwards held by the Yeo and Darke families. *Harwoods*, or *Stone Fishley*, now belongs to Mr. Wm. Pearse, of Chulmleigh. J. H. Veale, Esq., J. M. Woollcombe, Esq., W. C. Morris, Esq., and a number of smaller owners, have estates in the parish, mostly freehold and partly leasehold. The Hundred Court, formerly held here for the recovery of debts under 40s., has given place to the new County Courts. Freestone is got in the parish, and there was formerly a woollen manufactory here. The *Church* (St. John the Baptist,) was enlarged and beautified about 16 years ago, when the *Vicarage House* was rebuilt by the present incumbent, the Rev. Saml. Feild, M.A. The Trustees of the late Jas. Ireland are patrons of the *vicarage*, valued in K.B. at £20, and in 1831 at £241. The glebe is 51 acres, and the tithes were commuted in 1841, the vicarial for £224. 10s., and the rectorial for £335. 10s. The latter were formerly held by Tavistock Abbey, and now belong to the three daughters of the late Dr. Boughton. The Presbyterians had a meeting-house here as early as 1715, and there is now in the town a *Baptist Chapel*, erected about 20 years ago, at the cost of £200. The *Church Houses* comprise ten rooms, let for £5, and adjoining them are some old *Almshouses*, occupied at small rents by poor families. The poor have £7. 10s. yearly in three *rent-charges*, left by

Walter Bennett, Roger Walter, and Joseph Gliddon. For distribution in clothing, they have the dividends of £156. 2s. 10d. three per cent. consols, purchased with £82, left by John Lethbridge and Richd. Lucas. The interest of £100, left by *Chas. Luxmoore* in 1793, is applied in schooling poor children. The *National School*, built in 1838, is attended by 140 children. The POST-OFFICE is at Mr. John Hooper's, and letters are despatched daily by the mail to Exeter, &c. Money Orders are not paid here.

Allen Jas. tinner and brazier
Axford John, carrier to Exeter
Ayre Miss Martha, boarding school
Balkwill John, corn miller
Boles Jas. auctioneer, sheriff's officer, brick and tile maker, &c.
Bolt Wm. Henry, druggist, &c.
Brook Wm. travelling tea dealer
Chasty Robt. watchmaker, &c.
Clark Rev. Thos. (Baptist)
Day Mrs., *Reed House*
Dennaford Wm. brewer & maltster
Feild Rev. Saml., M.A. *Vicarage*
Gould John, surgeon
Heale John, millwright
Luxmoore Jno. gent. || Madge Mrs
Madge John, tax collector, &c.
Mitchell John, postman to Beafield
Morris Wm. C. Esq. *Fishley House*
Oldham Jph. Lang, Esq. *Strawbdg*
Pearse John, solicitor and master extraordinary in Chancery
Phillips John, *National School*
Reddaway J. gent. || Risdon Misses
Sanders Samuel, farrier
Short Jno. S. gent. *Redhill cottage*
Smale Wm. G. hatter
Truman Geo. Robert, surgeon
Veale Jas. Harris, Esq. *Passaford*
Wills John Collins, druggist, &c.

INNS AND TAVERNS.
Bridge Inn, James Boles
George Inn, Thomas Allen
London Inn, Wm. Andrews
New Inn, John Trace
Royal Oak, Thomas Bowden

BAKERS, &c.
Glanville Ptr. Hy. (& confectnr)
Lang Eliz.
Scott Joseph

BLACKSMITHS.
Edwards John
Petherick Wm.
Petherick W. jun.

BOOT&SHOE MKS.
Abell Joseph
Abell Henry
Madge John
Northcott Wm.
Pawley Richard
Petherick John
Squire Henry

CARPENTERS, &c.
Balkwill John
Bulleid Thomas
Chudley Thomas
Edwards James
Edwards John
Horn James

COOPERS.
Hockin John
Strange John

FARMERS.
(*are at Fishley.*)
*Abell Henry
Abell Rd. *Lake*
Acland Jas. *Hean*
Ash Rt. *Stepleford*
Beal Abm. *Pynd*
Bott My. *Upcott*
*Darke Henry
Duffty Eliz.
Ellicott Thomas
Hurford John
Johns James
Johns Ths. *Totley*
Keener Richard
King Thomas
*Luxton George
Luxton Wm.
*Morris Mrs J.
Rattenbury Wm.
*Risdon Mrs
Seldon Thomas
Southcombe Jno.
Squire Henry
Spear Richard
Tucker John

PLUMBERS, &c.
Essery James
Knight James
Strange Robert

SADDLERS.
Cardew Henry
White Wm.

SHOPKEEPERS.
Balkwill John

Essery Wm.
Luxton Thomas
Palmer Mary Ann and Eliz.
Williams Wm. (& ironmonger)

STONEMASONS.
Hooper John
Hooper Samuel
Hooper S. jun., *Stamp Office*

TAILORS.
Harwood John
Hooper John (& stationer, &c)
Petherick Rd.
Short John
Stevens Samuel
Stevens Wm.

THATCHERS.
Luxton Thos.
Medland Richd.

WHEELWRIGHTS.
Luxton John
Luxton Wm.
Pilefant Wm.

COACHES, &c.
Mail to Exeter, 3½ aftn. & to Bude, 9¼ morning
Coach to Plymth., M. Wed. & Fri. 10 morng. & to Barnstaple, Tu. Thu. & Sat. 3 aft
Omnibus to Plymouth, Tue. 7½ evg. & to Barnstaple, Sat. 8 mg
CARRIERS to *Exeter, &c.* call at the Inns daily
John Axford, to Exeter, Thursday, 4 aftn.

HIGH HAMPTON, a small village, on a bold eminence, 4 miles W. of Hatherleigh, has in its parish 365 souls, and 3200 acres of land. J. M.

Woollcombe, Esq., is lord of the manor, but Sir J. H. Williams and C. Burdon, Esq., have estates here. The latter resides at *Burdon*, which has been held by his family since the reign of Richard I. The *Church* (Holy Cross,) is a small structure, which was partly rebuilt in 1833, and has a tower and three bells. An ancient Norman doorway is preserved. The *rectory*, valued in K.B. at £8. 19s. 4½d., and in 1831 at £212, is in the patronage of J. M. Woollcombe, Esq., and incumbency of the Rev. Henry Woollcombe, M.A., who has held it since 1810, and rebuilt the Rectory house about 16 years ago. The glebe is 140 acres, and the tithes were commuted in 1844, for £197. 10s. per annum. The poor have the interest of £14. A small National School was built in 1834.

Blatchford Geo. jun. schoolmaster
Blatchford George, vict. Golden Lion
Bright John, wheelwright
Bright Robert, tailor
Burdon Charles, Esq. *Burdon House*
Isaacs John, farmer
Moorcombe John, farmer

Petherick Arthur, blacksmith
Woollcombe Rev Hy., M.A. *Rectory*

Post-Office at Joseph Crockford's.
Letters by *Bude and Exeter Mail*.
A foot-post to Black Torrington,
Sheepwash, Shebbear, &c. daily

HOLLACOMBE, a small parish, near the sources of the small river Claw, 2½ miles E. by S. of Holsworthy, has only 132 souls, and 1218 acres. Mr. Thomas Brown, of *Hayne*, owns about two thirds of the land, and the rest belongs to the Misses May, of Bath, and a few smaller owners. The *Church* (St. Petrock,) is a small antique fabric, with a low tower and three bells. The rectory, valued in K.B. at £4. 6s. 3d., and in 1831 at £78, is in the patronage of the Lord Chancellor, and incumbency of the Rev. J. C. D. Yule, M.A., of Bradford. The glebe is 32A. The FARMERS are, Thos. Brown, owner and cattle dealer, *Hayne* ; Ann Bailey, *Sellick* ; Wm. Brown, *East Coombe* ; James Boles, *Headon* ; Thomas Jordon, cattle dealer, *Eastdown* ; and John Sandercock, *West Coombe*.

HOLSWORTHY, a small market town, which gives name to a Deanery, Union, County Court District, and Petty Sessional Division, is pleasantly situated near the small river Deer and the Bude Canal, 9 miles E. of Bude Haven; 10 miles W. by S. of Hatherleigh; and 42 miles W. by N. of Exeter. Its parish contains 1857 souls, and about 8800 acres of land, including a tract of hilly moorland; the hamlets of *Staddon, Chilsworthy, Dunsteep,* and *Chesty ;* and many scattered farms. The weekly market for corn, cattle, &c., which had been long held on Saturday, was changed to Wednesday about 30 years ago, but here is also a provision market on Saturday. St. Peter's fair is recognised in a record of the reign of Edward I., as having belonged to the lord of the manor from time immemorial. The present fairs were granted or confirmed by James I. and Charles I. Here are *great markets* for cattle, &c., on the Wednesday after Candlemas-day, and on the first Wednesday in November; and three *fairs*, on April 27th, July 9th, 10th, and 11th, and Oct. 2nd. Earl Stanhope is lord of the *manor*, which anciently belonged to the baronial family of Brewer, and afterwards to the Chaworth, Paganell, Tracey, Holland, and other families. A *portreeve* and other officers are elected at the Court Leet and Baron. A great part of the parish belongs to Sir N. R. F. Davie, W. H. B. Coham, Esq., Mrs. Hart, and many smaller freeholders and leaseholders. *Petty Sessions* are held at the Stanhope Arms Inn, on the third Thursday of every month, by the magistrates of Holsworthy Division, to whom Mr. E. Shearm, of Stratton, is clerk. The *County Court,* for all the parishes in Holsworthy and Stratton Unions, is held at the same inn every fourth Friday, and Mr. John Darke, of Launceston, is the clerk, and Mr. Wm. Bassett high bailiff. In the civil wars, Holsworthy was occupied for the King, till February, 1646, when Sir

Thomas Fairfax sent a party to take possession, after the victory of Torrington. On the north-west side of the town is a curious plantation of beech, called the *Labyrinth*. It covers half an acre, and the puzzle consists in getting into the centre, where there is a tree, with a seat under it. The *Church* (St. Peter,) is a fine Gothic structure, with a tower and eight bells. There were formerly chapels at Chilsworthy and Thorne. The *rectory*, valued in K.B. at £30. 0s. 5d., and in 1831 at £605, is in the patronage and incumbency of the Rev. Roger Kingdon, who has a good residence, and 53A. of glebe. The tithes were commuted in 1842, for £725 per annum. The *Independents* and *Wesleyans* have chapels in the town. The Church House, occupied by poor families, has been vested with the parish officers from an early period. The poor have a share of Speccott's Charity, as noticed with Black Torrington. In 1812, Ann Bayley left 30s. a year for the poor, and 30s. a year for the Women's Friendly Society.

HOLSWORTHY UNION includes the 19 parishes marked thus * at page 778, and also those of Bridgerule-West, Virginstow, Broadwoodwidger, and North Tamerton. These 23 parishes embrace an area of 128 square miles, and in 1841 had 12,333 inhabitants, of whom 865 were in Cornwall. Their total average annual expenditure on the poor, during the three years preceding the formation of the Union, was £4173. Their expenditure in 1838 was £2903; in 1839, £3321; and in 1849, £3662, including £670 for county rates. Mr. Geo. Braund is the *union clerk and superintendent registrar*. Mr. T. Shapton is the *relieving officer;* Mr. Samuel Fry is *registrar of marriages;* and Messrs. S. Fry, P. Sanders, J. Gilbert, F. Hockaday, and R. Shipling, are *registrars of births and deaths*. A Workhouse has not yet been erected for this Union, but there is a small old Poorhouse in the town.

HOLSWORTHY DIRECTORY.

The POST-OFFICE is at Mr. George Downe's.—Letters are received by the Exeter and Bude Mail, &c., and Money Orders are granted and paid.

Allen Wm. gent || Rev. John, (Wes.)
Branwell Richard, solicitor
Braund George, union clerk, &c
Browne and Jennings, solicitors
Browne John Collins, solicitor
Cory Henry G. surgeon
Croker Chas. bookseller, printer, auctioneer, &c
Ford Michael, basket maker, &c
Fry Misses || Griffey E. dressmaker
Goode Thomas, druggist, &c
Hart Mrs A. || Heard Mrs E.
Hearle Stephen Doble, surgeon
Honey John, mechanic
Hoskin John, parish clerk
Jolliffe John, bookseller, printer, binder, &c
Kingdon Charles, solicitor
Kingdon Frederick, gentleman
Kingdon Rev Roger, *Rectory*
Lyle John, sub-clerk to County Court
Oliver Peter Hurdon, chemist, druggist, spirit merchant, &c
Pearce Thomas, surgeon
Petherick Emnl. beer and pot seller
Shipham Rev John, (Wesleyan)
Slee John, hatter || Meyrick Miss
Staddon John, game and pot seller

Treble Sarah, milliner, &c
Vanstone James, watch, &c. maker
Veale Thomas, butcher

BANKS.

Devon and Cornwall Banking Co. (draw on Barclay and Co.;) John Higgs, *agent*
National Provincial Bank of England, (on London & Westmnstr;) S. Fry, jun. *agent*

INNS & TAVERNS.

Crown and Sceptre, Philip Taylor
Globe, Richard Cole Lyle
Golden Fleece, Thomzn Penwarden
King's Arms, Wm. Priest
New Inn, George Drew
Stanhope Arms, Wm. Ireland
White Hart, John Dickson

FIRE AND LIFE OFFICES.

Argus, James Kingdon
Norwich Union, F. Honey
Royal Farmers', C. Croker
Temperance, &c. W. M. B. Sarell
Western, Chas. Croker
West of England, J. Fry

ACADEMIES.	FARMERS.	Webb Richard	SADDLERS.
Friend J.	Axford John	Webb Thomas	Downe George
Hewish —	Badcock Henry	Wickett Richard	Gimblett G. W.
Staddon Mary	Beale Richard	GROCERS, &c.	Ward Arscott
Vinson James	Bray Charles	Batten John	
BLACKSMITHS.	Branwell W.	Friend Mary	TAILORS.
Allen Geo. Jas.	Brimacombe M.	Goode Thomas	Beale Richard
Gimblett John	Browne Chas.	Johns Samuel	Treble John
BOOT&SHOE MKS.	Ching James	Oliver Peter H.	Treble Wm.
Braund John	Cole Matthew	Staddon John	
Cole Josias	Congdon John	HAIR DRESSERS.	WINE AND SPIRIT
Hoskin John	Daniel Edmund	Allen Thomas	MERCHANTS.
Lock Samuel	Daniel John	Badge Wm.	Fry Samuel
Pope John	Duffty John	IRONMONGERS.	Goode Thomas
Trim John	Friend Arthur	Griffey James	Oliver P. H.
CARPENTERS.	Gilbert John	Sarell W. M. B.	
Cole Philip	Harvey W. O.	L. & W. DRAPERS.	COACHES,&c.
Cory Wm.	Headon Wm.	Fry James	*Mail* to Exeter,
Sleeman Danl.	Jewell James	Higgs John	Bude, &c. daily
CORN MILLERS.	Jones Nathaniel	MALTSTERS.	*Coach* to Plymth.
Beer George	Millman Richd.	Fry Samuel	and Bideford,
Brimacombe Rt.	Mountjoy Edm.	Johns Thomas	alternate days
CURRIERS.	Nicholls Richd.	Strange John	
Cole Wm. *tanner*	Northcott Robt.	Ward John	CARRIERS to
Dunn Richard	Routley Richd.	PLUMBERS,	Exeter, Ply-
EATING HOUSES.	Taylor John	PAINTERS, &c.	mouth,&c.from
Beale Richard	Taylor J. jun.	Griffey James	the Inns, twice
Griffey James	Trible Samuel	Wonnacott John	a week

HONEYCHURCH, a small parish, 7 miles E. by S. of Hatherleigh, has only 69 souls, and about 500 acres of land. The Hon. Newton Fellowes is lord of the manor; but part of the soil belongs to and is occupied by Richard Sloman and Thomas and Wm. Brook. The other resident *farmers* are John Sloman and Saml. Vanstone. The *Church* is a small structure, and the *rectory*, valued in K.B. at £6. 7s. 8d., and in 1831 at £70, is in the gift of J. Alliston, Esq., and incumbency of the Rev. Hodgson Brailsford, LL.B., of Exbourne. The glebe is 50A., and the tithes were commuted, in 1841, for £48 per annum.

INWARDLEIGH, a large village and parish, 4¼ miles S. by E. of Hatherleigh, contains 715 souls, and about 6000 acres of land. The manor anciently belonged to the Coffins, and was divided among their co-heiresses. A great part of the parish now belongs to W. C. Morris, J. M. Woollcombe, and J. Burd, Esqrs.; and the remainder to Lord Clinton and several smaller owners. The *Church* is a neat structure, on a commanding eminence, and has a tower and five bells. The *rectory*, valued in K.B. at £16. 11s. 3d., and in 1831 at £301, is in the patronage and incumbency of the Rev. Peter Gunning, who has a good residence, built 14 years ago, and 242 acres of glebe. Here are four small *chapels*, belonging to Baptists, Independents, Wesleyans, and Bible Christians. The poor parishioners have £4. 4s. yearly from Newcombe's Charity. (See Crediton.)

	BLACKSMITHS.	FARMERS.
Bennet John, vict. New Inn	Bennett John	(* *are Owners*.)
Burd John, Esq. *Gouldbourn*	Percy John	Chasty George
Gunning Rev. Peter, *Rectory*	Percy J. jun.	*Chasty Thos.
Spear John, vict. Five Oaks		
Squire Jas. shopr. & vict. Sportsman		

Coombe James	Landick John	*Squire Jonas	Yeo John
Essery John	Medland Wm.	Stanbury Peter	Youlden Fras.
Finney Henry	Raddicliffe John	Stanbury Benj.	Youlden John
Frost George	Reddaway John	Vallance Thomas	
Fry Samuel	*Spark Angel	Ward Ralph	WHEELWRIGHTS.
Heale Thomas	*Spark Wm.	Ward Thos.	Hawking Wm.
Jeffery George	Spear Sarah	*Woolland Rd.	Heale John
King John	Spear Thomas	Yendall John	Vanstone Wm.
King Richard	Squire George		

JACOBSTOWE, a pleasant village, in the valley of the river Okement, $3\frac{1}{2}$ miles S.E. of Hatherleigh, has in its parish 309 souls, and 2836 acres of land. Thomas Burton, Esq., of Yarmouth, is lord of the manor; but a great part of the soil belongs to the Wayford, Luxmoore, Ash, and other families. The *Church* (St. James,) is a small neat fabric, with a tower and four bells. It has monuments belonging to the Oxendon and Burton families, and a handsome one, erected in 1849, to the memory of Lady Ellen Astley, wife of Lewis P. Madden, M.D., late of Clifton, Gloucestershire. The *rectory*, valued in K.B. at £11. 4s. $4\frac{1}{2}$d., and in 1831 at £201, is in the patronage of J. R. Vincent, Esq., and incumbency of the Rev. John Vincent, M.A., who has 80 acres of glebe, and a neat residence. The tithes have been commuted for £174 per annum.

Vincent Rev John, M.A., *Rectory*	Cole Thomas	Peak David
Madden Lewis P., M.D., *Rectory*	Davy John	Rattenbury Seth
Peak Lewis, schoolmaster	Hill My. & John	Rich Mrs Ann
Ward John, vict. Swan Inn	Hill Wm.	Rich James
Westlake Henry, wheelwright	Johns Daniel	Ward Thos.
FARMERS.	Lavis Edward	Westlake Mtw.
Blatchford Danl.	Brittain Samuel	Orchard Charles	Willen Wm.

LUFFINCOTT, a small parish in the Tamar valley, 6 miles S. of Holsworthy, has only 93 souls, and 990 acres of land, mostly the property of Miss Venner and John Spettigue, Esq., who are joint owners of the manor, and patrons of the *rectory*, valued in K.B. at £5. 6s. 8d., and in 1831 at £67. The Rev. Franke Parker, M.A., is the *rector*, and has 61 acres of glebe, and a good residence, rebuilt and enlarged a few years ago. The tithes were commuted, in 1842, for £68. 5s. per annum. Sir Wm. Molesworth has an estate in the parish. The *Church* (S. James,) is a small ancient structure. DIRECTORY:—Rev. F. Parker, M.A., *Rectory* ; John and Edmund Spettigue, gentlemen, *West Peek* ; A. Trible, farmer, *Barton* ; and Wm. Parkin, *smith*.

MILTON-DAMERELL, a village and parish on the north side of the small river Waldon, 5 miles N.E. by N. of Holsworthy, comprises 813 inhabitants, and 4252 acres of land, including the hamlets of *East and West Wonford* and *Whitbeare*. The Earl of Devon is lord of the manor, which is held under him by Earl Stanhope; but a few smaller owners and leaseholders have estates here. The *Church* (Holy Trinity,) has a tower and three bells, and the living is a *rectory*, valued in K.B. at £26. 13s. $6\frac{1}{2}$d., and in 1831 at £441, with the perpetual curacy of Cookbury annexed to it. The Rev. Thos. Clack, B.A., is the incumbent, and has 75A. of glebe and a good old residence. A Sunday School for about 100 children is supported by subscription. The Earl of Devon is patron of the rectory.

Blake Jno. maltster& vict. Bridge Inn	Fishleigh J. vict. Courtenay Arms
Braund Wm. miller ; & Mr John	Glover John, blacksmith
Clack Rev Thomas, B.A. *Rectory*	Page Wm. parish clerk

2 L 3

Sanders Emanuel, machine maker
Slade John, blacksmith

FARMERS. *(2 at E.&3 W. Wonford.)*

3 Bremell Thos.	2 Fishleigh Fras.	
Cory Wm. *Ley*	Fishleigh John	
Fishley Barthw.	Fulford Robert	
Whitbeare	3 Harris George	

2 Heddon Wm.	Moore James	
Hill George	Priest Richard	
3 Hill Henry	2 Sanders John	
Hopper Samuel	Slee John	
Hutchings Robt.	SquireWm. *Venn*	
Jeffery John	2 Tapley Hubert	
2 Jollow John	Watkins John	

MONK-OKEHAMPTON, a pleasant village, on the east side of the small river Okement, 2½ miles E. by N. of Hatherleigh, has in its parish 259 souls, and 1488 acres of land, including *Burrows* hamlet and 23 acres of orchards. Hugh Mallett, Esq., is lord of the manor, which is supposed to have once belonged to some monastery. Wm. Hill, John Snell, and a few smaller owners, have estates in the parish. The *Church* is a small antique structure, with a tower and four bells. The *rectory*, valued in K.B. at £6. 14s. 7d., and in 1831 at £131, is in the patronage of Sir S. H. Northcote, and incumbency of the Rev. Joseph Ruse, who has a large residence and 45A. of glebe. The tithes have been commuted for £126 per annum. The National School was built eight years ago, at the cost of £120. The poor have 20s. a year out of Colehouse farm, at Broadwood-Kelly.

Bowden Wm. blacksmith
Buckingham Denis, shoemaker
Lane Geo. shopkeeper & shoemaker
Lock Catherine, schoolmistress
Rockey Emanuel Northey, miller
Ruse Rev Joseph, *Rectory*
Vanstone Tristram, vict. Swan

FARMERS.

Anstey Eliz.	Lane George
Cornall John	Smale Wm.
Hill Wm.	Snell Mary
Jones Jno.&Wm.	Tucker John
Kelland Wm.	Wreford John, *Fursdon*

NORTH LEW, 4 miles S.S.W. of Hatherleigh, is a large and pleasant village, on a lofty eminence, commanding delightful views, and having two ancient *crosses*, one in the centre, and the other at the cross roads. Its parish contains 1051 inhabitants, and 5306 acres of land, including 2000 acres of common, 200 acres of wood, and the hamlet of *Whitston*. Mr. Vowler is lord of the manor of North Lew, but that of *Harper's Hill* belongs to Mr. W. Honeychurch; and a great part of the parish belongs to J. M. Woollcombe, Esq., Mrs. Morris, and many smaller owners. *Redcliffe* belongs to Mr. Woollcombe, and has a fine freestone quarry and the remains of an ancient chapel. The *Church* (St. Thomas à Becket,) is a small antique fabric, with a tower and five bells, and is in a dilapidated state, but it is hoped that funds will shortly be raised for its reparation. The *rectory*, valued in K.B. at £27. 8s. 9d., and in 1831 at £342, is in the patronage of the Crown, and incumbency of the Rev. Thos. England, M.A., who has 39A. of glebe, and a neat residence, built in 1849. The tithes were commuted in 1841, for £370 per annum. The Bible Christians have a small chapel in the village, and another at Whitston, at the distance of two miles. The National School is held in the old Poor-house. The poor have the interest of £21, left by John Watkins.

England Rev Thomas, M.A. *Rectory*
Dennis Pp. vict. Honeychurch Arms
Friend James, saddler
Glass Wm. vict. Green Dragon
Gould George, surveyor, &c.
Major Joseph, builder, &c.
Sampson Samuel, schoolmaster

BLACKSMITHS.
Baker John
Dart Thomas

BOOT & SHOEMKS.
Coles James
Lobb Wm.
Smale Richard
Vanstone Thos.

CARPENTERS.
Gay John
Glass Edward
Glass James
Major Joseph

FARMERS.
Adams John
Bickle John

Brayley James
Brayley Alex.
Dennis Philip
Evaly James, and miller
Evaly Robert
Evaly Henry
Friend John
Friend James
Glass Wm.
Glass Ts. & jun.

Glass John, and miller
Glass Edward
Gloyn Thomas
Hicks Wm.
Karslake Roger
Miller Edward
Phara Thomas
Rich John
Smale John
Smale Richard

Smale Emanuel
Tucker John
Weekes George
Whitelock John
Wood Samuel
Woollen George
WoolridgeTrstrm
Woolridge James
Worth Philip

SHOPKEEPERS.
Gratton Thomas
Major Thomas
Wood Mary

TAILORS.
Coles John
Cross Thomas
Hood Wm.
Harford John
King John

PANCRASWEEK, or *Week St. Pancras*, a village and parish, on the east side of Tamar valley, four miles W.N.W. of Holsworthy, has 540 inhabitants, and 3782 acres of land, including the hamlets of *Kingford, Dunsdon*, and *Dexbeer.* L. W. Buck, Esq., is lord of the manor, but part of the soil belongs to Earl Stanhope, C. H. Hotchkys, Esq., and a few smaller owners. The *Church* (St. Pancras,) was anciently appropriated to Tor Abbey, and has a tower and five bells. The living is a perpetual curacy, annexed to Bradworthy vicarage. The Rev. Roger Kingdon is impropriator of the great tithes, which have been commuted for £260, and the small tithes for £100 per annum. The glebe is 7A., and the Parsonage is a small cottage. DIRECTORY :—Wm. Bickley and Nathl. Gilbert, *wheelwrights ;* Robt. Lott and John Jeffery, *blacksmiths ;* and Jas. Baker, Wm. Burnard, John Gilbert, Rd. Hodge, Jas. Penwarden, and Peter Stacey, *farmers.*

PETHERWIN, (NORTH) is a large village and parish, in the Archdeaconry of Cornwall and Deanery of Trigg Major, 5 miles N.W. of Launceston. It contains 1066 souls, and about 8000 acres of land, bounded on three sides by Cornwall, and including the hamlets of *Holscott, Brassacott*, and *Maxworthy*, and many scattered houses. It is mostly in the Duke of Bedford's manor of Werrington, but D. Kingdon, Esq., and many smaller freeholders and leaseholders, have estates here. The *Church* (St. Paternus,) is an ancient structure, with a fine tower and five bells. It contains memorials of the Yeo and other families. The *vicarage*, valued in K.B. at £9. 10s. 10d., and in 1831 at £135, is in the patronage of the Duke of Bedford, and incumbency of the Rev. G. T. Kingdon, M.A. The patron is impropriator of half of the great tithes, and one fourth belongs to Mr. J. Veale, and the rest to the land owners. The poor have 25s. a year, left by John Credacott and another donor. Whickett estate is charged with 10s. a year for a sermon on New Year's day. There are five small *chapels* in the parish, two belonging to Wesleyans, two to Bible Christians, and one to Association Methodists. The National School is partly supported by subscription.

Bray John, vict. New Inn
Hooper Wm. parish clerk
Kingdon Dennis, Esq. *Barton*
Kingdon RevGeo.Ths.,M.A. *Vicarage*
Pellow Christopher, schoolmaster
Uglow Wm. *Post Office*

BLACKSMITHS.
Ellacott Wm.
Gilbert Samuel
Ham Wm.
Perkin Wm.

FARMERS.
Banbury Samuel

Banbury Thos.
Box John
Box Mary Ann
Braund Lewis
Bray George
Colwill George
Colwill Wm.

Colwill Thomas
Dawe John
Dennis George
Dennis Wm.
Gilbert John
Gubbin Francis
Hake Richard
Martin John
Mason Richard
Pearse Hugh
Reed NathanielC.
Reed Thomas
Strike John

Thomas Samuel
Veal Thomas
Veal John
Walter John

SHOPKEEPERS.
Bellamy Wm.
Gilbert Emanuel
Marshall Wm.

WHEELWRIGHTS.
Bray Wm.
Budd John
Cann Thomas
Pickle Thomas

PUTFORD, (WEST) in the Torridge valley, 8½ miles N. of Holsworthy, is a village and parish, containing 490 souls, and 2620 acres of land, including the small hamlets of *Colscot, Thriverden*, and *Wedfield.* Wm. May, Esq., is lord of the manor, but a great part of the soil belongs to the Trustees of the late Lord Rolle, the Rev. P. Thomas, Archdeacon Stevens, and a few smaller owners. The *Church* is a fine cruciform structure, in the perpendicular style, with a tower at the west end, containing three bells. The *rectory*, valued in K.B. at £9. 11s. 0½d., and in 1831 at £204, is in the patronage of Wm. May, Esq., and incumbency of the Rev. J. L. May, B.A., who has 89A. of glebe, and a good residence, recently erected. The tithes were commuted in 1842 for £203 per annum. The poor have the interest of £40, given by unknown donors.

Arnold Richard, wheelwright
Harris John, parish clerk, &c

May Rev J. L., B.A. *Rectory*
Rouse Eusibuis, surgeon

Sanguin John, blacksmith

FARMERS. (* are Owners.)

*Lane Richard || Johns Richard

*May Thomas Robins

*Walter John, *Cary Barton*

*Walter Richard, *Churchtown*

PYWORTHY, a village and parish, two miles W.S.W. of Holsworthy, contains 758 souls, and 5021 acres of land, including the small hamlets of *Derriton* and *Killatree*, and a number of scattered houses. Sir Wm. Molesworth is lord of the manor. J. Vowler, Esq., and several smaller owners and leaseholders, have estates here. The *Church* (St. Swithen,) is a neat Gothic structure, with a tower and five bells, and the living is a *rectory*, valued in K.B. at £27. 8s. 4d., and in 1831 at £318. The Rev. T. H. Kingdon, B.D., is patron and incumbent, and has 172A. of glebe, and a handsome residence, lately erected. The tithes were commuted in 1838, for £370 per annum. In 1711, the *Rev. Robert Beckley* left for the poor about 11A. of land, let for about £11, and two cottages, occupied by paupers. The poor have also the interest of £10, and here is a National School.

Coombe John, shopkeeper

Gilbert Richard, carpenter

Kingdon Rev Thomas Hockin, B.D. *Rectory*

Vowler Jno. & J. N., Esqrs. *Parnacott*

BLACKSMITHS.

Bray John

Short Joseph

BOOT & SHOE MKS.

Andrew Wm.

Wonnacott Saml.

FARMERS.

Burnard John

Carter Peter

Cole John

Gilbert John

Hancock Thos.

Mills John

Mills David

Oliver Francis

Oliver Richard

Petherick Arthur

Philp John

Rundle Wm.

Sanders Wm.

Sanguin Wm.

Sluggett Wm.

Turner Thomas

SAMPFORD COURTENAY, a pleasant village, five miles N.E. by N. of Okehampton, has in its parish 1239 souls, and 7962 acres of land, including 342 acres of waste; the hamlets of *Willey* and *Croscombe*; and the large village of STICKLEPATH. The latter is on the Exeter and Launceston road, about 2½ miles E. of Okehampton, on the banks of the Taw, and has two chapels, two inns, and corn, bone, and woollen mills. Sampford Courtenay formerly belonged to the Courtenay family, as part of the barony of Okehampton. It is remarkable as the place where the western rebellion, occasioned by the alteration of the church service, broke out in 1549. (See page 56.) The Masters and Fellows of King's College, Cambridge, are lords of the manor, and patrons of the *rectory*, valued in K.B. at £47. 2s. 1d., and in 1831 at £580, and now in the incumbency of the Rev. G. P. Richards, M.A., who has 80A. of glebe. The tithes were commuted in 1842, for £650 per annum. The *Church* (St. Andrew,) is a handsome structure, with a tower and six bells. The Snell, Lethbridge, Tickle, and other families, have estates in the parish, but about 4000 acres are copyhold, under King's College, and nearly 2000 acres are moors and commons. *Sticklepath* has an ancient chapel of ease, said to have been built by Joan Courtenay, in 1146, and endowed as a chantry with lands, &c., valued at £9. 10s. 8d. per annum, in 1547. This chapel has been lately repaired, and the Rev. H. G. Fothergill, of Belston, is the curate. There is also a Wesleyan chapel in the village. The poor parishioners have the dividends of £111. 13s. 8d. three per cent. consols, purchased with £100, left by John Tickle, in 1801, and the interest of £33, given by various donors. They have also a small cottage, left by John Slowman, and an annuity of 10s., left by John Langmead.

Marked 2, are at Sticklepath.

2 Brooks John, vict. Devonshire Inn

2 Cook Jas. vict., Cornish Arms

Fewins Thos. shopkeeper & tailor

2 Finch & Sons, edge tool mfrs. &c

Easterbrook Thomas, sexton, &c

2 German John, saddler & shopkpr

Hammat John, vict., Courtenay Arms

2 Hooper Wm. corn miller

2 Lagassic Wm. shopkeeper

2 Pearce Geo. & Ts. *woollen manfrs*

2 Phillips Henry, corn miller

Pyke Elizabeth, schoolmistress

Richards Rev G. Pearce, M.A. *Rectory*

2 Watts Thomas, bone miller

2 Watts Mr Wm. || Wills Mr Geo.

Yeo John, shopkeeper and tailor

BLACKSMITHS.

2 Cann John

Fewins Wm.

Heathman Solan

2 Rowe John

FARMERS.

Arscott Wm.

Ash Robert

Bolt Wm.

Brewer J.

Brook Isaac

Brook John

Cockram Wm.

Cook Jno. *butcher*

Coombe Wm.

Cooper Wm.

Dart Philip

Daymont Henry

Dennaford Edm.

Dennaford Mor.

Gibbins Richard

Hawkins Wm.

Heathman John

Heathman Solan

Hern John & Ts.

Hill John

Huxtable Jno. (& land agent)

Isaac John

Jackman Samuel

Jackman Wm.

Keener Wm.

Kelland Wm.

Lang Wm.

Legg Bernard	Reddaway Bros.	Stanley John	Northway Saml.
Legg John	Reddaway Wm.	Steer Wm.	Potter James
Lethbridge Thos.	Sanders George	Tucker Wm.	Ward George
Lock Mark	Sanders Wm.	Westway J. & W.	
Matters Thos.	Smith Richard	Wills Geo. U.	CARRIERS to
Newcombe Rd.	Snell John	Woodman John	Exeter, &c. call
Page Richard	Snell Sus.	WHEELWRIGHTS.	at *Sticklepath*,
Quick George	Southcombe Jno.	Brailey Wm.	where there is a
Rayment Richd.	Southcombe Stn.	Heathman Thos.	*post-office*, at J.
Reddaway Geo.	Squire John	2 Heathman Wm.	Cann's

SUTCOMBE, a pleasant village, on the north side of the small river Waldon, **five** miles N. by W. of Holsworthy, has in its parish 523 souls, and 3593 acres of land. The manorial rights are very small, and the nominal lord of the manor is Mr. Walter, of West Putford. Earl Stanhope owns a great part of the parish, and the rest belongs to Wm. Allin, Esq., of Theoborough, or Thoborough, and a number of smaller owners. The *Church* (St. Andrew,) is an ancient structure, with a fine Norman porch, and a tower and three bells. The *rectory*, valued in K.B. at £17. 10s. 7½d., and in 1831 at £201, is in the patronage of the Rev. W. B. Coham, LL.B., and incumbency of the Rev. F. B. Briggs, M.A., who has 67½ acres of glebe, and a handsome residence, built in 1849-'50, and having tasteful grounds. The tithes were commuted in 1842, for £300 per annum. Here is an ALMSHOUSE for six poor people, founded by *Sir Wm. Morice*, in 1674, and endowed with 42A. 1R. 38P., called Upcott Parks; and an annuity of £20, out of the great tithes of Broad Clist. The poor parishioners have the interest of £20. 10s., vested with the overseers.

Allin Robert, shopkeeper and miller	FARMERS.	Bridgeman.W.jn.
Allin Wm., Esq. *Thoborough*	Allin George	Fisher Francis
Allin Thomas, parish clerk	Allin John	Grylls Thomas
Briggs Rev. Fras. B., M.A. *Rectory*	Allin Philip	Millman Wm.
Carter Eliz. & Fry Hy. *millers*	Allin Thomas	Stacey Peter
Jennings Richard, carpenter	Axford Richard	Walter Hugh
Lee Samuel, blacksmith	Bartlett Thomas	Walter Wm.
Mason Wm. schoolmaster	Bridgeman Wm.	Wickett John
Mason Wm. jun. vict., New Inn		

TETCOTT is a village and parish, near the confluence of the rivers Tamar and Claw, **five** miles S. of Holsworthy. It has 300 inhabitants, and 1885 acres of land. Sir Wm. Molesworth is lord of the manor, owner of most of the soil, and patron of the *rectory*, valued in K.B. at £13. 16s. 8d., and in 1831 at £147. The Rev. P. W. Molesworth, B.A., is the incumbent, and has 40A. of glebe, and a good residence, recently erected. The tithes were commuted in 1841, for £140 per annum. The poor have the dividends of £50 four per cent stock, and of £83. 6s. 8d. three per cent. consols, left by John Arscott and the Rev. John Rouse, in 1789 and 1819. The *Church* (Holy Cross,) is a small ancient structure, with a tower and one bell.

Drown Richard, blacksmith	FARMERS.
Hart John, carpenter	Chapple Wm., Barton
Hart Samuel, wheelwright	Ball John, *Fernhill*
Hatch Eliz. vict. Tetcott Inn	Congdon Lewis, *West Lana*
Molesworth Rev Paul W., B.A.*Rectory*	Trible Martha ‖ Toms Thomas

THORNBURY, on the banks of the small river Waldon, **five** miles N.E. of Holsworthy, is a pleasant village and parish, containing 524 souls, and about 2006 acres of land. Mrs. Freer and Mrs. Fowke, (two sisters,) of Leicestershire, are ladies of the manor, and owners of most of the soil, held on life leases, not to be renewed. They have also the patronage of the rectory, valued in K.B. at £11. 3s. 11½d., and in 1831 at £221, and now in the incumbency of the Rev. Wm. Edgcumbe, B.A., who has 90A. of glebe, and a good residence, lately put in thorough repair. The *Church* (St. Peter,) is an ancient structure, with a tower and three bells.

Edgcumbe Rev Wm., B.A. *Rectory*	FARMERS.
Priest Richard, vict., New Inn	Allin Richard, *Brendon*
Sanders Lewis, blacksmith	Carter Rd. ‖ Cole Matthew, ditto
Skinner Sml.parish clerk, *Woodacott*	Hutchings Arthur ‖ Penwarden Dd.
Ward Robert, shopkeeper	Mountjoy John, *Bagbeare*
	Priest John ‖ Trible Abraham

WERRINGTON, a village and parish, on the banks of a rivulet, near the river Tamar and the Bude Canal, two miles N. of Launceston, has 685 souls, and about 5000 acres of land, adjoining Cornwall, and including *Yeolmbridge, Druxen, Eggbeer,* and other farms, &c. The *Duke of Bedford* is lord of the manor,˙but the Barton estate belongs to the Duke of Northumberland, who resides occasionally at *Werrington House,* a neat mansion, with a well-wooded park, which was purchased by his grandfather of the Morice family, who were seated here in the 17th century. E. Coote, Esq., and several smaller owners, have estates here. The manor was given by Ordulph to Tavistock Abbey, and was granted at the dissolution to John Lord Russell. The parish is in the Archdeaconry of Cornwall, and Deanery of Trigg Major. The *Church* (St. Martin and St. Giles,) was rebuilt in 1742, and is a handsome structure, with a large tower, and two small ones at the west end. In the transepts are sittings for the Duke of Northumberland's family and servants. His Grace is patron of the living, which is a *donative,* endowed with £120 a year out of the tithes, which are partly in the impropriation of the Marquis of Lothian, the Earl of Mount Edgcumbe, and the Dowager Lady Suffield, and have been commuted for £290 per annum. The Rev. J. B. Messinger is the incumbent, and has a handsome residence, built about five years ago, by the Duke of Northumberland, at the cost of £1000.

DUKE OF NORTHUMBERLAND, *Werrington House* (& Alnwick Castle, Northumberland)

Messenger Rev Jas. Bryant, B.A. incumbent, *Parsonage*

Bennett Rd. & Hawke Rd. *smiths*

Shapton Jno. & Smith Chas. *wheelgts*

FARMERS.

Adams Chas. & Eliz. || Bickle B.

Brendon Richard || Bridges Thos.

Chubb Richard || Holman John

Martin Wm. || Palmer James

Rowland Wm. || Toll Henry

Stanlake Robert || Stanbury Samuel

SHERWILL HUNDRED

Is a highly picturesque district of hill and dale at the northern extremity of Devon, adjoining Exmoor, and bounded on the east by Somersetshire, on the north by the Bristol Channel, on the west by Braunton Hundred, and on the south by the latter, and South Molton Hundred. It is in the Northern Parliamentary Division of Devon ; in Lynton and Barnstaple Polling Districts, in Braunton Petty Sessional Division, in the Archdeaconry of Barnstaple, and in Sherwill Deanery. It comprises the 12 *parishes of Arlington, Brendon, Challacombe, Charles, Countisbury, High Bray, Lynton, Loxhore, Martinhoe, Parracombe, Sherwill, and Stoke Rivers,* which contain about 50,000 acres of land, including a large portion of open moors and commons. They had 4643 inhabitants in 1841, and are all in *Barnstaple Union,* except Charles parish, which is in South Molton Union.

ARLINGTON, a village and parish, 6 miles N.E. of Barnstaple, has 206 inhabitants and about 2000 acres of land, including the hamlet of *Becott,* nearly 2 miles N. of the church. *Sir John Palmer Bruce Chichester,* who was created a *baronet* in 1840, is lord of the manor and owner of most of the soil, and has a handsome seat here, called ARLINGTON COURT, but is at present in Malta. The manor was settled on his family in the reign of Henry VII. He is patron of the *rectory,* valued in K.B. at £13. 18s. 1¼d., and in 1831 at £300. The Rev. James Hamilton Chichester is the incumbent, and has a neat *Rectory House* and 85A. of glebe. The tithes have been commuted for £275 per annum, and the *church* (St. James,) is an ancient structure, containing many memorials of the Chichesters. The *Rev. Wm. Bampfield,* who held the rectory 50 years, died in 1719, and left a farm of 54A. at Goodleigh, and a house and 16A. 3R. 2P. at Barnstaple, in trust for the education of a boy at school till he is 19 years of age, and at one of the Universities till he is 26, or has taken the degree of M.A. The donor directed that one of his name and kindred should have the preference. The property is now let for about £85 a year ; and the rectors of Eastdown, Bratton-Fleming, and Goodleigh are the trustees, and are also patrons of the rectory of Bradford, which is always presented to a clergyman who has been a scholar under this trust. The poor of Arlington have about 58s. a year from the gifts of Rebecca Crocombe, Rebecca Hayes, and a Mr. Burgoyne. In 1669, the Rev. G. Canham left the interest of £40 for apprenticing poor children.

Chichester Sir J. P. B., Bart., *Court*

Chichester Rev J. H., *Rectory*

Mock James, Post-office

Rockley John, corn miller

FARMERS. (* at Becott.)

Abrahams Wm. || Bale Samuel

* Blackmore Chas. || Fry James
* Penberthy Thos. || Ridge Wm.
* Tucker Henry || Tucker James

Vickery John, *Combeshead*
Yeo Henry, *Briscombe*

BRENDON, a small village, 1¼ mile E.S.E. of Lynton, and 15 miles W. of Mine-head, is in the picturesque valley of the river Lyn, and has in its parish 271 souls, and 6733 acres of land, including *Leeford* hamlet, and a large tract of high moorland on the borders of Somersetshire, where the rivers Exe, Lyn, and Barle have their sources. F. W. Knight, Esq., is lord of the manor, owner of most of the soil, and patron of the *rectory*, valued in K.B. at £9. 4s., and in 1831 at £148. The Rev. T. Roe, of Oare, Somerset-shire, is the incumbent, and has 57A. 2R. 22P. of glebe. The parsonage is a small cottage; and the *Church* (St. Brendon,) is an ancient structure, with a tower and four bells. DIRECTORY:—Elizabeth Bromham, vict., Hunters' Inn; Wm. Burnell, blacksmith; P. Richards, tailor and vict. Millslade Inn; and Richd. and Thos. Crick, John and Richard Crocombe, Anthony and John French, Richard Hobbs, Sarah Jones, Hy. Litson, R. G. McDonald, and Wm. Sloley, *farmers*.

CHALLACOMBE, among the hills, near the sources of the river Bray, 10 miles N.E. of Barnstaple, has in its parish 305 souls, and 5450 acres of land, including a large por-tion of high moorland wastes, extending eastward to the borders of Somersetshire. Earl Fortescue is lord of the manor, owner of most of the soil, and patron of the *rectory*, va-lued in K.B. at £11. 9s. 2d., and in 1831 at £164. The Rev. J. C. Carwithen, M.A., is the incumbent, and has a good cottage residence, in a romantic dell, and about 40A. of glebe. The tithes have been commuted for £180 per annum. The *Church* (Holy Trinity,) is a small dilapidated structure, which is about to be rebuilt, except the tower, which contains four bells. The poor have the interest of £40, given by Wm. Partridge and Thos. Facche, and an annuity of 20s. left by Rebecca Crocombe.

Baker Thomas, blacksmith
Carwithen Rev. J. C., M.A. *Rectory*
Huxtable Richard, miller and vict. New Inn
Huxtable Wm. & Jones D., wheelgts.
Leworthy Samuel, shopkeeper
Leworthy James, blacksmith
Webber James, beer seller

FARMERS.
Crang Wm. || Dallyn Thomas
Dallyn John || Dallyn Wm.
Huxtable Wm. || Lancey Susan
Leworthy Wm. || Ridd Humphy.
Ridd Partridge, *Oldclose*
Vellacott Nathl. C. || Webber James

CHARLES, a village and parish, in the picturesque valley of the river Bray, 6 miles N. by W. of South Molton, contains 362 souls, and 2432 acres of land, including *Brayford* hamlet and a number of scattered houses. Sir Peregrine Fuller Palmer Acland, Bart., of Fairfield, Somersetshire, is lord of the manor, and owner of the pleasant seat called *Little Bray*, in the valley, 2 miles N. of the village. A great part of the parish belongs to Earl Fortescue. J. Davy, Esq., H. Karslake, Esq., Jno. Loosemoore, Jno. Smyth, and several smaller owners. The *Church* (St. John,) has a tower and five bells, and the living is a *rectory*, valued in K.B. at £9. 10s., and in 1831 at £160, in the patronage and incumbency of the Rev. Richard Blackmore, M.A., who has 13CA. of glebe, and a large and commodious *Rectory House*, recently rebuilt, and commanding extensive views, in which are seen Haldon and Dartmoor hills. The tithes were commuted in 1842, for £240 per annum. Here are two chapels, belonging to Baptists and Wesleyans.

Blackmore Rev Rd., M.A., *Rectory*
Cutcliffe George, tailor
Cutcliffe Rev. Wm. (Baptist)
Dallyn Thomas, shoemaker
Dallyn Wm. blacksmith
Hill Wm. vict. Plough
King Mrs H., *Little Bray*
Thorne George, carpenter

FARMERS.
Greenslade John || Hill Wm.
Hill John || Hunt Edward
Hutchins Thomas || Mogridge Geo.
Passmore Michael, *Deer Park*
Rudd John || Skinner Alex.
Smyth John || Widlake George

COUNTESBURY, or *Countisbury*, a small village, on the coast of the Bristol Channel, near the borders of Somersetshire, 2 miles E. of Lynton, and 14 miles W. of Minehead, has in its parish 185 souls, and 2941 acres of land, including *Wilsham* hamlet and part of Lynmouth. The Rev. W. S. Halliday is lord of the manor and owner of a great part of the soil, and has a pleasant seat called *Glynthorne*, at the foot of a bold acclivity, facing the sea. *East Lynmouth House* belongs to the Rev. Thomas Roe, and a few smaller owners have estates in the parish. The *Church* (St. John,) was repaired and the tower rebuilt about 14 years ago, when a school was built near it. The *perpetual curacy* is consolidated with that of Lynton, and is in the same patronage, appropriation, and in-cumbency.

Elworthy John, butcher
Halliday Rev W. S., *Glynthorne*
Ley John, corn miller
Newton James, vict. Blue Ball

Roe Rev Thomas, *East Lynmouth*
FARMERS. (* *at Wilsham.*)
* Jones John ‖ Jones Wm., *Ashton*
* Litson John ‖ Lock John

HIGH-BRAY, a pleasant village, on the eastern acclivity of the Bray valley, 6 miles N. by W. of South Molton, has in its parish 314 souls, and 4259 acres of land, including part of Brayford hamlet, and a number of scattered farms. Sir P. F. Acland, Bart., is lord of the manor and patron of the *rectory*, valued in K.B. at £14. 6s. 8d , and in 1831 at £300, and now in the incumbency of the Rev. Charles Melhuish, who has a neat small residence, and nearly 64A. of glebe. The tithes were commuted in 1842, for £360 per annum. The *Church* is an ancient structure, in the perpendicular style, with a tower and four bells. The Rev. J. W. Bryan, R. Harding, Esq., and a few smaller owners, have estates in the parish. In 1703, *Jacob Sloly* left two annuities, namely, 36s. for the poor, and £3. 12s. for schooling poor children. The poor have also the interest of £14 left by R. Dalling and Henry Moreman.

Huxtable John, blacksmith
Huxtable Richard, wheelwright
Melhuish Rev. Chas., Rectory
　FARMERS.
Burrow John
Channings Nchs.
Parminter John
Pattison Aaron
Radley George
Robins Thomas
Rook Philip
Rook John D.
Skinner James
Slader Peter
Squire James
Thorne J. & Rd.
Thorne Wm.

LYNTON, or *Linton*, 18 miles W. of Minehead, and N.E. by N. of Barnstaple, is one of the most fascinating villages on the north coast of Devon, picturesquely seated on a high hill immediately above the little seaport, fishing station, and delightful bathing place of LYNMOUTH, which lies on the shore of the Bristol Channel, at the feet of august rocky hills, which beetle over it in every direction, except in the bottom, where the united waters of the East and West Lyn fall into the sea. The parish of Lynton is subject to the port of Barnstaple, and contains 1027 inhabitants, and about 7000 acres of land, including *Lynmouth, Ilkerton*, many scattered houses, and a large tract of high moorland hills and wastes. Here nature and art combine in producing scenes which alternate between the wild and romantic, and the magnificent and beautiful. The *valleys* are sunk into deep and narrow glens, with gurgling rivulets running through them, and their steep sides adorned with mantling woods and beetling rocks. No scenery in Europe surpasses in picturesque beauties the valleys of the *East and West Lyn*, which unite at Lynmouth, where the two alpine brooks, flashing over their craggy beds, rush from deep ravines that open upon the village to the east and south, and throw their waters under two small stone bridges, which are profusely mantled with ivy. A little west of Lynton is the *Valley of Rocks*, where the lofty heights on either side are of mountainous magnitude, but composed chiefly of stupendous masses of naked rocks, piled one above another, forming here and there rude natural columns, and so fantastically arranged on the summits as to resemble gigantic ruins impending over the pass. Vast fragments overspread this extraordinary valley in every direction, and the whole scene is evidently the result of a desolating convulsion of nature, at some remote period. Some of the heights command extensive and delightful views of the coast and the channel; and the magnificent scenery of the three valleys has often been vividly pourtrayed by the pencils of London and provincial artists. There are three good Inns at Lynton, and another at Lynmouth, were there are salt-water baths, a library, a fancy repository, a billiard room, and a small quay. Both villages have been much improved during the last twenty years, and they now contain many neat villas and commodious lodging houses for the accommodation of the numerous visitors who throng hither in summer, to enjoy the sea air and bathing, and the magnificent scenery of the neighbourhood. The rivers produce trout and salmon, and there is a herring fishery in the channel. The Rev. Thomas Roe is lord of the manor and owner of a great part of the parish. The *Church* (St. Mary,) has a tower and three bells, and was enlarged by the addition of two aisles in 1817 and 1833. The *perpetual curacy*, valued at £120, is united with that of Countesbury, in the patronage of the Archdeacon of Barnstaple, and incumbency of the Rev. Matthew Mundy, M.A. The tithes have been commuted for £274 per annum, and belong, with a glebe of 100A., to the Archdeacon, but are held by a lessee. The *National School* was established in 1818, and a new building was erected for it in 1844. A handsome *Independent Chapel* was built here in 1850, in the early English style, at the cost of about £400. *Marked * are at Lynmouth, and the rest at Lynton or where specified.*

Barley Chas. Esq. ‖ Cox Captain
* Bale Eliz., stocking knitter
Collard Wm., *Combe Park*
Cowell Wm., M.D. ‖ Heath A., gent
Hayes Rev H. H. ‖ * Delevaud Mrs

Herries Major General Sir Wm. L., K.C.H.
* Hunter Stephen, coast guard
Litson J., surveyor, &c. *Croft House*
Mundy Rev Mattw., M.A., incmbt.

* O'Neil Mr John || Robinson Mr
Powell Rev Edw. H., B.A., curate
* Rawdon Col. J. Dawson, M.P.
Rendle W., plumber, ironmonger,&c.
* Roe Rev Thomas (and *Brendon)*
Roe John C. Esq., *Woolhanger*
Sanford Mrs Mary, *Lynton Cottage*
Slater John, corn miller
Toone Mrs and Miss, bdg. school
* Trix Hy., stationer, and bath and
library owner
Westcott George, saddler, &c.
FARMERS. (+ *at Ilkerton.)*
Baker James || Bromham M. C.
Burnell Wm., *Kibsworthy*
Challacombe Wm. || Jones Rd.
Jones Wm. || Latham Wm.
Pyle James, *East Lyn*
+ Squire John || + Squire Pp.
Turner Wm., *West Lyn*
+ Tapper Thomas || Vellacott Jas.
Ward Richard, *West Lyn*
INNS AND TAVERNS.
Castle Hotel, Thomas Baker
Crown Hotel, Wm. Crook
Globe Inn, David Hill
* Lyndale Hotel, Nicholas Jones,
bathing machine owner, &c.
Litson's Valley of Rocks Hotel, N.
Jones
* Rising Sun, John Boyle
BAKERS, &c.
Greer George
Heywood James

BEER SELLERS.
Bale John
Heywood James,
(&portr.&c.dlr.)
BLACKSMITHS.
Burnell John
Burnell Wm.
BOOT & SHOEMKS.
Allen John
* Bale Henry
Hooper John
Hooper Wm.
Lord Joseph
Rawle Wm.
BUILDERS.
Crick John
Jones Nicholas
Jones Robert
BUTCHERS.
Crick John
Latham Wm.
GROCERS, &c.
Fry George
* Heywood Jas.
Latham Wm.
Southwood John
Ward Wm.
LODGINGS.
Arnold David
* Beven Thomas
* Blackmore My.
Branch Edw.
Busby Chas.

Catlin Wm.
Fry Charles
* Fry Charlotte
* Fry H.
Geen Thomas
* Geen T. jun
Gill Mary
Jones Mary Ann
Litson John
* Litson William,
Prospect Hs.
Richards Wm.
Shute Joseph
Taylor Mary
SHOPKEEPERS.
* Apley Fdk. G.
* Bale Henry
Blackmore Wm.
* Corbett Mary
SURGEONS.
Bencraft Henry
Clarke John
Mansell —
POST-OFFICE
at Mrs Maria
Litson's. Letters *via* Minehead
OMNIBUS.
Wm. Richards, to
Barnstaple,Tu.
an d Friday

LOXHORE, a scattered village and parish, 5½ miles N.N.E. of Barnstaple, has 306 inhabitants, and 1250 acres of land. Sir J. P. B. Chichester, Bart., is lord of the manor, owner of most of the soil, and patron of the *rectory*, valued in K.B. at £9. 16s. 4½d., and in 1831 at £190. The Rev. J. H. Chichester, of Arlington, is the incumbent, and has 21A. of glebe. The tithes were commuted in 1842, for £150. 10s. per annum. The *Church* (St. Michael,) is an ancient structure, with a tower and four bells. The poor have the interest of £21 left by several donors. DIRECTORY :—Wm. Delve, blacksmith and beer seller ; and John Clark, John Comer, Michael Dart, Geo. Gould, John Pugsley, and John Skinner, *farmers.*

MARTINHOE, a picturesque village, on the coast of the Bristol Channel, 3 miles W. of Lynton, is sheltered on the south by lofty moorland hills, rising above the rocky valleys of several small rivulets. Sir Robt. George Throckmorton, Bart., is lord of the manor and owner of a great part of the soil, and the rest belongs to C. Bailey, Esq., and a few smaller owners. The *Church* (St. Martin,) is an antique fabric, with a tower and two bells. The *rectory,* valued in K.B. at £8. 10s. 10d., and in 1831 at £130, is in the patronage of the Rev. John Pike, and incumbency of the Rev. Joseph Dovell, M.A., who has 35A. of glebe, and a neat residence, which was new fronted in 1843. The tithes were commuted in 1841, for £120 per annum. The poor have 5s. a year.

Dovell Rev Jph., M.A., Rectory
Dovell Charles, beer seller
Richards John, vict. Hunters' Inn
FARMERS.
Crang John C. || Crocombe Rd.
Dovell James, *Hillington*

Dovell Charles, *Manacott*
Fry Walter, *Kittatree*
Hoyles Wm., *Mill*
Jones Richd., *Kimacott*
Latham John, *Manacott*
Sloly Amos, *Slatenslade*

PARRACOMBE, a village and parish among the high moorland hills, five miles S.S.W. of Lynton, and E. of Combe-Martin, has 446 souls, and 4363 acres of land, in-

cluding the picturesque hamlets of *Parracombe Mill, Heal,* and *Rowley.* L. St. Aubyn, Esq., is lord of the manor and patron of the *rectory,* valued in K.B. at £13. 10s. 10d., and in 1831 at £259. The Rev. John Pyke, M.A., is the incumbent, and has 64A. 3R. 25P. of glebe, and a handsome *Rectory House,* built in 1827, at the cost of £1000, and seated in a romantic valley. The *Church* is an ancient structure, with a tower and three bells. Sir P. F. P. Acland, John Knott, Esq., (owner of Rowley manor,) Mr. Richard Dovell, and a number of smaller owners, have estates in the parish. At Holywell is a circular mound, called the *Castle.* The poor have the interest of £28, vested with the overseers.

Blackmore Charles, schoolmaster
Howe Wm. corn miller
Lancey John, shopkeeper
Lock John, butcher
Lovering John, maltster
Lovering Richard, corn miller
Mackenzie K. revenue officer
Palmer Noah, parish clerk
Polkinghorne Alfred, baker and vict. London Inn
Pyke Rev John, M.A. *Rectory*
Scamp Thomas, shoemaker
Somerville John, vict. Fox & Goose
Somerville Bartholomew, mechanic
Tucker Richard, blacksmith

Watts Wm. schoolmaster
Whitefield James and Son, tailors
Lock Wm.

FARMERS.
(* are Owners.)
Berry Wm.
*Blackmore John
Blackmore Wm.
Carr James, *Heal*
*Crang John
Dovell Nathaniel
*Dovell Richard
*Dovell Philip
*Gammon John
Harton Richard
Leworthy John

*Lovering John
*Smyth Jas. H.
*Smyth John
*Smyth George
Stribling John
Tamlyn James
*Tucker Richard
WHEELWRIGHTS.
Burden Wm.
Hatton —
Tamlyn John

SHERWILL, the pleasant village which gives name to this Hundred, is four miles N.E. by N. of Barnstaple, and has in its parish 686 souls, and 4762 acres of land. *Sir Arthur Chichester, Bart.,* whose baronetcy was created in 1641, is lord of the manor, and owner of most of the soil, and has a handsome seat here, called *Youlston Park,* which one of his ancestors obtained by marrying the heiress of the Beaumonts, in the reign of Henry VII. He is patron of the *rectory,* valued in K.B. at £30. 3s. 11½d., and in 1831 at £472. The Rev. R. J. Beadon, M.A., is the incumbent, and has 85A. of glebe, and a good residence, recently erected. The *Church* (St. Peter,) is a neat structure, and contains several memorials of the Chichesters. The poor have the interest of £56. 10s., given by various donors.

Beadon Rev Rd. John, M.A. *Rectory*
Chichester Sir Arthur, Bart. *Youlston Park*
Gregg Thomas, smith, *Post Office*
Kidwell George, shopkeeper
Kidwell James, shoemaker
Parkin John, vict. Old Inn
Robins Samuel, machine maker
Smith Richard, vict. Cross Inn
Symons John, tailor

FARMERS.
Alford Wm.
Bagster Wm.
Copp John
Combeer Wm.
Davey George
Delve John
Drake Charles
Ford John
Fry John

Kingdon Wm.
Parminter Thos.
Prestcott Wm.
Quance Mary
Richards Lewis
Stevens John
Stoles Wm.
Yeo Wm.

STOKE-RIVERS, which anciently belonged to the Rivers family, is a village and parish, 5 miles E. by N. of Barnstaple, containing 299 inhabitants, and 2426A. of land, including the hamlet of *North Horridge.* Sir A. Chichester, Bart., is lord of the manor, and owner of most of the soil, and the rest belongs to J. and P. Tamlyn, and several smaller owners. The *Church* (Holy Ascension,) is a Gothic structure, with a tower and five bells. The *rectory,* valued in K.B. at £14. 14s. 7d., and in 1831 at £260, is in the patronage and incumbency of the Rev. Henry Hiern, LL.B., who has 59A. 1R. 32P. of glebe, and a good old residence. The *School* has recently been endowed with the dividends of £200 consolidated Bank annuities, left by Amos Tamlyn, Esq.

Combeer Mary, schoolmistress
Cutland Edward, blacksmith
Hiern Rev Henry, LL.B. *Rectory*
Hutchings Edward, wheelwright
Parkin Wm. & Thos. wheelwrights
Vickery Christopher, blacksmith

FARMERS.
Fry Abraham
Fry Thomas
Lee Wm.
Tamlyn Peter

Tamlyn John, *Orswell*
Tucker James
Tucker John

LIFTON HUNDRED,

On the western side of Devon, extends over about 140,000 acres of land, more than a third of which is in the wild and hilly district of *Dartmoor Forest*. (See page 38.) The forest portion extends about 16 miles from north to south, and from 4 to 6 in breadth, and the rest of the hundred is generally a fertile district, about 12 miles in length and breadth, extending westward to the river Tamar, on the borders of Cornwall; northward to Okehampton, and southward to the vicinity of Tavistock. It gives rise to many rivers and brooks, and is in the Southern Parliamentary Division of Devon; in Tavistock and Okehampton Polling Districts; in Lifton and Tavistock Petty Sessional Divisions; in the Archdeaconry of Totnes; and mostly in the Deanery of Tavistock, and partly in that of Okehampton. The following enumeration of its 21 parishes shews their territorial extent, and their population in 1841:—

Parishes.	Acres.	Pop.	Parishes.	Acres.	Pop.
†Bradstone	1257	166	*Marystowe	2895	574
*Bratton-Clovelly	8316	870	*Okehampton Borough	9552	2194
*Bridestowe	5661	1128	*Sourton	5018	732
§Broadwoodwidger	8780	923	†Stowford	2066	647
†Coryton	1334	374	†Sydenham Damerel	2250	369
†Dunterton	1161	212	†Tavy St. Mary	4180	1552
*Germansweek	2595	414	†Thrushelton	3714	628
†Kelly	1722	258	§Virginstow	1275	167
†Lamerton	6788	1288	†Willsworthy‖	2450	—
†Lewtrenchard	2819	527			
†Lifton	5982	1784	Total	137,319	16,020
†Lidford Parish	3604	280			
†Dartmoor *quarter*	53,900	933			

☞ UNIONS.—Those marked thus * are in *Okehampton Union;* † in *Tavistock Union;* and § in *Holsworthy Union.*

‖ *Willsworthy* is a hamlet in Tavy St. Peter parish. (See page 742.)

OKEHAMPTON UNION comprises the 28 parishes of Ashbury, Beaworthy, Belston, Bondleigh, Bratton-Clovelly, Bridestowe, Broadwood-Kelly, Chagford, Drewsteignton, Exbourne, Germansweek, Gidleigh, Hatherleigh, Highampton, Honeychurch, Iddesleigh, Inwardleigh, Jacobstowe, Meeth, Monk-Okehampton, Northlew, North Tawton, Okehampton, Sampford-Courtenay, South Tawton, Sourton, Spreyton, and Throwleigh. They extend over an area of 201 square miles, and their total population amounted in 1841 to 22,001 souls. Their average annual expenditure on the poor during the three years preceding the formation of the Union, was £9157; but in 1838 it was only £6201, and in 1840, £7243. The expenditure for the half-year ending September, 1849, was £4645. The *Workhouse*, built in 1838, at the cost of £3600, has room for about 230 paupers. Mr. Henry Hawkes is the *union clerk* and *superintendent registrar ;* and Rd. Gibbings, of Okehampton, and Thos. Banbury, of South Tawton, are the *relieving officers.* Mr. Peter Paltridge and wife are *master* and *matron of the Workhouse;* and Messrs. T. C. Hawkes, Rd. Thorn, John Chapple, J. S. Day, and Richard Evely are *registrars of births and deaths.* Henry Newton, of Okehampton, and Thomas Pearse, of Sticklepath, are *registrars of marriages.*

BRADSTONE, on the east side of the Tamar valley, 8 miles N.W. by W. of Tavistock, has in its parish 166 souls, and 1257 acres of land. The houses are scattered. H. Blagrove, Esq., is lord of the manor and owner of two-thirds of the soil, and the rest belongs chiefly to A. Kelly, Esq. The manor house, which was the seat of the Cloberry family till 1750, is an old Tudor building, occupied by a farmer, and approached through a large gate-house. The *Church* (St. Nun,) is an ancient structure, with a tower and five bells. It still retains all its old carved benches, and part of the screen. The *rectory,* valued in K.B. at £6. 7s. 2d., and in 1831 at £222, is in the patronage of the Bishop of Exeter, and incumbency of the Rev. Thomas Johnes, B.A., who has a good residence, and 64A. of glebe. The tithes were commuted in 1843 for £210 per annum. *John Doble* died here in 1604, aged 120 years. *Directory:*—Matthew Hawkins, smith and wheelwright; Rev. Thomas Johnes, B.A, *Rectory;* Saml. Martin, corn miller; and Susan Brown, Henry Corry, Wm. Niles, Peters Brothers *(Barton,)* Thomas Ryall, and Philip Spear, *farmers.*

BRATTON-CLOVELLY, a small village, on a bold eminence, 8 miles W.S.W. of Okehampton, has in its parish 870 inhabitants, and 8316A. of land, including 2000A. of moorland; the hamlets of *Brockscombe, Burnaby,* and *Burrow,* and many scattered houses. The soil belongs to J. G. Newton, Esq., J. M. Woollcombe, Esq., Sir William Molesworth, S. Wreford, Esq., Rev. H. Coham, S. C. Hamlyn, Esq., and several smaller owners. The *Church* is a large and handsome structure, in the early decorated style, with a tower and six bells. The *rectory,* valued in K.B. at £21. 5s. 2½d., and in 1831 at £468, is in the patronage of the Bishop of Exeter, and incumbency of the Rev. Edward Budge, B.A., who has a good old residence, and 161A. 1R. 27P. of glebe. The

tithes were commuted in 1845, for £460 per annum. The Barton was long the seat of the ancient family of Burnaby.

Baker Wm. beer seller
Budge Rev Edward, B.A., *Rectory*
Bevan Richard, mason
Hortop Wm. corn miller
Palmer John, vict. Royal Oak
Phear Walter, saddler, and Mr John
Small John, shoemaker
Tucker John, vict. Pack Horse

BLACKSMITHS.
Pyne John
Roberts Thomas

CARPENTERS.
Dawe John
Guy Wm.
Hortop Wm. wheelgt

FARMERS.
(* *are Owners.*)
*Abell Wm.

*Hilson Thomas
Hortop James
Jackman John
Jackman Roger
Jackson Wm.
Kennard Richard
Kennard Nicholas
Kennard Wm.
Kerslake John
Lovell John
Luxton Henry
Martyn John
Palmer Nicholas
*Phear Samuel
Phear Wm.
Rice George
Rice John

*Baker Wm.
*Butler John
*Brown W. R.
Brown Thomas
Coy James
Down John
Hacker Edward
*Ham Philip
Hearn Henry
Higgadon Thomas

Rice Charlotte
Rich John
Rundle Jane
Shopland Thomas
Spear Wm.
Taylor James
*Tickle Wm.
Tucker John
Westlake Richard
Woolridge Wm.

SHOPKEEPERS.
Brown Peter
Smallcombe Roger

TAILORS.
Burd Thomas
Palmer Nicholas
Phear James

BRIDESTOWE, a neat and improving village, in a pleasant valley near Dartmoor, six miles S.W. of Okehampton, has in its parish 1128 souls, and 5661 acres of land, including *Combe-Ball, Watergate, Fernworthy, Bidluke,* many scattered houses, and a large tract of moorland hills, in which are the *lead and copper mines* of Wheal-Mary, Wheal-Newton, &c. The manors and their resident owners are, *Cobham-Wick* and *Blatchford,* J. G. Newton, Esq.; and *Leawood,* S. C. Hamlyn, Esq.; but J. M. Woollcombe, Esq., the Rev. J. Woollcombe, and many smaller owners, have estates in the parish. *Millaton,* a handsome mansion, with tasteful grounds, is the seat of J. G. Newton, Esq., and was rebuilt about the close of the 17th century, but was much enlarged and beautified some years ago. In the house is a fine museum of stuffed birds, &c., and a richly carved oak bedstead, of the Elizabethan age. On the site of the ancient domestic chapel, some coins of Louis IX. of France were found some years ago. *Leawood,* the seat of S. C. Hamlyn, Esq., is a fine old mansion, which was long the seat of the Calmady family. *Cattle fairs* are held in the village, on the first Wednesday in June, and July 29th. The *Church* (St. Bridget,) is a small antique fabric, with a tower and six bells, and several neat monuments. The chancel was rebuilt some years ago. The entrance gate to the churchyard is a fine Norman arch, supposed to be the remains of the original church. The *rectory,* valued in K.B. at £32. 17s. 11d., and in 1831 at £513, with the curacy of Sourton annexed to it, is in the patronage of the Bishop of Exeter, and incumbency of the Rev. H. Howell, who built the present large and handsome Rectory House, and has 70A. of glebe, and the manor of *Bridestowe Sanctuary.* The tithes were commuted in 1846, for £317. 5s. per annum. A field of 3A. has been long vested for the reparation of the church. The Baptists and Bible Christians have small chapels here. The *National School,* established about ten years ago, is attended by about 200 children.

Brock Betsy, vict., Royal Oak
Brownson John H. schoolmaster
Churchward Henry, auctioneer, land surveyor, &c. *Stone*
Gill and Rundle, lime burners
Gould James, butcher
Hamlyn Shilston Calmady, Esq. *Leawood*
Hockin Wm. cooper
Howell Rev Hinds, *Rectory*
Jackman Rt. vict. Fox and Hounds
Linton James and John, masons
Newcombe Wm. currier, &c
Newton John Gubbins, Esq. *Millaton*
Palmer James, brewer and maltster
Pike John, shoemaker
Youlden Samuel, millwright, &c
Younge Rd. J. G. vict., White Hart

BLACKSMITHS.
Alford Wm.
Bowden John
Coombe Edward
Sercombe Samuel

CARPENTERS.
(* *Wheelwrights.*)
*Alford Walter
Chebb Robert
*Shopland James

Weekes John
FARMERS.
Bailey Wm.
Baker Thomas
Ball Geo. *Bidlake*
Ball Wm. *Mill*
Batten Daniel
Bickle John
Bolt John
Brook John
Brook Philip
Doidge Arthur
Ellis Wm.
Friend James
Hill Wm.
Hortop Roger
Jackman Robert
Kennard John
Kennard Thomas
Lavis Edward
Lock Wm.
Martin John

Mason John
Orchard Richard
Palmer John
Palmer Wm.
Rule George
Stanbury Wm.
Vodden Wm.
Yelland David
Yelland Wm.

SADDLERS.
Bevan John
Joyce James

SHOPKEEPERS.
Coombe John
Peard John
Rundle John

TAILORS.
Peard John
Southcombe Thos.

POST-OFFICE at J. Bowden's

BROADWOODWIDGER, or *Broadwood Wiger,* is a village of old cob buildings, on the acclivity of a valley, six miles N.E. of Launceston. Its parish contains 923 souls, and 8780A. of land, including 1500A. of common, 140A. of wood, 100A. of orchards, the hamlets of *Rixton* and *Kallacott,* and many scattered houses. The manors and their

owners are, *Broadwoodwidger and Upcott*, Hy. Blagrove, Esq.; *Norden Bason*, Lord Clinton; *More Malherbe*, Rev C. T. C. Luxmoore; and *Deanacary*, Hy. Hawkes, Esq. Lord Ashburton, Sir Wm. Molesworth, the Misses May, Jas. Lay, Esq., and several smaller owners, have estates here, mostly freehold. The *Church* is an ancient structure, with a tower and five bells. It retains most of its old carved oak benches, and has some remains of stained glass in its windows. The Dean and Chapter of Bristol are appropriators of the tithes, and patrons of the *perpetual curacy*, now held by the Rev. Ponsford Cann, of Virginstow, who has yearly £67. 18s. 8d. from Queen Anne's Bounty, and £24. 6s. 8d. from the tithes, which were commuted in 1844, for £410 per annum, and are leased to the Rev. C. T. C. Luxmoore. Here are two small chapels, belonging to the Wesleyans and Bible Christians.

Squires Jph. vict., Hare and Hounds
Walters Thomas, vict., *Thorn Moor*

BLACKSMITHS.
Brown John
Burden Henry
Newbury James
Routley Richard
Shopland Wm.

CARPENTERS.
Clifton John
Hicks Wm.
Squires John

BOOT & SHOE MKRS.
Andrews Wm.
Kerslake George

FARMERS.
(* are Owners.)
Axworthy John
Bailey Walter
Bale James

Banbury Richard
Barsett Jacob
*Bickle George
Bickle John & Rd.
Boscobell Richard
Braund John
Bray Nathaniel
Brimmicombe J.
Cornish George
Davey Wm.
Down Rd. & Thos.
Down Wm.
*Eastcott Richard
Fursman J.
Gregory Susanna
*Hall John
Harris T. & W.
*Helson Robert

Jennings James
Kitton John
Martin Richard
Meadows Thomas
Meathrell Philip
Newcombe Wm.
Northcott James
Page John
*Palmer Richard
*Perkins Richard
*Perkins Thomas
*Reap Wm.
Rice George
*Rich James
*Rockey John & E.
Rogers Richard
Rowe Wm.
*Smale Jas. & T.
Spry Peter & S.

Squance Wm.
*Squire John & Jph.
Taunton Richard
Vale John
Veale Michael
Vicary Christopher

MILLERS.
Fry John
Martin John
Perkins James
Spry Sampson

SHOEMAKERS.
Andrews Wm.
Kerslake George

SHOPKEEPERS.
Eastcott Wm.
Raymont Augustus
Shopland Wm.
Squires John

CORYTON, a small scattered parish, between and near the confluence of the rivers Lyd and Lew, 6½ miles N.N.W. of Tavistock, contains 374 souls, and 1335A. of land, including 283A. of woods and plantations, and a large and excellent *slate quarry*, first opened in 1778, and celebrated for roofing, flooring, tombstones, chimney pieces, billiard tables, &c. Slabs, containing 140 superficial feet, and perfectly level, have been got by Messrs. Symons, who have worked the quarry 37 years. Thomas Newman, Esq., is owner of the soil, lord of the manor, and patron of the *rectory*, valued in K.B. at £8. 13s. 9d., and in 1831 at £218. The Rev Rd. Newman is the incumbent, and has 71A. 3R. 10P. of glebe, and a large and handsome residence, in the Elizabethan style, erected in 1836. The tithes were commuted in 1841, for £160. 16s. per annum. The *Church* (St. Andrew,) is a small antique structure, with a tower and three bells, and was completely renovated in 1838, when it was re-seated, and a new north transept added. At the coronation of Queen Victoria, here were great rejoicings, but the festivities were unhappily terminated by the explosion of a large cannon, while re-loading, which killed two men and four boys, and wounded many others. The parish school was built in 1839, at the expense of Sir R. W. Newman and Thomas Newman, Esq. The poor parishioners have the interest of £10, and also a fourth share of an annuity of £80, left in 1808, by *Arthur Tremayne*, for the poor of Coryton, Lamerton, South Sydenham, and Marystowe.

Blatchford Thomas, blacksmith
Davey Henry, carpenter
Hoidge —, *hind* to T. Newman, Esq.
Newman Rev Richard, *Rectory*

Symons Thos.& Chas slate merchants, &c.
Manor Cottage
FARMERS—John and Wm. Cumming, Ts.
Sloman, and Rd. Hamley

GERMANSWEEK, or *Week St. Germans*, on a bold acclivity, 11 miles W. by S. of Okehampton, has in its parish 414 souls, and 2595 acres of land, including *Heyworthy* hamlet, and nearly 800 acres of commons, about to be enclosed. The soil belongs to the Rev C. T. C. Luxmoore, Lord Clinton, J. Squire, H. Hawkes, C. Brown, and a few smaller owners. The *Church* is mostly in the early English style, and has a tower and three bells. The Dean and Chapter of Bristol are appropriators of the tithes, and patrons of the *perpetual curacy*, now held by the Rev. Chas. Carpenter, B.A., of Lifton, who has yearly £82. 7s. from Queen Anne's Bounty, and £9 from the tithes, now leased to the Rev. C. T. C. Luxmoore, and commuted for £117 per annum. Here is a small Baptist chapel. DIRECTORY :—Samuel Gerry, tailor and shopkeeper; John Reddicliff, shopkeeper and shoemaker; Wm. Short, blacksmith; Peter Spry, smith and vict., *Fortescue Arms ;* and Wm. Axworthy, Thomas Burnard, Thos. Moorcombe, John Northey, Thos. Northcott, Wm. and Walter Palmer, John Perkin, Roger and Thomas Seccombe, Wm. Symons, Wm. White, and Isaac Yeo, *farmers.*

KELLY, a pleasant scattered parish, 5 miles E.S.E. of Launceston, has 258 inhabitants, and 1722 acres of land, nearly all the property of *Arthur Kelly, Esq.,* whose family

has held the manor and advowson from the time of Henry II., and has been seated since that early period at *Kelly House*, which was greatly enlarged and partly rebuilt about a century ago. It stands on a commanding eminence, in a richly wooded park, from which a road descends to a sylvan valley, where a rivulet supplies a small lake, and gushes over several rocky heights, in beautiful cascades. The *Church* (St. Mary,) is a handsome structure, in the perpendicular style, with a tower and six bells. It was new roofed and repaired about six years ago, at the expense of the patron. Two of its windows are enriched with stained glass, and under a chapel at the east end is the vault of the ancient family of Kelly. The *rectory*, valued in K.B. at £9. 8s. 9d., and in 1831 at £285, is in the patronage of A. Kelly, Esq., and incumbency of the Rev. H. J. Morshead, who has a good residence, and 73A. 1R. 16P. of glebe. The tithes were commuted in 1838, for £265 per annum. The *School* was built by Mr. Kelly, in 1842. The parish includes *Meadwell* hamlet. DIRECTORY: Arthur Kelly, Esq., *Kelly House;* Rev. Hy. John Morshead, *Rectory;* Hugh Pedlar and Thos. Yole, *millers;* Geo. Rice, *shoemaker;* and Richard Brendon, John Cater, John and Wm. Eastcott, Richard Hill, John Larke, John Mason, Thomas Palmer, Wm. Perry, and Wm. Youldon, *farmers*.

LEWTRENCHARD, on the banks of the small river Lew, about 8½ miles N. of Tavistock, and E. by N. of Launceston, has in its parish 527 souls, and 2818 acres of land, rising boldly from the valley, and abounding in slate and limestone. It includes a great part of the village of LEW DOWN, which is on the turnpike road, and is partly in the parishes of Marystowe and Thrushelton; and has a *cattle fair*, on the Wednesday before the third Thursday in April. E. B. Gould, Esq., is lord of the manor, and owner of most of the soil, and resides occasionally at *Lew House*, a neat mansion with tasteful grounds, commanding delightful views. Orchard Barton, formerly the seat of the Woods, is an interesting Elizabethan house. The *Church* (St. Peter,) is a small antique fabric, with a tower and five bells, and was repewed in 1831, and cleaned and repaired a few years ago. The *rectory*, valued in K.B. at £9. 13s. 4d., is in the patronage of E. B. Gould, Esq., and incumbency of the Rev. Charles B. Gould, who has 80A. of glebe and a good residence. The tithes were commuted in 1839, for £270 per ann. The National School was built in 1841. A manganese mine was formerly worked in the parish, and yielded for some time 10,000 tons per annum.

*Marked * are at Lew Down; † in Marystowe; and § in Thrushelton parish.*

*Bevan George and Robert, masons
*Blatchfold John, blacksmith
*Brock John, vict. Lew Down Inn
Clatworthy Thomas, butcher
*Creber Mrs || Payne A. school
*†Davey Jonathan, schoolmaster
*Dawes Samuel, carpenter
Gould Rev Charles Baring, *Rectory*
Gould Edward Baring, Esq. *Lew House*
*Luxmore John, saddler
*§Parsons John, vict. New Inn
*†Reddicliffe Richard, gent
*Smith Thomas Wm. surgeon
*†Spry Richard, wheelwright

*Symons Thomas, saddler
Yelland David, corn miller

FARMERS.
Ash Thomas
Chowen Henry
Facey Samuel
Ham Thomas
Hortop Robert
Langmead James
Perry Wm. & Jehu
Reddicliff John
Stobie Matthew
Symons Henry
Symons Wm.
Symons Thomas

Westlake John
White Thomas
Yeo John, *Orchard*
SHOEMAKERS.
*Hockaday Thomas
*Rattenbury Wm.
SHOPKEEPERS.
*Frise James
*Johns Samuel
*Rice Ann
*POST OFFICE at Ann Rice's. Letters *via* Okehampton.

LIDFORD, or *Lydford*, is a small ancient village, on the banks of the small river Lyd, and on the western side of Dartmoor, 7½ miles N. by E. of Tavistock. Its parish contains 280 souls, and 3604 acres of land, exclusive of DARTMOOR FOREST QUARTER, which has a scattered population of 933 souls, and extends over about 53,900 acres of wild moorland hills and dales, including the hamlets of *Prince Town, Hexworthy, Huckaby, Dinnabridge, Two Bridges*, and the extensive but now unoccupied *Prison of War*; as already noticed with the general description of Dartmoor, at pages 38 to 40. There are *cattle fairs*, at Lidford on the Tuesday after July 20th, at Two Bridges on the Thursday after August 2nd, and at Prince Town on the 23rd of August. The Prince of Wales is lord of the manor, which forms, with the forest, part of his Duchy of Cornwall. Lidford, though now only an indifferent village, was anciently a borough, and had a grant for a market in 1267. It is said to have had the honour of entertaining Julius Cæsar and his army on his second expedition to Britain. In the Saxon Heptarchy it was a town of some note, and had a mint. In 997, it was ravaged and despoiled by the Danes, when they destroyed Tavistock Abbey. At Domesday Survey, it was evidently a walled town, and it sent burgesses to Parliament twice in the reign of Edward I. Vestiges of the walls and gates were often found in Risdon's time. *Lidford Castle*, which has been long reduced to a mere shell, is the place where the *stannary courts* were held till the latter part of the last century, and within it was the prison in which offenders against the *stannary laws* were confined. (See page 28.) In an Act of 1512, this prison is described as "one of the most heinous, contagious, and detestable places in the realm," and it had not improved in its reputation a century afterwards, when Browne wrote,—
"To lie therein one night 'tis guest, 'Twere better to be stoned and prest." The arbitrary nature of Lydford law is proverbial in the saying, "hang first and try afterwards."

The infamous Jeffries is reported to have been the last judge who presided in the court. *Crockern tor, Wistman's Wood,* and many of the romantic scenes and *Druidical remains* in Dartmoor are already noticed. (See page 40.) *Lidford Bridge* crosses, by a single arch of only a few feet span, over a dark and apparently interminable chasm, under which the river Lyd is heard falling 50 or 60 feet beneath. Many stories are told of tragical events and remarkable occurrences which have taken place at this romantic bridge, near which is the much admired *Lidford Waterfall,* where the river falls down a deep rocky ravine, beautifully festooned with thick foliage. Higher up the river is a smaller waterfall, called *Kitt's Hole,* from a woman said to have been drowned there. Some portions of Dartmoor have been planted and cultivated during the last and present centuries; and, since 1846, G. W. Fowler, Esq., of *Prince Hall,* (see page 40,) has greatly improved that estate, where he has now 130 acres in tillage, and 30 acres in grass, besides a large extent of rough pasture land. He has cleared much of his extensive farm of stones, and used them in constructing drains and fence walls; and the abundant crops which he now reaps shew that many other of the extensive Dartmoor wastes may be profitably cultivated, even to the altitude of 1000 to 1500 feet above the level of the sea. *Lidford Church* (St. Petrock,) is an ancient structure, with a tower and five bells, and is in the lancet style of the 13th century. The *rectory,* valued in K.B. at £15. 13s. 9d., and in 1831 at £197, is in the patronage of the Lord Chancellor, and incumbency of the Rev. John Rooke Fletcher, D.D., of Quethiock, Cornwall, who has 25A. of glebe, and a small house, occupied by a farmer. The Wesleyans have a small chapel in the village. *Dartmoor Chapel of Ease,* at Prince Town, was built by Government, in 1812, for the use of the prisoners of war and the soldiers in the barracks, as noticed at page 40. The *curacy* is in the patronage of the Duchy of Cornwall, and incumbency of the Rev. J. H. Mason, of Widecombe-in-the-Moor, who has a yearly stipend of £300. The formation of a large portion of Dartmoor into a *district parish* is in contemplation.

In the following Directory, those marked 1 are in Lidford; 2, at Prince Town; 3, at Two Bridges, and the rest mostly in other parts of Dartmoor Forest Quarter.

Fowler Geo. Wm. Esq., *Prince Hall*
1 Horn John, corn miller
1 Marsh Rev T. H., curate
INNS AND TAVERNS.
Dartmoor Inn, George Blatchford
2 Duchy Hotel, (empty)
Greyhound, Wm. Connybear, *Post Bridge*
Moreton Inn, Joseph Warne
2 Plume of Feathers, John Leger
2 Railway Hotel, James Rowe
Rundlestone Inn, Wm. Friend
3 Saracen's Head, Peter Chaffe
1 White Horse, Nicholas Rayment
1 *Beerhouse,* Richard Gregory

BLACKSMITHS.
1 Bickle Henry
3 Finch John
1 Millman Thomas
1 May John
BOOT & SHOE MKS.
1 Newton John
1 Parsons Thomas
CARPENTERS.
1 Bickle John
1 Bickle Henry
2 Caunter Edward
2 Creber James
FARMERS.
(* *are Owners.*)
Barker John
Bickle Henry
Bishop Thomas
Brooking Robert
Caunter Edward
Cleave James
Cleave Richard

Coaker John
Coaker Richard
Coaker Thomas
Creber John
Frear George
* French John
French Richard
Friend Richard
* German John
Gill James
* Gill Wm.
Gregory Richard
* Hamlyn James
Hannaford John
* Hext James
Heydon Richard
Heydon W., *Foxtor*
* Hill Hugh
Hunter John
Irish Thomas
Mann Peter
Mason James
Matters Caunter
* Michelmore Pp.
Michelmore John

Morris George
Mudge Wm.
Nichols Kennard
* Nosworthy John
* Paull John
* Phillips Roger
Powell Valentine
* Russell James
Scott Gilbert
* Sherwill T. H.
Stanbury Wm.
Stranger George
Tapson Thomas
* Taverner Thomas
Tuckett Richard
Tuckett Samuel
1 Veale John
Williams Pp., *Dury*
White W. H., *Babny*
MASONS.
3 Chaffe Peter
1 Gregory Richard
1 Higgins W. L.
2 Stevens Wm.
2 Toop John

LIFTON is a considerable village, pleasantly situated in the valley of the river Lyd, about a mile from its confluence with the Tamar, 4 miles E. of Launceston, and 15 miles W.S.W. of Okehampton, on the mail road. Its parish contains 784 inhabitants, and 5982 acres of land, including about 600 acres of plantation; the hamlets of *Tinney, High Cookworthy, Beara,* and *West Week,* and many scattered houses. A large *cattle fair* is held in the village on the 13th of February, and a *cattle show* on the first Thursday in June. *Petty Sessions* are held here at the Arundel Arms, on the last Thursday of every month, by the magistrates of Lifton Division, to whom S. Pattison and J. L. Cowland, of Launceston, are clerks. The manor of Lifton was given by King John to Agatha, who had been his mother's nurse. It afterwards passed to various families, and was sold, with 4580 acres, in September, 1845, by *W. A. H. Arundell, Esq.,* to the trustees of the late R. H. Bradshaw, Esq., for *Henry Blagrove, Esq.,* but to be held in trust till he attains the age of 36 years, or till 1856. Mr. Blagrove married Mr. Arundell's eldest daughter, and has a handsome seat here, called *Lifton Park,* and sometimes *Castle Park.* The mansion is large, and in the Tudor style, and was erected in 1815 and subsequent years, by Mr. Arundell, who now resides on the continent. It is encompassed by about 300 acres of lawn and woods, stretching into the Tamar valley, and commanding de-

lightful views. The Rev. W. Rayer, Sir W. Molesworth, the Rev. C. T. C. Luxmoore, and many smaller proprietors, have estates in the parish, which contains *limestone, lead ore, manganese, &c.* An argentiferous lead mine has lately been opened at *Gatherley*, and is likely to be profitable. The *Church* (St. Mary,) is a large antique fabric, with a lofty tower, containing eight bells, and crowned by a crocketted spire. It has several handsome monuments, belonging to the Harris family. The *rectory*, valued in K.B. at £31. 2*s.* 11*d.*, and in 1831 at £423, is in the patronage of Henry Blagrove, Esq., and incumbency of the Rev. Henry Townend, M.A., who has a good residence and 21A. of glebe. The tithes were commuted in 1841, for £540. 3*s.* 4*d.* per annum. The Baptists, Wesleyans, and Bible Christians have small chapels here; but there is no public school in the parish.

Bartlett Richard, butcher
Bickle Richard, butcher, *Stone*
Blagrove Henry, Esq. *Lifton Park*
Bluet Richard, surgeon
Brook John, schoolmaster
Carpenter Rev. Charles, *Heale*
Cater Miss P. || Martin Miss
Doidge John G. surgeon
Martyn Wm. baker, &c.
Palmer Richard, gent. *Corner House*
Penwarden John, plumber, &c.
Pyett George, brushmaker
Saunders Lawrence, miller
Sibbell Thomas W. gent. *Underhill*
Smale Thomas, tax collector, *Tinney*
Townend Rev. Henry, M.A. *Rectory*

INNS AND TAVERNS.
Arundell Arms, Elizabeth Ball
Bell, Wm. Davey
Fox and Grapes, Joseph May, *Tinney*
Gardeners' Arms, John Mason, *Tinney*
Plough, John Ball

BLACKSMITHS.
Bickle John
Fox John
Knight Robert

CARPENTERS.
Ball John
Bevan Richard
Harvey John
Beath Richard
Stenlake Richard

FARMERS.
(* *are Owners.*)
Bloye Thomas
*Braund John
Braund George
Brendon Richard
Colwell Wm.
*Davy Wm.
*Doidge Henry
Facey Peter

Fletcher John
Glanfield Jhna.
Hamlyn John
Hamlyn Richd.
Hanns Agnes
Harris Eliz.
*Hearne John
Hilson George
Hocking Fras.
Jackman Roger
Jackson Wm.
Jeffery Wm.
Kneeborn George
Mason Thomas
Medland Wm.
Northey Wm., *Lake*
Northey W. & Jno.
*Northey Wm. sen.
Palmer John D.
*Palmer Thos.
*Palmer T. Rowe
Parsons Amos
*Rowe Thomas
*Smale George
Tucker Wm.
Uglow Wm.
Walter John

LIME MERCHANTS.
Brendon and Co.
Northey Rd. & Co.

MASONS.
Ball John
Bullen John
Bullen J. jun.
Bullen Jonth.
Bullen Henry
Bullen James
Davey Wm.

SADDLERS.
Chubb Benj. (and auctioneer, &c.)
Croot Robert

SHOEMAKERS.
Hamley John
Wise James

SHOPKEEPERS.
Kellaway John
Maddaver John
Prout John
Truscott Thomas

TAILORS.
Palmer & Bullen
Vaudon Js., *Tinney*

POST-OFFICE at Robert Palmer's. Letters desp. at 2 afternoon *Mail, Coaches & Carriers* to *Exeter, Falmouth,* &c., pass daily

MARYSTOWE, or *Stowe St. Mary*, is a scattered parish on both sides of the Lyd valley, from 6 to 8 miles N.W. by N. of Tavistock. It contains 574 souls, and 2895 acres of land, including the hamlets of *Cholwell* and *Dipperton*, and part of the village of *Lew Down*. (See page 802.) It is mostly in the manors of Sydenham and Raddon Allerford, which belong to J. H. Tremayne, Esq., of *Sydenham House*, a large Elizabethan mansion, with tasteful grounds, on the banks of the Lyd. It was built by Sir Thomas Wise, who was knighted at the coronation of James I. It contains some fine portraits of the Wise and Tremayne families; and was garrisoned for the king, till taken by Colonel Holbourn, in January, 1645. The Gould, Harris, Pellow, and other families, have estates in the parish. The *Church* is a handsome structure, with a tower and six bells, and was cleansed and renovated about ten years ago. J. H. Tremayne, Esq., is impropriator of the great tithes, and patron of the *vicarage*, valued in K.B. at £12. 16*s.* 0¼*d.*, and in 1831 at £321, with that of Thrushelton annexed to it. The Rev. E. E. Rimell is the incumbent, and has a good residence and 114A. of glebe. The tithes were commuted in 1849, the rectorial for £186. 19*s.*, and the vicarial for £168. 7*s.* The poor have £20 a year from *Tremayne's Charity*. (See page 801.)

Davey Jonth. schoolmaster, *Lew Down*
Gough Wm. Henry, beer seller
Reddicliff Rd. gentleman, *Lew Down*
Rimell Rev. Edw. Edgcumbe, vicar
Smale Thomas, house steward
Soper Wm. blacksmith
Spry Rd. wheelwright, *Lew Down*
Tremayne John Hearle, Esq., *Sydenham House*

FARMERS.
Bickle Wm. || Burnard John
Chown John || Cory Richard
Cudlipp Joseph || Cornelius Mary
Doidge George || Gimlett Robert
Helson George || Mason Thomas
Steer Sampson Luscombe, *Barton*
White John || Walters Brothers
Post and *Carriers* from Lew Down

For the remainder of LIFTON HUNDRED, see pages 18 to 24.

ROBERT LEADER, PRINTER, SHEFFIELD.

22462